AT LAST—THE REPORT THE WORLD HAS BEEN WAITING FOR!

"If, as many people suspect, our planet is being visited clandestinely by spacecraft, manned or controlled by intelligent creatures from another world, it is the most momentous development in human history. . . .

"Now for the first time a full-fledged scientific study has been carried out. Over a two-year period hundreds of cases were investigated. . . .

"The result has been a series of case histories that reads like a modern, real-life collection of Sherlock Holmes episodes. The cases range from the eerily perplexing to the preposterously naive. The reader is given a taste of the scientific method, even though the cases are often such that they defy anything approaching deductive analysis."

From the Introduction
by Walter Sullivan

PUBLISHER'S NOTE

Bantam is publishing the text of SCIENTIFIC STUDY OF UNIDENTIFIED FLYING OBJECTS as it was released to the press on January 8, 1969.

The plates and legends in the center of the book include not only plates in the case study section (*IV*) but all plates in the report.

COVER PHOTOGRAPH

Photograph of an aurora made by an astronomer who sent it to the Colorado Project with the comment that it shows how "a complex lens system used in present day cameras can produce a strange image from stray light."

The hour-glass-shaped image is technically known as a "lens flare" (see Section III, Chapter 2) as is produced by moonlight reflected from the lens components.

FINAL REPORT OF THE

SCIENTIFIC STUDY OF UNIDENTIFIED FLYING OBJECTS

CONDUCTED BY THE UNIVERSITY OF COLORADO
UNDER CONTRACT TO THE UNITED STATES AIR FORCE

DR. EDWARD U. CONDON
Scientific Director

This research was supported by the Air Force Office of Scientific Research, Office of Aerospace Research, USAF, under contract F44620-67-C-0035

DANIEL S. GILLMOR
Editor

1968

With an introduction by
WALTER SULLIVAN
of *The New York Times*

BANTAM BOOKS • NEW YORK • TORONTO • LONDON

This low-priced Bantam Book has been completely reset in a type face designed for easy reading, and was printed from new plates. It contains the complete text of the original edition.
NOT ONE WORD HAS BEEN OMITTED.

SCIENTIFIC STUDY OF
UNIDENTIFIED FLYING OBJECTS
A Bantam Book / published by arrangement with the University of Colorado

Bantam edition published January 1969

With the exception of correction of grammatical and typographical errors made in this edition, it is a reproduction of the report submitted to the National Academy of Sciences on November 15, 1968 for its scientific review.
*For information address:
University of Colorado, Boulder, Colorado.*

Published simultaneously in the United States and Canada

Bantam Books are published by Bantam Books, Inc., a subsidiary of Grosset & Dunlap, Inc. Its trade-mark, consisting of the words "Bantam Books" and the portrayal of a bantam, is registered in the United States Patent Office and in other countries. Marca Registrada. Bantam Books, Inc., 271 Madison Avenue, New York, N.Y. 10016.

PRINTED IN THE UNITED STATES OF AMERICA

INTRODUCTION

If, as many people suspect, our planet is being visited clandestinely by spacecraft, manned or controlled by intelligent creatures from another world, it is the most momentous development in human history.

Opinion surveys indicate that several million Americans believe they have seen objects that could be described as unidentified flying objects (UFOs), or "flying saucers." What, in fact, have they seen?

It appears that the Central Intelligence Agency, in 1953, was party to a scheme to "debunk" the UFOs. (The previously-secret document relating to this proposal is Appendix U in this book.) Has the government, in fact, been aware for some years that earth was under surveillance and has there been an effort to avoid panic by concealing the fact?

Or has the Air Force, in fulfilling its responsibility to deny our skies to hostile vehicles, been too lax to recognize the threat? Project Blue Book, the Air Force office responsible for assembling UFO reports at Wright-Patterson Air Force Base near Dayton, Ohio, is a low-priority operation, long manned by one officer, a sergeant and secretary.

In 1966 rumblings of discontent, both on Capitol Hill and among the public at large, led the Air Force to seek an independent assessment of the situation. It was a remarkable fact that, despite the enormous public interest in UFOs, the big guns of science had never been brought to bear on the problem.

Now for the first time a full-fledged scientific study has been carried out. Over a two-year period hundreds of cases were investigated. Case studies on 59 of the most important or most representative are presented in this report. Of these, ten relate to incidents that occurred before the project but were sufficiently well documented to merit pursuit.

A number of alleged UFO photographs have been analyzed in depth, with measurements being made at the scenes where the photographs were taken and of the film itself. Some have been explained, but at least one, showing a disk-shaped object in flight over Oregon, (plates 23 through 26), is classed as difficult to explain in a conventional way.

The study, at a cost of about half a million dollars, was carried out by the University of Colorado under the direction of Dr. Edward U. Condon. He was clearly chosen, not only because of his scientific eminence, but because of his unquestionable independence. He has served as President of the American Association for the Advancement of Science, the

American Physical Society and as head of the National Bureau of Standards. The latter operated a complex of laboratories in Boulder, home of the University of Colorado. They now come under the recently-created Environmental Science Services Administration. Also in Boulder, on a mesa overlooking the town, is the National Center for Atmospheric Research. These centers offered Dr. Condon a wide range of experts in many fields of science.

Dr. Condon has the build of a football halfback. In his mid-sixties, he is a bit old for the game. Nevertheless, as the reader will see in this report, he has a tendency in scientific matters to lower his knowledgeable head and charge the line.

His independence has been many times demonstrated in his support of liberal (and sometimes unpopular) causes. He was one of the few who tangled with the House Committee on Un-American Activities and, to all intents and purposes, came out on top. Richard M. Nixon was associated with attempts to challenge his security clearance, and early in 1969 the Air Force, mindful that little love was lost between the two men, clearly wanted to get the Condon Report out of the way before Nixon became President.

The report concludes that there is no evidence to justify a belief that extraterrestrial visitors have penetrated our skies and not enough evidence to warrant any further scientific investigation. As Condon himself anticipated, this will not gladden UFO enthusiasts. There is no question but that a great many people want to believe the extraterrestrial hypothesis.

Why they do so is beyond the scope of the report—or this introduction. The feeling has been attributed to a hope that some sort of superior beings are watching over our world, prepared to intervene if things get too bad. Some people, too, are suspicious of "The Establishment" or resentful of what seems to them arrogant disregard by scientists of "evidence" for the existence of UFOs.

Although people have been reporting "flying saucers" for more than 20 years, there has been no machinery for bringing to bear on such sightings the many techniques for objective analysis available to modern science. When a citizen saw a UFO he tended to call the police who, in many cases, had no idea what to do about it. Those who knew that the nearest Air Force base was responsible for investigating such reported intrusions into American air space often found that the man at the base assigned to such duty was preoccupied with other tasks.

Some private organizations of concerned citizens, notably the National Investigations Committee for Aerial Phenomena (NICAP) and the Aerial Phenomena Research Organization (APRO) did the best they could. However, their resources were limited and they were handicapped, particularly in their dealings with government agencies, by their unofficial status and the fact that their membership consisted largely of people sympathetic to the view that UFOs may be controlled by an alien civilization (the so-called ETI, or Extra-Terrestrial Intelligence, hypothesis).

For the University of Colorado study, experts in radar, in plasma physics, in mirages, in photographic analysis and problems of perception were called in. Upon receipt of a promising UFO report scientists armed with a variety of observational tools flew to the scene, in some cases to witness the phenomena themselves.

The result has been a series of case histories that reads like a modern, real-life collection of Sherlock Holmes episodes. The cases range from the eerily perplexing to the preposterously naive. The reader is given a taste of the scientific method, even though the cases are often such that they defy anything approaching deductive analysis.

The reader can also exercise his own judgment by comparing this report with efforts to dispute it. For example a book has been published by a former member of the University of Colorado project who was dismissed. He and his co-author argue that the project may have been organized—without the knowledge of most of its staff—as a cover to divert attention from the real nature of UFOs.

He supports this conspiracy hypothesis with what he considers evidence that two members of a panel of top scientists convened by the government in 1953 to assess the UFO situation refused to sign the resulting report. That report found there was no threat to the nation in the UFOs and urged that they be stripped of their "aura of mystery." The panel feared that an enemy could exploit the tendency of the public toward hysterical behavior through "clogging of channels of communication by irrelevant reports." Real indications of hostile action would then be ignored.

The chairman of the panel was Dr. H. P. Robertson of the California Institute of Technology. According to surviving members of the panel no one dissented from its findings, although the name of one member was deleted before the report was declassified in 1966. The time was one of sensitivity about involvement of the Central Intelligence Agency in activities beyond its intelligence-gathering role and all references to the CIA's role in the panel's work, as well as names of its employees and others involved in intelligence work, were deleted.

Apart from these deletions, this document (Appendix U), like all other aspects of this report, is uncensored. Some of the documents presented here, as well as many of the UFO episodes, are offered to the public for the first time.

Despite the efforts of some UFO enthusiasts to discredit the report in advance, a panel of the nation's most eminent scientists, chosen by the prestigious National Academy of Sciences, has examined it, chapter by chapter, and given it "straight As," so to speak.

This "grading" of the report was performed at the request of the Air Force, which foresaw charges of "whitewash" if—as it earnestly expected—the Colorado study echoed earlier findings that even the most mysterious UFOs have not been shown to be of exotic origin.

Concurrence by the Academy, representing the nation's most distinguished scientists, would help divert such criticism. It was understood originally that the Academy panel would be asked merely to assess the working methods of the Colorado team, rather than to endorse its conclusions, but the panel went further than that. It expressed clear-cut agreement with the findings.

"We are unanimous in the opinion," the panel said, "that this has been a very creditable effort to apply objectively the relevant techniques of science to the solution of the UFO problem. The report recognizes that there remain UFO sightings that are not easily explained. The report does suggest, however, so many reasonable and possible directions in which an explanation may eventually be found, that there seems to be no reason to attribute them to an extraterrestrial source without evidence that is much more convincing. The report also shows how difficult it is to apply scientific methods to the occasional transient sightings with any chance of success. While further study of particular aspects of the topic (e.g., atmospheric phenomena) may be useful, a study of UFOs in general is not a promising way to expand scientific understanding of the phenomena. On the basis of present knowledge the least likely explanation of UFOs is the hypothesis of extraterrestrial visitations by intelligent beings."

The Chairman of this panel was Dr. Gerald M. Clemence of Yale University, former Scientific Director of the United States Naval Observatory. The others included leading specialists in fields relevant to the UFO problem—astronomy, atmospheric physics, meteorology and psychology. They were:

Dr. Horace R. Crane, Professor of Physics, University of Michigan.

Dr. David M. Dennison, Professor of Physics, University of Michigan.

Dr. Wallace O. Fenn, physiologist and former Director of the Space Science Center at the University of Rochester.

Dr. H. Keffer Hartline, biophysicist, Professor at Rockefeller University and 1967 co-winner of the Nobel Prize in medicine and physiology.

Dr. Ernest R. Hilgard, Professor of Psychology at Stanford University.

Dr. Mark Kac, mathematician, Professor at Rockefeller University.

Dr. Francis W. Reichelderfer, former head of the United States Weather Bureau.

Dr. William W. Rubey, Professor of Geology and Geophysics at the University of California at Los Angeles.

Dr. Charles D. Shane, Emeritus Astronomer at the Lick Observatory in California.

Dr. Oswald G. Villard, Jr., Director of the Radio Science Laboratory, Stanford University.

The panel did a certain amount of homework, in addition to reviewing the Colorado report. It read scientific papers prepared by outspoken scientific protagonists on both sides of the controversy. Two of these, Dr. William Markowitz, former head of the time service at the Naval Observatory, and Dr. Donald H. Menzel, former director of the Harvard College Observatory, have scoffed at the extraterrestrial hypothesis. Another author, Dr. James E. McDonald of the University of Arizona, has argued that UFOs are one of the biggest scientific puzzles of our time and that visitations from afar are the best explanation for UFOs that cannot otherwise be explained.

In forwarding the panel's assessment to the Air Force Dr. Frederick Seitz, President of the Academy, said: "Substantial questions have been raised as to the adequacy of our research and investigation programs to explain or to determine the nature of these sometimes puzzling reports of observed phenomena. It is my hope that the Colorado report, together with our panel review, will be helpful to you and other responsible officials in determining the nature and scope of any continuing research effort in this area."

The panel report was copyrighted to prevent its appearance in unauthorized publications. The review was done, Dr. Seitz said, "for the sole purpose of assisting the government in reaching a decision on its future course of action. Its use in whole or in part for any other purpose would be incompatible with the purpose of the review and the conditions under which it was conducted."

Apparently the Academy and its panel members did not want their review to appear between the covers of some of the more far-out UFO books. However, the review was distributed to the press on January 8, 1969, with the Colorado report itself, for release the next day.

The report is a memorable document. While the case histories read like detective stories, it is also a scientific study. There are sections here and there that most readers will find technical and difficult to follow. They are easily skipped. However, in the technical sections there are also nuggets that no one will want to miss. For example in Chapter 7, on atmospheric electricity and plasma interpretations of UFOs, there are accounts of collisions of Soviet and American aircraft with a peculiar phenomenon known as ball lightning, as well as a description of the extraordinary behavior of lightning inside a tornado. Also of special interest is the section describing UFOs observed by astronauts (all presumably manmade objects in earth orbit).

Efforts have been made by UFO enthusiasts to blunt the effect of this report by arguing that Dr. Condon and his colleagues were too biased for a meaningful finding. These attempts to discredit the report have concentrated in large measure on an episode that occurred when much of the on-the-spot investigation had been done.

Early in the project things seemed to be going smoothly. The two largest quasi-scientific organizations of UFO "buffs" cooperated by tipping off the Colorado project to new sightings. They also made available samples from their files of interviews, photographs and the like.

Then, however, a certain amount of infighting developed. One of the UFO groups, NICAP, is headed by Donald Keyhoe who, as author of *Flying Saucers Are Real,* has a vested interest in the confirmation of his thesis. Various statements attributed to Dr. Condon suggested to NICAP that he did not take very seriously the possibility that UFOs come from another civilization.

In this respect it should be pointed out that Dr. Condon is a somewhat garrulous soul who loves to spin a good yarn. The inquiry into UFOs was a rich source of such material and he found it hard, on various occasions, not to recount some of the sillier episodes.

This infuriated those, like Dr. McDonald at the University of Arizona, who believed in the possibility of an extraterrestrial origin. They charged that the Colorado project was wasting its time on crackpot reports and turning its back on the more solid evidence. Anyone who reads the following pages will see that this is untrue. It is obvious that the project concentrated on the best documented and most substantial cases and it did not hesitate to conclude that, on the basis of available evidence, some are difficult to explain by conventional means.

The most severe blow to the project came when one of its staff members, going through the files, came across a memorandum written by Robert J. Low before the University undertook the project. Low, who was serving as project coordinator, had been an assistant dean in the graduate school. His memo, to University officials, sought to analyze the pros and cons of the Air Force proposal. Could the University undertake the project in a manner that would satisfy public concern, yet not subject the University to ridicule by the academic community? He argued that the study would perforce be done almost entirely by nonbelievers and, while the project could never "prove" that no UFOs have ever come from another world, it could contribute impressive evidence for such a conclusion. "The trick," he wrote, "would be, I think, to describe the project so that, to the public, it would appear a totally objective study but, to the scientific community, would present the image of a group of nonbelievers trying their best to be objective, but having an almost zero expectation of finding a saucer."

He proposed, to this end, that the emphasis be on the psychological and sociological investigation of those reporting UFOs, rather than on checking out the physical evidence for alleged visitations.

Condon apparently never saw this memo at the time it was written and, in fact, rejected suggestions that the emphasis be on the psychology of UFO witnesses. As the case histories in this report show, the stress was on the search for physical evidence and physical explanations. However, the Low memo fell into the hands of Dr. McDonald and of NICAP. It was brought to the attention of John G. Fuller, author of two books *(Incident at Exeter* and *Interrupted Journey)* supporting the extraterrestrial explanation for UFOs. In an article in *Look* magazine, which had published parts of his two books, Fuller quoted the memo and reported dissension among staff members of the Colorado project. His article was entitled "Flying Saucer Fiasco," with the subtitle: "The Extraordinary Story of the Half-Million-Dollar 'Trick' to Make Americans Believe the Condon Committee Was Conducting an Objective Investigation."

Two men whom Condon considered responsible for leaking the memo to disgruntled UFO believers were discharged from the project.

In exploring possible roots of this controversy the journal *Science* quoted a statement by James and Coral Lorenzen, who run the Aerial Phenomena Research Organization (APRO) in Tucson, Arizona, which rivals NICAP as a comparatively sober association of UFO buffs. They suggested that there was "a strong attempt by the NICAP group (McDonald and Saunders are both close to NICAP) to control the study. When they found they couldn't control it, they attempted to scuttle it."

Whatever the merits of this analysis, the Condon Report and the challenges to it must stand or fall on their own merits —not on the degree of squabbling that may, or may not have occurred in its preparation. That Condon, an old scientific pro, was well aware of this shines forth from the pages of this document.

There is probably no such thing as a scientific researcher without bias. It is rare indeed for someone to undertake an experiment with no inkling as to its outcome. More commonly the scientist has formulated a hypothesis and he carries out a series of experiments that, he hopes, will convince himself—and all the world—of its correctness. Those experiments, to assure him of a place in scientific history, must, insofar as possible, be such that any other scientist can confirm his results.

The extent to which such tests can be applied to UFOs is limited. More often, as the case histories show, the judgement must be based on common sense. If, for example, it can be shown that a UFO photograph could have been faked, and if the story told by the person who took the picture displays suspicious inconsistencies, then Condon and his colleagues have tended to reject the picture as evidence. Those inclined to be believers might be more willing to accept the picture as genuine, but they could not use it as "proof" of the extra-terrestrial hypothesis.

A reading of the case histories in this report forces on the reader a certain humility regarding human perception. We do not see only with our eyes and hear only with our ears. We see and hear with that complex and little-understood organ, the brain, crammed with memories and earlier impressions.

It is the ingenuity of this brain that enables us to read fast or recognize a friend at a glance. If we had to read every letter of every word, or had to scrutinize the entire physiognomy of a person to recognize him, the pace of our lives would be slow indeed. Instead we have learned to deduce entire words or phrases and entire people from a limited number of observed clues.

However, when the circumstances are unusual we can easily be fooled by misleading clues. Nicolaas Tinbergen, Professor of Animal Behavior at Oxford and a founder of the young science of ethology (the study of animal behavior in the wild), told me of a personal experience that illustrates this.

In east Greenland he was once atop a mountain a number of miles inland. Offshore wind had blown the pack ice beyond the horizon some days earlier and now, to his horror, he saw the distant sea in violent motion. Giant waves were racing toward shore. "We must get down off the mountain," he told his Eskimo companion excitedly. "That gale could hit any minute and blow us off the mountain!"

Then suddenly the motion of the sea stopped as though a moving picture had been brought to a halt. This occurred at the moment when his mind realized that he was looking at pack ice that had blown back onshore, not at waves. The motion was a fiction of his brain.

It was not many generations ago that ghosts seemed plausible, and night visions, be they wisps of luminous gas rising from a swamp, or play of moonlight on a blowing curtain, could raise palpitations in the most stalwart heart. Today, if one hears a creak in the night or sees a peculiar glow, the usual reaction is to investigate, rather than duck under the covers. However, UFOs are often too far away for such intimate checking.

This report, in showing the fallibility of even such sober observers as policemen, airline pilots and radar operators, raises questions as to the role of conditioning in many other fields of human activity. The purveyors of advertising are well versed in the techniques of conditioning, but one wonders to what extent this phenomenon affects such basic attitudes as our nationalism, our theological point of view and our moral standards.

Are they really founded on logic and the ultimate truth?

One cannot help but view our points of view on a great many things with new skepticism.

Anyone who reads this study will, I believe, lay it down with a new perspective on human values and limitations.

WALTER SULLIVAN

UNIVERSITY OF COLORADO
President's Office
Boulder, Colorado 80302
October 31, 1968

The Honorable Harold Brown
Secretary of the Air Force
The Pentagon
Washington, D. C.

Dear Dr. Brown:

Pursuant to Contract No. F44620-67-C-0035 between the United States Air Force and the University of Colorado, I transmit herewith the final report of the Scientific Study of Unidentified Flying Objects.

As you know, the University undertook this study at the urging of the Air Force, not only for its purely scientific aspects, but in order that there might be no question that any of the matters reported herein reflect anything other than strict attention to the discovery and disclosure of the facts. I want to take this occasion to assure you that, under the direction of Dr. Edward U. Condon, the study has been made and the report prepared with this thought constantly in mind. The Air Force has been most cooperative, both in respect to furnishing the project with all information in its possession bearing upon the subject matter of the investigation and, equally important, in pursuing most scrupulously a policy of complete non-interference with the work of Dr. Condon and his staff. There has never been the slightest suggestion of any effort on the part of the Air Force to influence either the conduct of the investigation or the content of this report.

As a consequence of this cooperation and of a diligent effort on the part of scientists at this University, at the Environmental Science Services Administration, at the National Center for Atmospheric Research, and at other universities and scientific institutions, the report transmitted to you herewith is, I believe, as thorough as the time and funds allotted for the purpose could possibly permit.

We hope and believe that it will have the effect of placing the controversy as to the nature of unidentified flying objects in a proper scientific perspective. We also trust that it will stimulate scientific research along lines that may yield important new knowledge.

Sincerely yours,

J. R. Smiley
President

PREFACE

On 31 August 1966, Colonel Ivan C. Atkinson, Deputy Executive Director of the Air Force Office of Scientific Research, addressed a letter to the University of Colorado. In it he outlined the belief of AFOSR that a scientific investigation of unidentified flying objects conducted wholly outside the jurisdiction of the Air Force would be of unusual significance from the standpoint of both scientific interest in and public concern with the subject. Colonel Atkinson requested "that the University of Colorado participate in this investigation as the grantee institution." The University was asked to undertake this scientific study with the unconditional guarantee that "the scientists involved will have complete freedom to design and develop techniques for the investigation of the varied physical and psychological questions raised in conjunction with this phenomenon according to their best scientific judgment."

The request of AFOSR was pursuant to the recommendation made in March, 1966, of an *ad hoc* panel of the United States Air Force Scientific Advisory Board, chaired by Dr. Brian O'Brien. Subsequently, as chairman of the Advisory Committee to the Air Force Systems Command of the National Academy Sciences–National Research Council, Dr. O'Brien had advised AFOSR on the suitability of the University of Colorado as the grantee institution.

Following receipt of Colonel Atkinson's request in behalf of AFOSR, the University administration and interested members of the faculty discussed the proposed study project. The subject was recognized as being both elusive and controversial in its scientific aspects. For this reason alone, there was an understandable reluctance on the part of many scientists to undertake such a study. Scientists hesitate to commit their time to research that does not apppear to offer reasonably clear avenues by which definite progress may be made. In addition, the subject had achieved considerable notoriety over the years. Many popular books and magazine articles had criticized the Air Force for not devoting more attention to the subject; others criticized the Air Force for paying any attention whatever to UFOs.

Bearing these facts in mind, the University administration concluded that it had an obligation to the country to do what it could to clarify a tangled and confused issue while making entirely certain that the highest academic and scientific standards would be maintained. Fortunately, Dr. Edward U. Condon, Professor of Physics and Fellow of the Joint Institute for

Laboratory Astrophysics, shared this concern and was willing to accept appointment as scientific director of the project. Designated as principal investigators with Dr. Condon were Dr. Stuart Cook, Professor and Chairman of the Department of Psychology, and Dr. Franklin E. Roach, physicist specializing in atmospheric physics at the Environmental Science Services Administration. Assistant Dean Robert J. Low of the Graduate School was appointed project coordinator.

The University undertook the study only on condition that it would be conducted as a normal scientific research project, subject only to the professional scientific judgment of the director and his aides. Freedom from control by the granting agency was guaranteed not only by the assertions of Colonel Atkinson, but also by the provision that the complete report of the findings of the study would be made available to the public.

In addition the University recognized that this study, as the first undertaken on a broad scale in this field, would have seminal effect. It therefore desired the cooperation of the scientific community at large. Assurances of support and counsel were forthcoming from such institutions as the National Center for Atmospheric Research (NCAR) and the Environmental Science Services Administration (ESSA), and from many scientists and scientific institutions in other parts of the country.

The University also welcomed an arrangement whereby the methods and results of the study would be critically examined at the conclusion of the project. This cooperation was extended by the National Academy of Sciences, which announced in its October 1966 *News Report* that the Academy had agreed to review the University of Colorado study upon its completion in 1968. Unhesitatingly agreeing to this independent examination of the study, the ASOFR announced that it would consider the NAS review a "further independent check on the scientific validity of the method of investigation."

In October, 1966, the scientific director assembled a modest staff centered at the University campus in Boulder and work began. In addition, agreements were entered into between the University and such institutions as NCAR, the Institutes of ESSA, the Stanford Research Institute and the University of Arizona for the scientific and technical services of persons in specialized fields of knowledge bearing upon the subject under investigation. Thus it became possible to study specific topics both at Boulder and elsewhere and to bring to bear upon the data gathered by the project's field investigation teams whatever expertise might be required for full analysis of the information.

The report of the study that was conducted over the ensuing 18 months is presented on the following pages. It is lengthy and diverse in the subjects it treats, which range from history to critical examination of eye-witness reports; from laboratory analysis to presentation of general scientific principles. No claim of perfection is made for this study or for its results, since like any scientific endeavor, it could have been improved upon—especially from the vantage-point of hindsight. The reader should thus bear in mind that this study represents the first attempt by a group of highly qualified scientists and specialists to examine coldly and dispassionately a subject that has aroused the imagination and emotions of some persons and has intrigued many others. No one study can answer all questions; but it can point out new lines for research, it can cross off some ideas as not fruitful for further inquiry, and it can lay to rest at least some rumors, exaggerations, and imaginings.

Thurston E. Manning
Vice President for Academic Affairs

Boulder, Colorado
October 31, 1968

CONTENTS

Section I

CONCLUSIONS AND RECOMMENDATIONS

Edward U. Condon

We believe that the existing record and the results of the Scientific Study of Unidentified Flying Objects of the University of Colorado, which are presented in detail in subsequent sections of this report, support the conclusions and recommendations which follow.

As indicated by its title, the emphasis of this study has been on attempting to learn from UFO reports anything that could be considered as adding to scientific knowledge. Our general conclusion is that nothing has come from the study of UFOs in the past 21 years that has added to scientific knowledge. Careful consideration of the record as it is available to us leads us to conclude that further extensive study of UFOs probably cannot be justified in the expectation that science will be advanced thereby.

It has been argued that this lack of contribution to science is due to the fact that very little scientific effort has been put on the subject. We do not agree. We feel that the reason that there has been very little scientific study of the subject is that those scientists who are most directly concerned, astronomers, atmospheric physicists, chemists, and psychologists, having had ample opportunity to look into the matter, have individually decided that UFO phenomena do not offer a fruitful field in which to look for major scientific discoveries.

This conclusion is so important, and the public seems in general to have so little understanding of how scientists work, that some more comment on it seems desirable. Each person who sets out to make a career of scientific research, chooses a general field of broad specialization in which to acquire proficiency. Within that field he looks for specific fields in which to work. To do this he keeps abreast of the published scientific literature, attends scientific meetings, where reports on current progress are given, and energetically discusses his interests and those of his colleagues both face-to-face and by correspondence with them. He is motivated by an active curiosity about nature and by a personal desire to make a contribution to science. He is constantly probing for error and incompleteness in the efforts that have been made in his fields of interest, and looking for new ideas about new ways to attack new problems. From this effort he arrives at personal decisions as to where his own effort can be most fruitful. These decisions are personal in the sense that he must estimate his own intellectual limitations, and the limitations inherent in the working situation in which he finds himself, including limits on the support of his work, or his involvement with other pre-existing scientific commitments. While individual errors of judgment may arise, it is generally not true that all of the scientists who are actively cultivating a given field of science are wrong for very long.

Even conceding that the entire body of "official" science might be in error for a time, we believe that there is no better way to correct error than to give free reign to the ideas of individual scientists to make decisions as to the directions in which scientific progress is most likely to be made. For legal work sensible people seek an attorney, and for medical treatment sensible people seek a qualified physician. The nation's surest guarantee of scientific excellence is to leave the decision-making process to the individual and collective judgment of its scientists.

Scientists are no respecters of authority. Our conclusion that study of UFO reports is not likely to advance science will not be uncritically accepted by them. Nor should it be, nor do we wish it to be. For scientists, it is our hope that the detailed analytical presentation of what we were able to do, and of what we were unable to do, will assist them in deciding whether or not they agree with our conclusions. Our hope is that the details of this report will help other scientists in seeing what the problems are and the difficulties of coping with them.

If they agree with our conclusions, they will turn their valuable attention and talents elsewhere. If they disagree it will be because our report has helped them reach a clear picture of wherein existing studies are faulty or incomplete and thereby will have stimulated ideas for more accurate studies. If they do get such ideas and can formulate them clearly, we have no doubt that support will be forthcoming to carry on with such clearly-defined, specific studies. We think that such ideas for work should be supported.

Some readers may think that we have now wandered into a contradiction. Earlier we said that we do not think study of UFO reports is likely to be a fruitful direction of scientific advance; now we have just said that persons with good ideas for specific studies in this field should be supported. This is no contradiction. Although we conclude after nearly two years of intensive study, that we do not see any fruitful lines of advance from the study of UFO reports, we believe that any scientist with adequate training and credentials who does come up with a clearly defined, specific proposal for study should be supported.

What we are saying here was said in a more general context nearly a century ago by William Kingdon Clifford, a great English mathematical physicist. In his "Aims and Instruments of Scientific Thought" he expressed himself this way:

> Remember, then, that [scientific thought] is the guide of action; that the truth which it arrives at is not that which we can ideally contemplate without error, but that which we may act upon without fear; and you cannot fail to see that scientific thought is not an accompaniment or condition of human progress, but human progress itself.

Just as individual scientists may make errors of judgment about fruitful directions for scientific effort, so also any individual administrator or committee which is charged with deciding on financial support for research proposals may also make an error of judgment. This possibility is minimized by the existence of parallel channels, for consideration by more than one group, of proposals for research projects. In the period since 1945, the federal government has evolved flexible and effective machinery for giving careful consideration to proposals from properly qualified scientists. What to some may seem like duplicated machinery actually acts as a safeguard against errors being made by some single official body. Even so, some errors could be made but the hazard is reduced nearly to zero.

Therefore we think that all of the agencies of the federal government, and the private foundations as well, ought to be willing to consider UFO research proposals along with the others submitted to them on an open-minded, unprejudiced basis. While we do not think at present that anything worthwhile is likely to come of such research each individual case ought to be carefully considered on its own merits.

This formulation carries with it the corollary that we do not think that at this time the federal government ought to set up a major new agency, as some have suggested, for the scientific study of UFOs. This conclusion may not be true for all time. If, by the progress of research based on new ideas in this field, it then appears worthwhile to create such an agency, the decision to do so may be taken at that time.

We find that there are important areas of atmospheric optics, including radio wave propagation, and of atmospheric electricity in which present knowledge is quite incomplete. These topics came to our attention in connection with the interpretation of some UFO reports, but they are also of fundamental scientific interest, and they are relevant to practical problems related to the improvement of safety of military and civilian flying.

Research efforts are being carried out in these areas by the Department of Defense, the Environmental Science Services Administration, the National Aeronautics and Space Administration, and by universities and nonprofit research organizations such as the National Center for Atmospheric Research, whose work is sponsored by the National Science Foundation. We commend these efforts. By no means should our lack of enthusiasm for study of UFO reports as such be misconstrued as a recommendation that these important related fields of scientific work not be adequately supported in the future. In an era of major development of air travel, of space exploration, and of military aerospace activities, everything possible should be done to improve our basic understanding of all atmospheric phenomena, and to improve the training of astronauts and aircraft pilots in the recognition and understanding of such phenomena.

As the reader of this report will readily judge, we have focussed attention almost entirely on the physical sciences. This was in part a matter of determining priorities and in part because we found rather less than some persons may have expected in the way of psychiatric problems related to belief in the reality of UFOs as craft from remote galactic or intergalactic civilizations. We believe that the rigorous study of the beliefs—unsupported by valid evidence—held by individuals and even by some groups might prove of scientific value to the social and behavioral sciences. There is no implication here that individual or group psychopathology is a principal area of study. Reports of UFOs offer interesting challenges to the student of cognitive processes as they are affected by individual and social variables. By this connection, we conclude that a content-analysis of press and television coverage of UFO reports might yield data of value both to the social scientist and the communications specialist. The lack of such a study in the present report is due to a judgment on our part that other areas of investigation were of much higher priority. We do not suggest, however, that the UFO phenomenon is, by its nature, more amenable to study in these disciplines than in the physical sciences. On the contrary, we conclude that the same specificity in proposed research in these areas is as desirable as it is in the physical sciences.

The question remains as to what, if anything, the federal government should do about the UFO reports it receives from the general public. We are inclined to think that nothing should be done with them in the expectation that they are going to contribute to the advance of science.

This question is inseparable from the question of the national defense interest of these reports. The history of the past 21 years has repeatedly led Air Force officers to the conclusion that none of the things seen, or thought to have been seen, which pass by the name of UFO reports, constituted any hazard or threat to national security.

We felt that it was out of our province to attempt an independent evaluation of this conclusion. We adopted the attitude that, without attempting to assume the defense responsibility which is that of the Air Force, if we came across any evidence whatever that seemed to us to indicate a defense hazard we would call it to the attention of the Air Force at once. We did not find any such evidence. We know of no reason to question the finding of the Air Force that the whole class of UFO reports so far considered does not pose a defense problem.

At the same time, however, the basis for reaching an opinion of this kind is that such reports have been given attention, one by one, as they are received. Had no attention whatever been given to any of them, we would not be in a position to feel confident of this conclusion. Therefore it seems that only so much attention to the subject should be given as the Department of Defense deems to be necessary strictly from a defense point of view. The level of effort should not be raised because of arguments that the subject has scientific importance, so far as present indications go.

It is our impression that the defense function could be performed within the framework established for intelligence and surveillance operations without the continuance of a special unit such as Project Blue Book, but this is a question for defense specialists rather than research scientists.

It has been contended that the subject has been shrouded in official secrecy. We conclude otherwise. We have no evidence of secrecy concerning UFO reports. What has been miscalled secrecy has been no more than an intelligent policy of delay in releasing data so that the public does not become confused by premature publication of incomplete studies of reports.

The subject of UFOs has been widely misrepresented to the public by a small number of individuals who have given sensationalized presentations in writings and public lectures. So far as we can judge, not many people have been misled by such irresponsible behavior, but whatever effect there has been has been bad.

A related problem to which we wish to direct public attention is the miseducation in our schools which arises from the fact that many children are being allowed, if not actively encouraged, to devote their science study time to the reading of UFO books and magazine articles of the type referred to in the preceding paragraph. We feel that children are educationally harmed by absorbing unsound and erroneous material as if it were scientifically well founded. Such study is harmful not merely because of the erroneous nature of the material itself, but also because such study retards the development of a critical faculty with regard to scientific evidence, which to some degree ought to be part of the education of every American.

Therefore we strongly recommend that teachers refrain from giving students credit for school work based on their reading of the presently available UFO books and magazine articles. Teachers who find their students strongly motivated in this direction should attempt to channel their interests in the direction of serious study of astronomy and meteorology, and in the direction of critical analysis of arguments for fantastic propositions that are being supported by appeals to fallacious reasoning or false data.

We hope that the results of our study will prove useful to scientists and those responsible for the formation of public policy generally in dealing with this problem which has now been with us for 21 years.

Section II

SUMMARY OF THE STUDY

Edward U. Condon

1. Origin of the Colorado Project

The decision to establish this project for the Scientific Study of Unidentified Flying Objects stems from recommendations in a report dated March 1966 of an Ad Hoc Committee of the Air Force Scientific Advisory Board set up under the chairmanship of Dr. Brian O'Brien to review the work of Project Blue Book. Details of the history of work on UFOs are set forth in Section V, Chapter 2. (See also Appendix A.) The recommendation was:

> It is the opinion of the Committee that the present Air Force program dealing with UFO sightings has been well organized, although the resources assigned to it (only one officer, a sergeant, and a secretary) have been quite limited. In 19 years and more than 10,000 sightings recorded and classified, there appears to be no verified and fully satisfactory evidence of any case that is clearly outside the framework of presently known science and technology. Nevertheless, there is always the possibility that analysis of new sightings may provide some additions to scientific knowledge of value to the Air Force. Moreover, some of the case records at which the Committee looked that were listed as 'identified' were sightings where the evidence collected was too meager or too indefinite to permit positive listing in the identified category. Because of this the Committee recommends that the present program be strengthened to provide opportunity for scientific investigation of selected sightings in more detail than has been possible to date.
>
> To accomplish this it is recommended that:
>
> A. Contracts be negotiated with a few selected universities to provide scientific teams to investigate promptly and in depth certain selected sightings of UFO's. Each team should include at least one psychologist, preferably one interested in clinical psychology, and at least one physical scientist, preferably an astronomer or geophysicist familiar with atmospheric physics. The universities should be chosen to provide good geographical distribution, and should be within convenient distance of a base of the Air Force Systems Command (AFSC).
>
> B. At each AFSC base an officer skilled in investigation (but not necessarily with scientific training) should be desig-

nated to work with the corresponding university team for that geographical section. The local representative of the Air Force Office of Special Investigations (OSI) might be a logical choice for this.

C. One university or one not-for-profit organization should be selected to coordinate the work of the teams mentioned under A above, and also to make certain of very close communication and coordination with the office of Project Blue Book.

It is thought that perhaps 100 sightings a year might be subjected to this close study, and that possibly an average of 10 man days might be required per sighting so studied. The information provided by such a program might bring to light new facts of scientific value, and would almost certainly provide a far better basis than we have today for decision on a long term UFO program.

These recommendations were referred by the Secretary of the Air Force to the Air Force Office of Scientific Research for implementation, which, after study, decided to combine recommendations A and C so as to have a single contracting university with authority to subcontract with other research groups as needed. Recommendation B was implemented by the issuance of Air Force Regulation 80-17 (Appendix B) which establishes procedures for handling UFO reports at the Air Force bases.

In setting up the Colorado project, as already stated in Section I, the emphasis was on whether deeper study of unidentified flying objects might provide some "additions to scientific knowledge."

After considering various possibilities, the AFOSR staff decided to ask the University of Colorado to undertake the project (see Preface). Dr. J. Thomas Ratchford visited Boulder in late July 1966 to learn whether the University would be willing to undertake the task. A second meeting was held on 10 August 1966 in which the scope of the proposed study was outlined to an interested group of the administrative staff and faculty of the University by Dr. Ratchford and Dr. William Price, executive director of AFOSR. After due deliberation, University officials decided to undertake the project.

The contract provided that the planning, direction and conclusions of the Colorado project were to be conducted wholly independently of the Air Force. To avoid duplication of effort, the Air Force was ordered to furnish the project with the records of its own earlier work and to provide the support of personnel at AF bases when requested by our field teams.

We were assured that the federal government would withhold no information on the subject, and that all essential information about UFOs could be included in this report. Where UFO sightings involve classified missile launchings or involve the use of classified radar systems, this fact is merely stated as to do more would involve violation of security on these military subjects. In our actual experience these reservations have affected a negligible fraction of the total material and have not affected the conclusions (Section I) which we draw from our work.

The first research contract with AFOSR provided $313,000 for the first 15 months from 1 November 1966 to 31 January 1968. The contract was publicly announced on 7 October 1966. It then became our task to investigate those curious entities distinguished by lack of knowledge of what they are, rather than in terms of what they are known to be, namely, unidentified flying objects.

2. *Definition of an UFO*

An unidentified flying object (UFO, pronounced OOFO) is here defined as the stimulus for a report made by one or more individuals of something seen in the sky (or an object thought to be capable of flight but seen when landed on the earth) which the observer could not identify as having an ordinary natural origin, and which seemed to him sufficiently puzzling that he undertook to make a report of it to police, to government officials, to the press, or perhaps to a representative of a private organization devoted to the study of such objects.

Defined in this way, there is no question as to the existence of UFOs, because UFO reports exist in fairly large numbers, and the stimulus for each report is, by this definition, an UFO. The problem then becomes that of learning to recognize the various kinds of stimuli that give rise to UFO reports.

The UFO is "the stimulus for a report . . . ." This language refrains from saying whether the reported object was a real, physical, material thing, or a visual impression of an ordinary physical thing distorted by atmospheric conditions or by faulty vision so as to be unrecognizable, or whether it was a purely mental delusion existing in the mind of the observer without an accompanying visual stimulus.

The definition includes insincere reports in which the alleged sighter undertakes for whatever reason to deceive. In the case of a delusion, the reporter is not aware of the lack of a visual stimulus. In the case of a deception, the reporter knows that he is not telling the truth about his alleged experience.

The words "which he could not identify . . ." are of crucial importance. The stimulus gives rise to an UFO report precisely because the observer could not identify the thing seen. A woman and her husband reported a strange thing seen flying in the sky and reported quite correctly that she knew "it was unidentified because neither of us knew what it was."

The thing seen and reported may have been an object as commonplace as the planet Venus, but it became an UFO because the observer did not know what it was. With this usage it is clear that less well informed individuals are more likely to see an UFO than those who are more knowledgeable because the latter are better able to make direct identification of what they see. A related complication is that less well informed persons are often inaccurate observers who are unable to give an accurate account of what they believe that they have seen.

If additional study of a report later provides an ordinary interpretation of what was seen, some have suggested that we should change its name to IFO, for identified flying object. But we have elected to go on calling it an UFO because some identifications are tentative or controversial, due to lack of sufficient data on which to base a definite identification. A wide variety of ordinary objects have through misinterpretation given rise to UFO reports. This topic is discussed in detail in Section VI, Chapter 2. (The Air Force has published a pamphlet entitled, "Aids to Identification of Flying Objects" (USAF, 1968) which is a useful aid in the interpretation of something seen which might otherwise be an UFO.)

The words "sufficiently puzzling that they undertook to make a report . . . " are essential. As a practical matter, we can not study something that is not reported, so a puzzling thing seen but not reported is not here classed as an UFO.

3. *UFO Reports*

In our experience, the persons making reports seem in nearly all cases to be normal, responsible individuals. In most cases they are quite calm, at least by the time they make a report. They are simply puzzled about what they saw and hope that they can be helped to a better understanding of it. Only a very few are obviously quite emotionally disturbed, their minds being filled with pseudo-scientific, pseudo-religious or other fantasies. Cases of this kind range from slight disturbance to those who are manifestly in need of psychiatric care. The latter form an extremely small minority of all the persons encountered in this study. While the existence of a few mentally unbalanced persons among UFO observers is part of the total situation, it is completely incorrect and unfair to imply that all who report UFOs are "crazy kooks," just as it is equally incorrect to ignore the fact that there are mentally disturbed persons among them.

Individuals differ greatly as to their tendency to make reports. Among the reasons for not reporting UFOs are apathy, lack of awareness of public interest, fear of ridicule, lack of knowledge as to where to report and the time and cost of making a report.

We found that reports are not useful unless they are made promptly. Even so, because of the short duration of most UFO stimuli, the report usually can not be made until after the UFO has disappeared. A few people telephoned to us from great distances to describe something seen a year or two earlier. Such reports are of little value.

Early in the study we tried to estimate the fraction of all of the sightings that are reported. In social conversations many persons would tell us about some remarkable and puzzling thing that they had seen at some time in the past which would sound just as remarkable as many of the things that are to be found in UFO report files. Then we would ask whether they had made a report and in most cases would be told that they had not. As a rough guess based on this uncontrolled sample, we estimate that perhaps 10% of the sightings that people are willing to talk about later are all that get reported at the time. This point was later covered in a more formal public attitude survey (Section III, Chapter 7) made for this study in which only 7% of those who said they had seen an UFO had reported it previously. Thus if all people reported sightings that are like those that some people do report, the number of reports that would be received would be at least ten times greater than the number actually received.

At first we thought it would be desirable to undertake an extensive publicity campaign to try to get more complete reporting from the public. It was decided not to do this, because about 90% of all UFO reports prove to be quite plausibly related to ordinary objects. A tenfold increase in the number of reports would have multiplied by ten the task of eliminating the ordinary cases which would have to be analyzed. Our available resources for field study enabled us to deal only with a small fraction of the reports coming in. No useful purpose would have been served under these circumstances by stimulating the receipt of an even greater number.

Study of records of some UFO reports from other parts of the world gave us the strong impression that these were made up of a mix of cases of similar kind to those being reported in the United States. For example, in August 1967 Prof. James McDonald of Arizona made a 20-day trip to Australia, Tasmania and New Zealand in the course of which he interviewed some 80 persons who had made UFO reports there at various times. On his return he gave us an account of these experiences that confirmed our impression that the reports from these other parts of the world were, as a class, similar to those being received in the United States. Therefore we decided to restrict our field studies to the United States and to one or two cases in Canada (See Section III, Chapter 1). This was done on the practical grounds of reducing travel expense and of avoiding diplomatic and language difficulties. The policy was decided on after preliminary study had indicated that in broad generality the spectrum of kinds of UFO reports being received in other countries was very similar to our own.

4. *Prologue to the Project*

Official interest in UFOs, or "flying saucers" as they were called, at first dates from June 1947. On 24 June, Kenneth

Arnold, a business man of Boise, Idaho was flying a private airplane near Mt. Rainier, Washington. He reported seeing a group of objects flying along in a line which he said looked "like pie plates skipping over the water." The newspaper reports called the things seen "flying saucers" and they have been so termed ever since, although not all UFOs are described as being of this shape.

Soon reports of flying saucers were coming in from various parts of the country. Many received prominent press coverage (Bloecher, 1967). UFOs were also reported from other countries; in fact, more than a thousand such reports were made in Sweden in 1946.

The details of reports vary so greatly that it is impossible to relate them all to any single explanation. The broad range of things reported is much the same in different countries. This means that a general explanation peculiar to any one country has to be ruled out, since it is utterly improbable that the secret military aircraft of any one country would be undergoing test flights in different countries. Similarly it is most unlikely that military forces of different countries would be testing similar developments all over the world at the same time in secrecy from each other.

Defense authorities had to reckon with the possibility that UFOs might represent flights of a novel military aircraft of some foreign power. Private citizens speculated that the UFOs were test flights of secret American aircraft. Cognizance of the UFO problem was naturally assumed by the Department of the Air Force in the then newly established Department of Defense. Early investigations were carried on in secrecy by the Air Force, and also by the governments of other nations.

Such studies in the period 1947-52 convinced the responsible authorities of the Air Force that the UFOs, as observed up to that time, do not constitute a threat to national security. In consequence, ever since that time, a minimal amount of attention has been given to them.

The year 1952 brought an unusually large number of UFO reports, including many in the vicinity of the Washington National Airport, during a period of several days in July. Such a concentration of reports in a small region in a short time is called a "flap." The Washington flap of 1952 received a great deal of attention at the time (Section III, Chapter 5).

At times in 1952, UFO reports were coming in to the Air Force from the general public in such numbers as to produce some clogging of military communications channels. It was thought that an enemy planning a sneak attack might deliberately stimulate a great wave of UFO reports for the very purpose of clogging communication facilities. This consideration was in the forefront of a study that was made in January 1953 by a panel of scientists under the chairmanship of the late H. P. Robertson, professor of mathematical physics at the California Institute of Technology (Section V, Chapter 2). This panel recommended that efforts be made to remove the aura of mystery surrounding the subject and to conduct a campaign of public education designed to produce a better understanding of the situation. This group also concluded that there was no evidence in the available data of any real threat to national security.

Since 1953 the results of UFO study have been unclassified, except where tangential reasons exist for withholding details, as, for example, where sightings are related to launchings of classified missiles, or to the use of classified radar systems.

During the period from March 1952 to the present, the structure for handling UFO reports in the Air Force has been called Project Blue Book. As already mentioned the work of Project Blue Book was reviewed in early 1966 by the committee headed by Dr. Brian O'Brien. This review led to the reaffirmation that no security threat is posed by the existence of a few unexplained UFO reports, but the committee suggested a study of the possibility that something of scientific value might come from a more detailed study of some of the reports than was considered necessary from a strictly military viewpoint. This recommendation eventuated in the setting up of the Colorado project.

The story of Air Force interest, presented in Section V, Chapter 2, shows that from the beginning the possibility that some UFOs might be manned vehicles from outer space was considered, but naturally no publicity was given to this idea because of the total lack of evidence for it.

Paralleling the official government interest, was a burgeoning of amateur interest stimulated by newspaper and magazine reports. By 1950 popular books on the subject began to appear on the newsstands. In January 1950 the idea that UFOs were extraterrestrial vehicles was put forward as a reality in an article entitled "Flying Saucers are Real" in *True* magazine written by Donald E. Keyhoe, a retired Marine Corps major. Thereafter a steady stream of sensational writing about UFOs has aroused a considerable amount of interest among laymen in studying the subject.

Many amateur organizations exist, some of them rather transiently, so that it would be difficult to compile an accurate listing of them. Two such organizations in the United States have a national structure. These are the Aerial Phenomena Research Organization (APRO), with headquarters in Tucson, Arizona, claiming about 8000 members; and the National Investigations Committee for Aerial Phenomena (NICAP) with headquarters in Washington, D. C. and claiming some 12,000 members. James and Coral Lorenzen head APRO, while Keyhoe is the director of NICAP, which, despite the name and Washington address is not a government agency. Many other smaller groups exist, among them Saucers and Unexplained

Celestial Events Research Society (SAUCERS) operated by James Moseley.

Of these organizations, NICAP devotes a considerable amount of its attention to attacking the Air Force and to trying to influence members of Congress to hold hearings and in other ways to join in these attacks. It maintained a friendly relation to the Colorado project during about the first year, while warning its members to be on guard lest the project turn out to have been "hired to whitewash the Air Force." During this period NICAP made several efforts to influence the course of our study. When it became clear that these would fail, NICAP attacked the Colorado project as "biased" and therefore without merit.

The organizations mentioned espouse a scientific approach to the study of the subject. In addition there are a number of others that have a primarily religious orientation.

From 1947 to 1966 almost no attention was paid to the UFO problem by well qualified scientists. Some of the reasons for this lack of interest have been clearly stated by Prof. Gerard P. Kuiper of the University of Arizona (Appendix C). Concerning the difficulty of establishing that some UFOs may come from outer space, he makes the following cogent observation: "The problem is more difficult than finding a needle in a haystack; it is finding a piece of extra-terrestrial hay in a terrestrial haystack, often on the basis of reports of believers in extra-terrestrial hay."

5. *Initial Planning*

A scientific approach to the UFO phenomenon must embrace a wide range of disciplines. It involves such physical sciences as physics, chemistry, aerodynamics, and meteorology. Since the primary material consists mostly of reports of individual observers, the psychology of perception, the physiology of defects of vision, and the study of mental states are also involved.

Social psychology and social psychiatry are likewise involved in seeking to understand group motivations which act to induce belief in extraordinary hypotheses on the basis of what most scientists and indeed most laymen would regard as little or no evidence. These problems of medical and social psychology deserve more attention than we were able to give them. They fell distinctly outside of the field of expertise of our staff, which concentrated more on the study of the UFOs themselves than on the personal and social problems generated by them.

Among those who write and speak on the subject, some strongly espouse the view that the federal government really knows a great deal more about UFOs than is made public. Some have gone so far as to assert that the government has actually captured extraterrestrial flying saucers and has their crews in secret captivity, if not in the Pentagon, then at some secret military base. We believe that such teachings are fantastic nonsense, that it would be impossible to keep a secret of such enormity over two decades, and that no useful purpose would be served by engaging in such an alleged conspiracy of silence. One person with whom we have dealt actually maintains that the Air Force has nothing to do with UFOs, claiming that this super-secret matter is in the hands of the Central Intelligence Agency which, he says, installed one of its own agents as scientific director of the Colorado study. This story, if true, is indeed a well kept secret. These allegations of a conspiracy on the part of our own government to conceal knowledge of the existence of "flying saucers" have, so far as any evidence that has come to our attention, no factual basis whatever.

The project's first attention was given to becoming familiar with past work in the subject. This was more difficult than in more orthodox fields because almost none of the many books and magazine articles dealing with UFOs could be regarded as scientifically reliable. There were the two books of Donald H. Menzel, director emeritus of the Harvard College Observatory and now a member of the staff of the Smithsonian Astrophysical Observatory (Menzel, 1952; Menzel and Boyd, 1963). Two other useful books were *The UFO Evidence* (1964), a compilation of UFO cases by Richard Hall, and *The Report on Unidentified Flying Objects* by E. J. Ruppelt (1956), the first head of Project Blue Book. In this initial stage we were also helped by "briefings" given by Lt. Col. Hector Quintanilla, the present head of Project Blue Book, Dr. J. Allen Hynek, astronomical consultant to Project Blue Book, and by Donald Keyhoe and Richard Hall of NICAP.

Out of this preliminary study came the recognition of a variety of topics that would require detailed attention. These included the effects of optical mirages, the analogous anomalies of radio wave propagation as they affect radar, critical analysis of alleged UFO photographs, problems of statistical analysis of UFO reports, chemical analysis of alleged material from UFOs, and reports of disturbances to automobile ignition and to headlights from the presence of UFOs. Results of the project's study of these and other topics are presented in this section and in Sections III and VI of this report.

6. *Field Investigations*

Early attention was given to the question of investigation of individual cases, either by detailed critical study of old records or by field trip investigation of current cases. From this study we concluded that there was little to be gained from the study of old cases, except perhaps to get ideas on mistakes to be avoided in studies of new cases. We therefore decided not to make field trips to investigate cases that were more than a year old, although in a few cases we did do some work on such cases when their study could be combined with a field investigation of a new case.

At first we hoped that field teams could respond to early warning so quickly that they would be able to get to the site while the UFO was still there, and that our teams would not only get their own photographs, but even obtain spectrograms of the light of the UFO, and make radioactive, magnetic, and sound measurements while the UFO was still present.

Such expectations were found to be in vain. Nearly all UFO sightings are of very short duration, seldom lasting as long as an hour and usually lasting for a few minutes. The observers often become so excited that they do not report at all until the UFO has gone away. With communication and travel delays, the field team was unable to get to the scene until long after the UFO had vanished.

This was, of course, a highly unsatisfactory situation. We gave much thought to how it could be overcome and concluded that this could only be done by a great publicity campaign designed to get the public to report sightings much more promptly than it does, coupled with a nationwide scheme of having many trained field teams scattered at many points across the nation. These teams would have had to be ready to respond at a moment's notice. Even so, in the vast majority of the cases, they would not have arrived in time for direct observation of the reported UFO. Moreover, the national publicity designed to insure more prompt reporting would have had the effect of arousing exaggerated public concern over the subject, and certainly would have vastly increased the number of nonsense reports to which response would have had to be made. In recruiting the large number of field teams, great care would have had to be exercised to make sure that they were staffed with people of adequate scientific training, rather than with persons emotionally committed to extreme *pro* or *con* views on the subject.

Clearly this was quite beyond the means of our study. Such a program to cover the entire United States would cost many millions of dollars a year, and even then there would have been little likelihood that anything of importance would have been uncovered.

In a few cases some physical evidence could be gathered by examination of a site where an UFO was reported to have landed. In such a case it did not matter that the field team arrived after the UFO had gone. But in no case did we obtain any convincing evidence of this kind although every effort was made to do so. (See below and in Section III, Chapters 3 and 4).

Thus most of the field investigation, as it turned out, consisted in the interviewing of persons who made the report. By all odds the most used piece of physical equipment was the tape recorder.

The question of a number of investigators on a field team was an important one. In most work done in the past by the Air Force, UFO observers were interviewed by a single Air Force officer, who usually had no special training and whose freedom to devote much time to the study was limited by the fact that he also had other responsibilities. When field studies are made by amateur organizations like APRO or NICAP, there are often several members present on a team, but usually they are persons without technical training, and often with a strong bias toward the sensational aspects of the subject.

Prof. Hynek strongly believes that the teams should have four or more members. He recommends giving each report what he calls the "FBI treatment," by which he means not only thorough interviewing of the persons who made the report, but in addition an active quest in the neighborhood where the sighting occurred to try to discover additional witnesses. Against such thoroughness must be balanced the consideration that the cost per case goes up proportionately to the number of persons in a team, so that the larger the team, the fewer the cases that can be studied.

The detailed discussions in Section III, Chapter 1 and in Section IV make it clear that the field work is associated with many frustrations. Many of the trips turn out to be wild goose chases and the team members often feel as if they are members of the fire department that mostly answers false alarms.

We found that it was always worthwhile to do a great deal of initial interviewing by long distance telephone. A great many reports that seem at first to be worthy of full field investigation could be disposed of in this way with comparatively little trouble and expense. Each case presented its own special problems. No hard-and-fast rule was found by which to decide in advance whether a particular report was worth the trouble of a field trip.

After careful consideration of these various factors, we decided to operate with two-man teams, composed whenever possible of one person with training in physical science and one with training in psychology. When the study became fully operational in 1967 we had three such teams. Dr. Roy Craig describes the work of these teams in Section III, Chapters 1, 3, and 4. Reports of field investigations are presented in Section IV.

7. *Explaining UFO Reports*

By definition UFOs exist because UFO reports exist. What makes the whole subject intriguing is the possibility that some of these reports cannot be reconciled with ordinary explanations, so that some extraordinarily sensational explanation for them might have to be invoked. A fuller discussion of some misinterpretations of ordinary events by Dr. W. K. Hartmann is given in Section VI, Chapter 2.

A great many reports are readily identified with ordinary phenomena seen under unusual circumstances, or noted by someone who is an inexperienced, inept, or unduly excited observer. Because such reports are vague and inaccurate, it is often impossible to make an identification with certainty.

This gives rise to controversy. In some cases, an identification that the UFO was "probably" an aircraft is all that can be made from the available data. After the event no amount of further interviewing of one or more witnesses can usually change such a probable into a certain identification. Field workers who would like to identify as many as possible are naturally disposed to claim certainty when this is at all possible, but others who desire to have a residue of unexplained cases in order to add mystery and importance to the UFO problem incline to set impossibly high standards of certainty in the evidence before they are willing to accept a simple explanation for a report.

This dilemma is nicely illustrated by a question asked in the House of Commons of Prime Minister Harold Wilson, as reported in *Hansard* for 19 December 1967:

> Unidentified Flying Objects. Question 14. Sir J. Langford-Holt asked the Prime Minister whether he is satisfied that all sightings of unidentified flying objects which are reported from service sources are explainable, what inquiries he has authorised into these objects outside the defence aspect, and whether he will now appoint one Minister to look into all aspects of reports.
>
> The Prime Minister: The answers are 'Yes, except when the information given is insufficient,' 'None' and 'No.'

Obviously there is a nice bit of semantics here in that the definition of "when the information is sufficient" is that it is sufficient when an explanation can be given.

Discussions of whether a marginal case should be regarded for statistical purposes as having been explained or not have proved to be futile. Some investigators take the position that, where a plausible interpretation in terms of commonplace events can be made, then the UFO is regarded as having been identified. Others take the opposite view that an UFO cannot be regarded as having been given an ordinary identification unless there is complete and binding evidence amounting to certainty about the proposed identification.

For example, in January 1968 near Castle Rock, Colo., some 30 persons reported UFOs, including spacecraft with flashing lights, fantastic maneuverability, and even with occupants presumed to be from outer space. Two days later it was more modestly reported that two high school boys had launched a polyethylene hot-air balloon.

Locally that was the end of the story. But there is a sequel. A man in Florida makes a practice of collecting newspaper stories about UFOs and sending them out in a mimeographed UFO news letter which he mails to various UFO journals and local clubs. He gave currency to the Castle Rock reports but not to the explanation that followed. When he was chided for not having done so, he declared that no one could be *absolutely* sure that *all* the Castle Rock reports arose from sightings of the balloon. There might also have been an UFO from outer space among the sightings. No one would dispute his logic, but one may with propriety wonder why he neglected to tell his readers that at least *some* of the reports were actually misidentifications of a hot-air balloon.

As a practical matter, we take the position that if an UFO report can be plausibly explained in ordinary terms, then we accept that explanation even though not enough evidence may be available to prove it beyond all doubt. This point is so important that perhaps an analogy is needed to make it clear. Several centuries ago, the most generally accepted theory of human disease was that it was caused by the patient's being possessed or inhabited by a devil or evil spirit. Different diseases were supposed to be caused by different devils. The guiding principle for medical research was then the study and classification of different kinds of devils, and progress in therapy was sought in the search for and discovery of means for exorcising each kind of devil.

Gradually medical research discovered bacteria, toxins and viruses, and their causative relation to various diseases. More and more diseases came to be described by their causes.

Suppose now that instead, medicine had clung to the devil theory of disease. As long as there exists one human illness that is not yet fully understood in modern terms such a theory cannot be disproved. It is always possible, while granting that *some* diseases are caused by viruses, etc. to maintain that those that are not yet understood are the ones that are really caused by devils.

In some instances the same sort of UFO is observed night after night under similar circumstances. In our experience this has been a sure sign that the UFO could be correlated with some ordinary phenomenon.

For example, rather early in our work, a Colorado farmer reported seeing an UFO land west of his farm nearly every evening about 6:00 p.m. A field team went to see him and quickly and unambiguously identified the UFO as the planet Saturn. The nights on which he did not see it land were those in which the western sky was cloudy.

But the farmer did not easily accept our identification of his UFO as Saturn. He contended that, while his UFO had landed behind the mountains on the particular evening that we visited him, on most nights, he insisted, it landed in front of the mountains, and therefore could not be a planet. The identification with Saturn from the ephemeris was so precise that we did not visit his farm night after night in order to see for ourselves whether his UFO ever landed in front of the mountains. We did not regard it as part of our duty to persuade observers of the correctness of our interpretations. In most cases observers readily accepted our explanation, and some expressed relief at having an everyday explanation available to them.

We sought to hold to a minimum delays in arriving at the site of an UFO report, even where it was clear that it was going to be impossible to get there in time actually to see the reported UFO. Once an observer made a report, the fact of his having done so usually becomes known to friends and neighbors, local newspapermen, and local UFO enthusiasts. The witness becomes the center of attention and will usually have told his story over and over again to such listeners, before the field team can arrive. With each telling of the story it is apt to be varied and embellished a little. This need not be from dishonest motives. We all like to tell an interesting story. We would rather not bore our listeners if we can help it, so embellishment is sometimes added to maximize the interest value of the narration.

It is not easy to detect how a story has grown under retelling in this way. Listeners usually will have asked leading questions and the story will have developed in response to such suggestions, so that it soon becomes impossible for the field team to hear the witness's story as he told it the first time. In some cases when the witness had been interviewed in this way by local UFO enthusiasts, his story was larded with vivid language about visitors from outer space that was probably not there in the first telling.

Another kind of difficulty arises in interviewing multiple associated witnesses, that is, witnesses who were together at the time that all of them saw the UFO. Whenever several individuals go through an exciting experience together, they are apt to spend a good deal of time discussing it afterward among themselves, telling and retelling it to each other, unconsciously ironing out discrepancies between their various recollections, and gradually converging on a single uniform account of the experience. Dominant personalities will have contributed more to the final version than the less dominant. Thus the story told by a group of associated witnesses who have had ample opportunity to "compare notes" will be more uniform than the accounts these individuals would have given if interviewed separately before they had talked the matter over together.

One of the earliest of our field trips (December 1966) was made to Washington, D. C. to interview separately two air traffic control operators who had been involved in the great UFO flap there in the summer of 1952. Fourteen years later, these two men were still quite annoyed at the newspaper publicity they had received, because it had tended to ridicule their reports. Our conclusion from this trip was that these men were telling in 1966 stories that were thoroughly consistent with the main points of their stories as told in 1952. Possibly this was due to the fact that because of their strong emotional involvement they had recounted the incident to many persons at many times over the intervening years. Although it was true that the stories had not changed appreciably in 14 years, it was also true for this very reason that we acquired no new material by interviewing these men again. (See Section III, Chapter 5.)

On the basis of this experience we decided that it was not profitable to devote much effort to re-interviewing persons who had already been interviewed rather thoroughly at a previous time. We do not say that nothing can be gained in this way, but merely that it did not seem to us that this would be a profitable way to spend our effort in this study.

In our experience those who report UFOs are often very articulate, but not necessarily reliable. One evening in 1967 a most articulate gentleman told us with calm good manners all of the circumstances of a number of UFOs he had seen that had come from outer space, and in particular went into some detail about how his wife's grandfather had immigrated to America from the Andromeda nebula, a galaxy located 2,000,000 light years from the earth.

In a few cases study of old reports may give the investigator a clue to a possible interpretation that had not occurred to the original investigator. In such a case, a later interview of the witness may elicit new information that was not brought out in the earlier interview. But we found that such interviews need to be conducted with great care as it is easily possible that the "new" information may have been generated through the unconscious use of leading questions pointing toward the new interpretation, and so may not be reliable for that reason.

8. *Sources of UFO Reports*

Usually the first report of an UFO is made to a local police officer or to a local news reporter. In some cases, members of UFO study organizations are sufficiently well known in the community that reports are made directly to them. In spite of the very considerable publicity that has been given to this subject, a large part of the public still does not know of the official Air Force interest.

Even some policemen and newsmen do not know of it and so do not pass on the UFO report. In other cases, we found that the anti-Air Force publicity efforts of some UFO enthusiasts had persuaded observers, who would otherwise have done so, not to report to the Air Force. We have already commented on the fact that for a variety of reasons many persons who do have UFO experiences do not report promptly.

Ideally the entire public would have known that each Air Force base must, according to AFR 80-17, have an UFO officer and would have reported promptly any extraordinary thing seen in the sky. Or, if this were too much to expect, then all police and news agencies would ideally have known of Air Force interest and would have passed information along to the nearest Air Force base. But none of these ideal things were true, and as a result our collection of UFO reports is extremely haphazard and incomplete.

When a report is made to an Air Force base, it is handled by an UFO officer whose form of investigation and report is prescribed by AFR 80-17 (Appendix A). If the explanation of the report is immediately obvious and trivial—some persons will telephone a base to report a contrail from a high-flying jet that is particularly bright in the light of the setting sun—the UFO officer tells the person what it was he saw, and there the matter ends. No permanent record of such calls is made. As a result there is no record of the total number of UFO reports made to AF bases. Only those that require more than cursory consideration are reported to Project Blue Book. Air Force officers are human, and therefore interpret their duty quite differently. Some went to great lengths not to submit a report. Others took special delight in reporting all of the "easy" ones out of a zealous loyalty to their service, because the more "identifieds" they turned in, the higher would be the over-all percentage of UFO reports explained. When in June 1967 Air Force UFO officers from the various bases convened in Boulder some of them quite vigorously debated the relative merits of these two different extreme views of their duty.

Many people have from time to time tried to learn something significant about UFOs by studying statistically the distribution of UFO reports geographically, in time, and both factors together. In our opinion these efforts have proved to be quite fruitless. The difficulties are discussed in Section VI, Chapter 10.

The geographical distribution of reports correlates roughly with population density of the non-urban population. Very few reports come from the densely-populated urban areas. Whether this is due to urban sophistication or to the scattering of city lights is not known, but it is more probably the latter.

There apparently exists no single complete collection of UFO reports. The largest file is that maintained by Project Blue Book at Wright-Patterson Air Force Base, Ohio. Other files are maintained by APRO in Tucson and NICAP in Washington. The files of Project Blue Book are arranged by date and place of occurrence of the report, so that one must know these data in order to find a particular case. Proposals have been made from time to time for a computer-indexing of these reports by various categories but this has not been carried out. Two publications are available which partially supply this lack: one is *The UFO Evidence* (Hall, 1964) and the other is a collection of reports called *The Reference for Outstanding UFO Reports* (Olsen,).

We have already mentioned the existence of flaps, that is, the tendency of reports to come in clusters at certain times in certain areas. No quantitative study of this is available, but we believe that the clustering tendency is partly due to changing amounts of attention devoted to the subject by the news media. Publicity for some reports stimulates more reports, both because people pay more attention to the sky at such a time, and because they are more likely to make a report of something which attracts their attention.

In the summer of 1967 there was a large UFO flap in the neighborhood of Harrisburg, Pa. This may have been in part produced by the efforts of a local NICAP member working in close association with a reporter for the local afternoon newspaper who wrote an exciting UFO story for his paper almost daily. Curiously enough, the morning paper scarcely ever had an UFO story from which we conclude that one editor's news is another's filler. We stationed one of our investigators there during August with results that are described in Case 27.

Many UFO reports were made by the public to Olmsted Air Force Base a few miles south of Harrisburg, but when this base was deactivated during the summer UFO reports had to be made to McGuire Air Force Base near Trenton, N. J. This required a toll call, and the frequency of receipt of UFO reports from the Harrisburg area dropped abruptly.

For all of these various reasons, we feel that the fluctuations geographically and in time of UFO reports are so greatly influenced by sociological factors, that any variations due to changes in underlying physical phenomena are completely masked.

In sensational UFO journalism the statement is often made that UFOs show a marked tendency to be seen more often near military installations. There is no statistically significant evidence that this is true. For sensational writers, this alleged but unproven concentration of UFO sightings is taken as evidence that extra-terrestrial visitors are reconnoitering our military defenses, preparatory to launching a military attack at some time in the future. Even if a slight effect of this kind were to be established by careful statistical studies, we feel that it could be easily accounted for by the fact that at every base men stand all night guard duty and so unusual things in the sky are more likely to be seen. Moreover civilians living near a military base are more likely to make a report to the base than those living at some distance from it.

AFR 80-17a directed UFO officers at each base to send to

the Colorado project a duplicate of each report sent to Project Blue Book. This enabled us to keep track of the quality of the investigations and to be informed about puzzling uninterpreted cases. Such reporting was useful in cases whose study extended over a long period, but the slowness of receipt of such reports made this arrangement not completely satisfactory as a source of reports on the basis of which to direct the activity of our own field teams. A few reports that seemed quite interesting to Air Force personnel caused them to notify us by teletype or telephone. Some of our field studies arose from reports received in this way.

To supplement Air Force reporting, we set up our own Early Warning Network, a group of about 60 active volunteer field reporters, most of whom were connected with APRO or NICAP. They telephoned or telegraphed to us intelligence of UFO sightings in their own territory and conducted some preliminary investigation for us while our team was en route. Some of this cooperation was quite valuable. In the spring of 1968, Donald Keyhoe, director of NICAP, ordered discontinuation of this arrangement, but many NICAP field teams continued to cooperate.

All of these sources provided many more quickly reported, fresh cases than our field teams could study in detail. In consequence we had to develope criteria for quickly selecting which of the cases reported to us would be handled with a field trip (See Section III, Chapter 1).

9. Extra-terrestrial Hypothesis

The idea that some UFOs *may* be spacecraft sent to Earth from another civilization, residing on another planet of the solar system, or on a planet associated with a more distant star than the Sun, is called the Extra-terrestrial Hypothesis (ETH). Some few persons profess to hold a stronger level of belief in the *actuality* of UFOs being visitors from outer space, controlled by intelligent beings, rather than merely of the *possibility*, not yet fully established as an observational fact. We shall call this level of belief ETA, for extra-terrestrial actuality.

It is often difficult to be sure just what level of belief is held by various persons, because of the vagueness with which they state their ideas.

For example, addressing the American Society of Newspaper Editors in Washington on 22 April 1967, Dr. McDonald declared: "There is, in my present opinion, no sensible alternative to the utterly shocking hypothesis that the UFOs are extraterrestrial probes from somewhere else." Then in an Australian broadcast on 20 August 1967 McDonald said: ". . . you find yourself ending up with the seemingly absurd, seemingly improbable hypothesis that these things may come from somewhere else."

A number of other scientists have also expressed themselves as believers in ETH, if not ETA, but usually in more cautious terms.

The general idea of space travel by humans from Earth and visitors to Earth from other civilizations is an old one and has been the subject of many works of fiction. In the past 250 years the topic has been widely developed in science fiction. A fascinating account of the development of this literary form is given in *Pilgrims through Space and Time—Trends and Patterns in Scientific and Utopian Fiction* (Bailey, 1947).

The first published suggestion that some UFOs are visitors from other civilizations is contained in an article in *True*, entitled "Flying Saucers are Real" by Donald E. Keyhoe (1950).

Direct, convincing and unequivocal evidence of the truth of ETA would be the greatest single scientific discovery in the history of mankind. Going beyond its interest for science, it would undoubtedly have consequences of surpassing significance for every phase of human life. Some persons who have written speculatively on this subject, profess to believe that the supposed extraterrestrial visitors come with beneficent motives, to help humanity clean up the terrible mess that it has made. Others say they believe that the visitors are hostile. Whether their coming would be favorable or unfavorable to mankind, it is almost certain that they would make great changes in the conditions of human existence.

It is characteristic of most reports of actual visitors from outer space that there is no corroborating witness to the alleged incident, so that the story must be accepted, if at all, solely on the basis of belief in the veracity of the one person who claims to have had the experience. In the cases which we studied, there was only one in which the observer claimed to have had contact with a visitor from outer space. On the basis of of our experience with that one, and our own unwillingness to believe the literal truth of the Villas-Boas incident, or the one from Truckee, Calif. reported by Prof. James Harder (see Section V, Chapter 2), we found that no direct evidence whatever of a convincing nature now exists for the claim that any UFOs represent spacecraft visiting Earth from another civilization.

Some persons are temperamentally ready, even eager, to accept ETA without clear observational evidence. One lady remarked, "It would be so wonderfully exciting if it were true!" It certainly would be exciting, but that does not make it true. When confronted with a proposition of such great import, responsible scientists adopt a cautiously critical attitude toward whatever evidence is adduced to support it. Persons without scientific training, often confuse this with basic opposition to the idea, with a biased desire or hope, or even of willingness to distort the evidence in order to conclude that ETA is not true.

The scientists' caution in such a situation does not represent opposition to the idea. It represents a determination not to accept the proposition as true in the absence of evidence that clearly, unambiguously and with certainty establishes its truth or falsity.

Scientifically it is not necessary—it is not even desirable—to adopt a position about the truth or falsity of ETA in order to investigate the question. There is a widespread misconception that scientific inquiry represents some kind of debate in which the truth is adjudged to be on the side of the team that has scored the most points. Scientists investigate an undecided proposition by seeking to find ways to get decisive observational material. Sometimes the ways to get such data are difficult to conceive, difficult to carry out, and so indirect that the rest of the scientific world remains uncertain of the probative value of the results for a long time. Progress in science can be painfully slow—at other times it can be sudden and dramatic. The question of ETA would be settled in a few minutes if a flying saucer were to land on the lawn of a hotel where a convention of the American Physical Society was in progress, and its occupants were to emerge and present a special paper to the assembled physicists, revealing where they came from, and the technology of how their craft operates. Searching questions from the audience would follow.

In saying that thus far no convincing evidence exists for the truth of ETA, no prediction is made about the future. If evidence appears soon after this report is published, that will not alter the truth of the statement that we do not *now* have such evidence. If new evidence appears later, this report can be appropriately revised in a second printing.

10. *Intelligent Life Elsewhere*

Whether there is intelligent life elsewhere (ILE) in the Universe is a question that has received a great deal of serious speculative attention in recent years. A good popular review of thinking on the subject is *We Are Not Alone* by Walter Sullivan (1964). More advanced discussions are *Interstellar Communication,* a collection of papers edited by A. G. W. Cameron (1963), and *Intelligent Life in the Universe* (Shklovskii and Sagan, 1966). Thus far we have no observational evidence whatever on the question, so therefore it remains open. An early unpublished discussion is a letter of 13 December 1948 of J. E. Lipp to Gen. Donald Putt (Appendix D). This letter is Appendix D of the Project Sign report dated February 1949 from Air Materiel Command Headquarters No. F-TR-2274-IA.

The ILE question has some relation to the ETH or ETA for UFOs as discussed in the preceding section. Clearly, if ETH is true, then ILE must also be true because some UFOs have then to come from some unearthly civilization. Conversely, if we could know conclusively that ILE does not exist, then ETH could not be true. But even if ILE exists, it does not follow that the ETH is true.

For it could be that the ILE, though existent, might not have reached a stage of development in which the beings have the technical capacity or the desire to visit the Earth's surface. Much speculative writing assumes implicitly that intelligent life progresses steadily both in intellectual and in its technological development. Life began on Earth more than a billion years ago, whereas the known geological age of the Earth is some five billion years, so that life in any form has only existed for the most recent one-fifth of the Earth's life as a solid ball orbiting the Sun. Man as an intelligent being has only lived on Earth for some 5,000 years, or about one-millionth of the Earth's age. Technological development is even more recent. Moreover the greater part of what we think of as advanced technology has only been developed in the last 100 years. Even today we do not yet have a technology capable of putting men on other planets of the solar system. Travel of men over interstellar distances in the forseeable future seems now to be quite out of the question. (Purcell, 1960; Markowitz, 1967.)

The dimensions of the universe are hard for the mind of man to conceive. A light-year is the distance light travels in one year of 31.56 million seconds, at the rate of 186,000 miles per second, that is, a distance of 5.88 million million miles. The nearest known star is at a distance of 4.2 light-years.

Fifteen stars are known to be within 11.5 light-years of the Sun. Our own galaxy, the Milky Way, is a vast flattened distribution of some 10^{11} stars about 80,000 light-years in diameter, with the Sun located about 26,000 light-years from the center. To gain a little perspective on the meaning of such distances relative to human affairs, we may observe that the news of Christ's life on Earth could not yet have reached as much as a tenth of the distance from the Earth to the center of our galaxy.

Other galaxies are inconceivably remote. The faintest observable galaxies are at a distance of some two billion light-years. There are some 100 million such galaxies within that distance, the average distance between galaxies being some eight million light-years.

Authors of UFO fantasy literature casually set all of the laws of physics aside in order to try to evade this conclusion, but serious consideration of their ideas hardly belongs in a report on the scientific study of UFOs.

Even assuming that difficulties of this sort could be overcome, we have no right to assume that in life communities everywhere there is a steady evolution in the directions of both greater intelligence and greater technological competence. Human beings now know enough to destroy all life on Earth, and they may lack the intelligence to work out social controls to keep themselves from doing so. If other civilizations have the same limitation then it might be that they develop to the point where they destroy themselves utterly before they have developed the technology needed to enable them to make long space voyages.

Another possibility is that the growth of intelligence precedes the growth of technology in such a way that by the time a society would be technically capable of interstellar space travel, it would have reached a level of intelligence at which it had not the slightest interest in interstellar travel. We must not assume that we are capable of imagining now the scope and extent of future technological development of our own or any other civilization, and so we must guard against assuming that we have any capacity to imagine what a more advanced society would regard as intelligent conduct.

In addition to the great distances involved, and the difficulties which they present to interstellar space travel, there is still another problem: If we assume that civilizations annihilate themselves in such a way that their effective intelligent life span is less than, say, 100,000 years, then such a short time span also works against the likelihood of successful interstellar communication. The different civilizations would probably reach the culmination of their development at different epochs in cosmic history. Moreover, according to present views, stars are being formed constantly by the condensation of interstellar dust and gases. They exist for perhaps 10 billion years, of which a civilization lasting 100,000 years is only 1/100,000 of the life span of the star. It follows that there is an extremely small likelihood that two nearby civilizations would be in a state of high development at the same epoch.

Astronomers now generally agree that a fairly large number of all main-sequence stars are probably accompanied by planets at the right distance from their Sun to provide for habitable conditions for life as we know it. That is, where stars are, there are probably habitable planets. This belief favors the possibility of interstellar communication, but it must be remembered that even this view is entirely speculation: we are quite unable directly to observe any planets associated with stars other than the Sun.

In view of the foregoing, we consider that it is safe to assume that no ILE outside of our solar system has any possibility of visiting Earth in the next 10,000 years.

This conclusion does not rule out the possibility of the existence of ILE, as contrasted with the ability of such civilizations to visit Earth. It is estimated that 10^{21} stars can be seen using the 200-inch Hale telescope on Mount Palomar. Astronomers surmise that possibly as few as one in a million or as many as one in ten of these have a planet in which physical and chemical conditions are such as to make them habitable by life based on the same kind of biochemistry as the life we know on Earth. Even if the lower figure is taken, this would mean there are 10^{15} stars in the visible universe which have planets suitable for an abode of life. In our own galaxy there are 10^{11} stars, so perhaps as many as 10^{8} have habitable planets in orbit around them.

Biologists feel confident that wherever physical and chemical conditions are right, life will actually emerge. In short, astronomers tell us that there are a vast number of stars in the universe accompanied by planets where the physical and chemical conditions are suitable, and biologists tell us that habitable places are sure to become inhabited. (Rush, 1957.)

An important advance was made when Stanley L. Miller (1955) showed experimentally that electrical discharges such as those in natural lightning when passed through a mixture of methane and ammonia, such as may have been present in the Earth's primitive atmosphere, will initiate chemical reactions which yield various amino acids. These are the raw materials from which are constructed the proteins that are essential to life. Miller's work has been followed up and extended by many others, particularly P. H. Abelson of the Carnegie Institution of Washington.

The story is by no means fully worked out. The evidence in hand seems to convince biochemists that natural processes, such as lightning, or the absorption of solar ultraviolet light, could generate the necessary starting materials from which life could evolve. On this basis they generally hold the belief that where conditions make it possible that life could appear, there life actually will appear.

It is regarded by scientists today as essentially certain that ILE exists, but with essentially no possibility of contact between the communities on planets associated with different stars. We therefore conclude that there is no relation between ILE at other solar systems and the UFO phenomenon as observed on Earth.

There remains the question of ILE within our solar system. Here only the planets Venus and Mars need be given consideration as possible abodes of life.

Mercury, the planet nearest the Sun, is certainly too hot to support life. The side of Mercury that is turned toward the Sun has an average temperature of 660°F. Since the orbit is rather eccentric this temperature becomes as high as 770°F, hot enough to melt lead, when Mercury is closest to the Sun. The opposite side is extremely cold, its temperature not being known.* Gravity on Mercury is about one-fourth that on Earth. This fact combined with the high temperature makes it certain that Mercury has no atmosphere, which is consistent with observational data on this point. It is quite impossible that life as found on Earth could exist on Mercury.

* Mercury rotates in 59 days and the orbital period is 88 days, so there is a slow relative rotation.

Jupiter, Saturn, Uranus, Neptune and Pluto are so far from the Sun that they are too cold for life to exist there.

Although it has long been thought that Venus might provide a suitable abode for life, it is now known that the surface of Venus is also too hot for advanced forms of life, although it is possible that some primitive forms may exist. Some uncertainty and controversy exists about the interpretation of observations of Venus because the planet is always enveloped in dense clouds so that the solid surface is never seen. The absorption spectrum of sunlight coming from Venus indicates that the principal constituent of the atmosphere is carbon dioxide. There is no evidence of oxygen or water vapor. With so little oxygen in the atmosphere there could not be animal life there resembling that on Earth.

Although it is safe to conclude that there is no intelligent life on Venus, the contrary idea is held quite tenaciously by certain groups in America. There are small religious groups who maintain that Jesus Christ now sojourns on Venus, and that some of their members have travelled there by flying saucers supplied by the Venusians and have been greatly refreshed spiritually by visiting Him. There is no observational evidence in support of this teaching.

In the fantasy literature of believers in ETH, some attention is given to a purely hypothetical planet named Clarion. Not only is there no direct evidence for its existence, but there is conclusive indirect evidence for its non-existence. Those UFO writers who try not to be totally inconsistent with scientific findings, recognizing that Venus and Mars are unsuitable as abodes of life, have invented Clarion to meet the need for a home for the visitors who they believe come on some UFOs.

They postulate that Clarion moves in an orbit exactly like that of the Earth around the Sun, but with the orbit rotated through half a revolution in its plane so that the two orbits have the same line of apsides, but with Clarion's perihelion in the same direction from the Sun as the Earth's aphelion. The two planets, Earth and Clarion, are postulated to move in their orbits in such a way that they are always opposite each other, so that the line Earth-Sun-Clarion is a straight line. Thus persons on Earth would never see Clarion because it is permanently eclipsed by the Sun.

If the two orbits were exactly circular, the two planets would move along their common orbit at the same speed and so would remain exactly opposite each other. But even if the orbits are elliptical, so that the speed in the orbit is variable, the two planets would vary in speed during the year in just such a way as always to remain opposite each other and thus continue to be permanently eclipsed.

However, this tidy arrangement would not occur in actuality because the motion of each of these two planets would be perturbed by the gravitational attractions between them and the other planets of the solar system, principally Venus and Mars. It is a quite complicated and difficult problem to calculate the way in which these perturbations would affect the motion of Earth and Clarion.

At the request of the Colorado project, Dr. R. L. Duncombe, director of the Nautical Almanac office at U.S. Naval Observatory in Washington, D. C., kindly arranged to calculate the effect of the introduction of the hypothetical planet Clarion into the solar system. The exact result depends to some extent on the location of the Earth-Sun-Clarion line relative to the line of apsides and the computations were carried out merely for one case (see Appendix E).

These calculations show that the effect of the perturbations would be to make Clarion become visible from Earth beyond the Sun's limb after about thirty years. In other words, Clarion would long since have become visible from Earth if many years ago it were started out in such a special way as has been postulated.

The computations revealed further that if Clarion were there it would reveal its presence indirectly in a much shorter time. Its attraction on Venus would cause Venus to move in a different way than if Clarion were not there. Calculation shows that Venus would pull away from its otherwise correct motion by about 1″ of arc in about three months time. Venus is routinely kept under observation to this accuracy, and therefore if Clarion were there it would reveal its presence by its effect on the motion of Venus. No such effect is observed, that is, the motion of Venus as actually observed is accurately in accord with the absence of Clarion, so therefore we may safely conclude that Clarion is nonexistent.*

In his letter of transmittal Dr. Duncombe comments "I feel this is definite proof that the presence of such a body could not remain undetected for long. However, I am afraid it will not change the minds of those people who believe in the existence of Clarion."

We first heard about Clarion from a lady who is prominent in American political life who was intrigued with the idea that this is where UFOs come from. When the results of the Naval Observatory computations were told to her she exclaimed, "That's what I don't like about computers! They are always dealing death blows to our fondest notions!"

Mars has long been considered as a possible abode of life in the solar system. There is still no direct evidence that life exists there, but the question is being actively studied in the space research programs of both the United States and Soviet Russia, so it may well be clarified within the coming decade.

At present all indications are that Mars could not be the habitation of an advanced civilization capable of sending

* These calculations assume Clarion's mass roughly equal to that of the Earth.

spacecraft to visit the Earth. Conditions for life there are so harsh that it is generally believed that at best Mars could only support the simpler forms of plant life.

An excellent recent survey of the rapidly increasing knowledge of Mars is *Handbook of the Physical Properties of the Planet Mars* compiled by C. M. Michaux (NASA publication SP-3030, 1967). A brief discussion of American research programs for study of life on Mars is given in *Biology and Exploration of Mars,* a 19-page pamphlet prepared by the Space Science Board of the National Academy of Sciences, published in April 1965.

The orbit of Mars is considerably more eccentric than that of the Earth. Consequently the distance of Mars from the Sun varies from 128 to 155 million miles during the year of 687 days. The synodic period, or mean time between successive oppositions, is 800 days.

The most favorable time for observation of Mars is at opposition, when Mars is opposite the Sun from Earth. These distances of closest approach of Mars and Earth vary from 35 to 60 million miles. The most recent favorable time of closest approach was the opposition of 10 September 1956, and the next favorable opposition will be that of 10 August 1971. At that time undoubtedly great efforts will be made to study Mars in the space programs of the U.S.S.R. and the United States.

Some of the UFO literature has contended that a larger than usual number of UFO reports occur at the times of Martian oppositions. The contention is that this indicates that some UFOs come from Mars at these particularly favorable times. The claimed correlation is quite unfounded; the idea is not supported by observational data. (Vallee and Vallee, 1966, p. 138.)

Mars is much smaller than Earth, having a diameter of 4,200 miles, in comparison with 8,000 miles. Mars' mass is about one-tenth the Earth's, and gravity at Mars' surface is about 0.38 that of Earth. The Martian escape velocity is 3.1 mile/sec.

At the favorable opposition of 1877, G. V. Schiaparelli, an Italian astronomer, observed and mapped some surface marking on Mars which he called "canali," meaning "channels" in Italian. The word was mistranslated as "canals" in English and the idea was put forward, particularly vigorously by Percival Lowell, founder of the Lowell Observatory of Flagstaff, Arizona, that the canals on Mars were evidence of a gigantic planetary irrigation scheme, developed by the supposed inhabitants of Mars (Lowell, 1908). These markings have been the subject of a great deal of study since their discovery. Astronomers generally now reject the idea that they afford any kind of indication that Mars is inhabited by intelligent beings.

Mars has two moons named Phobos and Deimos. These are

exceedingly small, Phobos being estimated at ten miles in diameter and Deimos at five miles, based on their brightness, assuming the reflecting power of their material to be the same as that of the planet. The periods are 7^h39^m for Phobos and 30^h18^m for Deimos. They were discovered in August 1877 by Asaph Hall using the then new 26-inch refractor of the U.S. Naval Observatory in Washington. An unsuccessful search for moons of Mars was made with a 48-inch mirror during the opposition of 1862.

I. S. Shklovskii (1959) published a sensational suggestion in a Moscow newspaper that these moons were really artificial satellites which had been put up by supposed inhabitants of Mars as a place of refuge when the supposed oceans of several million years ago began to dry up (Sullivan, 1966, p. 169). There is no observational evidence to support this idea. Continuing the same line of speculation Salisbury (1962), after pointing out that the satellites were looked for in 1862 but not found until 1877, then asks, "Should we attribute the failure of 1862 to imperfections in existing telescopes, or may we imagine that the satellites were launched between 1862 and 1877?" This is a slender reed indeed with which to prop up so sensational an inference, and we reject it.

11. Light Propagation and Visual Perception

Most UFO reports refer to things seen by an observer. Seeing is a complicated process. It involves the emission or scattering of light by the thing seen, the propagation of that light through the atmosphere to the eye of the observer, the formation of an image on the retina of the eye by the lens of the eye, the generation there of a stimulus in the optic nerve, and the perceptual process in the brain which enables the mind to make judgments about the nature of the thing seen.

Under ordinary circumstances all of these steps are in fairly good working order with the result that our eyes give reasonably accurate information about the objects in their field of view. However, each step in the process is capable of malfunctioning, often in unsuspected ways. It is therefore essential to understand these physical and psychological processes in order to be able to interpret all things seen, including those reported as UFOs.

The study of propagation of light through the atmosphere is included in atmospheric optics or meteorological optics. Although a great deal is known about the physical principles involved, in practice it is usually difficult to make specific statements about an UFO report because not enough has been observed and recorded about the condition of the atmosphere at the time and place named in the report.

Application of the knowledge of atmospheric optics to the interpretation of UFO reports has been especially stressed by Menzel (1952); (Menzel and Boyd, 1963). A valuable treatise on atmospheric effects on seeing is Middleton's *Vision through the Atmosphere* (1952). A survey of the literature of atmospheric optics with emphasis on topics relevant to understanding UFO reports was prepared for the Colorado project by Dr. William Viezee of the Stanford Research Institute (Section VI, Chapter 4).

Coming to the observer himself, Menzel stressed in consulting visits to the Colorado project that more ought to be known about defects of vision of the observer. He urged careful interviews to determine the observer's defects of vision, how well they are corrected, and whether spectacles were being worn at the time the UFO sighting was made. Besides the defects of vision that can be corrected by spectacles, inquiry ought to be made where relevant into the degree of color blindness of the observer, since this visual defect is more common than is generally appreciated.

Problems connected with the psychology of perception were studied for the Colorado project by Prof. Michael Wertheimer of the Department of Psychology of the University of Colorado. He prepared an elementary presentation of the main points of interest for the use of the project staff (Section VI, Chapter 1).

Perhaps the commonest difficulty is the lack of appreciation of size-distance relations in the description of an unknown object. When we see an airplane in the sky, especially if it is one of a particular model with which we are familiar, we know from prior experience approximately what its size really is. Then from its apparent size as we see it, we have some basis for estimating its distance. Conversely, when we know something about the distance of an unknown object, we can say something about its size. Although not usually expressed this way, what is really "seen" is the size of the image on the retina of the eye, which may be produced by a smaller object that is nearer or a larger object that is farther away. Despite this elementary fact, many people persist in saying that the full moon looks the same size as a quarter or as a washtub. The statement means nothing. Statements such as that an object looks to be of the same size as a coin *held at arm's length* do, however, convey some meaningful information.

Another limitation of normal vision that is often not appreciated is the color blindness of the dark-adapted eye. The human eye really has two different mechanisms in the retina for the conversion of light energy into nerve stimulus. Photopic vision is the kind that applies in the daytime or at moderate levels of artificial illumination. It involves the cones of the retina, and is involved in color vision. Scotopic vision is the kind that comes into play at low levels of illumination. It involves the rods of the retina which are unable to distinguish colors, hence the saying that in the dark all cats are gray. The transition from photopic to scotopic vision normally takes place at about the level of illumination that corresponds to the light of the full moon high in the sky. When one goes from a brightly lighted area into a dark room he is blind at first but gradually dark adaptation occurs and a transition is made from photopic to scotopic vision. The ability to see, but without color discrimination, then returns. Nyctalopia is the name of a deficiency of vision whereby dark adaptation does not occur and is often connected with a Vitamin A dietary deficiency.

If one stares directly at a bright light which is then turned off, an afterimage will be seen; that is, the image of the light, but less bright and usually out of focus, continues to be seen and gradually fades away. Positive afterimages are those in which the image looks bright like the original stimulus, but this may reverse to a negative afterimage which looks darker than the surrounding field of view. Afterimages have undoubtedly given rise to some UFO reports.

The afterimage is the result of a temporary change in the retina and so remains at a fixed point on the retina. When one then moves his eyes to look in a different direction, the afterimage seems to move relative to the surroundings. If it is believed by the observer to be a real object it will seem to him to have moved at an enormous velocity. A light going out will seem to shrink and move away from the observer as it does so. If one light goes on while another is going off, it may appear as if the light that is going off is moving to the place where the other light is going on.

Autokinesis is another property of the eye which needs to be understood by persons who are interested in looking for UFOs. A bright light in a field of view which has no reference objects in it, such as a single star in a part of the sky which has very few other stars in it, will appear to move when stared at, even though it is in reality stationary. This effect has given rise to UFO reports in which observers were looking at a bright star and believed that it was rapidly moving, usually in an erratic way.

12. Study of UFO photographs

The popular UFO literature abounds with photographs of alleged strange objects in the sky, many of which are clearly in the form of flying saucers. Some of these have been published in magazines of wide circulation. The editors of *Look* in collaboration with the editors of United Press International and Cowles Communications, Inc. published a *Look* "Special" in 1967 that is entirely devoted to "Flying Saucers," which contains many examples of UFO pictures.

Photographic evidence has a particularly strong appeal to many people. The Colorado study therefore undertook to look into the available photographs with great care. Chapter 2 of Section III gives the story of most of this work and Chapter 3 of Section IV gives the detailed reports on individual cases.

It is important to distinguish between photographic prints and the negatives from which they are made. There are many ways in which an image can be added to a print, for example, by double-printing from two negatives. Negatives, on the other hand, are somewhat more difficult to alter without leaving evidence of the fact. We therefore decided wherever possible to concentrate our study of photographic case upon the negatives. This was not, of course, possible in every instance examined.

A barber whose shop is in Zanesville, Ohio, but whose home is in the suburb of Roseville, has made a widely publicized pair of UFO photographs. He did not attempt to exploit them in a big way. He merely exhibited them for local interest (and stimulation of his barbering business) in the window of his shop. There they remained for more than two months until they were discovered by a big city newspaperman from Columbus, Ohio, who arranged to sell them to the Associated Press. They were distributed in February 1967 and have been often printed in various magazines after their original presentation in many newspapers.

Early in the project we became acquainted with Everitt Merritt, photogrammetrist on the staff of the Autometrics Division of the Raytheon Company of Alexandria, Virginia. He undertook to do an analysis of the photographs. A pair of prints was supplied to Merritt by NICAP.

Each of the pair shows the home of the photographer, a small bungalow, with a flying saucer flying over it. The flying saucer looks like it might be almost as large as the house in its horizontal dimension. The photographer says that he was leaving home with a camera when he chanced to look back and see the saucer flying over his home. He says he quickly snapped what we call picture A. Thinking the UFO was about to disappear behind a tree, he ran to the left about 30 ft. and snapped picture B, having spoiled one exposure in between. He estimated that there was less than a two minute interval between the two pictures, with A followed by B.

Merritt studied the negatives themselves by quantitative photogrammetric methods, and also did some surveying in the front yard of the Roseville home, as a check on the calculations based on the photographs. From a study of the shadows appearing in the picture, he could show conclusively that actually picture B was taken earlier than picture A, and that the time interval between the two pictures was more than an hour, rather than being less than two minutes as claimed.

The photographic evidence contained in the negatives themselves is therefore in disagreement with the story told by the man who took the pictures. Two letters written to him by the Colorado project requesting his clarification of the discrepancy remain unanswered.

We made arrangements with Merritt for his services to be available for photogrammetric analysis of other cases. These methods require a pair of pictures showing substantially the same scene taken from two different camera locations. Unfortunately this condition is seldom met in UFO photographs. Only one other pair came to our attention which met this criterion. These were the much publicized pictures taken on 11 May 1950 near McMinnville, Ore. (Case 46). But in this case the UFO images turned out to be too fuzzy to allow worthwhile photogrammetric analysis.

Other photographic studies were made for the Colorado project by Dr. William K. Hartmann, (Section III, Chapter 2).

Hartmann made a detailed study of 35 photographic cases, (Section IV, Chapter 3) referring to the period 1966-68, and a selection of 18 older cases, some of which have been widely acclaimed in the UFO literature. This photographic study led to the identification of a number of widely publicized photographs as being ordinary objects, others as fabrications, and others as innocent misidentifications of things photographed under unusual conditions.

On p. 43 of the *Look* Special on "Flying Saucers" there is a picture of an allegedly "claw-shaped" marking on the dry sand of a beach. Some of the dark colored moist sand making up the "claw mark" was shipped to Wright-Patterson AFB and analyzed. The liquid was found to be urine. Some person or animal had performed an act of micturition there.

A report by Staff Sergeant Earl Schroeder which says "Being a native of this area and having spent a good share of my life hunting and fishing this area, I believe that the so-called 'monster' (if there was such) could very well have been a large black bear." His report also notes that "during the week of July 26 the local TV stations showed a program called 'Lost in Space.' In this program there were two monsters fitting their description controlled by a human being."

Summarizing, the investigation report says, "There was food missing from the picnic table which leads to the belief that some animal was responsible for the black shape portion of the total sighting. There are numerous bears and raccoons in the area."

Another photograph presented in the *Look* Special is of a pentagonal image, though called hexagonal. Photographic images of this kind arise from a malfunctioning of the iris of the camera and are quite commonplace. It is hard to understand how the editors of a national illustrated magazine could be unfamiliar with this kind of camera defect.

13. Direct and Indirect Physical Evidence

A wide variety of physical effects of UFOs have been claimed in the UFO literature. The most direct physical evidence, of course, would be the actual discovery of a flying saucer, with or without occupants, living or dead. None were found. Claims which we studied as direct evidence are those of the finding of pieces of material which allegedly came from outer space because it is a product of a different technology, so it is said, than any known on earth. Another kind of direct evidence studied were allegations that disturbance of vegetation on the ground, or of the soil was due to an UFO having landed at the place in question.

The claimed indirect physical evidence of the presence of an UFO is of the nature of effects produced at a distance by the UFO. Accounts of sounds, or the lack of sounds, associated with UFOs, even though reports of visual observation indicated speeds of the UFO far in excess of the velocity of sound were common. Whenever a terrestrial solid object travels through the atmosphere faster than the speed of sound, a sonic boom is generated. The argument has been advanced that the absence of a sonic boom associated with UFOs moving faster than cutoff Mach (see Section VI, Chapter 6) is an indication of their being a product of a technology more advanced than our own because we do not know how to avoid the generation of sonic booms. Another category of indirect physical effects are those associated with claims that UFOs possess strong magnetic fields, vastly stronger than those that would be produced by the strongest magnets that we know how to make.

There are many UFO reports in which it is claimed that an automobile's ignition failed and the motor stopped, and in some cases that the headlights failed also, and that after this happened, an UFO was seen nearby. Usually such reports are discussed on the supposition that this is an indication that the UFO had been the source of strong magnetic field.

Reports of both direct and indirect physical evidence were studied by various staff members of the Colorado project, principally by Dr. Roy Craig, whose account of these studies is contained in Chapters 3 and 4 of Section III.

These studies resulted mostly in lack of substantiation of the claims that have been made. Claims of terrestrial magnetic disturbances at various Antarctic bases were either unconfirmed or seemed to be closely related to a practical joke that was played on a base commander.

During the period of field study of this project only one case of automobile engine malfunction came to our attention. There was some ground for skepticism about the report in that it was made by a diabetic patient who had been drinking and was returning home alone from a party at 3:00 a.m.

Some laboratory tests showed that engine failure due to the action of an external magnetic field on the car's ignition coil would require fields in excess of 20,000 gauss, at the coil. Owing to the magnetic shielding action of the sheet steel in the car body, the strength of the field outside the car would have to be considerably greater than this. But magnetic fields of such intensity would alter the state of magnetization of the car itself.

The process of forming car bodies by cold-forming the sheet steel introduces some quasi-permanent magnetization into all car bodies. Since all of the bodies of a given make in a given year are usually made with the same molds on the same presses they are all magnetized in the same pattern.

In the case in question we found that the car body that had been subjected to the presence of the UFO was magnetized. The pattern of magnetization quite closely resembled that of a car of the same make and year that was found a thousand miles away in a used car lot in Boulder, Colo. From this we can infer that the car that was supposedly near the UFO had not been subjected to a strong magnetic field, otherwise this would have permanently changed the state of magnetization of the body of the exposed car.

In the area of direct physical evidence, probably the most interesting result of investigation was the analysis of a piece of metallic magnesium which was alleged to have come from an UFO that exploded over a stretch of tidal water at Ubatuba, São Paulo, Brazil in 1957. This was one of several pieces of magnesium from the same source that had been sent to the society editor of a Rio de Janeiro newspaper at the time.

Later one of the pieces was subjected to elaborate chemical analyses in government laboratories in Brazil. The results of the analysis are given in great detail in the first of the Lorenzen books (1962), the full account occupying some forty pages. The claimed result of these studies was that the laboratory work showed the metallic magnesium to be purer than any ever made by man on Earth. Therefore it could not have been a product of earthly technology, therefore it came from an extraterrestrial source.

Mrs. Lorenzen kindly supplied one of the magnesium specimens to the Colorado project. We arranged to have it studied by the method of neutron activation analysis in a laboratory in Washington, D. C. The result, which is presented in detail in Chapter 3 of Section III, was that the magnesium metal was found to be much less pure than the regular commercial metal produced in 1957 by the Dow Chemical Company at Midland, Michigan. Therefore it need not have come from an extraterrestrial source, leaving us with no basis for rational belief that it did.

14. Radar Sightings of UFOs

The public became generally aware of radar at the end of World War II when the story of its important use in that war was told, after having been kept secret for some 12 years. A good non-technical account of this development is given in R. M. Page, *The Origin of Radar* (1962).

The word radar is an acronym for *RA*dio *D*etection *a*nd *R*anging. Basically, most radar systems operate in the following way. A transmitter sends out short pulses of electromagnetic energy at regular intervals. These are sent out through an antenna designed to radiate a narrow beam within a small angle of its main direction. This beam of pulses travels outward at the speed of light. If it encounters an obstacle, which may be a metallic object like an airplane, a rain storm, or a bird or a flock of birds, it is partially scattered in all directions from the obstacle. In particular a part of the beam is scattered back toward the transmitter. When it arrives back at the transmitter it is received and indicated or displayed in various ways, depending on the special purpose for which the system was designed. By the fact of there being a returned signal at all, the function of detection is accomplished. By the time delay involved between the transmission of the outgoing signal and the return of the back-scattered signal, the distance of the scattering object is inferred, thus accomplishing the function of ranging.

To get a beam of sufficiently narrow distribution in angle as to enable inferring from what direction the scattered signal was returned, the antenna must have a diameter of the order of ten times the wavelength of the radio waves which it uses.

In the period since 1945 the technology has had an enormous development so that nowadays there are elaborate networks of land and ship-based radar systems, as well as radar systems carried by most airplanes, which have become vitally necessary to the safe operation of civil and military aircraft. In addition to the use of radar in connection with navigation, it has become a valuable tool in meteorological work in that distant rain storms can be detected by radar. Also the trails of ionized air left by meteorites can be detected and studied by radar, providing for the first time the means for observing meteorites in the daytime.

There are many popular misconceptions about radar. It is important at the outset to realize that the returned radar signal does *not* give a sharply focussed image or picture of the obstacle that has been detected. What one gets when it is displayed on a cathode-ray screen is simply a diffuse blob of light indicating that *something* is there, in the direction the antenna is pointed (with some exceptions) and at the distance indicated by the time delay between transmission and reception of the back-scattered pulse. Of course, a large airplane gives a more intense signal than a flock of small birds at the same range, and skilled operators learn to make valid inferences about the nature of the object detected from other things that they know about the general situation together with the magnitude of the returned signal.

It is important also to recognize that the propagation of the outgoing and the back-scattered pulses is ordinarily assumed to be rectilinear and at the normal speed of light. But the actual propagation is affected by temperature and humidity differences in the air path along which the radio pulse travels. This can give rise to anomalous propagation that is analogous to but in detail not identical with the effects which give rise to mirages in the propagation of light through such an atmosphere. Usually the radar set operator does not know enough about the actual atmospheric conditions to make allowance for effects of this kind and, if they happen to be pronounced, can be led to make erroneous decisions. Another point is that, although the antenna sends out most of its energy in a single narrow beam, small amounts of energy go out in several other directions, known as sidelobes, so that a large or a nearby object in the direction of a sidelobe can give rise to a received signal that is indistinguishable from a small or distant object in the direction of the main beam.

The overall radar system is a rather complicated set of electronic equipment which can malfunction in various ways giving rise to internally generated signals which the operator will tend to regard as reflections made by outside obstacles which are in reality not there.

Usually the returned radar signals are displayed on the screen of a cathode ray tube and observed visually by the operator. On this account, subjective judgments of the operator enter into the final determination of what is seen, how it is interpreted and how it is reported. The data obtained from radar systems are thus not as completely objective as is often assumed. In some few instances subjectiveness is somewhat reduced by the fact that the cathode ray screen is photographed, but even when this is done there is a subjective element introduced at the stage where a human observer has to interpret the photograph of the radar screen.

Radar operators do report unidentified targets from time to time and so there exists a category of UFO cases in which the unidentified flying object was seen on a radar screen. In a few cases there is a close correlation between an unknown thing in the sky seen visually and something also displayed on radar.

However in view of the many difficulties associated with unambiguous interpretation of all blobs of light on a radar screen it does not follow directly and easily that the radar reports support or "prove" that UFOs exist as moving vehicles scattering the radio pulses as would a metallic object. The Colorado project engaged the services of the Stanford Research Institute to make a general study of the functioning of radar systems from the point of view of the relation of their indications to UFOs. The study which was carried out resulted in the production of Section VI Chapter 5, by Dr. Roy H. Blackmer, Jr. and his associates, R. J. Allen, R. T. H. Collis, C. Herold and R. I. Presnell.

Studies of specific UFO radar reports and their interpretation are presented in Section III, Chapter 5 by Gordon Thayer. Thayer is a radio propagation specialist on the staff of the Environmental Science Services Administration in Boulder. In his chapter, Thayer presents a detailed analysis of some 35 cases, some of which are visual, others radar, and some are both. Both optical and radar phenomena are treated together because of the similarity in the wave propagation problems involved.

In his summary of results he says: ". . . there was no case where the meteorological data available tended to negate the anomalous propagation hypothesis . . ." However, Thayer points out that adequate meteorological data for a thorough interpretation is often lacking so that a great deal more observational material of this kind would be needed in order to deal with a larger proportion of all of the reported UFO radar cases.

In view of the importance of radar to the safe operation of all aircraft, it is essential that further research be done leading to the most precise knowledge possible of anomalous propagation of radar signals. However, it is felt that this can best be done by a direct attack on the problem itself rather than by detailed field investigation of UFO cases.

15. Visual Observation made by U.S. Astronauts

The popular UFO literature makes occasional reference to UFOs seen by the U.S. astronauts in the space program operated by the National Aeronautics and Space Administration. We do not know of similar reports by Soviet astronauts but they may well have seen similar things.

In flights conducted between 12 April 1961 and 15 November 1966, thirty U.S. and Russian astronauts spent a total of 2,503 hours in orbit. The Colorado project was fortunate in that Dr. Franklin Roach, one of the principal investigators, has worked closely with the astronaut program in connection with their visual observations and so was already quite familiar with what they had seen and also was able to conduct further interviews with several of them on the basis of close personal acquaintances already established.

Roach presents a detailed account of what they saw as related to the UFO question in Section III, Chapter 6. Nothing was seen that could be construed as a "flying saucer" or manned vehicle from outer space. Some things were seen that were identified as debris from previous space experiments. Three sightings that are described in detail remain quite unidentified and are, Roach says, "a challenge to the analyst."

Roach emphasizes that the conditions for simple visual observation of objects near the satellite are not as good as might be naively supposed. As he describes them, "The conditions under which astronauts made their observations are similar to those which would be encountered by one or two persons in the front seat of a small car having no side or rear windows and a partially covered, very smudged windshield." Moreover, the astronauts were kept occupied with other observations and activities during their flight and so did not have extended periods of time in which to concentrate on visual observation of their surroundings. Most of the available visual observations therefore have to be regarded as a by product rather than a primary purpose of the program in which they were engaged.

The conclusion is that nothing definite relating to the ETH aspect of UFOs has been established as a result of these rather sporadic observations.

16. Public Attitudes Toward UFOs

Opinion polls are widely employed nowadays to measure public attitudes on various important and trivial issues. It is natural therefore to apply the same method to a determination of public attitudes toward various phases of the UFO question. Studies of this sort are not studies of the UFOs themselves, but an attempt at determination of what the American public thinks about UFOs. Some UFOs either do or do not come from outer space, and the fact of the matter would not be determined by finding out what the opinion of the American people about it may be. Nevertheless we considered that public attitudes do play a role in policy formation in America, and therefore it was appropriate to carry on some work in this area.

In 1947, 1950 and 1966 brief surveys of public attitudes on UFOs or flying saucers were conducted by the American Institute of Public Opinion, popularly known as the Gallup poll. Arrangements were made by the Colorado project for a more detailed study to be made during the spring of 1968. This was done for us by the Opinion Research Corporation. Findings of the earlier studies and of the study made for us are presented in Chapter 7 of Section III.

The first two studies indicated respectively that 90% and 94% of the American adult public had heard of flying saucers. The first of these results, taken within months of the original June 1947 sightings at Mt. Rainier indicates the extraordinary interest which the subject aroused from the outset. The 1966 survey indicated that 96% of the adult public had heard of flying saucers.

In the 1966 poll people were asked,

> "Have you, yourself, ever seen anything you thought was a 'flying saucer'?"

The result was that 5% of the 96% who had heard of them answered yes to this question. The sample was designed to be representative of the American population, 21 years of age and older, of whom there are some 100 million. This is the basis of the oft-quoted statistic that five million Americans have said that they think they have seen a flying saucer.

In the same 1966 poll, 48% said they thought the things called flying saucers were "something real," and 31% said that they were "just people's imagination." The question does not distinguish between various kinds of "real" things, such as weather balloons, aircraft, planets, mirages, etc., so the result by no means indicated that 48% believe they are visitors from outer space. That question was not included in the 1966 poll.

The 1966 poll asked whether the person interviewed thinks "there are people somewhat like ourselves living on other planets in the universe?" The question thus bears solely on ILE, not on whether such intelligences do in fact visit the Earth. Of the 1,575 interviewed 34% thought yes, 45% thought no, and 21% had no opinion.

There were no statistically significant regional differences between East, Midwest, South and West with regard to the proportion of the population which had heard of, had seen, or believed in the reality of flying saucers. However, as to belief in ILE, the existence of people on other planets, this belief was held by only 27% of southerners, as compared with 36% of easterners, 37% of midwesterners and 36% of westerners. The lower proportion of southerners who believe in ILE is statistically significant, that is, outside the range of chance variation due to finite size of sample. Although statistically significant, it is causally unexplained.

Significant variation with age is shown in response to belief in the reality of flying saucers, and to belief in intelligent life on other planets. About 50% of persons under 60 believe in the reality of flying saucers as compared with about 33% of persons over 60. On the other hand, a significantly smaller proportion of those under 50 believe in ILE, than do those over 50. On both of these points, the decline in the number of "believers" among older people is mostly due to the increase of those having "no opinion" rather than to an increase of the number of "non-believers." Here again the poll gives no basis for conclusions as to the reasons for these differences.

As to dependence on sex, 22% of men or women have no opinion as to the "reality" of flying saucers. Significantly more women than men believe in their reality:

	% Real	% Imaginary
Men	43	35
Women	52	26

The poll showed that increased amount of formal education is associated with an increased tendency to believe in the reality of flying saucers. Perhaps this result says something about how the school system trains students in critical thinking.

An interesting correlation is found between tendency to

believe in UFO reality, and to believe in ILE with having had a personal experience of having seen an UFO. The results are:

	% believing UFOs are real	% believing in ILE
Sighters	76	51
Non-sighters	46	34

As before, causal relations are unexplored, we do not know whether seeing is believing, or believing is seeing.

In the 1968 study conducted for the Colorado project by the Opinion Research Corporation, 2,050 adults over 17 years of age, living in private households in the continental United States were interviewed. In addition teenagers in the same household with an adult who was interviewed were also interviewed to give a sample of their views. Separate studies of opinions held by college students were conducted. These are reported in Section III, Chapter 7.

In the 1968 survey, 3% of adults replied affirmatively to "Have you, yourself, ever seen an UFO?" This parallels the 5% who answered affirmatively in the 1966 Gallup poll to the similar question, "Have you ever seen anything that you thought was a 'flying saucer'?" One might think that the smaller number in 1968 could be explained by perhaps less familiarity of the public with the term UFO than with the term flying saucer. This seems hardly likely, however, in that the question was part of a total interview in which the meaning of the term UFO would have become clear from the general context of other questions in the interview. It seems to us therefore that this poll actually indicated a smaller percentage of sighters than the earlier one.

An important finding is that 87% of those who said that they had seen an UFO, also declared that they had reported it to no one, other than to family or friends, that is, to no one by which it would have received official attention. Thus only about one-eighth of sightings were reported anywhere, and not all of these were reported to the Air Force. Hence if all sightings were reported to the Air Force, this result indicates that the number of reports received would be more than eight times as many as are now being received. From the small fraction who did report to the Air Force, it seems a fair inference that most of these non-reporting sighters did not think that what they saw constituted a security hazard.

In contrast, 56% of the non-sighters declared that they would report it to the police if they saw an UFO. We find this rather large discrepancy between the promised reporting behavior of the non-sighters and the actual reporting behavior of the sighters quite puzzling.

17. Other Psychological Studies

Consideration was given to a variety of modes of conducting psychological and psychiatric research into the UFO phenomenon. The possibility that an "experimental UFO" might be launched and reports of its sighting studied was given serious consideration and rejected on three grounds: In view of the fact that this was a government-sponsored, university-based study, it was felt that experiments in which the public might regard itself as having been victimized by what amounted to a hoax were unwise. Such experiments also might give rise, we thought, to the erroneous notion that the study regarded UFO phenomena *solely* as the result of misinterpretation of natural or man-made phenomena. Finally, we were advised by some of our experts in the psychological disciplines, that a "mock-up" UFO would introduce unknown variables that would render inconclusive any results derived from the conduct of experiments with it (see Section VI, Chapter 10).

Turning to the realm of psychiatry, we decided to refrain from mounting a major effort in this area on the ground that such a study could not be given priority over other investigations. This decision was buttressed by the evidence that we rapidly gathered, pointing to the fact that only a very small proportion of sighters can be categorized as exhibiting psychopathology and that, therefore, there is no reason to consider them any more suitable for study than psychotic or psychoneurotic individuals who belong to any other statistical class of the population as a whole (see Section VI, Chapter 3).

18. Instrumentation for UFO Searches

As remarked earlier, the short duration of most UFO sightings, the delays in reporting them and the delays caused by communication and travel, make it essentially impossible that investigators can bring physical observing equipment to a report site quickly enough to make UFO observations in that way. There is another way that is often proposed for getting better observational data than is now available; namely, to set up a permanently manned network of observing stations at various places in the country to observe such UFOs as might come within their range.

Such a network of stations might be set up solely for the purpose of UFO study, or it might be established in conjunction with one of the networks of stations which exist for other astronomical or meteorological purposes. This latter alternative, of course, would be much less expensive than the former, or could give a greater coverage for the same expenditure.

We gave considerable attention to the possibilities and difficulties in this direction (Section VI, Chapter 9). At first we hoped that some definite results could be obtained by such cooperation with existing stations in a way that would make results available for this report. An all-sky camera was operated during most of August 1967 at Harrisburg, Penna. during an UFO flap in that locality (Case 25) but no interesting results were found on some 9,000 photographs. It would be quite expensive to operate a network of such cameras on a routine basis all over the United States. The likelihood of interesting images being recorded would be very small. Because of the short duration of an UFO appearance a proper plan for use of the all-sky camera would involve frequent processing and examination of the film, otherwise the presence of an UFO would not be recognized until long after it had disappeared. This would greatly increase the cost of operation of such a network.

Another suggestion that is often made is to make UFO studies in connection with the radar networks operating in this country for air traffic control under auspices of the Federal Aviation Agency. Consideration was given to this possibility and it was concluded that it is quite out of the question to burden this network with additional duties of any kind. The air traffic control operators are now heavily burdened with the work of safely guiding civil and military aviation. During the summer of 1968 especially, the heavy overloads that sometimes exist on the system were emphasized by troublesome traffic delays in the neighborhood of several of the nation's major airports. It would be quite out of the question to ask the air traffic controllers to assume the responsibility of watching for UFOs in addition to their primary responsibilities. It would likewise be impracticable for a separate group of personnel to be installed at these stations to watch the same radars for UFOs.

The Prairie Network is a group of camera stations operated in the mid-west by the Smithsonian Institution in connection with the Harvard Meteor Program. Its primary purpose is to detect and record meteor trails in such a way as to guide a search for actual meteoritic bodies that strike the earth's surface. The field headquarters of this network is at Lincoln, Neb.

We prepared a listing of reported UFO sightings since 1965 that fell within the geographic limits of this network and through the kind cooperation of the Smithsonian Institution obtained the records of the network for the times and locations of these sightings. About half of the sightings were so lacking in specific information that, Frederick Ayer reports, (Section VI, Chapter 9) "even if an object had been recorded by the film it would have been impossible to correlate it with the sighting." About one-third of the sightings could not be traced on the film because of overcast skies. Some 18% of all the UFO sightings were identified on the network's records with a fair degree of probability. Nearly all of these were identified as astronomical objects. Some consideration was given to the costs and likelihood of success of adapting the Prairie Network instruments to UFO searches without interfering with their primary purpose. We think that something might be done along this line at reasonable expense, but we do not make a positive recommendation that such a program be undertaken because of the inconclusiveness of the information that we believe would be gathered.

Another existing program that was studied for unrecognized UFO records was that of scanning the night sky for study of air glow from the upper atmosphere, and of zodiacal light. Detailed study was made of two records obtained from a station on the Hawaiian Islands. One of these remains unidentified but is thought to be related to an artificial satellite for which no information is readly available. The other was definitely identified as a sub-orbital missile launched from Vandenberg AFB on the coast of southern California. Mr. Ayer, p. 1233, concludes that "because of their relatively extensive sky coverage, scanning photometers can be considered useful instruments in the conduct of UFO searches." This, however, is not to be construed as a recommendation that a network of scanning photometer stations be established for this purpose.

Consideration was also given to the adaptability to UFO search purposes of radars of the type used by the Weather Bureau, and the radar station of the Radar Meteor Project of the Smithsonian Institution located near Havana, Ill.

Although frequent claims are made in the UFO popular literature of magnetic disturbances due to the presence of UFOs, a consideration of various official magnetometer records produced no evidence of an effect of this kind that, in our judgment would warrant the setting up of an observational program to look for UFOs by their alleged magnetic effects.

19. *Conclusion*

In our study we gave consideration to every possibility that we could think of for getting objective scientific data about the kind of thing that is the subject of UFO reports. As the preceding summary shows, and as is fully documented in the detailed chapters which follow, all such efforts are beset with great difficulties. We place very little value for scientific purposes on the past accumulation of anecdotal records, most of which have been explained as arising from sightings of ordinary objects. Accordingly in Section I we have recommended against the mounting of a major effort for continuing UFO study for scientific reasons.

This conclusion is controversial. It will not be accepted without much dispute by the UFO amateurs, by the authors of popular UFO books and magazine articles, or even by a small number of academic scientists whose public statements indicate that they feel that this is a subject of great scientific promise.

We trust that out of the clash of opinions among scientists a policy decision will emerge. Current policy must be based on current knowledge and estimates of the probability that further efforts are likely to produce further additions to that knowledge. Additions to knowledge in the future may alter policy judgments either in the direction of greater, or of less attention being paid to UFO phenomena than is being done at present.

We hope that the critical analysis of the UFO situation among scientists and government officials that must precede the determination of official policy can be carried out on a strictly objective basis. Attacks on the integrity of various individuals on either side of this controversy ought to be avoided. The question of an individual's integrity is wholly distinct from the issue of what science should do in the future about UFOs.

In the Congress of the United States concern about the UFO problem from a defense viewpoint is the province of the House Committee on Armed Services. Concern about it from the point of view of the nation's scientific research program comes under the House Committee on Science and Astronautics. Here there seems to be a valid situation of overlapping jurisdictions because the UFO problem can be approached from both viewpoints.

A particular interest in the UFO problem has been shown by Congressman J. Edward Roush of Indiana, who is a member of the House Committee on Science and Astronautics. He performed a valuable service by arranging for the holding of a "Symposium on Unidentified Fying Objects" in Washington on 29 July 1968 (see references). As pointed out by one of the symposium participants, Prof. Carl Sagan of the department of astronomy of Cornell University, the presentations made in that symposium incline rather strongly to the side of belief that large-scale investigations of the UFO phenomenon ought to be supported in the expectation that they would be justified by what some speakers called "scientific paydirt."

Several of the contributors to that symposium have become trenchant advocates in the past several years of a continuing major government investment in an UFO program. Several have long urged a greater degree of congressional interest in this subject. The symposium of 29 July afforded them an occasion on which, with the utmost seriousness, they could put before the Congress and the public the best possible data and the most favorable arguments for larger government activity in this field. Hence it is fair to assume that the statements presented in that symposium represent the maximum case that this group feels could be made. We welcome the fact that this symposium is available to the public and expect that its data and arguments will be compared with those in this report of this study by those whose duty it is to make responsible decisions in this area.

We have studied this symposium record with great care and find nothing in it which requires that we alter the conclusions and recommendations that we have presented in Section I, nor that we modify any presentation of the specific data contained in other sections of this report.

References

Bailey, J. O. *Pilgrims Through Space and Time—Trends and Patterns in Scientific and Utopian Fiction,* New York: Argus Books, 1947.

Bloecher, T. E. *Report of the UFO Wave of 1947,* Washington (?), 1967.

Cameron, A. G. W. *Interstellar Communication,* New York: Benjamin, 1963.

Hall, Richard H. *The UFO Evidence,* Washington: NICAP, 1964.

Keyhoe, Donald E. "Flying Saucers are Real," *True,* 1950.

Lorenzen, Coral E. *The Great Flying Saucer Hoax,* New York: William-Frederick Press, 1962.

Lowell, Percival H. *Mars and its Canals,* New York: The Macmillan Company, 1908.

Markowitz, William. "The Physics and Metaphysics of Unidentified Flying Objects," *Science,* 157 (1967), 1274-79.

Menzel, Donald H. *Flying Saucers,* Cambridge: Harvard University Press, 1952.

———, and Lyle G. Boyd. *The World of Flying Saucers,* New York: Doubleday, 1963.

Miller, Stanley L. "Production of Organic Compounds under Possible Primitive Earth Conditions," *Journal American Chemical Society,* 77 (1955), 2351-61.

Olsen, T. *The Reference for Outstanding UFO Sighting Reports,* Ridenwood, Maryland: UFOIRC, Inc.

Page, R. M. *The Origin of Radar,* Garden City, New York: Doubleday, Anchor Books, 1962.

Purcell, Edwin. "Radioastronomy and Communication Through Space," Brookhaven Lecture Series No. 1, Brookhaven National Laboratory, New York, 16 November 1960.

Ruppelt, E. J. *The Report on Unidentified Flying Objects,* New York: Doubleday and Company, Ace Books, 1956.

Rush, J. H. *The Dawn of Life,* New York: Doubleday & Co., Inc. 1957 (also Signet Library of Science, New American Library, N.Y. 1962).

Salisbury, Frank B. "Martian Biology," *Science,* 136 (1962), 17-26.

Sullivan, Walter. *We Are Not Alone,* New York: McGraw-Hill Book Co., 1964, New York: New American Library (paper back edition), 1966.

Shklovskii, I. S. *Artificial Satellites of Mars* and *Riddle of the Martian Satellites,* Moskow: Komsomal'skaya Pravda, 1 May and 31 May 1959, English translation, FTD-TT-62-488-1, Wright Patterson AFB, 18 May 1962.

———, and Carl Sagan. *Intelligent Life in the Universe,* San Francisco: Holden-Day, 1966.

U.S. Ninetieth Congress, Second Session, Hearings before the Committee on Science and Astronautics, 29 July 1968. *Symposium on Unidentified Flying Objects,* Washington: Govt. Print. Off., 1968.

Vallee, Jacques, and Janine Vallee. *Challenge to Science—The UFO Enigma,* Chicago: Henry Regnery Co., 1966.

Section III

THE WORK OF THE COLORADO PROJECT

The seven chapters that follow describe the details of the scientific studies carried out by members of the project staff in the physical and social sciences. Most of the studies were, as Dr. Craig points out, closely related to the project's examination of specific cases. Detailed reports of the cases are found in Section IV.

Chapter 1 Field Studies / Ray Craig

1. Introduction

Reports of UFO observations, elaborate in description as they sometimes are, are usually lacking information which would concretely define the nature of the object observed or the experience described. When specific information describing an unidentifiable object is presented, the reliability of that information must also be evaluated, and some corroboration or independent verification is necessary.

At its outset in November 1966, the information with which this project had to work consisted of old reports, some of which had been investigated quite thoroughly by official and private agencies, and press accounts of current sightings, in which the information was generally fragmentary. New information regarding sightings which had never been revealed to the public also occasionally came to our attention. In all cases, additional information, varying in nature for different cases, was desired. Field investigations were undertaken in an effort to obtain such information.

2. Old UFO Cases

The project acquired copies of Project Blue Book and NICAP reports of UFO cases which had been discussed in popular UFO writings or which were regarded as having unusual scientific interest. Some of these reported sightings had been so extensively publicized that they have acquired the status of "Classic" cases.

In December 1966, early in the project history, we attempted to augment available information regarding one such case: the 1952 Washington, D.C., radar sightings (see Section III Chapter 5), by on-site re-investigation of the case. While this inquiry provided valuable new experience in the problems of investigating UFO phenomena, it brought little or no new information to light.

In general, testimony of witnesses recorded shortly after their experiences can be considered more reliable than their re-telling of the story two to 20 years later, both because of failures of memory and because of a tendency to crystallization of the story upon repeated retelling. For this reason, re-examination of witnesses in "classic" cases was not considered a useful way for the project to invest time. Field investigation of classic cases was therefore limited to those in which existing reports contained a serious discrepancy which might be resolved.

In one classic case, field investigation was undertaken primarily to locate that portion of a strip of 16mm. motion picture film made in 1950 which, the photographer said, showed most clearly the structure of UFOs he had photographed (Case 47). The photographer had claimed that this portion had been removed from his film when he lent it to the Air Force for study before the film was returned to him by ATIC experts.

The results of the investigation emphasized the vicissitudes of memory and the difficulties of establishing a crucial fact some 18 years after the event. Rather than reducing the uncertainty in the case, the investigation created greater uncertainty because it revealed further discrepancies in accounts of the sighting.

The case also was of special interest because earlier photographic analysis by Dr. R. M. L. Baker, then of Douglas Aircraft Corporation, indicated that the photographed objects probably were not aircraft, contrary to their "identification" in Project Blue Book records. Identification as other man-made or natural objects apparently had been ruled out primarily on the basis of wind direction on the alleged date of the sighting.

Since a detailed account of this sighting is given in Chapter 3, Section IV, only that information is presented here which illustrates the difficulties arising in attempts to investigate an event which occurred years previously, even when the primary and most of the principal secondary witnesses are still available.

This writer visited the photographer seeking details that might confirm or disprove his claim that the Air Force had admitted confiscating part of the film. The photographer had asserted that he possessed a letter from the Air Force containing precisely such an admission. If the letter could be produced, it might then be possible for the project to recover the allegedly missing film for study. A first-hand account of the sighting also was desired. At Great Falls, Mont. where the film was made, residents who had seen the film before it was sent to the Air Force were interviewed, newspaper accounts were searched, and attempts were made to resolve discrepancies in these reports. The only other person who reportedly witnessed the filming was, at the time of the event, serving as secretary to the photographer. She was interviewed by telephone.

1) The photographer had an extensive accumulation of papers and news clippings relating to his UFO film, much of it referring to his participation in a commercially produced documentary on UFOs released in 1956. No Air Force (or other) letter admitting that part of the film had been removed could be found among these accumulated papers. The photographer nevertheless insisted that he had such a letter, and suggested that many such items had been misplaced when he had changed his residence.

2) He also professed to no knowledge of the Air Force's "identification" of the filmed objects as two F-94 airplanes circling to land at the Great Falls Air Base, now renamed Malmstrom AFB. He remembered no aircraft in the sky near the time of his UFO sighting, and thought the aircraft explanation absurd. Nor did he recall that he had claimed in the documentary film, and in letters which are part of the Blue Book case file, to have seen two airplanes approaching Great Falls Air Base just after he took his UFO movies.

3) Several residents of Great Falls who were said to have seen the UFO film before it was loaned to the Air Force denied having seen it at that time. Others who had seen it both before and after it was lent to the Air Force firmly believed that not all the original film was returned by the Air Force. This claim was generally accepted as true by Great Falls residents. However, no measurements of film footage had been made before and after the loan to the Air Force, so that claims of film cropping could not be verified. Blue Book files contained some evidence lending credence to this claim. The original letter of transmittal of the film from Great Falls AFB to Wright-Patterson AFB stated that approximately 15 ft. of film were being transmitted. Only some 7 ft. were analyzed by Dr. Baker in 1956.

4) The secretary was the only witness to the UFO filming. She remembered distinctly seeing a single object and rushing outside the baseball stadium with her employer to watch him film it. She was certain it could not have been an airplane, because its appearance was quite different from that of a plane. She remembers seeing only one object, while the movie unambiguously shows two, almost identical objects moving across the sky.

5) Records had shown that two F-94s did land at Great Falls Air Base at 11:30 and 11.33 a.m. on 15 August 1950, about the time the UFO film was assumed to have been made. Local newspapers for this period, however, revealed that the semi-professional baseball team that the photographer managed did not play in Great Falls on that date but, rather, played

in Twin Falls, Idaho, several hundred miles away. The team played no home games in Great Falls between 9 August and 18 August. According to the account of the UFO sighting, the photographer was at the baseball park to prepare for the game to be played that afternoon; if this general account of the conditions of the UFO filming is accepted, the 15 August date must be erroneous. The relevance of the landing of the particular airplanes to which official identification of the filmed objects was assigned thus became highly questionable. Weather data which indicated the objects were moving against the wind, and thus could not have been balloons, also became irrelevant.

Reexamination of the record, in view of this date discrepancy, shows some early uncertainty as to whether the movies were taken on 5 August or 15 August. Acceptance by the Air Force of 15 August as the sighting date, and explanation of the filmed objects in terms of aircraft in the vicinity on that date, seems somewhat careless, since the presence of the photographer in Great Falls on that date of the photograph appears improbable. There is no question that the film was made in Great Falls, Mont. An identifiable water tower located there appears on the film. The date the movie was made is entirely open to question, however. Elimination of a balloon explanation depends upon knowledge of wind direction and that knowledge is available only if the date is known. Information regarding the date is not now available.

6) An indication of the manner in which representatives of the Air Force dealt with the photographer, after the original UFO report was submitted in 1950, is given in a written statement to him from Air Materiel Command Headquarters. After examination of the film, which clearly showed two images crossing the sky and passing behind the distant water tower, the statement read ". . . our photo analysts were unable to find on it anything identifiable of an unusual nature. Our report of analysis must therefore be negative." This writer prefers to leave interpretation of this statement to the reader.

This limited field investigation of a classic case revealed more discrepancies in the file record reports than it resolved. It produced no firm evidence that part of the film had been retained by the Air Force, and no leads through which such film might be located, if it had been retained.

Other field investigations of "classic" sightings involving photographs were somewhat more productive of new information. In the Ft. Belvoir photographic case for example, the doughnut-shaped structure in the photos was unequivocally identified when Dr. Hartmann showed the photographs to Army experts at Ft. Belvoir (Case 50).

During review of other classic cases it was possible, in some instances, for project investigators to develop new, pertinent information. This information generally depended upon recorded data, such as weather data, which could be acquired by telephone, mail, or library reference. Knowledge of atmospheric conditions prevailing at the time of radar UFO sightings, for example, allowed analysis of sighting reports in the light of current knowledge of radar propagation. Thus, atmospheric information was useful in evaluating classic cases such as the 1952 Washington, D.C. sightings (see Section III, Chapter 5), in which on-site interviewing had contributed no new information. Since our experience generally showed that new interviews of witnesses in classic cases did not produce dependable new information, few on-site investigations of such cases were undertaken.

3. Old Cases Not on Record:

Because of the existence of our study, people told us of UFO sightings that had never previously been reported to any study group. A graduate student described three large craft which flew in 1956, slowly just above tree-top level, over a clearing in woods where, as a Boy Scout he and other Scouts were camping.

A U.S. Navy captain related such an unreported experience. In 1962, he and four members of his family saw what appeared to be an elongated cylindrical object silhouetted against stars. His brief account reads:

> While returning from a movie at about 9:30 p.m., on Palatine Road about 5 mi. west of (location X), an object was sighted above the tree tops crossing from South to North at a slow rate of speed. At first it appeared like the lighted windows of a railroad passenger car, although on continued observation the lighted windows appeared in a more circular arrangement. We stopped the car and the entire family stepped outside and watched as it slowly moved away. There was no sound whatsoever. The night was warm, clear, and with no wind. The object (appeared) to be about 1000-2000 ft. in altitude on a level course.

The captain has served in the Navy for 25 years and had been a pilot for 26 years.

An Air Force major, on active duty at an air base described an experience he and his family had several years ago while driving across Texas. While stopped at a remote gasoline station just after dawn, the major and his son heard and watched two strange conical vehicles. They rose from behind a small hill, crossed the highway near them, and soared off into the sky, according to the major's account.

The numerous reports of this type were extremely interesting, and often puzzling. Many incidents were reported by apparently reliable witnesses. However, since they had happened in the relatively distant past, these events did not offer the project much prospect of obtaining significant information about the objects apparently sighted. There was no possibility of finding residual physical evidence at the site, and, in the typical case, the date of the event was uncertain, making it impossible to locate recorded relevant information such as weather data.

One old case (Case 5) which was not on public record did seem to warrant investigation. Our early information, from an apparently highly reliable source, indicated that radar scope pictures, electronic counter-measure graphic data, and U.S. Air Force Intelligence debriefing records regarding the event should be in existence and available for our study.

The case came to our attention when an Air Force officer attending the project's conference for base UFO officers mentioned that he had encountered an unknown aerial phenomenon about ten years earlier. At the time of the event he reported it to Air Force intelligence personnel.

The incident involved the crew of a B-47 equipped with radar surveillance devices. The B-47 was operating from a Strategic Air Command base, and the report of the incident was thought to have been sent to Air Defense Command Intelligence. No report of the incident was found in Blue Book files or in the files of NORAD headquarters at Ent AFB. Lacking adequate information on an impressive case, project investigators sought to locate and interview members of the original B-47 crew, hoping to determine how the incident had been officially identified and to trace AF reports on it.

The B-47 crew consisted of pilot, co-pilot, navigator, and three officers who operated special radar-monitoring equipment. The three officers most directly involved with the UFO incident were pilot, co-pilot, and the operator of #2 monitoring unit. Their descriptions of the 1957 experience over the Dallas-Ft. Worth area were in broad agreement. Details of the experience are given in Case 5.

The UFO encountered was a glowing ball of light, as "big as a barn," which apparently emitted or reflected electromagnetic radiation at both 2800 MHz and visible frequencies. For an extended period it maintained a constant position relative to the moving airplane, at 10-mi. range. It disappeared suddenly and reappeared at a different location, both visually and on airborne and ground radars. Since visual and radar observation seemed to coincide, reflection of ground radar did not seem a satisfactory explanation. Other explanations such as airplanes, meteors, and plasma also seemed unsatisfactory.

At first glance, the case seemed ideal for investigation by the project, since B-47s engaged in such operations routinely wire-record all conversations within the aircraft and between the ground during missions and are equipped with radar scope cameras and devices for recording graphically electronic counter-measure data. The pilot believed that such records had been turned over to intelligence officers after landing at the air base. The co-pilot and radar specialist were interviewed, but they said that since this mission was only for equipment checkout, neither wire nor film was taken aboard, and no data were recorded. The three crew members agreed that a full account of the experience had been given to Intelligence personnel at the air base from which the plane was operating. The pilot recalled the crew's completing a lengthy standard questionnaire regarding the experience some days after the event. However, the other two crew members recalled only an Intelligence debriefing just after landing and believed it was not more than two days after this event that the entire crew left for temporary duty in England. Thereafter they heard nothing further about the UFO.

Efforts to locate an intelligence report of this event were made at our request by Aerospace Defense Command Headquarters. Neither intelligence files nor operations records contained any such report, according to the information we received. An inquiry directed to Strategic Air Command Headquarters elicited response from the Deputy Commander for Operations of the Air Wing involved. He said a thorough review of the Wing history failed to disclose any reference to an UFO incident on 19 September 1957.

UFO reports filed in Wing Intelligence are destroyed routinely after six months. Since Project Blue Book, which maintains permanent UFO records, had no report of this event, we concluded that there existed no Air Force record that we could study.

The question of reliability of the crew's oral report remains. The individuals involved were trained, experienced observers of aerial events. None had encountered anything else of this nature before or since, and all were deeply impressed by the experience. Inconsistencies in the various accounts of the event itself were minor, and of a nature expected for recollection of an impressive event ten years past. There was serious lack of agreement regarding information recorded during the flight and events subsequent to landing. On the basis of criteria commonly applied, however, these observers would be judged reliable.

If the report is accurate, it describes an unusual, intriguing, and puzzling phenomenon, which, in the absence of additional information, must be listed as unidentified. In view of the date and nature of the mission, it may be assumed that radar "chaff" and a temperature inversion may have been factors in the incident. (See Section VI, Chapter 5.) A temperature inversion did exist at 34,000 ft. The fact that the electromagnetic energy received by the monitor was of the same frequency as that emitted by the ground radar units makes one suspect the ground units as the ultimate source of this energy. Whether such factors are pertinent or coincidental to the experience of this B-47 crew remains however, open to debate. For a detailed analysis of this case see Section III, Chapter 5, pp. 203-207.

For the purposes of this discussion the case typifies one of the difficulties inherent in the investigation of older sighting reports: The first information that the investigator receives leads him to believe that further inquiry may well adduce reliable records of a strange event, for example, recordings of intercommunication within the aircraft and between air and ground; photographs of radarscope targets; graphic data from other instrumentation; written reports of crew debriefings. Yet the most diligent efforts by project investigators failed to disclose the existence of any record.

4. Emphasis on Current Reports:

Such experiences convinced project investigators that field investigation should concentrate on current UFO reports. A properly equipped investigator might obtain accurate descriptive information about an unidentified object if he arrived on the scene shortly after a sighting, or during a sustained or repetitive sighting. Early in the study a few field trips had already been made to check current sighting reports, but the investigators had not been adequately equipped to gather quantitative data. In some interesting cases, the project had depended upon the reports of members of civilian UFO organizations who investigate UFO reports in their localities. In some instances their findings supplemented information from official Air Force investigation.

While the cooperation of private groups was helpful, objective evaluation of the sighting required obtaining as much first-hand information as possible. This could be done only when sustained or repetitive sighting situations occurred. In the case of isolated sightings, the project sought to send an investigator to the location as soon as possible, since the possibility of gathering meaningful data decreased rapidly with time, particularly when residual physical evidence was reported. For this reason, it was essential that the project receive immediate notification of any significant sighting.

Reports of apparently significant sightings usually reached us days or weeks after the event. Notification through official channels was inadequate because many sightings reported to news media apparently were not reported to the Air Force. Although Air Force Regulation 80-17A (Appendix B) stipulated that Air Force bases were to submit all UFO reports to the project, few reports were received from this source during the Spring of 1967. During this time Frank Edwards (1967) claimed that he and NICAP were each receiving some 100 UFO reports per week. Since many of these reports would not have been judged significant by any investigator, the project established an early notification network designed to filter out obviously insignificant reports and to notify us immediately of apparently significant sightings anywhere in the continental United States.

5. The Early Warning System:

Our organization for providing early notification of UFO sightings utilized official and semi-official agencies, and private groups. Reporters and editors, although operating outside this structure, occasionally supplemented the system by telephoning us about sightings in their areas. The Federal Aviation Agency assisted by providing a mechanism (see Appendix F) whereby air traffic controllers were to report unidentified radar targets to us immediately, and several reports were received from this source. Similar assistance was extended (see Appendices G and H) by the U.S. Weather Bureau and by Region 2 of the U.S. Forest Service. Cooperation also was obtained from the Volunteer Flight Officer Network (VFON), a cooperative organization of more than 30,000 flight personnel of more than 100 airlines in about 50 countries. This organization, under the direction of Mr. H. E. Roth of United Airlines, transmits reports of sightings deemed to be satellite re-entries, whether or not the object observed is immediately identifiable. Arrangements were made with VFON for rapid transmittal to us of all unidentified aerial objects. Although few such reports were received from this network, its coverage of over 2,000,000 unduplicated route miles and its efficient system of communication promised monitoring of a large portion of the earth's atmosphere and quick reporting of observations.

A major component of our system for early notification consisted of a network of civilian observers distributed in carefully selected locations across the United States, and designated as the Early Warning Network (see Appendix I). Selected individuals were asked to serve as early warning coordinators for their areas, evaluating UFO sightings in their vicinities, and immediately notifying us of apparently significant sightings. Most of the coordinates were recommended by NICAP or APRO, and the majority were associated with one or both of these organizations. Many of the coordinators were technically trained. All served without compensation, sometimes at considerable personal sacrifice. They were a major source of information received regarding current UFO sightings, and the project is grateful for their generous assistance.

Reports of current UFO sightings were received by telephone and details specified on a standard early warning report form (Appendix J) were immediately recorded. If the report seemed promising, additional checking by telephone was begun immediately. This generally included calling a law enforcement agency, air base, newspaper editor, or others to get independent descriptions of the local situation. When possible witnesses were also phoned for additional information.

Since the aim was to have field teams at the site as quickly as possible, the decision whether to send a team to investigate had to be made on information available at this point. That information was often disturbingly incomplete. Rather than risk missing opportunities to get first-hand photographic, spectroscopic, magnetic, electromagnetic, or visual data, however, the project elected to err in the direction of dispatching a team even though the case might later prove valueless.

The decision to investigate was made by a standing committee of three or four senior staff members. The decision was based upon the committee's evaluation of the expectation that significant information could be obtained through field investigation. This expectation was judged on the basis of the apparent reliability of the source and the nature of the reported event. If the event had been observed independently by different groups of people, was reported to differ markedly from known or expected phenomena, and particularly if the sighting was a continuing event or one that had recurred frequently, field investigation was undertaken. Special attention was given to events in which physical evidence, such as alleged landing marks, residues, or measurable alterations in properties of objects in the environment, might be discovered and studied.

6. *Investigation Capability and Philosophy*

By May 1967 teams of project investigators were available at all times for field investigations and were geared to reach a sighting location anywhere in the United States within 24 hours from receipt of the initial report. Equipment carried varied according to expected requirements. A standard field kit enabled the team to take 35mm photographs and 8mm motion pictures, check the spectrum of a light source, measure radioactivity, check magnetic characteristics, collect samples, measure distances and angles. and to tape record interviews and sounds (see inventory list, Appendix K). Special equipment, such as an ultrasonic detector (Case 20) and two-way radio equipment, was ultilized in some instances. An all-sky camera was installed and used for one series of field investigations (Case 27). In this case, the investigator established a base of operations at a location from which UFO reports were generated, publicized his presence, and had an aide who received telephone calls and relayed UFO reports immediately to him in his telephone-equipped automobile. He surveyed the area in this manner for several weeks.

In some investigations, a single investigator was deemed sufficient, but most investigating teams consisted of a physical scientist and a psychologist. Although each had his own area of special interest, they assisted each other in all aspects of the investigation. In a few cases, psychological testing of individuals who reported UFO sightings was done in the field (see, for example cases 33, 38, 42).

The aim of the field investigation was always to obtain useful information about UFO phenomena. We did not consider it our function to prove beyond doubt that a case was fraudulent if it appeared to be so. When an investigation reached the point, as sometimes happened, that the reality of the reported experience became highly doubtful, there was little to be learned from further inquiry. If unlawful or unethical practice were involved, we considered obtaining proof of this outside the realm of our study.

7. *Types of Current Cases Studied*

A. TYPICAL INVESTIGATION

Although field teams entered a wide variety of situations and were often able to establish firm identifications, a common situation was one in which the lack of evidence made the investigation totally inconclusive.

Near Haynesville, La., for example, (Case 10) a family had reported observing a pulsating light which changed from a red-orange glow to a white brilliance which washed out their car headlights and illuminated the woods on both sides of the highway. The driver had to shield his eyes to see the highway. About 0.6 mi. farther down the highway, the driver reportedly stopped the car and, from outside the automobile, watched the light, which had returned to its original glow. The light was still there when he stopped observing and left the area about five minutes later.

Although our investigating team made an aerial survey of the area and watched for reappearance of the phenomenon, and the principal witness continued to search the area after the team left, no revealing new information was discovered, and the source remains unidentified.

In another case (39) a lone observer reported that his car had been stalled by an UFO he observed passing over the highway in front of his car. While the project generally did not investigate single-observer cases, this one presented us with the opportunity to check the car to see if it had been subjected to a strong magnetic field. Our tests showed it had not. Lacking any other means of obtaining additional information, the investigators left with the open question of what, if anything, the gentleman had actually experienced.

A series of sightings around Cape Ann, Mass. (Case 29) offered testimony of numerous witnesses as evidence of the presence of a strange object, described as a large object with numerous lights which lit and disappeared in sequence. The investigating team was convinced, after interviewing several of the witnesses, that they had indeed seen something in the sky. The team was not able, at the time, to identify what had been seen. The chairman of the NICAP Massachusetts Subcommittee, Mr. Raymond E. Fowler, continued the investigation and subsequently learned that an aircrew from the 99th Bomb Wing, Westover AFB, had dropped 16 white flares while on a practice mission about 30 mi. NE of Cape Ann. The flare drop coincided in time and direction with the observed "UFO." As Mr. Fowler suggested, the "object" enclosing the string of lights must have been constructed by imagination.

In this case as in others, the key to the solution to the puzzle of a previously unexplained sighting was discovered. Additional cases probably were not identified as ordinary phenomena merely because of lack of information. Hence the label "unidentified" does not necessarily imply that an unusual or strange object was present. On the other hand, some cases involve testimony which, if taken at face value, describes experiences which can be explained only in terms of the presence of strange vehicles (see, for example, Case 6). These cases are puzzling, and conclusions regarding them depend entirely upon the weight one gives to the personal testimony as presented.

B. PRANKS AND HOAXES

For varying reasons, UFO-related pranks are commonly perpetrated by the young, the young at heart, and the lonely and bored. Our field teams were brought to the scene more frequently by victims of pranksters than by the pranksters themselves.

In one instance, (Case 7) the individual chiefly involved expressed serious concern that this project might conclude that flying saucers do not exist. Whether or not this concern was a factor in production of his photographs, this gentleman, would, by normal standards, be given the highest possible credibility rating. A recently retired military officer, he now holds a responsible civilian job. He is a man in his mid-forties who is held in high regard in the community. According to Air Force records, he served as an officer for 16 yr. and was rated a Command Pilot. He logged over 150 hr. flying time in C-47's in 1965. He presented two 35mm color slides of a flying saucer asserting that he took the photographs from an Air Force C-47 aircraft he was piloting. The object photographed was clearly a solid object of saucer shape. He claimed the pictures were taken in 1966, while he was off flight status and piloting the plane "unofficially" when he was aboard as a passenger. It was because of this circumstance, he claimed, that he did not report the UFO incident to the Air Force.

While the latter argument seemed reasonable, it was puzzling that no one else on the plane apparently reported the UFO. According to the officer, the co-pilot who remained in the cockpit was unaware that he had taken the UFO pictures. The reason the officer had not been taken off flight status was never revealed, but the Air Force Office of Special Investigations informed us that there was "nothing on file in his medical records to cast doubt on his veracity."

In spite of the officer's apparent reliability, investigation disclosed that the photographs were probably not taken at the time or place claimed. While he asserted that he barely had time to snap the two photographs through the window of the C-47, the numbers on the sides of the slide frames showed that the two slides had not been taken in immediate sequence. Comparison of these numbers with the numbers on other slides from the same roll of film also showed the UFO photographs to have been made after the officer retired from the Air Force and had moved to a new community. While the frame numbers stamped on mountings of the slides might conceivably have been erroneously stamped, as the officer claimed, such an error would not account for discrepancies in the frame numbers on the film itself, which are present when the film leaves the factory. The officer did not know that the film itself was prenumbered.

Case 23 is an example of a simple prank by the young at heart. A pilot, about to take off from an Air Force base in an airplane equipped with a powerful, movable searchlight, suggested to his co-pilot, "Let's see if we can't spook some UFO reports." By judicious use of the searchlight from the air, particularly when flashes of light from the ground were noticed, the pilots succeeded remarkably well. Members of the ground party, hunting raccoons at the time, did report an impressive UFO sighting. Our field team found, in this case, an interesting opportunity to study the reliability of testimony.

A common prank is the launching of hot-air balloons, with small candles burning to keep the air heated. Instructions for making such balloon using plastic dry-cleaners' bags and birthday candles have appeared in newspapers and magazines across the nation.

UFO reports frequently result from such balloon launchings. The lights are reported to go out one by one, and sometimes the UFO "drops brilliant streams of light" as burning candles fall from their balsa-wood or drinking-straw mountings. Cases 18 and 45 are examples of this type prank.

The instance described in case 18 was a flight of three plastic bags over Boulder, Colo., on 1 April 1967. The date is probably significant. They were observed and reported as UFOs by students, housewives, teachers, university professors, and a nationally prominent scientist. A newspaper reported one student's claim that the telephone he was using went dead when the UFO passed over the outdoor booth which housed it. Although plastic bags were suspected as the explanation, we were not certain of this until several days after the event. Because of unexpected publicity given the UFO sightings, the students who launched the balloons decided to inform the project of their role in the event.

Case 45 is noteworthy as an example of extreme misperception of such a balloon. One adult observer described this 2 ft. x 3 ft. plastic bag floating over a building in Castle Rock, Colo., as a transparent object 75 ft. long, 20 ft. wide, and 20 ft. high, with about 12 lights in a circle underneath. He thought the object was about 75 ft. away. According to his description, the lights were much brighter than his car headlights; although the lights did not blind him, they lit up the ground near by.

While this observer may still believe he saw something other than the plastic balloon bag, such a balloon was launched at the time of his observation and was observed by others to rise over the same building.

The last three examples mentioned are ones in which the UFO observer was the victim of pranksters. We conclude that in similar cases the prank is never discovered, and the UFO report remains in the "unknown" or "unresolved" category. Undiscovered pranks, deliberate hoaxes, and hallucinations, were suspected in some other field investigations.

C. PRANKS OUT OF HAND

What starts out as a prank occasionally develops a notoriety so widespread that the prankster becomes enmeshed in a monstrous web of publicity from which he can no longer extricate himself. One elderly security guard (Case 26) on lonely, boring, pre-dawn duty in a waterfront area, fired his pistol at an oil drum used as a waste container. He was within the city limits of Los Angeles, but the site was isolated. Invention of an UFO, either to "explain" his illegal firing of a weapon within the city limits or to generate a bit of excitement, would be understandable under such circumstances. His tale of a 90 ft., cigar-shaped UFO, against which his bullets flattened and fell back to earth, where he picked up four of them, was a sensation. This gentleman was bewildered by the reaction to his nationally broadcast story. He and his wife were harassed by phone calls from coast to coast. The police, civilians, and Colorado project investigated. Even after admitting to police that his shots had been fired at the steel drum which bore bullet-size holes and dents, he could not disconnect himself from the widely publicized UFO version of his story.

In any instance in which commitment to an apparently faked story seemed so strong that hoax or ignorance could no longer be admitted without serious psychological sequence, project members considered it neither desirable from the individual's standpoint nor useful from the project's standpoint to pursue the case further.

D. NAIVE MISINTERPRETATIONS

Unfettered imaginations, triggered into action by the view of an ordinary object under conditions which made it appear to be extraordinary, caused reports of UFOs having such impressive features that our field teams investigated. Such a case was 15, in which the observer reported evening observations of a green light as large as a two-story building, sometimes round and sometimes oblong, which landed several times per week 5-20 mi. to the west of his house. He reported having seen through binoculars two rows of windows on a dome-shaped object that seemed to have jets firing from the bottom and that lit up a very large surrounding area. The motion was always a very gradual descent to the western horizon, where the object would "land" and shortly thereafter "cut off its lights." Our investigators found this gentleman watching the planet Venus, then about 15° above the western horizon. He agreed that the light now looked like a planet, and, had he not seen the object on other occasions when it looked closer and larger, he would not have known it was really an UFO.

Light diffusion and scintillation effects (see Section VI, Chapter 4) were also responsible for early morning UFO observations, and Venus was again most frequently the unknowing culprit. Case 37, as initially reported to us, was a particularly exciting event, for not only had numerous law enforcement officers in neighboring communities observed, chased, and been chased by an UFO of impressive description, but, according to the report, the pilot of a small aircraft sent aloft to chase the UFO had watched it rise from the swamp and fly directly away from him at such speed that he was unable to gain on it in the chase. Both the light plane and the unidentified object, according to the initial report, were observed on the local Air Traffic Control radar screen. According to the descriptions, the object displayed various and changing colors and shapes. Appearing as big as the moon in the sky, it once stopped about 500 ft. above a police car, lighting up the surroundings so brightly that the officers inside the car could read their wrist watches. As indicated in the detailed report of this case, supporting aspects of the main sighting report fell apart one by one as they were investigated, leaving us again pointing to Venus and finding the law enforcement officers surprised that she could be seen at mid-day near the position in the sky their UFO had taken after the early morning chase.

E. MISINTERPRETATION SUPPORTED BY OFFICIAL MISINFORMATION

One case impressed us not so much because of the description of the UFO as because of official information given to the observers by Air Force representatives. The Air Force not only failed to correct the observers' misinterpretation but by giving erroneous information, caused the proper interpretation to be withdrawn from consideration. Details of the case are reported by project investigator James E. Wadsworth in

Section IV, Case 28. The discussion presented here is designed to serve as a basis for comment regarding the failure to recognize and reveal misinterpretations of known phenomena.

A series of recurring sightings by multiple witnesses was reported from near Coarsegold, Calif. Coarsegold is in the Sierra Nevada foothills northeast of Fresno. The sightings were of special interest because they had been recurring for several months and remained unidentified after preliminary investigation by NICAP members in the area. These sightings offered the project the unusual opportunity of observing, photographing, and studying an object or objects which were being reported as UFOs.

Dr. Franklin E. Roach and Mr. Wadsworth were sent by the project to conduct the investigation, NICAP members on the scene furnished results of their preliminary investigation and names and addresses of principal witnesses. The witnesses had organized a loose network for UFO surveillance using Citizens Band radio for communication covering an area of about 80 mi. radius. They not only had observed strange lights in the sky over several months, but also had photographed them and recorded the dates and times of their appearance and descriptions of their motions.

One to six UFOs had been sighted per week, sometimes several during the same night. About 85% of the sightings followed a recognizable pattern: Orange-white lights above the valley at night moved, hovered, disappeared and reappeared, and occasionally merged with one another. Other sightings were of varying nature, and some seemed to warrant separate investigation. Most of the observations had been made from a ranch 1,800 ft. above the valley floor. Several others often in radio communication with the ranch owner, had witnessed the same events, and the witnesses were of apparently high reliability. The ranch owner, for example, had a background of police and military investigative experience.

After interviewing primary witnesses, looking at photographs, and listening to tape recordings of descriptions of previous sightings, the project field team joined the ranch owner and his wife in night watches. At 10:30 p.m. on the second night of observation, a light appeared low in the southern sky travelling W to E at approximately 1° of arc per second. After about 10 sec. more detail became visible. The source of this light was identified as a probable aircraft with conventional running lights and anticollision beacon.

At the same time, another light had appeared to the east of the presumed aircraft, moving W to E at about the same rate. It appeared as a dull orange light, showing some variation in intensity as it moved. No accurate estimates of distance could be made. Although this light was not manifestly on an aircraft, the possibility that it was could not be ruled out. The rancher, however, said that this was exactly the sort of thing they had been observing frequently as UFOs. He was disappointed that this one had not appeared as close and bright as on other occasions.

After about 15 sec., the UFO seemed to flicker and then vanish. The original object continued eastward, disappearing into the distance in the manner of an ordinary aircraft. Duration of observation was less than a minute. Photographs of the unidentified light were taken by the project team on a high-speed Ektachrome film.

Dr. Roach withdrew from the investigation taking the camera containing the exposed film to the Eastman Laboratories at Rochester, N.Y., for special processing, film calibration, and color analysis of film images. Mr. Wadsworth continued the investigation. The next night, he and the rancher observed UFOs at midnight and again at 12:42 a.m. They appeared as bright orange lights, showing no extended size but varying in intensity. They hovered, moved horizontally, and vanished. The rancher said that these were good, solid sightings of UFOs. Mr. Wadsworth thought they might be the lights of low-flying aircraft whose flight path produced the illusion of hovering when the plane was flying along the observer's line of sight. The presence of planes in the vicinity at the time, however, was not established.

The next morning it was learned that at least two other persons had observed the UFOs at midnight and 12:42 a.m. The rancher telephoned the UFO officer at Castle Air Force Base about 30 mi. west of Coarsegold. The officer declared that no aircraft from the base were aloft at the time of the sighting and promised that the sighting would be investigated and appropriate action taken.

Since the presence of aircraft as a possible explanation of the UFOs had been denied by the local air base, Mr. Wadsworth arranged to observe the UFO activity from the vantage point of the highest fire lookout tower in the area. The tower afforded an excellent view of the valley area below. The observers were equipped with cameras, binoculars, compass, and other field-kit items, and maintained two-way radio contact with the rancher for coordination of observations.

At midnight one orange light after another appeared over the valley. The lights, observed simultaneously by the project investigator and a NICAP member at the tower and by the rancher at his house, appeared to brighten, dim, go out completely, reappear, hover, and move back and forth. Sometimes two lights would move together for a few moments and then separate. Only point source lights were observed, and there was no sound. The visible paths of the lights were not continuous. The lights would repeatedly go out, to reappear elsewhere or not at all. At times they became so dim as to be almost impossible to follow with binoculars. At other times they appeared to hover, flare up, then go out completely. The rancher believed the lights flared up in response to signals flashed at them with a spotlight, and it was true that many times when he flashed there followed a flare up of the UFOs. Mr. Wadsworth felt, however, that this was a coincidence, since the lights exhibited frequent flare-ups independently of signals. This behavior continued for about 1.5 hr.

From the higher vantage point of the tower it was possible to determine a general pattern of movement that was not apparent from below, since the pattern's northern most end was not within the rancher's field of view.

Mr. Wadsworth concluded that these lights, and the similar ones of the previous night, notwithstanding assertions to the contrary from the base UFO officer, must be aircraft operating out of Castle Air Force Base. Careful observations through binoculars of the extreme northern end of the pattern had revealed lights moving along what must have been a runway lifting off, circling southwards, and following the behavior pattern previously observed before returning to land at a northern location coinciding with that of Castle AFB.

The rancher was skeptical of this identification. The following night he drove with Mr. Wadsworth toward the air base. En route, more orange lights appeared as before, but through binoculars these could now be identified as aircraft. As they approached the base, they could plainly see landings and takeoffs in progress.

Subsequently it was learned that most of the night-flying at Castle AFB involved tankers and B-52s in practice aerial refuelling operations. Castle AFB is a training center for midair refuelling with 400 to 500 sorties launched from the base each month, both day and night. Flight schedules from the base, obtained later, showed planes scheduled to be in the air at the times the UFOs were observed. The planes carried large spotlights which were switched on and off repeatedly. This accounted for the observed flare-ups and disappear-reappear phenomena. The apparent hovering was due to the fact that part of the flight pattern was on a heading toward Coarsegold. Closings followed by separations were the actual refuelling procedures. The absence of sound was accounted for by distance, and the color variation, orange to white, by variable haze scattering of the light.

Maps obtained from Castle AFB show flight patterns for these operations wholly consistent with the sightings. Descriptions of lighting configurations of the tankers and bombers also were consistent with this identification.

While these sightings were not particularly impressive individually, being essentially lights in the night sky, the frequency of reports was sustained at a high level for nearly a year, and the observers had noted the UFOs occasionally since the fall of 1960. Observations were widespread and attracted much attention. The phenomenon seemed strange to the observers, defying simple explanation. Although the stimulus was conventional aircraft, the aircraft behavior, lighting, and flight paths presented an unconventional appearance to witnesses who were not familiar with inflight refuelling practice.

Prior to the Colorado project investigation none of the observers had driven to the airbase while sightings were occurring to check the aircraft hypothesis. This was true in part because the rancher had called the air base on several occasions to report sightings, and had received misleading information several times to the effect that the sightings could not be accounted for by planes from that base. On one occasion, Mr. Wadsworth took the telephone to hear this information conveyed to the rancher.

It should have been simple enough for representatives from Castle AFB to explain to inquiring citizens that the sightings were of practice refuelling operations, and to identify the UFOs as aircraft from their base. Why was this not done? Was the Public Information Office at Castle AFB actually not aware of the activities of its own base? Was misinformation released deliberately? If base representatives investigated the reports of UFOs and were not able to explain the sightings, the UFO report should have been sent to Project Blue Book at Wright-Patterson AFB and to the University of Colorado. The project had received no such report. Had Project Blue Book? If not, why not?

It is Air Force practice not to investigate reports of UFOs which are described merely as lights in the sky, particularly lights near an air base, and such reports need not be forwarded to Blue Book. In the Coarsegold sightings, however, according to the rancher and his wife, their reports had been investigated by officers from Castle AFB and the UFOs had remained unidentified. Thus, the reports should have been forwarded to Blue Book.

Blue Book files yield a single report on this series of sightings, describing the Castle AFB officers' interview with the rancher's wife after the rancher had reported numerous sightings by himself and neighbors during the two week period starting 9 October, 1966. (The rancher was absent when Castle AFB officers investigated his report.) The report to Blue Book stated, "Officers who interviewed Mrs.——can offer no explanations as to what those individuals have been sighting. Descriptions do not compare with any known aircraft activity or capability."

The file also carried a notation that Castle AFB was to forward to Blue Book information required in AFR 80-17, but this information had not been received; therefore, the case was being carried as "insufficient data." There was no evidence of any follow-up or further effort to get the information.

What were the UFO descriptions which did not, in the view of investigating officers, compare with any known aircraft activity or capability? The housewife's description of what she and others had seen, as recorded by the interviewing officers, referred to pulsating and glowing lights varying between shades of white, red and green occasionally remaining stationary on a nearby ridge and capable of moving in any direction at greatly variable speeds, generally exceeding that of jets observed in the area. In particular, she once noted a vertical ascent at a very rapid speed. On one occasion, her husband was able to distinguish a rectangular-shaped object with very bright lights at the corners.

The description contained other references to appearance and motion. However, it is obvious that, when taken literally and without allowance for common errors in perception and cognition and without allowance for subjective interpretations, the descriptions, as the officers stated, did not conform with aircraft capability. Failure to make such allowance left the sightings unidentified.

F. NON-EVENTS

Two types of non-events received brief attention of our field teams. One involved predicted events revealed to us by persons claiming special psychic and communication powers. The other involved claimed UFO events at Air Force bases.

Predictions of UFO landings and close appearances were received from several sources (e.g. Case 19). One or two such psychic predictions were checked. The predicted flying saucer failed to materialize.

One non-event of the second type is presented as Case 30. Others were recorded only as internal project memoranda, and are not presented as case reports. In each instance, conflicting information was received by this project. The initial information that an UFO event had occurred sometimes reached us as a rumor. A phone call to the Air Base UFO Officer or to the reported internal source of the information yielded confirmation that an event that should be of interest to a UFO study had occurred, but further information would have to be obtained through official channels. Unless such confirmation was obtained, the information, although received from a source which was usually reliable, was rejected as rumor.

In Case 30, a civilian employee at an air base in California, contacted by telephone regarding a rumored sighting, confirmed that an UFO event had occurred at that base, and that a report of the event had passed across his desk and had been sent on to proper authorities. Those authorities, contacted with difficulty by telephone, insisted that no UFO event occurred at that base on or near that date. The employee, when contacted again later for additional information, replied only that he had been told to "stay out of that."

Conflicting information regarding a fast-moving radar track

which was claimed to be unidentified and later "classified" similarly leaves nothing for study when official notification is received that there was no such event at the given time and place.

In one instance, the base UFO officer had no knowledge of a supposed UFO alert at his base on a given date and time. According to our information, jet interceptors alerted to scramble after a UFO were rolled out armed with rockets, taxied to the runway, but did not take off. The UFO officer, however, realized that such an event would have involved fighter craft at his base which are under a different command than the SAC command which he represented. Air Defense Command personnel could have an UFO report, the officer indicated, without telling SAC personnel about it. He then checked with the fighter defense squadron stationed at this SAC base, talking with people who were on duty at the time of the rumored event. He reported to us that there was an alert at the indicated date and time and that fighters were deployed to the runway ready to scramble. This action was taken on orders from the squadron's headquarters at another base. The alert to scramble was said to be definitely not UFO-related but any other information regarding the cause of the alert would have to come from that headquarters. Further inquiry, through Pentagon channels, elicited only a denial that there had been an alert to that particular fighter squadron on the given date. In the absence of some independent source of information, we had no means of determining whether or not there was an alert and, if so, whether or not it was in fact triggered by the report of an unidentified flying object.

8. Remarks and Recommendations:

Instances in which there was less than full cooperation with our study by elements of the military services were extremely rare. Our field teams invariably were cordially received and given full cooperation by members of the services. When air bases were visited, the base commander himself often took personal interest in the investigation, and made certain that all needed access and facilities were placed at our disposal.

Field teams observed marked difference in the handling of UFO reports at individual air bases. At some bases, the UFO officer diligently checked each report received. On the other hand, at one base, which we visited to learn what a local Air Force investigation had revealed regarding a series of UFO sightings in the area, we found that none had been conducted, nor was one likely to be. Sighting reports received at the base by telephone, including one we knew to have been reported by the wife of a retired Naval officer, resulted in partial completion of a standard sighting form by the airman who received the call. This fragmentary information was then filed. The UFO officer argued that such reports contained too little information for identification of what was seen. He insisted that the information was insufficient to warrant his sending them to Project Blue Book. There was no apparent attempt to get more information. In this instance, what the woman had seen was later identified by interested civilians as a flare drop from an Air Force plane.

While Air Force cooperation with our field teams was excellent and commendable, the teams frequently encountered situations in which air base public relations at the local level left much to be desired.

Official secrecy and classification of information were seldom encountered by project investigators. In the few instances when secrecy was known to be involved, the classified reports were reviewed and found to contain no significant information regarding UFOs.

Reviewing the results of our field investigations, one must note the consistent erosion of information contained in the initial report. Instead of an accumulation of evidence to support a claim of the sighting of an unusual flying vehicle, erosion of claimed supporting evidence to the vanishing point was a common investigative experience. As shown by examples in the above discussion, this was true of both current and older cases. As an investigation progressed, the extraordinary aspects of the sighting became less and less dominant, and what was left tended to be an observation of a quite ordinary phenomenon.

Current sightings which we investigated and left unresolved were often of the same general character as those resolved. The inconclusiveness of these investigations is felt to be a result of lack of information with which to work, rather than of a strangeness which survived careful scrutiny of adequate information. In each current report in which the evidence and narrative that were presented were adequate to define what was observed, and in which the defined phenomenon was not ordinary—that is, each observation that could be explained only in terms of the presence of a flying vehicle apparently representing an alien culture—there were invariably discrepancies, flaws or contradictions in the narrative and evidence which cast strong doubt upon the physical reality of the event reported.

Of the current cases involving radar observations, one remained particularly puzzling after analysis of the information, since anomalous propagation and other common explanations apparently could not account for the observation (see Section III, Chapter 5 and Case 21).

While the current cases investigated did not yield impressive residual evidence, even in the narrative content, to support an hypothesis that an alien vehicle was physically present, narratives of past events, such as the 1966 incident at Beverly, Mass., (Case 6), would fit no other explanation if the testimony of witnesses is taken at full face vaue. The weight one should place on such anecdotal information might be determined through psychological testing of witnesses; however, advice given us by psychologists at the University of Colorado Medical Center indicated that such testing would be of questionable significance if done as long as a year or two after the event. Since we had no such impressive cases among more recent sightings, the opportunity for significant psychological testing of witnesses in such cases was not presented. Depending upon the weight given to old anecdotal information it permits one to support any conclusion regarding the nature of UFOs that the individual wishes to draw.

If UFO sighting reports are to be checked and studied, this should be done as soon as possible after the event, before witnesses' stories become crystallized by retelling and discussion. Such field investigation, undertaken on any scale for any purpose, should be done by trained investigators. The Coarsegold incident described above exemplifies the futility of an investigation which does not take into account subjective and perceptual considerations, as well as knowledge of events occurring in and above the atmosphere. The experience of seeing the planet Venus as a UFO that trips a magnetic UFO-detector, chases police cars at 70 mph, flies away from aircraft, changes size and shape drastically, lands about ten mi. from a farmhouse, and descends to 500 ft. above a car and lights up the inside of the vehicle; of seeing a plastic dry cleaners' bag, of sufficient size to cover a single garment, as a UFO 75 ft. long and 20 ft. wide when only 30 ft. away; of seeing rows of windows in planets and in burning pieces of satellite debris which have re-entered the atmosphere, of seeing the star Sirius as an UFO which spews out glowing streams of red and green matter; seeing aircraft lights as flying saucers because the observer could not believe there are that many airplanes flying around her town; or other experiences of this general type are ones with which an effective investigator must be familiar.

It is obvious that not all UFO reports are worthy of investigation. What kinds of reports should be investigated? Persons who have lengthy experience working with UFO reports give varying answers to this question. NICAP discards unsubstantiated tales of rides in flying saucers, on the basis that their investigators have found no evidence to support these claims but have found considerable evidence of fraud (NICAP 1964). Air Force practice is to neglect reports of mere lights in the sky, particularly around air bases or civil landing fields, for experience has shown the UFOs in such reports to be lights of aircraft or other common lighted or reflecting objects. Both Dr. J. Allen Hynek, scientific consultant to the Air Force on UFOs, and Dr. Peter M. Millman (1968), who is presently in charge of the handling of UFO reports in Canada and has had an active interest in UFO reports for nearly 20 years, have said they do not favor any field investigation of single-observer sightings because of the difficulty in deriving useful scientific information from such reports.

Such policies and recommendations have grown out of much experience and practical considerations. Their authors are very much aware of the fact that a rare event certainly might be witnessed by a single observer. It also is obvious that if an extraterrestrial intelligence were assumed to be present, there is no logical reason to assume that it would not or did not make contact with a human being. Yet those who have worked with UFO reports for decades with a conscious attempt to be objective have encountered so many nonproductive reports of certain types that they have concluded that those classes of reports are not worth the effort of field investigation.

Our own field experience leads this writer to question the value of field investigations of any UFO reports other than which a) offer a strong likelihood that information of value regarding meteors, satellites, optics, atmospheric properties, electrical phenomena, or other physical or biological phenomena would be generated by the investigation; b) present clear indication of a possible threat to a nation or community whether in the form of international or intra-national hostilities, physical or biological contamination of environment, panic, or other emotional upheaval; or c) are of interest as sources of information regarding the individual and collective needs and desires of human beings.

If there were an observation of a vehicle which was actually from an alien culture, the report of this observation certainly would deserve the fullest investigation. Our experience indicates that, unless the sighting were of a truly spectacular and verifiable nature, such a report would be buried in hundreds or thousands of similar reports triggered by ordinary earthly phenomena. While a large fraction of these reports could be discarded after establishment of the earthly cause, the report of interest would remain buried in others which contained too little evidence for identification and the report itself probably would not be distinguishable from them. For this reason, this writer would not recommend field investigations of routine UFO reports if the intent of that investigation is to determine whether or not an alien vehicle was physically present. A verifiable report of a spectacular event, such as an actual landing of an alien vehicle, conceivably could thus be missed by neglect; however this is unlikely, since such a report would probably be so unusual in character as to attract immediate attention.

Edwards, F. *Flying Saucers—Here and Now,* Lyle Stuart: N.Y., 1967.
Hall, R. H. *The UFO Evidence,* NICAP, publication: Washington D.C., 1964.
Kohl, Mrs. L. Reference Librarian, Great Falls Public Library, private communication.
Millman, P. M. Personal communication dated 8 July 1968.

Chapter 2 Analysis of UFO Photographic Evidence / William K. Hartmann

1. Introduction

The first reported photograph of a UFO after the Arnold sighting of 24 June 1947, was made on 4 July 1947 in Seattle, Washington. (Ruppelt, 1956, p. 32) The object was identified as a weather balloon. This first photograph is typical of the photographic evidence that has accrued since: It accompanied a "wave" of reports and was inconclusive in establishing the existence of any extraordinary aircraft.

Although photographic evidence, in contrast to verbal testimony, might be considered "hard" data, experience has indicated that one cannot assume that a photograph of an airborne disk is more credible than a verbal report. Even if it were true that cameras never lie, photographers sometimes do. A photograph may be more interesting than a verbal account; indeed, if we knew that "flying saucers" existed, the best documented photographs would be extremely valuable in establishing their properties. But in the absence of proof of the existence of such aircraft, we are concerned at this stage with the credibility of reports.

The most convincing case of photographic evidence would involve not only multiple photographs but multiple photographers, unrelated and unknown to each other, a considerable distance apart (preferably tens of miles), whose photographs demonstrably show the same UFO. No such case is known to the Colorado project.

The Colorado project studies of UFO photographs are based on this approach. The question that is central to the study is: *does the report have any probative value in establishing the existence of flying saucers?* A question definitely secondary in importance (and conducive to unproductive arguments) is: What is the final explanation of each photograph?

That is to say, our principal task is to examine UFO photographic evidence that is alleged to indicate the existence of "flying saucers," and make a judgment as to whether the evidence supports this assertion. Photographic evidence is peculiarly open to the contention that one must establish what is shown, before one can say that it is not a "flying saucer." This argument is invalid. It is not necessary to prove that an object is an orange before establishing that it is not a mushroom. Exhaustive attempts to establish the identity of each object or image recorded were therefore not made. Yet possible interpretations were suggested in many cases where it was concluded (for one reason or another) that there was no evidence of an unusual phenomenon.

2. *Selection of Cases*

Time and funds did not permit exhaustive investigation of all interesting cases. About 90% of the cases could be assigned second or third priority upon inspection or brief study. Such a priority rating was based on a judgment that the case had little potential value in establishing the existence of "flying saucers." The remaining 10% of the cases were of first priority and required intensive study, some as much as a month of full-time effort. A "residual" of about 2% to 5% of all cases remained unexplained after this process. It is such a residual that is the core of the UFO problem (both in photographic cases and more generally).

The O'Brien committee (see Appendix A) suggested that the proposed university study of UFOs give emphasis to current reports. However, certain older, "classic" cases from the last two decades contain the most significant photographic evidence. Neglect of them would justifiably be open to criticism. Hence, the present photographic study includes both new cases and independent reevaluations of older cases.

3. *Sources of Data*

1. PROJECT BLUE BOOK

Material on a number of older cases was obtained from the Aerial Phenomena Office (Project Blue Book) at Wright-Patterson Air Force Base, Ohio. In many cases, these files were not sufficiently organized or complete to permit an intelligent evaluation of the report. Further investigation was carried out in these instances.

2. APRO

Cordial relations were maintained with APRO, and through the kind assistance of Mr. and Mrs. J. Lorenzen much first- or second-generation photographic material was made available.

3. NICAP

Contacts for the exchange of information on photographic cases were established with NICAP in the spring of 1967, and files on a number of cases were made available to us at that time.

4. J. E. MC DONALD

The help of Dr. McDonald, Institute for Atmospheric Physics, University of Arizona, who conducted a study of UFO phenomena concurrently with this study, was invaluable in bringing a number of cases to our attention.

5. OTHER

Many individuals submitted reports directly to us and other recent cases were investigated by our field teams. Certain news organizations, in particular BBC, Time-Life, Inc., and United Press International were very helpful in obtaining material. Dr. R. M. L. Baker, Computer Sciences, Inc., kindly made available to us his files on the Great Falls, Tremonton, and Vandenberg AFB motion pictures, Dr. J. Allen Hynek, of Northwestern University also rendered valued assistance in providing materials for analysis.

4. Hidden Data

The problem of hidden data is characteristic of the study of UFO phenomena. Only about 12% of those persons who have seen flying objects they cannot identify actually report the sighting (Section III, Chapter 7). The indication that we are aware of only a small fraction of all sightings of UFOs and the experience of investigators in uncovering photographs suggest that we have considerably less than half the photographs considered by their owners to show UFOs. Of the photographs that may have a bearing on the existence of extraordinary *aircraft* we probably have a larger fraction, since they are more interesting to their owners. The distinction is that an UFO photo may show just a point source of light, or an amorphous blob, while an alleged "flying saucer" photo must exhibit some detail. But even in these cases, the fraction may well be less than half.

Reasons for the existence of hidden data include: (1) apathy on the part of the photographer, (2) ignorance of what to do with the photographs, (3) fear of ridicule, (4) fear of becoming involved with authorities in situations involving security or military restrictions (e.g. Ft. Belvoir case), (5) fear of restrictions in JANAP-146.

It is also possible that data, generated by various technical recording equipment, such as all-sky auroral cameras, or the Prairie Network are another "hidden" source (Section VI, Chapter 9).

Finally, there is another class of "hidden data": sightings supposed to have occurred on various military bases but allegedly suppressed by military or intelligence authorities. We have heard many allegations of such cases. Usually they were not detailed enough to be fruitful, and in only one case was it possible for us, even with the cooperation of the Air Force, to locate any alleged photographs of UFOs. Such allegations of suppression may typically arise as a result of incidents like that described in Case 51. In this instance a bright UFO was recorded by several tracking cameras at Vandenberg AFB. The UFO was described as "streaking up past" a rocket during a launch. Project investigators recovered the films in question without difficulty. Study of them conclusively identified the

UFO as the planet Venus. Meanwhile, however, the story had reached the rumor stage, and it is likely that belief that an UFO had paced a rocket was widespread as a result.

5. *Quality of UFO Photographic Data*

The statistical properties or the quantity of photographic data are less important than the content of a single case that might strongly indicate the existence of a hitherto unrecognized phenomenon. Nonetheless, it is a part of the problem that most of the data are of very low quality. A glance through typical UFO periodicals and books illustrates this. Many of the photographs are blurred, usually due to poor focus. Many are badly processed or light-struck. Many, usually because they are fabrications made with small models too close to the camera, show, against sharp backgrounds, objects that are hopelessly out of focus. Many photographs do not give the subjective impression of a metallic or luminous entity flying through the air at some moderate distance from the observers.

More specifically a large part of the data is inappropriate for analysis. Night-time photographs that show either point sources or amorphous blobs with no background or foreground fall in this category. Daytime photographs of objects of very small angular size are also of little value. A large number of reports consist of only one photograph, and single photographs are of much less photogrammetric value than sets.

Damage to negatives frequently renders them valueless for investigative purposes. An investigator visiting one witness found a baby playing on the floor with the negatives. (McMinnville, Case 46.) A crucial spot on another set of negatives was burned out by a dropped match, assertedly by accident. (North Eastern, Case 53.) Loss of original negatives or prints is reported, as in Santa Ana (Case 52).

Accurate descriptive testimony, even in photographic cases is also difficult to obtain. For example, a witness described an UFO as "half as large as the moon"; his photograph and sketch show a disk having an angular diameter of about 15°.

6. *Natural Phenomena Photographed as UFOs*

A number of natural phenomena, well known in various branches of the scientific community, but little known to the general public, have been reported as UFOs. Three classes of these are meteorological, astronomical, and photographic.

Plate 1 shows an excellent example of a lenticular cloud. These thin clouds are usually related to irregularities in ground elevation (hence classified as "orographic" clouds), and sometimes appear stacked, one above the other, like a pile of saucers. A number have appeared in UFO reports.

Plate 2 illustrates a sub-sun, produced by reflection of the sun off a laminar arrangement of flat ice crystals (Minnaert,

1954, p. 203). The Gulfstream aircraft case is tentatively attributed to a sub-sun (see Case 54).

Plate 3 is a time exposure of the moon, showing trailing due to the earth's rotation. The explanation of such a photograph of the moon is obvious to anyone familiar with astronomical photographs. Yet a similar picture showing the trails of the moon and Venus was widely printed in newspapers across the country in March 1966. The trails were described as two UFOs.

Although aurora displays can produce colored, fast-moving arcs of light of various shapes and brightnesses, it does not appear that auroras are involved in a substantial number of UFO reports. No UFO photographs were attributed to auroras in this study.

A number of purely photographic effects can result in UFO-like images. Two classes are very common. The first is film damage. Creases or unusual pressure produce dark images on negatives and bright spots on prints made from them. Chemical damage during development can produce either bright or dark spots on negatives or prints. The second class is internal reflections, or lens flares produced by unwanted light paths through the camera optics. Many widely circulated UFO photographs are unquestionably the result of lens flares. Symmetry about a line connecting the flare to a bright light source in the photograph is usually the clue to identification of a lens flare photograph.

Plates 4 and 5 show examples of reported "UFOs" identified as film defects, and Plate 6 shows an example of a lens flare (see also Menzel and Boyd, 1963).

Man-made objects such as balloons and rocket exhaust trails, especially illuminated by a low sun during twilight have also produced many UFO reports (N.M. aircraft Case 55). A number of photographs of bright, nearly stationary point sources in a daylight or twilight sky may be balloons.

7. *Fabrications*

Fabrications represent a delicate problem. Nowhere in the discussion of photographic cases have I conclusively labeled one as a hoax, although I have shown that this hypothesis is entirely satisfactory in a number of cases.

Hoaxes are not new in UFO investigations. The Maury Island (Wash.) incident of 1947 has been called "the first, possibly the second-best, and the dirtiest hoax in UFO history." (Ruppelt, 1956). Photographs allegedly taken by one of the witnesses to the incident had been "misplaced," he said. Eventually, he, a companion, and an "investigator" hired by a magazine publisher admitted that the incident was a fabrication. Before the case was closed, much money and time had been spent, and two Air Force investigating officers had been killed when their Air Force B-25 crashed during the inquiry into the "sighting." According to Ruppelt, the federal government considered prosecuting the hoaxers, but later abandoned the idea.

Often a photograph apparently fabricated to amuse friends results in a full-blown UFO report. The friends take the photograph seriously and tell others. Eventually a local newspaper prints both picture and story. From there it may be distributed nationally by the press wire services, or one of the private UFO investigating organizations such as APRO or NICAP. In view of the demonstrable avocational interest of some persons, especially young persons, in producing "flying saucer photos," one must be especially wary of any alleged UFO photo that *could* have been easily fabricated under the circumstances.

Fabrications may be thought of in two broad categories: "physical," of a real *object,* which is then alleged to be an UFO; or "optical," the producing by optical and other means of an *image* falsely alleged to be a real physical entity at the scene. Retouched negatives, double exposures, and superimposed images are examples of the latter. Generally, physical fabrications meet tests of consistence in lighting and shadow but fail tests of size or distance. Most commonly, photographs of models are out of focus, or have inconsistent focus between the "UFO" and other objects at its alleged distance. Optical fabrications, on the other hand, may show inconsistencies in lighting between background and UFO details, or in the case of montages, image flaws.

Plate 7 is an example of the simplest and most common type of physical fabrication—a disk-shaped model thrown into the air by hand. Plates 8 and 9 are examples of more complex fabrications—a model suspended from a string and a nighttime photograph of a hand-held model illuminated by flashlight. These three photographs were made by the writer. Plates 8 and 9 were made for comparison with the Santa Ana and North East UFO photographs (Cases 52 and 53). Plates 10, 11, and 12 are examples of optical fabrications made by the writer.

8. *Techniques of Analysis*

Photographic evidence acquires probative value only when known natural phenomena can be ruled out and it can be shown that a fabrication was not easy or convenient.

Early in the study, it was decided not to select or analyze each case by a predetermined routine. Rather, cases were studied in terms of their individual characteristics. Diagnostic characteristics included such properties as (1) potential stereoscopy, (2) reports by multiple visual witnesses, (3) cloud motions, (4) use of haze to define distance, (5) accurate altitude and azimuth data, (6) structure and shape of object, (7) geometry of motion, and (8) geometry of lighting and shadows. Initial selection of cases to be studied was also influenced by the degree to which other students of UFO phenomena regarded them as significant.

In the course of the investigation, analysis of the foregoing characteristics of UFO photographs resulted in our developing a set of protocols useful in the assigning priorities to UFO photographs for study. These results are described in section 10 of this chapter.

The cases selected for investigation were analyzed as completely as possible. The techniques are demonstrated in the case reports themselves (Part IV, Chapter 3).

9. *Review and Summary*

The project gathered information on 35 photographic cases that occurred in 1966-68. These may be assumed to be a more or less representative cross-section of photographic cases. Of this 35-case current cross-section only two, Calgary and North Pacific (Cases 57 and 56), were initially selected as first priority cases. On investigation, neither case yielded data deemed to be of probative value. Second priority cases among the 1966-68 group were Camarillo (identified probably as airborn debris), Gulfstream Aircraft (sub-sun), and Sonora (airborn debris). Many of the remaining 1966-68 cases of lower priority had low strangeness or insufficient data for analysis.

The final disposition of the 35 cases is summarized in Table 1. The figures are thought to be representative of UFO photographic cases. That is, roughly one quarter are fabrications, one quarter are misidentifications, a quarter have such low information content as to be unfit for analysis, another quarter are clearly recorded but lack sufficient data for analysis. The residual cases that are genuinely puzzling constitute at most a very small percentage.

In addition to these current cases, 18 older reports, including some by advocates of the existence of "flying saucers," were also studied.

Of the 35 cases only those in which the nature of the evidence or the credentials of the witness were judged to have the highest *a priori* probability of producing evidence for an unknown phenomenon were assigned first priority for study. Table 2 shows the classifications finally assigned to these first priority cases. Of them some 60% were found to be identifiable or to lack probative value. Two cases survived analysis:

Table 1. Classification of 35 Current Photographic Cases

Evidence for probable fabrication	9
Misidentified natural or man-made phenomena	7
Insufficient data for analysis (night-time shots, point sources, amorphous blobs, etc.)	12
Inconclusive data (unidentified unusual objects shown, but little or no analysis possible; possible fabrications)	7
Unidentified after analysis (real objects with high strangeness)	0
	35

Table 2. Classification of 11 First-Priority Cases

Inconsistencies between testimony and photos, internal inconsistencies in photos, or evidence for fabrication	Barra da Tijuca North Eastern North Pacific Santa Ana
Identified natural or man-made phenomena	Fort Belvoir Vandenberg AFB Tremonton
Not amenable to analysis	Calgary
Unidentified after analysis (indication of real objects with high strangeness), conceivable but unlikely misidentification of birds, aircraft, etc.	Great Falls
Clearly either a fabrication or an extraordinary object ("flying saucer")	McMinnville

Great Falls (motion pictures of two bright light sources difficult to reconcile with known aircraft) and McMinnville (two photographs of a saucer-shaped craft).

Since the selection of older, "classic" cases was limited, it is probable that the "residual" of unexplained photographic cases could be increased well beyond these three cases if there were additional research. Whether or not anything of probative value would be found is a matter of speculation.

10. Conclusions

Our experience also leads us to conclude that UFO photographic cases can best be selected for study and analyzed on the basis of the following criteria:

(1) *Subjective evaluation* Do various photographic factors (focus, clarity, sharpness, contrast) and the testimony combine to make the case appear credible? Does it have *potential* in providing probative evidence for the reality of an unusual phenomenon?

(2) *Known phenomena* Is any known phenomenon rationally acceptable as an explanation of the observation?

Phenomena considered must be based on a wide experience with meteorological, astronomical, optical, and photographic effects. Can the report be a case of mistaken interpretation?

(3) *Fabrications* Can the case be accepted as having been made in good faith? Are there any signs of tampering with the negative? (Are the negatives or original prints available?) Do the negatives represent a continuous sequence? Are focus, sharpness and other characteristics quantitatively in accord with the alleged sightings? Are light and shadows internally consistent on each photo?

(4) *Consistency with testimony* In addition to the internal evidence of the photographs themselves, are the photographs consistent with the witness testimony? Is lighting consistent with alleged time and direction of sighting? Are time intervals between photos consistent with testimony?

(5) *Physical and geometric tests* What peculiar characteristics suggest tests? Is the object in front of or behind any landscape features? Is contrast and focus consistent with alleged distance? What can be learned from motions and time intervals? Can the flight path be estimated from the sequence of positions and angular sizes?

The Colorado study of UFO photographic evidence failed to disclose conclusive evidence of the existence of "flying saucers." Nor did it, of course, establish that such objects do not exist. I believe that it is significant, however, that a number of the most widely heralded "classic" cases were either identified or were shown to be of little probative value in the present study. This finding suggests that much of the case for the reality of "flying saucers" has been built on very inadequate research into widely publicized reports. Some examples of such cases, the reality of which has been rejected after intensive study by the project, are summarized briefly below:

Barra da Tijuca, Brazil, (Case 48): A magazine photographer and a reporter allegedly saw and made five photographs of a large disk that passed overhead. The photographic sequence shows the disk approaching (edge on) in the distance and passing by in a credible series. A report on the case by O. T. Fontes, of Brazil, (APRO, 1961) "pronounce(s) them authentic" and purports to establish their authenticity with "top-secret documents" from Brazilian Air Force files kept since 1951. The documents purport to demonstrate "the absolute impossibility of a hoax." Study of photographs enlarged from the APRO copies shows that the disk in the fourth photograph (Plate 30) clearly illuminated from the left, with bold shadows, but a palm tree as well as other confused foliage on the hillside below appear to be illuminated from the right. The discrepancy was first pointed out by Menzel and Boyd (1963).

North Eastern (Case 53): Two photographs show a bright, amorphous object that reportedly swept past four boys who were photographing the moon at night. The image on the photographs is strikingly suggestive of an out-of-focus plate-like object supported by a human arm and hand photographed by time-exposure. According to the original report, (NICAP, 1965) the "arm" was an invisible gaseous discharge from the UFO. A photograph (Plate 9) that demonstrates how such an image can be fabricated was made by taping a plate to a small handle. The apparent transparency of the "gaseous discharge" was simulated by moving the arm during the time exposure. In the light of such simple reproduction of these photographs, I have concluded that this case is of no probative value.

Fort Belvoir, Va., (Case 50): Six exposures made on this Army base show a ring-shaped object being enveloped in a white, puffy cloud. The photographs were proclaimed as "First Published Photos of the Amazing Ring-Shaped UFO" (Rankow, 1967). Aides of the commanding officer at Fort Belvoir demonstrated to a project investigator that this was a vortex cloud generated by atomic bomb simulation demonstrations that were frequently carried out at the base some years ago. Positive identification was obtained.

North Pacific (Case 57): Three boys in their back yard photographed a disk that allegedly passed overhead. The object was not reported by any other witnesses. The incident was given considerable publicity and the two photographs were published by APRO. In an interview the boys stressed that they had accurately re-enacted the event and that the time interval between the two photographs was very short, about eight seconds; however, the cloud patterns were markedly different. Separately confronted with the marked discrepancy in cloud structure between the two photographs, the boys each said they could not account for it, though they reaffirmed the story of the sighting. The photographs cannot therefore be considered as satisfactory evidence for the existence of "flying saucers."

Santa Ana, Calif., (Case 52): A traffic engineer, of good reputation, with excellent references, and with experience as a former policeman, allegedly saw and made three photographs of a metallic disk and a fourth photograph of a vortex smoke ring allegedly left by the departing disk. Interruption of radio transmissions from his vehicle, reportedly associated with the presence of the disk, was confirmed by the engineer's supervisor. The series of photographs has been widely published and widely regarded as one of the best cases. Detailed investigation revealed several serious discrepancies. For example, a study of the weather data at surrounding stations indicates that an early morning cloud cover had entirely dissipated well before the report was made, yet the fourth photograph shows a background of moderately dense, gray clouds. Other circumstances surrounding these photographs reduce further their probative value.

In the course of my study I was able to simulate effectively the first three photographs by suspending a model by a thread attached to a rod resting on the roof of a truck and photographing it (Plate 8). Without assuming the truth or untruth of the witness' story, this has led me to conclude that the case is of little probative value.

Vandenberg AFB, Calif., (Case 51): Tracking films from a rocket launch show a bright object apparently rushing up past the rocket just after second stage ignition. The films were first described in a textbook (Baker, 1967). The film sequence was taken very seriously because several cameras in different locations simultaneously recorded the object. Interest in the case was heightened by its resemblance to a number of apocryphal accounts of UFOs pacing rockets. The Colorado project at once obtained the films through official channels. Tracking data showed that the rocket was moving toward the horizon past the calculated position of Venus at the time.

To summarize conclusions relating to UFO photographs:

1. About half of the photographic reports are clearly identifiable as known phenomena or can be demonstrated to contain internal geometric or other inconsistencies.
2. About half can be ultimately classified as being inconclusive or presenting insufficient data to furnish probative evidence of an unknown phenomenon. Most single-witness cases must fall in the latter category. Most night-time photographs, point-source objects, and amorphous objects without background or foreground must be relegated to this category for lack of satisfactory quantitative tests that can be performed on them.
3. A number of cases initially described publicly by UFO enthusiasts as representative of the strongest evidence for the reality of extraordinary aircraft were either conclusively identified as ordinary phenomena or shown to have serious internal inconsistencies.
4. The number of identified or fraudulent cases is irrelevant to the existence or non-existence of extraordinary objects or "flying saucers."
5. A very small fraction of potentially identifiable and interesting photographic cases remain unidentified.

Some conclusions relating to these residual photographic cases are:

1. None of them conclusively establishes the existence of "flying saucers," or any extraordinary aircraft, or hitherto unknown phenomenon. For any of these cases, no matter how strange or intriguing, it is always possible to "explain" the observations, either by hypothesizing some extraordinary circumstance or by alleging a hoax. That is to say, none of the residual photographic cases investigated here is compelling enough to be conclusive on its own.

2. Some of the cases are sufficiently explicit that the choice is limited to the existence of an extraordinary aircraft or to a hoax.

3. The residual group of unidentifieds is not inconsistent with the hypothesis that unknown and extraordinary aircraft have penetrated the airspace of the United States, but none yields sufficient evidence to establish this hypothesis.

In summary, about 10% of the photographic cases can initially be selected as "first priority" cases, i.e. interesting and detailed enough to investigate. After investigation, there remains a small residual, of the order of 2% of all cases, that appears to represent well recorded but unidentified or unidentifiable objects that are airborne—i.e. UFOs. Yet there is insufficient evidence to assert that any one of these represents an unusual or extraordinary phenomenon. We find no conclusive evidence of unidentified aircraft or "flying saucers." The photographic data has been poorly presented in the past, and the frequency of hypothetical "flying saucers" appears much smaller than has been popularly assumed; it may be zero. The present data are compatible with, but do not establish either the hypothesis that (1) the entire UFO phenomenon is a product of misidentification, poor reporting, and fabrication, or that (2) a very small part of the UFO phenomenon involves extraordinary events.

References

Baker, R. M., Jr. and Maud W. Makemson, *An Introduction to Astrodynamics*, N. Y.: Academic Press, 1967.
Menzel, D. H. and Lyle G. Boyd, *The World of Flying Saucers*, Garden City, N. Y.: Doubleday, 1963.
Rankow, Ralph. "The Ring-Shaped UFO," *Flying Saucers*, No. 4, Fall, (1967).
Ruppelt, E. J., *The Report on Unidentified Flying Objects*, Garden City, N. Y.: Doubleday, 1956.

Chapter 3 Direct Physical Evidence / Roy Craig

Several types of physical effects have been presented as evidence that an object of unusual nature had been present at a given location. Such effects consist of: (1) markings on ground, vegetation, or objects with which an UFO, as something from an UFO, reportedly made direct or indirect physical contact; (2) material residue allegedly deposited from or by an UFO; and (3) articles or portions of articles manufactured by intelligent beings, but reportedly not produced by known cultures. A fourth known conceivable type of physical evidence, consisting of a non-earthly or captured "flying saucer," would be most impressive as evidence. The existence of this type of evidence has been suggested by some reporters, such as Moseley (1967), who reported the claim that a captured flying saucer was held at a military base in Ohio, and Allen (1959), who presented a photograph of a tiny humanoid creature and four adult Earth residents, claiming that the creature was a crewman of a saucer which crashed near Mexico City in 1950. During the course of this study, however, no indication was found that this fourth type of evidence has ever existed.

1. *Markings Allegedly Made By UFOs*

Claims of evidence of the first type are common. UFO reports contain numerous descriptions, often with supporting photographs of saucer "nests"—areas where soil, grass, cattails, or other vegetation had been flattened, burned, broken off, or blown away, allegedly by an UFO that landed or hovered there. The Lorenzens (1967) also have described six cases in which sets of circular or wedge-shaped depressions were allegedly made by the landing legs of unidentified vehicles. A number of other cases of the landing-gear imprint type have been reported, including incidents at Presque Isle State Park, Pa., 31 July 1966; South Hill, Va., 21 April 1967; and Tucson, Ariz., 9 October 1967. These three cases were examined and analyzed by Project Blue Book. Hall (1964) and others have listed other cases in which ground impressions are claimed as evidence that unknown physical objects had been present. Hall's listing also includes a half dozen "nest" reports, and a 13-ft. ring imprint of a general type earlier reported in a case described by Maney and Hall (1961).

Reports of ring imprints are not uncommon. Four cases, involving ring imprints generally about 30 ft. in diameter and 6-12 in. wide were reported in August and September, 1967, in three different Canadian provinces. In Camrose, Alberta six different rings were reported. Photographs of the Camrose rings were received by this project for evaluation.

Claims of the saucer nest type of evidence were made in a few of the current cases investigated by the field teams (e. g. Cases 22, 25, 38). In some cases, the "nest" seemed imaginary. In other cases, the reality of an imprint, of a type which conceivably could have been made by a large saucer or by a being from a saucer, was evident (as in Case 22). However, in all such cases, it was impossible to establish as factual the claims that the imprints actually were made by an extraordinary object or being.

If the evidence displayed could have been the result of human or animal activity, or lightning or other natural events, the probability that it was so caused is much greater, in absence of independent evidence to the contrary, than the probability of its creation by an extraterrestrial vehicle or being: therefore, the burden of proof must lie with the person claiming a strange origin.

The independent evidence most frequently claimed is presence of unusual radioactivity at the site. In cases where such claims were checked by our field teams, (32, 42) the claim was found to be untrue. In one case (22), radioactive material was found to be present by Canadian investigators and in other cases, (e. g. Fisherville, Va., 12-21-64) which could no longer be checked, testimony by persons other than the UFO observer supported a claim that the site was found to be radioactive. In such cases, however, if radioactive material actually were present, the possibility that it was placed there by humans cannot be ignored. If humans are known to have visited the site before official confirmation of presence of radioactive material has been made, and the material found is either a naturally occurring radioactive mineral or a commercially available luminous paint, the presence of this material serves to weaken any claim of strange origin of the markings.

The existence of an imprint of odd shape or a circular area of crushed vegetation often can be established. Its mere existence does not prove, however, that the marking was made by a strange being or vehicle. Demonstration of a connection between such markings and strange objects has thus far not been accomplished. Attempts to establish such connection must still depend upon personal testimony. Generally, personal testimony includes the reported sighting of an UFO in the area of the discovered imprints or nest. Quite frequently, however, UFO origin of the markings is assumed, even though no UFO was seen in the area near the time the markings must have been made. This was true of the Camrose rings, whose appearance did not differ markedly from tracks left by wheels of farm vehicles. In case 38, "nests" were reportedly discovered in the forest just after the field team investigated a multitude of UFO reports in the region. The project sent photographs of these circular patches of forest damage to Dr. Carl E. Ostrom, Director of Timber Management Research, U.S. Forest Service, for comment. Dr. Ostrom listed four natural causes of such patches of forest damage. He indicated that members of the Forest Service had observed similar damage in other regions under ecological conditions similar to those in the area in which these "saucer nests" were reported. Although UFOs had been reported in the general region, there again was no direct connection between them and the patches of timber damage, the existence of which could be accounted for by quite earthly processes.

Generally there are no physical tests which can be applied to a claimed saucer landing site to prove the origin of the imprints. Occasionally, the degree of compaction of soil by UFO "landing legs" is presented as evidence that the force was extraordinary. However, if the compaction could have been achieved by a human with a sledge hammer, for example, compaction measurements are of little significance, since they do not yield information regarding the cause of compaction.

Chemical tests of soil can sometimes be used to disaprove a claim, but are not likely to support a claim of strange origin of markings, since there is no obvious reason to expect chemical alteration. For example, samples of soil from a golf course at Port Townsend, Wash. were submitted to this project for analysis (Case 1406P, 1074T, project files). One sample was taken from a burned area where an UFO, reportedly observed earlier by several youngsters, was assumed to have touched down. Comparison samples from unaffected areas nearby were also studied. Gas chromatography showed the existence of hydrocarbon residues in the sample from the burned area, indicating that gasoline or other hydrocarbon had been used to make this particular "saucer nest." An empty lighter-fluid can was found in the area a few hundred yards away.

2. *Material Allegedly Deposited by UFOs*

An elusive material, called "angel hair" in UFO publications, is sometimes reported to have been deposited by UFOs. Seventeen cases involving "angel hair" were listed by Maney and Hall (1961) for the period 1952 through 1955. In fourteen there was an associated sighting reported of an UFO. The "angel hair" is described as a fibrous material which falls in large quantities, but is unstable and disintegrates and vanishes soon after falling. It has also been described as filaments resembling spider webs, floating down to earth, hanging from telephone wires and tree branches and forming candy-floss-like streamers. These streamers, which sometimes are reported to cover areas as large as 0.25 sq. mi., also are reported to vanish on touch, burn like cellophane when ignited, and sublime and disappear while under observation. A somewhat similar evanescent residue, described as a luminous haze or a misty, smoke-like deposit, was reported in three cases discussed by the Lorenzens (1967), and "angel hair" cases are also described by Michel (1958), who suggested that the material be collected and preserved at low temperature for crystal structure study by X-ray diffraction. Hall (1964) has stated that many deposits of "angel's hair" have been nothing but cobwebs spun by ballooning spiders. On at least one occasion, he wrote, small spiders have actually been found in the material. In other cases, the composition or origin of the "angel's hair" is uncertain. During the course of this study, one sample of dry white powder was submitted to the project for analysis. It had been collected from beneath the eaves of a house over which "angel hair" was reported to have settled, leaving a sticky deposit. (Project files 1406P. 1074T). Since the major cationic component of this powder was titanium, it was concluded that the powder was the residue of a commonly used house paint containing a titanium oxide pigment. Few recent UFO reports have been involved material of the "angel hair" type.

A second type of material often is assumed, because of the circumstances of its appearance, to have been dumped by

UFOs. The material is commonly referred to as "space grass," and has appeared unexpectedly in fields and yards after falling from the sky. Generally, no sighting of identified or unidentified objects is associated with the fall. The material is composed of metallic threads of lengths varying from a fraction of an inch to a foot or more, generally with many threads intertwined into a loose mass. Typical material of this type is described by Keel (1967), who suggests that UFOs are using the earth as a kind of garbage dump. Actually, "space grass" is aluminum "chaff" of the various sizes and types used by military aircraft to confuse tracking radar (see Section VI, Chapter 5).

Samples of material sent to the project for analysis because of their assumed UFO association were most commonly "space grass." The first sample was received from observers of two "space ships" reported over Manhattan Beach, Calif., on 5 February 1957. The material appeared 24 hr. after the sighting and was reported to have been radioactive when found. It was not radioactive when received. Analysis demonstrated it to be 1145 alloy hard aluminum foil chaff dipoles with both a slip and a stripe coating applied to the surface of the foil. Since the slip coating was color coded red, it could be identified as a product of the Foil Division of Revere Copper and Brass Incorporated, Brooklyn, N. Y. The company identified the chaff as its product. This chaff could have been dropped by aircraft. It also could have been carried aloft by sounding rockets or balloons, and released at high altitudes for radar tracking. It is certain, however, that this sample of "space grass," like other such samples submitted to the project for analysis, had a quite earthly origin, and was not deposited by vehicles of extra-terrestrial origin.

3. Parts of UFOs, or UFO Equipment

Frank Edwards (1966) discusses three cases in which an UFO or part of an UFO is claimed to have been recovered: (1) a flying disc was reported to have crashed on Spitzbergen Island in 1952 and to have been recovered, badly damaged but intact, by the Norwegian Air Force; (2) a 1 lb. fragment from a 2 ft. diameter glowing disk which was reportedly intercepted over Washington, D. C., in 1952; and (3) a 3,000 lb. mass of "strange metal" was found about 1 July 1960, in the St. Lawrence River in Quebec, and considered by a Canadian UFO investigator to be possibly a portion of a very large interstellar device which came into this solar system at an unknown time in the past.

Efforts have been made to determine to what degree any of these claims might be factual. In the Spitzbergen case, Mr. Finn Lied, Director, Norwegian Defence Research Establishment, replied that the only articles he knew of having been recovered in Norway have been traced back to rocket and satellite hardware. Mr. Tage Eriksson, of the Research Institute of National Defence, Sweden, replied that neither the Swedish Air Force nor the Research Institute of National Defence has at any time taken part in an investigation of a crashed UFO in Spitzbergen or elsewhere. A U.S. Air Intelligence Information Report, dated 12 September 1952, revealed that the Norwegian government knew nothing of such an object. The story apparently was the work of a West German reporter. It first appeared in the German newspaper "Berliner Volksblatt" for 9 July 1952. The original newspaper report stated definitely that the silver discus-like body was 48.88 m. in diameter and made of an unknown metal compound; its meters and instruments had Russian symbols, and it appeared to have a range of some 30,000 km. Significantly, the aspects of this first report implying that the vehicle was of Russian origin have been selectively neglected by subsequent writers, particularly those who urge that the claimed wreckage is extra-terrestrial in origin. It seems well established that this story has no basis in fact.

Representatives of Air Force Project Blue Book claimed no knowledge of the disc fragment discussed by Edwards, who claimed the successful search for this fragment was confirmed by Lt. Cdr. Frank Thompson of the U.S. Navy. The fragment, said to have been dislodged by gunfire from a Navy jet, reportedly fell to the ground, where it was found, still glowing, an hour later by U.S. military ground search crews. Reports of UFO events over Washington, D. C., in 1952 contain no reference to such a gunfire incident. If such a fragment did exist and was classified "Secret" as was claimed, its existence and whereabouts would not necessarily be revealed to this project. A request for official confirmation that the claimed fragment did or did not exist and does or does not exist was forwarded to U.S. Air Force Headquarters. A reply was received from J. W. Clinton, by direction of the Chief of Information, Department of the Navy. Mr. Clinton indicated that a thorough search of all Navy records available failed to reveal any account of a Navy jet fighter's encounter with an UFO in July 1952 or at any other time. Perhaps more significant, however, were the facts that Navy records of the year 1952 carried only one Frank Thompson, an individual who had retired from active duty several years before 1952 with the rank of lieutenant, not lieutenant commander. Navy fighters based near Washington were armed only for firing practice conducted far out at sea over a restricted firing area. Navy aircraft armed with live ammunition, Mr. Clinton pointed out, would have been usurping an Air Force function if they had been present over Washington, D. C., as interceptors. Mr. Clinton concluded: "The incident is not beyond the realm of possibility, but due to the nature of the Navy's jet operations about the Washington, D. C. area at the time, it was very highly unlikely."

The 3,000-lb. mass of metallic material from the St. Lawrence River was the subject of several communications received by this project. Among these was a letter from Mrs. Carol Halford-Watkins, Secretary of the Ottawa New Sciences Club (Project file 1326-P). The Club now has custody of the specimen. The Club does not claim that the piece of metal is, in fact, part of a spaceship; however, its members do not reject this possibility. Mrs. Halford-Watkins generously offered samples of the material for analysis and provided photographs of the object and a description of details of the find and analyses of the material. The Canadian Arsenals Research and Development Establishment (CARDE) had examined the non-homogeneous material, and described it as high-manganese austenitic steel. CARDE personnel considered the material the normal product of a foundry, consisting of slag with semi-molten scrap imbedded in it. The object was not believed to have fallen in the location where it was found, which is near Quebec City, in a channel of the St. Lawrence River which carries water only at high tide, for there was no crater nor splattered material in the vicinity.

A Quebec newspaper had reported that a fiery object fell out of the sky with an accompanying sonic boom rocking the area, prior to discovery of the massive metal in the river. Members of Ottawa New Sciences Club who investigated, however, were unable to find anyone in the area who had actually heard or seen the object fall. Since no connection could be seen between the existence of this metal of slag and the UFO question, no further analysis of the material was undertaken by the project. This writer examined the metallic mass at Ottawa and agreed with the CARDE conclusion that it was ordinary foundry waste.

Examination of claimed evidence of any of the three general types revealed a tendency of some persons to attribute to UFOs any track material, or artifact which seemed unusual and strange, even when there had been no sighting of an UFO in the vicinity. The 3,000 lb. metallic mass is one example. Another example was a ground depression and connecting system of crooked, thread-like tunnels found near Marliens, France, on 9 May 1967, and reported in *The Flying Saucer Review* (1967). The radar chaff "space grass" described above also illustrates this tendency. Metal spheres, a foot or two in diameter have also been found in fields or woods and reported as mysterious UFOs or UFO evidence. These hollow spheres actually are targets used to calibrate radar sets. One such object, not considered an "UFO" by the finder in this case, but arousing widespread interest, was found on an Arkansas farm on 3 November 1967. The sphere had been manufactured by the Universal Metal Spinning Company of Albuquerque, N. M. for the Physical Science Laboratory of New Mexico State University at Las Cruces. These spheres, according to the manufacturer, are made of aluminum, vary in diameter from 3³⁄₁₆ in. to 28 in., and are deployed from aircraft, balloons, or rockets. In ordinary use, they fall freely, reaching a terminal velocity of about 90 mph. They are normally dropped only in uninhabited regions. Such spheres, found in Australia, were mentioned in an UFO context by Edwards (1967).

A 5 in. metal object found on a lawn in Colorado, near a burned spot its own size where it evidently had struck while still hot was thought perhaps to have fallen from outer space during the night, since it was not on the lawn when it had been mowed the previous day. This object was easily identified as the power lawn mover's muffler.

Any artifact reportedly found at the site of an alleged UFO landing, collision, or explosion presents the primary problem of establishing a relationship between the artifact and the UFO. During the course of this study reports reaching us of events from which such artifacts might be recovered have invariably been sufficiently vague and uncertain to make doubtful the reality of the event described. Analysis of the artifact is therefore meaningless unless the analysis itself can demonstrate that the artifact is not of earthly origin. Samples of material were submitted to this project from two reported events which occurred during project operation. In one case (42) a tiny irregular piece of thin metal had reportedly been picked up from among the beer-can tubs and other earthly debris in an area beneath the reported location of a hovering UFO. It was said to have been picked up because it was the only object in the area that the local investigator could not identify immediately. Analysis showed the sample to be composed chiefly of iron. No additional effort was made to prove that it was or was not a piece of corroded metal can, for project investigators saw no reason to assume it was related to the UFO, even if the reported UFO were real. In the other case, two metal samples were submitted, through APRO headquarters, reportedly from the site of an UFO-automobile collision of 16 July 1967. One of these, a tiny piece of thin, rolled metal, was shown by analysis to be an alloy of magnesium, aluminum, and zinc. The other sample, weighing several grams, was an iron—chromium—manganese alloy in unworked, crystalline state. Large crystals extending from one surface suggested this sample had solidified at the edge of a vessel from which the rest of the melt had been poured. Both of these materials could be produced by conventional technology. Proof that they are residue from a strange object would require demonstration that they were actually found at the site; that they were not there prior to the reported UFO event and could not have been brought there by the automobile or by other means subsequent to the event; that there was dependable continuity of custody of samples between discovery and analysis; and that there was, indeed, an UFO involved in the reported event. In other words, the existence of these materials, since they are easily producible by earthly technology, can not serve as evidence that a strange flying object collided with the automobile in question.

One case described at great length in UFO literature (Lorenzen, 1962) emphasizes metal fragments that purportedly fell to earth at Ubatuba, Sao Paulo, Brazil from an exploding extra-terrestrial vehicle. The metal was alleged to be of such extreme purity that it could not have been produced by earthly technology. For that reason, this particular material has been widely acclaimed as a fragment of an exploded flying disc. Descriptions of the material's origin and analyses occupy 46 pages of the Lorenzen book and the material is referred to in a high percentage of UFO writings. These fragments of magnesium metal—undoubtedly the most famous bits of physical evidence in UFO lore—were generously loaned to the Colorado project by Jim and Coral Lorenzen of APRO for analysis.

The story which associated these fragments with an UFO is even more tenuous than most UFO reports, since the observers could never be identified or contacted because of the illegibility of the signature on the letter which described the event. According to the account by Olavo T. Fontes, M.D., a Rio de Janeiro society columnist wrote, under the heading, "A Fragment From a Flying Disc."

> We received the letter: "Dear Mr. Ibrahim Sued. As a faithful reader of your column and your admirer, I wish to give you something of the highest interest to a newspaperman, about the flying discs. If you believe that they are real, of course. I didn't believe anything said or published about them. But just a few days ago I was forced to change my mind. I was fishing together with some friends, at a place close to the town of Ubatuba, Sao Paulo, when I sighted a flying disc. It approached the beach at unbelievable speed and an accident, i.e. a crash into the sea seemed imminent. At the last moment, however, when it was almost striking the waters, it made a sharp turn upward and climbed rapidly on a fantastic impulse. We followed the spectacle with our eyes, startled, when we saw the disc explode in flames. It disintegrated into thousands of fiery fragments, which fell sparkling with magnificent brightness. They looked like fireworks, despite the time of the accident, at noon, i.e. at midday. Most of these fragments, almost all, fell into the sea. But a number of small pieces fell close to the beach and we picked up a large amount of this material—which was light as paper. I am enclosing a sample of it. I don't know anyone that could be trusted to whom I might send it for analysis. I never read about a flying disc being found, or about fragments or parts of a saucer that had been picked up. Unless the finding was made by military authorities and the whole thing kept as a top-secret subject. I am certain the matter will be of great interest to the brilliant columnist and I am sending two copies of this letter—to the newspaper and to your home address."
>
> From the admirer (the signature was not legible), together with the above letter, I received fragments of a strange metal. . . .

Following the appearance of this account, the claim was published that analyses of the fragments, performed by a

Brazilian government agency and others, showed the fragments to be magnesium of a purity unattainable by production and purification techniques known to man at that time. If this proved to be true, the origin of the fragments would be puzzling indeed. If it could then be established that the fragments had actually been part of a flying vehicle, that vehicle could then be assumed to have been manufactured by a culture unknown to man.

The first step in checking this claim was independent analysis of the magnesium fragments, and comparison of their purity with commercially produced pure magnesium. A comparison sample of triply sublimed magnesium, similar to samples which the Dow Chemical Company has suppied on request for at least 25 years, was acquired from Dr. R. S. Busk, Research Director of the Dow Metal Products Dept., Midland, Mich. Since it was assumed that extremely small quantities of impurities would need to be measured, neutron-activation analysis was selected as the analytical method. The samples were taken to the National Office Laboratory, Alcohol and Tobacco Tax Division, Bureau of Internal Revenue, at which the personnel had no special interest in the UFO question. The neutron irradiation and gamma spectrometry were personally observed by this writer. The analysis was performed by Mr. Maynard J. Pro, Assistant Chief, Research and Methods Evaluation, and his associates. Original irradiation data and gamma-spectrometer read-out tapes are preserved in project files.

The material irradiated was a chip broken from the main fragment. It was immersed in HC1 to remove surface contamination. After washing, the sample presented a bright, shiny, metallic surface. The absence of chlorine emissions in the gamma-ray spectra after neutron activation showed both that washing had been thorough and that chlorine was not present in the sample itself. The concentrations of eight impurity elements were measured. Results are given in parts per million parts of sample, with limits of error estimated on the basis of greatest conceivable error. The "UFO fragment" compared with the Dow material as follows:

	Parts Per Million	
Element	Dow Mg.	Brazil UFO
Mn	4.8 ± 0.5	$35.0 \pm 5.$
Al	not detected (<5)	not detected (<10)
Zn	$5. \pm 1.$	$500. \pm 100.$
Hg	2.6 ± 0.5	not detected
Cr	$5.9 \pm .12$	$32.0 \pm 10.$
Cu	0.4 ± 0.2	3.3 ± 1.0
Ba	not detected	$160. \pm 20.$
Sr	not detected	$500. \pm 100.$

Mn, Al, Zn, Hg, and Cr values were obtained from direct gamma spectrometry and half-life measurement; Cu, Ba, and Sr values were obtained by gamma spectrometry after radiochemical separation of the elements. In the latter cases, known standard samples of these elements were irradiated and analyzed concurrently with the specimen. Results, within the limits of error indicated, should be quite dependable. Since spectrographic analyses routinely performed on purified magnesium show no other elements present at concentrations of more than a few parts per million, the analytical results presented above show that the claimed UFO fragment is not nearly as pure as magnesium produced by known earthly technology prior to 1957, the year of the UFO report.

The neutron activation analysis also was utilized as a means of checking the magnesium isotopic content. The suggestion had been made (Jueneman, 1968) that the fragment might be composed of pure Mg^{26}, and therefore the magnesium isotopic content of this fragment should be determined. The suggestion was based on assumed qualities of such a pure isotope and on a density figure of 1.866 gm/cc, which had been reported for the center of one of the magnesium pieces "as determined in replicate using a Jolly balance" (Lorenzen, 1962). It is interesting that this figure was chosen over the density figure of 1.7513 gm/cc, also reported in the Lorenzen book, which was determined at a U.S. Atomic Energy Commission laboratory by creating a liquid mixture in which the fragment would neither float nor sink, and measuring the density of the liquid. The quantity of Mg^{27} isotope produced by neutron activation [Mg^{26} (n, gamma) Mg^{27}], as determined by gamma spectrometry after activation, showed that the Brazil sample did not differ significantly in Mg^{26} isotope content from other magnesium samples.

Although the Brazil fragment proved not to be pure, as claimed, the possibility remained that the material was unique. The high content of Sr was particularly interesting, since Sr is not an expected impurity in magnesium made by usual production methods, and Dr. Busk knew of no one who intentionally added strontium to commercial magnesium. The sample was, therefore, subjected also to a metallographic and microprobe analysis at the magnesium Metallurgical Laboratory of the Dow Chemical Company, through the cooperation of Dr. Busk and Dr. D. R. Beaman. Again, all work was monitored by this writer. Microprobe analysis confirmed the presence of strontium and showed it to be uniformly distributed in the sample (see Case 4). In all probability, the strontium was added intentionally during manufacture of the material from which the sample came. Metallographic examinations show large, elongated magnesium grains, indicating that the metal had not been worked after solidification from the liquid or vapor state. It therefore seems doubtful that this sample had been a part of a fabricated metal object.

A check of Dow Metallurgical Laboratory records revealed that, over the years, this laboratory made experimental batches of Mg allow containing from 0.1% - 40% Sr. As early as 25

March 1940, it produced a 700 gm. batch of Mg containing nominally the same concentration of Sr as was continued in the Ubatuba sample.

Since only a few grams of the Ubatuba magnesium are known to exist, and these could have been produced by common earthly technology known prior to 1957, the existence and composition of these samples themselves reveal no information about the samples' origin. The claim of unusual purity of the magnesium fragments has been disproved. The fragments do not show unique or unearthly composition, and therefore they cannot be used as valid evidence of the extra-terrestrial origin of a vehicle of which they are claimed to have been a part.

4. *Conclusion*

This project has found no physical evidence which, in itself, clearly indicates the existence in the atmosphere of vehicles of extraordinary nature. Belief in the existence of such vehicles, if such belief is held, must rest on other arguments.

References

Allen, W. Gordon. *Space Craft from Beyond Three Dimensions,* Exposition Press: New York, (1959), 51 and 98.

Edward, Frank. *Flying Saucers—Here and Now,* Lyle Stuart, Inc.: New York, (1967), 199.

———. *Flying Saucers, Serious Business,* Bantam Book S3378, (1966), 41ff.

Hall, Richard H. *The UFO Evidence,* NICAP publication, (1964), 97.

Jueneman, Frederick B. Private communication to Mrs. Coral Lorenzen, 4 January 1968.

Keel, John A. "Are UFOs Using the Earth For a Garbage Dump?" *Flying Saucers, No. 4,* Dell Publication, (1967), 32ff.

Lorenzen, Coral E. *The Great Flying Saucer Hoax,* The William Frederick Press: New York, (1962), 89ff. Also reprinted, paperbound, as *Flying Saucers, the Startling Evidence of the Invasion from Outer Space,* Signet Book T3058, 104ff.

Lorenzen, Coral and Jim. *Flying Saucer Occupants,* Signet Book T3205, (1967), 19-32.

Maney, C. A. and R. H. Hall. *The Challenge of Unidentified Flying Objects,* NICAP publication, (1961), iii.

Michel, Aime. *Flying Saucers and the Straight Line Mystery,* S. G. Phillips, Inc.: New York, (1958), 170.

Moseley, James W. *Saucer News,* (Spring 1967).

The Flying Saucer Review, Courier Printing and Publishing Co., Ltd.: Tunbridge Wells, Kent, England, (Sept.-Oct., 1967), 14.

Chapter 4 Indirect Physical Evidence / Roy Craig

1. *Introduction*

Reports of unidentified flying objects, particularly those reported to have come quite close to the observer, frequently describe physical effects due to the presence of the UFO. The most frequently claimed effects are electric or electromagnetic in nature. They include unexplained stoppage of automobile motors; failure of automobile headlights; interference with radio, TV, and electric clock operation; power failures; magnetic field disturbances; and sudden temporary increases in gamma radiation levels. One publication (Hall, 1964) lists

106 UFO cases in which electromagnetic effects are a significant feature of the UFO report. Forty-five of these involve stalled automobile motors, generally accompanied by headlight failure.

Physiological effects of UFOs are also frequently reported. They include strange reactions of animals, feelings of pressure, heat, or "prickly sensations," and, occasionally, lapse of consciousness by a human observer.

While such physical or physiological effects are frequently reported, they are not invariably a part of UFO reports. Some report stoppage of the observer's automobile, while others chase the UFOs in their cars, the operation of which is unimpaired. Our field teams also have noted that strange animal reactions, and even interference with telephone operation, have been claimed in cases in which the UFO was later identified as a bird or a plastic balloon. Such instances confuse the issue, but do not prove that in other cases there is no relation between claimed unusual physical and psychological effects and UFO sightings.

Claims of strange animal reactions or unusual human sensations when an UFO is near cannot be verified by examination of residual evidence, for no physical evidence remains after the event. Certain physical effects, however, might be expected to leave a detectable alteration in the affected object, or a permanent record of an instrumented measurement of a physical quantity. Attempts to find and examine such evidence are reported in this chapter.

One expected physical effect is noteworthy because of its absence. In numerous reports, the UFO is seen, visually or by radar, to be moving at presumed speeds far exceeding the speed of sound, yet no sound, particularly no sonic boom, is heard. Our present knowledge of physics indicates that any material object moving through the atmosphere at such speeds would *necessarily* create a pressure wave in the atmosphere resulting in a sonic boom. This expected physical effect is discussed in Section VI, Chapter 6.

2. *Radiation Level Excursions*

In 1952-53, Project Blue Book personnel investigated claimed correlations of visual sightings of UFOs with rapid rises of radiation counts on radiation-detecting devices (Blue Book, 1953). The events allegedly occurred near Mt. Palomar Observatory in October 1949, and at the Los Alamos Scientific Laboratory in 1950, 1951, and 1952. Air Force investigators examined their records and searched, as well, for reports of unrecorded UFO sightings. They found no evidence of UFO observations which would correlate with the Los Alamos high-radiation occurrences.

The Blue Book investigators also reviewed a Navy report of the October 1949 incidents at Mt. Palomar. According to the Air Force report, on two occasions at Mt. Palomar at the same time that radiation detectors indicated a sudden burst of radiation, "personnel from the observatory observed something in the air."

In one instance, according to the Navy report, the observed object was judged to have appeared similar to a bird. In the other the similarity was to a formation of aircraft. There was strong inidcation that, whatever the identities of the observed object, the observations and the radiation excursions were strictly coincidental.

No instances of radiation excursions coincident with UFO sightings were reported to the Colorado project, which has therefore not had an opportunity to study at firsthand any possible relationship between such events.

3. *Terrestrial Magnetic Disturbances*

Popular lore associates the presence of UFOs with local disturbances of the earth's magnetic field. "UFO detectors" have been designed to sense such disturbances, sounding an alarm when a sudden change in the magnetic field alters the orientation of a magnet in the "detector."

During the investigative phase of this project, an observer near Denver, Colo., reported that his detector had sounded. He telephoned project headquarters to inform us that he had sighted an UFO overhead. Responding to this call, project investigators drove to the scene and observed a light in the daylight sky pointed out to them by the observer. They watched the light move westward at a rate later calculated to be 15°/hr. Its coordinates during the period of observation were those of the planet Venus.

The project attempted to verify reports of the association of magnetic disturbances with UFO sightings in the Antarctic during the period March-September 1965 (Project file 1257-P). In this effort the project was greatly assisted by Commander Jehu Blades of the NROTC unit at the University of Colorado. Cmdr. Blades had served as commanding officer of the U.S. Antarctic "wintering-over" party at McMurdo Station in 1965. Argentine newspapers had given extensive coverage to a report that on 3 July 1965 personnel of the Orcadas Naval Station in the Antarctic observed the presence of a strange luminous body simultaneously with a small deviation in the earth's magnetic field. The episode lasted for 40 min. Information from the British Antarctic Survey (Blades, 1967) indicated that the British station at Deception Island had received reports of moving colored lights seen from the Argentine station on Deception Island on 7 June, 20 June, and 3 July 1965; from the Chilean station on the latter two dates, and from the British station on 2 July. An UFO observed by two men on 20 November 1965, at an Antarctic field approximately 74° 30′S, 17°00′W, was judged to have been a radiosonde balloon launched from the British station at Halley Bay.

Base Commander C. D. Walter, of the British base at Deception Island recalled receipt, during the early winter of 1965, of a variety of UFO reports from the Argentine station. Reports subsequently came from the Chilean station. The phenomena seen by the Chileans were reported as being above the Argentine base, while those seen by the Argentinians were reported as located above the Chilean base.

Mr. Walter reported that the one observation reported by a member of the British base was made by the cook at the base and was looked upon as rather a joke. There also was a suggestion that practical jokes were being played upon the commandant of the Argentine base.

No UFO observations on Deception Island were made by scientific personnel. Mr. Walter also mentioned that a nacreous cloud was observed at the British Base F on the Argentine Islands on 4 July at the same time as a defect developed in the magnetic instruments. While the instrument fault was soon corrected, misinterpreted radio reports of the event may have led to UFO interpretations, and even to claims of magnetic effects of the UFO.

Dr. Erich Paul Heilmaier, Director of the Astronomical Observatory, Catholic University of Chile, reported that observations of white luminous flying objects, made by nine people at the Chilean "Presidente Aquirre Cerda" Antarctic base on 3 July 1965, were made by untrained persons, and suggested that reports of the observations should be accepted with reserve. The objects were said to have been seen for 20 minutes as they crossed the SW end of Deception Island travelling at "full speed" in a NW-SE direction, at 45° elevation.

According to Dr. Heilmaier's information, the phenomenon was also observed at the British base and the Argentine station, and variations of the magnetic field were recorded by magnetometers at the Argentine station. Dr. Heilmaier was unable to supply details of these observations.

Capt. Jose Maria Cohen, Argentine Navy, reported that the magnetic variations registered on the Deception Island instruments were not outside the limits of normal variation.

Microfilm copies of magnetograms recorded at the Orcadas Observatory on 3 July 1965 were obtained and examined. The magnetic deviation recorded during the reported UFO sighting was small, an order of magnitude lower than deviations observed during magnetic storms, and well within normal daily fluctuations. Consequently, we must conclude that the 1965 Antarctic expedition reports offer little convincing evidence that an unidentified object caused a terrestrial magnetic disturbance. No data which could serve as firm evidence that an UFO caused a magnetic disturbance have been brought to our attention.

4. Automobile Engine Malfunction and Headlight Failure

Reports of temporary stalling of automobile motors by

UFOs constitute one of the more puzzling aspects of UFO reports. The automobiles are invariably reported to operate normally after the UFO leaves the vicinity, and no permanent damage to the car's ignition or lighting system is indicated.

One explanation advanced for such effects has been that UFOs somehow ionize the air to such an extent that normal internal combustion is prevented. This is considered unlikely because no concomitant physiological or physical effects that such ionization would cause are reported. Mechanisms capable of short-circuiting automobile electrical systems do not take into account the claim that normal operation resumes after departure of the UFO.

There remains the hypothesis that automobile motors are stopped or their performance interfered with by magnetic fields associated with UFOs. To test this hypothesis, the project sought, as the first step, to determine the minimum magnetic field strength that would cause motor malfunction. Tests of the effect of a high intensity magnetic field on individual components of an automobile ignition system have been carried out at a major national laboratory using an electromagnet capable of producing a field up to 10 kg (kilogauss) across an area 9 in. in diameter. The engineer has requested that his identity not be disclosed in this report. At a meeting sponsored by the project in Boulder, he presented his experimental results. He used a simplified simulated automobile ignition system, placing each component in turn in the magnetic field, which was increased slowly from −20 kg. The distributor was turned by an electric motor outside the magnetic field. His results are shown in the following table:

Item in Field	Field Direction	Effects
Spark Plug	Coaxial with arc	Slightly brighter spark
Spark Plug	Perpendicular to arc	Moved arc to side of electrodes, 20 kilogauss did not stop arcing.
Coil (Steel Container)	Perpendicular to center line	Occasionally interrupted spark at 20 kilogauss.
Coil (Aluminum Container)	Perpendicular to center line	Spark started missing at about 4 kilogauss, stopped at 17 kilogauss.
Lead acid battery with resistive load (1A current)	Parallel to battery plates	Voltage dropped from 12.3 at zero field to 12.0 volt at 20 kilogauss.
Light	Parallel and perpendicular to filament	No effect on brightness or current (resistance) up to 20 kilogauss.

The spark plug was at atmospheric pressure with a normal gap of about 0.025 inches.

Two coils were used, a 12V aluminum-cased coil, without a voltage-dropping resistor, typical of European cars, and a 6V steel-cased coil of American manufacture. The iron core of the aluminum-cased coil saturated at 16 kg. When the core is saturated, the charging current does not change the magnetism enough to generate a high voltage. The steel casing of the 6V coil apparently provided enough magnetic shielding to extend the saturation point to something greater than 20kg. external field.

If we accept these measurements, they indicate that a car with its ignition coil in a steel container (standard in cars of American manufacture) would continue to operate in magnetic fields less than 20 kg. However, since the entire ignition system is shielded by the steel hood and body of the car, it is apparent that very intense magnetic fields external to the car would be required if automobile stoppage should be due to magnetic effects.

Rather than attempt to assess the probability that intense magnetic fields are generated by UFOs, or to calculate hypothetical field intensities at variable distances from an UFO, we chose to test the magnetic field hypothesis by looking for direct evidence that automobiles reportedly affected by the presence of UFOs had in fact been subjected to the effects of a magnetic field that was sufficiently intense to cause motor malfunction. Magnetic mapping of car bodies as a means of obtaining information about the magnetic history of an automobile was suggested by Mr. Frederick J. Hooven, formerly of the Ford Motor Company, and now Adjunct Professor of Engineering Science at the Thayer School of Engineering, Darthmouth College. Hanover, N. H. Mr. Hooven and members of the General Parts Division of Ford Motor Company, notably Mr. David F. Moyer, manager of advanced manufacturing engineering, applied the magnetic mapping technique to an automobile that had allegedly been directly beneath an UFO for several minutes. During that time, the driver reportedly could not accelerate the automobile, which seemed to be moving under the control of the UFO. Residual radio and car instrument malfunctions also were claimed. The full study of this case, carried out at the expense of the Ford Motor Company, is reported as Case 12. A summary of the magnetic signature aspects of the case is presented by Mr. Hooven as follows:

> When a piece of ordinary low-carbon steel, such as automotive sheet metal, is stressed beyond the elastic limit, as in forming or stretching, it becomes "work-hardened" to an extent sufficient to enable it to retain a substantial degree of permanent magnetism. Thus, it ordinarily will retain a substantial portion of the earth's magnetic field as it existed at the time of form-

ing. This can easily be demonstrated by hammering a nail on an anvil, with the nail pointing north/south, which will result in permanently magnetizing the nail in the direction of the earth's field.

The external sheet metal parts of an automobile, such as the door panels, hood, deck lid, roof, and minor body panels, are ordinarily formed under conditions that remain constant for the duration of the yearly model, and often for three or four years. Thus, the parts of a given make and model car are all likely to have come from a single source, or at the most two sources, no matter where the car is assembled. The dies that form these parts ordinarily remain undisturbed during the service life, subject to repeated blows that cause them to become magnetized by the magnetic field of the earth, and forming parts that all take on a similar pattern of magnetism.

Other processes that leave their magnetic imprint on the sheet metal parts of the car, are the use of magnetic lifting devices, spot-welding, and (where used) chrome-plating, with the result that each make and model car has a pattern of magnetism retained in its sheet metal parts that is as distinctive of that make and model as a finger print is of an individual.

This characteristic was utilized in the tests reported in Case 12, as a suggested technique whereby vehicles could be examined for some indication of their history so far as magnetic environment is concerned. The vehicle was carefully mapped with a magnetometer, and the complex pattern of magnetic remanence was compared with that of three other vehicles of the same make, model, and year chosen at random. It proved to be identical to two of them; it was established that the third had been wrecked and repaired.

It was not established by these tests just what strength of magnetic field would be required to change the established pattern of the production vehicle, but it is obviously a greater amount than a car experiences in the normal course of its life. It was likewise assumed that this value would be smaller than any field capable of interfering with the car's operation.

Since the magnetic pattern on the tested car was substantially unchanged from new, it was concluded on the basis of the above assumptions that the car has not been subject to any ambient magnetic field, either unidirectional or alternating, of sufficient intensity to interfere with its normal functioning. This would have been sufficient to conclude that the permanent magnets in the car could not have been demagnetized, as was at first suspected, without the necessity of removing the instruments for testing, since any field that would have affected the permanent magnets in the car would have been sufficient to change the retained magnetism in the car's sheet metal.

Magnetic effects have been considered to be the most plausible causes of reported automobile malfunctioning in UFO encounters, and the magnetic-mapping technique offers an effective means of determining whether or not a given vehicle has been subjected to intense fields. It does not provide information respecting other possible environmental causes of vehicle malfunction.

Mr. Hooven's assumption that the minimum strength of

magnetic field required to change the established magnetic pattern would be smaller than any field capable of interfering with the car's operation has been verified by a test with 1 kg. field. A magnetron magnet was passed over specified points on the front deck of a 1962 Chevrolet Corvair, and the alteration in magnetic pattern was noted. A 0.4 cm. paper tablet was kept between the magnet and the car deck to prevent physical contact. The maximum field strength penetrating the tablet was measured with a Bell "120" gaussmeter, with Model T-1201 probe, and was found to be 1 kg. (one inch away from the tablet, which was held against the magnet poles, the maximum field was measured as 235 g.). The observed alterations in magnetic pattern are shown in Table 1 which gives the directions a compass needle pointed when the compass was placed on the selected test points 6 in. apart located as shown in Fig. 1. The measurements also demonstrate both the permanence of pattern alteration and alteration due to bending and straightening of the car deck. The car was facing 180° T. during all measurements.

The third and fourth columns of Table 1 show definitely that the passage of 1-kg. magnetic field completely determines the residual magnetic pattern. Subsequent compass readings, except for unexplained anomaly at point 29, show the last alteration to be the one retained. The car under study was involved in a collision on 21 August. Figures in the right column of Table 1 show the magnetic pattern after straightening and repainting. All compass readings shown are accurate to within 2°-3°. Each set of readings was recorded without reference to prior readings, with which they were compared only subsequently. The reproductibility, in most cases, is surprising. When test points were near sharp changes in magnetic orientation, a slight error in point relocation would cause major variation in compass readings. Such slight location error probably accounts for the lack of agreement in the 5 August and 15 August columns of Table 1, which shows data taken to test the permanency of a pattern previously scrambled by twisting the magnet over the area. Points A-1 through A-12 are specific points 1 in. apart on each of two parallel lines 2 in. apart within Area A. The agreement of the two right columns shows both that the test points were accurately relocated and that the pattern was retained.

While we did not determine the minimum magnetic field which would alter the car pattern, an indication that its value would be only a few gauss is given in data shown in Tables 1 and 2, and Table 1 is included here for that reason.

As seen in Table 3, 5 August readings were significantly different from the original values for all points other than 16 and 18. After the original values were determined on 18 July, the magnet had been passed directly over point 13 and

Table 1

Test Point Number	Compass Readings 18 July 1968			Subsequent Compass Readings		
	Original	After passage of magnet, N pole on E side of point	After passage of magnet, N pole on W side of point	5 August	15 August	After collision and repair
25	29	295	68	66	68	60
13	38	275	80	78	78	70
26	349	275	89	90	89	44
27	10	275	91	90	90	67
28	22	280	85	72*	67	53
29	13	265	85	52*	39	1
30	13	271	76	12*	10	352
31	6	305	26	355*	2	3

*After readings were taken on 18 July, the magnet was brought to Area A and twisted over it. The altered readings for points 28-31 on 5 August can be assumed to have been altered 18 July by the nearness of the magnet to these points. (See Fig. 1) (It was not noticed how close the magnet was to these points. Estimated minimum is 2 to 6 in.)

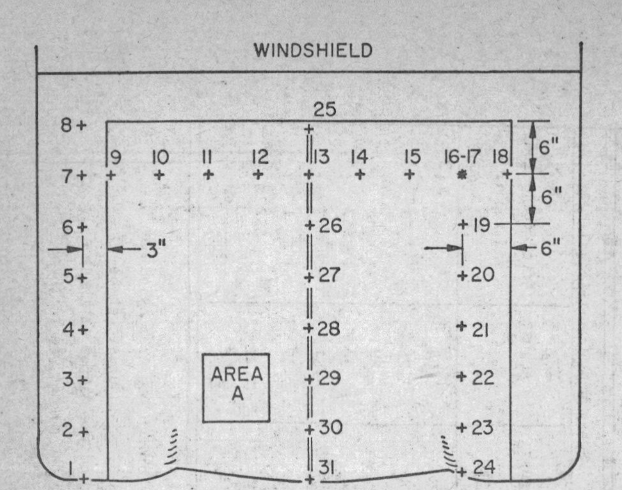

180° M.

FRONT DECK OF CORVAIR
Figure 1

within an inch of point 9 (The magnet was passed over points 1-8 in variable orientation, showing initially that the pattern was thus changed. The data for passage over points 25-31 were chosen for presentation in Table 1 because of the observable determination of residual orientation.) These passes of the magnet, plus its passage over Area A, apparently altered the magnetic pattern at all points which were less than a foot from the magnet (note altered values on 5 August for points 9-15 in Table 3, points 28-31 in Table 1).

More precise quantitative tests of the effect of magnetic fields of varying strength on the residual magnetic pattern of automobiles would be interesting. The above tests, however, show that a 1 kg. field is more than adequate to alter this pattern permanently.

One case of reported car stoppage, occurring during the term of the Colorado project, was studied in the field (Case 39) using a simple compass of good quality. The correspondence of magnetic signature of the affected car with that of a comparison car of the same make and model in a different geographical location was striking. The correspondence showed that the automobile in question had not been subjected to a magnetic field of high intensity.

Table 2

Test Point No.	Compass Readings		
	18 July	5 August	15 August
A-1	74	69	63
A-2	98	105	108
A-3	127	150	147
A-4	153	178	175
A-5	171	192	190
A-6	176	200	207
A-7	58	48	45
A-8	79	66	72
A-9	104	112	112
A-10	132	162	158
A-11	159	195	192
A-12	176	221	220

Table 3

Test Point No.	Compass Readings			
	Original 18 July	5 August	15 August	Post Wreck 4 September
9	310	266	263	275
10	292	236	228	256
11	197	130	143	65
12	56	350	337	56
13	38	78	78	70
14	25	317	327	20
15	22	347	351	5
16	332	328	331	356
18	67	69	69	72

Magnetic mapping of the bodies of automobiles involved in particularly puzzling UFO reports of past years, such as the November 1957 incidents at Levelland, Texas, would have been most desirable, but the cars were no longer available for study.

The technique is simple and would be quite useful to any field team studying an event in which stalling of a car by an UFO is claimed. Investigators should interpret the results with caution, however, since denting and straightening of the car body does alter the magnetic signature. As demonstrated in the test reported above, the signature also can be changed easily with a simple horeshoe magnet.

5. Unexplained Electric Power Interruptions

(This section prepared by Mr. R. J. Low)

A listing of electrical power interruptions from 1954 through 1966 appears as Appendix E of the Federal Power Commission report, Prevention of Power Failures. This list contains none of the 15 disturbances of power systems tabulated in *The UFO Evidence* (NICAP, 1964), and its supplement as having been coincidental with sightings of UFOs near the affected power systems.

The 148 power interruptions listed in the resume are those "which were sufficiently important to gain publicity." Since none of the reported UFO-related power failures tabulated by NICAP is reflected in the FPC resume, we may conclude that none of them was of major public consequence. This is also apparent from the descriptions of the incidents given by the authors of *The UFO Evidence*.

Rather than investigate events that, from the standpoint of power systems operations and impact on the public, were not significant, it appeared more fruitful to determine whether there were power failures that could not be satisfactorily explained. The FPC report for the 13 years from 1954 through 1966 includes a total of 148 failures. In three instances although the events that initiated the disturbances were identified, the causes are listed as "unknown." In one case (Los Angeles, 19 July 1966), the event is described: "Breaker Operations—Cause Unknown"; in the second (Chicago, 22 Nov. 1966) "Transformer Relay Operation—Cause Unknown"; and in the third (Austin, Texas, 14 Dec. 1966): "Lines Tripped Out—Cause Unknown." It has not been suggested, so far as we are aware, that these outages are related to UFO sightings. No sighting is listed in the Colorado project's printout of sighting reports for 19 July or 22 November; a sighting recorded for 14 December occurred elsewhere.

An FPC Order No. 331, issued 20 December 1966, requires all entities engaged in the generation and transmission of electric power to report significant interruptions of bulk power supply to the Commission. Through 12 June 1967, 52 power interruptions were reported in accordance with Order No. 331.

Of the 52, three were not explained. These are, together with the explanatory material given, the following:

> Tennessee Valley Authority, 25 February 1967—A high-temperature detector removed a transformer from service at Johnson City, Tenn. No damage was apparent and when restored to service the transformer continued to function normally. Loads of 36,700 kw. were interrupted for 36 min.
>
> Carolina Power & Light Company, 1 May 1967—25,000 kw. of load in the city of Rocky Mount, N.C., was interrupted for about 1 hr. when the 110 kw. bus at the Rocky Mount substation tripped. Cause of the interruption is unknown.
>
> Pennsylvania Power & Light Company, 12 June 1967—Approximately 78,000 customers and 163,000 kw. of load in Lycoming and Schuylkill counties were interrupted at 2:01 p.m., EDT, when a 330 kv. lightning arrester failed on a 220/66 kv. transformer bank at Frackville Substation. The failure occurred during clear weather and the cause was unknown. Service was restored to 113,000 kw. within 15 min. and to the remaining 50,000 kw. within 24 min.

Eight UFO sightings are recorded in the project's printout on the date of the first outage, none of them in Tennessee; three on the date of the second, none in North Carolina; and one, not in Pennsylvania, on the date of the third.

The causes of power failures are usually not announced until after the period of most intense public interest has passed. Although usually the cause of the outage will be traced very quickly, power officials may be and often are reluctant to make prompt announcement of it, for fear that subsequent analysis will reveal the initial conclusion to be incorrect. Occasionally, it is several days before the cause is located. The public, however, begins to lose interest in what happened very soon after power is restored, so that circumstances of outages, because they can be determined immediately, are usually reported more fully and covered more prominently than their underlying causes.

J. L. McKinley, Manager of System Operations, Public Service Company of Colorado, assisted us with the technical aspects of the study of possible UFO-related electric power system failures. As a member of the North American Power Systems Interconnection Committee, Mr. McKinley is concerned with and informed about all aspects of power generation, transmission, and distribution in the local area and in the nation as a whole. We asked him whether there are power outages, the underlying cause of which remains unexplained. In a letter dated 11 October 1967, he answered as follows:

> I am not aware of any major power disturbances the causes of

which are concealed behind a cloak of mystery. When we say that a 'cause is unknown,' we mean that we have not found, after reasonable inspection, physical evidence of the cause. For example, a transmission line faults, circuit breakers open, and the relays sensing the fault causing the tripout show a ground target, which means that one of the phase conductors has been grounded. If the fault is instantaneous from a lightning strike, the circuit breakers will close, restoring the line in service. If the fault is permanent the circuit breakers will close and again open. In either event an inspection will result; in the case of the lightning strike, some physical evidence of the strike may be evident; in the case of the permanent fault, the cause will be found, perhaps a tree has fallen into the line, etc. If no physical evidence is apparent upon inspection, a subsequent breakdown of some component may result, improper functioning of control or protection equipment may be found on routine tests, or, if the same fault occurs frequently, a much more intensive effort will locate the cause. Sometimes large birds will cause transmission lines to trip and it it very difficult to find evidence of physical damage, the dead bird or feathers, etc. being the only evidence.

Equipment failures causing power outages are usually very easy to locate unless such outages result from the malfunctioning of the more sophisticated types of control or protection devices. Then specialized technicians must resort to extensive testing of the performance of these devices.

The Rocky Mountain Power Pool at Casper meeting on 13 June 1967, the North American Power Systems Interconnection Committee meeting at Vancouver, B. C., on 17-18 July 1967, and the Western Operating Committee meeting at Boise on 25-26 July 1967 were asked whether there is reason to suppose that some power interruptions are caused by or related to the appearance of UFOs. None of these experts replied in the affirmative.

In *Incident at Exeter* (Fuller, 1966), the massive power failure in Northeast of 9 November 1965 is described as follows:

The blackout caused by the failure of the Northeast Power Grid created one of the biggest mysteries in the history of modern civilization . . .

By November 11, *The New York Times* was reporting that the Northeast was slowly struggling back toward normal, but that the cause of the blackout was still unknown. Authorities frankly admitted that there was no assurance whatever that the incredible blackout could not occur again, without warning.

There was a curious lack of physical damage . . . only a few generators were out of action as a result of the power failure, not a cause. What's more, the utilities were able to restore service with the exact same equipment that was in use at the time of the blackout. What happened that night was not only far from normal; it was mystifying. If there had been a mechanical flaw, a fire, a breakdown, a short circuit, a toppling transmission tower, the cause would have been quickly and easily detected. Mechanically, however, the system as a whole was in perfect repair before and after the failure.

William W. Kobelt, of Walkill, N.Y., is one of the thousands of line patrol observers who, according to *The New York Times* went into action to try to discover the trouble. He is typical of all the others. He flew over the lines of the Central Hudson Gas and Electric Corporation at daybreak after the blackout. Cruising close to treetop level, he checked wires, insulators, cross arms and structures of the high-power transmission lines. He looked for trees, branches which might have fallen over the wires. "We looked for trouble—but couldn't find any at all," he said.

Robert Ginna, Chairman of the Rochester Gas and Electric Corporation, said that his utility had been receiving 200,000 kw. under an agreement with the New York State Power Authority, which operates the hydroelectric plants at Niagara Falls. "Suddenly, we didn't have it," he said. "We don't know what happened to the 200,000 kilowatts. It just wasn't there."

The difficulty was traced to a remote-controlled substation at Clay, N. Y., near Syracuse, where, according to Mr. Fuller, all was found to be in order. "Something else happened outside Syracuse, however, which was noted briefly in the press, and then immediately dropped without follow-up comment," according to the Fuller account. The "something else" was the sighting of a huge red ball of brilliant intensity about 100 ft. in diameter just over the power lines near the Clay substation. The reported observation by a private flight instructor and his student passenger was made from a plane approaching Hancock Field, Syracuse. Five persons, according to Fuller, including Robert C. Walsh, Deputy Commissioner for the Federal Aviation Agency, reported this UFO sighting, which was said to have occurred at 5:16 p.m., the moment the outrage commenced. Observations of other unusual aerial objects, according to Mr. Fuller, were reported from New York City, N. Y., West Orange and Newark, N. J., Philadelphia, Pa., Holyoke and Amherst, Mass., and Woonsocket, R. I. Here is author Fuller's conclusion:

> In spite of the lengthy report issued by the FCC (sic) the Great Blackout has still not been adequately explained. Ostensibly, backup Relay #Q-29 at the Sir Adam Beck generating station, Queenston, Ontario, was eventually pinpointed as the source of the massive failure. But further investigation, hardly noted in the press, showed that nothing in the relay was broken when it was removed for inspection. In fact, it went back into operation normally when power was restored. The line it was protecting was totally undamaged. "Why did everything go berserk?" *Life* Magazine asks in an article about the blackout. "Tests on the wayward sensing device have thus far been to no avail." A later statement by Arthur J. Harris, a supervising engineer of the Ontario Hydroelectric Commission, indicated that the cause was still a mystery. "Although the blackout has been traced to the tripping of a circuit breaker at the Sir Adam

Beck No. 2 plant, it is practically impossible to pinpoint the initial cause." As late as January 4, 1966, *The New York Times* in a follow-up story indicated a series of questions regarding the prevention of future blackouts. The news item says:

"These questions more or less are related to the cause, still not fully understood, of last November's blackout . . ."

The A.P.R.O. Bulletin of November-December 1965 expresses a similar view of the events of that night.

Finally, in testimony before a symposium on UFOs conducted by the House Committee on Science and Astronautics on 29 July 1968, Dr. James E. McDonald referred to the possibility that UFOs might have caused the power failure.

Let us now examine the FPC report. Volume I states that "the Commission's initial report, published December 6, 1965, pinpointed the initiating cause of the interruption as the operation of a backup relay on one of the five main transmission lines taking power to Toronto from Ontario Hydro's Sir Adam Beck No. 2 Hydroelectric Plant on the Niagara River. This relay, which was set too low for the load which the line was carrying, disconnected the line." Volume III gives a detailed chronology (to the hundredth of a second) of the events following the initial output of Q-29, as follows:

> The initial event was the operation of a backup relay at Beck Generating Station which opened circuit Q29BD, one of five 230-kv. circuits connecting the generation of Beck to the Toronto-Hamilton load area. Prior to the opening of circuit Q29BD at Beck, these circuits were loaded with Beck generation plus almost 500 megawatts of power flowing to Beck over the two tie lines from New York State. Of this 500 megawatts, about 300 megawatts were scheduled for use in Ontario and the remaining 200 megawatts were in replacement of power flowing from the Saunders plant into New York at Massena. The loading on Q29BD, based on digital computer flows and examination of the Beck Station tie line and totalizing graphic charts, was indicated to be 361 megawatts at about 0.93 power factor and a voltage of 248 kv. This pickup setting was, therefore, in excess of the indicated average line loading. The precise cause of the backup relay energization is not known. A momentary and relatively small change in voltage might have been responsible as the pickup setting is inversely proportional to the square of the voltage. Alternatively the line megawatt loading could have increased slightly above 361 megawatts due to a change in system loading or a change in tap position of the phase shifting transformer at Saunders, St. Lawrence. Shortly before circuit Q29BD tripped, a tap setting change had been made in such a direction as to increase the power flow. In any event the pickup setting of the line backup relay was reached and the circuit opened at the Beck end.
>
> The opening of circuit Q29BD resulted in the sequential tripping of circuits Q23BW, Q25BW, Q24BD, and Q30AW. After the opening of the first two circuits, determined by an event recorder at Beck, the oscillograph at Beck started and

established the sequential openings of circuits Q25BW, Q24BD, and Q30AW.

The opening of the five Beck 230-kv. circuits occurred over a period of 2.7 seconds, during which the initial flow of 500 megawatts from the western New York area toward Beck reversed and reached an estimated value of about 1,200 megawatts into western New York for a total change of 1,700 megawatts. This surge of excess power continued eastward and southward from Niagara, and back into Canada over the 230-kv. tie line at St. Lawrence. This line was opened by protective relaying and separated the Ontario system, with the exception of Beck and its adjacent area, from the remainder of the interconnection.

Generators in western New York and at the Beck Station accelerated toward an out-of-step condition and separated from the remaining system. The separation from the New York State Electric & Gas system was effected by the opening of the Meyer-Hillside 230-kv. circuit at 3.53 seconds and the Stolle Road-Meyer circuit at 3.57 seconds, as recorded by oscillographs at Niagara and Stolle Road. Simultaneously with the separation from New York State Gas & Electric, the PJM system separated from western New York due to the tripping of the Dunkirk-Erie 230-kv. line and the lines running east and west from Warren, Pa.

At almost the same time, separation from central New York began when line protective relays operated to open the two Rochester-Clay 345-kv. circuits at 3.56 and 3.61 seconds. The computer simulation demonstrated that the parallel lower voltage circuits opened immediately thereafter.

Moses-St. Lawrence generating station in northern New York, now connected to New England and central New York, continued to accelerate toward an out-of-step condition, tripping the two Moses-Adirondack circuits at 3.98 and 4.01 seconds. This was followed by automatic generator droppings at Moses-St. Lawrence in an attempt to maintain area stability. At this late stage, this did not prevent the opening of the Plattsburgh-Essex 230-kv. circuit at 4.11 seconds. Automatic reclosure was unsuccessful on the two Moses-Adirondack 230-kv. circuits at 4.79 and 4.81 seconds. Northern New York was now effectively separated from central New York and New England. The switching sequences in the St. Lawrence area separation were determined from oscillographic records at Moses-St. Lawrence, and were not duplicated successfully in the computer simulation.

The separation of western New York from central New York was followed by the separation of central New York from PJM at approximately 4 seconds with the opening of the 230-kv. Hillside-East Towanda line, the North Waverly-East Sayre line and the Goudey-Lennox line. This separation was followed by a surge of about 900 megawatts from New Jersey to Consolidated Edison across the Fresh Kills-Linden circuit. This caused two lines in series with the Fresh Kills-Linden circuit to open at Greenwood approximately 7 seconds after the initial event. The opening of these circuits separated eastern New York and New England from PJM.

Within 12 min. power generation in lower Ontario, N. Y.,

and New England (except for Maine and eastern New Hampshire) virtually ceased.

Volume I of the FPC report states that "the causes which can trigger severe disturbances are practically unlimited. Many of them are derivatives of severe storms, seemingly unaccountable equipment failures, or even the fallibility of well trained system operators and maintenance men." The initial disturbances themselves are often quite minor and are sometimes difficult to trace, but the initiating event in the Great Northeast blackout holds no mystery. Quoting from IEEE *Spectrum* (February 1966):

> At 5:16:11 p.m., a backup relay, protecting line Q29BD, operated normally and caused the circuit breaker at Beck to trip the unfaulted line. The power flow on the disconnected line shifted to the remaining four lines, each of which then became loaded beyond the critical level at which its backup protective relay was set to function. Thus the four remaining lines tripped out in cascade in 161 cycles' time (2.7 seconds).
>
> The relay that triggered the disturbance was one of five backup sensing devices (one backup relay per line) that protect the lines against failure of the Beck primary relays, or of circuit breakers at remote locations. According to the FPC report, the five backup relays were installed in 1951, and, in 1956, a breaker on one of the 230-kv. lines failed to open (reason not explained) following a fault. In January 1963, as a result of a re-evaluation study of its backup protection requirements, Ontario Hydro modified these relay settings to increase the scope of their protective functions.
>
> Figure 6 indicates the set of conditions under which this type of relay would trip. The evidence suggests that, at 5:16:11, the load and generation characteristics of the Canada-United States interchange caused such a condition to be reached.
>
> The FPC report further states that the relay settings made in 1963 at the Beck plant were in effect at the time of the November 9 power failure. The backup relay on the line Q29BD was set in 1963 to operate at about 375 MW and the 160 Mvar at a bus voltage of 248 kV and, although the load-carrying capacity of each of these lines is considerably higher, it was necessary to set each backup relay to operate at a power level below the line's capacity to provide the desired protection and to achieve coordination with other relays on the system. This setting was believed to be sufficiently high to provide a safe margin above expected power flows.
>
> When the backup relays were modified and the power levels were set in 1963, the load on the northbound lines from Beck No. 2 was appreciably lower than the trip setting of the backup relay. Recently, the megawatt and megavar loadings on the transmission lines from Beck to the north, because of emergency outages in a new Ontario Hydro steam-electric plant, have been very heavy. This temporary situation produced a deficiency in Ontario generation, with the result that a heavier inflow of power from the United States interconnections was necessary.
>
> According to Ontario Hydro spokesmen, the average flow had reached 356 MW (and approximately 160 Mvar) in the line

that tripped out first, but momentary fluctuation in the flow is normal. Therefore, at 5:16 p.m., as already mentioned, the power flow apparently reached the level at which the relay was set; it functioned in accordance with its setting, and its circuit breaker tripped out the line. Ontario Hydro also informed the FPC that its operating personnel were not aware that the relay on line Q29BD was set to operate at a load of 375 MW.

6. *Conclusions*

Of all physical effects claimed to be due to the presence of UFOs, the alleged malfunction of automobile motors is perhaps the most puzzling. The claim is frequently made, sometimes in reports which are impressive because they involve multiple independent witnesses. Witnesses seem certain that the function of their cars was affected by the unidentified object, which sometimes reportedly was not seen until after the malfunction was noted. No satisfactory explanation for such effects, if indeed they occurred, is apparent.

A search for residual indirect physical evidence failed to yield any recorded or otherwise verified instances which establish a relationship between an UFO and an alteration in electric or local magnetic fields or in radiation intensity. The Northeast electric power failure appears adequately explained without reference to the action of UFOs. No evidence has been presented to this project that supports the claim that any such power failure was UFO related.

In addition to instrument readings, residual effects on materials can also be investigated. Magnetic mapping of affected automobile bodies, if used with proper reservation, is suggested as one useful procedure for obtaining such evidence, since the original magnetic pattern of the body of a given automobile can be determined.

References

Blades, Jehu, Cdr, USN, Communication. Project File 1257-P, 1967.
Hall, Richard H., *The UFO Evidence,* NICAP, Washington, D.C., 1964, 73ff.
Project Blue Book *Status Report No. 10;* 27 February 1953, 2.

Chapter 5 Optical and Radar Analyses of Field Cases / Gordon D. Thayer

1. *Introduction*

In Chapters 4 and 5 of Section VI unusual atmospheric conditions causing anomalous propagation of electromagnetic waves are described. In the present chapter an analysis is made of some of the most puzzling UFO phenomena. Most of them involve combined radar and visual contacts. All 31 combined radar-visual sightings, two visual-only, and two radar-only cases in the project files are analyzed in an effort to determine whether or not anomalous modes of propagation could account for the details of such sights. Since both visual and radar sightings are analyzed below, readers whose familiarity with atmospheric propagation of light and radio waves is limited are urged to read Chapters 4 and 5, Section VI, before reading what follows in the present chapter.

In evaluating UFO phenomena it is seldom possible to arrive at an incontrovertible conclusion; rather, it is necessary to introduce admissible hypotheses and then attempt to determine the probability of their correctness through the study of generally inadequate data. In the case of the anomalous propagation hypothesis, extreme examples of anomalous propagation imply extreme conditions in the state of the atmosphere, and data on these unusual atmospheric conditions are either scarce or non-existent. Meteorological measurements that may be on record for a time and place appropriate to a particular UFO incident will usually be only generally indicative of the propagation conditions that existed during the incident. The meteorological instrumentation necessary to record the extremely sharp gradients of temperature of humidity that are associated with strong partial reflections of electromagnetic waves is either beyond the state of the art or so difficult to construct and operate that the measurements required have not yet been attempted.

Nevertheless, there is strong inferential evidence that such sharp gradients do exist in the atmosphere (see Section VI, Chapter 4), but experiments capable of detecting such gradients have not been made. The fact that, for example, a temperature change of 10° C over a distance of 1 cm. has not yet been observed in the free atmosphere is not proof that such gradients do not exist.

The following set of hypotheses were considered as possible explanations for each of the UFO phenomena studied:

1. That the phenomenon was caused by a mechanical or other device designed for transportation, surveillance, or other related objectives, and which may or may not have been controlled by extraterrestrial beings.
2. That the phenomenon was caused by a conventional airplane, balloon, blimp, or other man-made device.
3. That it was a natural phenomenon, star, meteor, etc., perhaps seen under unusual circumstances.
4. That it was an unknown natural phenomenon;
5. That it was a product of unusual conditions of radar or optical propagation, possibly involving natural or artificial phenomena observed and/or recorded in unusual aspect.

The purpose of the investigation reported in this chapter was to determine, for the 35 cases included, the extent to which hypothesis No. 5, either alone or in combination with Nos. 2

and 3 could satisfactorily account for the circumstances of the UFO report. In each case the probability that some other hypothesis, such as Nos. 1 or 4, could more satisfactorily account for the sighting had to be evaluated.

There is always the danger in this sort of procedure that the true explanation for a particular event is not contained in a given set of *a priori* hypotheses. One obvious omission from the list above is the hypothesis that a particular UFO report was a hoax. Since hoaxes are not part of the subject matter of this chapter, all cases have been studied under the assumption that all observers involved were reporting, to the best of their abilities and beliefs, the details of an event which they did not fully understand.

The 35 UFO cases examined in this chapter were classified using the following criteria:

1. *Primarily visual.* This class includes those cases where the first and most significant contact was visual, or where the visual contact was preponderant and more positive than any radar contacts.
A. *Star-like.* Cases where the visual reports were of one or more small, bright objects without pronounced motion, round or without definite shape. Cases where visual description appeared to be similar to a diffracted star-like object were also included.
B. *Meteor-like.* Cases where visual reports resembled meteor phenomena: rapidly moving star-like object, or small glowing object, with or without "smoke trails," sparks, fragmentation, etc.
C. *Blurry light or glow.* Cases where descriptions were of a blurry or glowing object of undefined or amorphous shape.
D. *Other.* Cases not fitting any of the above three criteria. Six cases were in this sub-group, including one dark, opaque, "jelly-fish" shaped object, three balloon-like objects, one aircraft-like object and one well-defined, structured saucer-shaped object.
II. *Primarily radar.* This class includes those cases where the first and most significant contact was by radar, or where the radar contact was preponderant and more positive than any visual contacts.
A. *AP-like.* Cases where the radar scopes showed a confused or random distribution of images, blips that showed erratic or discontinuous motion, or other patterns bearing a general similarity to anomalous propagation (AP) returns.
B. *Blip-like.* Cases where the radar target (or targets) showed characteristics similar to the return from a solid object (such as an aircraft, etc.), and where the target did not display erratic or discontinuous behavior. Acceleration or velocity in excess of known aircraft capabilities, or

periods of immobility, were not considered to be contrary to normal target behavior.

In the following section cases of particular interest are treated in detail; these cases generally fall into one of three categories:

(a) Cases that are good examples of inconsistencies tending to confuse any conclusions that might be arrived at;
(b) Cases that are typical of a sub-group of UFO reports that have the same probable explanation;
(c) Cases that are difficult or seemingly impossible to explain in terms of known phenomena.

2. Presentation of Radio Refractive Index Data

Two methods of presenting vertical profiles of radio refractivity in graphical form are used in this chapter. Both methods are based on the use of the radio refractivity, N, wherc

$$N = (n - 1) \times 10^6.$$

since the radio refractive index, n, is always very close to unity in the atmosphere. The maximum value of N that is likely to be encountered in the atmosphere is not much over 400; values close to 500 may occasionally be experienced over the surface of the Dead Sea, 1200 ft. below sea level, in the summer months.

A feature of all vertical profiles of N is a general decrease with height; the departures of any given profile from the average decrease with height are the significant features for anomalous propagation of radio waves. Therefore the refractive index profiles illustrated for many of the UFO cases in the following section are given in terms of A-units (Bean, 1966a) where

$$A(z) = N(z) + 313 [1 - \exp\{-0.14386z\}];$$

here N(z) is the actual refractivity profile, a function of height, z, in kilometers, and the last term represents the average decrease with height of an average radio refractivity profile

$$N(z) = 313 \exp\{-0.14386z\}.$$

The number 313 is an average surface refractivity value. An N-profile that is not abnormal will, when plotted on a graph with A(z) as abscissa and z as ordinate, appear as a fairly straight vertical line, perhaps with a slight tilt in one direction or the other. On the other hand, an N-profile with strongly super-refractive or subrefractive display a marked zigzag character on an A(z) vs. z plot. The use of A-units allows a more generous scale size for the abscissa than would be the case for N-unit plots.

Ray tracings, calculated and plotted by a digital computer, are illustrated for a few of the refractivity profiles. The computer also calculates the M-profile, and plots it on the same graph as the ray tracing. M-units are defined by

$$M(z) = N(z) + \frac{z}{a},$$

where "a" is the radius of the earth. This is equivalent to adding 156.9 N-units per km. to the observed profile. Since the ducting gradient (see Chapter VI—4) is -156.9 N. km^{-1}, any layer with such a gradient will be represented on an M(z) plot as a vertical line. Layers with $dN/dz > -156.9\ km^{-1}$ (not ducting) will show a trace slanting up to the right, whereas strong ducts with $dN/dz < -156.9\ km^{-1}$ will show a trace slanting up to the left. Hence the M-unit plot is very convenient for exposing the existence or non-existence of radio ducts in N(z) data.

3. *Analysis of Selected UFO Incidents by Classes.*

In the discussions that follow the UFO incidents are referred to by the case numbers assigned to them in the UFO project files. The letter refers to the origin of the case: B-number cases are from USAF Project Blue Book files, N-numbers are for cases supplied by NICAP (National Investigations Committee for Aerial Phenomena), C-numbers refer to cases that were investigated by personnel of the Colorado project, and X-numbers were given to cases that were received after the cut-off date for inclusion in the regular files (i.e., after the computer analysis of all project file cases had already been completed). X-number cases are also identified by their B−, N−, or C− number.

Class I-A Primarily visual, star-like cases.

1321-B. This is a good example of a misidentified star combined with an apparently uncorrelated radar return causing an UFO report to be generated. The incident took place at Finland Air Force Base (60 mi. NE of Duluth), Minn., with a civilian sighting near Grand Marais, Minn., (50 mi. NE of Finland AFB) on the night of 5-6 September 1966, between 2130 and 0015 LST (0330-0615 GMT). The weather was clear, ceiling unlimited, visibility more than 15 mi.; a display of Aurora Borealis was in progress. Applicable radio refractivity profile is shown in Fig. 1. Visual reports of a "white-red-green" object "moving but not leaving its general location" were received at Finland AFB about 2130 LST. An FPS-90 search radar was activated but there was "too much clutter to see anything in that area . . ." At 2200 LST a return was detected; it "flitted around in range from 13 to 54 mi., but always stayed on the

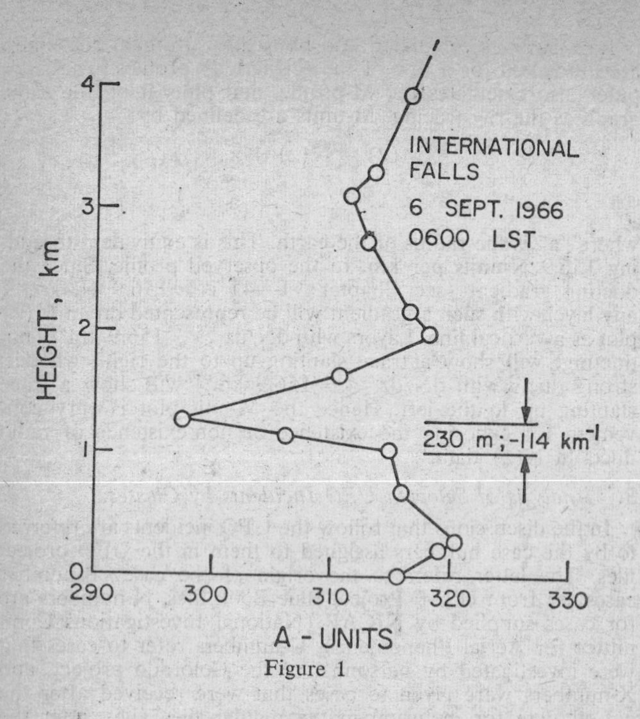

Figure 1

270° azimuth." A pair of F-89s was scrambled from Duluth AFB and searched the area at altitudes of 8,000-10,000 ft. The two aircraft "merged with blip, apparently wrong altitude, no airborne sighting"; the radar operators insisted the target was at 8,000-10,000 ft., the same altitude at which the scrambled aircraft were flying. The pilots reported that they "only observed what was interpreted to be a beacon reflection."

Available meteorological data show that the winds were southwesterly, 7 knots at the surface, and northerly (320° to 30°) at 25 to 65 knots aloft. The closest available radiosonde data (International Falls 1200 GMT 0600 LST) 6 September, show a temperature inversion and strong humidity lapse through a layer extending from 1029-1259 m. above the surface. The gradient of radio refractivity through this layer averaged −114N/km (corrected for radiosonde sensor lag). This layer would be expected to show a significant partial reflection at radio frequencies. If the layer were present over Finland AFB at the same elevation, it could have produced false targets by partial reflection of real ground targets, which would have appeared to be at altitudes of from 8,300-9,800 feet because of the geometry of such reflected targets (see Section VI, Chapter 5). This agrees well with the reported "UFO" altitudes of 8,000-10,000 ft.

Anomalous propagation echoes are not usually confined to a single direction. There are three possible explanations in this case and in other similar cases: a single real object was being tracked; the radar operators were not looking for targets on other azimuths; the partially reflecting layer may have been anisotropic (i.e. displaying a preferred direction for strongest reflection). There is no direct physical evidence for the existence of such anisotropic layers, but no studies have been made to determine whether or not they might exist. Apparent anisotropy in radar AP returns has often been observed, although not usually over such a narrow azimuth range as was apparently the case at Finland AFB.

Regarding the visual reports submitted, the comment of the investigating officer at Finland AFB is of particular interest:

> The next evening, at 2200 hours, the "white-red-green" object reappeared in the sky at exactly the same position it had appeared on 5 September. This officer observed it and determined it to be a star which was near the horizon and would settle beneath the horizon after midnight. It did appear to "sparkle" in red-green-white colors, but so do other stars which can be pointed out from this mountain top.

The officer refers to Rangoon Mountain, elevation 1,927 ft., from which many of the visual observations were made.

The star that the officer saw was in all probability λ Scorpio (Shaula) a magnitude 1.7 star at $-37°$ declination and 17 hr. 31 min. right ascension. It would have set at just about 1:30 a.m. 90th meridian time, if the horizon were unobstructed. An obstruction of only 4° would cause λ Scorpio to "set" at 1:15 a.m. CST; a 4° angle is equivalent to a 35 ft. tree or building at a distance of 500 ft. The southerly declination would indicate that the star was in the southwest, which is compatible with the visual reports that were submitted.

Additional meteorological effects may have been present in this case. In particular, the southwesterly surface winds present are quite likely to have advected relatively cool, moist air from nearby Lake Superior under the elevated warm, dry layer noted previously, thus tending to increase the strength of the inversion and associated humidity lapse. Some of the optical effects noticed by the observers in this instance, strong red-green scintillation, apparent stretching of the image into a somewhat oval shape, and the red fringe on the bottom, may have been due to strong and irregular local refraction effects in the inversion layer (or layers).

This UFO report seems to have resulted from a combination of an unusually scintillating star and false radar targets caused by AP from a strong elevated layer in the atmosphere. This pattern is found in a number of other cases.

Reports with elements similar to the preceding case are:

*113-B**. Nemuro AF Detachment, Hokkaido, Japan, 7 February 1953, 2230 LST (1230 GMT). Weather was clear. Visual description fits a scintillating star (flashing red and green, later white with intermittent red and green flashes, then later steady white) rising in the east (only motion was slow gain in altitude, "[I believe] that the object did not move with respect to the stars in its vicinity"). CPS-5 radar painted a single pip at 85° azimuth, range 165 mi., which operator regarded as interference. Visual object was boresighted with radar antenna and azimuth read as 91° ± 2°. Elevation estimated as 15° initially (2230 LST). No stars brighter than magnitude 3 were in this azimuth between 0° and 30° elevation angle at that time. Blue Book file suggests Deneb or Regulus as likely objects, but their positions are far away from the sighted object. In view of two observers' comments that light "shown from beneath" object, it is very probable that they saw a lighted Pibal balloon, possibly launched from the Russian-held Kurile Islands to the east and northeast of Hokkaido (launch time 1200 GMT). The investigating officer noted the exceptionally good visibility prevalent in the area on clear nights.

1306-B. Edwards AFB, Kernville, Calif., 30 July 1967, 2217-2400 LST. Weather: clear, calm, warm (83°F). Two civilians reported observing one or two blue, star-like objects that appeared to circle, bob, and zigzag about a seemingly fixed star; these objects "instantly disappeared" about 1 hr. 45 min. after sighting. Edwards AFB RAPCON radar picked up "something" at about 2230 LST "for several sweeps." Blip seemed to be moving south at about 50-60 mph. There is no apparent connection between the radar and visual reports. The visual UFO did not appear to move at 50-60 mph. Data, including weather data, on this report are insufficient to form an opinion. The most likely possibility seems to be that the visual UFO consisted of the direct image plus one or two reflected images of the "fixed star" that the observer reported. What may have produced the reflected images remains conjectural. For example, a turbulent layer of air with strong temperature contrasts could produce images similar to those described by the witnesses. The instantaneous disappearance of the UFOs is consistent with an optical phenomenon. As for the radar "track," a blip appearing for only "a few sweeps" could be almost anything: noise, AP, or possibly a real target flying near the lower limits of the radar beam.

1212-B. Tillamook, Ore., 13-14 March 1967, 2230-0008 LST. Weather: clear with "stars plainly visible," some ground

* Case numbers referred to thusly are so listed in the project's files.

fog, thin broken cirriform clouds estimated at 10,000 ft., visibility 15 mi. This is a good example of some of the confusion that arises in reporting UFO incidents. Initial visual observer reports indicated object at about 45° to 50° elevation angle, yet when the Mt. Hebo radar station "contacted target" it was at 39 mi. range, 9,200 ft. height. This is an elevation angle of only about 2°. This inconsistency seems to have gone unnoticed in the Project Blue Book file on the case. The radar target, as plotted, stayed at 39 mi. range and slowly increased height to 11,200 ft., then shifted almost instantaneously to 48 mi. range. Subsequently the radar target slowly gained altitude and range, disappearing at 55 mi. and 14,000 ft. (still at about a 2° elevation angle). The azimuth varied between 332° and 341° during this time. Average apparent speed of the radar track was low: the first part of the track was at zero ground speed and a climb rate of about 100 ft/min., the second part of the track was at an average ground speed of about 16 mph. and a climb rate of about 100 ft/min. In between there is a jump of 9 mi. range in one minute, a speed of 540 mph. The characteristics of this radar track are suggestive of radar false targets or slow-moving AP echoes. The jump may be a point where one echo was lost, and another, different echo began coming in. This effect is apparently a frequent cause of very high reported speeds of UFOs (Borden, 1953). The visual reports are suggestive of either a scintillating star if the reported angle is higher than actual, or an aircraft. There was an electronic warfare aircraft "orbiting" at high altitude seaward of Tillamook at the time of the sighting, and it seems quite plausible that this was the visual UFO. However, this was discounted in the Blue Book report because the aircraft's position did not check with the radar contact.

115-B. Carswell AFB (Fort Worth area), Tex., 13 February 1953, 0235 LST. Weather: clear with visibility unlimited; temperature inversion layer with sharp humidity lapse at 3,070 ft. altitude, elevated radio duct at 4,240 ft. altitude. Applicable refractivity profile for 0300 LST shown in Fig. 2. Visual observers saw a "formation" of three bright lights which performed a series of maneuvers suggestive of an aircraft with landing lights doing several rolls and then climbing rapidly and heading away. Operators then attempted to pick up the object on an APG 41 radar, and after about two minutes they brought in two apparently stationary targets on the correct azimuth. It seems likely that these returns were from ground objects seen via partial reflection from the strong elevated layers (gradients -154 and -311 km^{-1}). The visual sighting was probably an aircraft.

237-B. Haneda AFB (Tokyo), Japan, 5-6 August 1952, 2330-0030 LST. Weather: "exceptionally good," 0.3 cloud cover about 10 mi. north and 10 mi. south of the contact area,

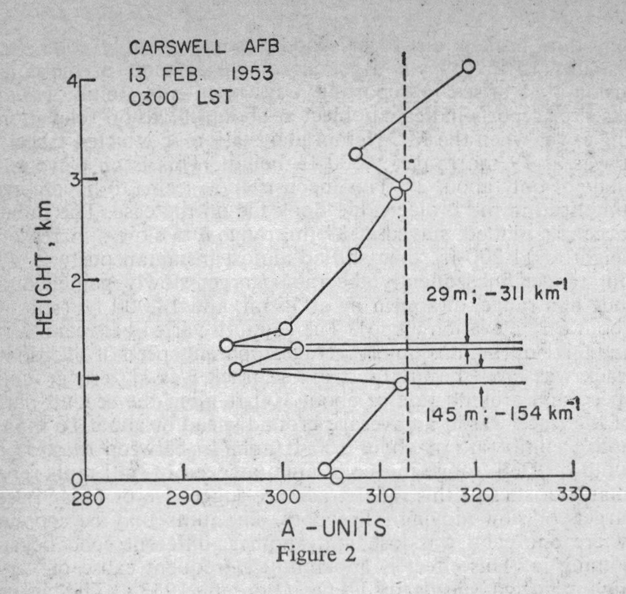

Figure 2

"excellent visibility," isolated patches of low clouds, Mt. Fuji (60 n. mi.) "clearly discernible," scattered thunderstorms in mountains northwest, temperature at Haneda 78°F, dew point 73°F. Observers saw a bright, round light (about 1 mrad arc) surrounded by an apparently dark field four times larger, the lower circumference of which tended to show some bright beading. It was low in the sky at about 30°-50° azimuth. Object appeared to fade twice, during which time it appeared as a dim point source. It disappeared, possibly becoming obscured by clouds, after about an hour. The sky at Haneda AFB was overcast by 0100 LST. One of the visual observers noted that near the end of the sighting the object seemed somewhat higher in the sky and that the moon seemed proportionately higher in elevation. The pilot of a C-54 aircraft coming in for a landing was directed to observe the object and he replied that it looked like a brilliant star, and he dismissed the sighting as such.

When the controller at Shiroi AFB was asked to look for target on GCI radar, he could find nothing for 15 min. He stated: "There were three or four blips on low beam but none I could definitely get a movement on or none I could get a reading on the RHI (range-height indicator) scope." A new controller taking over at 2345 LST "believed" he made radar contact with the object and an F-94 was scrambled. This officer stated: "The target was in a right orbit moving at varying speeds. It was impossible to estimate speed due to the short distances and times involved." By the time the F-94 arrived in the area of the "bogie," Shiroi GCI had lost radar contact; regaining contact at 0017 LST "on a starboard orbit in the same area as before." The F-94 was vectored in to the target, and at this point the timing becomes confused. The Shiroi controller states that the F-94 "reported contact at 0025 (LST) and reported losing contact at 0028 (LST)." The F-94 radar operator states: "At 0016 (LST) I picked up a radar contact at 10° port, 10° below, at 6,000 yd. The target was rapidly moving from port to starboard and a lock-on could not be accomplished. A turn to the starboard was instigated [sic] to intercept target which disappeared on scope in approximately 90 sec. No visual contact was made with the unidentified target." Shiroi GCI had lost the F-94 in ground clutter, and had also lost the target. It is not clear whether the GCI radar ever tracked the fast-moving target described by the F-94 crew. The maximum range of the F-94's radar is not given in the Blue Book report.

The F-94 pilot stated that the weather was very good with "exceptional visibility of 60-70 miles," yet this fast-moving UFO, obviously far exceeding the F-94's airspeed (about 375 knots), was seen by neither the aircraft crew nor the observers on the ground at Shiroi GCI even though the UFO track crossed over very close to Shiroi GCI number four. There are many other inconsistencies in the report of the incident besides the timing and the lack of visual contact by the F-94 crew. The bright, quasi-stationary object sighted NE of Haneda AFB, and seen also from Tachikawa AFB (about 30 mi. west of Haneda AFB), should have been visible to the south of Shiroi AFB, but was never seen by any of a large number of persons there who attempted such observations. Also, at 0012 LST the object being tracked by GCI's CPS-1 radar reportedly "broke into three smaller contacts maintaining an interval of about ¼ mile." The blips on the CPS-1 were described as small and relatively weak, but sharply defined.

Two things seem apparent: (1) the object seen at Haneda and Tachikawa AFB was much farther away than the observers realized; (2) the visual UFO and the target tracked by radar were not the same. The first statement is supported by the inability of the observers at Shiroi to see anything to the south; the second statement is supported by numerous inconsistencies between the visual and radar sightings. The two most important of these latter are: (1) During times when the GCI radar could not find the target, the visual object was in about the same location as during those times when it could be found on radar; (2) The visual object was seen for at least five min. after the time when the airborne radar on the F-94 indicated that the UFO had left the area at a speed well in excess of 300 mph.

The most likely light source to have produced the visual object is the star Capella (magnitude 0.2), which was 8° above horizon at 37° azimuth at 2400 LST. The precise nature of the optical propagation mechanism that would have produced such a strangely diffracted image as reported by the Haneda AFB observers must remain conjectural. Complete weather data are not available for this case, but it is known that the light SSE circulation of moist air from Tokyo Bay was overlain by a drier SW flow aloft. A sharp temperature inversion may have existed at the top of this moist layer, below which patches of fog or mist could collect. The observed diffraction pattern could have been produced by either (1) interference effects associated with propagation within and near the top of an inversion, or (2) a corona with a dark aureole produced by a mist of droplets of water of about 0.2 mm. diameter spaced at regular intervals as described by Minnaert (1954). In either event, the phenomenon must be quite rare. The brightness of the image may have been due in part to "Raman brightening" of an image seen through an inversion layer.

Nor can exact nature of the radar propagation effects be evaluated, due to the lack of complete weather data. However, a substantial inference that the radar returns were of an anomalous propagation nature is derived from:

(1) the tendency for targets to disappear and reappear;
(2) the tendency for the target to break up into smaller targets;
(3) the apparent lack of correlation between the targets seen on the GCI and airborne radars;
(4) the radar invisibility of the target when visibility was "exceptionally good."

Singly, each of the above could be interpreted in a different light, but taken together they are quite suggestive of an anomalous propagation cause.

In summary, it appears that the most probable causes of this UFO report are an optical effect on a bright light source that produced the visual sighting and unusual radar propagation effects that produced the apparent UFO tracks on radar.

104-B. Goose AFB, Labrador, 15 December 1952, 1915-1940 Local Mean Solar Time. Weather: clear and visibility unlimited (30 mi.). The crews of an F-94B fighter and a T-33 jet trainer saw a bright red and white object at 270° azimuth while flying at 14,000 ft. The aircraft attempted an intercept at 375 knots indicated air speed, but could not close on the UFO. After 25 min. of reported chase, although the aircraft had covered a distance of only about 20 mi. (about 3.5 min. at 350 knots ground speed) the object faded and disappeared. During the chase, the radar operator in the F-94B had a momentary lock-on to an unknown target at about the correct azimuth for the UFO. Since this was so brief, it was felt (by Air Intelligence, presumably) that the set had malfunctioned. No GCI contact was made.

The official Air Force explanation for this UFO incident is that the aircraft were chasing Venus which was setting about the time of the sighting, and that the radar "target" was simply a malfunction. It seems likely that this explanation is essentially correct. However, it is unlikely that experienced pilots would have chased a normal-appearing setting Venus. It is more probable that the image of Venus was distorted by some optical effect, possibly a slight superior mirage, and that loss of the mirage-effect (or the interposing of a cloud layer) caused the image to fade away. All items of the account may be explained by this hypothesis, including the report that the object had "no definite size or shape," as the image would no doubt be somewhat "smeared" by imperfections in the mirage-producing surface. The small-angle requirement of a mirage is satisfied since the pilots reported the object seemed to stay at the same level as the aircraft, regardless of altitude changes that they made (another indication of great distance).

14-N. This file actually consists of two similar cases reported by a Capital Airlines pilot with 17 years and 3,000,000 mi. logged. The first case occurred over central Alabama the night of 14 November 1956; the second case was on the night of 30 August 1957, over Chesapeake Bay near Norfolk, Va.

The first sighting took place about 60 mi. NNE of Mobile, Ala. while on a flight from New York to Mobile in a Viscount as "high altitude," probably about 25,000 ft. It was a moonless, starry night and there was an occasionally broken undercast. The object seen was described as an intense blue-white light about 1/10 the size of the moon ($\sim 3'$ arc) and about "seven or eight times as bright as Venus at its brightest magnitude." It first appeared 2210 LST at the upper left of the Viscount's windshield falling towards the right and decelerating rapidly as a normal meteor would. Pilot and copilot both took it to be an unusually brilliant meteor. However, this "meteor" did not burn out as expected, but "abruptly halted directly in front of us and began to hover motionless." The aircraft at this time was over Jackson, Ala. and had descended to 10,000 ft. The pilot contacted Bates Field control tower in Mobile and asked if they could see the object which he described to them as "a brilliant white light bulb." They could not see it. The pilot then asked Bates to contact nearby Brookley AFB to see if they could plot the object on radar. He never learned what the result of this request had been. The object began maneuvering "darting hither and yon, rising and falling in undulating flight, making sharper turns than any known aircraft, sometimes changing direction 90° in an instant—the color remained constant, —and the object did not grow or lessen in size." After a "half minute or so" of this maneuvering, the object suddenly became motionless again. Again, the object "began another series of crazy gyrations, lazy eights, square chandelles, all the while weaving through the air with a sort of rhythmic, undulating cadence." Following this last exhibition, the object "shot out over the Gulf of Mexico, rising at the most breathtaking angle and at such a fantastic speed that it diminished rapidly to a pinpoint and was swallowed up in the night."

The whole incident took about two minutes. The pilot remembers noting that the time was 2212 EST. The object appeared to be at the same distance from the aircraft, which was flying a little faster than 300 mph. during the entire episode.

The second incident reported by this pilot, the 30 August 1957, Chesapeake Bay report, occurred as he was flying another Capital Airlines Viscount at 12,000 ft. approaching Norfolk, Va. There was a Northeast Airlines DC-6 flying at 20,000 ft. "directly above" the Viscount. In this case, the object "was brilliant; it flew fast and then abruptly halted 20 mi. in front of us at 60,000 ft. altitude." The Northeast pilot looked for the object on radar and "could get no return on his screen with the antenna straight ahead but when tilted upward 15° he got an excellent blip right where I told him to look for the object."

This object "dissolved right in front of my eyes, and the crew above lost it from the scope at the same time. They said it just faded away. This sighting covered "several minutes."

These two similar sightings are very difficult to account for. The first sighting over Alabama has most of the characteristics of an optical mirage: an object at about the same altitude seeming to "pace" the aircraft, the meanderings being easily accountable for as normal "image wander." However, there are two aspects that negate this hypothesis: (1) the manner of appearance and disappearance of the UFO is inconsistent with the geometry of a mirage; the high angle of appearance at the top of the windshield is particularly damaging in this regard; (2) there was no known natural or astronomical object in the proper direction to have caused such a mirage. Venus, the only astronomical object of sufficient brightness, was west of the sun that date; Saturn had set 4 hr. 30 min. earlier, and there was not even a first magnitude star near 190°-210° azimuth, 0° elevation angle.

The second sighting is equally difficult to explain as a mirage, which seems to be the only admissible natural explanation in view of the pilot's experience as an observer. The reasons are twofold: (1) the apparent angle at which the object was observed is incompatible with a mirage; (2) there was apparently a radar return obtained from the object which is incompatible with the hypothesis that it was an astronomical object, the most likely mirage-producer.

The pilot stated that the Northeast DC-6 flying at 20,000 ft. "painted" the UFO at 15° elevation and a range of 20 mi. This would place the UFO at about 48,500 ft., the pilot's estimate of 60,000 ft. apparently being in error. Presumably then, the elevation angle as viewed from the Capital Viscount was about 19°. It is very unlikely that any temperature inversion sufficient to produce a mirage would be tilted at such an angle. For a near-horizontal layer to have produced such an image (plus the radar return) by partial reflection of a ground-based object seems equally unlikely. The largest optical partial reflection that such a layer might produce at an angle of 19° would be about 10^{-14} as bright as the object reflected (see Section VI, Chapter 4). This is a decrease of 35 magnitudes. Such a dim object would be ordinarily invisible to the unaided eye.

In summary, these two cases must be considered as unknowns.

1065-B. Charleston, S. C., 16 January 1967, 1810 LST. The observational data in this case are insufficient to determine a probable cause for the sighting. A civilian "walked out of his house and saw" two round objects. He estimated that they were about 30° above the horizon. They appeared to be "silver and blue, with a red ring." These objects were alternately side by side and one above the other, and a beam of light issued "from the tail end." The observer does not state how he knew which was the "tail end," or even at what azimuth he saw the objects. They "vanished in place," still at 30° elevation.

After the Charleston AFB was notified of the sighting, some unidentified returns were picked up on an MPS-14 search radar. An investigating officer later determined that these returns were spurious. The case file states:

> [The officer] called [8 March 1967] to provide additional information in regard to the radar sighting. [The officer] was informed by the Charleston AFB that the radar paints were not of UFOs. A check of the equipment was made and it was learned that the individual monitoring the radar set had the "gain" [control] on the height finder turned up to the "high" position. This caused the appearance of a lot of interference on the radar scope. Personnel at Charleston AFB determined the paints on the radar to be this interference. The personnel turned the gain on high again and picked up more "UFOs." When the gain was turned down the UFOs disappeared.

There apparently were no radar UFOs in this case. The residue is a visual sighting by a single observer with insufficient data for evaluation. What the observer saw could conceivably have been (a) a mirage with direct and reflected images of a planet (Jupiter was at 68° azimuth, 5° elevation) or a bright star, (b) an aircraft, or (c) a genuine unknown (i.e., a possible

ETI object). There is no real evidence either for or against any of these possibilities.

I-B: Primarily visual, meteor-like cases.

1323-B. Sault Saint Marie AFB, Mich., 18 September 1966, 0100 LST. Weather: clear, calm. There is a very brief Blue Book file on this incident. Two sergeants of the 753rd Radar Squadron saw a bright light, elliptical in shape and apparently multicolored of unsaturated hues, which appeared low over the treetops to the SE and moved in a straight line toward the west, disappearing "instantaneously" in the WSW. Duration of this sighting was 2-5 sec. The report states that the object was also tracked by a long-range AN/FPS-90 heightfinder with azimuth, range, and altitude "available on request." Since this information is not included in the folder, no firm conclusion may be reached as to the probable cause of the radar sighting or even as to whether or not the radar and visual objects were correlated.

The general visual appearance, brightness range, motion and mode of disappearance are all compatible with the hypothesis that the object was a large meteor. Some large meteors display even more unusual appearance than this report. If it was a meteor, the radar may have actually tracked it; radar tracks of large meteors are not unknown. Of course, the radar track may have been spurious, or may have indicated that the object was unnatural. The tracking data would be required to settle the point.

The radio refractivity profile for 0600 LST, shown in Fig. 3 indicates that an intense super-refractive layer existed within the first 372 m. (1220 ft.) above the surface. This profile is conducive to the formation of AP echoes on ground-based radar, so there is some possibility that the observed radar data in this UFO incident may have been spurious. This case would seem to merit further investigation.

1206-N. Edmonton, Alberta, 6 April 1967, 2125-2200 LST. Weather: "very clear," cool, temperature about 35°F, little or no wind at surface, stars "bright," no moon. Observers state that a bright object appeared in the NNW low on the horizon, moving fast, appeared to hover, and then disappeared. The night before, a whitish object like a normal star "only much larger" had appeared in the same place (NNW). A Pacific Western Airlines pilot independently reported "chasing" a UFO whose position was relayed to him by GCA radar from Edmonton International Airport. This UFO appeared to move somewhat erratically, was seen only briefly by the pilot as a "reddish-orange lighted effect," and did not travel the same course as the visual object described above.

The general atmospheric conditions prevailing during this sighting were conductive to AP. The description of the GCA radar track is suggestive of AP (quasi-stationary target appearing to "jump" in position), and the description of the

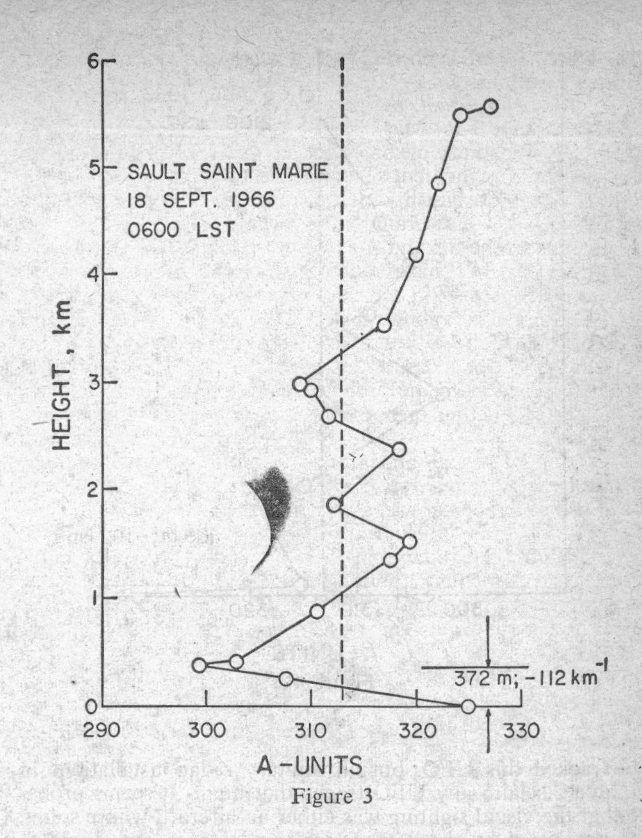

Figure 3

UFO of 5 April is suggestive of the diffracted image of a star seen through a sharp temperature inversion. In the absence of detailed meteorological data, the most probable conclusion seems to be that the primary sighting was a meteor and that no genuine UFO case exists here. However, this case also might merit a more intensive investigation.

1207-B. Paris, Tex., 7 March 1967, 1645 LST. Weather: clear, visibility 15 mi. This is an unconfirmed report by a single observer who could not even be reached for verification of the report by members of this proiect staff. He claimed to have seen two lights that "made a 90° turn at high speed, appeared to separate and come back together again and then went straight up. Speed varied from fast to slow to fast, in excess of known aircraft speed." The last statement is the witness's interpretation. He stated that radar at Paris AFB

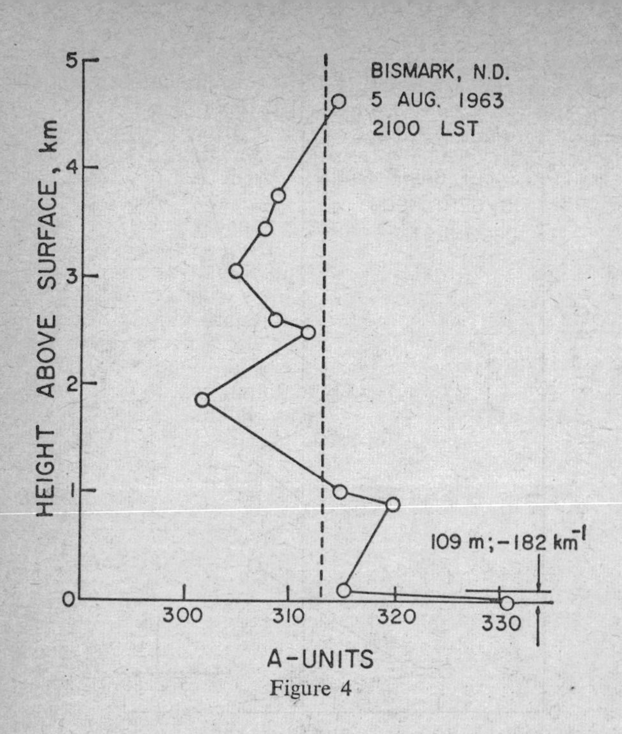

Figure 4

had tracked this UFO, but all military radar installations in the area disclaim any UFO tracks that night. It seems probable that the visual sighting was either an aircraft, whose sound was not heard by the witness for some reason, or a pair of meteors on close, nearly parallel paths. The quick dimming of a meteor burning out may be interpreted as a 90° turn with sudden acceleration away from the observer of a nearly-constant light source, which then seems to disappear in the distance.

I-C: Primarily visual, blurry light or glow.

15-B. Blackhawk and Rapid City, S. Dak., and Bismarck, N. Dak., 5-6 August 1953, 2005-0250 LST. Weather: clear, excellent visibility, stable conditions, temperature inversions and radio surface ducts prevalent. See Fig. 4. The night was dark and moonless.

The initial incident in this chain of UFO sightings was the sighting by a GOC (Ground Observers Corps) observer of a stationary "red glowing light" at 2005 LST near Blackhawk, S. Dak. This light soon began to move some 30° to the right, "shot straight up," and moved to the left, returning to its original position. A companion thought it was "just the red tower light" (a warning light on an FM transmitter tower normally just visible from their location). The report was relayed to the Rapid City Filter Center, and three airmen from the radar site were sent outside to look for the UFO. They saw what was undoubtedly a meteor, judging from their description. The radar operator when informed of the new sighting began to search for unidentified targets. He found many.

Over the course of the next four hours a large number of unidentified blips appeared on the Rapid City radar. Many of those were transitory, moving blips with a fairly short lifetime, usually being "lost in the ground clutter." An F-84 fighter was vectored in to a stationary blip near Blackhawk, and the pilot "chased" a UFO which he found at the location on a heading of 320° M. without gaining on it. The F-84 was probably chasing a star, in this case Pollux (mag. 1.2) which was in the correct location (335° true azimuth, near the horizon).

When the Blackhawk GOC post called in that the original object had returned for a third time, another F-84 was vectored in on the visual report, as no radar contact could be made. The pilot made a "visual contact" and headed out on a 360° magnetic (~ 15° true) vector. At this point the radar picked up what apparently was ghost echo, that is, one that "paced" the aircraft, always on the far side from the radar. The fighter in this instance was probably chasing another star, the image of which may have been somewhat distorted. The pilot's report that the visual UFO was "pacing" him appears to have strengthened the radar operator's belief that he was actually tracking the UFO, and not a ghost echo. The star in this instance may well have been Mirfak (mag. 1.9), which, at 2040 LST, was at azimuth 15° and about 5° to 7° elevation angle. The second pilot, upon being interviewed by Dr. Hynek, stated that he felt he had been chasing a star, although there were some aspects of the appearance of the object that disturbed him. He also stated that the radar gunlock, which he had reported by radio during the chase, was due to equipment malfunction, and that the radar gunsight continued to malfunction on his way back to the base. This equipment was never subsequently checked for malfunctioning (i.e., not before or during the official AF investigation of the incident).

The Bismarck, N. Dak. sightings began when the Bismarck Filter Center was alerted to the "presence of UFO's" by Rapid City. At 2342 LST the sergeant on duty there and several volunteer observers went out on the roof and shortly spotted four objects. The descriptions of these objects by the various observers were consistent with the hypothesis that they were stars, although some apparent discrepancies caused early AF investigators to deduce by crude triangulations that the sighted objects must have been nearby. It now appears that all four objects were stars viewed through a temperature inversion layer. The observers stated that the objects resembled stars, but that their apparent motion and color changes seemed to rule out this possibility.

Dr. Hynek's summary of the probable nature of the four Bismarck objects is enlightening:

> Object #1, which was low on the horizon in the west and disappeared between midnight and 0100 hr. was the star Arcturus observed through a surface inversion. Arcturus was low on the horizon in the west and set at approximately 1220 (LST) at 289° azimuth.
>
> Object #2—was the star Capella observed through a surface inversion. At 0011 CST Capella was at 40° azimuth and 15° elevation . . . [and] at 0200 CST [it] was at 53° azimuth and 30° elevation, which agrees with the positions given by [the two witnesses].
>
> Object #3 and #4 were, with a high degree of probability, the planet Jupiter and the star Betelgeuse, observed through a surface inversion. Jupiter's . . . stellar magnitude was −1.7 [and it] was low on the eastern horizon at approximately 92° azimuth. Betelgeuse . . . was also low on the eastern horizon at approximately 81° azimuth.

The statement of one of the witnesses at Bismarck includes the following comments:

> . . . they appeared much brighter than most of the stars and at times appeared to take on a rather dull bluish tint.
>
> They appeared to move in the heavens, but at a rather slow rate and unless a person braced his head against some stationary object to eliminate head movement it would be hard to tell that they were moving.
>
> The one in the west eventually disappeared below the horizon and the one in the northeast gradually seemed to blend in with the rest of the stars until it was no longer visible.

The last statement is typical of the description given by witnesses who have apparently observed a bright star rising through an inversion layer. It would seem to be circumstantial evidence of the diffraction-brightening predicted by Raman for propagation along an inversion layer (see Section VI Chapter 4). However, there is an alternative explanation that simple diffractive blurring or smearing of a star's image, by spreading the available light over a larger area of the eye's retina, may cause a psychological illusion of brightening of the object.

The meteorological conditions were generally favorable for anomalous propagation at both locations. The refractivity profile for Rapid City 2000 LST 5 August shows a 0.5°C temperature inversion over a layer 109 m. thick, although the resulting refractivity gradient is only -77 km^{-1} (Fig. 5). The

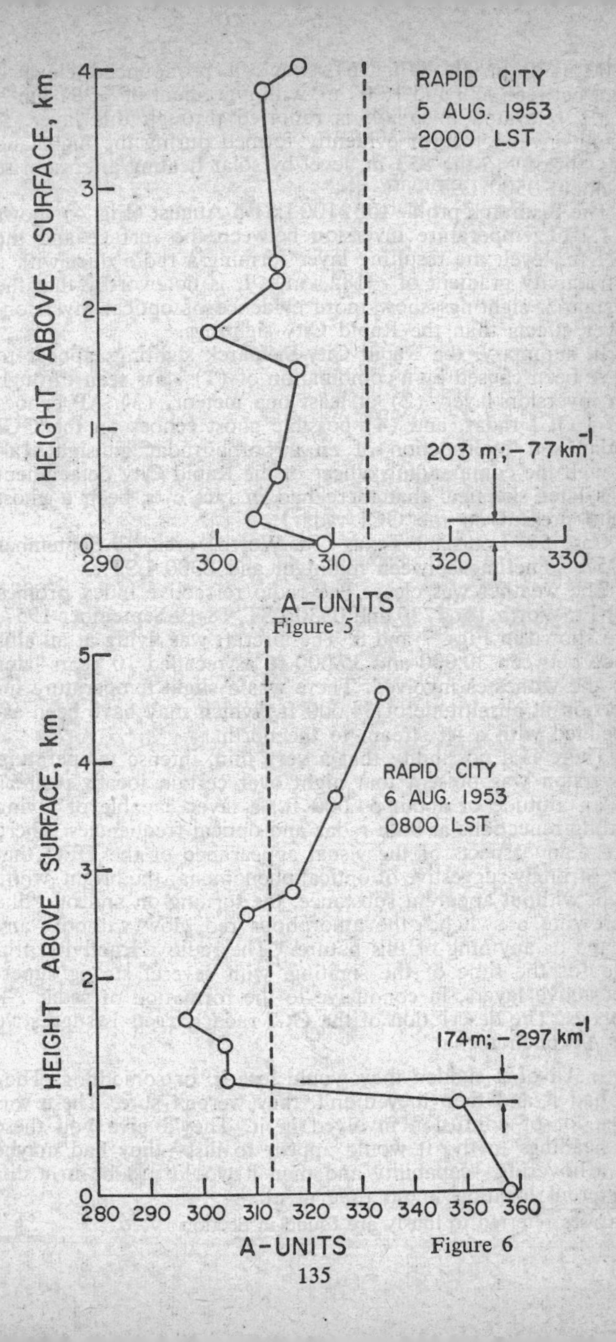

Figure 5

Figure 6

0800 LST profile (Fig. 6) shows a pronounced elevated duct between 833 and 1,007 m. with a gradient of -297 km^{-1}; a 3.2° elevated inversion is reported through this layer. A strong inversion layer evidently formed during the night and was "lifted" to the 833 m. level by solar heating after sunrise at about 0500 LST.

The Bismarck profile for 2100 LST 5 August (Fig. 4) shows a 1.2°C temperature inversion between the surface and the 109 m. level, the resulting layer forming a radio duct with a refractivity gradient of -182 km^{-1}. It is noteworthy that the Bismarck sightings show more evidence of optical inversion-layer effects than the Rapid City sightings.

In summary, the Rapid City-Bismarck sightings appear to have been caused by a combination of (1) stars seen through an inversion layer, (2) at least one meteor, (3) AP echoes on a GCI radar, and (4) possible ghost echoes on the GCI radar and malfunction of an airborne radar gunsight (although the commanding officer of the Rapid City detachment was later skeptical that there had in fact ever been a ghost echo present on the GCI radar).

Case 5*. Louisiana-Texas (Ft. Worth) area, 19 September 1957, sometime between midnight and 0300 LST.

The weather was clear. The radio refractive index profiles for Ft. Worth, for 1730 and 0530 LST, 18-19 September 1957, are shown in Figs. 7 and 8. The aircraft was flying at an altitude between 30,000 and 35,000 ft. as recalled 10 years later by the witnesses involved. There was a slight temperature inversion at an altitude of 34,000 ft., which may have been associated with a jet stream to the north.

There is a possibility that a very thin, intense temperature inversion was present that night over certain localized areas at an altitude of about 34,000 ft., a layer capable of giving strong reflections at both radar and optical frequencies. There are many aspects of the visual appearance of the UFO that are strongly suggestive of optical phenomena: the bright, white light without apparent substance, the turning on and off "like throwing a switch," the amorphous red glow without "any shape or anything of this nature." The radio refractivity profile for the time of the sighting, with several strong superrefractive layers, in conducive to the formation of radar AP echoes. The description of the GCI radar targets is suggestive of AP phenomena:

> All of a sudden they would lose it, or something. They had it and then they didn't, they weren't sure. There was a lot of confusion involved in it. They'd give you these headings to fly. It would appear to just—they had maybe a hovering—capability and then it would just be in a different location in no time at all.

---

* Cases referred to thusly are found in Section IV.

This type of behavior is typical of moving AP targets. The elevated duct shown on the Fort Worth profiles is very thick, and seems fully capable of causing these effects.

In summary, it is possible to account for the major details of the sighting through three hypotheses:

(1) The UFO at 30,000 to 35,000 ft. may have been a combined radio-optical mirage of another aircraft, at great distance, flying just below a thin inversion layer which was also just above the B-47's flight path. This aircraft would have had to have (a) displayed landing lights which were turned off

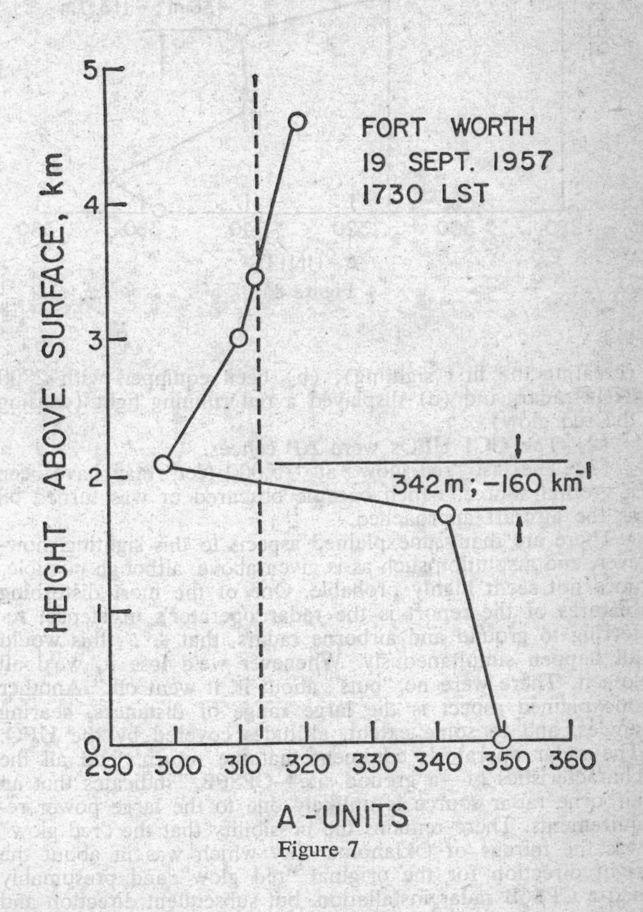

Figure 7

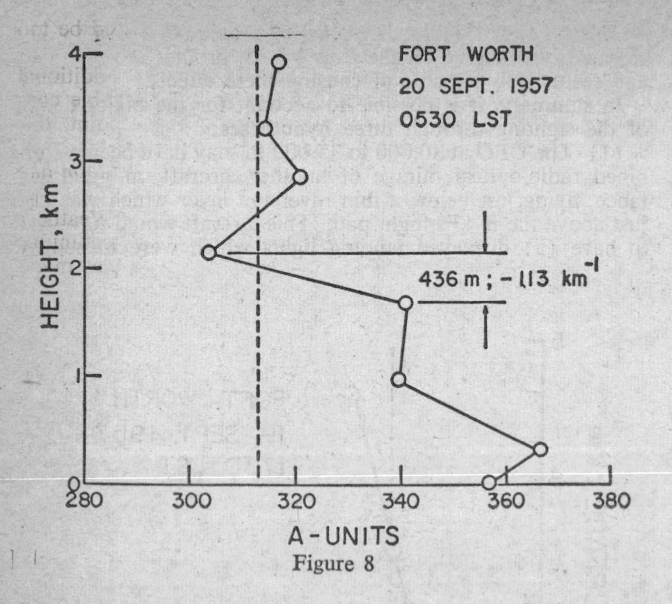

Figure 8

(creating the first sighting), (b) been equipped with 2800 MHz radar, and (c) displayed a red running light (causing the red glow).

(2) The GCI UFOs were AP echoes.

(3) The last "red glow" at "15,000 feet" may have been a ground source, which became obscured or was turned off as the aircraft approached.

There are many unexplained aspects to this sighting, however, and a solution such as is given above, although possible, does not seem highly probable. One of the most disturbing features of the report is the radar operator's insistence, referring to ground and airborne radars, that ". . . this would all happen simultaneously. Whenever we'd lose it, we'd all lose it. There were no "buts" about it, it went off." Another unexplained aspect is the large range of distances, bearing angles, and to some extent, altitudes covered by the UFO. The radar operator's comment that the return "had all the characteristics of—a ground site—CPS6B," indicates that an airborne radar source is unlikely due to the large power requirements. There remains the possibility that the "red glow" was the mirage of Oklahoma City which was in about the right direction for the original "red glow" and presumably had a CPS6B radar installation, but subsequent direction and location changes would seem to rule out this possibility and the grazing angle at the elevated inversion layer would be too large for a normal mirage to take place.

In view of these considerations, and the fact that additional information on this incident is not available, no tenable conclusion can be reached. From a propagation standpoint, this sighting must be tentatively classified as an unknown.

I-D: Primarily visual, misellaneous appearance: balloon-like aircraft-like, etc.

Over Labrador, 30 June 1954, 2105-2127 LST. Weather: (at 19,000 ft.) clear, with a broken layer of stratocumulus clouds below, excellent visibility. No radar contact was made in this incident.

A summary of the pilot's first-hand account of his experience reads:

> I was in command of a BOAC Boeing Strato cruiser en route from New York to London via Goose Bay Labrador (refuelling stop). Soon after crossing overhead Seven Islands at 19,000 feet, True Airspeed 230 kts, both my copilot and I became aware of something moving along off our port beam at a lower altitude at a distance of maybe five miles, in and out of a broken layer of Strato Cumulus cloud. As we watched, these objects climbed above the cloud and we could now clearly see one large and six small. As we flew on towards Goose Bay the large object began to change shape and the smaller to move relative to the larger. . . .
>
> We informed Goose Bay that we had something odd in sight and they made arrangements to vector a fighter (F94?) on to us. Later I changed radio frequency to contact this fighter; the pilot told me he had me in sight on radar closing me head-on at 20 miles. At that the small objects seemed to enter the larger, and then the big one shrank. I gave a description of this to the fighter and a bearing of the objects from me. I then had to change back to Goose frequency for descent clearance. I don't know if the fighter saw anything, as he hadn't landed when I left Goose for London.

The description of the UFO in this case, an opaque, dark "jelly-fish-like" object, constantly changing shape, is suggestive of an optical cause. Very little meteorological data are available for this part of the world on the date in question, so that the presence of significant optical propagation mechanisms can be neither confirmed nor ruled out. Nevertheless, certain facts in the case are strongly suggestive of an optical mirage phenomenon:

(1) The UFO was always within a few degrees of a horizontal plane containing the aircraft, thus satisfying the small-angle requirement;

(2) The aircraft flew at a steady altitude of 19,000 ft. for the 85 n. mi. over which the UFO appeared to "pace" the aircraft, thus the plane maintained a constant relationship to any atmospheric layer at a fixed altitude;

(3) The dark UFO was seen against a bright sky back-

ground within 15°-20° of the setting sun; nearly identical images, displaying "jellyfish-like" behavior may be commonly observed wherever mirages are observed with strong light-contrast present. The reflection of the moon on gently rippling water presents quite similar behavior.

The suggestion is strong that the UFO in this case was a mirage: a reflection of the dark terrain below seen against the bright, "silvery" sky to the left of the setting sun. The reflecting layer would be a thin, sharp temperature inversion located at an altitude just above that of the crusing aircraft. Most of the facts in this incident can be accounted for by this hypothesis. The dark, opaque nature of the image arises from the contrast in brightness and the phenomenon of "total reflection." The arrangement of the large and small objects in a thin line just above the aircraft's flight path, as well as the manner of disappearance, are commensurate with a mirage. As the mirage-producing layer weakens (with distance) or the viewing angle increases (was the aircraft beginning its descent at the time?), the mirage appears to dwindle to a point and disappears. This type of mirage is referred to as a superior mirage and has often been reported over the ocean (see Section VI, Chapter 4).

The principal difficulty with this explanation, besides having to hypothesize the existence of the mirage-producing layer, is how to account for the anisotropy of the mirage. Anisotropy of this sort, i.e. a mirage limited to certain viewing azimuths, is common in earthbound mirages when viewed from a single location. But a mirage layer through which a reflected image could be seen only in one, constant principal direction (plus a few small "satellite" images) over a distance of 85 n. mi. is quite unusual.

There remains the slim possibility that the aircraft itself produced the mirage layer through intensification (by compression induced by the shock wave of the aircraft's passage through the air) of a barely subcritical layer, i.e. one in which the temperature gradient is just a little bit less than the value required to produce a mirage. This hypothesis would satisfy the directional requirement of the sighting, but the resulting scheme of hypotheses is too speculative to form an acceptable solution to the incident.

This unusual sighting should therefore be assigned to the category of some almost certainly natural phenomenon, which is so rare that it apparently has never been reported before or since.

304-B. Odessa, Wash., 10 December 1952, 1915 LST. Weather: clear above undercast at 3,000 ft.; aircraft at 26,000-27,000 ft. Two pilots in an F-94 aircraft sighted a large, round white object "larger than any known type of aircraft." A dim reddish-white light seemed to come from two "windows." It appeared to be able to "reverse direction almost instantly," and did a chandelle in front of the aircraft. After this the object appeared to rush toward the aircraft head-on and then would "suddenly stop and be pulling off." The pilot banked away to avoid an apparently imminent collision, and lost visual contact. Fifteen minutes later the aircraft radar picked up something which the crew assumed was the UFO, although there is no evidence that it was. The object was reported to be moving generally from west to east at 75 knots. It was never sighted.

This sighting has been described as a mirage of Venus, although the reported 75 knot speed and 270° direction of motion is in contradiction to this hypothesis. The general description of the object as well as the reported motion is suggestive of a weather balloon. However, the peculiar reversals of direction, although they could have been illusory, and particularly the loss of visual contact are at odds with the balloon hypothesis.

The radiosonde profile for Spokane, 1900 LST, is shown in Fig. 9 and is inconclusive. The tropopause, where the sharpest temperature inversions are likely, is at about 30,500 ft. above sea level, too high to have produced a mirage visible at 26,000-27,000 ft.

The closeness of the timing between the radiosonde release at 1900 LST and the sighting at 1915 LST suggests that the F-94 crew may have seen a lighted pibal balloon. The description given, including the two dimly-lit "windows," is typical of the description of a pibal balloon by those not familiar with weather instrumentation. Such a balloon would rise to at least 17,000 ft. in 15 min., and the reported motion, 270° at 75 knots, is in excellent agreement with the upper winds at the highest level plotted for the Spokane profile: 280° at 66 knots at 18,000 ft.

19-X. 361-B. Kirtland AFB, Albuquerque, N.M., 4 Nov. 1957, 2245-2305 LST. Weather: scattered clouds with high overcast, visibility good, thunderstorms and rain showers in vicinity, light rain over airfield. Observers in the CAA (now FAA) control tower saw an unidentified dark object with a white light underneath, about the "shape of an automobile on end," that crossed the field at about 1500 ft. and circled as if to come in for a landing on the E-W runway. This unidentified object appeared to reverse direction at low altitude, while out of sight of the observers behind some buildings, and climbed suddenly to about 200-300 ft., heading away from the field on a 120° course. Then it went into a steep climb and disappeared into the overcast.

The Air Force view is that this UFO was a small, powerful private aircraft, flying without flight plan, that became confused and attempted a landing at the wrong airport. The pilot apparently realized his error when he saw a brightly-lit restricted area, which was at the point where the object reversed

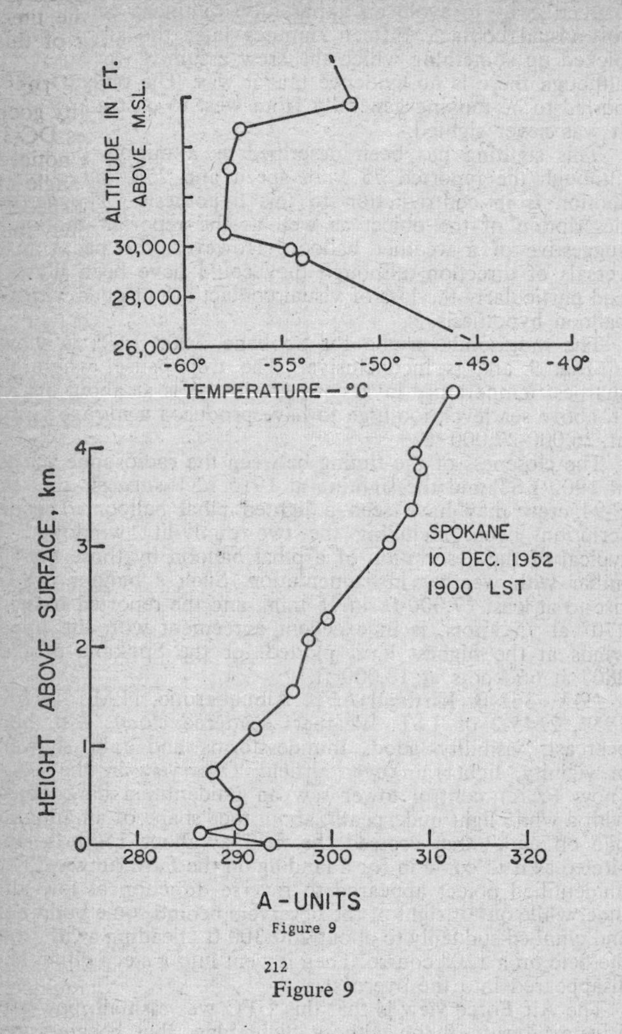

Figure 9

212

Figure 9

direction. The radar blip was described by the operator as a "perfectly normal aircraft return," and the radar track showed no characteristics that would have been beyond the capabilities of the more powerful private aircraft available at the time. There seems to be no reason to doubt the accuracy of this analysis.

1482-N. About 15 mi. east of Utica, N. Y., 23 June 1955, 1215-1245 LST. Weather: overcast at 4,000 ft., visibility good below. Reported by the co-pilot of a Mohawk Airlines DC-3. They were cruising at 3,000 ft. at 160 knots, when he noticed an object passing approximately 500 ft. above at an angle of about 70° (20° from vertical). It was moving at "great speed." The body was "light gray, almost round, with a center line. . . . Beneath the line there were several (at least four) windows which emitted a bright blue-green light. It was not rotating but went straight." The pilot also saw this UFO; they watched it for several miles. As the distance between the DC-3 and the UFO increased, the lights "seemed to change color slightly from greenish to bluish or vice versa. A few minutes after it went out of sight, two other aircraft (one, a Colonial DC-3, the other I did not catch the number) reported that they saw it and wondered if anyone else had seen it. The Albany control tower also reported that they had seen an object go by on Victor-2 [airway]. As we approached Albany, we overheard that Boston radar had also tracked an object along Victor-2, passing Boston and still eastbound."

The pilot and co-pilot computed the "speed" of the UFO at 4,500-4,800 mph. from the times of contact near Utica and at Boston. There are a number of inconsistencies in this report, aside from the most obvious one: the absence of a devastating sonic boom, which should be generated by a 150 ft. ellipsoidal object travelling at Mach 6 or better in level flight at 3,500 ft. It does seem likely that the Boston GCA report was coincidental and involved a different object.

The residue is a most intriguing report, that must certainly be classed as an unknown pending further study, which it certainly deserves. Statements from some of the other witnesses involved would help in analyzing the event, and should prove useful even 13 years after the fact. It does appear that this sighting defies explanation by conventional means.

10-X [371-B.] Continental Divide, N. M., 26 January 1953, 2115-2200 LST. Weather: high, thin overcast, low scattered clouds, very good visibility. An airman stationed at the 769th AC&W Squadron at Continental Divide (elevation 7,500 ft.) observed a "bright reddish-white object" about 10 mi. west of the radar site and approximately 2,000 ft. above the terrain. The radar subsequently painted a strong, steady return at 9 mi. range and about 2,500-7,500 ft. above the surface. This object passed behind a nearby hill and reappeared, heading north at about 10-15 mph. Radar track confirmed this. The object then moved to the west at 12-15 mph to a point 18 mi. west of the radar site. It then turned north for about 10 mi., and subsequently turned back on a heading of 128° inbound to the station. Radar and visual contact was lost near the area where the object was first detected. Before disappearing, the object seemed to shrink in size and fade in color to a dull red.

There seems to be little doubt in this case that the visual and radar contacts were in fact of the same object. The obvious interpretation is that the object seen and tracked on radar was a weather balloon, a lighted pibal used for obtaining data on upper winds. This explanation was considered and rejected by Air Force investigators for two reasons:

(1) The sighting occurred 1 hr. 15 min. after the scheduled release of the Winslow, Ariz. pibal, the only one that seemed likely to have showed up in the sighting area, and the balloon ought to have burst by then, since they generally burst at 30,000 ft., an altitude the Winslow pibal should have reached 25 min. after launch;

(2) The reported direction of movement was, at least part of the time, directly opposite to the reported upper winds as derived from the Albuquerque radiosonde flight. These winds were reported from the "west between 10,000 and 30,000 feet."

Actually, neither of these two reasons is sufficient to discount the balloon theory. In the first place, weather balloons are often released later than the scheduled time, and this possibility was apparently not checked. In the second place, pibal ballons are often known to leak and consequently to rise at a much slower rate than normal. Often they have so little bouyancy that they may be caught in local updrafts or downdrafts. These leaking balloons are usually carried away by the horizontal wind flow at such a rate that they are lost from sight of the observing station before they reach burst altitude. The pibal data from Winslow, Ariz. for 0300 GMT 27 January 1953, (2000 LST 26 January) is listed as "missing" above the 500 mb level (about 19,000 ft. m.s.l.), which is a strong indication that the balloon may have been leaking. It is therefore entirely conceivable that the Winslow pibal balloon could have been in the vicinity of Gallup, N. M. (west of the radar site) at 2115 LST on the night in question.

The problem of the observed direction of movement cannot be completely resolved, because it depends largely on an analysis of mesoscale winds in the lower atmosphere, that is, on a scale smaller than ordinarily analyzed on synoptic weather maps. The synoptic maps for 2000 LST 26 January 1953, for the 700 mb (about 10,000 ft.), 500 mb (about 19,000 ft.), and 300 mb (about 27,000 ft.) levels are shown in Figs. 10 and 11.

Although the general windflow in the Arizona-New Merico area for at least the 700 and 500 mb maps is from the west, there are indications of a secondary mesoscale circulation somewhere in the vicinity of the Arizona-New Mexico border, which is embedded in the general trough overlying the southwestern states. Especially significant are the winds at the 700 and 500 mb levels at Tucson and at Phoenix, mainly at the 500 mb level, which show evidence of a mesoscale cyclonic circulation in the area.

In view of the general meteorological situation at the time, a quite likely explanation for the Continental Divide sighting is as follows: The Winslow pibal balloon, which was leaking, was carried away to the east, probably sinking slowly as it went, and was lost from view of the Winslow weather station. Upon reaching the general vicinity of Gallup, N. M. the leaking balloon was probably caught up in a local cyclonic vortex and updraft, which, being instigated by the mesoscale cyclonic flow in the region may have formed on the windward side of the range of low mountains forming the Divide in that area. This would have caused the balloon to be carried toward the north, slowly rising, as first observed. This would be followed in sequence by a turn to the west, and ultimately, upon reaching a somewhat higher level, a turn toward the southeast again as the balloon became caught in the more general flow from the west and northwest prevailing at middle levels in the atmosphere.

This hypothesis fits the details of the observations rather well, and considering the lack of additional information or data pertaining to this incident, the UFO should probably be tentatively identified as a weather balloon.

321-B. Niagara Falls, N. Y., 25 July 1957, 0025 LST. Weather: clear, excellent visibility. Observers saw a "circular brilliant white object with pale green smaller lights around its perimeter." Object appeared to move slowly at nearly constant altitude, and then went into a "fast, steep climb," disappearing in about 5-8 min. The object was tracked on a CPS-6B radar for about 3 min. moving from SW to NE, in agreement with prevailing winds in the area.

The rate of climb could not have been very great, or the object would not have remained in sight for "five to eight" minutes. The official AF view is that the object was a lighted balloon, and in the absence of other data or a more complete file on the case, there seems to be no more likely explanation.

Class II: UFO incidents that are primarily radar contacts, with or without secondary visual observations.

Class II-A: Primarily radar, with radar returns of an AP-like nature: fuzzy, vague, or erratic returns, multiple returns, sporadic returns, etc.

1211-B. McChord AFB, Seattle, Wash., 2 October 1959, 0020-0320 LST. Weather: clear, fog moved in at 0150 LST after initial sighting, wind from 10° at 10 knots (approx.).

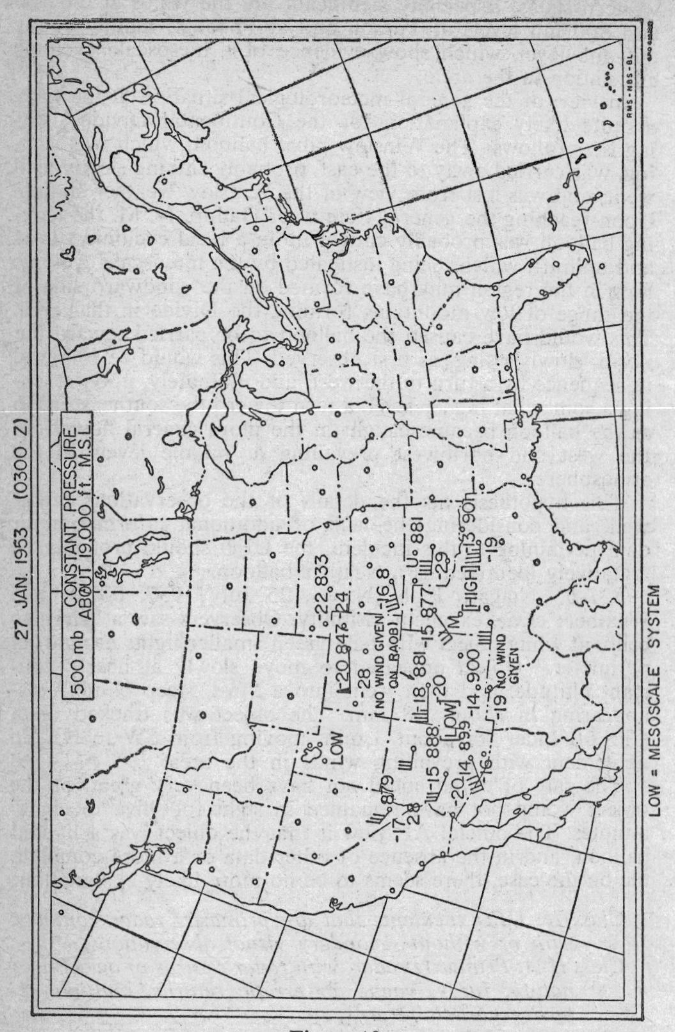
27 JAN. 1953 (0300 Z)
500 mb CONSTANT PRESSURE
ABOUT 19,000 ft. M.S.L.
LOW
NO WIND GIVEN ON RAOB
HIGH
LOW
NO WIND GIVEN
LOW = MESOSCALE SYSTEM

Figure 10

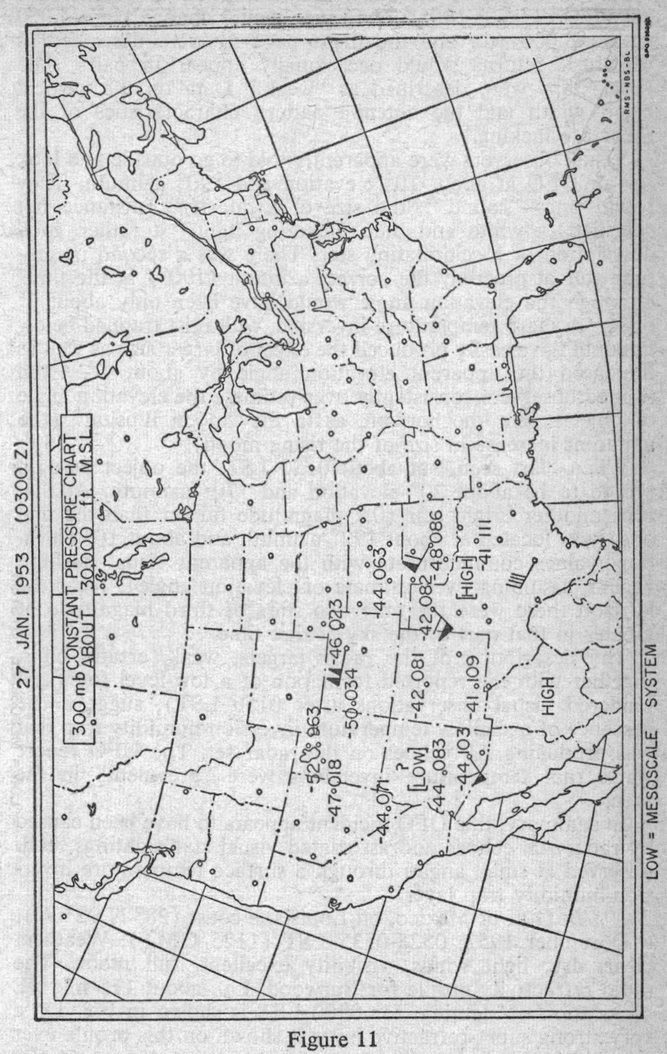
27 JAN. 1953 (0300 Z)
300 mb CONSTANT PRESSURE CHART
ABOUT 30,000 ft. M.S.L.
[LOW]
[HIGH]
HIGH
LOW = MESOSCALE SYSTEM

Figure 11

Radar at McChord AFB picked up a total of five or more unidentified tracks between 0020 to 0320 LST. These targets appeared to be at elevation angles of about 10°-20° and azimuths of 170°-190°. The range would change from 4,000 yd. to 8,000 yd., and the flight patterns were described as "erratic;" returns would occasionally appear in pairs. The radar blips were described as "weak." Data on the vertical beam width and the antenna pattern characteristics of the radar are lacking.

Visual observers were apparently told to go outside and look for an UFO at about 10° elevation and 190° azimuth. They found one—"round," "the size of a quarter" (distance not specified), "white and blue flickering light," a rather good description of a scintillating star. There was a second magnitude star at precisely the correct azimuth (190°) at the time, although the elevation angle would have been only about 1° or so. A sharp temperature inversion, with mist trapped below it, could have easily produced the effect of larger size as well as increased the apparent elevation angle by about 1°. Even trained observers consistently over-estimate the elevation angle of objects near the horizon, as in the "moon illusion" (the apparent increase in size of the rising moon).

When "last seen," at about 0150 LST, the object was reported to be about 20° elevation and 170° azimuth. At that time another bright star (0.7 magnitude fainter than the first one) was located at about 172° azimuth and about 10° elevation, values commensurate with the apparent visual position (again, assuming over-estimate of elevation angle). Near the horizon these were the only two stars of third magnitude or greater in that part of the sky at that time.

The description of the radar targets, weak, erratic blips, together with the reported formation of a low-level fog (that hindered visual observations after 0150 LST), suggests the presence of a shallow temperature inversion-humidity trap that was producing AP echoes on the radar set. The UFO report states that temperature inversions were "prevalent" in the area.

In summary, this UFO incident appears to have been caused by radar AP echoes and associated visual star sightings, both observed at small angles through a surface temperature inversion-humidity trap layer.

103-B. Gulf of Mexico, off Louisiana coast (28° N 92° W), 6 December 1952, 0525-0535 LST (1125 GMT). Weather: clear, dry, light winds, visibility excellent, full moon. The radio refractivity profile for Burwood, La., about 175 mi. NE of location of sighting, for 0900 LST is shown in Fig. 12; a very strong super-refractive layer is shown on this profile over a height interval extending from the surface to 456 m. (1,500 ft.). A sharp temperature inversion existed at the top of this layer. As an aircraft was returning to Galveston, Tex. at

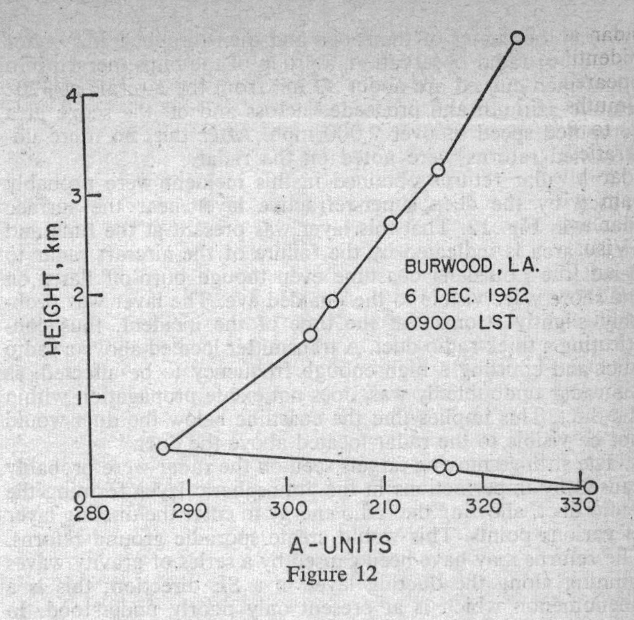

Figure 12

20,000 ft. burn-off flares from oil refineries became visible. The radar was activated on 100 mi. range to check for the Louisiana coastline. The range to the nearest point on the coastline was about 89 mi. and assuming standard propagation conditions, the range to the radar horizon should have been on the order of 140 mi. Surprisingly, the coastline could not be seen on the radarscope. Instead a number of unusual echoes were observed. Initially there were four moving on a course of 120° true azimuth. These blips moved at apparent speeds of over 5,000 mph., coming within 15-20 mi. of the aircraft's position. Eventually they disappeared from the scope. The radar set was calibrated, but more blips appeared still moving SE across the scope.

Visual observations consisted of one or two blue-white flashes, one of which, as viewed from the waist blister, appeared to pass under a wing of the aircraft. All of these may have been above the horizon, since the wingtip would appear well above the horizon as viewed from this position. The observers stated that the flashes "did not alter course whatsoever." These visual sightings were probably Geminid meteors; the wing operations officer stated: "Visual sightings are indecisive and of little confirmatory value."

One of the radar witnesses stated: "One object came directly towards the center of the scope and then disappeared." After 10 min. of radar observation, a group of the blips merged into a half-inch curved arc about 30 mi. from the aircraft at 320° relative azimuth and proceeded across and off the scope at a computed speed of over 9,000 mph. After this, no more unidentified returns were noted on the radar.

The radar returns obtained in this incident were probably caused by the deep super-refractive layer near the surface shown in Fig. 12. That this layer was present at the time and in the area is indicated by the failure of the aircraft radar to detect the Louisiana coastline even though burn-off flares on the shore were visible to the unaided eye. The layer was probably slightly stronger at the time of the incident, thus constituting a thick radio duct. A transmitter located above a radio duct and emitting a high enough frequency to be affected, as the radar undoubtedly was, does not excite propagation within the duct. This implies that the coastline below the duct would not be visible to the radar located above the duct.

The strange moving targets seen on the radar were probably caused by imperfections in the atmospheric layer forming the radio duct, allowing the radio energy to enter the ducting layer at various points. This would create sporadic ground returns. The returns may have been caused by a series of gravity waves running along the ducting layer in a SE direction; this is a phenomenon which is at present only poorly understood. In any event, spurious radar images have often been noted under propagation conditions of this sort, often moving at apparent speeds of from tens to thousands of miles per hour.

In summary, it seems most likely that the cause of this sighting can be assigned to radar AP, for which there is meteorological evidence, and meteors.

7-C. White Sands Missile Range, N. M., 2 March 1967, 1025-1132 LST. Weather: apparently clear (few meteorological data are available). A single witness at the summit of highway 70 over the Sacramento Mountains (Apache Summit, 9,000 ft. elevation) reported seeing "silvery specks" passing overhead from north to south. The witness called Holloman AFB, and range surveillance radar was requested to look for the objects. Two aircraft were scrambled, but neither reported a sighting, although they searched the area where the UFOs were reported.

Two radars were in operation. Both tracked a number of targets, most of which were stationary and so intermittent in nature as to prevent lock-on (see Case 16). Significantly, none of the radar targets was behaving in the manner described by this witness (i.e., moving steadily south at high altitude). Therefore, this incident is considered to be primarily a radar contact.

The probable nature of each of the three types of radar contact made is examined below.

(1) The stationary, intermittent targets. Most of these can be identified with terrain features, peaks or ridges, that would normally be just below the radar's line of sight. If the atmospheric conditions were such as to render these points just barely detectable by the radars, they would probably appear as intermittent, stationary targets of the type described.

(2) The object at 25,000 ft. that "drifted east three or four miles in about 10 minutes" was apparently moving with the prevailing upper winds from the west; it may have been a weather balloon, or some similar device.

(3) The circular track executed by the Holloman radar was interpreted by the radar engineers on the base as being a noise track. This seems quite likely, despite some apparent discrepancies noted in the report. If this track represented a real target, it is strange that the Elephant Mountain radar never picked it up, in spite of the fact that the apparent track passed within about 6.5 mi. of the second radar's location.

190-N. Detroit, Mich., March 1953, about 1000 to 1100 LST (exact date and time unknown). Weather: "perfectly clear." A USAF pilot and a radar operator, flying in an F-94B fighter on a practice training mission, were directed by GCI radar at Selfridge AFB to intercept some unknown targets which appeared to be over downtown Detroit. The pilot and radar operator looked in that direction and saw "tiny specks in the sky, which appeared to look like a ragged formation of aircraft."

The aircraft at this time was about 30 mi. NW of downtown Detroit, and the targets "appeared to be over the city's central section." The pilot turned the aircraft to an intercept course. During this time, perhaps "three or four minutes," the objects were visible to the pilot as "a ragged formation traveling slowly in a westward direction;" the objects appeared to be "a little lower than our aircraft." The pilot started his intercept run under full military power, without afterburner, at approximately 500 mph.

The pilot recalls thinking several times that details of the unknowns, like wings, tails, etc. should have "popped out" as they approached, so that identification could be made, but they did not. The ground radar had both the F-94B and the unknowns "painted as good, strong targets." The unknowns could still not be identified, but "seemed to get a little larger all the time."

The F-94B's radar operator began to get returns and "thought he was picking up the targets." The pilot looked at his instruments to see if he could "inch out a little more speed without going into afterburner," and when he looked up again "every last one" of the objects was gone. The pilot asked GCI where the UFOs were, and was told they were still there, "loud and clear." They continued to fly headings given by GCI right into the center of the targets, flying and turning in "every direction," but there was nothing in sight. The pilot states: "Gradually the targets disappeared from ground radar after we had been amongst them for three or four minutes." The F-94B then returned to base.

Since the exact date of this sighting is unknown, no applicable meteorological data are available. Any explanation of this incident must therefore remain speculative in nature. If the UFOs are considered to have been material objects, then they would have had to have shifted position some tens of miles in the "two to four" seconds while the pilot was looking down at his instruments. This does not explain why they continued to appear on the ground radar. The only admissible hypothesis would seem to be that they became invisible as the fighter approached, but this does not account for the fact that they could not be picked up on airborne radar while the aircraft was searching the area.

There is one hypothesis that seems to fit all of the observed facts: that the "ragged formation" was actually an inferior mirage (see Section VI, Chapter 4). The angular conditions are satisfied: the objects appeared "slightly below the level of the aircraft," and reflections of the sky above the horizon would seem dark when seen projected against the hazy sky directly over the city. A layer of heated air, trapped temporarily below a cooler layer by a stable vertical wind shear, could produce a wavy interface that would reflect the sky in a few spots. This phenomenon is quite similar to the familiar road mirage. Like a road mirage it suddenly disappears when one gets too close and the viewing angle becomes either too large or too small.

If the warm air below, the source of which would presumably have been the downtown area of Detroit, were also considerably moister than the cooler air above as is quite probable, then the radio refractive index would decrease quite suddenly across the interface. This would tend to produce anomalous propagation effects, including false echoes, on radar, and would explain why ground radar could continue tracking the unknowns when the pilot and airborne radar operator could no longer see them. The airborne radar, being immersed in the layer would probably not receive AP echoes of any duration other than, perhaps, occasional random blips.

After the aircraft had thoroughly mixed the opposing air currents by flying repeatedly through the interface as it searched for the targets, the ground radar returns would gradually fade away. This corresponds to what was actually observed.

In summary, without the data to make a more definitive evaluation of this case, the most likely cause seems to be a combined radio-optical mirage as described above. If so, this is another example of a natural phenomenon so rare that it is seldom observed: for a 0.25° critical mirage angle, the temperature contrast required is on the order of 10° or 15°C in the space of about 1 cm.

Washington, D.C. (see Appendix L) 19-20 and 26-27 July 1952.

Weather: mostly clear, a few scattered clouds, visibility 10 to 15 mi., temperature 76° to 87° F, dewpoint 61° to 72° F, surface winds from SE, light, near surface, from 300° to 320° aloft, light. Radio refractive index profiles are shown in Figs. 13, 14, and 15, in Md., at an elevation of 88 m. (289 ft.) above sea level. There are a tremendous number of reports of UFOs observed on these two nights. In most instances visual observers, especially in scrambled aircraft, were unable to see targets indicated on ground radar, or to make airborne radar contact. Ground radar observers were often able to find a return in the general area of reported visual contacts, especially in the case of ground visual reports where only an azimuth was given. A few excerpts from typical reports during these incidents are given below:

Control tower operator, Andrews AFB, 0100 to 0500 EST, 20 July 1952:

> An airman became excited during the conversation and suddenly yelled "there goes one." I saw a falling star go from overhead a short distance south and burn out. About two minutes later (the airman) said, "There's another one; did you see the orange glow to the south?" I said I thought I saw it, but he pointed south and I had been looking southwest. I went up on

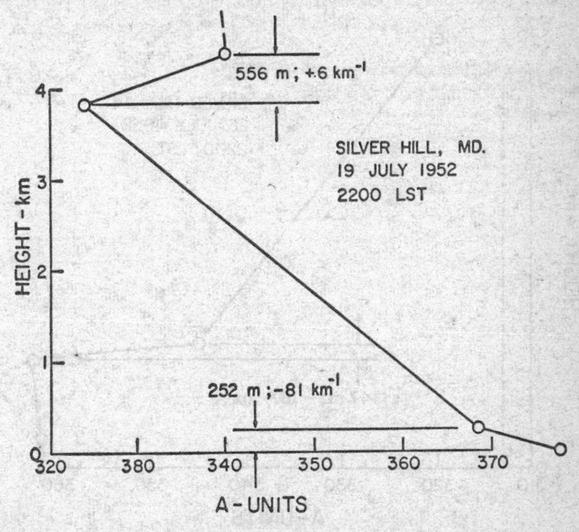

Figure 13

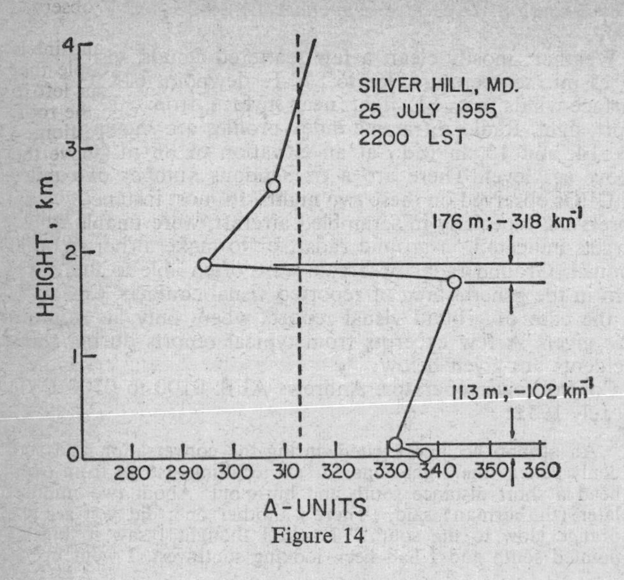

Figure 14

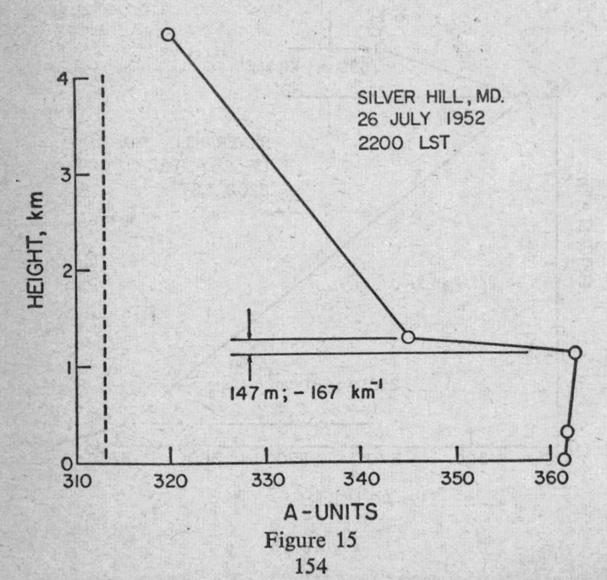

Figure 15

the roof—and watched the sky in all directions. In the meantime Washington Center was reporting targets on their radar screen over Andrews. Andrews Approach Control observed nothing.

[The airman] was in the tower talking on the phone and interphones. He was watching a star and telling various people that it was moving up and descending rapidly and going from left to right, and [another airman] and I, listening to him from the roof, believed we saw it move too. Such is the power of suggestion.

This star was to the east slightly to the left of and above the rotating beacon. [The airman] reported the star as two miles east of Andrews and at an altitude of 2,000 ft.

A short time later, approximately 0200 hours, I saw a falling star go from overhead to the north. A few minutes later another went in the same direction. They faded and went out within two seconds. The sky was full of stars, the Milky Way was bright, and I was surprised that we did not see more falling stars.

All night Washington Center was reporting objects near or over Andrews, but Andrews Approach Control could see nothing, however they could see the various aircraft reported so their [radar] screen was apparently in good operation.

At 0500 hours Washington Center called me and reported an unknown object five miles southeast of Andrews field. I looked and saw nothing. That was the last report I heard.

A USAF Captain at Andrews AFB radar center:

At about 0200 EST Washington Center advised that their radar had a target five miles east of Andrews Field. Andrews tower reported seeing a light, which changed color, and said it was moving towards Andrews. I went outside as no target appeared on Andrews radar and saw a light as reported by the tower. It was between 10° and 15° above the horizon and seemed to change color, from red to orange to green to red again. It seemed to float, but at times to dip suddenly and appear to lose altitude. It did not have the appearance of any star I have ever observed before. At the time of observation there was a star due east of my position. Its brilliance was approximately the same as the object and it appeared at about the same angle, 10° to 15° above the horizon. The star did not change color or have any apparent movement. I estimated the object to be between three and four miles east of Andrews Field at approximately 2,000 ft. During the next hour very few reports were received from Washington Center. [According to Washington Center's account, however, the 0200 EST object was seen on radar to pass over Andrews and fade out to the southwest of Andrews—G. D. T.] At approximately 0300 EST I again went outside to look at the object. At this time both the star and the object had increased elevation by about 10°. [The azimuth would have also increased about 10°, so that the observed change was apparently equal to the sidereal rate, 15° of right ascension per hour—G. D. T.] The object had ceased to have any apparent movement, but still appeared to be changing color. On the basis of the second observation, I believe the unidentified object was a star.

The account of the airman referred to by the Andrews AFB control tower operator:

Airman [X] called the tower and reported he had seen objects in the air around Andrews; while we were discussing them he advised me to look to the south immediately. When I looked there was an object which appeared to be like an orange ball of fire, trailing a tail; it appeared to be about two miles south and one half mile east of the Andrews Range [station]. It was very bright and definite, and unlike anything I had ever seen before. The position of something like that is hard to determine accurately. It made kind of a circular movement, and then took off at an unbelievable speed; it disappeared in a split second. This took place around 0005 EST. Seconds later, I saw another one, same description as the one before; it made an arc-like pattern and then disappeared. I only saw each object for about a second. The second one was over the Andrews Range; the direction appeared to be southerly.

The account of a staff sergeant at Andrews AFB follows. He was apparently describing the same object that the radar center Captain had observed.

Later on we spotted what seemed to be a star northeast of the field, which was in the general direction of Baltimore. It was about tree top level from where I was watching. It was very bright but not the same color (as some apparent meteors). This was a bluish silver. It was very erratic in motion; it moved up from side to side. Its motion was very fast. Three times I saw a red object leave the silver object at a high rate of speed and move east out of sight. At this time I had to service a C-47 and lost sight of it for the night. The time was about 0330.

The visual sightings in these incidents seem to be either meteors, apparently quite numerous at the time, or stars, but a few descriptions are not adequate to make an identification and hence may represent unknowns.

The radar tracks reported, at various times, from Washington National Airport, Andrews AFB, and Bolling AFB are generally not correlated with each other, with airborne radar/visual observations, or with ground visual reports, except in a very general way, e.g., a star sighted on the azimuth supplied by the radar track.

An investigation of the radar tracks reported by Borden and Vickers (1953) is very informative. The authors observed, on the night of 13-14 August 1952, radar tracks very similar to those described in the 19-20 and 25-27 July incidents. The targets appeared to move with the upper winds at various levels at twice the observed wind speed, suggesting that they were ground returns seen by partial reflections from moving atmospheric layers of relatively small horizontal extent (i.e., patches of local intensification of a general super-refractive stratum). Borden and Vickers state:

The almost simultaneous appearance of the first moving targets with the [stationary] ground returns, [the latter] signifying the beginning of the temperature inversion, suggested that the target display was perhaps caused by some effects existing in or near the inversion layers.

The authors also relate similar target patterns observed during testing of a new radar at Indianapolis in November, 1952. They state:

> Targets were larger, stronger, and more numerous than those observed by the writers during the Washington observations. At times the clutter made it difficult to keep track of actual aircraft targets on the scope.

In all major respects this report (Borden, 1953) is an excellent analysis of the probable radar situation during the July 1952, Washington sightings.

The atmospheric conditions in existence at the times of these UFO incidents, as shown in Figs. 13, 14, and 15, are rather peculiar. Refractivity profile for 19 July 2200 LST shows a surface inversion of 1.7°C (3.1°F) but the resulting refractivity gradient is only -81 km^{-1}, about twice the "standard" value. There is a rather unusual subrefractive layer at 3833 to 4389 m. produced by overlying moist air. Relative humidity drops from 84% at surface to 20% at base of this layer, then climbs to 70% at top of the layer. A number of significant levels are missing from this profile, which is common in 1952 Silver Hill profiles, but even so it is indicative of unusual atmospheric conditions. The radar sightings were made between 2340 LST and 0540 LST (July 20), and the atmospheric stratification was no doubt more strongly developed by that time. In addition, Silver Hill is at an elevation of 88 m. (289 ft.) above MSL, whereas Washington National Airport is at an elevation of only 13 m. (43 ft.). The intervening 75 m. is precisely that part of the atmosphere in which some of the most spectacular super-refractive and ducting layers would be expected to develop. Indeed, records for 1945-1950, during which radiosonde upper-air soundings were launched from Washington National Airport, reveal a much stronger tendency for the formation of anomalous propagation conditions than the Silver Hill data.

The profiles for 25 July and 26 July, 2200 LST are more complete than the 19 July profile, although some significant levels were noted as missing from the 26 July profile. Otherwise, the foregoing comments apply to these profiles as well. The 25 July profile shows a super-refractive surface layer and a strong elevated duct; there is a 4.6°C (8.3°F) temperature inversion through the elevated duct. It is perhaps significant that unidentified radar targets began appearing at 2030 LST on 25 July. The 26 July profile has a 1.2°C (2.2°F) surface inversion without a humidity lapse sufficient to cause super-refraction; however, a 0.9°C inversion between 1115 and 1275 m. is associated with a sharp humidity drop and a resulting elevated duct with a gradient of -167 km^{-1}. This elevated layer is quite strong enough to produce AP effects on radar. Unidentified radar targets began appearing at 2050 LST on 26 July and continued until after midnight.

In summary, the following statements appear to be correct:

(1) The atmospheric conditions during the period 19-20 and 25-27 July, 1952, in the Washington, D. C., area, were conducive to anomalous propagation of radar signals;

(2) The unidentified radar returns obtained during these incidents were most likely the result of anomalous propagation (AP);

(3) The visual objects were, with one or two possible exceptions, identifiable as most probably meteors and scintillating stars.

Wichita, Kans. area, 2 August 1965, "early morning hours" up to "shortly after 0600" LST. Weather: clear, temperature 61°F to 70°F, wind at surface: light from WSW. This is classed as primarily radar since the bulk of the reports were from radar and the first visual object was never described. The refractivity profiles for Topeka, Kans. and Oklahoma City, Okla. are shown in Figs. 16 and 17.

During the early morning hours of 2 August 1965, the Wichita Weather Bureau Airport Station was contacted by the dispatcher of the Sedgwick County Sheriffs Department with regard to an object sighted in the sky near Wellington, Kans. (25 mi. south of Wichita). The radar operator, Mr. John S. Shockley observed what appeared to be an aircraft target near Udall, Kans., 15 mi. northeast of Wellington. This target moved northward at 40 to 50 mph.

During the next hour and a half several of these targets were observed on the radar scope over central Kansas moving slowly northward occasionally remaining stationary, or moving about erratically. Mr. Shockley checked with the Wichita Radar Approach Control, however they were not able to observe a target simultaneously, with the exception of one aircraft south of McConnell Air Force Base near Wichita.

Later, a target was observed about seven miles NNW of Wellington, Kans., moving slowly southward. The Wellington Police Department was contacted and two officers went three miles west of the city, to see if they could observe anything. The target passed about one mile west of the city as observed on radar. The officers did not observe it until it was southwest of the city. They described it as a greenish-blue light that moved slowly away from them.

The dispatcher called again, with a report that two officers at Caldwell, Kans. (35 mi. south of Wichita) had sighted an object near the ground east of the city. A target was observed about two miles northwest of the city that moved northward and disappeared.

At daybreak, the dispatcher reported that the Wellington

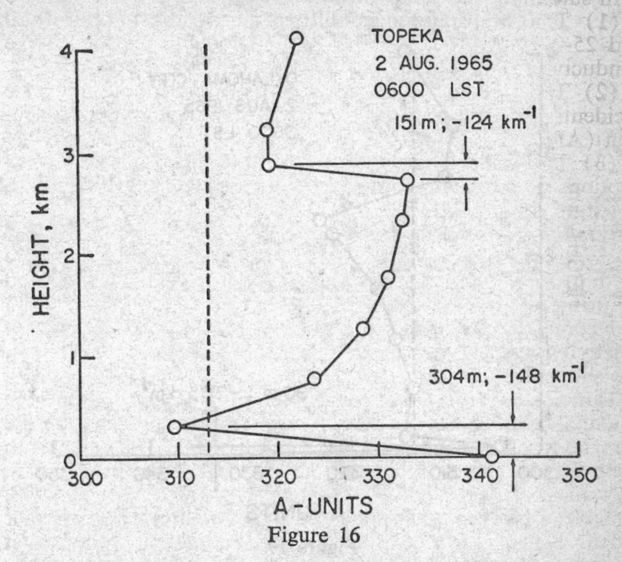

Figure 16

officers had an object in sight east of the city. Radar indicated a target in that area moving southward about 45 mph. Four or five people stopped their cars and watched the object with the officers. It was described as an egg-shaped object about the size of three automobiles, made of a highly polished silver metal.

Shortly after 0600C, a target was observed five miles north of Wellington moving southward. The target moved directly over the city to a point ten miles south of the city where it disappeared. The officers in Wellington were contacted but were able to observe absolutely nothing in the sky overhead during that time.

The radar was operated in long pulse, at 50 mi. range, with STC off. The targets were coherent and appeared from six to nine thousand feet on the RHI scope during the early morning and about four or five thousand feet later in the morning.

The descriptions of most of the visual objects in this sighting are too cursory to allow for any reasonable conjecture as to the real nature of the objects. One of the objects, described as "a greenish-blue light that moved slowly away," may have been a star.

In most instances the radar targets did not seem directly

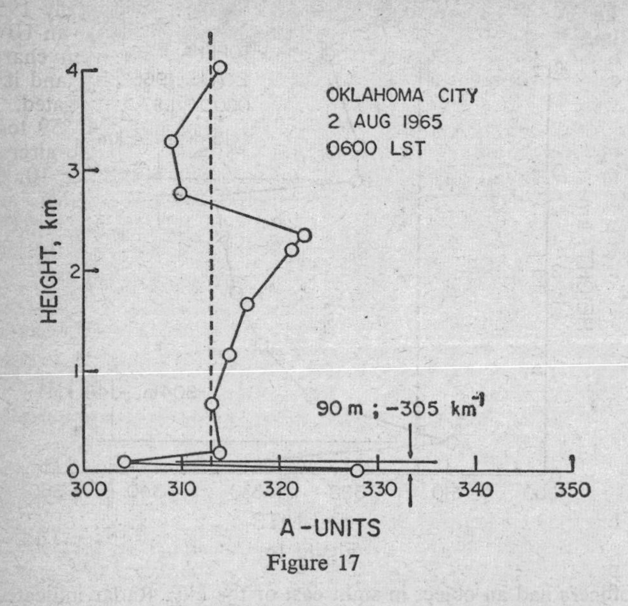

Figure 17

related to the visual UFOs. This is characteristic of radar anomalous propagation returns.

The refractivity profiles both show highly refractive surface layers, with a 6.7°C (12.1°F) surface inversion at Topeka and a 9.7°C (17.5°F) surface inversion at Oklahoma City. In addition, the Topeka profile shows a strong elevated layer at 2720 m. with a 0.6°C inversion. The temperature inversion at Oklahoma City produced a surface layer having an optical refractivity gradient (at 5570Å) of -101 km^{-1}; this layer would extend the theoretical optical horizon for the eye of an observer 2 m. above the surface of a smooth earth from the normal value of 5.6 km. (9 mi.) to 8.5 km. (about 14 mi.). Such inversions can produce many strange effects, including the visibility of objects normally well below the horizon.

In summary, since the atmospheric conditions were conducive to anomalous radar propagation, and the radar targets displayed AP-like characteristics, this incident may probably be classified as consisting of radar false targets, with associated optical sightings that may have been enhanced by a strong temperature inversion at the surface.

Class II-B. Primarily radar, returns mostly single, sharp, aircraft-like blips, behaving in a continuous manner (i.e., no sudden jumps, etc.).

19-B. Walesville-Westmorland, N. Y., 1-2 July 1954, 1105-1127 LST. Weather: apparently clear. On 1 July 1954 reports came into the AF Depot at Rome, N. Y. of an UFO having the appearance of a balloon. The officer in charge said he believed it to be a partially deflated balloon, and if it were still there the next day, he would have it investigated.

On 1105 LST 2 July 1954, F-94C aircraft 51-13559 took off on a routine training mission. GCI requested the aircraft to change mission to intercept an unknown aircraft at 10,000 ft. The pilot identified a C-47 aircraft by tail number, and was then requested to check a second unidentified aircraft that was at low altitude and apparently letting down to land at Griffith AFB. The AF account states:

> As the pilot started a descent, he noted that the cockpit temperature increased abruptly. The increase in temperature caused the pilot to scan the instruments. The fire warning light was on and the pilot informed the radar observer of this fact. The fire warning light remained on after the throttle was placed in "idle" so the engine was shut down and both crew members ejected successfully.

The aircraft crashed at the "Walesville Intersection," and was destroyed. The aircraft struck a house and an automobile, fatally injuring four persons.

The above account is from the official USAF accident report ("Summary of Circumstances"). There is no Blue Book file because no UFO was involved.

Conclusion:

(1) The first object was probably a balloon;

(2) There was no UFO in the aircraft accident case.

93-B. Wright-Patterson AFB, Ohio, August 1952, 1050-1113 LST. Weather: scattered clouds at 25,000 ft. This case, occurring almost over Project Blue Book's home base, is a very good example of confusion or contradictory evidence tending to obscure the true nature of a UFO incident.

At 1051 LST an unidentified radar track appeared 20 mi. NNW of Wright-Patterson AFB on the 664th AC&W Squadron's GCI radar at Bellefontaine. The radar operator stated that the course was 240° at 400 knots. Elsewhere the report states 450 knots; how he determined this is not made clear. Two F-86 aircraft from the 97th Fighter-Interceptor Squadron, Wright-Patterson AFB, were vectored in and made visual contact at 1055 LST. Fighters stayed with the object until 1113 LST. The F-86s climbed to 48,000 ft., fell off, and made a second climb. One aircraft had airborne radar activated and received a "weak" return. The object was described as "silver in color, round in shape," and its altitude was estimated as 60,000-70,000 ft. The object appeared on the radar gunsight film as a "fuzzy, small image . . . with discernible motion . . . that could be any darn thing."

In this incident it is apparent that (1) the UFO was a real object and (2) the visual and radar sightings (both ground and airborne) were of the same object. All of the evidence points to a weather balloon except for the 400-450 knot speed, and the 240° flight path, which is against the prevailing upper winds. Known aircraft were ruled out because of the altitude. A U-2 would "fit," but the first one was not flown until 1955, and the visual appearance was all wrong. The radar returns eliminated astronomical objects, mirage was ruled out because of the high angles, and the sighting occurred "above the weather." The conclusion was: unknown.

However, buried deep in the report was the radar operator's note that "At the time it was dropped (1113 LST) object was five miles northwest of Springfield, Ohio." This allows the UFO's course to be plotted on a map; Figs. 18 and 19, shows such a map plot. It is readily apparent from this that the UFO's true heading was about 111° at an average speed of only 44 knots. Apparently no one thought to make this simple check. Since the highest reported winds from the radiosonde launched at Dayton at 1000 LST were 260°/31 knots at 50,000 ft. and 270°/33 knots at 55,000 ft. the plotted track of the UFO is consistent with the observed upper winds. The blip was first "painted" at a 240° azimuth, which may explain where that quantity originated in the UFO movement report.

Conclusion: almost certainly a weather balloon. Note that the winds reported for the Wright-Patterson AFB 1000 LST show winds blowing first from the east, then from the SSE, ultimately from the west at higher altitudes. These winds were blowing in such a manner that it is conceivable that

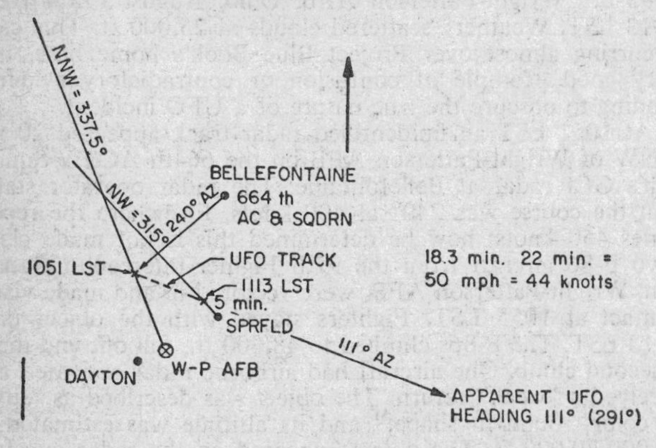

Figure 18

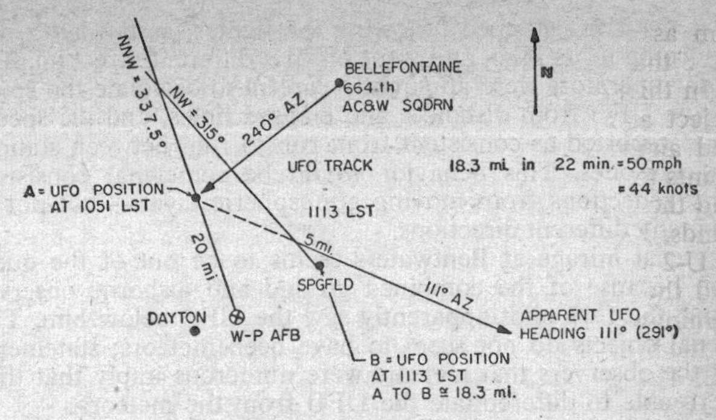

Figure 19

Wright-Patterson's own radiosonde balloon may have been the UFO in this incident.

76-B. Near Charleston, W. Va., 4 May 1966, 0340 LST. Weather: Severe thunderstorms in area. Pilot of a Braniff Airlines Boeing 707 flying at 33,000 ft. observed on his left side what appeared to be a fast-flying aircraft with landing lights. Braniff's airborne radar recorded this unknown. Pilot requested the radar operator at Charleston sector of Indianapolis ARTC to look for traffic at his 8:30 or 9:00 position, and the radar picked up a track in this position. Return made a sweeping turn and disappeared off scope to the southwest.

An American Airlines pilot flying 20 mi. behind the Braniff plane saw the object. It appeared to him to be a normal aircraft with landing lights. This pilot stated he had often seen such aircraft with lights during AF refueling missions.

Estimated speed of the unknown was 750-800 mph. No unusual maneuvers were performed or any that were beyond known military aircraft capabilities at the time. AF explanation is that the unknown was an aircraft with landing lights on. This is consistent with the reported facts.

Case 2. Lakenheath, England, 13-14 August 1956, 2230-0330 LST. Weather: generally clear until 0300 LST on the 14th. (For details see Section IV.)

The probability that anomalous propagation of radar signals may have been involved in this case seems to be small. One or two details are suggestive of AP, particularly the reported disappearance of the first track as the UFO appeared to overfly the Bentwaters GCA radar. Against this must be weighed the Lakenheath controller's statement that there was "little or no traffic or targets on scope," which is not at all suggestive of AP conditions, and the behavior of the target near Lakenheath—apparently continuous and easily tracked. The "tailing" of the RAF fighter, taken alone, seems to indicate a possible ghost image, but this does not jibe with the report that the UFO stopped following the fighter, as the latter was returning to its base, and went off in a different direction. The radar operators were apparently careful to calculate the speed of the UFO from distances and elapsed times, and the speeds were reported as consistent from run to run, between stationary episodes. This behavior would be somewhat consistent with reflections from moving atmospheric layers—but not in so many different directions.

Visual mirage at Bentwaters seems to be out of the question because of the combined ground and airborne observations; the C47 pilot apparently saw the UFO below him. The visual objects do not seem to have been meteors; statements by the observers that meteors were numerous imply that they were able to differentiate the UFO from the meteors.

In summary, this is the most puzzling and unusual case in the radar-visual files. The apparently rational, intelligent behavior of the UFO suggests a mechanical device of unknown origin as the most probable explanation of this sighting. However, in view of the inevitable fallibility of witnesses, more conventional explanations of this report cannot be entirely ruled out.

Kincheloe AFB, Sault Saint Marie, Mich., 11-12 September 1967, 2200-2330 LST. Weather: clear, ceiling unlimited, visibility unlimited (over 20 mi.), no thunderstorms in area, wind at surface 140°/4 knots, aloft 240°-270°/15-35 knots. The radio refractivity profile from Sault Saint Marie for the most applicable time is shown in Fig. 21.

This is a good example of moving radar targets that cannot be seen visually, where there is a "forbidden cone" over the radar site. Some of the returns were even seen to approach within 5-15 mi. of the radar and disappear, apparently subsequently reappearing on the other side of the radar scope at about the same range that they disappeared. This sort of behavior is symptomatic of AP-echoes.

The meteorological data tend to confirm this interpretation. The refractivity profile shown in Fig. 21 displays three peculiarities: a strong subrefractive layer at the surface, a strong elevated duct at 325-520 m. (about 1100-1700 ft.) and a super-refractive layer at 1070-1360 m. (about 3,500-4,500 ft.). A ray-tracing is shown for this profile in Fig. 20. The ray shows noticeable changes in curvature as it passes through the different layers, an indication that strong partial reflections would be expected. With this profile, moving AP-echoes, produced in the manner described by Borden and Vickers (1953), could be expected to appear at apparent heights of between 2,000-3,000 ft. and 7,000-9,000 ft. No height information was supplied with this report, so the calculation above cannot be verified.

In summary, it appears that this is a case of observations

of moving AP-echoes produced by unusually well stratified atmospheric conditions.

156-B. Gulf of Mexico, Coast Guard Cutter "Sebago," 25°47'N 89°24'W, 5 November 1957, 0510-1537 LST. Weather: not given, but apparently some clouds in area. The most applicable radio refractivity data available are for Key West, Fla., 0600 and 1800 LST, 5 November 1957. They are shown in Figs. 22 and 23. One visual and three radar objects were included in this case. The ship's heading was 23° true. The first contact was a radar blip picked up at 0510 LST at 290° true azimuth, 14 mi. It moved south, approached the ship within 2 mi., and returned north along ship's port side. Contact was lost at 0514 LST. Average speed of this UFO was calculated as 250 mph. At 0516 LST a new blip was picked up at 188°, 22 mi.; this target departed at a computed 650 mph., disappearing at 0516 LST at 190°, 55 mi. The third radar target was acquired at 0520 LST at 350°, 7 mi.; it appeared to be stationary. While the third radar target was being watched on the scope, a visual object was observed for about 5 sec. at 0521 LST travelling from south to north at about 31° elevation between 270° and 310° azimuth. The third radar target remained stationary for about 1 min. and then slowly moved to the northeast, finally accelerating rapidly and moving off scope at 15°, 175 mi.

The visual object was described as "like a brilliant planet"; it was undoubtedly a meteor, and in any event obviously was unrelated to radar target number three, the only radar target visible at the same time.

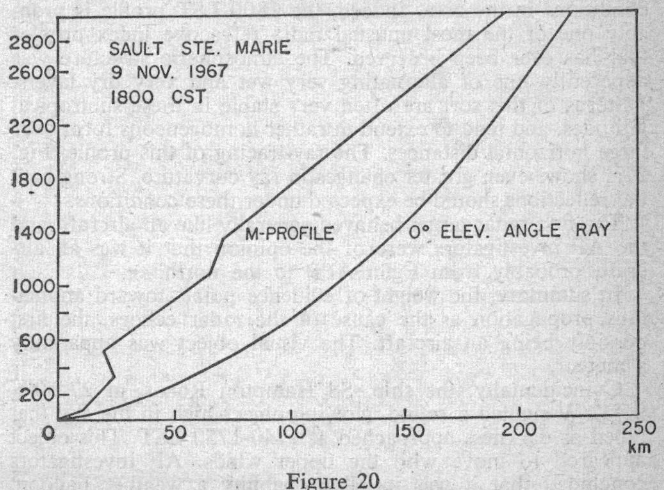

Figure 20

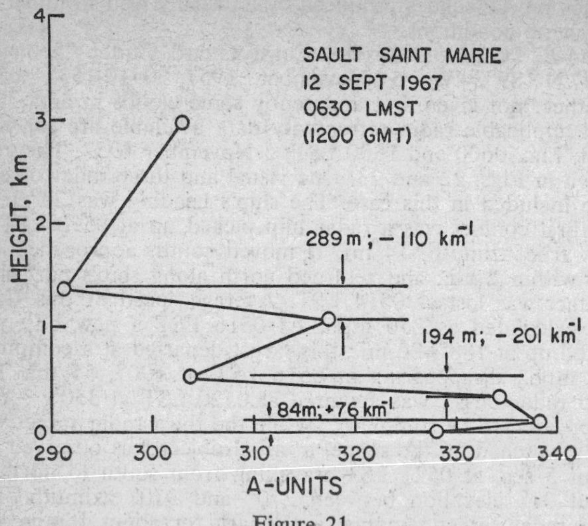

Figure 21

The radar targets were, with the possible exception of the first one, erratic and unpredictable in their movements. The second and third radar blips appeared suddenly, well within the normal pick-up range of the ship's radar. These two blips were probably caused by anomalous propagation. The two Key West profiles, although taken at some distance from the ship's position, are indicative of rather unusual atmospheric conditions in the area. Indeed, the 1800 LST profile is probably one of the most unusual radio refractive index profiles that has ever been observed. The atmospheric structure was apparently one of alternating very wet and very dry layers. Patterns of this sort are often very stable in these subtropical latitudes, and tend to extend in rather homogeneous form over large horizontal distances. The ray-tracing of this profile, Fig. 23a, shows even greater changes in ray curvature. Strong partial reflections should be expected under these conditions.

The first radar target behaved generally like an aircraft, and the AF investigators were of the opinion that it was an aircraft, probably from Eglin AFB to the north.

In summary, the weight of evidence points toward anomalous propagation as the cause of the radar echoes, the first possibly being an aircraft. The visual object was apparently a meteor.

Coincidentally, the ship, SS Hampton Roads, at 27°50′N 91°12′W sighted a round, glowing object high in the sky that faded as darkness approached at 1740-1750 LST. This object appeared to move with the upper winds. AF investigators concluded that it was in all probability a weather balloon.

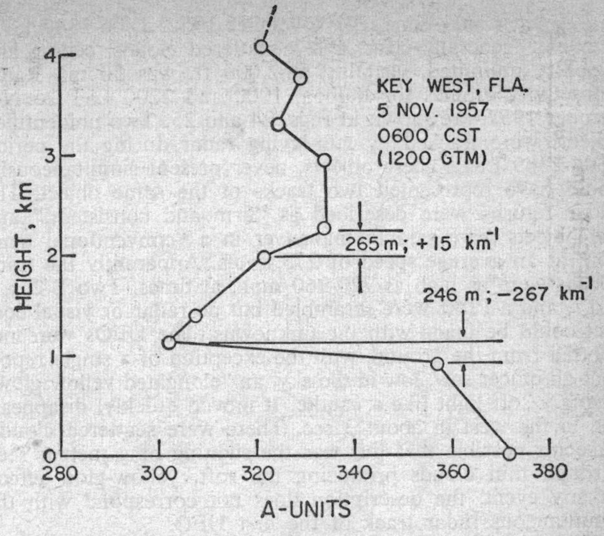

Figure 22

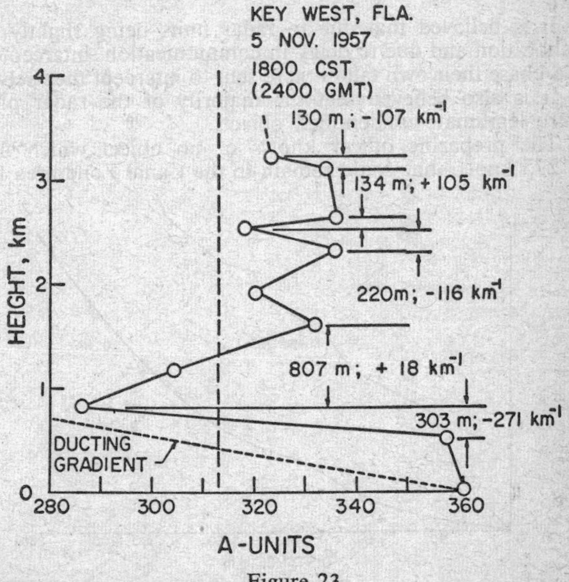

Figure 23

101-B. Canal Zone, 25 November 1952, 1806-2349 LST. Weather: generally clear, a few scattered clouds, ceiling and visibility unlimited, visibility at 2,000 ft. was 50 mi. Radio refractivity profiles for Balboa, 1000 and 2200 LST 25 November 1952, are shown in Figs. 24 and 25. Two unidentified objects were tracked by gun-laying radar during the period 1806-2349 LST. These objects, never present simultaneously, could have represented two tracks of the same object. The radar returns were described as "firm and consistent," and the objects were said to maneuver in a "conventional manner" at an average speed of 275 knots. Apparently the track speeds were as high as 720-960 mph. at times. Two B-26s, a B-17, and a PBM were scrambled but no radar or visual contact could be made with the unknowns. The UFOs were not spotted from the ground, with the exception of a single report that an officer saw, low in the sky, an "elongated yellow glow" giving a soft light like a candle. It moved quickly, disappearing in the west in about 3 sec. There were scattered clouds. It seems possible that this was the sighting of a meteor seen through thin clouds producing the soft, yellow-glow effect. In any event, the description does not correspond with the simultaneous radar track of the first UFO.

With visibility of 50 mi. it seems strange that the scrambled aircraft could not sight either of the UFOs. The Air Force report comments:

> It is believed that due to radar units being slightly off calibration and due to delay in communication, interceptors did chase their own tail or were sent to intercept themselves.
>
> It is also believed that the majority of the radar plots were legitimate unidentified objects.
>
> The preparing officer knows of no object which flies at 275 knots, that could remain in the Canal Zone area for

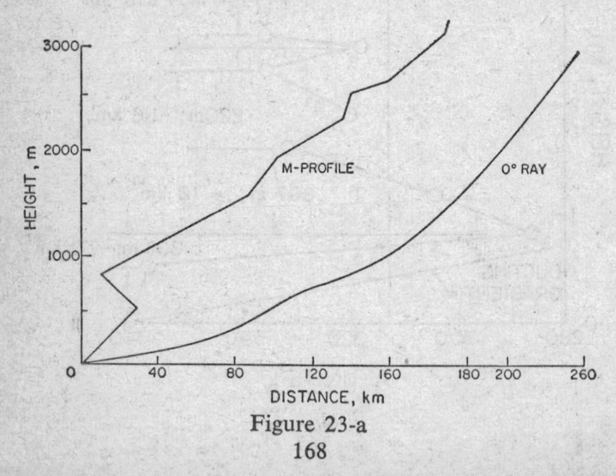

Figure 23-a

nearly six hours, maneuver from 1000 through 28,000 feet altitude, make no sound, and evade interception.

In fact, it is difficult to imagine any material object that could accomplish all these feats. The strange radar tracks were probably the product of anomalous propagation conditions, an hypothesis that would account for the facts above. The atmospheric conditions were certainly favorable for AP, as can be seen from the A-profiles in Figs. 24 and 25. How-

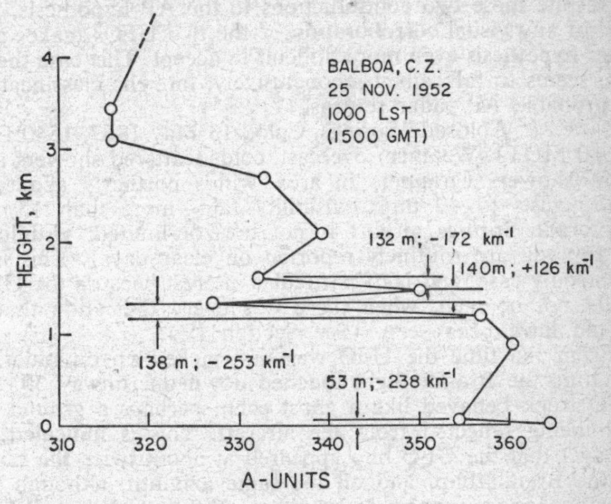

Figure 24

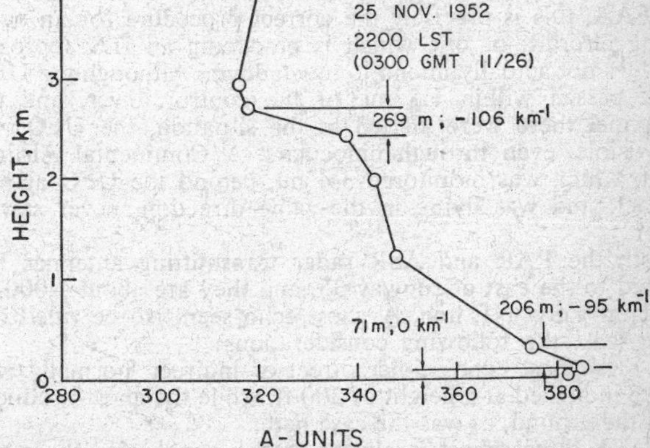

Figure 25

ever, there are two considerations that argue against this hypothesis.

(1) The targets tracked behaved in a more rational, continuous manner, and covered a greater altitude range, than AP echoes of the type usually observed;

(2) If they were AP echoes, should these targets have appeared at not only 1806-2349 LST but around 1000 LST when the profile was obviously more favorable for AP than the 2200 LST profile?

Despite these two contradictions to the AP hypothesis, the lack of any visual corroboration of the two UFOs makes any other hypothesis even more difficult to accept. This case therefore seems to fall, albeit inconclusively, into the classification of probable AP radar returns.

Case 21. Colorado Springs, Colo., 13 May 1967, 1540 LST (1640 MDT). Weather: overcast, cold, scattered showers and snow showers (graupel) in area, winds northerly about 30 mph., gusts to 40 mph., visibility fair—more than 15 mi. (Colorado Springs airport is not horizon-limited; visibilities of 100 mi. are routinely reported on clear days). This is a radar-only case, and is of particular interest because the UFO could not be seen, when there was every indication that it should have been seen. (See Section IV).

From the time the UFO was first picked up on radar to the time the Braniff flight touched down on runway 35, the UFO track behaved like a ghost echo, perhaps a ground return being reflected from the aircraft. This is indicated by the fact that the UFO blip appeared at about twice the range of the Braniff blip, and on the same azimuth, although the elevation angle appears to have been different. When Braniff touched down, however, the situation changed radically. The UFO blip pulled to the right (east) and passed over the airport at an indicated height of about 200 ft. As pointed out by the FAA, this is precisely the correct procedure for an overtaking aircraft, or one which is practicing an ILS approach but does not actually intend to touch down. Although the UFO track passed within 1.5 mi. of the control tower, and the personnel there were alerted to the situation, the UFO was not visible, even through binoculars. A Continental Airlines flight, which was monitored 3-4 mi. behind the UFO at first contact, and was flying in the same direction, never saw it either.

Both the PAR and ASR radar transmitting antennas are located to the east of runway 35, and they are about 1,000 ft. apart on a SW-NE line. A ghost echo seems to be ruled out by at least the following considerations:

(1) A ghost echo, either direct or indirect, normally will not be indicated at a height of 200 ft. while the ghost-producer is on the ground, as was the case here;

(2) A direct ghost is always at the same azimuth as the

moving target, and an indirect ghost is on the same azimuth as the fixed reflector involved. (See Section VI Chapter 5). If an indirect ghost were involved here, the ghost echo would thus have always appeared well to the east of Braniff, not at the same azimuth.

The radar flight characteristics of the UFO in this care were all compatible with the hypothesis that the unknown was a century-series jet (F100, F104, etc.), yet nothing was ever seen or heard.

This must remain as one of the most puzzling radar cases on record, and no conclusion is possible at this time. It seems inconceivable that an anomalous propagation echo would behave in the manner described, particularly with respect to the reported altitude changes, even if AP had been likely at the time. In view of the meteorological situation, it would seem that AP was rather unlikely. Besides, what is the probability that an AP return would appear only once, and at that time appear to execute a perfect practice ILS approach?

Case 53. Vandenberg AFB, Lompoc, Calif., 6-7 October 1967, 1900-0130 LST. Weather: clear, good visibility, strong temperature inversions near the surface caused by advection of very warm (80°-90°F), dry air over the cool ocean surface (water temperature 58°-59°F). This sighting begins with an apparent mirage (of a ship probably 60 mi. beyond the normal horizon) and continues with a very large number of unknown targets that were found on tracking radars which were being used in a search mode (they normally are not used in this way). The project case file contains a good analysis of the probable nature of the radar targets, some of which were apparently birds and some apparently ships tracked at 80 mi. ranges as well as other AP-like returns that may have been associated with local intensification of the ducting layer. The nature of the visual objects is not as clear, although at least two of them appear to have been superior images of ships beyond the normal horizon. There were possibly some meteor sightings involved.

The meteorological conditions were quite interesting. The warm, dry air was apparently quite close to the water surface, at least in places. Data from Vandenberg and San Nicholas island indicate that in places the inversion was no thicker than about 90 m. (10 mb pressure difference). The contrast that may have existed can be calculated from these data:

		At or Near Sea Surface:	At 90 Meters or Less:
Pressure:		1004 mb	994 mb
Temperature:	°F:	58°F	90°F
	°C:	14°C	32°C
	°K:	287°K	305°K
Optical N (5570Å)		275 (ppm)	256 (ppm)

The optical refractive index gradient that may have existed at the time was therefore on the order of -210 pp. km^{-1}, or a somewhat greater negative value, depending upon the thickness chosen for the layer. The value above is computed as (256-275) /0.090, based on the 90 m. maximum thickness assumed. Since the critical value of the gradient for a superior mirage is -157 ppm. km^{-1}, it is quite apparent that the conditions required for the formation of extended superior mirages were most likely present on the date in question. The only problem with this explanation is the reported elevation angle of 10°, but as pointed out in the conclusions to this chapter such estimates by visual observers are invariably over-estimated by a large factor.

In summary, the conclusions arrived at by the investigators in this case seem to be adequately supported by the meteorological data available.

The sighting reported for 12 October 1967, 0025 LST, seems to be a classic example of the description of a scintillating, wandering star image seen through a strong inversion layer. Note particularly the estimated ratio of vertical and horizontal movements. Two very bright stars would have been close to the horizon at this time: Altair, magnitude 0.9, would have been at 277° azimuth and about 4° elevation angle; Vega, magnitude 0.1, would have been at about 313° azimuth and about 12° elevation angle. Of the two, Altair seems the more likely target because of the smaller elevation angle; the observers gave no estimate of either azimuth or elevation angle.

3. *Summary of Results.*

A summary of the results of this investigation is given in Table 1.

The reader should note that the assignment of cases into the probable AP cause category could have been made on the basis of the observational testimony alone. That is to say, there was no case where the meteorological data available tended to negate the anomalous propagation hypothesis, thereby causing that case to be assigned to some other category. Therefore, a review of the meteorological data available for the 19 probable-AP cases is in order.

(1) Every one of the 19 cases is associated with clear or nearly clear weather. In 15 cases weather is described as "clear and visibility unlimited" (CAVU), in many of these "exceptional visibility" is noted; in four cases the weather is "generally clear," with some scattered clouds, or a "high, thin broken" condition (usually meaning cirriform clouds). Such weather is indicative of stable atmospheric conditions that are favorable for the formation of layered, stratified refractive index profiles, i.e., they are conducive to anomalous propagation effects. The *a priori* probability of such a result, from a truly random sample of dates-times-places is roughly on the

Table 1

Frequency of Occurrence of Most Probable UFO Causes

Class	Most Likely or Most Plausible Explanation				Class
	Anomalous Propagation	Man-Made Device	Unknown	No UFO	Total
I-A	6	1	2	0	9
I-B	2	1	0	0	3
I-C	1	0	1	0	2
I-D	0	4	2	0	6
All Class I	9	6	5	0	19
II-A	6	0	0	0	6
II-B	4	2	2	1	9
All Class II	10	2	2	1	15
All Classes	19	8	7	1	35

order of one chance in 200,000 (assuming that the probability of clear weather is roughly 0.5 in any single case).

(2) Of the 19 cases, all but two occur during the night. Although AP often occurs during the daytime, the nighttime hours are generally more favorable, and tend to greatly increase the *a priori* probability of encountering AP.

(3) In the 11 cases for which pertinent meteorological data are available, in every case the refractive index profile is favorable, to a greater or lesser degree, for the presence of anomalous propagation effects. The weakest case, the data for Silver Hill, 19 July 1952, (see p. 47), where inadequacies in the data were pointed out, has a near-super-refractive surface layer (gradient -81 ppm. km^{-1}) and an elevated subrefractive layer. Of the remaining 11 profiles, seven showing decting gradients (-157 ppm. km^{-1} or greater negative value) and four show super-refractive gradients (-100 to -157 ppm. km^{-1}). Since the *a priori* probability of the occurrence of such profiles is on the order of 0.25 (Bean, 1966b), the *a priori*

probability of this result, given a truly random sample, is on the order of one in 10^6.

In overall summary of these results, as they pertain to anomalous propagation of radio or optical waves, it seems that where the observational data pointed to anomalous propagation as the probable cause of an UFO incident, the meteorological data are overwhelmingly in favor of the plausibility of the AP hypothesis. That this result could have been only coincidental has been shown to be only remotely probable.

4. *Conclusions and Recommendations for Further Work*

The following conclusions can be stated as a result of the investigation reported in this chapter:

(1) Anomalous Propagation (AP) effects are probably responsible for a large number of UFO reports in cases involving radar and visual sightings.

(2) There are two common patterns that are evidenced in radar-visual cases involving anomalous propagation effects:

(a) Unusual AP radar targets are detected, and visual observers are instructed where to look for apparent UFOs and usually "find" them in the form of a star or other convenient object.

(b) Unusual optical effects cause visual observers to report UFOs and radar operators are directed where to look for them. As above, they usually "find" them, most often in the form of intermittent AP echoes, occasionally of the unusual moving variety.

(3) In radar-visual UFO sightings there is a pronounced tendency for observers to assume that radar and visual targets are correlated, often despite glaring discrepancies in the reported positions. There is a perhaps related tendency to accept radar information without checking it as carefully as the observer might normally do; hence errors are promulgated such as, direction of UFO movement confused with the azimuth at which is was observed on the radar scope, and UFO speed reported that is grossly at variance with plotted positions at times (both of these effects are well illustrated in Case 93-B).

(4) There is a general tendency among even experienced visual observers to grossly over-estimate small elevation angles. Minnaert (1954) states that the average "moon illusion" involves a factor of 2.5-3.5. The results of the present investigation imply that objects at elevation angles as small as 1° are estimated to be at angles larger than the true value by at least this factor or more. Interestingly, all of the elevation angles reported of visual objects in the cases examined in this chapter, not a single one is reported to be less than 10°. The fact that radar may subsequently "see" the UFOs at angles of only 1° to 4° seems not to bother the visual observers at all; in fact when the visual observers report apparent height-range, these

values often turn out to be equivalent to elevation angles of only a degree or two. There seems to be a sort of "quantum effect" at work here, where an object must be either "on the horizon" (i.e., at 0°) or at an elevation of greater than 10°.

(5) There are apparently some very unusual propagation effects, rarely encountered or reported, that occur under atmospheric conditions so rare that they may constitute unknown phenomena; if so, they deserve study. This seems to be the only conclusion one can reasonably reach from examination of some of the strangest cases (e.g., 190-N, 5 and 21).

(6) There is a small, but significant, residue of cases from the radar-visual files (i.e., 1482-N, Case 2) that have no plausible explanation as propagation phenomena and/or misinterpreted man-made objects.

A number of recommendations for future UFO investigative procedures are indicated by the results of this chapter:

(1) In any investigation of a UFO report, extremely careful efforts should be made to determine the correct azimuth and elevation angles of any visual or radar objects, by "post mortem" re-creation of sightings if necessary. This information is probably more useful in analysis of the case than the description of the objects or targets.

(2) Reported speeds and directions of UFOs, especially of radar UFOs, should be carefully checked (again, "post mortem" if necessary) and cross-checked for validity. This information is also often critical for subsequent analysis.

(3) Every effort should be made to get the most comprehensive and applicable meteorological data available for an UFO incident as quickly as possible. Many types of weather data are not retained permanently, and it is difficult or impossible to retrieve the appropriate data for a sighting months or years after the fact. Copies of original radiosonde recordings should be obtained for the closest sites, since these may be analyzed in more detail than that routinely practiced by weather bureaus for synoptic purposes. It should be emphasized that, for example, a nighttime profile is usually more germane to a nighttime sighting than is a daytime profile. For example, if an UFO incident occurs at 2100 to 2200 LST, an 0600 LST (next day) raob will generally be more pertinent to the propagation conditions involved than will an 1800 LST raob. The converse is also true.

(4) Any field team investigating UFO reports and seeking to explore all radio/optical propagation aspects of the sighting (a highly desirable goal), should be equipped with the following personnel as a minimum:

(1) An expert on the unusual aspects of electromagnetic wave propagation, at both radio and optical wave lengths;

(2) An expert in the interpretation and theory of radar targets, who is acquainted with all types of anomalous propagation and other spurious radar returns;

(3) An expert with wide experience in the physiology and psychology of human eyesight, and familiarity with optical illusory effects, etc.;

(4) A meteorologist, with specialized experience in micro-meteorology-climatology, mesoscale meteorology, and atmospheric physics.

References

Bean, B. R., B. A. Cahoon, C. A. Samson, & G. D. Thayer. *A World Atlas of Atmospheric Radio Refractivity,* ESSA Monograph No. 1, U.S.G.P.O., (1966).

Bean, B. R., & E. J. Dutton. *Radio Meteorology,* National Bureau of Standards Monograph No. 92, U.S.G.P.O., (1966).

Borden, R. C., and T. K. Vickers. "A Preliminary Study of Unidentified Targets Observed on Air Traffic Control Radars," *CAA Technical Development Report No. 180,* (1953).

Minnaert, M. *The Nature of Light and Colour in the Open Air,* New York City, N. Y.: Dover, 1954.

Chapter 6 Visual Observations Made by Astronauts / Franklin E. Roach

Astronauts in orbit view the earth, its atmosphere and the astronomical sky from altitudes ranging from 100 to 800+ nautical miles (160 to 1300 km.) above mean sea level, well above many of the restrictions of the ground-based observer. They are skilled in accurate observations, their eyesight is excellent, they have intimate familiarity with navigational astronomy and a broad understanding of the basic physical sciences. Their reports from orbit of visual sightings therefore deserve careful consideration.

Between 12 April 1961 and 15 November 1966, 30 astronauts spent a total of 2503 hours in orbit (see Tables 1 and 2). During the flights the astronauts carried out assigned tasks of several general categories, viz: defense, engineering, medical, and scientific. A list of the assigned tasks that were part of the Mercury program is provided in Table 3 to give an idea of the kinds of visual observations the astronauts were asked to make.

As part of the program, debriefings were held following each U.S. mission. At these sessions, the astronauts were questioned by scientists involved in the design of the experiments about their observations, unplanned as well as specifically assigned. The debriefings complemented on-the-spot reports made by the astronauts during the mission in radio contacts with the ground-control center. In this way, a comprehensive summary was obtained of what the astronauts had seen while in orbit.

This chapter discusses the conditions under which the astronauts observed, with particular reference to the Mercury and

Table 1

Astronauts' Time in Orbit

Name	Total Time In Orbit HOURS	MINUTES	Flight Designation*
Aldrin	94	34	GT-12
Armstrong	10	42	GT-8
Borman	330	55	GT-7
Belayeyev	27	2	Voshkod II
Bykovsky	119	6	Vostok V
Carpenter	4	56	MA-7
Cernan	72	21	GT-9
Collins	70	47	GT-10
Conrad	262	13	GT-5, GT-11
Cooper	225	16	MA-9, GT-5
Feoktisov	24	17	Voshkod I
Gagarin	1	48	Vostok I
Glenn	4	56	MA-6
Gordon	71	17	GT-11
Grissom	5	10	MR-4, GT-3
Komarov	24	17	Voshkod I
Leonov	27	2	Voshkod II
Lovell	425	29	GT-7, GT-12
McDivitt	97	50	GT-4
Nikoyalev	94	35	Vostok III
Popovich	70	57	Vostok IV
Schirra	35	4	MA-8, GT-6
Scott	10	42	GT-8
Shepherd	0	15	MR-3
Stafford	98	12	GT-6, GT-9
Tereshkova	70	50	Vostok VI
Titov	25	18	Vostok II
White	97	50	GT-4
Yegorov	24	17	Voshkod I
Young	75	41	GT-3, GT-10
Total (for 30 astronauts)	2503	39	Total Man-flights 37

* GT = Gemini series; MA and MR = Mercury series; flights designated by words beginning with "V" refer to Soviet flights.

Table 2

Log of Manned Flights

Flight	Astronauts	Launch Date	Number of Revolutions	Duration Hr.	Duration Min.	Altitudes (Statute Miles) Perigee	Altitudes (Statute Miles) Apogee
Vostok I	Gagarin	12 April 61	1	1	48	110	187
MR-3	Shepherd	5 May 61	Suborbital		15	116	-
MR-4	Grissom	21 July 61	Suborbital		16	118	-
Vostok II	Titov	6 Aug 61	17	25	18	100	159
MA-6	Glenn	20 Feb 62	3	4	56	100	162
MA-7	Carpenter	24 May 62	3	4	56	99	167
Vostok III	Nikoyalev	11 Aug 62	64	94	35	114	156
Vostok IV	Popovich	12 Aug 62	48	70	57	112	158
MA-8	Schirra	3 Oct 62	6	9	13	100	176
MA-9	Cooper	15 May 63	22	34	20	100	166
Vostok V	Bykovsky	14 June 63	81	119	6	107	146
Vostok VI	Tereshkova	16 June 63	48	70	50	113	144
Voshkod I	Komarov, Yegorov, Feoktisov	16 Oct 64	16	24	17	110	255
Voshkod II	Belayayev, Leonov	18 Mar 65	17	27	2	107	307
GT-3	Grissom, Young	23 Mar 65	3	4	54	100	139
GT-4	McDivitt, White	3 June 65	63	97	50	100	175
GT-5	Cooper, Conrad	21 Aug 65	120	190	56	100	189
GT-6	Schirra, Stafford	15 Dec 65	16	25	51	100	140
GT-7	Borman, Lovell	4 Dec 65	205	330	55	100	177
GT-8	Armstrong, Scott	16 Mar 66	7	10	42	99	147
GT-9	Stafford, Cernan	3 June 66	46	72	21	99	144
*GT-10	Young, Collins	18 July 66	44	70	47	99	145
*GT-11	Conrad, Gordon	12 Sept 66	45	71	17	100	151
GT-12	Lovell, Aldrin	11 Nov 66	59	94	34	100	185
Total (of 24 flights)			934	1457	56		

*Extreme altitudes of 475 and 850, respectively, were achieved in GT-10 and GT-11 by powered departures from the "stable" orbits indicated by the perigee and apogee given in the table.

Table 3

Assigned Scientific Observations Mercury Program

Assigned Observations	Mission Numbers	Equipment	Results
Observe dimlight phenomena to increase our knowledge of auroras, faint comets near the sun, faint magnitude limit of stars, gegenschein, libration, clouds, meteorite flashes, zodiacal light.	6,9	Unaided eye Camera Voasmeter photometer	MA-6 not dark adapted. MA-9 saw zodiacal light and airglow. Photographs of airglow obtained.
Measure atmospheric attenuation of sunlight and starlight intensity.	6	Voasmeter photometer	No result
Determine intensity, distribution structure, variation and color of visual airglow.	6,7,8,9	Unaided eye with 5577 A filter Camera	Airglow was seen on all flights; was photographed on MA-9. Filter was used on MA-7.
Determine danger of micrometeorite impact and relate to spacecraft protection.	6,7,8,9	Visual and microscopic inspection	One impact found on MA-9 window.
Determine intensity, distribution structure, variation and color of red airglow.	8,9	Unaided eye	Detected visually on MA-8; Confirmed visually on MA-9.
Test and refine theory of optics vis à vis refraction of images near horizon.	6,7,9	Unaided eye Camera	Photographs MA-6, MA-7. Visual MA-7, MA-9

Table 3 (cont'd)

Assigned Observations	Mission Numbers	Equipment	Results
Determine nature and source of the so-called "Glenn effect" or particles.	6,7,8,9	Unaided eye Camera	Discovered on MA-6; all others saw visually; MA-7 photographs.
Compare observations of albedo intensities, day and night times with theory and refine theory.	6	Unaided eye Voasmeter photometer	Not obtained due to instrument malfunction.
Photograph cloud structure for comparison with Liros photos. Improve map forecasts.	6,7,8,9	Camera with filters of various wavelengths	MA-8 and MA-9 obtained scheduled photographs.
Take general weather photographs and make general meteorological observation for comparison with those made by Liros satellite.	6,7,8,9	Unaided eye Camera	All obtained photographs.
Determine best wavelength for definition of horizon for navigation.	7,9	Camera with red and blue filters.	Successful. The red photographs were sharper; the blue more stable.
Obtain ultraviolet spectra of Orion stars for extension of knowledge below 3000 A	6	Ultraviolet spectrograph.	Spectra were obtained but window did not transmit to expected wavelength.

Table 3 (cont'd)

Assigned Observations	Mission Numbers	Equipment	Results
Identify geological and topographical features from high altitude photographs for comparison with surface features as mapped.	6,7,8,9	Unaided eye Camera	Photographs obtained on all. Quality best on MA-9.
Identification of photographs of surface targets by comparison with known geological features.	8	Unaided eye Camera	Few selected ones obtained. Quality fair.

Gemini series, and the observations, both planned and unplanned, made by them. The sources of information are: (1) the official National Aeronautics and Space Administration reports (see references), (2) transcripts of press discussions during and following the missions, (3) mission commentaries released systematically to the press during the missions, (4) transcripts of astronaut reports based on tapes made shortly after return from the mission, (5) personal notes made by me during scientific briefings and debriefing of the astronauts, and (6) conversations with many of the astronauts.

2. *The Spacecraft as an Observatory*

The conditions under which astronauts made their observations are similar to those which would be encountered by one or two persons in the front seat of a small car having no side or rear windows and a partially covered, smudged windshield.

The dimensions and configuration of the spacecraft windows, which are inclined 30° toward the astronauts, are given in Figure 1. The windows are small and permit only a limited forward (with respect to the astronauts) view of the sky. The sphere of view around a capsule in space contains 41,253 square degrees, but the astronauts are able to see only 1200 square degrees or about 3% of that sphere, and only 6% of a hemisphere. The spacecraft can be turned to enable the astronauts to see a different area than the one they face, but fuel must be conserved and maneuvers were not usually made simply to provide a better or different view. In effect, therefore, 94% of the solid angle of space around the capsule was, at any given moment, out of view of the spacecraft occupants.

In addition to this restricted field of vision, the windows themselves were never entirely clean, and the difficulties imposed by the scattering of light from deposits on the window were severe. The deposits apparently occured during the firing of third-stage rockets, when gases were swept past the windows. Attempts were made to eliminate the smudging by use of temporary covers jettisoned once orbit was achieved, but even then deposits were present on the inside of the outer pane of glass. Another source of contamination was apparently the material used to seal the glass to the frames. The net result was that the windows were never entirely clean, and scattered light hampered the astronauts' observations.

There were differences from one flight to another in viewing quality of the windows and from one window to the other on the same flight. For example on Gemini 7, the command pilot in the left seat was able to identify stars to magnitude 6 during satellite night, while the pilot on the right seat was limited to magnitude 4.4. The difference of 1.6 magnitudes (a factor of 4.4) was undoubtedly due to a difference in window transmission. It should be noted that stars as faint as magnitude 6 can be identified from the ground only under superb condi-

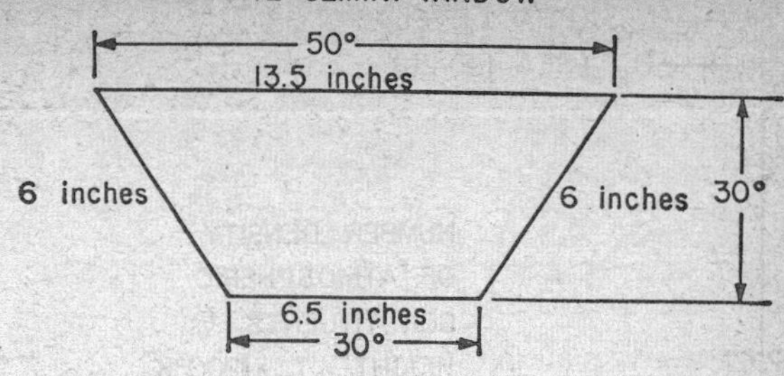

Figure 1

tions (absence of artificial lights and moonlight plus a very clear sky).

The astronauts who had relatively clean windows often referred to the appearance of the night sky as seen in orbit, as similar to that seen by the pilot of a jet aircraft at 40,000 feet.

The smudged windows affected the visibility of objects during satellite night due to the decrease in the window transmission, but the effect was even more serious during satellite daytime when the glare from the light scattered by the smudge often was so bright as to destroy the contrast by which objects could be easily distinguished.

3. *Orbital Dynamics*

Satellites in orbit are subjected to atmospheric drag, which ultimately causes them to reenter the earth's atmosphere, often producing a brilliant display as they do so. Reentries are sometimes reported as UFOs. One recent case in particular stands

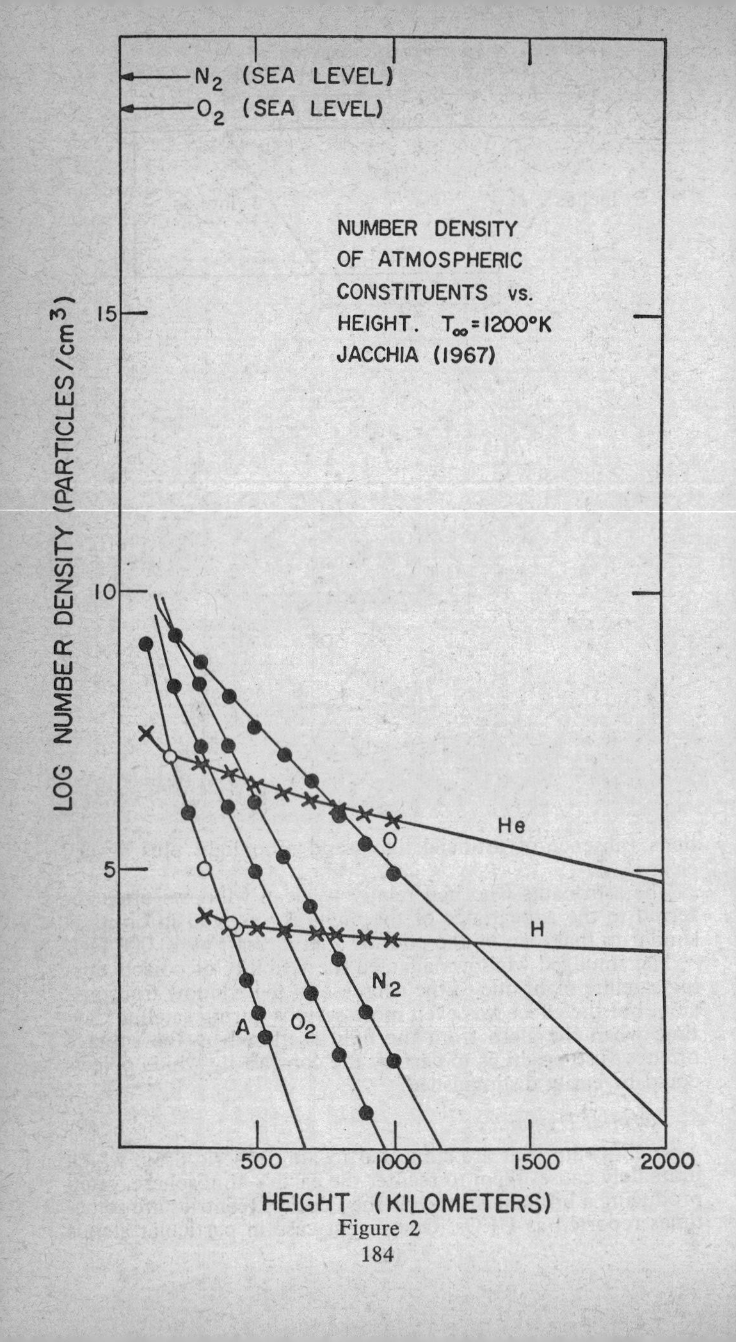
N2 (SEA LEVEL)
O2 (SEA LEVEL)
NUMBER DENSITY
OF ATMOSPHERIC
CONSTITUENTS vs.
HEIGHT. T∞ = 1200°K
JACCHIA (1967)
LOG NUMBER DENSITY (PARTICLES/cm3)
15
10
5
He
O
H
N2
A
O2
500
1000
1500
2000
HEIGHT (KILOMETERS)

Figure 2

as an example of a reentry reported as an UFO and later identified tentatively as the reentries of Agena of Gemini II (Case 11) and Zond IV (see Section VI, Chapter 2).

Space from 100 to 1000 km. is not a perfect vacuum, nor is it isothermal. At about 100 km. the mean molecular weight of the atmosphere undergoes a marked change, where O_2 becomes dissociated by sunlight into atomic oxygen (see Fig. 2). Up to about 100 km. the temperature profile varies between

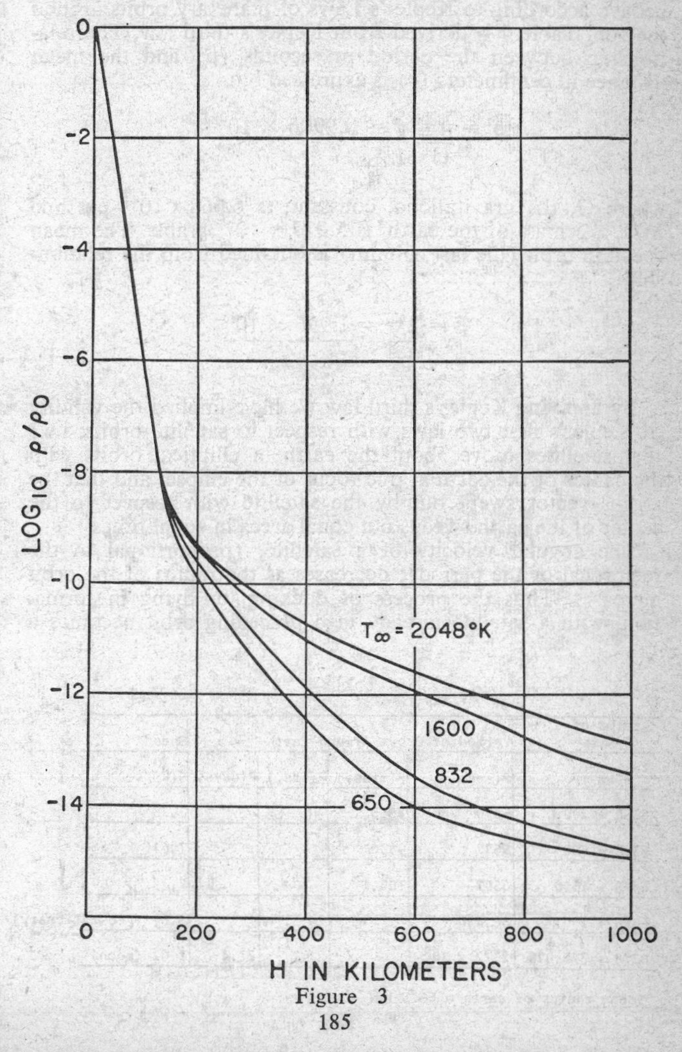

Figure 3

about 200°K. and 300°K. Above 100 km. the temperature undergoes a steady increase to 1000°K. or more. Fig. 3 shows how the relative density of the atmosphere varies with height up to a height of 1000 km. Above 200 km. the density is sensitive to the asymptotic high-level temperature, too, which varies with the solar cycle and geomagnetic activity.

If the earth were a perfect sphere and if there were no atmospheric drag, satellites in orbit around our planet would behave according to Kepler's Laws of planetary orbits around the sun. Table 4 is derived from Kepler's third law. The relationship between the period in seconds (p) and the mean distance in centimeters (r) is expressed by:

$$p^2 = \frac{4\pi^2 r^3}{G M_\oplus} = 0.9906 \times 10^{-19} \cdot r^3$$

where G, the gravitational constant, is 6.668×10^{-8} cgs and $M_\oplus$, the mass of the earth, is 5.977×10^{27} grams. The mean speed in orbit (the last column) is obtained from the relationship:

$$S = \frac{2\pi r}{p} = \frac{1.996 \times 10^{10}}{\sqrt{r}}$$

By applying Kepler's third law we have implied the validity of Kepler's first two laws with respect to satellite orbits; i.e.: that satellites move about the earth in elliptical orbits with the center of the earth at one focus of the ellipse; and that the radius vector swept out by the satellite with respect to the center of the earth sweeps out equal areas in equal times.

The angular velocity of a satellite, (proportional to the reciprocal of the period), decreases as the radius of the orbit increases. Thus the process of docking, or flying in formation, with a satellite already in a preceding orbit becomes a

Table 4

Radius of Orbit	Period of Orbit Around Earth				Speed
r(km.)	P(secs.)	P(mins.)	P(hrs.)	P(days)	S(km/sec)
6378 + 200	5310	88.5			7.78
6378 + 500	5677	94.6			7.61
6378 + 1000	6307	105.1			7.35
6378 + 35,862	86,400		24		3.07 (geostationary)
6378 + 378,025	2372×10^6			27.4	1.02 (moon)

*mean radius of earth = 6378 km.

complicated and difficult maneuver involving descent to a lower, and therefore smaller, orbit with the resultant increase in angular velocity causing the following orbiting body to approach the preceding.

Atmospheric drag slows the satellite speed, especially near perigee, and this causes the satellite to swing out to a smaller subsequent apogee. The orbit contracts and becomes more circular. Eventually the satellite descends to an altitude where the drag causes the satellite to reenter the earth's atmosphere.

Table 5 shows some calculated decelerations for a massive object such as a satellite, and a small meteoritic particle of 0.1 cm. diameter and density of 0.4 gm/cm^{-3} (mass = 2.09 x 10^{-4} grams). At 160 km. (the perigee of many of the manned spacecraft orbits) the deceleration on the spacecraft is not trivial (0.017 cm/sec^{-2}) and the orbit will slowly, but surely degrade to a reentry. Of interest in connection with the observation of small particles by the astronauts is the differential acceleration between the spacecraft and the particles. In a period of ten seconds small particles will "drift" away from the spacecraft a distance of some meters. Typical relative speeds of small particles with respect to the spacecraft have been estimated by the astronauts as 1 or 2 m/sec.

During reentry, the spacecraft and fragments flaked off of its surface become luminous, producing the displays sometimes reported as UFOs. A satellite reentry normally occurs along a grazing path, but the trajectories of meteorites are more radial, and therefore the duration of luminosity is usually no more than two to three seconds.

Table 6 shows the masses of objects for given apparent stellar magnitudes and varying periods of luminosity, calculated on the assumption that all the orbital kinetic energy of the object is converted into light as a consequence of its deceleration on reentry.

4. *Brightness of Objects Illuminated by the Sun*

Astronauts have reported observations they have made, while in orbit, of artifacts (defined here as man-made objects) as well as observations made of natural geophysical and astronomical phenomena during flight. It is among the observations of artifacts that unidentified sightings are most likely to occur, if at all.

A man-made satellite moving slowly against the star background has become a familiar sight. Even though the sun may be below the observer's horizon, the satellite, some hundreds of kilometers above the earth's surface catches the sun's rays and reflects them back to the ground-based observer. Since artifact sightings made from a spacecraft are frequently also the result of reflection of sunlight from a solid object, the question of the brightness of objects illuminated by the sun is pertinent to the consideration of observations from the space

Table 5

Deceleration Calculations

Satellite

mass	diameter	Ratio area/mass	Altitude	Air density	Deceleration
3.63×10^{6} gm.	400 cm.	0.00865	160 km.	8.271×10^{-13}	1.741×10^{-2} cm. sec^{-2}
			200 km.	1.098×10^{-13}	2.311×10^{-3} cm. sec^{-2}

Small Particle

mass	diameter	Ratio area/mass	Altitude	Air density	Deceleration	Separation from craft after: 1 sec.	10 sec.	100 sec.
2.09×10^{-4} gm.	0.1 cm.	37.5	160 km.	8.271×10^{-13}	18.86 cm. sec^{-2}			
			200 km.	1.098×10^{-13}	2.50 cm. sec^{-2}	1.25 cm.	125 cm.	12500 cm.

vehicles. One observation was reported of a dark object against the bright day sky (window?) background (see Section 9 of this chapter).

Satellite brightness, as observed from the ground, is usually given in apparent stellar magnitudes because of the convenience of comparing a satellite with the star background. The unaided eye on a clear moonless night can perceive magnitudes as faint as between +5 and +6. Telescopic satellite searches are able to detect fainter magnitudes; for example, the United Kingdom optical tracking stations can acquire satellites as faint as +9 (Pilkington, 1967). The brightness of artificial satellites and their visual acquisition has been discussed by several writers (Pilkington, 1967; Roach, J. R., 1967; Sumners, et al, 1966; and Zink, 1963).

Table 6

Masses of objects (grams) for given duration of visibility and apparent magnitudes.

APPARENT MAGNITUDE \ DURATION OF VISIBILITY	1 Second	10 Seconds	100 Seconds
5	.000078 gm	.00078 gm.	.0078 gm.
0	.0078	.078	.78
-5	.79	7.8	78.
-10	79.	780	7800.

initial speed = 30 km/sec.

APPARENT MAGNITUDE \ DURATION OF VISIBILITY	100 Seconds
-5	1000 gm.
-10	100,000 (100 kilograms)

initial speed 7.5 km/sec.

Plots of the apparent visual magnitude of sun-illuminated objects as a function of slant distance (in kilometers) and of diameter (in centimeters) of the object are shown in Figs. 4 and 5 respectively.

In curve A of Fig. 4 and in Fig. 5 the illuminated object is assumed to be a sphere. In curve B of Fig. 4 the object is the Orbiting Solar Observatory (OSO) with its sails broadside to the observer (Roach, J. R., 1967). The plots for the sphere are based on the assumption that a sun-illuminated sphere of diameter 1 meter at a distance of 1000 kilometers has an apparent magnitude of 7.84 (Pilkington, 1967). From this, a general relationship between apparent magnitude, m, diameter, d in meters, and slant distance, r in kilometers, is obtained:

$$m = -7.16 - 5.0 \log d + 5.0 \log r \ldots \qquad (1)$$

Fig. 5 indicates that artifacts 1 m. in diameter are brighter than m = +5 and therefore visible to the normal unaided eye to distances of 100 km. The same spacecraft becomes brighter than Venus at her brightest (m = −3) if closer to the observer than 10 km. In the case of a non-spherical object with an albedo that is less than unity, equation (1) is only a guide and the references in the bibliography should be consulted for details.

Fig. 5 is pertinent to the observation of the Glenn "fireflies" and the "uriglow" (see pp. 202-203) and shows that seen close up, i.e.; at 1 to 10 m., even very small sun-illuminated particles are dazzlingly bright.

Legend

Figure 5. Apparent magnitude of spheres illuminated by the sun as a function of the diameter of the spheres. It is assumed that the distance from the observer to the spheres is 1 meter (Curve A) and 10 meters (Curve B). See equation (1) above.

Figure 4. The apparent visual magnitude of objects illuminated by the sun as a function of distance between observer and object. Curve A is for a sphere of 1 meter diameter (see equation 1 above). Curve B is for the OSO spacecraft assuming an albedo of 0.4, a window transmission of 0.5, a solar cosine of 0.5, and the OSO sails broadside to the observer (Roach, J. R., 1967).

---

5. *Visual Acuity of the Astronauts*

Reports by the Mercury astronauts that they were able to observe very small objects on the ground aroused considerable interest in the general matter of the visual acuity of the astronauts. One of the criteria in the selection of the astronauts

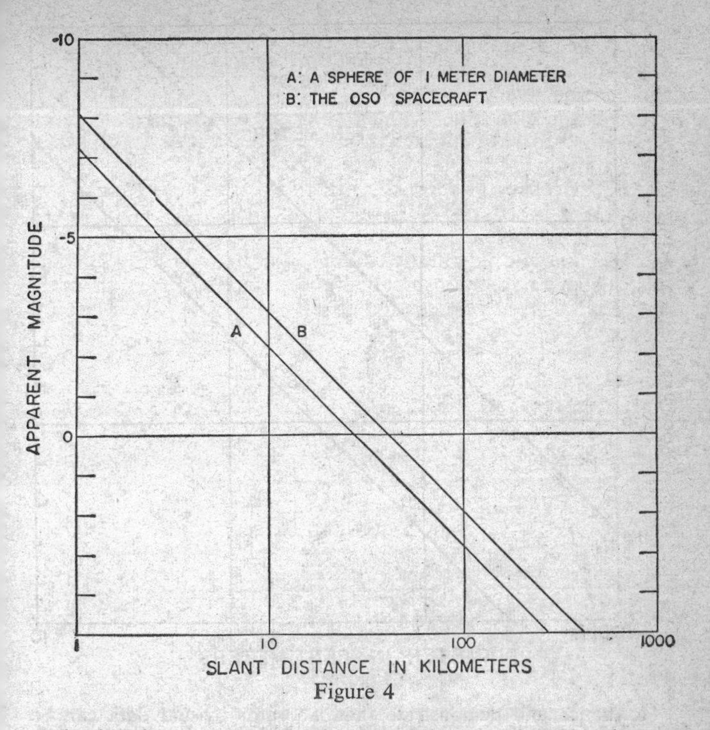

Figure 4

to begin with was that they have excellent eyesight, but it was not known whether their high level of visual acuity would be sustained during flight. Therefore, experiments were designed to test whether any significant change is visual acuity could be detected during extended flights. These experiments were carried out during Gemini 5 (8 days) and Gemini 7 (14 days).

An in-flight vision tester was used one or more times per day, and the results were compared with preflight tests made with the same equipment. In addition, a test pattern was laid out on the ground near Laredo, Tex. for observation during flight. The reader is referred to the original report for the details of the carefully controlled experiments, which led to the following conclusions:

> Data from the inflight vision tester show that no change was detected in the visual performance of any of the four astronauts who composed the crews of Gemini 5 and Gemini 7. Results from observations of the ground site near Laredo, Tex., confirm that the visual performance of the astronauts during space flight was within the statistical range of their preflight visual per-

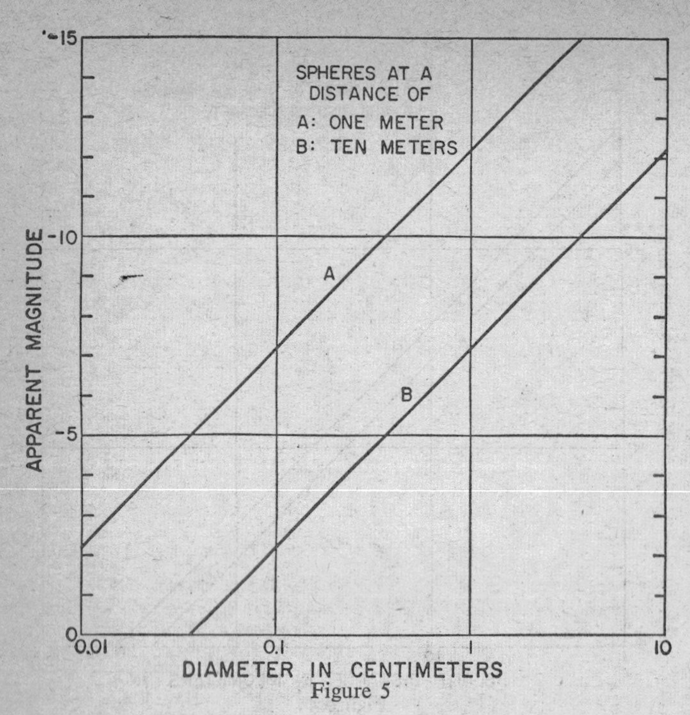

Figure 5

formance and demonstrate that laboratory visual data can be combined with environmental optical data to predict correctly the limiting visual capability of astronauts to discriminate small objects on the surface of the earth in the daylight.

In addition, the astronauts' vision was tested both before and after the flights and the test results were compared with preflight measurements. There were no significant differences in the level of their acuity, as shown in the following tabulation of test results:

Astronaut		Preflight		+Postflight	
		O.S.	O.D.	O.S.	O.D.
Cooper	Far	20/15	20/15	20/15	20/15
	Near	20/15	20/15	20/20	20/20
Conrad	Far	20/15	20/15	20/12.5	20/12.5
	Near	20/15	20/15	20/15	20/15
Borman	Far	20/15	20/15	20/15	20/15
	Near	20/15	20/15	20/15	20/15
Lovell	Far	20/15	20/15	20/15	20/15
	Near	20/15	20/15	20/15	20/15

It is clear that the men selected to participate in the space program of the U.S. have excellent eyesight and that the level of performance is sustained over long and tiring flights.

At the same time, a hindrance to top observing performance was that the astronauts were never thoroughly dark-adapted for any length of time. Good dark-adaptation is achieved some 30 minutes after the eyes are initially subjected to darkness. A typical orbit period was 90 minutes during which the astronauts were in full sunlight for 45 minutes and in darkness for 45 minutes. The astronauts therefore were fully dark-adapted for only 15 minutes out of every 90 minute orbit (assuming no cabin lights).

6. *Sample Observations of Natural Phenomena*

THE NIGHT AIRGLOW

The first American to go into orbit, astronaut John Glenn, (MA-6) reported observing an annular ring around the horizon during satellite night. It appeared to him to be several degrees above the solid earth surface and he noted that stars seemed to dim as they "set" behind the layer. Astronaut Carpenter (MA-7) made careful measurements of the angular height of the layer above the earth's surface and estimated its brightness. All the astronauts have since become familiar with the phenomenon. Soon after Glenn's report (Plate 13) the ring was identified as an airglow layer seen tangentially. It is especially noticeable when there is no moon in the sky and the solid earth surface is barely discernible (Plate 14); as a matter of fact it is easier to use the airglow layer than the earth edge as a reference in making sextant measurements of angular elevations of stars.

Ground-based studies of the night airglow show that it is composed of a number of separate and distinct layers. The layer visible to the astronauts is a narrow one at a height of about 100 km. which, seen tangentially by the astronauts, is easily visible. (It can be seen from the earth's surface only marginally but is easily measured with photometers.)

At a height of about 250 km. there is another airglow layer which is especially prominent in the tropics. It is probable that airglow from this higher level was seen on two occasions. Astronaut Schirra (MA-8) reported a faint luminosity of a patchy nature while south of Madagascar, looking in the general direction of India (NASA SP-12, page 53, 3 October 1962) as follows:

> A smog-appearing layer was evident during the fourth pass while I was in drifting flight on the night side, almost at 32° south latitude. I would say that this layer represented about a quarter of the field of view out of the window and this surprised me. I thought I was looking at clouds all the time until I saw stars down at the bottom or underneath the glowing layer.

Seeing the stars below the glowing layer was probably the biggest surprise I had during the flight. I expect that future flights may help to clarify the nature of this band of light, which appeared to be thicker than that reported by Scott Carpenter.

All the astronauts of later flights knew of astronauts Schirra's sighting, but on only one other occasion was an observation made of a similar phenomenon. At 05h 11m 34s into the Mercury flight, astronaut Cooper reported "Right now I can make out a lot of luminous activities in an easterly direction at 180° yaw . . . I wouldn't say it was much like a layer. It wasn't distinct and it didn't last long; but it was higher than I was. It wasn't even in the vicinity of the horizon and was not well defined. A good size." I had occasion to query him a bit more about his report during a debriefing following the flight:

Roach: More like a patch?
Cooper: Smoother. It was a good sized area.
Roach: You didn't feel this had a discrete shape?
Cooper: It was very indistinct in shape. It was a faint glow with a reddish brown cast."

The phenomenon was estimated to be at about 50° west longitude and about 0° latitude.

The hypothesis has been advanced that the two observations are of the tropical airglow. We know from ground observations of this phenomenon that it is often observed to be patchy. The spectroscopic composition of the phenomenon is about 80% 6300Å and 20% 5577Å. If a bright patchy region of 1000 km. extension (horizontal) came into the view of an astronaut it could appear to be "smog appearing" (Schirra) or "reddish brown" (Cooper). The tropical airglow was relatively bright during 1962 and 1963, and became quite faint during 1964 to 1966, the sunspot minimum. During 1967, as the new sunspot maximum approached, the tropical airglow underwent a significant enhancement. This solar cycle dependence could account for the fact that the Gemini astronauts (1965-1966), although alerted to look for this "high airglow," did not see it.

THE AURORA

The Mercury and Gemini orbits were confined within geographic latitudes of 32°N and 32°S. Since the auroral zones are at geomagnetic latitudes of 67°N and 67°S it would seem unlikely that auroras could be seen by the astronauts. However two circumstances were favorable for such sightings. First, the "dip" of the horizon at orbital heights puts the viewed horizon at a considerable distance from the sub-satellite point. For example at a satellite height of 166 km. (perigee for GT-4) the dip of the horizon is about 13° and at a height of 297 km.

(apogee for GT-4) it is about 17°. Second, the auroral zone, being controlled by the geomagnetic field, is inclined to parallels of geographic latitude as illustrated in Plate 15. Nighttime passes over the eastern United States or over southern Australia bring the spacecraft closest to the auroral zone. On several occasions auroras were seen in the Australia-New Zealand region. Plate 16 (Fig. 32-7 of NASA SP-121) shows a reproduction of a sketch made by the Gemini 7 crew. An auroral arch is seen below the airglow layer.

THE VISIBILITY OF STARS

Satellite orbits are at a minimum height of about 160 km. where the "sky" above is not the familiar blue as it is from the earth's surface. Since the small fraction of the atmosphere above the spacecraft produces a very low amount of scattering, even in full sunlight, it was anticipated that the day sky from a spacecraft would therefore display the full astronomical panoply. This was decidedly *not* the case. All the American astronauts have expressed themselves most forcefully that during satellite daytime, i.e., when the sun is above the horizon, they could not see the stars, even the brighter ones. Only on a few occasions, if the low sun was completely occulted by the spacecraft were some bright stars noted. The inability to observe the stars as anticipated is ascribed to two reasons; (1) the satellite window surfaces scattered light from the oblique sun or even from the earth sufficiently to destroy the visibility of stars, just as does the scattered light of our daytime sky at the earth's surface; and (2) the astronauts are generally not well dark-adapted, as mentioned in section 5 of this Chapter.

Mention has already been made of the dispersion in star visibility during satellite night because of the smudging of the windows. Under the best window conditions the astronomical sky is reported to be similar to that from an aircraft at 40,000 ft. Under the particularly poor conditions of Mercury 8, astronaut Schirra, who is very familiar with the constellations, could not distinguish the Milky Way.

METEORS

In general, meteors become luminous below 100 km., well below any stable orbit. Although organized searches for meteor trails were not part of the scientific planning of the NASA programs, sporadic observations were made by the astronauts who reported that the meteor trails could be readily distinguished from lightning flashes. Because of their sporadic nature, these observations cannot be systematically compared with the ground-observed statistics of the known variation of meteors during the year as the earth crosses the paths of interplanetary debris. However, Gemini 5 was put into orbit shortly after the peak of the August Leonid shower and ground observations of the shower were confirmed in a rough way when astronauts Cooper and Conrad observed a significant number of meteor flashes.

THE ZODIACAL LIGHT BAND

Two factors tend to offset each other in the observation of the zodiacal light band from a spacecraft. A favorable factor is that the zodiacal band gets very rapidly brighter as it is observed as close as some 5° or 6° to the sun, as is possible from spacecraft in contrast with the twilight restriction on the earth's surface of about 25°. The ratio of brightness at an elongation of 5°, B(5), to that at 25°, B(25), is

$$\frac{B\ (5)}{B\ (25)} = 50$$

At the same time, it is difficult to detect the zodiacal band through the spacecraft window with its restricted angular view since one cannot sweep his eyes over a wide enough arc to see the bright band standing out with respect to the darker adjacent sky. By contrast, to locate the zodiacal band observing from the earth's surface, one can sweep over an arc of some 90°, in the center of which the bright band can be readily distinguished.

The most convincing description of a visual sighting of the zodiacal band was by astronaut Cooper (Mercury 9). From his description, I concluded that he distinguished the zodiacal band some 6° from the sun.

TWILIGHT BANDS

The satellite "day" for orbits relatively near the earth is about 45 min. long. The sunrise and sunset sequence occurs during each satellite day. The bright twilight band extending along the earth's surface and centered above the sun is referred to by the astronauts as of spectacular beauty.

8. *Observations of Artifacts in Space*

In the decade since the launching of Sputnik 1 (4 October 1957) a large number of objects have been put in orbit. With each launch, an average of five objects go into orbit. As of 1 January 1967, a total of 2,606 objects had been identified from 512 launchings, of which 1,139 were still in orbit and 1,467 had reentered. The objects in quasi-stable orbits are catalogued by the North American Air Defense Command (NORAD), and up-to-date lists of orbital characteristics are given annually in Planetary and Space Science (Quinn and King-Hele, 1967) from which tabular and graphic statistics have been prepared for this report. (Tables 7 and 8 and Fig. 6.)

Table 7

Number of Satellite (piece) decays or Reentries

Calendar year	1957	1958	1959	1960	1961	1962	1963	1964	1965	1966	Total to date	Reentries during preceding year
Pieces put in orbit during calendar year	5	12	15	50	297	190	204	329	950	554	2606	
Decays as of: 1 Jan. 1963	5	8	10	22	64	92					201	
1 Jan. 1964	5	8	10	22	66	139	83				333	132
1 Jan. 1965	5	8	10	22	66	141	87	210			549	216
1 Jan. 1966	5	8	10	23	68	141	93	233	380		961	412
1 Jan. 1967	5	8	10	23	71	142	98	241	455	414	1467	506
Still in orbit as of 1 Jan. 1967	0	4	5	27	226	48	106	88	495	140	1139	

Table 8

Summary of artificial satellites for the decade 1957-1966

Total Launchings 512

	Pieces put in Orbit	Decayed	Still in Orbit (1 Jan. 1967)
Instrumented satellites	643	379	264
Separate rockets	298	179	119
Other fragments	1665	909	756
Total	2606	1467	1139
Percent	100.0	56.3	43.7

At any given moment during the two-year period of the Gemini program (1965 and 1966) approximately 1000 know objects were in orbit. During the same biennium, there was a total of 918 known reentries. Even though the probability of a collision with an orbiting artifact is statistically trivial, NASA and NORAD coordinated closely to keep track of the relative positions in space of the objects orbiting there.

PROTON III

An interesting example of an unexpected sighting of another spacecraft was made by the Gemini 11 astronauts. Quoting from the transcript (GT-11, tape 133, page 1)

> We had a wingman flying wing on us going into sunset here, off to my left. A large object that was tumbling at about 1 rps and we flew—we had him in sight, I say fairly close to us, I don't know, it could depend on how big he is and I guess he could have been anything from our ELSS* to something else. We took pictures of it.

The identification of the sighting (tape 209, page 2) was given as follows:

> We have a report on the object sighted by Pete Conrad over Tananarive yesterday on the 18th revolution. It has been identified by NORAD as the Proton III satellite. Since Proton III was more than 450 kilometers from Gemini 11, it is unlikely that any photographs would show more than a point of light.

* ELSS = extravehicular life support system

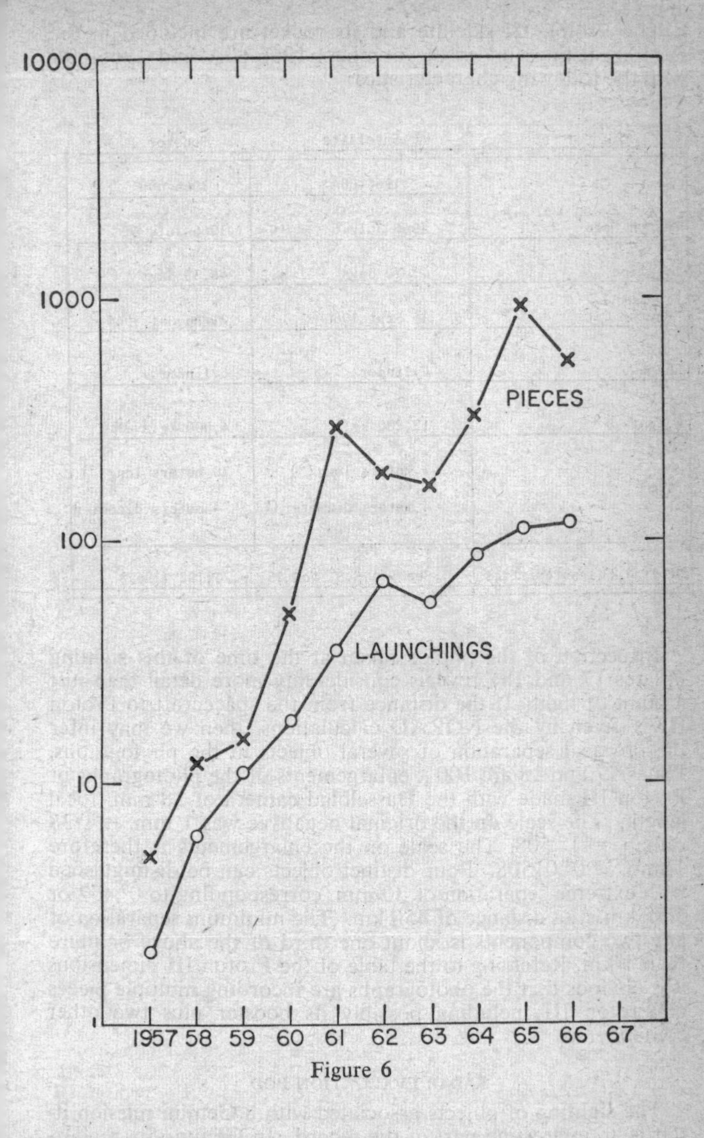
10000
1000
100
10
1
1957
58
59
60
61
62
63
64
65
66
67
PIECES
LAUNCHINGS

Figure 6

The pictures referred to are shown in enlargement in Plates 17 and 18.

The Proton III satellite and its rocket are included in the P.A.S.S. listings under the numbers 1966-60A and 1966-60B with the following characteristics:

	Satellite	Booster
	1966-60A	1966-60B
Launch Date	1966 July 6	1966 July 6
Lifetime	72.20 days	46.33 days
Predicted Reentry Date	16 Sept 1966	21 August 1966
Shape	Cylinder	Cylinder
Weight	12,200 kg.	4,000 kg. (?)
Size	3 meters long (?) 4 meters diameter (?)	10 meters long (?) 4 meters diameter (?)
Orbital Characteristics	See P.A.S.S. Vol.15, p. 1,192 (1967)	

Inspection of the photos taken at the time of this sighting (Plates 17 and 18) reveals considerably more detail than just a point of light. If the distance from the spacecraft to Proton III is given by the NORAD calculations, then we may infer the physical separation of several objects in the photographs. Plates 17 and 18 are 100 x enlargements of the photographs of Proton III made with the Hasselblad camera of 38 mm. focal length. The scale on the original negatives was 1 mm. = 1/38 radian = 1°.508. The scale on the enlargements is therefore 1 mm. = 0°.01508. Four distinct objects can be distinguished with extreme separation of 30 mm. corresponding to 0°.452 or 3.55 km. at a distance of 450 km. The minimum separation of any two components is about one third of the above or more than 1 km. Referring to the table of the Proton III dimensions it is obvious that the photographs are recording multiple pieces of Proton III including possibly its booster plus two other components.

RADAR EVALUATION POD

The sighting of objects associated with a Gemini mission itself is an interesting part of the record. In Gemini 5 a rendezvous exercise was performed with a Radar Evaluation Pod

(REP), a package equipped with flashing lights and ejected from the spacecraft early in the mission. Although the primary aim of the rendezvous exercise was to test radar techniques, the Gemini astronauts, in their conversations with NASA control, commented (Table 9) on the visibility or non-visibility of the REP. Plate 19 shows a photograph of the REP made by the astronauts.

Referring to Fig. 4, Section 4 of this chapter, the REP illuminated by sunlight should be of apparent magnitude −2 at a distance of 10 km. (assuming a 1 meter effective diameter) and magnitude +3 at a distance of 100 km.

THE AGENA RENDEZVOUS

The rendezvous with the REP was a rehearsal for the rendezvous and docking exercises with the Agena. In turn the Agena exercises were rehearsals for the coming Apollo program in which space dockings will be a part of both the terrestrial and lunar flights.

The Agena vehicle is a cylindrical object 8 m. long with a diameter of 1.5 m. Its size makes it a conspicuous object at considerable distances when illuminated by the sun. Plate 20 illustrates its appearance at distances varying between 25 and 250 ft. At 250 ft. its apparent magnitude when sun-illuminated is −9.74 (about 1/13 the brightness of the full moon).

The original plan was to rendezvous with an Agena on the Gemini missions 6-12 inclusive. The planned procedure was to send up the Agena prior to the launching of the manned spacecraft. In the case of the GT-6, the associated Agena did not achieve orbit, so a rendezvous with GT-7 was substituted.

Table 9

Tabulations of REP sightings

Tape	Page	Comment
40	1	REP about 1 mile away
60	1, 3	REP near spacecraft (~1000 ft.) and is visible (flashing light)
62	1, 23	
67	3, 4	Looked for REP—Could not see
68	1	Looked for REP—Could not see
76	1	Looked for REP—Could not see
80	2	Looked for REP at distance of 75 mi. Did *not* see.
234	2, 3	Discussion of photography of REP

The sun-illuminated Agena, when close to the astronauts, was of blinding brightness. Details could be made out at a distance of 26 km. (GT-11, tape 216, page 2). It was picked up visually at distances up to 122 km. (GT-11, tape 50, page 7). Assuming an effective diameter of 4.0 meters, we note from equation (1) that its apparent magnitude was about +0.3 at a distance of 122 km.

The Rendezvous of GT-6 and GT-7

The rendezvous of these two spacecraft involved close coordinations of radar and visual acquisitions and of ground and on-board calculations. Some of the most spectacular photographs of the entire Mercury-Gemini program were obtained during the rendezvous and one is included in this report (Plate 21).

Some of the drama of the rendezvous which also suggests the nature of the visual sightings is brought out in the words of astronaut Lovell during the post-flight press conference (tape 5, page 1). The question was asked of both astronauts — "What was your first reaction when you realized you had successfully carried off rendezvous?"

Answer (Lovell):

> I can only talk for myself, looking at it from a passive point of view. I think Frank (Borman) and I expressed the same feeling—it was night time just become light, we were face down and, coming out of the murky blackness of the dark clouds this little point of light. The sun was just coming up and it was not illuminating the ground yet, but on the adapter of 6 (Gemini 6) we could see this illumination. As it got closer and closer, it became a half moon and, it was just like it was on rails. At about half a mile, we could see the thrusters firing like light hazes, something like a water hose coming out—just in front of us without moving it stopped, fantastic.

THE GLENN "FIREFLIES", LOCAL DEBRIS

During the first Mercury manned orbital space flight, astronaut Glenn reported as follows:

> The biggest surprise of the flight occurred at dawn. Coming out of the night on the first orbit, at the first glint of sunlight on the spacecraft, I was looking inside the spacecraft checking instruments for perhaps 15 to 20 seconds. When I glanced back through the window my initial reaction was that the spacecraft had tumbled and that I could see nothing but stars through the window. I realized, however, that I was still in the normal attitude. The spacecraft was surrounded by luminous particles.
>
> These particles were a light yellowish green color. It was as if the spacecraft were moving through a field of fireflies. They were about the brightness of a first magnitude star and appeared to vary in size from a pinhead up to possibly ⅜ inch. They were about 8 to 10 feet apart and evenly distributed through the space around the spacecraft. Occasionally, one or two of them would move slowly up around the spacecraft and across the window, drifting very, very slowly, and would then gradually move off, back in the direction I was looking. I observed these luminous objects for approximately 4 minutes each time the sun came up.
>
> During the third sunrise I turned the spacecraft around and faced forward to see if I could determine where the particles were coming from. Facing forwards I could see only about 10

percent as many particles as I had when my back was to the sun. Still, they seemed to be coming towards me from some distance so that they appeared not to be coming from the spacecraft.

Dr. John A. O'Keefe has concluded that "the most probable explanation of the Glenn effect is millimeter-size flakes of material liberated at or near sunrise by the spacecraft" (NASA, 1965, pp. 199-203).

Reference is here made to Fig. 5. We note that the apparent magnitude of the sun-illuminated sphere of diameter 1 mm. at 1 m. is −7. This is in general agreement with the description of brightness given by Glenn who referred to them as looking like steady fireflies.

Observations by astronauts in subsequent flights showed that O'Keefe's interpretation is almost certainly correct. Astronaut Carpenter in Mercury 7 found for example that (NASA SP-6, p. 72).

> At dawn on the third orbit as I reached for the densitometer. I inadvertently hit the spacecraft hatch and a cloud of particles flew by the window . . . I continued to knock on the hatch and on other portions of the spacecraft walls, and each time a cloud of particles came past the window. The particles varied in size, brightness, and color. Some were grey and others were white. The largest were 4 to 5 times the size of the smaller ones. One that I saw was a half inch long. It was shaped like a curlicue and looked like a lathe turning.

A modification of the "knocking" technique used by astronaut Carpenter to get the "firefly" effect was used by some of the Gemini astronauts who discovered that a brilliant display resulted from a urine dump at sunrise. The crystals which formed near the spacecraft, when illuminated by the sun, looked like brilliant stars. Plate 22 illustrates the effect (GT-6, Magazine B, Frame 29).

Similar spectacular effects were obtained by venting one of the on-board storage tanks when the sun was low. One such event is described by astronaut Conrad (GT-5, tape 269, page 2) speaking to the ground crew:

> We just had one of our more spectacular sights of our flight coming into sunset just before you acquired us. Either our cryo-hydrogen or our cryo-oxygen tank vented, and it just all froze when it came out and it looked like we had 7 billion stars passing by the windows which was really quite a sight.

The Glenn particles were observed to move with respect to the spacecraft at velocities of 1 to 2 m/sec. Thus the particles and the spacecraft have velocities identical within about 1 part in 4000 in all three coordinates. According to O'Keefe this implies that the orbital inclinations were the same within ±0.01°.

THE ROCKET BOOSTERS

The rocket booster often achieves orbit along with the primary spacecraft, and can often be seen by the astronauts until the relative orbits have diverged to put the booster out of sight.

EXTRA-VEHICULAR ACTIVITY DISCARDS

Because of the crowded conditions in the Gemini spacecraft, the usual procedure after completion of extra-vehicular activity (EVA) was to discard all the equipment and material that had been essential to the EVA but was now useless. This material stayed in essentially the same orbit as the spacecraft and was visible to the astronauts after the disposal. An interesting example occurred in Gemini 12 mission when four discarded objects were seen some time later as four "stars" (GT-12, Astronaut debriefing, page K/3, 4).

Lovell:

> I did not see any objects in space other than the ones we had put there except for several meteors that whistled in below us during the night passes. I might mention we—during the last standup EVA we discarded, *in addition to the ELSS, three bags,* one of which was the umbilical bag and the other had some food in it and the third one had several hoses that we were discarding. And I pushed these forward with a velocity, I would guess, might be 3 or 4 feet per second. And we watched these for quite some time period until they finally disappeared about 2 maybe 3 or possibly 4 orbits later at sunrise condition; we looked out again and saw 4 objects lined up in a row and they weren't stars I know. They must have been these same things we tossed overboard.

Much has been made of this event by John A. Keel, who apparently thought there was discrepancy between the number of objects thrown out by the astronauts (three) and the number of objects later seen as illuminated objects (four). The pertinent part of Keel's article follows (Keel, 1967):

> You never read about it in your local newspaper but during the last successful manned space shot—the flight of *Gemini 12* in November 1966—astronauts James Lovell and Edwin Aldrin reported seeing four unidentifiable objects near their orbit.
>
> "We saw four objects lined up in a row" Captain Lovell told a press conference on November 23rd, "and they weren't stars I know." Several orbits earlier, he explained, they had thrown three small plastic bags of garbage out of the spacecraft. He hinted that these four starlike objects standing in a neat row were, somehow, that trio of nonluminous garbage bags.

A careful reading of the original transcript however shows that four objects were discarded, i.e. *the ELSS, plus three bags.*

9. *Unidentified Flying Objects.*

There are three visual sightings made by the astronauts while in orbit which, in the judgment of the writer, have not been adequately explained. These are:

1. Gemini 4, astronaut McDivitt. Observation of a cylindrical object with a protuberance.
2. Gemini 4, astronaut McDivitt. Observation of a moving bright light at a higher level than the Gemini spacecraft.
3. Gemini 7, astronaut Borman saw what he referred to as a "bogey" flying in formation with the spacecraft.

1. Gemini 4, cylindrical object with protuberance.

Astronaut McDivitt described seeing at 3:00 CST, on 4 June 1965, a cylindrical object that appeared to have arms sticking out, a description suggesting a spacecraft with an antenna.

I had a conversation with astronaut McDivitt on 3 October 1967, about this sighting and reproduced here my summary of the conversation.

McDivitt saw a cylindrical-shaped object with an antenna-like extension. The appearance was something like the second phase of a Titan (not necessarily implying that that is actually what he saw). It was not possible to estimate its distance but it did have angular extension, that is it did not appear as a "point.'" It gave a white or silvery appearance as seen against the day sky. The spacecraft was in free drifting flight somewhere over the Pacific Ocean. One still picture was taken plus some movie exposures on black and white film. The impression was not that the object was moving parallel with the spacecraft but rather that it was closing in and that it was nearby. The reaction of the astronaut was that it might be necessary to take action to avoid a collision. The object was lost to view when the sun shone on the window (which was rather dirty). He tried to get the object back into view by maneuvering so the sun was not on the window but was not able to pick it up again.

When they landed, the film was sent from the carrier to land and was not seen again by McDivitt for four days. The NASA photo interpreter had released three or four pictures but McDivitt says that the pictures released were definitely not of the object he had seen. His personal inspection of the film later revealed what he had seen although the quality of the image and of the blown-up point was such that the object was seen only "hazily" against the sky. But he feels that a positive identification had been made.

It is McDivitt's opinion that the object was *probably* some unmanned satellite. NORAD made an investigation of possible satellites and came up with the suggestion that the object might have been Pegasus which was 1200 miles away at the time. McDivitt questions this identification.

The NORAD computer facility's determination of the distances from GT-4 to other known objects in space at the time of the astronaut McDivitt's sighting yielded the following tabulation.

Object	Number Spodats (NORAD)	Number International (PASS)	Time (C.S.T.)	Distance in km. from GT-4
Fragment	975		2:56	439
Tank	932		3:01	740
Fragment	514		3:04	427
Omicron	646		3:06	905
Omicron	477		3:07	979
Fragment	726		3:09	625
Fragment	874		3:13	905
Omicron	124		3:13	722
Pegasus Debris	1385		3:16	757
Yo-Yo Despin Weight	167		3:18	684
Pegasus B		1965-39A	3:06	2000

Table 10

(Source: Gemini News Center, Release Number 17, 4 June 1965)

A preliminary identification of the object as Pegasus B is suspect. When fully extended Pegasus B has maximum dimension of 29.3 meters, which corresponds to 1/20 minute of arc at a distance of 2000 km. This is much too small an angular extension for the structure of the craft to be resolved and thus does not agree with the description of "arms sticking out." Later in the mission Pegasus B was at a much more favorable distance (497 km.) from the Gemini 4 spacecraft or four times as close as during the reported sighting. Astronauts McDivitt and White reported that they were *not* successful in a serious attempt to visually identify the Pegasus B satellite during this encounter.

The ten objects in addition to Pegasus B in the NORAD list were all at considerably greater distances away from GT-4 than an admittedly crude estimate of 10 miles (16 km.) made by McDivitt, and were of the same or smaller size than Pegasus B. They would not appear to be likely candidates for the object sighted by the astronaut.

2. Gemini 4, moving bright light, higher than spacecraft.

At 50h 58m 03s of elapsed time of GT-4, astronaut McDivitt made the following report.

> Just saw a satellite, very high . . . spotted away just like a star on the ground when you see one go by, a long, long ways away. When I saw this satellite go by we were pointed just about directly overhead. It looked like it was going from left to right . . . back toward the west, so it must have been going from south to north.

Although McDivitt referred to this sighting as a satellite, I have included it among the puzzlers because it was higher than the GT-4 and moving in a polar orbit. It was reported as looking like a "star" so we have no indication of an angular extension.

The suggestion at the time of sighting that this was a satellite has not been confirmed, so far as I know, by a definite identification of a known satellite.

Conversations with McDivitt indicate that on one other occasion, off the coast of China, he saw a "light" that was moving with respect to the star background. No details could be made out by him.

3. Gemini 7, "bogey."

Portions of the transcript (GT 7/6, tape 51, pages 4,5,6) from Gemini 7 are reproduced here. The following conversation took place between the spacecraft and the ground control at Houston and referred to a sighting at the start of the second revolution of the flight:

Spacecraft:	Gemini 7 here, Houston how do you read?
Capcom:	Loud and clear. 7, go ahead.
Spacecraft:	Bogey at 10 o'clock high.
Capcom:	This is Houston. Say again 7.
Spacecraft:	Said we have a bogey at 10 o'clock high.
Capcom:	Roger. Gemini 7, is that the booster or is that an actual sighting?
Spacecraft:	We have several, looks like debris up here. Actual sighting.
Capcom:	You have any more information? Estimate distance or size?
Spacecraft:	We also have the booster in sight.
Capcom:	Understand you also have the booster in sight, Roger.
Spacecraft:	Yea, we have a very, very many—look like hundreds of little particles banked on the left out about 3 to 7 miles.
Capcom:	Understand you have many small particles going by on the left. At what distance?
Spacecraft:	Oh about—it looks like a path of the vehicle at 90 degrees.
Capcom:	Roger, understand that they are about 3 to 4 miles away.
Spacecraft:	They are passed now they are in polar orbit.
Capcom:	Roger, understand they were about 3 or 4 miles away.
Spacecraft:	That's what it appeared like. That's roger.
Capcom:	Were these particles in addition to the booster and the bogey at 10 o'clock high?
Spacecraft:	Roger—Spacecraft (Lovell) I have the booster on *my* side, it's a brilliant body in the sun, against a black background with trillions of particles on it.
Capcom:	Roger. What direction is it from you?
Spacecraft:	It's about at my 2 o'clock position. (Lovell)
Capcom:	Does that mean that it's ahead of you?
Spacecraft:	It's ahead of us at 2 o'clock, slowly tumbling.

The general reconstruction of the sighting based on the above conversation is that in addition to the booster travelling in an orbit similar to that of the spacecraft there was another bright object (bogey) together with many illuminated particles. It might be conjectured that the bogey and particles were fragments from the launching of Gemini 7, but this is impossible if they were travelling in a polar orbit as they appeared to the astronauts to be doing.

10. Summary and Evaluation

Many of the engineering problems involved in putting men into orbit would have been alleviated if it had been decided to omit the windows in the spacecraft, although it is questionable whether the astronauts would have accepted assignments in such a vehicle. The windows did make possible many planned experiments but the observations discussed in this chapter are largely sporadic and unplanned. The program of engineering, medical and scientific experiments was sufficiently heavy to keep the astronauts moderately busy on a regular working schedule but left reasonable opportunity for the inspection of natural phenomena.

The training and perspicacity of the astronauts put their reports of sightings in the highest category of credibility. They are always meticulous in describing the "facts," avoiding any tendentious "interpretations." The negative factors inherent in spacecraft observations which have been mentioned in this chapter would seem to be more or less balanced by the positive advantages of good observers in a favorable region.

The three unexplained sightings which have been gleaned from a great mass of reports are a challenge to the analyst. Especially puzzling is the first one on the list, the daytime sighting of an object showing details such as arms (antennas?) protruding from a body having a noticeable angular extension. If the NORAD listing of objects near the GT-4 spacecraft at the time of the sighting is complete as it presumably is, we shall have to find a rational explanation or, alternatively, keep it on our list of unidentifieds.

References

Air Force Cambridge Research Center, The U.S. Extension to the ICAO Standard Atmosphere, 1958.

Duntley, Seibert Q., Roswell W. Austin, J. H. Taylor, and J. L. Harris. "Visual acuity and astronaut visibility, *NASA SP-138,* (1967).

Hymen, A. "Utilizing the human environment in space," *Human Factors,* Vol. 5, No. 3, (3 June 1963).

Jacchia, L. G. *Philosophical Transactions,* Royal Society, London A262 (1967), 157.

Keel, John A. "The astronauts report UFOs in outer space," *Flying Saucers—UFO Reports,* Dell No. 4, (1967), 32.

King-Hele, D. G. *Theory of Satellite Orbits in an Atmosphere,* London: Butterworths, 1964.

McCue, G. A., J. G. Williams, H. J. Der Prie and R. C. Hoy. *North American Aviation Report,* No. S 10 65-1176, 1965.

NASA Reports on Mercury and Gemini Flights as follows:

Results of the First United States Manned Orbital Space Flight (20 February 1962). Transcript of Air-Ground Communications of the MA-6 flight is included.

NASA SP-6. Results of the Second United States Manned Orbital Space Flight (24 May 1962). Transcript of the Air-Ground Voice Communications of this MA-7 flight is included.

NASA SP-12. Results of the Third United States Manned Orbital Space Flight (3 October 1962). Transcript of the Air-Ground Communications of this MA-8 flight is included.

NASA SP-45. Mercury Project Summary including results of the Fourth Manned Orbital Flight (15-16 May 1963). Includes a transcript of Air-Ground Voice Communication for MA-9.

MA-9 Scientific Debriefing held on (2 June 1963).

Manned Space Flight Experiments Symposium, Gemini Missions III and IV, (18-19 October 1965).

NASA SP-121, Gemini Mid Program Conference, (February 1966).

NASA SP-138, Gemini Summary Conference, (February 1967).

Pilkington, J. A. "The visual appearance of artificial earth satellites," *Planetary and Space Science,* Vol. 15, (1967), 1535.

Quinn, E. and D. G. King-Nele. "Table of earth satellites launched in 1966," *Planetary and Space Science,* Vol. 15, (1967), 1181.

Roach, J. R., R. E. Hathaway, V. L. Easterly and R. H. Sahlehouse. *Final Report, F67-05, Contract NAS 8-18119,* (1967), 3-23, 24, 25.

Summers, L. G., R. A. Shea and K. Ziedman. "Unaided visual detection of target satellites," *Journal of Spacecraft and Rockets,* Vol. 3, No. 1, (January 1966).

Zink, D. L. "Visual experiences of the astronauts and cosmonauts," *Human Factors,* Vol. 5, No. 3, (June 1963).

Chapter 7 Public Attitudes Toward UFO Phenomena / Aldora Lee

1. *Introduction*

Reported in this chapter are the findings of four opinion surveys conducted during the spring of 1968. The major surveys were of 2050 adults and 451 teen-agers, representing a cross-section of the U.S. population. The other two surveys concerned college students and UFO sighters. These latter two however, are not representative samples of college students and UFO sighters. In this report, findings regarding the proportion of sighters in the United States, opinions regarding the reporting of UFOs, and attitudes toward UFOs and related phenomena are considered.

It has been suggested that UFO phenomena should be studied by both physical and social scientists. Although some events are easily categorized as physical and others as social, some do not belong exclusively in one or the other domain of investigation. A focus of the study of tornadoes or other natural disasters, for example, may be upon the physical origin, evolution and demise of the phenomenon, a problem for the physical scientist; another focus may be upon the behavior and attitudes of individuals regarding the phenomenon, a problem for the social or behavioral scientist. In such cases not only does the phenomenon have potential implications regarding the physical world, but it also has implications for the behavior of individuals as a function of that kind of situation.

Still, another condition may obtain. If a reported phenomenon is as yet ill-defined, it is particularly appropriate to investigate both its physical and social aspects in order to maximize the amount of information to be gained and to delimit the parameters of that phenomenon.

Two other considerations also support the study of opinions and attitudes regarding UFO phenomena. First, the great majority of UFO reports consist entirely of verbal reports; material or physical evidence is infrequently available. Even when evidence of some kind is provided, there is still necessarily a heavy reliance on the description provided by the observer. Second, most UFO reports are dependent on the perceptual and cognitive processes (Considerations regarding the nature of perception and misinterpretation are examined in Section VI Chapters 1, 2, & 3). But perception influences and is influenced by the attitudes and beliefs of the perceiver. Equally important is the fact that the attitudes and beliefs of any individual exist in a social context and are either congruent or incongruent with the attitudes and beliefs of others. In the case of attitudes regarding UFOs and related topics, it is not known whether the beliefs of for example, sighters and nonsighters differ, much less what degrees of opinion characterize the public at large.

Finally, a study of opinions and attitudes toward UFO phenomena gains support from the fact that public opinion, concerning an apparently ill-defined phenomenon, was one reason for the establishment of the Scientific Study of Unidentified Flying Objects of the University of Colorado.

In the past three public opinion polls regarding "flying saucers" have been conducted by the American Institute of Public Opinion, more familiarly known as the Gallup Poll. The report of the first poll appeared in August of 1947, shortly after Kenneth Arnold's widely publicized report of flying saucers. The Gallup news release indicate that 90% of the American public had heard of flying saucers (Gallup, 1947). About three years later, a second poll was conducted; at that time 94% of those polled had heard or read about flying saucers (Gallup, 1950). Sixteen years had passed when in 1966, the report of the third poll announced that "more than five million Americans claim to have seen something they believed to be a 'flying saucer' " (Gallup, 1966).

Because of the substantial public interest in UFO phenomena and the absence of information in the area of attitudes and opinions on the subject, opinion surveys were undertaken for the Colorado project in February 1968. The primary surveys were of adults and teen-agers, representing a cross-section of the population of the United States and were conducted for the project by the ORC Caravan Surveys Division of Opinion Research Corporation, Princeton, N. J. Two ancillary surveys, one of UFO sighters and another of college students, were also conducted. Before these surveys are described previous research in the area of attitudes and opinions toward UFOs and related phenomena will be considered.

2. *Prior Research*

In the 1966 Gallup Poll, 1,575 persons were interviewed according to a stratified area sampling procedure. The interview included the following four questions:

(1) "Have you ever heard or read about 'flying saucers'?"
(2) "Have you, yourself, ever seen anything you thought was a 'flying saucer'?"
(3) "In your opinion, are they something real, or just people's imagination?"
(4) "Do you think there are people somewhat like ourselves living on other planets in the universe?"

No further explanations or elaborations of the questions were provided, so that replies necessarily were contingent on the respondent's interpretation of such words and expressions as "real" and "people somewhat like ourselves." For example, that 48% of the respondents felt that flying saucers are real does not imply that the respondents necessarily view them as space-vehicles; "real" in this context suggests a multitude of alternatives (such as weather balloons, or secret weaponry, or airplanes), all of which would afford explanations other than "people's imagination."

The major findings of this poll appear in Table 1. As also indicated by the 1947 and 1950 polls, all but a very small proportion of the respondents had heard or read about flying saucers. From the replies to the second question in Table 1, the Gallup organization estimated that over 5,000,000 persons had seen a flying saucer. Responses to the third and fourth questions reveal that opinion is clearly divided among those who voice an opinion, and that over 20% say that they have no opinion.

Table 1

Major Findings of the 1966 Gallup Poll

Question	Yes	No	No Opinion	Total	N
1. Have you heard or read about "flying saucers?"	96%	4	—	100%	(1575)
2. Have you ever seen anything you thought was a "flying saucer?"	5%	94	1	100%*	(1518)
3. In your opinion, are they something real, or just people's imagination?	48%**	31***	22	100%*	(1518)
4. Do you think there are people somewhat like ourselves living on other planets in the universe?	34%	45	21	100%	(1575)

* Percents are based on the number of respondents who indicated that they had heard or read about flying saucers.
** Real
*** Imaginary

In general, the results of opinion polls may be used in two ways: first simply to represent or typify public opinion; and second, to delineate characteristics which are related to differences in opinion. Taking the latter approach, the raw data from the 1966 poll were obtained from the Gallup Organization in order to examine the relationships between demographic characteristics of the respondents and their replies to the Gallup Poll questions. The finding presented here (including those of Table 1) are based on the Colorado project's statistical analyses of these data.

To determine whether those holding different opinions differ or whether sighters and nonsighters differ with respect to other characteristics, the replies to the four poll questions were examined with regard to the region of the country in which the respondents lived, age, sex, education, and where appropriate, whether the respondents were sighters.

The four regions of the country, East, Midwest, South, and West, did not differ from each other in the proportion of respondents who had heard of flying saucers. The differences among the proportions having seen a flying saucer, by region, also were not statistically significant. (To say that a difference *is* statistically significant is to indicate that the difference is not likely to be due to chance alone. For example, a difference which is significant at the .05 level is said to be so large that that or one greater would occur only 5 times out of 100 if only chance were operating.) The proportion of respondents within each region indicating that flying saucers are "real" varied somewhat, with the largest percentage to say "real," 52% from the West, and the smallest, 45% from the South, with 48% and 47% for Easterners and Midwesterners, respectively. However these differences are not large enough to be statistically significant. When it came to consideration of "people on other planets," the percentage of Southerners, 27% to say "yes," was smaller than those from the other areas of the country. The percent of those from the East, Midwest, and West were 36%, 37%, and 35% respectively. The difference between southerners and others is statistically significant at the .05 level. No sufficient explanation can be offered for this regional difference on the basis of the present analyses.

In addition, the data were analysed according to age. Respondents were categorized as being in their 20's, 30's, 40's, 50's, 60's, or 70 and above .The percentage having heard of flying saucers is constant across age groups, as is the percentage who identify themselves as sighters. On the other hand, the age of the respondents does appear to be related to the replies to the other questions, as to whether flying saucers are real and whether there are people on other planets. The results of the analysis appear in Table 2. They show that the younger the respondents, the greater the proportion willing to indicate that they feel that flying saucers are "real." About twice as many persons in the youngest group answer "real" as answer "imagination," while in the oldest group the proportion answering "imagination" outweighs those replying "real." It can also be seen that the percent reporting "no opinion" varies, with a larger proportion of the older people than of the younger reporting "no opinion."

The analysis by age of the question concerning "people on other planets" appears in Table 3. Again, response is related to age, with more of the younger respondents indicating an opinion. Of those who voice an opinion, the youngest persons are fairly evenly divided between "yes" and "no," while "no's" outweigh "yesses" two to one among the eldest. The above analyses of these two opinion questions strongly suggest that age is, in some way, an important factor in beliefs regarding UFOs and related topics. The implications of these findings are considered later in conjunction with the analyses of the opinion surveys of the Colorado study.

When the questions are analysed according to sex, it is found that men and women *do not* differ in their replies, except to the question which asks whether flying saucers are real or imaginary. 43% of the men and 52% of the women indicate they think flying saucers are real; 35% and 26%, respectively, hold them to be imaginary and 22% of each group have no opinion.

Although the relationships are not strong, the results of the 1966 Gallup poll suggest that education is related to opinions.

The greater the education, the higher the proportion who indicated they have heard of flying saucers, who think they are real rather than the product of imagination and who believe that there are people somewhat like ourselves living on other planets.

Table 2

Responses to the Question:

"In your opinion, are they something real, or just people's imagination?"

Age	Real	Imagination	No Opinion	Total
21-29	55%	26	19	100%
30-39	51%	27	22	100%
40-49	51%	30	20	100%
50-59	53%	31	16	100%
60-69	38%	33	29	100%
70 and above	32%	42	26	100%

Table 3

Responses to the Question:

"Do you think there are people somewhat like ourselves living on other planets in the universe?"

Age	Yes	No	No Opinion	Total
21-29	42%	41	17	100%
30-39	41%	39	21	100%
40-49	35%	48	18	100%
50-59	29%	51	20	100%
60-69	29%	44	27	100%
70 and above	23%	47	30	100%

A comparison of sighters and nonsighters shows that sighters are more inclined to say that flying saucers are real, 76% of the sighters as compared with 46% of the nonsighters, and that there are people on other planets, 51% as compared with 34%.

In summary, the analysis of the 1966 Gallup data indicate the following:

(1) Most Americans, 96%, have heard of flying saucers.
(2) About 5% of the population claim to have seen a flying saucer.
(3) About one-half of the population feel that they are real.
(4) About one-third feel that there are people on other planets.
(5) People who are better educated are more likely to have heard of flying saucers.
(6) Sighters do not differ from nonsighters with respect to education, region of the country, age, or sex.

(7) Age, sex, and education all appear to be related to whether flying saucers are considered to be real or imaginary. That is, younger persons, women, and those who are better educated tend to be more inclined than older persons, men, and the less educated, respectively, to consider flying saucers to be real.

(8) Age, education, and respondent's region of the country appear to be related to whether it seems possible that there are people on other planets in the universe. That is, younger persons, those who are better educated, and individuals from the East, Midwest, and West are more inclined than older persons, the less well educated, and those who reside in the South to think that there are "people somewhat like ourselves on other planets in the universe."

The findings of Scott (1966) provide a different kind of information about the investigation of attitudes regarding UFOs. His study was concerned with the problem of an individual's public association with UFO phenomena. Because it is commonly said that people will not report a flying saucer because they are reluctant to be associated with such a controversial topic, he undertook a small study to determine whether individuals would be less inclined to indicate acquaintance with the phenomena under public than under private conditions.

As the instructor of a class of 210 students in introductory psychology, he explained that he was collecting some data for a colleague and asked the students to indicate, by raising their hands, if they had seen each of the objects he was about to name. Each of the 11 objects that were named referred to one of three sets: neutral items, taboo (socially unacceptable or negatively sanctioned) items, and unidentified flying objects. Seven of the items were neutral, two taboo, and two UFO. The two items in the UFO set were "UFO" and "flying saucer." The number of responses to each item was recorded. A short time later, an assistant arrived with questionnaire forms listing all 11 items. The instructor indicated that he had already completed the survey; the assistant said that there must have been some misunderstanding because the students were to have indicated their answers on the forms he had brought. Subsequently the students filled in the forms. Later the written responses were tallied and compared with the results of the previous inquiry. The study thus involved the comparison of public response when the response of the individual was visible to others, versus a private response, when the responses could not be observed and would remain anonymous.

A comparison of the number of students indicating that they had seen a given object under the public condition and the number under the private condition revealed a general increase for all items. The mean percent increase for the seven neutral items, which may serve as a baseline for comparison, was 24%. The mean increase for the two taboo items was 85% and for the two UFO items 61%. Comparisons among the three classes of items suggest that the public-private discrepancy for "UFO" and "flying saucer" is more like that for taboo words than that for neutral objects. That is, the subjects appeared to be nearly as reluctant to be associated publicly with these words as with the taboo words.

3. *The Colorado Study of Public Attitudes*

Turning now to the 1968 Colorado Study, the objectives of the research to be reported in the remainder of this chapter are: 1) To estimate the proportion of the adult American population which represents sighters; 2) to compare sighters and nonsighters with respect to age, sex, education, and region of the country in which they live; 3) to determine the attitudes of both sighters and nonsighters regarding the reporting of sightings; 4) to assess attitudes regarding various aspects of UFO phenomena and related topics.

Method

SURVEY SAMPLE

In the 1968 Colorado study, four surveys were carried out: a survey of adults, a survey of teen-agers, a survey of sighters, and a survey of college students.

A. Adult sample, national opinion survey.

The data in this survey were obtained by means of a personal interview research survey, conducted by the Opinion Research Corporation, of 2,050 adults 18 years of age and over residing in private households in the continental United States. Interviewing took place between 21 February and 13 March 1968. Sample selection was made by an equal-probability sample technique. A detailed description of the sampling procedure provided by Opinion Research Corporation appears in Appendix O. Comparisons of population and survey sample characteristic appear in Tables 4 and 5, provided by the Opinion Research Corporation. The size of the sample and the method of sampling make it possible to make inferences regarding the American public at large and to make comparisons among subgroups.

B. Teen-age sample, national opinion survey.

This survey of 451 teen-agers was conducted in conjunction with the adult survey; each teen-ager who participated was a member of a household in which an adult was also interviewed. Comparisons of population and sample characteristics for teen-agers appear in Table 5, also provided by Opinion Research Corporation.

C. Sighter survey

Data were obtained from 94 sighters of UFOs whose names were drawn from the project sighting files. In addition to reports made directly to the project, there were report files,

Table 4

Sample Characteristics, February 1968, ORC Caravan Surveys: Adult Sample

The data in the table below compare the characteristics of the weighted [1/] Caravan sample with those of the total population, 18 years of age or over. The table shows that the distribution of the total sample parallels very closely that of the population under study.

	Total		Men		Women	
	Population [2/]	Caravan Sample	Population [2/]	Caravan Sample	Population [2/]	Caravan Sample
Age						
18 - 29	26%	26%	25%	25%	26%	27%
30 - 39	18	18	19	17	17	19
40 - 49	19	20	20	20	19	19
50 - 59	16	16	16	18	16	15
60 or over	21	20	20	20	22	20
Race						
White	89%	89%	90%	89%	89%	89%
Nonwhite	11	11	10	11	11	11
City Size						
Rural, under 2,500 population	29%	31%	30%	35%	27%	27%
2,500 - 99,999	19	21	)			
100,000 - 999,999	23	23	) 70	65	73	73
1,000,000 or over	29	25	)			
Geographic Region						
Northeast	25%	25%	25%	25%	25%	25%
North Central	28	26	28	26	28	26
South	30	33	30	33	30	32
West	17	16	17	16	17	17

[1/] Weights were introduced into the tabulations to compensate for differences in size of household and variations in completion rates between rural and urban areas.

[2/] Source: Latest data from U. S. Bureau of the Census, regular and interim reports.

duplicating in part cases on file with the Air Force's Project Blue Book and with NICAP. The names drawn came from four major sources: case reports from Blue Book, case reports from NICAP, personal reports (i.e., cases from individuals who directly contacted the project), and reports from the file of all cases which have been investigated or extensively reviewed by the project staff.

An attempt to obtain approximately 50 completed questionnaires each from the Blue Book, NICAP, and "Personal" files was undertaken by a systematic sampling procedure. In the case of the Colorado investigation file, the names and addresses of sighters were taken from all files extant at the time the sample was drawn. When more than one sighter per

Table 5

Sample Characteristics, February 1968, ORC Caravan Surveys: Teen Sample

The data in the table below compare the characteristics of the Caravan sample households with those of all households in the United States.

	U. S. Households[1/]	Caravan Sample
Geographic region		
Northeast	25%	24%
North Central	28	27
South	30	32
West	17	17
City size		
Rural	28%	29%
2,500 - 99,999	19	22
100,000 - 999,999	23	23
1,000,000 or over	30	26
Race		
White	90%	89%
Nonwhite	10	11
Family composition		
No children	51%	48%
Children under 18	49	52
With teen-agers 12 - 17	21%	23%

[1/] Source: Latest data from U.S. Bureau of the Census, regular and interim reports.

report was listed, the case was reviewed to determine who was the principal sighter, and only that person's name was drawn.

A large number of cases did not include satisfactory mailing addresses for sighters. Consequently, it was necessary to select the next occurring file that did include a complete address in either the United States or Canada. Following this procedure, a total of 139 cases were drawn from the Blue Book file to obtain 106 names and addresses, 140 cases from the NICAP file to obtain 95 names and addresses, and 55 cases from the Personal file to obtain 54 names and addresses.

In the spring of 1968, each person whose name was thus drawn was sent a letter explaining the purpose of the intended opinion survey and requesting his participation. Anonymity of the individual was assured. Enclosed with the letter was a reply postcard on which the sighter could indicate whether or not he would be able to participate. Some letters were returned by the post office for insufficient address; no reply was received to some letters. Of those from whom we received affirmative replies (and therefore to whom we sent questionnaires), most participated in the survey. A comparison of the percents participating, not participating, failing to reply to the request letter, and failing to receive the letter, for lack of sufficient address, for the four file sources appear in Table 6.

As would be expected, the rate of response is best for the "Personal" file. Most individuals represented in this file are those who volunteered information. In addition, a larger proportion of these cases occurred since the beginning of the

Table 6

Response of Sighters from Project Files to Questionnaire

	Blue Book	NICAP	Personal Letters	Colorado	Total
Participants	20%	29%	57%	36%	32
Non-participants	14	12	17	18	14
No Reply	47	55	22	44	45
Insufficient Address	19	4	4	2	9
Total Mailing	100%	100%	100%	100%	100
N =	(106)	(95)	(54)	(39)	(294)

project. Among the four files, the greatest proportion of letters returned for insufficient address were sent to sighters whose names were drawn from the Blue Book file. The proportion of "no reply" persons is difficult to interpret, because it is impossible to know how many letters were never received and how many were received but went unanswered. Both Blue Book and NICAP files have the greatest proportion of older sightings, which in part accounts for their relatively poorer rate of return. The final sighter sample, on which the analyses are based, consists of 21 sighters form the Blue Book file, 28 from the NICAP file, 31 from the Personal file, and 14 from the Colorado investigations file.

D. College survey

College survey data were obtained between 4 April and 13 May 1968 from 12 college samples, representing 10 colleges and universities. The total number of students participating in the survey is 719. The names of the institutions participating and those individuals who assisted us in obtaining subjects appear in Appendix M. All but three sources of respondents were courses in the behavioral sciences; one participating class was in a physical science department and two were special courses in flying saucers, one offered at the University of California at Davis and the other at Wesleyan University. A description of the samples appears in Table 7. In this table, sample numbers correspond to the order in which completed questionnaires were received; however, the order of schools in Appndix M, referred to above, is alphabetical. Most questionnaires were filled out during a class period by students present on the day the questionnaire was administered. In a few cases, volunteers, rather than every student present, provided the data. In most instances students were not aware, until after they had completed filling out the questionnaire, that the research was being sponsored by the Colorado project.

Although group, rather than individual responses were of interest, students were asked to place their names on the questionnaires, in order to discourage careless or irresponsible answers. (A few students chose not to provide their names; one class was required by its instructor to fill in the questionnaires anonymously). The results of Scott's study (1968) indicate that responses regarding UFO material under public conditions may be more cautious than under private conditions. Consequently, it was felt that if there were any sample bias in assessing students' views on UFOs and related topics, it would be in the direction of obtaining cautious answers. Moreover, national opinion survey respondents were assessed by personal interview (though anonymity was assured), and the participants of the sighter survey were aware that their names were known to the investigator (though, again, anonymity was assured). Requesting names from students, then, also make the conditions under which this information was obtained more comparable to the other surveys.

Table 7

College—University Sample Characteristics

Sample	N	Administered To	Course Title	Aware of CU Sponsorship
1	118	Class	Intro. Psychology	No
2	29	Class	Flying Saucers	No
3	88	Class	General Psychology	No
4	76	Class	Abnormal Psychology	No
5	99	Class	Psychology of Personality	No
6	95	Class	Child Psychology	No
7	26	Class	General Physics	No
8	19	Class	Flying Saucers	No
9	91	Class	Intro. Psychology; Psychology of Adult Life	No
10	44	Volunteers	Intro. Sociology	No
11	15	Volunteers	Intro. Sociology, Anthropology	Yes
12	19	Volunteers	Intro. Psychopathology	Yes

Because the results of the national survey of adults serve to reflect the opinions and attitudes of the American adult public, they are given the greatest emphasis in the following analyses. Because of time limitations, only a portion of the data collected on each of the four groups could be analysed.

Survey Instruments

The instruments of this study are both attitude scales and questionnaires. Because some instruments are common to all four surveys (adult, teen, college, and sighter) while others are not, the instruments are listed according to survey, so that the set of instruments used in each is apparent. A brief description of each instrument is provided the first time it is mentioned, except in those few instances in which the data from them are not included in the present analyses. In such cases, the description of the instrument will be found in Appendix N, where it precedes the instrument.

A. Adult sample, national opinion survey

1) UFO Opinion Questionnaire. This instrument is comprised of 29 statements regarding UFOs and related topics. All are presented as opinion statements; the respondent indicates whether he feels that the statement is definitely false, probably false, probably true, or definitely true.

The items are considered singly, as expression of opinion on separate topics, and as sets comprising the following scales:

a) Outer Space scale—measures the degree to which respondents accept the hypothesis that UFOs are from outer space:

b) Evidence scale—measures the degree to which respondents believe that there is evidence for the existance of UFOs (This scale, however, does not include items which suggest the origin of UFOs. The respondent may, if he wishes, reject the extraterrestrial or outer space hypothesis, but still indicate that he believes there is evidence to support the hypothesis that UFOs do exist;

c) Adequacy scale—measures the degree to which efforts of the government and its agencies in investigating UFO reports are perceived to be adequate;

d) Secrecy scale—measures the degree to which government secrecy regarding information about UFOs is believed to exist.

A respondent's scale score was determined first by scoring the answer to each statement in the scale either zero or one, according to whether the response was in the direction of acceptance (1) or rejection (0) of the variable measured by the scale itself, then obtaining the mean score for those items of the scale which were answered.

Scale composition was determined jointly by manifest content and inter-item correlations, based on a sample of 205 of the surveyed adults, chosen by a systematic sampling procedure. The composition of each of the scales may be found in Table 8. Homogeneity rates (Scott, 1960) and coefficient alphas (Cronbach, 1951) for the scales appear in Table 8a.

Scale intercorrelations (Pearson Product Moment Coefficients (McNemar, 1962) may be found in Table 9.

2) A-B Scale—(The instrument is not included in the present analyses. Its description appears in Appendix 0).

3) Adult Background Questionnaire—Includes questions concerning the following:

a) demographic information;
b) opinions regarding the reporting of UFO sightings;

Table 8

Item Composition of Attitude Scales

Scale	Question Number	Question
1. Outer Space	1.	Some flying saucers have tried to communicate with us.
	11.	Earth has been visited at least once in its history by beings from another world.
	13.	Intelligent forms of life cannot exist elsewhere in the universe.
	15.	Some UFOs have landed and left marks in the ground.
	23.	People have seen space ships that did not come from this planet.
2. Evidence	6.	No airline pilots have seen UFOs.
	8.	No authentic photographs have ever been taken of UFOs.
	24.	Some UFO reports have come from astronomers.
3. Competence	3.	The Air Force is doing an adequate job of investigation of UFO reports and UFOs generally.
	12.	The government should spend more money than it does now to study what UFOs are and where they come from.
	18.	The government has done a good job of examining UFO reports.
4. Secrecy	19.	There have never been any UFO sightings in Soviet Russia.
	22.	There is no government secrecy about UFOs.
	28.	Government secrecy about UFOs is an idea made up by the newspapers.

Table 8a

Reliability of Opinion Scales

(based on adult sample)

Scale	Homogeneity Ratio	Coefficient Alpha
Outer Space	.31	.69
Evidence	.22	.46
Adequacy	.19	.40
Secrecy	.24	.49

Table 9
Intercorrelation of Opinion Scales
(based on the adult sample)

Scale	1	2	3	4
1. Outer Space	—			
2. Evidence	.40	—		
3. Adequacy	−.32	−.26	—	
4. Secrecy	.22	.32	−.18	—

c) acquaintance with UFO phenomena.

4) Background Questionnaire of the Opinion Research Corporation—Contains questions frequently asked by them for all clients.

B. Teen sample, national opinion survey

1) UFO Opinion Questionnaire.

2) Teen Background Questionnaire—comprised of background questions appropriate for teen-agers.

C. Sighter survey

1) UFO Opinion Questionnaire.

2) Sighter Background Questionnaire—includes demographic measures, questions regarding the reporting of UFOs, and questions about information sources.

D. College survey

1) College information sheet.

2) UFO Opinion Questionnaire.

3) A-B Scale.

4) Current Events Questionnaire. (Neither the A-B Scale nor the Current Events Questionnaire is included in the present analyses. Their descriptions appear in Appendix P).

5) College Background Questionnaire—comprised of background questions appropriate for college students.

Results and Discussion

The analyses of the data which are to be reported are of three kinds. The first section concerns the proportion of the population who identify themselves as sighters and the demographic characteristics of sighters and nonsighters. In the second section, the reporting of UFOs and attitudes toward reporting are examined. In the final section attitudes toward UFOs and related topics are discussed; data from each of the four groups surveyed are presented.

SIGHTERS AND NONSIGHTERS

All adults in the national survey were asked the question, "Have you, yourself, ever seen a UFO?" Three percent of the sample indicated that they had. In order to provide an analysis parallel to our analysis of the Gallup study's question, "Have you ever seen anything you thought was a 'flying saucer'?" the replies to the above question were examined with respect to four demographic variables: region, sex, age, and education. It was found that the proportion of sighters in the various regions of the country, East, Midwest, South, and West, are similar. Equal percentages of men and women say that they have seen an UFO. There are also no differences among age or educational levels. Differences with respect to these demographic variables, except for region of the country, were also absent in the projects analysis of the 1966 Gallup data.

A point at which the results of the above analyses do not agree with those of the Gallup survey concerns the proportion of the public who say that they have seen an UFO. Three percent of our sample said they had seen an UFO while 5% of those polled in the Gallup survey indicated that they had seen as the question was worded, a "flying saucer." The difference between the results of the two surveys approaches statistical significance. The apparent discrepancy between the findings of the Gallup and the Colorado project surveys may be due to one or more variables, such as the difference in the wording of the two questions, or difference in sampling techniques.

The findings of the study undertaken by the Colorado project suggest that the actual number of sighters in the United States is approximately 3.75 million. This estimate is based on the continental U.S. civilian population, 18 years of age and over (*Current Population Reports*, 14 February 1968), the parameters of which were used in determining the survey sample characteristics.

The actual number of sighters may, however range from as few as 1,000,000 to as many as 5,000,000. (A range, as compared with a specific number, takes into account possible sampling variation).

VIEWS ON REPORTING

Attitudes toward the reporting of UFOs were covered in one of the Colorado project questionnaires by nine questions, five addressed to sighters and four to nonsighters. The previously conducted opinion surveys, by Gallup (1947, 1950, 1966) attempted to estimate the percentage of the American population who had heard of flying saucers and, in the 1966 survey, the number of sighters in the American population. However, the Gallup organization did not attempt to determine what proportion of these self-designated sighters actually reported their sightings.

A study which provides a basis for comparison is one concerned with the reporting of crimes. It was made for the President's Commission on Law Enforcement and Administration by the National Opinion Research Center under the direction of Philip Ennis (1967a, 1967b). This study revealed that 51% of those interviewed who had been the victims of crimes did not report them to the police (1967b). After reviewing the reasons people gave for not notifying the police, Ennis made the following observations (Ennis, 1967b):

> First there is a strong resistance to invoking the law enforcement process even in matters that are clearly criminal. Second, there is considerable skepticism as to the effectiveness of police action.

Inasmuch as people show reluctance to report crimes, it should not be surprising to find that something thought to be an UFO frequently goes unreported by the sighter. In fact, it is commonly said that sighters are reluctant to report such events because of ridicule. (There are, in fact, some cases in which publicity and ridicule appear to have influenced the sighter to change jobs or move to another town).

The questions designed to assess the reporting process in the present study were asked of sighters to ascertain whether or not they had reported their sightings and the reasons for their decisions, and of nonsighters, under a hypothetical circumstance of having seen an unusual object suspected to be an UFO, to determine whether they thought they would report a sighting and their reasons for their decision. In addition, sighters who had reported their sightings were asked to express their degree of satisfaction with the way in which the report was handled.

The first of the questions concerns the agency to which sighters had reported an UFO; the second, the agency to which nonsighters would report an UFO. The responses of national survey nonsighters appear in Table 10. Data for sighters identified in the national survey are not presented in the table because they are based on so few individuals that the results have no statistical validity. Data for sighters drawn from

Table 10

Preference of Nonsighters for Agency to Which to Report an UFO

Agency	Percent
Town or city official	10%
Police	56
Newspaper	10
Radio station	9
NICAP	5
APRO	3
Local UFO organization	8
Air Force	15
Airport	5
Weather bureau	5
Other	1
No one (other than family or friends)	16
Total	143%*
N =	(1608)

* In this and subsequent tables, percents are based on the total number answering the question.

project case files are also not presented, because the percentages obtained primarily reflect the sources from which the sighters' names were drawn.

The primary finding from the sighters' question is that 87% of sighters indicated that they reported the sighting to no one other than family or friends. It would seem, then, that most sightings have little chance of coming to the attention of an agency, whether official, semi-official, or private. The failure to report UFO sightings appears to be more prevalent, 87%, than the failure to report crime, 51%, as indicated in the Ennis reports (1967a, 1967b).

By contrast, only 16% of the nonsighters indicated that they would notify no one save family or friends. In addition, over half of the nonsighters, 56%, indicated they would notify the police. There is clearly, a considerable discrepancy between results for sighters and for nonsighters.

At least two possible explanations may account for the discrepancy between what people say they would do (responses of nonsighters) and what they in fact do, (responses of sighters) given the actual circumstance of a sighting:

(1) The number of sighters in the study is small and thus may not accurately reflect the action of all sighters;

(2) Entertaining the hypothetical situation of having seen something suspected to be an UFO and actually being confronted with the decision precipitated by a sighting are quite different events.

Although both sighters and nonsighters were asked for their reasons for reporting, responses from sighters identified in the national survey were not statistically meaningful because the answers are from so few respondents. Reasons given by nonsighters, which represent a response to a hypothetical situation, are interesting primarily in that they may be regarded as reflecting the views of most of the American public. As can be seen in Table 11, the dominant reason of nonsighters is "I would want to know what it was." The other alternative frequently endorsed is "because strange objects should be reported."

In the questionnaire for project sighters was an identical question. Project sighters' reasons appear in Table 12. These

Table 11

Major Reason for Reporting Given by Nonsighters Who Indicated They Would Report an UFO

Reason	Percent
I would want to know what it was	49%
Because strange objects should be reported	36
I would be worried about it	7
Because other people have seen UFOs	—
It is the best way to convince people that UFOs really exist	4
Other	3
Total	100%
N=	(1382)

Table 12

Reasons for Reporting Indicated by Sighters from Project Files

Reason	Percent
I wanted to know what it was	29%
Because strange objects should be reported	43
I was worried about it	6
Because other people have seen UFOs	2
It is the best way to convince people that UFOs really exist	11
Other	31
Total	122%*
N=	(94)

* Percents total more than 100% because multiple reasons were permitted.

sighters, who filled in a questionnaire sent to them, tended to give more than one "major reason." The alternatives "because a strange object should be reported," "other" (reasons supplied by the respondent), and "I wanted to know what it was" were most frequently indicated, in that order.

The sighters in the national survey who reported their sightings and the project sighters both were asked: "How satisfied were you with the way your report of the UFO was handled?" Those few sighters in the national survey who reported were about evenly divided between satisfaction and dissatisfaction; again problems of interpretation arise because the results are based on *only seven sighters*. The responses of project sighters are presented with qualifications. These individuals received their questionnaires directly from the project and the fact that they had been asked by us for further information may have altered their evaluations of the "handling of the report." More than two-thirds were satisfied. Not to be overlooked in the interpretation of these findings is the fact that their reports had survived the reporting process and had become case files.

The remaining national survey respondents, sighters who did not report and nonsighters who said they would not report a sighting, were asked to indicate which reasons influenced their decisions. Respondents were permitted to indicate as many reasons as influenced their decision, and they were asked to indicate the one reason that was the most important. A comparison of Table 13, a summary of sighter responses, and Table 14, a summary of nonsighter responses, shows that the sighter and nonsighter groups are quite similar. The most important reason of both for not reporting was that the event was probably "something normal that must have looked funny for one reason or another." Fear of ridicule was the reason second in order of importance for both sighters and nonsighters. The combined replies to alternatives 6 and 8 which are concerned with knowledge about whom to notify and how to notify is third in order of importance, and the combined replies to alternatives 4 and 5 which suggest ineffectiveness and indifference on the part of authorities rank only fourth.

These findings contrast markedly with those of Ennis, who found that more than one-half of the victims who did not

Table 13

Sighters' Reasons for Not Reporting the Sighting to Anyone Other Than Family or Friends

	Reasons Influencing Decision	Most Important Reason
1. Did not want to take the time, might mean time lost from work	0%	0%
2. Afraid of ridicule; people would think I was a nut or crazy	28	19
3. Thought it was a private matter	26	8
4. Authorities couldn't do anything	19	4
5. Authorities wouldn't want to be bothered about it	23	6
6. Didn't know how to notify them or know that they should be notified	26	10
7. Too confused or upset to notify them	4	0
8. Didn't know to whom to report it	13	6
9. It was probably something normal that just looked funny for one reason or another	58	40
Total	197%*	92%**
N =	(35)	(34)

* Percents do not total 100 because multiple reasons were permitted.

** Percents are based on the total number on non-reporters answering the question. Eight percent of the respondents are not represented because they indicated more than one reason.

Table 14

Nonsighters' Reasons for Not Reporting the Sighting to Anyone Other Than Family or Friends

	Reasons Influencing Decision	Most Important Reason
1. Would not want to take the time, might mean time lost from work	7%	1%
2. Afraid of ridicule; people might think I was a nut or crazy	38	20
3. Would think it is a private matter	12	4
4. Authorities could not do anything about it	21	7
5. Authorities would not want to be bothered about it	16	4
6. Do not know how to notify them or that they should be notified	22	4
7. Would be too confused or upset to notify them	9	3
8. Would not know to whom to report	31	12
9. Probably the thing seen would be something normal that just looks funny for one reason or another	63	43
Total	219%*	98%**
N =	(219)	(196)

* Percents do not total 100 because multiple reasons were permitted.

** Percents are based on the total number of nonsighters answering the question. Two percent of the respondents are not represented because they indicated more than one reason.

report crimes had a negative view of the effectiveness of the police (1967a). Although the present study is concerned not only with the police, but also with other agencies to which UFO phenomena might be reported, it appears that the treatment expected from such an agency is not the primary deterrent to reporting. If failure to report possible UFOs had the same origins as failure to report crime, ineffectiveness and indifference on the part of authorities should have attained a higher ranking among the alternatives.

The finding that most sighters do not report their sightings, and the nature of the reasons for not reporting, given by sighters and nonsighters alike, suggest two considerations regarding the reporting process. The first is related to rapport between the public and officials of public agencies. Having assumed that the event is "something normal," the sighter apparently feels that it is inappropriate to report it. "Appropriateness" may be the key concept here; the question raised is: "When is it appropriate to report something as a 'possible UFO'?"

The second consideration is access. Not knowing whom to notify and how to notify them reveals that the appropriate avenue is not available or, at least, is not visible to the individual. Hence the concepts of appropriateness and access seem to be interdependent in considering the problem of reporting.

Further consideration of "appropriateness" is beyond the domain of this discussion, but various public agencies, although concerned with different problems, have attempted to solve the problem of access by making it clear to the public who is to be contacted. Examples of such efforts include the establishment of poison control centers and suicide prevention services, which—like the police and fire departments—may be reached by phone at any time of day.

If the public is uncertain as to what agency is to be notified about a possible UFO, its uncertainty may mirror uncertainty among agencies themselves as to which of them should handle UFO reports. If such is the case (and our survey research has no information either to confirm or negate this possibilty), it would account, in part, for both the uncertainty as to the correct procedure for reporting and the expectation that authorities may be either indifferent or ineffective. These findings clarify some of the factors which influence the reporting process, as seen by the respondents at the time of the survey.

ATTITUDES AND OPINIONS

The attitudes and opinion of the respondents in the four surveys will be discussed first in terms of responses to the single opinion statements and, second, in terms of scores on attitude scales measuring four general concepts.

Attitudes and opinions are very similar concepts. Hilgard (1962) provides these basic definitions:

> Attitude. An orientation toward or away from some object, concept, or situation; a readiness to respond in a predetermined manner to the object, concept, or situation.
>
> Opinion. A judgment or belief involving an expectation or prediction about behavior or events.

The reponses of the persons surveyed will be considered both as opinions and as attitudes.

The 29 opinion items used in the surveys and the percentages of adults and the percentages of teen-agers responding "true" and "false" to each statement appear in Table 15. Interpretation of these findings, however, requires a word of caution. First, it must be noted that the proportion in agreement with one item is not necessarily the same as that for an item similar to it. It appears that a change in wording or a slight change in emphasis results in different responses. For example, it is possible that the use of the word "science," instead of "scientists," or "government," instead of "government agency" or "Air

Table 15

Responses of Adults and Teen-agers to UFO Opinion Items

Item	Adults			Teen-agers		
	True	False	(N)	True	False	(N)
1. Some flying saucers have tried to communicate with us.	24%	76%	(1886)	37%	63%	(432)
2. All UFO reports can be explained either as well understood happenings or as hoaxes.	55%	45%	(1886)	53%	47%	(433)
3. The Air Force is doing an adequate job of investigation of UFO reports and UFO generally.	83%	17%	(1861)	72%	28%	(434)
4. No actual, physical evidence has ever been obtained from a UFO.	63%	37%	(1824)	54%	46%	(433)
5. A government agency maintains a Top Secret file of UFO reports that are deliberately withheld from the public.	69%	31%	(1852)	73%	27%	(434)
6. No airline pilots have seen UFOs.	41%	59%	(1820)	32%	68%	(432)
7. Most people would not report seeing a UFO for fear of losing a job.	33%	67%	(1839)	42%	58%	(445)
8. No authentic photographs have ever been taken of UFOs.	46%	54%	(1743)	34%	66%	(442)

Opinion Survey (cont.)	Adults True	Adults False	(N)	Teen-agers True	Teen-agers False	(N)
9. Persons who believe they have communicated with visitors from outer space are mentally ill.	44%	56%	(1823)	38%	62%	(444)
10. The Air Force has been told to explain all UFO sightings reported to them as natural or man-made happenings or events.	60%	40%	(1804)	60%	40%	(443)
11. Earth has been visited at least once in its history by beings from another world.	28%	72%	(1809)	47%	53%	(443)
12. The government should spend more money than it does now to study what UFOs are and where they come from.	46%	54%	(1815)	63%	37%	(433)
13. Intelligent forms of life cannot exist elsewhere in the universe.	30%	70%	(1812)	22%	78%	(434)
14. Flying saucers can be explained scientifically without any important new discoveries.	46%	54%	(1807)	35%	65%	(429)
15. Some UFOs have landed and left marks in the ground.	41%	59%	(1788)	54%	46%	(433)

Opinion Survey (cont.)	Adults True	False	(N)	Teen-agers True	False	(N)
16. Most UFOs are due to secret defense projects, either ours or another country's.	57%	43%	(1798)	54%	46%	(431)
17. UFOs are reported throughout the world.	87%	13%	(1801)	86%	14%	(433)
18. The government has done a good job of examining UFO reports.	71%	29%	(1796)	58%	42%	(431)
19. There have never been any UFO sightings in Soviet Russia.	27%	73%	(1698)	26%	74%	(433)
20. People want to believe that life exists elsewhere than on Earth.	82%	18%	(1813)	75%	25%	(429)
21. There have been good radar reports of UFOs.	62%	38%	(1736)	65%	35%	(429)
22. There is no government secrecy about UFOs.	37%	63%	(1830)	31%	69%	(431)
23. People have seen space ships that did not come from this planet.	40%	60%	(1807)	61%	39%	(430)
24. Some UFO reports have come from astronomers.	67%	33%	(1718)	77%	23%	(429)
25. Even the most unusual UFO report could be explained by the laws of science if we knew enough science.	73%	27%	(1818)	63%	37%	(423)

Opinion Survey (cont.)	Adults			Teenagers		
	True	False	(N)	True	False	(N)
26. People who do *not* believe in flying saucers must be stupid.	15%	85%	(1831)	15%	85%	(433)
27. UFO reports have not been taken seriously by any government agency.	30%	70%	(1801)	29%	71%	(430)
28. Government secrecy about UFOs is an idea made up by the newspapers.	26%	74%	(1779)	25%	75%	(442)
29. Science has established that there are such things as "Unidentified Flying Objects."	76%	24%	(1824)	78%	22%	(440)

Force," even in the same context will not render the same kinds of responses. Moreover, the items were initially selected to represent various beliefs which are frequently voiced with respect to the UFO problem. Consequently, some of the statements are fairly complex, and, as a result, complexity is another factor contributing to the variability in response. Therefore, the results appearing in Table 15 should be regarded simply as one way of describing public opinion.

Table 15 reveals some fairly consistent differences between the adult and teen samples. For example, a greater proportion of teen-agers tend to agree with statements which suggest evidence for the existence of UFOs. However, the use of attitude scales, rather than single items, provides a more reliable estimate of opinion and a better basis for making group comparisons regarding a general topic.

Four scales based on the UFO items (see Table 16 for scale composition) were employed to determine whether individuals felt that UFOs were from outer space, whether they felt there was evidence for the existence of UFOs, whether the government was seen as handling the problem adequately, and whether secrecy in this matter was attributable to the government. Any scale score larger than .50 is in the direction of acceptance of the scale concept, e.g., evidence exists, secrecy exists, etc., while any score smaller than .50 is in the direction of rejection of the scale concept. The farther the score from .50, the stronger the acceptance or rejection.

Analyses of the findings by scale may be found in Tables 16, 17, and 18. Table 16 presents scale information for the adult and teen samples of the national opinion survey. Table 17 provides information on the sighter and nonsighter groups in the adult sample and on the sighter sample drawn from project files. The project sighters are unique in that they are all reporting sighters as compared with the national sighters, of whom 87% are nonreporters and in their willingness to participate in an opinion survey conducted by mail. Because these respondents are essentially self-selected by their willingness to participate in the survey, they may not be assumed to be representative of all sighters whose reports are in the case files of the Colorado project. The kind of bias this self-selection might introduce is unknown. Table 18 presents the information collected by the project from the college samples. The data on college students in the first column exclude students enrolled in the UFO classes. These latter students are represented in the second column.

Responses of students in UFO classes are interesting because of their exposure to material concerning UFOs and because of their high interest in the topic. Rather than attribute differences between this group and any other group to exposure

Table 16

Opinion Scale Means and Standard Deviations for Adults and Teen-agers, National Opinion Survey

Scale	Adult Sample	Teen Sample
Outer Space		
Mean	.39	.55
Standard Deviation	.31	.31
N =	(1659)	(437)
Evidence		
Mean	.60	.71
Standard Deviation	.34	.30
N =	(1629)	(434)
Adequacy		
Mean	.69	.56
Standard Deviation	.30	.32
N =	(1656)	(434)
Secrecy		
Mean	.70	.74
Standard Deviation	.32	.29
N =	(1631)	(440)

Table 17

Opinion Scale Means and Standard Deviations for Respondents in National Sample and for Sample of Sighters from Project Files

Scale	Nonsighters*	Sighters Adult Sample	Sighters Project Sample
Outer Space			
Mean	.40	.65	.78
Standard Deviation	.31	.33	.27
N =	(1770)	(49)	(94)
Evidence			
Mean	.59	.83	.94
Standard Deviation	.34	.26	.14
N =	(1738)	(49)	(94)
Adequacy			
Mean	.70	.45	.34
Standard Deviation	.30	.36	.35
N =	(1769)	(49)	(94)
Secrecy			
Mean	.69	.83	.89
Standard Deviation	.32	.23	.21
N =	(1741)	(49)	(92)

* Adult Sample

Table 18

Opinion Scale Means and Standard Deviations for College Students and College UFO Classes

Scale	College Students*	UFO Classes
Outer Space		
Mean	.55	.79
Standard Deviation	.32	.26
N =	(670)	(48)
Evidence		
Mean	.78	.85
Standard Deviation	.29	.21
N =	(668)	(48)
Adequacy		
Mean	.51	.24
Standard Deviation	.38	.33
N =	(669)	(48)
Secrecy		
Mean	.88	.92
Standard Deviation	.22	.17
N =	(669)	(48)

* Not included are students enrolled in Flying Saucer Classes.

to an UFO course, one might assume that these students are essentially self-selected on the basis of their prior attitudes or interest.

On only two of the scales do the mean scale scores for any group represent views antithetical to those of another. Differences of mean opinion on the other two scales represent only differences in *degree* of acceptance or rejection.

On the outer space scale, adults tend to respond negatively to the hypothesis that UFOs are extra-terrestrial in origin, while teen-agers and college students, on the average, are almost neutral, and the two groups of sighters tend to react with greater degrees of acceptance of the possibility.

On the adequacy scale, both adults and teens are inclined to view the government's efforts as adequate. The mean scale value for sighters, though of a middle position, leans toward a negative view of the government's adequacy in investigating the UFO problem. This finding cannot be explained solely in terms of sighters' first-hand experience with reporting, because most of the sighters in the national survey were non-reporters. The mean score of college students falls between those of teen-agers and sighters.

On the remaining two scales, differences of opinion are merely a matter of degree, with the mean scale scores for all groups in the same direction. It would appear that the majority of respondents in all groups feel that there is some evidence for the existence of UFOs, with the adults and teen-agers tending to be the most neutral. The adults tend to be the most cautious in their view, with a mean close to the midpoint of the scale. Teen-agers tend to give more support to the *possibility* that evidence for UFOs does exist, and both groups of sighters seem nearly certain that evidence does exist.

A similar pattern is evident for the responses regarding secrecy. All groups to a greater or lesser degree, tend to suspect government secrecy with regard to UFOs and UFO reports.

Differences between adult and teen scores on three of the four scales, the outer space, evidence, and adequacy scales, were found to be significant at the .01 level. At *t* test (McNemar, 1962), modified for the present data was used; the sampling error for comparison of survey variable values was estimated, on the basis of sampling tolerances provided by ORC, to be approximately 20% greater than under the assumption of simple random sampling, yielding a design factor (Kish, 1965) of 1.20, which was incorporated in the *t* test.

Because these findings are the result of opinion surveys, they do not imply that, for example, evidence or secrecy actually exists. The findings only reflect opinions held by the adult, teen, college, and project sighter samples in our surveys, and only the findings for the adult and teen samples may be considered indicative of the opinions of adults and teens in the general population.

CORRELATES OF ATTITUDES

Our analysis of the 1966 Gallup data suggests that age and education, but particularly age, may be related to opinions regarding UFOs and related topics. In the analysis of the Gallup data, it appeared that the younger and the better educated persons are more likely to say that flying saucers are "real" and that there are "people somewhat like ourselves living on other planets in the universe." The differences between mean scores on four attitude scales for adults and teen-agers from the national opinion survey (Table 19) once again suggest that age may be a factor in determining attitude.

Two kinds of analyses of the adult survey sample were undertaken to examine the relationships between age and opinion and between education and opinion. In Table 19 are the scores for adults on the four scales by age. The younger the age group, the less the respondents tend to reject the extra-terrestrial hypothesis, the more inclined they are to believe that there is evidence for UFOs and government secrecy about them; younger respondents also tend to be slightly less satisfied with government handling of the "UFO problem."

Findings also related to age have been reported by David R. Deener (1967). In a survey of 1,200 persons conducted in New Orleans, La., he found that 61% of those pooled under 25 years of age, 48% of those aged 25 to 29, and 34% of those aged 50 and over felt that flying saucers are real. When

Table 19

UFO Opinion Scale Means and Standard Deviations by Age for Adults, National Opinion Survey

Age	Outer Space	Evidence	Adequacy	Secrecy
18-29				
Mean	.48	.68	.64	.77
Standard Deviation	.32	.33	.33	.29
N =	(474)	(473)	(477)	(472)
30-39				
Mean	.43	.63	.68	.76
Standard Deviation	.32	.34	.31	.28
N =	(369)	(366)	(370)	(366)
40-49				
Mean	.39	.59	.71	.69
Standard Deviation	.30	.33	.30	.33
N =	(361)	(357)	(362)	(360)
50-59				
Mean	.37	.58	.73	.66
Standard Deviation	.30	.32	.27	.34
N =	(290)	(283)	(291)	(286)
60-69				
Mean	.32	.52	.71	.58
Standard Deviation	.29	.31	.30	.33
N =	(190)	(182)	(187)	(182)
70 and above				
Mean	.27	.42	.77	.55
Standard Deviation	.28	.33	.22	.33
N =	(156)	(146)	(152)	(194)

asked if they thought flying saucers come from outer space, 47% of those under 25, 27% of those aged 25 to 49, and 19% of those 50 and over answered yes (*Times-Picayune*, 5 November 1967). According to Strentz (1967), Eugene J. Webb obtained data in 1966 that indicated that as age increases, the proportion of respondents who think UFOs are from some other planet decreases. In that study, a greater proportion of younger than older respondents also felt that the government is concealing information about UFOs.

Patterns are less clear for the analyses by education, Table 20. It does appear, however, that education is related to attitudes regarding evidence and secrecy. Better educated individuals feel more strongly that both evidence and secrecy exist.

Because education and income are frequently examined together as determinants of socio-economic status, family income was chosen as an additional variable for the analysis of correlates. Instead of using mean scores for groups, a correlational approach was employed. Pearson Product Moment Correlation Coefficients (McNemar, 1962) were calculated. It was found that the correlation between age and education is −0.37, age and family income, −0.33, and education and family income, +0.45. The correlations of these three demographic variables with the four scales appears in Table 21. All correlations are significant at the .01 level, except for the correlation between family income and the adequacy scale, which is not satatistically significant. Of the three demographic variables, age is the strongest single predictor of opinion.

The correlations of the scales with age seem strong enough to warrant some speculations regarding its role in the nature of opinion expressed. These findings reflect, perhaps, something interesting about either a) the change of beliefs and attitudes with age, or b) the changing nature of beliefs and attitudes. To test the former interpretation would necessitate a prospective study in which the same attitudes are assessed at five- or ten-year intervals, using the same respondents.

In consideration of the marked changes that have taken place in culture and technology during the past 40 years (noting that the oldest respondents in the sample were young adults 40 years ago) and particularly during the past 20 years (dur-

Table 20

UFO Opinion Scale Means and Standard Deviations by Education for Adults, National Opinion Survey

Education	Outer Space	Evidence	Adequacy	Secrecy
Less than 8th Grade				
Mean	.32	.49	.73	.55
Standard Deviation	.29	.32	.26	.36
N =	(188)	(177)	(188)	(179)
8th Grade				
Mean	.33	.51	.71	.60
Standard Deviation	.30	.33	.27	.33
N =	(200)	(193)	(196)	(189)
High School Incomplete				
Mean	.41	.58	.73	.67
Standard Deviation	.31	.32	.27	.31
N =	(431)	(408)	(416)	(409)
High School Completed				
Mean	.44	.64	.68	.73
Standard Deviation	.32	.34	.30	.30
N =	(632)	(618)	(621)	(618)
College Incomplete				
Mean	.45	.64	.63	.78
Standard Deviation	.32	.34	.35	.30
N =	(234)	(230)	(235)	(234)
College Completed				
Mean	.38	.67	.68	.80
Standard Deviation	.28	.34	.33	.29
N =	(221)	(220)	(222)	(220)

Table 21

*Correlation of Age, Education and Family Income with UFO Opinion Scales**

	Scale			
	Outer Space	Evidence	Adequacy	Secrecy
Age	−.21	−.20	+.13	−.23
Education	+.08	+.16	−.07	+.23
Family Income	+.10	+.11	−.02	+.18

* Correlation coefficients are based on the adult sample.

ing which time the youngest members of the sample were growing up and receiving most of their formal education), the second interpretation seems highly tenable. Because the younger people have been exposed exclusively or primarily to the "space age," an era of accelerated technological advance and an era in which educational objectives have moved from the acquisition of facts to an emphasis on inquiry and problem-solving, it may be that age differences for the outer space and the evidence scales may reflect a greater readiness on the part of younger people to accept as possible that which has not, at present, been demonstrated.

At one time flying to the moon was only fantasy; now the plans for the landing of the first manned spacecraft are being completed. In addition, not only the scientific community, but the general public are aware of special technical problems, such as those concerning "soft landings," and zero gravity conditions of space flight. At the same time, television, a major medium of entertainment and information, is able to give the appearance of reality to that which is technologically impossible—at least at this time. As a result of these and other factors, the younger person may have a greater range of acceptance for "what might be" than the older generation.

Given the findings of the present study, one might suspect that reactions to various projected or hypothesized social, scientific, and technological changes would reveal similar kinds of age- and, perhaps, education-differences. Such changes might include chemical methods to increase the capacity for memory, human hibernation, permanently inhabited undersea colonies, or the major use of rockets for commercial transportation—all of which have been included among projections for the future (Kahn and Wiener, 1967). The major implication of this discussion is that the present findings relating age and education to attitudes regarding UFO phenomena may, in large measure, reflect the changing technology and culture.

Inherent in the above speculations are at least two research questions which may be posed. The first of these concerns formal training in the sciences, the second concerns exposure to information sources.

The measure of education used in the present study simply represents years of schooling. If the above interpretations are correct in relating attitude to differential exposure to a changing technology and culture by way of age, it should prove interesting to examine further attitudes with respect to both the nature of the individual's education and to age. Attitudes of persons trained in the physical sciences might be compared with those of comparable levels of education in other fields; the views of older scientists within a discipline might be compared with those of the younger.

The second variable suggested by the present research is differential exposure to information sources. To what extent do age-related attitudes reflect differential exposure either to popular or to technical sources of scientific information? For example, do younger people have a greater knowledge of the sciences and in particular of recent scientific developments? Is interest in an exposure to science fiction predictive of attitudes about conditions not now technologically possible or culturally familiar? Such questions as these may clarify the apparent relationships which are suggested by the present findings regarding attitudes toward UFO phenomena.

Apart from these speculations, there are a number of procedures in the social psychology of UFO phenomena which merit consideration for further study, as William A. Scott has pointed out (1968), and which could not be studied by the Colorado Project.

Scott suggests that, for example, the cognitive correlates of UFO phenomena might be studied in terms of a) the subject's interest in and information about UFO phenomena; b) the degree and range of credibility that the subject attaches to reported sightings; c) the subject's knowledge of possibly confounding illusions and misinterpretations, e.g., atmospheric an astronomical phenomena; d) attitudes related to the process of hypothesis testing, the process of considering and rejecting alternative explanations, the rapidity with which the subject reaches a conclusion, and the certainty that he attaches to his interpretation; e) the degree of cognitive elaboration evidenced when the subject is exposed to a mock-up or experimental UFO.

Another area which the limitations of time and funds made it impracticable to study is that concerned with communication processes. Among the possible foci of study are the ways in which consensus develops among observers and the effects of communication upon that consensus. Still another approach might be the comparison of independent interpretations of the same UFO phenomenon. A related area of research might include studies of the effect of publicity on the frequency and nature of reports, the effect of the interviewers' (e.g., journalists', researchers') attitudes on the respondents' reports, and the effect of communication between subjects on the convergence and clarity of their reports.

Other suggestions for further studies of UFO phenomena, in the field of social psychiatry, are made by Rhine (Section VI, Chapter 3).

It is the writer's judgment that, in evaluating the feasibility and desirability of such further studies, their costs, material and non-material, need to be weighed against the potential usefulness of the resulting data. The ultimate value of further studies concerning the social psychological aspects of UFO phenomena may rest on the generality of the processes studied and the degree to which the research contributes to the advancement of the behavioral and social sciences.

References

Cronbach, L. J., "Coefficient Alpha and the Internal Structure of Tests," *Psychometrika*, 1951, 16, 297-334.

Ennis, P. H., *Criminal Victimization in the United States*, Washington, D.C.: U. S. Government Printing Office, 1967a.

———, "Crimes, Victims, and the Police," *Trans-action*, 4, 7, 1967b, 36-44.

Gallup, G., "Nine out of Ten People Heard of Flying Saucers," *Public Opinion News Service*, Princeton, N.J., 15 August 1947.

———, "Just What ARE Those Flying Saucers—A Secret Weapon?" *Public Opinion News Service*, Princeton, N.J., 20 May 1950.

———, "More than 5 Million Americans Claim to Have Seen 'Flying Saucers,'" *Gallup Poll,* Princeton, N.J., 8 May 1966.
Hilgard, E. R., *Introduction to Psychology*. New York: Harcourt, Brace, 1962.
Kahn, H. and A. J. Wiener. *The Year 2000*. New York: Macmillan, 1967.
Kish, L. *Survey Sampling*. New York: Wiley, 1965.
McNemar, Q. *Psychological Statistics*. New York: Wiley, 1962.
Rotter, J. B., "Generalized Expectancies for Internal versus External Control of Reinforcement" (see Appendix), *Psychological Monographs,* 80, 1, 1966.
Scott, W. A., "Measures of Test Homogeneity," *Educational and Psychological Measurement,* 1960, 20, 751-757.
———, Unpublished report minutes of the Fourth Meeting of the C.U. UFO-Investigators, Boulder, Colorado, 28 October 1966.
———, Personal Communication, 1968.
Strentz, H., Personal communication, 1967.
"Survey of Tulane Students Reveals Belief in Saucers." *Times Picayune,* New Orleans: 5 November 1967.
United States Bureau of the Census, *Current Population Reports, Population Estimates,* Series P-25, No. 385. Washington, D.C.: U. S. Government Printing Office, 14 February 1968.

Section IV

CASE STUDIES

In this section three kinds of specific cases are presented: 1) those of special interest that occurred prior to the commencement of the Colorado project; 2) those investigated in the field by project teams; and 3) those involving the analysis of photographs. In most instances, field investigation involved study of the sighting reports and, rarely, of the sighted object; in a few cases, only the analysis of purported UFO-related physical evidence was carried out. Information received regarding some older cases was reviewed but only when new information made new conclusions possible is it reported as a case. Examples are the 1952 sighting report of W. B. Nash and William Fortenberry and the 1954 sighting of J. H. Howard, both of which are discussed in Section III, Chapter 5. The renowned 1952 radar sightings at Washington, D. C., are also discussed in that chapter. Weather data concerning the Washington sightings are presented in Appendix L. None of these are presented as case studies in this section.

Many witnesses were willing to cooperate with the study only on the condition that their names be withheld. Consequently, a uniform policy of eliminating the name of the witness or witnesses in all cases has been followed, as their identities are irrelevant to the facts under study.

The region in which the sighting occurred is designated by its location in the northern or southern half of a time zone. Thus the designation "South Pacific" refers to the southern portion of the Pacific time zone. At the request of some of the witnesses to and participants in sightings, the names of places and other descriptive data have been changed. These changes have been invariably made, however, in such a way that every significant fact has been accurately presented and the case, as a whole, described in all its essentials.

Chapter I Case studies predating the term of the project (Cases 1–10)

Case 1
South Mountain
Spring 1950
Investigators: Low, staff

Abstract:

A professional meteorologist saw an unidentified object flying beneath clouds. He believed the object to be a powered craft three to five feet in diameter. Positive identification cannot be made, although the possibility that the object was common earth debris is suggested.

Background:

A UFO sighting from the grounds of an Observatory had attracted attention because the observation was made by a professional meteorologist who is highly regarded in the scientific community. The meteorologist wrote the following account within an hour of his observation:

> I saw the object between 12:15 and 12:20 p.m. . . . from the grounds of the . . . Observatory. It was moving from the Southeast to the Northwest. It was extremely prominent and showed some size to the naked eye, that is, it was not merely a pinpoint. During the last half of its visibility I observed it with 4-power binoculars. At first it looked like a parachute tipped at an angle to the vertical, but this same effect could have been produced by a sphere partly illuminated by the sun and partly shadowed, or by a disc-shaped object as well. Probably there are still other configurations which would give the same impression under proper inclination and illumination. I could see it well enough to be sure it was not an airplane (no propeller or wings were apparent) nor a bird. I saw no evidence of exhaust gases nor any markings on the object.
>
> Most fortunately the object passed between me and a small bright cumulus cloud in the Northwest. Thus it must have been at or below the cloud level. A few seconds later it disappeared, apparently into the cloud.
>
> Against the sky it was very bright but against the cloud it was dark. This could be produced by a grey body which would be bright against the relatively dark sky, but dark against the bright cloud. Alternatively, if the object were half in sunlight and half shadowed the sunlit part might have had no detectable contrast with the cloud while the shadowed part appeared dark.
>
> I immediately telephoned the U.S. Weather Bureau (2-3 miles S.W. of the Observatory). They were estimating the cloud to be 6000 feet above the ground. Now estimates of cloud heights are rather risky, so I obtained their observations of temperature and dew point, and from the known lapse rates of these quantities in a convective atmosphere, calculated the cloud base to be at 12,000 feet. I believe this latter figure to be the more

accurate one because later in the afternoon the cumulus clouds thickened but at all times remained well above the tops of our nearby mountains. These are about 6000 feet above us.

Thus, having some idea of the object's elevation and its angular diameter through the binoculars (about equivalent to a dime seen at 50 feet with the naked eye), I calculated its size to be 3 to 5 feet for a height of 6-12 thousand feet, and a zenith angle of about 45°. This size estimate could easily be in error by a factor or two, but I am sure it was a small object.

The clouds were drifting from the SW to the NE at right angles to the motion of the object. Therefore, it must have been powered in some way. I did not time it but for that elevation I would estimate its speed to be about 100 miles per hour, perhaps as high as 200 m.p.h. This too means a powered craft. However, I could hear no engine noise.

nvestigation:

The meteorologist who reported this observation was interviewed. He could offer no information beyond his original report written 17 years earlier. In earlier correspondence with project personnel, however, he furnished copies of letters exchanged in 1961 with another interested scientist who suggested alternate explanations of his observation.

The crucial point in question was the height of the object, coupled with the direction of wind at that elevation. Did the object disappear into a cloud, thus showing it to be at cloud level, or was its abrupt disappearance due to reorientation of the object relative to the observer, such as the turning of a sheet of paper edgewise to the observer, or to passage of a reflecting object into the shadow of a cloud? In either of the latter cases, the observed object could have been much lower than cloud level in which case its motion could be accounted for by winds, and the requirement of self-propulsion would no longer pertain.

Loren W. Crow, Certified Consulting Meteorologist, was commissioned to analyze records of weather pertinent to this observation. He studied surface weather records, and winds aloft data from this South Mountain area. According to his report, winds were light and variable at all stations. He presented a vertical profile of cloudiness and the following evidence of strong vertical mixing. (Crow's Fig. 4 is not included in this excerpt from his report).

Excerpts have been made from the detailed surface observations at three stations. It is worth noting that at approximately 12:30 (the observations actually being made prior to this filing time) . . . [two stations] carried a notation under remarks that dust devils were being observed. From the Glossary of Meteorology a *dust devil* is defined as a well-developed dust whirl. The following is a further quotation from that definition.

> . . . A rapidly rotating column of air over a dry and dusty or sandy area, carrying dust, leaves and other light material picked up from the ground. When well developed it is known

as a dust devil. Dust whirls form, typically, as the re… strong convection during sunny, hot, calm summer afternoo… This type is generally several yards in diameter at the base, narrowing for a short distance upward and then expanding again, like two cones apex to apex. Their height varies; normally it is only 100 to 300 feet, but in hot desert country they may be as high as 2000 feet. . . .

The actual lowering of temperature between 12:30 and 13:30 at . . . [airport A] indicates that strong vertical mixing took place during that hour. It could have started in the vicinity of . . . [city A], particularly over the warmer portions of local heat absorbing surfaces, a few minutes or an hour earlier.

The spread between dry bulb and wet bulb temperature was comparable at each of the three stations, indicating that they were in the same air mass. This spread was slightly less at the . . . [airport A] than at . . . [city B or C]. Super-adiabiatic temperature lapse rates would have been prevalent near the surface in the late morning hours.

Surface conditions were quite dry. The most recent rainfall above a trace recorded at both . . . [city A and airport A] occurred on May 4, sixteen days earlier. The amounts received at that time were .34 inch in . . . [city A and] .35 inch at the airport [A]. The maxima temperatures were well above normal for the month on May 20. The maximum of 83° at . . . [city C] was the first such maximum that had been reached in 1950. A warmer maximum temperature had been recorded on only one day previously at . . . [city A].

The vertical wind profiles show only light winds prevailing at the level of the sighting. The direction of air flow at the sighting level as indicated by the pressure pattern would have been from the northeast. Velocity would have been less than 10 mph and could have been overcome by local convective activity or the influence of any particularly large cloud development.

It is the author's opinion that within the hour prior to the sighting strong vertical mixing of the air in the first 3,000 feet above the surface would have been a typical pattern of air motion in the vicinity of the sighting. Horizontal flow of air would have been limited to velocities not exceeding 10 mph. Visibility would have been excellent.

In addition to his report, Crow expressed the opinion that some light, low density material must have been carried aloft by a localized dust whirl not too far from the observer. He suggested that at the time of sighting vertical motion no longer was being applied and the object was drifting slowly along a nearly horizontal path from NE toward NW. Although the witness reported cloud movement, Crow suggests that this observation could have been the result of movement of the object combined with very slight cloud movement, producing the impression that the cloud was drifting more than it actually was. A near-deflated child's balloon or a sheet of paper, carbon paper, or plastic at an altitude of 1500-3000 ft. could have caused observations similar to those reported.

no way to establish the altitude of the reported is not certain that the object was at cloud elevation, .e are other acceptable explanations of abrupt disap- .ice of such an object. Thus, the object may have been n. .n nearer to the observer than he assumed, and may have been airborne debris.

Case 2
Greenwich
Summer 1956
Investigator: Staff

Abstract:

At least one UFO was tracked by air traffic control radar (GCA) at two USAR-RAF stations, with apparently corresponding visual sightings of round, white rapidly moving objects which changed directions abruptly. Interception by RAF fighter aircraft was attempted; one aircraft was vectored to the UFO by GCA radar and the pilot reported airborne radar contact and radar "gunlock." The UFO appeared to circle around behind the aircraft and followed it in spite of the pilot's evasive maneuvers. Contact was broken when the aircraft returned to base, low on fuel. The preponderance of evidence indicates the possibility of a genuine UFO in this case. The weather was generally clear with good visibility.

Background:

The existence of this very interesting radar-visual case was first brought to the attention of the project staff in winter 1968 by the receipt of an unsolicited letter from one of the principal witnesses, a retired USAF non-commissioned officer who was the Watch Supervisor at the GCA station on the night in question. This letter is rather well written, and since it forms the most coherent account of this UFO case, it is reproduced below in its entirety.

> Reference your UFO Study: you probably already have this item in your file, but, in case you don't, I will briefly outline it and you can contact me for full details if you want them.
>
> I retired (20 years service) . . . from the USAF. I have placed my name, rank, and serial number at the top of the page if you want to check on my authenticity. I was an Air Traffic Controller throughout my service career and utilized radar the last 16 years in the control of Air Traffic. I won't bother listing the types and locations, although I could supply all this if needed.
>
> In 1956, . . . (I can't remember the exact date or month), I was on duty as Watch Supervisor at . . . [GCA A] in the Radar Air Traffic Control Center. It was the 5:00 p.m. to midnight shift. I had either four or five other controllers on my shift. I was sitting at the Supervisor's Coordinating desk and

received a call on the direct line (actually I'm not sure which line it was). Anyway, it was . . . [GCA B] calling and the radar operator asked me if we had any targets on our scopes travelling at 4,000 mph. They said they had watched a target on their scopes proceed from a point 30 or 40 miles east . . . to a point 40 miles west of . . . [GCA B]. The target passed directly over . . . [GCA B] RAF Station (also an USAF Station). He said the tower reported seeing it go by and it just appeared to be a blurry light. A C-47 flying over the base at 5,000 feet altitude also reported seeing it as a blurred light that passed under his aircraft. No report as to actual distance below the aircraft. I immediately had all controllers start scanning the radar scopes. I had each scope set on a different range—from 10 miles to 200 miles radius of . . . [GCA A]. At this time I did not contact anyone by telephone as I was rather skeptical of this report. We were using full MTI on our radar, which eliminated entirely all ground returns and stationary targets. There was very little or no traffic or targets on the scopes, as I recall. However one controller noticed a stationary target on the scopes about 20 to 25 miles southwest. This was unusual as a stationary target should have been eliminated unless it was moving at a speed of at least 40 to 45 knots. And yet we could detect no movement at all. We watched this target on all the different scopes for several minutes and I called the GCA Unit at . . . [A] to see if they had this target on their scopes also. They confirmed the target was on their scope in the same geographical location. As we watched the stationary target started moving at a speed of 400 to 600 mph in a north, northeast direction until it reached a point about 20 miles north northwest of . . . [A]. There was no slow start or build-up to this speed—it was constant from the second it started to move until it stopped.

I called and reported all the facts to this point, including . . . [B] GCA's initial report, to the . . . Command Post . . . . . . I also hooked in my local AFB Commanding Officer and my Unit (AFCS Communications Squadron) Commander on my switchboard. And there could have been others hooked in also that I was not aware of. I repeated all the facts known to this point and continued to give a detailed report on the target's movements and location. The target made several changes in location, always in a straight line, always at about 600 mph and always from a standing or stationary point to his next stop at constant speed—no build-up in speed at all—these changes in location varied from 8 miles to 20 miles in length—no set pattern at any time. Time spent stationary between movements also varied from 3 to 4 minutes to 5 or 6 minutes (possibly even longer as I was busy answering questions—listening to theories, guesses, etc. that the conference line people were saying). This continued for some time. After I imagine about 30 to 45 minutes, it was decided to scramble two RAF interceptors to investigate. This was done I believe by . . . Air Force calling the RAF and, after hearing what the score was, they scrambled one aircraft. (The second got off after as I will mention later.)

The interceptor aircraft took off from an RAF Station . . . and approached . . . [A] from the southwest. Radio and radar contact was established with the RAF intercept aircraft at a point about 30 to 35 miles southwest . . . [and] inbound to . . . [A]. On initial contact we gave the interceptor pilot all the background information on the UFO, his (the interceptor's) present distance and bearing from . . . [A], the UFO's (which was stationary at the time) distance and bearing from . . . [A]. We explained we did not know the altitude of the UFO but we could assume his altitude was above 15,000 feet and below 20,000 feet, due to the operational characteristics of the radar (CPS-5 type radar, I believe). Also we mentioned the report from the C-47 over . . . [B] that relayed the story about the light which passed below him. His altitude was 5,000 feet.

We immediately issued headings to the interceptor to guide him to the UFO. The UFO remained stationary throughout. This vectoring of the interceptor aircraft continued. We continually gave the intercept aircraft his heading to the UFO and his distance from the UFO at approximately 1 to 2 miles intervals. Shortly after we told the interceptor aircraft he was one-half mile from the UFO and it was twelve-o'clock from his position, he said. "Roger, . . . I've got my guns locked on him." Then he paused and said, "Where did he go? Do you still have him?" We replied, "Roger, it appeared he got behind you and he's still there." [There were now two targets; one behind the other, same speed, very close, but two separate distinct targets.]

The first movement by the UFO was so swift (circling behind the interceptor); I missed it entirely, but it was seen by the other controllers. However, the fact that this had occurred was confirmed by the pilot of the interceptor. The pilot of the interceptor told us he would try to shake the UFO and would try it again. He tried everything—he climbed, dived, circled, etc., but the UFO acted like it was glued right behind him, always the same distance, very close, but we always had two distinct targets. [Note: Target resolution on our radar at the range they were from the antenna (about 10 to 30 miles, all in the southerly sectors from . . . [A]) would be between 200 and 600 feet probably. Closer than that we would have got one target from both aircraft and UFO. Most specifications say 500 feet is the minimum, but I believe it varies and 200 to 600 feet is closer to the truth and, in addition, the tuning of the equipment, atmospheric conditions, etc., also help determine this figure.]

The interceptor pilot continued to try and shake the UFO for about ten minutes (approximate—it seemed longer both to him and us). He continued to comment occasionally and we could tell from the tonal quality he was getting worried, excited and also pretty scared.

He finally said, "I'm returning to Station . . . [A]. Let me know if he follows me. I'm getting low on petrol." The target (UFO) followed him only a short distance, as he headed south southwest, and the UFO stopped and remained stationary. We advised the interceptor that the UFO target had stopped following and was now stationary about 10 miles south of . . . [A]. He rogered this message and almost immediately the second interceptor called us on the same frequency. We replied and told him we would advise him when we had a radar target, so we could establish radar contact with his aircraft. (He was not on radar at this time, probably had just taken off and was too low for us to pick him up, or too far away—we had most of the scopes on short range, so we could watch the UFO closely on the smaller range.) The number two interceptor called the number one interceptor by name (Tom, Frank—whatever his name was) and asked him, "Did you see anything?" Number one replied, "I saw something, but I'll be damned if I know what it was." Number two said, "What happened?" Number one said, "He (or it) got behind me and I did everything I could to get behind him and I couldn't. It's the damnest thing I've ever seen." Number one also made a remark at this time to number two, that he had his radar locked on whatever it was for just a few seconds so there was something there that was solid. Number one then switched frequencies to his home base frequency. We gave number two the location of the UFO and advised him that we still didn't have him on radar, but probably would have shortly. He delayed answering for some seconds and then finally said, . . . [A] ____________ (Identification aircraft call sign)—can't remember what call sign these aircraft were using. Returning home, my engine is malfunctioning." He then left our frequency.

Throughout this we kept all the agencies, . . . advised on every aspect, every word that was said, everything.

We then inquired what action they wanted to take. They had no more suggestions and finally they told us to just keep watching the target and let them know if anything else happened. The target made a couple more short moves, then left our radar coverage in a northerly direction—speed still about 600 mph. We lost target outbound to the north at about 50 to 60 miles, which is normal if aircraft or target is at an altitude below 5,000 feet (because of the radiation lobe of that type radar). We notified . . . Air Division Command Post and they said they'd tell everybody for us.

I made out a written report on all this, in detail for the officers in charge of my facility, and was told that unless I was contacted later for further information, he would take care of it. I don't know if a CERVIS report was submitted on this or not —I heard no more about it.

All speeds in this report were calculated speeds based on time and distance covered on radar. This speed was calculated many times that evening and although this happened quite awhile ago, the basic elements are correct.

Fig. 1 shows a map of the contact as drawn by the witness.

Investigation:

Since this case was discovered so late in the project, investigation was limited to a follow-up request for additional information from Project Blue Book, and analysis of the available details of the case by investigators familiar with radar and optical propagation anomalies.

Copies of the Project Blue Book files on the case were received in late August of 1968. A considerable amount of this material is reproduced below. One of the interesting aspects of this case is the remarkable accuracy of the account of the witness as given in the letter reproduced above, which was apparently written from memory 12 yr. after the incident. There are a number of minor discrepancies, mostly a matter of figures (the C-47 at 5,000 ft. was evidently actually at 4,000 ft.), and he seems to have confused the identity of location C with B; however, all of the major details of his account seem to be well confirmed by the Blue Book account.

There were ancillary sightings at . . . [C] besides those which instigated the UFO search by the . . . [A] GCA Unit but as subsequent airborne intercept attempts yielded neither radar nor visual contact, these accounts are not detailed below.

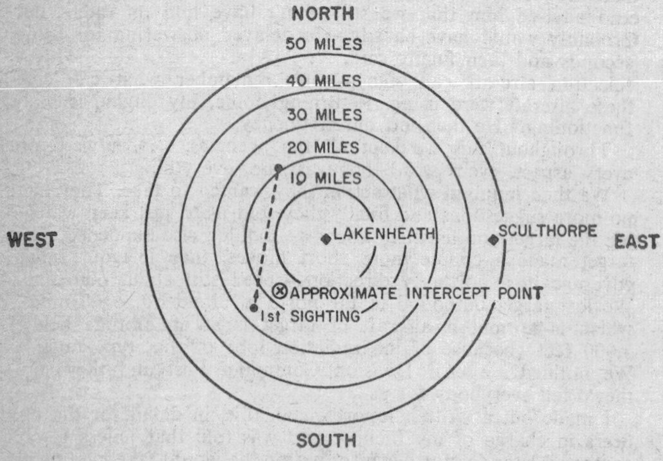

Fig. 1

At 22557, . . . [C] GCA sighted object thirty miles east of station traveling westerly at 2000-4000 mph. Object disappeared on scope two miles east of station and immediately appeared on scope three miles west of station where it disappeared thirty miles west of station on scope. Tower personnel at . . . [C] reported to GCA a bright light passed over the field east to west at terrific speed and at about 4000 feet alt. At same time pilot in aircraft at 4000 feet alt. over . . . [C] reported a bright light streaked under his aircraft traveling east to west at terrific speed.

At this time . . . [C] GCA checked with RAF station . . . [A] GCA to determine if unusual sightings were occurring . . . [A] GCA alerted [the] AAA stationed at . . . [A] and . . . [B] GCA to watch for unusual targets. Following info is the observations made by this station radar, tower and ground personnel placed in format required by AFR 2000-2: 1. Description of object(s): (A) Round white lights (B) One observer from ground stated on first observation object was about size of golf ball. As object continued in flight it became a "pin point." (C) Color was white. (D) Two from ground observation undetermined number of blips appearing and disappearing on radar scopes. (E) No formation as far as radar sightings concerned. Ground observers stated one white light joined up with another and both disappeared in formation together. (F) No features or details other than the white light. (G) Objects as seen by ground observers and GCA radar have feature of traveling at terrific speeds and then stopping and changing course immediately. 2. Description of course of objects: (A) Ground observers looked at sky and saw the object(s). RAF Station . . . [A] GCA was alerted by . . . [C] GCA to be on lookout for unusual targets. (B) Ground observers estimated objects were 20-2500 feet alt and were on a SW heading. Object stopped and immediately assumed an easterly heading. RAF Station . . . [A] GCA and Air Traffic Control Center reports radar tracking from 6 miles west to about twenty miles SW where target stopped and assumed a stationary position for five minutes. Target then assumed a reading north westerly into the Station and stopped two miles NW of Station. . . . [A] GCA reports three to four additional targets were doing the same. Radars reported these facts to occur at later hours than the ground observers. (C) Ground observers report no change in alt and objects disappeared on easterly heading. Radar sets stated no definite disappearance factors other than targets disappeared from scopes at approx 0330 GMT Aug 14. (D) Flight path was straight but jerky with object stopping instantly and then continuing. Maneuvers were of same pattern except one object was observed to "lock on" to fighter scrambled by RAF and followed all maneuvers of the jet fighter aircraft. In addition, . . . [A] Radar Air Traffic Control Center observed object 17 miles east of Station making sharp rectangular course of flight. This maneuver was not conducted by circular path but on right angles at speeds of 600-800 mph. Object would stop and start with amazing rapidity. (E) Objects simply disappeared. (F) Objects were observed intermittently by RAF Station . . . [A] radars from 140310 to 140330. 3. Manner of observation: (A) Ground-visual, air-electronic and ground-electronic. Ground-electronic equipment was TS-ID, CPS 5, and CPN4 radars. Air-electronic was A-1 airborne radar equipment in . . . jet aircraft. Type of aircraft, Venom, operating out of RAF Station. . . . 4. Time and date of sighting: (A) Summer 140010Z through 140330Z. (B) Night (sky clear and nin/th of clouds—moonlight). 5. Location of observers RAF Station

. . . [A] 52°24′N 0°33′E. 6. Weather and winds-aloft conditions at time and place of sightings: (A) Clear sky until 0300Z shortly thereafter scattered clouds at 3500 ft. (B) From midnight until 0600Z surface wind was 230 deg at 15 knots; 6000 ft 290 deg at 24 knots; 1000 ft 290 deg at 35 knots; 16,000 ft 290 deg at 45 knots; 20,000 ft 290 deg at 53 knots; 30,000 ft 290 deg at 62 knots; 50,000 ft 290 deg at 75 knots. (C) Ceiling unlimited. (D) Visibility from 0001Z to 04000Z was 10 nautical miles. (E) 1/10 of sky covered at 0300Z. 8. Ground observers report unusual amount of shooting stars in sky. Further state the objects seen were definitely not shooting stars as there were no trails behind as are usual with such sightings. 9. Interception was undertaken by one British jet fighter on alert by . . . [A] sector control. Aircraft is believed to have been a Venom. The aircraft flew over RAF Station . . . [A] and was vectored toward a target on radar 6 miles east of the field. Pilot advised he had a bright white light in sight and would investigate. At thirteen miles west he reported loss of target and white light. . . . [A] RATCC vectored him to a target 10 miles east of . . . [A] and pilot advised target was on radar and he was "locking on." Pilot reported he had lost target on his radar. . . . [A] RATCC reports that as the Venom passed the target on radar, the target began a tail chase of the friendly fighter. RATCC requested pilot acknowledge this chase. Pilot acknowledged and stated he would try to circle and get behind the target. Pilot advised he was unable to "shake" the target off his tail and requested assistance. One additional Venom was scrambled from the RAF Station. Original pilot stated; "clearest target I have ever seen on radar." Target disappeared and second aircraft did not establish contact. First aircraft returned to home Station due to being low on fuel. Second Venom was vectored to other radar targets but was unable to make contact. Shortly afterwards, second fighter returned to home Station due to malfunctions. No further interception activities were undertaken. All targets disappeared from scopes at approximately 0330Z. 10. Other aircraft in the area were properly identified by radar and flight logs as being friendly. All personnel interviewed and logs of RATCC lend reality to the existence of some unexplainable flying phenomena near this air field on this occasion. Not an Air Base; however, the controllers are experienced and technical skills were used in attempts to determine just what the objects were. When the target would stop on the scope the MTI was used. However, the target would still appear on the scope. All ground observers and reports from observers at . . . [C] agree on color, maneuvers and shape of object. My analysis of the sightings is that they were real and not figments of the imagination. The fact that three radar sets picked up the targets simultaneously is certainly conclusive that a target or object was in the air. The maneuvers of the object were extraordinary; however, the fact that radar and ground visual observations were made on its rapid acceleration and abrupt stops certainly lend credulance to the report. It is not believed these sightings were of any meteorological or astronomical origin.

The material on the . . . [C] sightings given at the beginning of the preceding account is typical; three other radar targets tracked by that station behaved in a similar manner and intercept attempts made from 2130 to 2215 GMT by an American T-33 jet aircraft were fruitless.

An analysis of this case from the viewpoint of possible anomalous propagation was made and appears in Chapter 7, Section VI.

Conclusions:

In view of the multiple radar sightings involved in this case, any conventional explanation for the occurrences reported would seem to require some sort of radar anomalous propagation. As pointed out in Chapter 7, the evidence for anomalous propagation in this case is rather uncertain. The temporary disappearance of the target as it appeared to overfly the . . . [C] GCA is quite suggestive of anomalous propagation. The generally clear weather was conducive to the formation of the atmospheric stratification that causes anomalous propagation, although it by no means follows that such formation would have actually occurred. In this connection, the apparent near-coincidence between the appearance of broken clouds (0330 GMT) and the disappearance of the radar targets (0330 GMT) could be significant.

On the other side must be balanced the generally continuous and consistent movements of the radar tracks reported by . . . [A], which are not at all typical of radar false targets caused by anomalous propagation. In addition, some of the maneuvers reported in the radar controller's letter to have been executed by the UFO are extremely unlikely to be duplicated by a false target, in particular stopping and assuming a new path after following the intercepting aircraft for some time. The comments of the Air Force officer who prepared the UFO message reproduced earlier are also significant.

In an early Air Force investigation it was suggested that the visual sightings might have been caused by the Perseid meteors. However, as Air Force Consultant Dr. Hynek pointed out:

> It seems highly unlikely, for instance, that the Perseid meteors could have been the cause of the sightings, especially in view of the statement of observers that shooting stars were exceptionally numerous that evening, thus implying that they were able to distinguish the two phenomena. Further, if any credence can be given to the maneuvers of the objects as sighted visually and by radar, the meteor hypothesis must be ruled out.

Dr. Hanek also remarked:

> The statement that radars reported these facts to occur at later hours than the ground observers' needs clarification inasmuch as it contradicts other portions of the report which indicate that at least at certain times visual and radar sightings were simultaneous.

In retrospect it appears that what the statement in question may have been meant to imply was that the radars *continued* to report target(s) after visual contact had been lost; the statement does not necessarily imply that no simultaneous radar-visual sightings occurred.

In conclusion, although conventional or natural explanations certainly cannot be ruled out, the probability of such seems low in this case and the probability that at least one genuine UFO was involved appears to be fairly high.

Case 3
South Pacific
Winter 1957
Investigators: Hauser Research and Engineering Co.

Abstract:

Material which reportedly had dropped from a spaceship was found to be radar chaff dipoles manufactured by Revere Copper and Brass, Inc., Brooklyn, N. Y.

Background:

The Colorado Project received a sample of metallic material, in the form of short pieces of narrow ribbon which was asserted to be material from a spaceship. A nested pile of the material reportedly was found in the front of the home of the witnesses who had observed "two space ships" overhead 24 hr. previously.

The sample was not radioactive when received by the Project, but was said to have been highly radioactive when it fell in the Winter of 1957. The sample was accompanied by an analytical report from a laboratory near the area of the sighting. This report stated that the composition of the material differed from the material used as radar "chaff," although aluminum was the main constituent.

Investigation:

The material was sent to the Hauser Research and Engineering Company, Boulder, Colo., for analysis and identification. Spectrographic analyses indicated a composition similar to that of radar "chaff," i.e.: aluminum foil coated with lead powder. The Hauser Company sent small samples of this material to major manufacturers of radar "chaff." Among their responses was the following, from Mr. V. B. Lane, Director of Technical Research, Foil Division, Revere Copper and Brass, Inc.

> The chaff dipoles sent to us in your letter of 21 June 1967 were manufactured by this company.
>
> The material is 1145 alloy hard aluminum foil with both a slip and a stripe coating applied to the surface of the foil. The stripe coating consists of lead powder suspended in Kerstyn lacquer. The slip coating is basically atomized Acruanx C sus-

pended in a lacquer. Identification is possible since the slip coating was color coded (red for Revere and, I believe, blue for Reynolds and green for Anaconda).

Generally speaking, the slip coat was last used in the fabrication of chaff units RR 39/AL and RR 44/AL. Your sample dipoles (tuned to S-band) could have come from either unit. These units were last produced in 1955-56 although a considerable supply was reworked in 1961-63. Since that time occasional small lots have been produced for test purposes. It is possible that some of this material was dropped by aircraft.

However, associating the chaff with a reported sighting of a UFO leads us to suspect another source. The chaff in question has been and is being used as a payload for sounding rockets and balloons. These devices are used to carry the chaff payload up to high altitudes and then the material is released for radar tracking. In some balloon devices, the chaff dipoles are supposed to remain within the balloon but occasionally they fall free.

Quite a few agencies employ these devices, among them Sandia Corp., Albuquerque, New Mexico and Dewey-Almy Chemical Corp., Cambridge, Mass. Perhaps they can associate a sounding device launch with the time of your reported sighting.

We can assure you, however, that the chaff in question was manufactured in Brooklyn, New York, USA and not in some remote corner of the galaxy.

Conclusion:

The material consisted of radar chaff dipoles manufactured by Revere Copper and Brass, Inc.

Case 4
Greenwich +3
Fall 1957
Investigator: Craig

Abstract:

A small piece of corroded magnesium metal, widely acclaimed as a fragment from an alien vehicle which exploded over a beach in Greenwich +3, was analyzed. The analysis disproved claims that the material was of greater purity than earthly metallurgical technology was capable of in 1957. Claims of extraterrestrial origin of the magnesium are thus based solely upon hearsay information which was never authenticated.

Background:

UFO writings commonly refer to pieces of ultra-pure magnesium which reportedly were once part of an alien vehicle which exploded over a beach in Greenwich +3 in 1957. According to the accounts, the claim of alien origin was supported by the fact that the magnesium was of a higher purity than human technology was then capable of producing; therefore, the material must have come from another culture. These claims are developed in great detail in *The Great Flying Saucer*

Hoax by Coral E. Lorenzen (1962). Mr. and Mrs. Lorenzen generously offered their magnesium samples to us for analysis.

The story of the origin of the samples had not been authenticated. A newspaper item, written by a society columnist, presented a letter which the columnist allegedly received, along with fragments of metal, from an "admirer" who could not be identified because his signature was illegible. The letter identified its writer as a fisherman who saw a flying disc approach the beach at unbelievable speed, turn sharply, and explode. The disc reportedly disintegrated into thousands of burning fragments, some of which fell into shallow water, where they were recovered by the fisherman, who said that some of these fragments accompanied the letter.

The fisherman has never been located or identified, and it has not been established that the columnist actually received the letter from a third party.

An interested civilian obtained the metal from the columnist, and, according to his account, took it to the Mineral Production Laboratory of the Agriculture Ministry of the country, where analysis showed it to be magnesium of greater purity than human technology could produce.

Investigation:

It was impossible to verify any relationship between the magnesium fragments and an UFO sighting. However, the degree of purity of the magnesium could be determined and since great weight has been given to the claim that the metal was of phenomenal purity, the project decided to have the Lorenzen sample analyzed.

Purified magnesium normally contains few impurities in sufficient quantity for detection by emission spectroscopy. An indication of the degree of purity attainable by known technology to 1957 was contained in a report of analysis (dated 23 May 1951) of magnesium which had been purified by eight successive sublimations. The analytic information furnished by Dr. R. S. Busk, Research Director, Metal Products Department, Dow Chemical Company, showed only Al, Zn, Ca, and Na present in detectable quantities as listed below, and given in parts per million of the sample. All other elements shown in the report were not present in quantities sufficient to be the symbol < merely indicate the limits of detectability for each element by the analytical method used.

Table

	PPM		*PPM*
Al	2	Sn	<10
Cu	<10	Zn	2
Fe	<4	Ba	<1
Mn	<2	Ca	8
Ni	<4	K	<5
Pb	<5	Na	3
Si	<10	Sr	<5

Dr. Busk informed us that his company has supplied samples of sublimed magnesium on request for at least 25 yr., and sent us a sample of triply-sublimed magnesium for purity comparison with the specimen.

Since we assumed we would be looking for extremely small quantities of impurity in the samples, we chose to analyze the two samples by neutron activation, the most sensitive analytical method currently available. The work was done by the Research and Methods Evaluation Group, Alcohol and Tobacco Tax Division, Internal Revenue Service, under the direction of Mr. Maynard J. Pro. The neutron irradiation and subsequent gamma spectrometry were observed by the project investigator and original analytical data are retained in project files. Results of neutron activation analysis showed the impurities listed below, given in parts of impurity per million parts of sample (PPM). Elements shown as N.D. (not detectable) were not present in sufficient quantity for detection. Limits of error in all cases are based upon most extreme estimates of analytical error, and the uncertainty indicated probably is overly generous. Figures for the first five elements shown were obtained by direct gamma spectrometry after neutron activation. Cu, Ba, and Sr values were obtained by gamma spectrometry after radio-chemical separation of the elements. It is obvious from these results that the magnesium is not nearly so pure as the Dow product.

Table

	Dow Mg	*UFO Mg*
Mn	4.8 ± 0.5	35.0 ± 5.
Al	N. D.(<5)	N. D. (<10)
Zn	5. ± 1.	500. ± 100.
Hg	2.6 ± 0.5	N. D.
Cr	5.9 ± 1.2	32.0 ± 10.
Cu	0.4 ± 0.2	3.3 ± 1.0
Ba	N. D.	160. ± 20.
Sr	N. D.	500. ± 100.

For the neutron activation analysis, a small portion of the sample was broken off, and leached in HC1 solution to remove surface impurities. After washing, this portion (which then had a bright metallic surface) was analyzed. The absence of C1 in the post-irradiation gamma spectrum showed both that C1 was not present in the sample itself and that washing of the leached sample was complete.

The quantity of MG^{27} isotope produced by neutron activation of Mg^{26} was also measured. This measurement showed that the magnesium isotopic ratio in the sample not differ significantly from that of other natural magnesium samples.

While the sample proved not to be especially pure, the relatively high strontium concentration was particularly interesting, since Sr is not an expected impurity in magnesium. Dr. Busk knew of no one who intentionally added Sr to commercial Mg. Additional work was therefore undertaken to determine if the sample, while not pure, might nonetheless be unique. The additional analytical work consisted of microprobe analysis and metallographic examination, and was done by Dr. Busk's staff at the Dow Metallurgical Laboratory. Again, the work was monitored by the project investigator.

Dr. D. R. Beaman's report of this work states:

> The electron microprobe analysis of the Mg-UFO revealed that Sr and Zn were present in extremely low concentrations and were not present in detectable localized regions of high concentrations. This does not preclude the possibility of a fine dispersion of precipitates. The metallographic examination of the clean matrix (negative numbers 64486-64499) by H. Diehl coupled with the probe results and the known solubilities of Sr and Zn in Mg suggests that these elements are present in solid solution.

Metallographic examination showed large, elongated magnesium grains, indicating that the metal had not been worked after solidification from the liquid or vapor state. The grain structure was thus not consistent with an assumption that the sample had been part of a fabricated metal object. Rapid quenching of a melted fragment was not indicated.

Since the strontium apparently had been added intentionally during manufacture of the material from which the sample came, Dow Metallurgical Laboratory records were checked to see if such material had been produced in the past by that particular laboratory. The records revealed that, over the years, experimental batches of magnesium alloy containing from 0.1% Sr to 40% Sr were produced. As early as 25 March 1940, the laboratory produced a 700 gm. batch of magnesium containing nominally the same concentration of Sr as was contained in the sample.

Conclusion:

Since only a few grams of the magnesium are known to exist, and these could easily have been produced prior to 1957 by common earthly technology, the composition and metallographic characteristics of these samples themselves reveal no information about their origin. The mere existence of these samples cannot serve to support an argument that they are fragments from material of extraterrestrial origin.

Since none of the additional information about this case is other than hearsay, it is not possible to establish any relationship between the small pieces of magnesium and a "flying disc."

Case 5
South Central
Fall 1957
Investigator: Craig

Abstract:

The crew of a B-47 aircraft described an encounter with a large ball of light which was also displayed for a sustained time for both airborne radar monitoring receivers and on ground radar units. The encounter had occurred ten years prior to this study. Project Blue Book had no record of it. Attempts to locate any records of the event, in an effort to learn the identity of the encountered phenomenon, failed to produce any information. The phenomenon remains unidentified.

Background:

At a project-sponsored conference for air base UFO officers, held in Boulder in June 1967, one of the officers revealed that he personally had experienced a puzzling UFO encounter some ten years previously. According to the officer, a Major at the time of the encounter, he was piloting a B-47 on a gunnery and electronic counter-measures training mission from an AFB. The mission had taken the crew over the gulf of Mexico, and back over South Central United States where they encountered a glowing source of both visual and 2,800 mHz. electromagnetic radiation of startling intensity, which, during part of the encounter, held a constant position relative to the B-47 for an extended period. Ground flight control radar also received a return from the "object," and reported its range to the B-47 crew, at a position in agreement with radar and visual observations from the aircraft.

According to the officer, upon return to the AFB, electronic countermeasures, graphic data, and radar scope pictures which had been taken during the flight were removed from the plane by Intelligence personnel. He recalled that an Intelligence questionnaire regarding the experience had later been completed by the B-47 crew; however, the "security lid" shut off further information regarding the encounter. The crew learned nothing more regarding the incident, and the pilot occasionally had wondered about the identity of the phenomena encountered ever since his experience.

Investigation:

When no report of this incident was found in Blue Book or Air Defense Command records, this project undertook to obtain leads to the location of data recorded during the event through detailed interview of all available members of the B-47 crew. Of the six crew members, the three most closely involved in the encounter were the pilot, co-pilot, and the officer who had been in charge of the most involved radar-monitoring unit.

Details of the encounter, as best they could be recalled, were obtained by interview with the pilot and, later, with the two other officers at another air base. All remained deeply impressed by the experience, and were surprised that a report of it was not part of Blue Book files. Their descriptions of the experience were generally consistent, although the pilot did not mention that the navigator also had received a radar return from the object in question, as was recalled by the other officers. (The navigator, on duty in Vietnam, was not available for interview). The two other crew members, each of whom had operated a radar monitoring unit in the B-47 during the UFO event, were involved to a lesser extent in the incident, and were not located for interview.

The crew's description of the experience follows:

Time: Early morning, Fall 1957.

Place: Over South Central United States

Plane's altitude: Above 30,000 ft. during the first part of the encounter.

Nature of Mission: (Pilot): Combined navigation, gunnery, and electronic counter-measure training mission.

(Other Crew): Check-out of plane and equipment, including electronic counter-measures equipment, prior to European assignment.

Weather: Witnesses recalled seeing, from 30,000 ft. altitude, lights of cities and burn-off flames at gas and oil refineries below. They have no recollection of other than clear weather.

Radar monitoring unit number two, in the back end of the B-47, picked up a strong signal, at a frequency of about 2,800 mHz., which moved up-scope while the plane was in straight flight. (A signal from a ground station necessarily moves down-scope under these conditions, because of forward motion of the airplane). This was noted, but not reported immediately to the rest of the crew. The officer operating this unit suspected equipment malfunction, and switched to a different monitoring frequency range. The pilot saw a white light ahead and warned the crew to be prepared for a sudden maneuver. Before any evasive action could be taken, the light crossed in front of the plane, moving to the right, at a velocity far higher than airplane speeds. The light was seen by pilot and co-pilot, and appeared to the pilot to be a glowing body as big as a barn. The light disappeared visually, but number two monitor was returned to the frequency at which the signal was noted a few moments earlier and again showed a target, now holding at the "two-o'clock" position. The pilot varied the plane's speed, but the radar source stayed at two o'clock. The pilot then requested and received permission to switch to ground interceptor control radar and check out the unidentified companion. Ground Control in the area informed the pilot that both his plane and the other target showed on their radar, the other target holding a range of ten miles from him.

After the UFO had held the two o'clock position and ten-mile range through various test changes in aircraft speed, the number two monitoring officer informed the pilot that the target was starting to move up-scope. It moved to a position dead ahead of the plane, holding a ten-mile range, and again became visible to the eye as a huge, steady, red glow. The pilot went to maximum speed. The target appeared to stop, and as the plane got close to it and flew over it, the target disappeared from visual observation, from monitor number two, and from ground radar. (The operator of monitor number two also recalled the B-47 navigator's having this target on his radar, and the target's disappearing from his radar scope at the same time). The pilot began to turn back. About half way around the turn, the target reappeared on both the monitor and ground radar scopes and visually at an estimated altitude of 15,000 ft. The pilot received permission from Ground Control to change altitude, and dove the plane at the target, which appeared stationary. As the plane approached to an estimated distance of five miles the target vanished again from both visual observation and radar. Limited fuel caused the pilot to abandon the chase at this point and head for his base. As the pilot leveled off at 20,000 ft. a target again appeared on number two monitor, this time behind the B-47. The officer operating the number two monitoring unit, however, believes that he may have been picking up the ground radar signal at this point. The signal faded out as the B-47 continued flight.

The co-pilot and number two monitoring officer were impressed by the sudden disappearance of the target and its reappearance at a new location. As they recalled the event, the target could be tracked part of the time on the radar monitoring screen, as described above, but, at least once, disappeared from the right side of the plane, appeared on their left, then suddenly on their right again, with no "trail" on the radar scope to indicate movement of the target between successive positions.

The monitoring officer recalled that the navigator, who reported receiving his own transmitted radar signals reflected from the target, not only had a target on his screen, but reported target bearings which coincided exactly with the bearings to the source on the monitoring scope. He also indicated that the officer operating the number one radar monitoring unit, which was of a different type, having a fixed APD-4 antenna instead of a spinning antenna as used with the number two unit, and covering all radar ranges, also observed the same display he observed on unit two. The sixth crew member, operating number three radar monitor, which covered a lower frequency range, was searching for something to tie in with the signals being observed on the other scopes, but found nothing.

The following questions are raised by this information:

1) Could the number two monitoring unit have received either direct or reflected ground radar signals which had no relation to the visual sighting?

The fact that the frequency received on number two, about 2,800 mHz., was one of the frequencies emitted from ground radar stations (CPS6B type antennas) at an airport and other airports nearby, makes one suspect this possibility. The number two monitoring officer felt that after the B-47 arrived over South Central U.S., signals from GCA sets were received, and this confused the question of whether an unidentified source which emitted or reflected this wave length was present. On original approach to the area, however, a direct ground signal could not have moved up-scope. Up-scope movement could not have been due to broken rotor leads or other equipment malfunction, for all other ground signals observed that night moved down-scope. A reflected signal would require a moving reflector in the region serving as apparent source, the movement being coordinated with the motion of the aircraft, particularly during periods when the UFO held constant position relative to the moving aircraft. Since the monitor scans 360°, if a reflected beam were displayed on the scope, the direct radar beam also would be displayed, unless the transmitter were below the horizon. As the event was recalled by the witnesses, only one signal was present during initial observations. If the UFO actually reflected radar signals transmitted from the B-47, and appeared in the *same* position on the navigator's scope as one, the number two monitoring scope, reflection of 2,800 mHz. ground signals from these same positions seems extremely unlikely.

2) Could the visual observations have been misinterpreted airplane lights, airplane afterburners, or meteors?

The persistence of the phenomenon rules out meteors. Observed speeds, plus instant re-position and hovering capabilities are not consistent with the aircraft hypothesis.

3) Were the visual observations necessarily of the same phenomenon as the radar observations?

Coincidence of disappearances, appearances, and indicated positions suggest a common cause.

4) If the reported observations are factual and accurate, what capabilities and properties were possessed by the UFO?

a) Rapid motion, hovering, and instant relocation.
b) Emission of electromagnetic radiation in the visible region and possibly in the 2,800 mHz. region.
c) Reflection of radar waves of various frequencies. (From airborne radar units as well as 2,800 mHz. ground units). Failure to transmit at the frequency of the number three radar monitor.
d) Ability to hold a constant position relative to an aircraft.

5) Could the observed phenomenon be explained as a plasma?

Ten scientists who specialize in plasma research, at our October 1967 plasma conference regarded an explanation of this experience in terms of known properties of a plasma as not tenable.

Further investigation of this case centered around efforts to trace reports of this event submitted by the crew after the B-47 returned to the AFB. Recollections of the nature and manner of submission of such reports or records were in sharp divergence. As the pilot recalled the incident, the landing plane was met by their Wing Intelligence personnel, who took all filmed and wire-recorded data from the "back-end" crew. The crew was never extensively questioned about the incident. Days or weeks later, however, the crew did receive from Air Defense Command, a lengthy questionnaire which they completed including sketches of what they had seen and narrative descriptions of the event. The questionnaire also had a section to be completed by the ground radar (GCI) personnel. The pilot could not recall where or exactly when the completed questionnaire had been sent.

In contrast with this recollection, the co-pilot and number two monitoring officer said that no data whatsoever had been recorded during the flight. The #1 monitoring unit was equipped for movie filming of its display, and #2 was equipped for wire recording of data. Since the flight had been merely for the purpose of checking equipment, however, neither film nor recording wire was taken aboard. Both these officers recalled intensive interrogation by their Intelligence personnel immediately after their return to the AFB. They did not recall writing anything about the event that day or later. According to their account, the B-47 crew left for England the following day, and heard nothing more of the incident.

Since it appeared that the filmed and recorded data we were seeking had never existed, we renewed the effort to locate any special intelligence reports of the incident that might have failed to reach Project Blue Book. A report form of the type described by the pilot could not be identified or located. The Public Information Officer at ADC Headquarters checked intelligence files and operations records, but found no record of this incident. The Deputy Commander for Operations of the particular SAC Air Wing in which the B-47 crew served in 1957 informed us that a thorough review of the Wing history failed to disclose any reference to an UFO incident in Fall 1957.

Conclusion:

If a report of this incident, written either by the B-47 crew or by Wing Intelligence personnel, was submitted in 1957, it apparently is no longer in existence. Moving pictures of radar scope displays and other data said to have been recorded during the incident apparently never existed. Evaluation of the experience must, therefore, rest entirely on the recollection of crew members ten years after the event. These descriptions are not adequate to allow identification of the phenomenon encountered (cf. Section III Chapters 2 & 6, Appendix Q).

Case 6
North Eastern
Spring 1966
Investigators: Craig, Levine

Abstract:

Three adult women went onto the high school athletic field to check the identity of a bright light which had frightened an 11-year-old girl in her home nearby, and reported that one of three lights they saw maneuvering in the sky above the school flew noiselessly toward them, coming directly overhead, 20-30 ft. above one of them. It was described as a flowing, solid, disc-like, automobile-sized object. Two policemen who responded to a telephone message that a UFO was under observation verified that an extraordinary object was flying over the high school. The object has not been identified. Most of the extended observation, however, apparently was an observation of the planet Jupiter.

Background:

The account of an incident which occurred some 16 mo. earlier was sufficiently impressive to a field team investigating current sightings in the general region of The Northeast to cause the team to interview some of the individuals involved in the earlier report.

According to the account, an 11-year-old girl heard a bump outside her bedroom window about 9:00 p.m. and looked out the window to see a football-shaped object with flashing red lights moving in the air. Frightened, she ran downstairs. Her father was watching T.V. and said that its reception was showing the effects of interference. Two neighbor women arrived at that time, saw the red light near the high school, and called the girl's mother. The three women agreed to go out toward the school grounds to show the girl, who stayed in the house, that what she saw was nothing but an airplane. However, when they got to the field, about 300 yd. from the school building, they saw three separate lights, generally red, but green or white at times, which were not like airplane lights. The center light was darting about over the school building, and the others were "sort of playing tag" with it. Still thinking they might be planes or helicopters, one of the women beckoned the nearest light with an arm motion, whereupon it came directly toward her.

She said that as it approached nearly overhead, she could see that it was a metal disc, about the size of a large automobile, with glowing lights around its top. She described the object as flat-bottomed and solid, with a round outline and a surface appearance like dull aluminum. The other two women ran. Looking back, they saw their friend directly beneath the object, which was only 20-30 ft. above her head. She had her hands clamped over her head in a self-protective manner, and later reported that she thought the object was going to crush her. The object tilted on edge, and returned to a position about 50 ft. over the high school as the women ran home to call more neighbors. A man and his wife came out and saw the lights that were pointed out to them. One of the lights appeared to be only 15-30 ft. above the roof of the school building. To this couple, the lights appeared oval-shaped, flashing, mostly red, but changing colors. The lights were star-like in appearance, but looked a little larger than stars. The man ran back and telephoned the police. As the group, now consisting of the three women, the girl, the girl's older brother and handicapped father, and the neighbor couple, awaited the arrival of police, the central object receded in the sky and looked like a star. Its two companions had left the scene unnoticed apparently while the observers' attention was focussed on the receding object. As two policemen arrived, the observers were concerned that the police would think the UFO was only a star. However, the star-like light did brighten and resume its motion over the high school. The officers reportedly jumped back into their police cruiser and drove down to the school parking lot, where they saw the object at close range before it sped off, with the police in pursuit. The object had been observed for a total of about 30-45 min. It had made no noise, and the observers felt no heat or wind from the object when it was overhead.

Investigation:

One of the police officers was interviewed. He confirmed the claim by the other observers that he and another officer had responded to the call and, after having the object pointed out to them by the group of observers near the school grounds, drove down to the school parking lot to get a closer look at the object. He said it was neither an airplane nor helicopter, but he did not know what it was. The object seemed to the officer to be shaped like a half dollar, with three lights of different colors in indentations at the "tail end," something like back-up lights It seemed to have a more or less circular motion but was always over the school. After the officers arrived at the parking lot, the object "flew around" the school two or three more times and departed apparently toward the airport. As it got farther away, it looked like just one light. It took off at a "normal speed," staying the same height in the sky. It dimmed and then disappeared quickly.

The three women, two children, and the girl's father granted a group interview to project investigators. Their story was generally quite consistent with that recorded a year earlier by NICAP interviewers. The fact was brought out that the school parking lot had been filled with cars during the early part of the UFO sighting, since there was a Friday evening basketball game at the school. None of their occupants, having driven away while the UFO over the school building was under observation, reported seeing an UFO. Some youngsters leaving the school grounds were told about the UFOs by the observers. The observers said the youngsters watched for a while, then left—apparently unimpressed.

Review of all reports indicated that all observers other than the young girl and the group of three women had seen something that looked like a star. Written reports by both policemen stated the object appeared "like a bright star," and the reports of the four said the objects "when standing still, looked like stars." The changing of colors could be due to ordinary scintillation of starlight, and some apparent motion of the object could be accounted for as autokinesis, even if a star were being observed (see Section VI, Chapters 1 and 2).

Descent of the object over the women's heads could not be attributed to autokinesis, or apparent motion of a motionless light. Could all other reported movements be accounted for if one assumed the observers actually were looking at a star or planet? The policeman had been asked how close he was to the object at its closest position when he was in the school parking lot, and he indicated a distance of about 200 yd. As shown in he accompanying sketch (Fig. 2), which was prepared by Raymond E. Fowler, chairman of the NICAP Mass. Subcommittee, the police were about 200 yd. from the high school when the object over the school was first pointed out to them (position marked FENCE on the sketch). They must, therefore, not have reduced the apparent distance to the object when they drove down to the parking lot next to the school building. Mr. Fowler's original report, written a few days after the incident, said of the police. "As they came into the school yard, the object moved off slowly into the SW toward [a factory] and disappeared from view." An observer approaching the school building on the driveway from the road (see sketch), as the police officers did, and looking at a star over the building, would see the same apparent motion of the star as a near object moving to the SW would have.

Motion attributed to the object (except for the descent overhead) was typically circular, or "up, down, and around." The object was thus not seen to move far from its original position. In response to the question "How did the object disappear from view?" the woman who had reported being directly beneath the object wrote, "Just vanished in a circular direction in plain view." One of the police officers wrote, "The object

Map/UFO Sighting Area

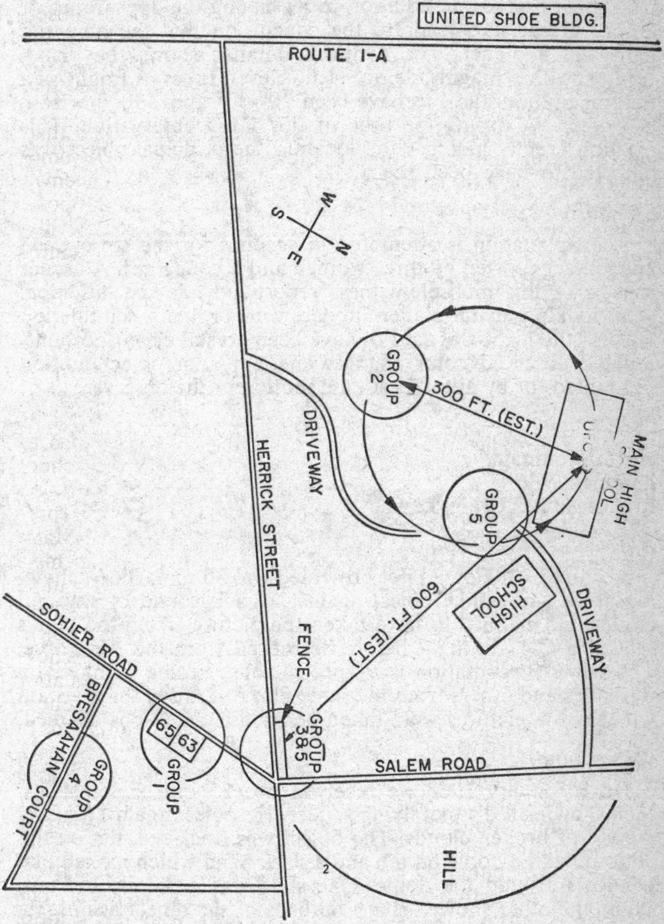

Fig. 2

seemed to stay at the same height and just move away very smoothly."

As shown in the sketch, in all views except the reported close encounter, the principal object was seen in the same WNW direction. This fact, plus the fact that it stayed in this general direction and disappeared as if going straight away from the observer, in addition to its having the appearance of a very bright star, leads to the conclusion that the observed light was a planet. The nautical almanac shows the planet Jupiter, with a magnitude of −1.6 (eleven times as bright as a first magnitude star), to have been 20°-30° above the horizon, 23° N of W, during the time of this UFO observation. This position exactly matches the location the principal object was reported to have been seen.

Conclusions:

No explanation is attempted to account for the close UFO encounter reported by three women and a young girl. All other aspects of this multiple-witness report indicate the observers were looking at the planet Jupiter, with ordinary scintillation effects (the night was said to have been crystal clear) accounting for observed color change, and apparent object motion accounted for by autokinesis and motion of the observer.

Case 7

North Mountain
Summer 1966
Investigators: Craig, Levine

Abstract:

A retired Air Force pilot presented two 35 mm. slides, showing a red saucer-like object against a background of sky and clouds. He claimed to have taken the pictures from the pilot's seat of a C-47 in flight before he retired from the Air Force. The witness' reputation is irreproachable. Frame numbers on the slides and others from the same film roll raised the question whether the pictures were taken under the conditions claimed.

Background:

On 9 January 1968 we received two 35 mm. color slides, each showing a distinct flying-saucer-like object against a background of broken clouds. The object was brick-red, flat on the bottom, with a dome on top and a dark band which looked like windows around the dome. One slide was generally blurred, while the other showed sharp outlines of the object against the clouds. A very bright area, spanning one portion of the window-like dark band and extending onto the metallic-appearing body of the object, had the appearance of specular reflection. The cloud background was similar in the two pictures, showing the object to have moved about 10° to the right in picture two as compared with number one.

According to accompanying information, the pictures were taken in Summer 1966 by an officer in the Air Force. He said he had been piloting a C-47 over the Rocky Mountains when he took the UFO pictures from his plane. The co-pilot was busy computing expected destination arrival times, and did not see the object, which was visible only a few seconds. No one else saw the object or knew that the pilot had taken the pictures. The now retired officer was currently employed at one of the FAA control centers, where he had shown the pictures to friends. As a result of this showing, the slides were obtained and, with the photographer's permission, sent to the project for evaluation.

Frames of the two slides carried the processing date of December 1966. The blurred slide carried the slide number 14, and the sharper slide carried the number 11 on its frame. There was no evidence of airplane window framing or window dirt or reflection on either slide. Lighting of the clouds gave the appearance that one was indeed looking at the tops of sunlit clouds. The pictures were said to have been taken consecutively at about 11:00 a.m. local time on a day in July, and to have been left in the camera, undeveloped, until the rest of the roll was exposed and commercially developed in December 1966. The incident had never been reported to the Air Force because the officer said he knew that people were ridiculed for reporting such things, and the pictures had not been shown to anyone outside the officer's family for a year after development.

The ex-pilot consented to our examination of his photographs on the condition that his identity would not be revealed.

Investigation:

Checking the window structure of DC-3 planes (courtesy of Frontier Airlines), which are the same as C-47s, revealed that it would be quite easy to take 35 mm. pictures through the windshield, at ten or twelve o'clock from the pilot's position, without getting any part of the windshield framework in the field of view of the camera.

The UFO photographer and his wife were interviewed at their home. According to the officer's account the UFO incident occurred about 11:00 a.m., when the plane was about 25 mi. SW of Provo. He had turned control of the C-47 over to the co-pilot and gotten his camera ready to take pictures of the mountains ahead. He had set the shutter of his camera [VITO CL Voightländer, Lanthar 2.8 lens] at 1/500 sec. exposure, and adjusted the iris reading to give proper exposure as indicated by the built-in coupled light meter. [This was f 5.6 to 8, he thought.] He was using high speed Ektachrome film, EH 35, ASA 160. He was thus ready to take pictures of the mountains, with camera held in his hands in his lap, when the unknown object appeared at about "ten o'clock." He quickly photographed the object, wound the camera, and got a second picture before the object sped upward and to the right, out of view. He had lost sight of the object momentarily as it went behind the compass at the center of the windshield, then saw it again briefly as it passed through the visible top left corner of the right windshield before the cockpit ceiling blocked his view of the object. The object had been in sight only a few seconds, and had moved in a sweeping path in front of the plane, appearing to accelerate, but making no sudden changes in direction or speed. The officer judged the time interval the object was visible by the time necessary for him to bring the camera up to his eye, snap a picture, wind the film (a single stroke, lever advance), and snap the second picture. This required only a few seconds, and the object vanished very soon after the second picture was taken.

The co-pilot was busy with computations, and did not look up in time to see the object. In earlier telephone conversation, the officer said he told the co-pilot he had just taken a picture of something and the co-pilot's response was a disinterested "that's nice." The officer stated that the co-pilot didn't know but that he had photographed the left wing of the plane, or something of that sort. In the taped interview, the officer stated that he had asked the co-pilot if he had seen the object that the officer had just photographed, and the co-pilot had said he did not. According to this account, the co-pilot should have known that the pilot had photographed an unidentified object but neither reported the incident upon landing.

From Provo to the next check point, Battle Mountain, Idaho, the direction of flight was slightly north of west. The witness felt they were flying SW at the time of sighting, and may have still been in a turn after passing the Provo checkpoint. If the bright spot on the picture of the object is a specular reflection as it appears, and if the object was at the photographer's twelve o'clock position at 11:00 a.m., the position of the specular reflection would require the plane to have been in a heading between east and north.

The officer's wife supported his story that they had had the roll of film developed several months after the UFO pictures were taken. The officer stated that there were pictures already on the roll before the UFO shots were taken and after the UFO pictures were taken in July, and the roll was finished during September and October. These later pictures showed park and mountain scenes, as well as a snow-storm scene.

The witness was aware that frame numbers printed on the slides (14 and 11) did not agree with his story that they were taken consecutively on the roll (14 before 11). He indicated, however, that all pictures on the roll were numbered erroneously.

Removal of slides from their mountings revealed that the numbers on the mountings were consistent with frame numbers on the edge of the film itself. Each number on the film was one integer lower than the number on the mounting. This held true also for the UFO shots, frame numbers 11 and 14 yielding pictures with numbers ten and 13 shown on the film edge. These numbers show rather conclusively that the UFO pictures were taken after the snow-storm, rather than in July when the witness was still in the Air Force. They also were not taken on consecutive frames of the roll, and were taken in an order reversed to that claimed. The numbering examination was witnessed by five project staff members.

Conclusion:

In view of the discrepancies, detailed analysis of the photographs did not seem justifiable. They were returned to the officer with our comment that they obviously could not be used by us to support claims that the object photographed was other than an ordinary object of earthly origin thrown into the air.

Case 8

North Central
Summer 1966
Investigators: Hynek, Low

Abstract:

Witness was driving in a rural area in late afternoon, when, he said, a silvery metallic-looking disk with dome, about 30 ft. diameter, descended with wobbling motion into the adjacent valley, hovered just above the ground about 200 ft. from the witness, then took off rapidly with a whooshing sound. Depressions in ground and overturned rocks near landing site were offered as evidence, but may have been caused by animals. The report is unexplained.

Background:

Project Bluebook records showed that the witness, a man employed by the U.S. Immigration Service, had reported a UFO sighting. He had been interviewed in the summer of 1966 by the Director of Operations at Minot AFB, who had visited the reported site of the UFO landing. The interview disclosed the following:

About 5:00 p.m. on a cloudy day, the witness was driving about one mile north of a town when bright flashes in a clear patch of sky low in the east caught his attention. He stopped and watched as a bright metallic, silvery object dropped below the horizon and moved down the slope opposite him into the shallow valley. It appeared to be tilted, so that he saw it as a disc. A domelike shape on top could be seen. It was about ten feet above the ground, and moved with a wobbly, "falling-leaf" motion. In its center was a dark spot, like smoked glass, about five feet in diameter, and around it three smaller spots.

When it reached the valley floor, it rose about 100 ft. and moved to a small reservoir, where it turned horizontal and hovered for about one minute. Then it moved up-slope to a small field and settled down within a few feet of the ground and about 250 ft. from the witness. Thereafter it slowly tilted back on edge, took off with a whooshing sound, and disappeared rapidly into the clouds. The witness' car radio, which had stopped working during the landing, came back to life.

A visit to the reported "landing" site disclosed nothing of interest except two groups of depressions and approximately ten rocks that had been recently displaced. The three depressions in each group were spaced about 9.5-12.5 ft. apart. The rocks were about one foot in diameter or less. The investigating officer commented that persons familiar with wild game in the area had pointed out that grouse make similar depressions in nesting, and that coyotes and badgers overturn rocks in the manner observed. He noted also that the witness impressed him as a steady, practical kind of person. He wished no publicity, and said he would deny the story if it got out.

Investigation:

Project investigator Low and Dr. J. Allen Hynek of Dearborn Observatory, Northwestern University, visited the town in the fall of 1966, interviewed the witness and went with him to the site he had reported. They were able to fill in some details: the witness had seen the discoid object at first about .75 mi. distant; it had approached as close as 100 ft.; there it had hovered about one minute, about ten feet off the ground; then it took off and disappeared in about three seconds. The entire observation of the object had taken about five minutes.

At the site, the investigators noted the depressions and the overturned rocks, but were unable to add anything significant to the earlier report. They learned at Minot AFB that no target corresponding to the sighting had appeared on radar.

Comment:

In the absence of supporting witnesses or unambiguous physical evidence, no significant confirmation of the witness' report could be developed. Like other spectacular one-witness sighting reports, it cannot be verified or refuted.

Case 9
North Central
Summer 1966
Investigators: Hynek, Low

Abstract:

Two guards on post about 10:00 p.m. reported that a glowing saucer-shaped object at 45° altitude in the NE descended toward them, then receded. Radar was alerted, and reported an unidentified target at 95 mi. due north, very near the horizon; a fighter was unable to locate it. A strike team sent out to the site of the first observation reported unexplained white lights near the southeast horizon. These may have been aircraft, and the original object Capella.

Investigation:

The investigators went to the AFB and talked with several persons involved in the reported UFO sightings. Their principal findings follow.

About 10:00 p.m. a guard walking his post at missile site Mike 6 reported a luminous shape at about 45° altitude in the northern sky. It exhibited limited lateral motion, but always came back to its original direction. It appeared about the width of a thumb, presumably at arm's length and continually changed color from green to red, to blue in turn. It seemed dim relating to stars. When it was apparently nearest, it appeared like a luminous inverted dinner plate.

The guard was frightened and woke his partner, who was due to relieve him at 11:00 p.m. Both watched the object. Meanwhile, their captain sent out a strike team to Mike 6 and alerted the south base radar crew.

The latter reported about 11:30 p.m. that they had an unidentified target on search radar at 95 mi., azimuth 357°. A little later, presumably the same target was picked up on the height finder radar at 95 mi., azimuth 360°, altitude 2,400 ft. Later it was reported at 4,400 ft. and changing altitude "every so often", it was observed from 2,400 to 8,200 ft. altitude and varied a degree or two in azimuth, but the range of 95 mi. did not vary The target remained continuously on the radar until the operator was relieved at 3:00 a.m. Except when a fighter was sent out. it was an isolated target; no other aircraft, ground clutter, or noise pips were seen within 20 mi. of it.

The pilot of the fighter sent to intercept the radar target reported that, guided by the radar crew, he had flown over the target location at 1,000 ,2,000, 3,000, 4,000, and 5,000 ft. The radar verified that the plane passed through or very near the target, but the pilot saw nothing, nor did he detect anything on his radar or on his infrared detector.

By the time a strike team reached Mike 6, about 11:20 p.m., the original object was gone. However, they and several other men noticed one or more yellow-white lights very low on the southeastern horizon, in the direction of the airstrip at the base 50 mi. distant. These moved irregularly over a range of about 35° in azimuth.

At the request of the Colorado investigators, an officer sometime later went with one of the Mike 6 guards and the two members of the strike team to the Mike 6 site at night. There they pointed out as accurately as possible the locations of the objects they had seen. The guard, relying on a nearby fence as reference, indicated that the object he and his partner had first seen had ranged in azimuth from about 0° to 55°, but had been at about 40° most of the time. It had been "very high." Soon after the strike team had arrived, he had been trying to watch the yellow-white light on the southeastern horizon, and when he looked again to the NE the original object was gone.

The leader of the strike team indicated that the original object had been pointed out to him by the guard at about 20° azimuth; it was "unusually bright and very high." His partner did not see it.

The officer stated also that it was possible from Mike 6 to see the lights of aircraft in their landing approaches at the AFB; they would have been very near the horizon because of the local topography. One large airplane had landed at the base at midnight, and two others at 12:29 a.m. The officer thought it highly probable that the white light reported in that sector had been the landing lights of one or more of these aircraft.

Comment:

A situation of this kind is difficult to evaluate, because of the number of people and objects involved and vagueness or inconsistencies as to various details. As to the original object seen by the guards, the fact that it continually changed color and oscillated about a fixed position suggests a star. The sky was clear, and the bright star Capella was a few degrees above the north-northeast horizon. If the guards' estimate of 45° altitude was accurate, the object could not have been Capella; but a sleepy man on a lone guard post might quite possibly have a distorted impression, especially if he is not used to making such judgments. One officer commented that most guards did not report UFOs, but the guard who reported this one was new and had not seen one before. However, he was supported by the leader of the strike team, who remembered the object was "very high."

Whatever the original object was, it appears unlikely that the unidentified radar target was the same object. Apparently the visual object disappeared at about the time the radar target was acquired. The latter was very near the horizon, and remained at a fixed range and very near 0° azimuth, a location and behavior entirely different from that reported for the visual object.

The radar target was practically stationary except in altitude; it was very near the horizon; and no object was detectable by an aircraft pilot searching the target location. All of these factors suggest strongly that the target was generated by anomalous atmospheric propagation from a stationary object at a quite different location.

Thus, what was ostensibly a single sighting was probably three; and there is much in the situation to suggest that the later two—radar target and white lights—were commonplace phenomena that were endowed with significance by the excitement generated by the first report. The weight of evidence suggests that the original object was Capella, dancing and twinkling near the horizon; however, the evidence is not sufficient to justify any definite conclusion.

Case 10
South Central
Winter 1966
Investigators: Saunders, Wadsworth

Abstract:

A pulsating reddish light seen below treetop level from a highway at night became brilliant white briefly, then resumed its earlier character. Its location was estimated by rough triangulation. By comparison with the car headlights, the white light was estimated to emanate from a source of several hundred megawatts. Inspection of the area ten weeks later revealed no explanation of the light.

Background:

The principal witness reported the sighting to Barksdale AFB; the report reached the CU project shortly afterward, and a telephone interview with the witness developed the following account.

The principal witness, with his wife and children, was driving north on U.S. Highway 79 through a wooded region near the eventual UFO site at about 8:30 p.m. The sky was heavily overcast, with fog and a light drizzle, ceiling about 300 feet; no lightning activity was noticed. The wife called her husband's attention to a red-orange glow appearing through and above the trees ahead and to the left (west), and both watched it as they continued driving. The light apparently emanated from a source below the tops of the trees, appearing as a luminous hemisphere through the fog and rain. It pulsated regularly, ranging from dull red to bright orange with a period of about two seconds.

As the witnesses reached a point on the road apparently nearest the source of the light, it suddenly brightened to a brilliant white, "washing out" the headlight illumination on the road, lighting up the landscape and casting shadows of trees, forcing the driver to shield his eyes from the glare, and waking the children. After about four seconds, the light subsided to its earlier red-orange pulsation. The driver then stopped to estimate the bearing of the source from the highway (it was then to the rear) and then proceeded on his way. No sound or other effect had been noted except the light.

The principal witness, a nuclear physicist, made rough estimates of his distance from the light source and the illumination it produced during the bright phase. From these estimates, he deduced a source power of about 800 megawatts, which he believed implied a nuclear-energy source. This figure was later revised somewhat.

Investigation:

Although the report did not relate specifically to an UFO, the qualifications of the principal witness, the similarity of the reported incident to many UFO reports, and the possibility of recurrence or observable effects of heat, all appeared to justify a field investigation.

In Spring, 1967, the project team, together with the principal witness and his astronomer friend, began a joint air-and-ground investigation of the area in which the light had appeared. While two men in a helicopter surveyed the area, the other two operated transits to fix the location of the helicopter whenever they were informed by radio that it was over a feature of interest. At night a watch was kept for a possible reappearance of the light. The following day, the vicinity of the presumed location of the light was explored on foot.

The area was found to contain little but trees, underbrush, and oil wells. A burned area that showed slightly higher radioactivity than background turned out to be a burned-over oil slick beside a pumping station. Similar radiation anomalies were found at other oil slicks. Nothing was found that suggested any relation to the unexplained light source.

The CU team returned home, while the principal witness carried out several follow-up investigations. He later reported the following results:

1. The chief dispatcher of a railroad which runs in the vicinity of the sighting, stated that no rolling stock was within 50 mi. of the site on the night in question.

2. The nearest high-tension power lines were about nine miles west of the area.

3. The five oil companies operating in the area concerned had no record of any burnoffs, or rupture of oil or gas lines, or other fires in the vicinity of the sighting. No fires, flares, or other night activity had occurred in the area for a year preceding the sighting.

4. Numerous areas in the region showed significant radiation levels. These appeared to relate to oil wells or old tank sites, but not all such places showed anomalies.

5. A local resident related that he had hunted in the area for many years, and that he had noted a sharp decrease in game since the end of 1966.

6. The principal witness revised his estimate of the power of the light source to a minimum of 500 megawatts. He estimated that he drove about 0.6 mi. from first sighting of the light until its bright phase, and had clocked 0.6 mi. on the odometer from that point to his final observation. He estimated that the bearing of the light relative to the highway was between 45° and 60°, forward in the first case and rearward in the second. The highway was not straight; but he estimated his distance from the light during its intense phase by plotting the bearings on an aerial photo of the area, obtaining a range of 1,000-1,400 yd.

He judged that the illumination during the intense phase was just noticeably stronger than that of his headlights ten meters in front of the automobile. His headlamps totalled 175 watts. On the basis of this rough photometry, he computed the power of the unknown source at about 500 megawatts. However, he noted that its total power might have been substantially less than this value if it was concentrated in a beam.

7. The witness reported several descriptions of sightings by others in the area; but these did not appear to offer anything to clarify the original sighting. However, one witness reported that about 8:30 p.m. six days before the sighting a similar bright white light had appeared near the location of the original sighting.

8. The principal witness arranged for the photointerpretation group at Barksdale AFB to examine aerial photographs of the vicinity of the sighting, and he and a companion went in on foot to check detailed features the AF analysts noted. Several features were not satisfactorily identified, but nothing was discovered that appeared to relate to the sighting.

Comment:

This case is of interest mainly because of the difficulty in accounting for any kind of a light in that area on such a night, and because of the very high power attributed to the source. However, the latter estimate involves great uncertainties.

Considering that it was a dark, rainy night and that the sighting was unexpected, the witness' judgment of his locations on the highway when he took bearings may have been seriously inaccurate. His comparison of the illumination during the intense phase of the unknown source with that of his headlights was subject to wide errors because of the rain, excitement, and difficulty in adapting to the sudden brilliant light. A significant discrepancy appears in the record: In a formal report of the sighting written 5 April 1967, the principal witness stated that the "intensity" (illumination) from the unknown source "at the highway" was estimated by JND "just noticeable difference" curves to be at least 100 times that of the headlamps. In a letter dated 3 June 1967, he stated that he estimated the illumination from the headlamps ten meters ahead of the car was one JND greater than that of the unknown source; this was the basis of the revised computation. In a follow-up telephone conversation 13 September 1968—admittedly a long time after the event—he stated that he did not recall that he had detected *any* difference in illumination by the unknown source and the headlamps on the road 20 ft. ahead.

Further uncertainties are involved in attempting to compare the source intensity of the unknown light with that of the headlamps. The light from the latter is concentrated in beams in which the distribution is unspecified, and which were incident on the road at an unknown angle (e.g., high or low beams).

The unknown light emanated apparently from a concentrated source seen through trees from a moving car, and also from a general glow (reflection from clouds?) above the trees; it would have been enhanced by this effect, and attenuated by the rain, fog, and obstructing trees. And it impinged on the roadway at an unknown—really undefinable—angle. In such circumstances, photometry is crude indeed.

Interpretation of even such a result as this in terms of the power dissipated in the light source introduces further wide uncertainties, since nothing whatever was known as to the mechanism of the light source or its radiative efficiency as compared with that of automobile headlamps, or whether it was radiating in a beam toward the witness or in all directions. All of these factors bear crucially on the power estimate, so that the value of several hundred megawatts is highly dubious.

Chapter II Case studies during the term of the project (Cases 11–45)

Case 11

South Central
Winter 1966
Investigator: Roach

Abstract:

Four members of the crew of a DC-8 aircraft on a night flight from Lima, Peru to Mexico, D. F. reported sighting two bright lights which appeared to increase their angular separation with time. At the greatest angular separation the lights appeared to one of the observers to be connected by a body which had a suggestion of windows. Protuberances from the main "body" were reported. The object appeared to fly "in formation" with the aircraft for about two minutes and then was lost to view behind the wing of the aircraft.

It is suggested that the sighting may have been the result of the reentry of fragments of the Agena from Gemini II.

Background:

During a regular flight of a DC-8 commercial airliner from Lima to Mexico City four crew members reported an interesting sighting to the left of the aircraft. Here is the description given by the captain.

> Two very bright lights, one of which was pulsating; from the two lights were two thin beams of light (like aircraft landing lights) which moved from a V initially to an inverted V finally. At one point the object seemed to emit a shower of sparks (similar to a firework). There appeared to be a solid shape between the two white lights, which was thicker in the middle and tapered outwards. There was also a strip of light between the white lights (not very bright and yellowish in color). Much like cabin lights of an aircraft.

The chronology and circumstances of events are given below:

Time: Winter 1966; 0803 GCT; 0238 local time.

Position of aircraft: Latitude 6°S; Longitude 81°42'W.

Moon: Almost full moon, high in the sky behind the aircraft.

Heading of aircraft: 318° magnetic, 324° geographic (36°W of N).

Table 1

Time (relative)	Description
0 min.	First sighting. Two lights, 70° left, about 10° above the horizon. Estimated separation of the lights about ½°.
4 min.	Lights now about 90° to the left, brighter than the full moon, separation of the lights estimated at about 9° or 10°. A suggestion of "windows" between the lights. Shower of sparks from more northerly light.
5 min.	"Pacing" the aircraft.
6 min.	"Pacing" the aircraft.
7 min.	Object lost to view behind the left wing.

Suggested explanation of the sighting:

The apparent "pacing" of the aircraft by the object for an estimated two minutes is a puzzling feature of the sighting. Also the captain's sketch is suggestive of some kind of a craft. These add up to the intriguing possibility of an intelligently guided craft which, in the words of the aircraft's captain, "is a craft with speed and maneuverability unknown to us."

In a discussion with the captain, who has had some 26 yr. of flying experience, I asked his opinion of the following possibilities:

Table 2

Explanation	Evaluation by Captain
Aircraft	Definitely no
Meteor	No
Reentry of satellite	Possible

The Agena from Gemini II (see Plate 20) had been predicted to reenter at 0730 GCT at latitude 21 N, and longitude 134 E (NE of the Philippine I.). This is some 33 min. earlier than the sighting and about ⅓ of the earth's circumference away. NORAD has made a calculation of a reentry of a fragment or fragments from the Agena which would have a much smaller drag coefficient than the Agena proper. The final computer predictions to represent an extended reentry of a low drag fragment in the vicinity of the aircraft are shown in Table 3. It is noteworthy that during the last two minutes from 08h 04m 30s to 08h 06m 21s the object is dropping almost vertically from 26 km. to 10 km. The aircraft was presumably flying at about the latter height.

The closest approach of the Agena and the aircraft is about 250 statute mi. The rapid deceleration of the reentering fragment at the end of its journey is consistent with the impression of the crew that the object was pacing the aircraft since it could have appeared close to 90° on the left side of the aircraft for some minutes during its final descent into the atmosphere. The time of the sighting was given by the report of the crew as 0803 GCT. It is not known whether this time was near the early or the late part of the event. Also there is some uncertainty as to the exact geographical location of the aircraft during the sighting. With these uncertainties it seems that the proposed explanation of the sighting as due to the reentry of the Agena from Gemini II is reasonable (but not proven) so far as the relative paths of the aircraft and the predicted reentry are concerned.

Table 3

NORAD Computer Predictions for Extended Reentry of Low Drag Fragment of Agena

Date	Hr.	Min.	Sec.	S. Lat.	E. Long.	Ht. (km.)
30 Dec. 1966	08	00	30	4°.498	268°.218	81
		01	30	6 .390	271 .476	74
		03	30	9 .264	276 .572	43
		04	30	9 .558	277 .106	26
		05	30	9 .577	277 .142	15
		06	21	9 .577	277 .142	10

Case 12

North Eastern
Winter 1967
Investigators: Fred Hooven and David Moyer of Ford Motor Company

Abstract:

Witness reported that, while she was driving alone at night, a luminous object hovered over her car for several miles, then moved rapidly into the distance, and that several mechanical and electrical functions of her car were found to be impaired afterward. Examination of the car two months later disclosed no faults that were not attributable to ordinary causes, nor any significant magnetic or radioactive anomaly in or on the car body.

Background:

The witness reported this and an earlier sighting to a sheriff who referred her to someone at a local university. The latter, in turn, reported the case to the Colorado project staff. Because the report indicated that the case would afford a good opportunity to test the possibility of electromagnetic effects on an automobile by an UFO, Hooven and Moyer were asked to carry out a detailed investigation.

Investigation:

In the spring of 1967 Moyer recorded an interview with the witness and drove her car back to Dearborn, where Ford engineers and laboratory staff under Hooven's direction examined it in detail.

The witness, a professional secretary, reported that, while driving on a rural road near her home about 2 a.m. one morning in the winter of 1967, she first noticed that the scene in front of her was brightly illuminated. Thinking at first that her headlamps were on high beam, she operated her foot switch but this made no difference, although the indicator light was responding. She then turned the headlamps out, but the illumination was undiminished. She then observed that its source was a luminous body over her car, which she perceived in the rear-view mirror and from the side windows. The object remained directly over her car for ten or fifteen minutes as she drove along the road rather slowly. The car would not accelerate. She depressed the accelerator all the way. Though the car went straight, she felt that she was not steering it, rather it—or her mind—was being steered from the mysterious object. She opened one window and could hear no sound. At the top of a rise the object drew away and "made a big check mark in the sky." It disappeared rapidly into the distance, growing redder as it did so. As it moved away, it resembled an inverted mushroom having a short stem on top and a uniform yellowish glow and two bright white lights and several smaller ones underneath.

The witness reported four instrument malfunctions after the incident that she had not noticed before: (1) the radio was weak and full of static; (2) the speedometer read low; (3) the battery did not charge properly and the ammeter did not read as usual; (4) the oil gauge was stuck at the maximum reading.

After his interview with the witness, Moyer drove her car, a 1964 Comet, to Detroit, where Ford engineers and research staff investigated its condition in detail. With respect to the malfunctions reported by the witness, they found that: (1) The radio antenna had been broken off the car, so that only local stations could be heard through the background noise.

(2) The fan belt, which operated the generator, was so loose that the generator was not delivering normal charging power to the battery. (3) In the speedometer, a die casting that provided alignment for the bearings had been broken, repaired, and apparently had broken again, causing bearing friction that caused the speedometer to read low. This condition was aggravated by sticky lubricant from the speedometer cable that had worked up. (4) The transmitter element of the oil gauge was malfunctioning because of electrical leakage due to corrosion.

All of the reported malfunctions were found to result from conditions that are commonplace in cars of the age and mileage of the witness' Comet.

The metal-forming operations in the manufacture of a car body produce a characteristic magnetization pattern for each model, which persists for years with little change unless the metal is reworked or subjected to a magnetic field substantially stronger than that of the earth. An examination of the magnetic "signature" of the witness' car body revealed no significant difference from that of three out of four other randomly selected similar cars of the same age. It was therefore concluded that no significant magnetic field had acted on the witness' car.

A Geiger beta-gamma survey counter showed no significant radio-activity from the car body. Scrapings of accumulated dirt and debris from hood and deck lid flanges, drip rail, etc., showed a low level radioactive contaminations, the strongest being about 5 gammas per sec. at 120 keV. A similar survey of material from another 1964 Comet showed a similar level of contamination, though with a different spectral distribution. The radioactivity found is not unusual; however, an accurate evaluation of its significance was impossible in the absence of detailed knowledge of the environmental history of the car.

Comments:

This case is especially interesting because of the specific and detailed information given by the witness, and the "strangeness" of the encounter. Her recorded testimony indicates a competent, practical personality, trained and accustomed to keeping her presence of mind in unexpected situations. By her account, her first intimation of something strange was the abnormally bright headlight field. Her practical response was to try the high-low beam switch, and she distinguished between the dash-signal indication and the lack of change in the illumination. Later she lowered the window to listen for any unusual sound. Most interesting is her comment that, after she realized something strange was above the car, she remembered stories of alleged mental influence by such apparitions and kept talking to herself to keep her mind actively busy. "I was not about to give it an opening." In short her testimony presents the picture of a woman alone on a deserted road confronted by a strange phenomenon, scared but coping intelligently with the situation.

However, her account is not free of discrepancies. She remembered bright moonlight, but the moon was at last quarter on 3 January, and would not have been very high even on that date. Her discription of what she saw of the UFO through the rear-view mirror is open to question. The Ford investigators noted that the internal mirror allows a field of only 3° above the horizontal. The UFO would have had to be about 20 times as wide as its elevation above the car to be seen in the mirror at all. She also reported several earlier UFO sightings by herself and friends and family in the vicinity of her home. These reports suggest the possibility of a preoccupation with the subject. However, she apparently was not seeking publicity. She mentioned the incident early in March to a local deputy sheriff, who reported it to a person at a local university. All of the malfunctions of the car that the witness stated had manifested themselves after the UFO experience were found to be the results of gradual wear and deterioration except the broken radio antenna, which was inconclusive. The case remains interesting but unexplained.

Case 13
North Eastern
Winter 1967
Investigators: Ayer, Wadsworth

Abstract:

Two women, joined later by a third, reported three appearances of a disc-shaped object with lights while they were driving in early darkness. Because of elapsed time and other factors, no evaluation was practicable.

Investigation:

Interviews with the three women in autumn 1967 developed the following account:

A woman (witness A), and her niece about 16 yr. old (witness B), were driving north toward town at about 5:45 p.m. They had just passed the lake and were about 0.5 mi. south of town, when they saw a "classical" disc-shaped object moving toward them from the general direction of the mountain on their right. The disc had several round lights or "portholes" on its equator, and bright beams pointed in all directions. It stopped and hovered about 200 yd. from the road at such an altitude that it appeared to be below the crest of the mountain. (Since the top of the mountain was 400 ft. higher than the road and 2,400 yd. away, the object would have been 33 ft. off the ground if it had been seen in line with the mountain top.)

The women stopped and observed this phenomenon for five minutes, until the lights went out and the craft vanished. They stayed in the car during this time, with the engine running and the lights on.

They then drove on to town to pick up a woman friend (witness C). Just before arriving in town they looked back and saw the same or another object overtaking them from the direction of the lake. This second object looked and behaved like the first, hovering over the ground, remaining for about the same time, and finally vanishing when its lights went out. This time the women got out of the car, but left the lights on and the motor running.

The women continued their drive, picked up their friend, and returned to a point just east of the town to see if the object(s) had reappeared. Seeing nothing, they drove around to the east of the mountain and continued south. About a mile south of the mountain, they saw another object similar in shape to the first two, but having dim red, square windows, hovering near the road on their right at the same altitude as before. The three women got out of the car and turned off the motor and lights, and watched the object until the lights went out and it disappeared.

Comments:

This case is stronger than most eyewitness accounts, because two original witnesses were corroborated by a third although the third is not independent. Unfortunately, the incidents occurred eight months before the interviews, thus affording opportunity for significant distortions of memories. Because of the time lapse, a search for other witnesses or other contributing evidence did not appear practicable. The case therefore must be regarded as unexplained for lack of knowledge of the context in which it occurred.

During the interview, the niece made a remark that seemed especially relevant to the numerous sighting reports in that region. When asked whether she had seen anything like the disc before, she said she had not, "But we frequently see moving lights." Questions about altitude and azimuth, characteristics of the lights and frequency of appearances, brought out that lights had been seen several times a week, mostly toward the northwest (15 to 20 mi. away), at a low altitude just above the tree line. The lights were white points and moved rather rapidly in a random manner.

Case 14
South Central
Winter 1967
Investigators: Low, Powers, Wadsworth, Crow

Abstract:

Six UFO reports in the area of two South Central cities were investigated in the winter of 1967. Of the six, three were promptly identified, two as astronomical objects and one as a chemical-release rocket shot. The other three remain unidentified as follows:

(1) The city police chief and several officers reported sighting an extended object of spherical shape one morning, winter, 1967. It was of whitish or metallic color and showed no surface features as it drifted slowly near the outskirts of the city. The officers watched it for about 1.5 hours before it drifted out of sight.

(2) Several town policemen reported a red-and-green light moving irregularly in the western sky in the morning in winter, 1967. The planet Jupiter was low in the western sky also, but according to the witnesses the object displayed movement which would rule out identification as an astronomical object. They also stated that a bright "star" was visible near the object.

(3) Three teenage boys in the city reported to the police that they had just seen a large elongated UFO at the edge of town. Their description closely matched that of a recently publicized set of pictures that have since come under suspicion as a probable hoax. Credibility of these witnesses was considered marginal.

Background and Investigation:

FIRST SIGHTING

One morning in the winter of 1967 about 1.5 hours before dawn, the city police received a call from the town police reporting that an unidentified object was headed southeast toward the city. A police lieutenant drove to a location approximately four miles north of the city, and within a few minutes saw what he described as a huge silvery object moving slowly in his direction. The object was low on the horizon at an estimated elevation of 1,000 ft.

Several minutes after the object first became visible, it turned in a southwesterly direction, heading toward a nearby town. At this point, additional officers were called as witnesses. They met at a point just west of the city, about four miles from the town. The object was visible to all until it drifted out of sight just before dawn.

There is no reason to doubt the credibility of the sighting; however, the question of *what* was seen remains unresolved. One bit of corroborating evidence was brought to light during the investigation. A periodic glow or reflection from the object was described by the Joplin lieutenant. He stated that the glow had a regular five-second period. One-half mile from the witnesses' first location was the local airport. The half-rotation period of the airport's two-way beacon is five seconds, and thus consistent with the periodic glow seen coming from the object. If the object was both low and nearby, it might have been illuminated by the beacon.

The possibility of conventional explanation as a balloon

was ruled out when a weather check indicated that lower winds were from south to southwest.

SECOND SIGHTING

At approximately 5:00 a.m., the following morning, a sergeant of the police department observed an unidentified object in the western sky. He described the object as a bright light one-fourth the diameter of the full moon, showing no distinct outline, and colored red on the left and greenish-blue on the right. The object first attracted attention because of its apparent motion, which was irregular, involving stopping and changing direction. After a period of observation during which time several other officers were present, the object suddenly dropped as though it were going to "crash," but stopped a short distance above the horizon. By comparing the remembered elevation of the object to a pencil held vertically at arm's length, it was estimated that the object, when first observed, was 12 degrees above the horizon, and then dropped 9 or 10 degrees before stopping.

The sergeant was questioned about Jupiter, which was low in the west at the time. He said that a bright "star" was also visible, but that the motion of the object was too pronounced for it to have been a star or planet. He also emphasized that all of the witnesses observed the motion simultaneously, and that the object moved relative to the fixed background of stars. The object was still visible when the witnesses left the scene.

On the basis of witness testimony, it seems unlikely that the object spotted was Jupiter; however, evidence was insufficient to establish this.

THIRD SIGHTING

A sheriff and a police chief reported seeing a bright bluish cloud-like display for over an hour just before dawn on a winter morning, 1967. As daylight approached the object disappeared.

This "object" was later identified as an active chemical rocket launched from Eglin AFB, Florida, at 5:40 a.m. CST. It rose to an altitude of approximately 100 mi., where it released for scientific purposes a cloud of barium particles that glowed brilliantly bluish through chemical reaction with the surrounding atmosphere. It has been determined that this display would have been clearly visible from the area where the sighting took place.

FOURTH SIGHTING

Three teenage boys reported having seen a large UFO at the edge of town about 11:30 p.m., one evening, winter 1967. They described structural details, fins, and lights. After first seeing the object directly in front of their car, they followed it as it drifted over a wooded area into which there was a narrow access road. There they got out of their car, but became frightened when the object appeared to move in their direction, whereupon they returned to their car and left to report the incident. The boys' description and a sketch drawn by one of them closely matched recently publicized photographs, one of which had appeared in a local newspaper a few days before the sighting. Nevertheless, during interviews, the boys showed no evidence of falsification and seemed to have been genuinely frightened by the experience. No corroborating evidence was found to support this report.

FIFTH SIGHTING

At 12:30 a.m., one morning, winter 1967, a report came into the city police station from the state patrol. The report stated that a UFO was at that moment under observation, that it was being photographed, and that it had caused an observer's car to stall. Low immediately investigated this report and identified the object as Jupiter. The stalled car was still at the scene with apparently a low battery. The observer who had photographed the object said it had moved markedly before coming to rest at its present position. Thus, the possibility exists that initially he was watching something other than Jupiter; but there was no doubt of the identity of the object that he photographed.

SIXTH SIGHTING

At approximately 1:30 a.m., one morning, winter 1967, the city police dispatcher reported an object low in the East. This was promptly identified as Arcturus, which was scintillating markedly.

WEATHER CONDITIONS:

The following are pertinent excerpts from the meteorological report for the area on the day of the first sighting as prepared by Loren W. Crow:

> The semi-stationary weak cold front lay in a north—northeast-south-southwest orientation approximately forty miles northwest of [the city]. Behind this front cloudiness was generally overcast at 10,000 feet or more above the ground. To the east of the front, the sky was generally clear with some patches of scattered clouds. Visibility was 15 miles or greater, and the flow of the air was from the south-southwest at the surface in the vicinity of [the city] . . . (at higher elevations).
>
> CLOUDS: It is of some interest to note that the clear condition being observed at [three local stations] at 5:00 a.m. changed to reports of at least two cloud layers by 7:00 a.m. at all three stations. Part of this would have been due to increasing amounts of light for the trained observers to be able to identify cloudiness which could not have been seen during the darker hours of the night . . .
>
> Although the type of clouds being reported at 10,000 feet over [the city] were not identified, the type of cloud in this height

range was identified as alto-cumulus over [nearby cities]. It is the Author's opinion that this type of cloud would have been *altocumulus castellatus*, which tends to have rounded edges. The initial formation of such clouds would constitute small individual cloud cells. Each may have shown for a matter of a few minutes then may have been replaced by another cloud cell nearby which may have been similar in shape. This could have indicated movement from the position of the first cloud parcel (which now would have disappeared) to the position of the newer cloud. At the same time, the individual clouds would be moving with the wind, which was from a westerly direction at those elevations.

It is fairly certain that cloudiness began to appear in this area sometime between 4:00 and 6:00 a.m. There may have been a few isolated cloud parcels visible with the limited moonlight available at 5:00 a.m. . . .

Conclusion

Of the six sightings investigated, three objects were identified. In only one case of an unidentified object was the evidence strong for both its reality and its strangeness. That was the first, which involved a slowly drifting sphere, metallic in color. We have little basis for speculation about *what* the object was, since the sighting occurred in pre-dawn darkness and no surface details or structural features were seen. In the other two unknown cases the evidence is less substantial, one case having low credibility and other marginal strangeness.

Case 15

South Mountain
Winter 1967
Investigator: Wadsworth

Background

A private observer had reported by telephone that for several months he had repeatedly seen in the west at evening a green light as large as a two-story building. Sometimes it appeared round, sometimes oblong. He reported that the object had been landing five to 20 miles west of his house several times per week, in the period about 4:30 to 7:30 p.m. Observing through binoculars, he had seen two rows of windows on a dome-shaped object that seemed to have jets firing from the bottom and that lit up a very large surrounding area.

Investigation

The investigator visited the site on a winter evening, 1967, arriving at the observer's home about 6:30 p.m. The observer pointed out as the object of his concern a bright planet 10-15 degrees above the western horizon. Wadsworth suggested that the object appeared to be a star or planet. (Both Venus and Saturn were visible about 1.3 degrees apart, Venus being the brighter.) The observer agreed, saying that, had he not seen it on other occasions when it appeared much nearer and larger, he would have the same opinion. Also, he held to his description of the surface features that he claimed to have seen through the binoculars. His wife concurred with this statement, supporting his allusion to windows. It was suggested that some object other than a planet might have been involved, but no other bright light was visible in that area of the sky.

The phenomena of scintillation and color change characteristic of light sources low on the horizon were described to the observer, and he seemed to accept the possibility that what he had seen was only a planet seen under conditions unusual in his experience. Thus what he had observed, even with the binoculars, apparently had not been sufficiently clear to be conclusive to him. The possibility of a second object seems very unlikely, although at times he may have observed stars or planets other than the one he noted at this time. This possibility would account for the long period during which the sightings had occurred.

Conclusion

The reported "landings" apparently were the nightly settings of the planet. The glow around the "landed" object probably was the bright moonlit snowscape seen through the binoculars. The motion was described as always the same, a very gradual descent to the western horizon, where the object would "land" and shortly thereafter cut off its lights. It is believed that the alleged size, brightness, and surface features were largely imagined.

The observer seemed quite sincere and curious; however, his description of the phenomena could not be considered scientifically reliable. He demonstrated an inadequate grasp of basic scientific information, and seemed unable to distinguish between objective observations and subjective impressions.

Case 16

South Mountain
Winter 1967
Investigators: Van Arsdale, Hynek

Abstract:

Daylight visual sightings of "silvery specks" overhead were reported, but pilots of aircraft sent to investigate saw nothing. Two radars concurrently detected several intermittent stationary targets in the reported area, and then a single target that moved slowly several minutes. Then it disappeared on one radar, and on the other described an approximately circular course at high speed. The visual sighting, and a later one, are impossible to evaluate. The radar targets are attributed to propagation anomalies, a balloon, and malfunction of one radar.

Background:

Reports of reliably witnessed visual and radar sightings in the vicinity of an Air Force base reached the project, leading to the decision to send an investigator there. It was arranged that Dr. Hynek, who was to be at the base on other business, should participate in the investigation.

Investigation:

The investigators examined the radar plots and talked with the base UFO officer, the Public Information Officer, and the radar operators who had reported the unidentified targets. From these inquiries, the following account developed.

At 10:25 a.m. a young man telephoned the base UFO officer to report that he was seeing "silvery specks" passing overhead. During about 30 min., he had seen two or three groups of 30 to 40 such objects moving southwest. He was at a point (Point "1," Fig. 1) in the mountains NE of the base.

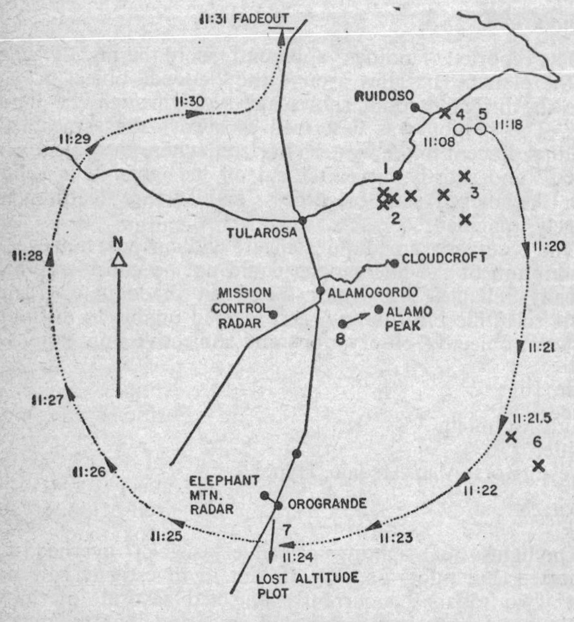

Fig. 1

The UFO officer finished his conversation with the witness at 10:50. He then had two aircraft sent to the reported location; but they reported nothing unusual.

He also asked range surveillance radar to seek the objects. (Being inexperienced in such investigations, he told the operators where to look, instead of simply asking them whether they had any unidentified targets.) Only two surveillance radars were operating, one at Mission Control on the base and the other 35 mi. south.

About 10:55 both radars plotted four objects about five miles south of the visual sighting, and a little later three other objects ("2" and "3" Fig. 1.) All of these objects were intermittent, appearing sometimes on one sweep of the radar screen and not on the next, so that the radar tracking equipment could not "lock on" them; but they appeared to be stationary.

Then at 11:08 both radars plotted a slow-moving object at 25,000 ft. altitude, and tracked it ten minutes while it moved three or four miles eastward ("4" and "5" Fig. 1). At this point, at 11:18 a.m., it disappeared from the south radar screen, while the radar at Mission Control showed it moving southward at Mach 1.2. It continued approximately on a circular course centered on Mission Control radar, while both radars scanned clockwise. At 11:21.5 both radars showed two stationary objects ("6" Fig. 1) that also flickered intermittently. Mission Control radar continued to follow the fast-moving target on its circular course until it abruptly climbed to 80,000 ft. ("7" Fig. 1), and followed it on around to the north until it appeared to go out of range at 100,000 ft. altitude, at 11:31.

During the tracking of the circular course, the operator stated that he thought the radar was not functioning properly. The UFO officer accordingly was advised that he should not consider the plotted tracks "firm and accurate" FAA radar did not confirm the circular track, and range-data radars were not operating. The following day, the radar supervisor reported that evaluation of the Mission Control radar record indicated that the instrument had plotted a noise track. Also, there exist unexplained discrepancies of 5 to 15 mi between the ranges of the various unidentified targets displayed on photographs of the radar plotting boards, compared with the written report issued by Mission Control the next day. Positions indicated on Fig. 1 are taken from the plots.

An electronics technician reported that at 11:20, while he was at location "8" (Fig. 1), he saw a saucer-shaped object moving rapidly away from him; it disappeared behind a neaby peak. His line of sight to the peak was approximately toward the point on the circular track traced at 11:20 by Mission Control radar.

Comment:

With the limited information available, the two visual sighting reports are impossible to evaluate. The "silvery specks" could have been plant seeds of the type that float like parachutes, but such a suggestion is speculative.

The radar observations offer a more substantial basis for

analysis, since they involved two trained operators and instrument records (See also Section III Chapter 5). However, the UFO officer remarked that the men on duty during the sightings were second-line operators having little experience with "track" (surveillance) radar. As noted earlier, they were told to look for unidentified objects at a specified location and had perhaps in consequence found them there ("2" on Fig. 1). It appears probable that these intermittent, stationary targets were mirage-like glimpses of peaks or other high points that were just below the radar line of sight, and were brought into view sporadically by fluctuations in the atmospheric path. There is the strong implication that the operators noticed these "objects" at location "2" because they were directed to look for something there, and that they could have found similar targets at other points on the mountain landscape In fact, they did just that, at locations "3" and "6" (Fig 1) These observations appear to be similar to some reported in other cases (e.g., Case 35) in which operators of highly specialized radar equipment have failed to notice extraneous objects on their screens because they were intent on the targets that they had been assigned to track. They became aware of such commonplace objects only when a "UFO flap" has diverted them from routine procedure and encouraged them to look for anomalies. It should be noted that such a habit of ignoring irrelevant information in the perceptual field unless attention is directed to it is common in other instrument observations, and indeed in ordinary experience. It has accounted for many visual UFO reports.

The slow-moving radar object ("4" and "5" on Fig. 1) was entirely compatible with a weather or research balloon drifting with the prevailing westerly winds.

The evidence indicates that the circular track plotted on Mission Control radar, but not on the south screen, was an instrumental anomaly. The operator at Mission Control judged that the instrument was malfunctioning, and the subsequent evaluation by the civilian radar supervisory staff attributed the circular trace to a "noise track." Why the slowly-drifting object should have disappeared from both radars at nearly the same time is not clear. However, if it is assumed that the circular track represented a real object, then it is much more difficult to explain why the south screen never picked it up, even though it passed within seven miles of that station when the radar was working as attested by its plotting the targets at location "6."

It is important to note that none of the radar targets exhibited motions agreeing even approximately with those reported in the two visual sightings. The "silvery specks" were moving southwest. The saucer-like object of the second sighting was moving "away from" the observer and disappeared behind the peak, which was ENE of him, while the radar "object" was moving south. Also, inspection of the contours of the region indicates that the radar "object" plotted at 25,000 ft. altitude would have been obscured by mountain ridges from the observer at location "6" throughout at least 25° of azimuth to the north of the peak.

This case is not fully clarified in all details; but the evidence indicates decisively that it is typical of many instances in which an initial sighting of dubious quality stimulates unusual attention and induces an expectant emotional state in which commonplace phenomena assume apparent significance.

Case 17

South Mountain
Spring 1967
Investigator: Wadsworth

Abstract:

A youth reported that a large, glowing object approached his car and accompanied it more than twenty miles. He described apparent electromagnetic effects on his automobile. Investigation revealed neither a natural explanation to account for the sighting, nor sufficient evidence to sustain an unconventional hypothesis.

Other reported sightings in the area were investigated without conclusive results.

Background:

THE PRIMARY SIGHTING

On a night in the spring of 1967 an 18 year-old high school boy (Witness I) was returning from a first-aid class in town to his parents' home, a general store. He reported that shortly after 11:00 p.m., when he was three miles west of the town, he noticed an object high in the sky directly ahead of him. He compared its apparent size and brightness to an ordinary incandescent light bulb seen at about twenty feet, or a slow-moving ball of fire. As he continued, the object descended at an angle toward his left, closed on his automobile, and accompanied it at a distance and elevation he estimated at one hundred feet each. He estimated the dimensions of the object as approximately 30 by 100 feet. It was shaped like an inverted bowl, flat on the bottom and arched on top. No surface features were visible, only an overall glow that was blue at the top and blended gradually through cream color and orange to bright red at the bottom. At times he noticed a white vapor associated with the object. The only other feature he noted was a periodic on-off manifestation of the glow.

The witness also reported a sensation of intense heat coming from the object, such that he began perspiring profusely even with the car windows down. At this same time, the automobile engine began to sputter and miss, the radio and headlights went out, the ammeter indicated "discharge," and shortly afterward the temperature light indicated "hot."

To see the road, he used a battery-powered spotlight that was independent of the car battery. It continued to function normally. He drove as rapidly as possible (50-60 mph) under the adverse conditions, and was paced the entire twenty-odd miles to his home. As he approached the family store, the object moved off ahead of him for the first time and stopped above the store as if to wait for him. As he turned in, the object blacked out and vanished into the darkness.

The witness reported that after the incident his car never recovered. Its condition worsened continually until it was beyond repair.

Investigation:

Wadsworth investigated this and other reports in the area, Spring 1967. Although no unequivocal corroborating evidence was uncovered, testimony from a game warden who is regarded as highly reliable by area residents, provided possible corroboration. He reported having seen a round, reddish object in the sky a little later on the same evening. He was travelling the same stretch of the road that was involved in the sighting already described. The object he saw was so distant that its identity with the other is uncertain.

Witness' automobile was monitored for high-energy radiation. Smear samples were analyzed for alpha, beta, and gamma radiation. Alpha and beta were at normal background levels, and gamma was a trace above; this result may relate to the presence of uranium deposits in the vicinity. The magnetization pattern of the automobile body was checked against a control auto and found to be normal.

The auto engine was found to be badly out of tune and in generally poor running condition. Unfortunately, it was impossible to determine whether any specific damages resulted from the effects of ordinary wear and tear. Nevertheless, the witness stated that his car was in good running condition before the incident.

The route on which the sighting occurred was inspected under both day and night conditions. No physical evidence was found that could be related to the sighting; however, terrain and highway features were consistent with the witness' account.

ADDITIONAL SIGHTINGS

After the initial report, additional sightings were reported in the area. Many of these were of marginal quality and insufficiently detailed to warrant further investigation. In a few cases, followup attempts were made. Most of the witnesses were Indians, who were difficult to locate because they live in remote places, and were extremely difficult to interview once found because they speak little English and are not familiar with such a procedure. It was thus almost impossible to obtain more than the barest details.

The most useful materials obtained from these witnesses were their sketches of the objects they reported having seen. These sketches show a considerable range of variation, suggesting several types of objects. It should be noted that the Navajo appear to be unsophisticated as to UFOs. That is, they are less likely than a member of the general population to know what an UFO is reported to look like. Also, these reports cannot be assessed in terms of the same psychosocial dynamics that are appropriate to most UFO reports.

Reported loss of UFO-caused power failures were checked with an official of the local Power Association. He stated that nothing out of the ordinary had been reported to him. In one case, an Indian witness reported loss of power at his cabin when an UFO landed nearby.

AVAILABLE DETAILS OF ADDITIONAL SIGHTINGS

(1) Evening of the first sighting, 9:00 p.m., Duration 2 min., two witnesses.

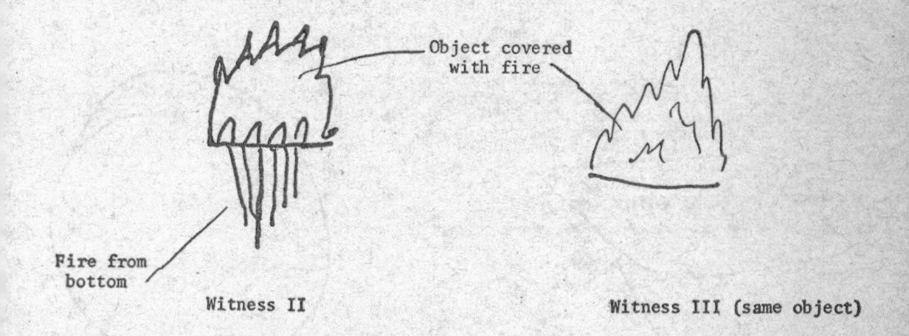

(2) Following evening, 9:00 p.m., one witness.

Object appeared to be 100 to 150 yards away. It was a reddish-white light, the apparent size of a car. There were lighted windows all around the edge. Fire coming from the bottom of the object left a trail; however, it left no evidence on the ground. The witness stopped his car and shut off his lights. When his lights went out, so did the lights of the object. It did not reappear.

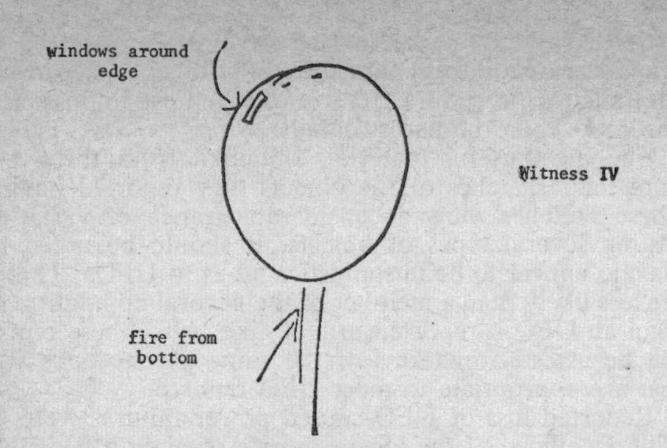

(3) 14 da. after original sighting, 3:00-3:30 a.m., duration 2 minutes, one witness, estimated altitude, 150 feet; estimated size, 20 feet long; weather clear.

Object had blue lights the color of a welding torch in a band around center. It was reddish at the bottom. It moved up and out, vanishing in the distance.

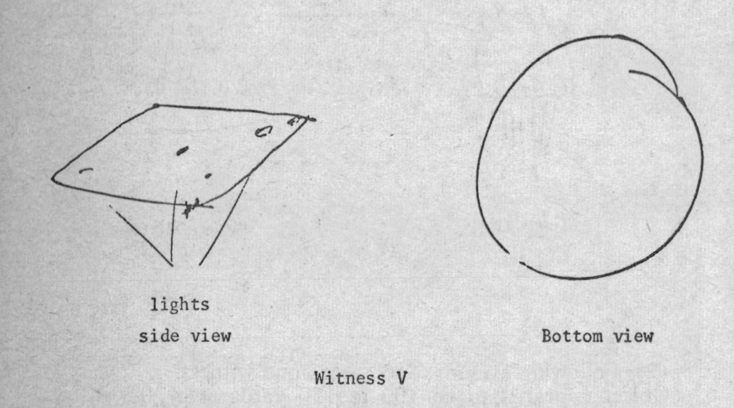

(4) 15 da. after original sighting, 11:20 p.m., duration 20 minutes. One witness.

Witness was on duty as hoistman at the mine at time of sighting. Object approached the mine, hovered nearby, then departed rapidly at an upward angle. He reported that the incident so scared him that he was still shaking when he went home.

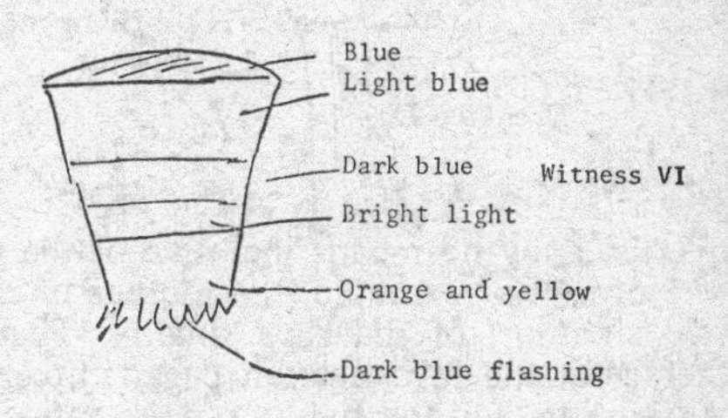

(5) 17 da. after original sighting, 9:58 p.m., duration 5 minutes, three witnesses including witness VI above.

Witness VI said the object looked very much like the one he had seen two nights previously.

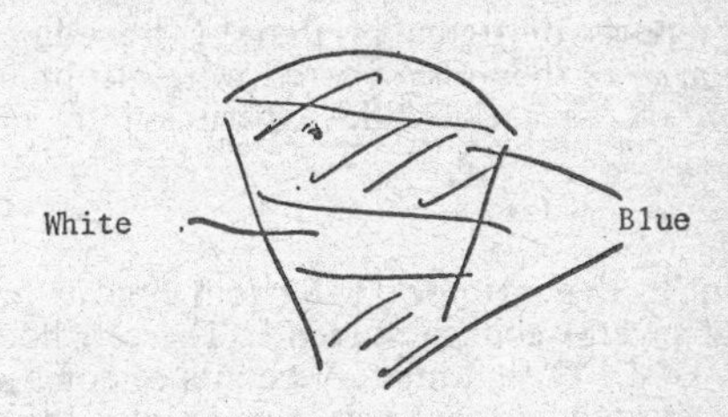

(6) Spring, 1967, night, duration 6 min. Two witnesses (IX and X).

Witness IX was in his cabin when the lights went out. He put on his miner's light, went out to investigate, and saw an object on the ground near his cabin. He then went inside to get a rifle. When he came out again, he saw the object departing into the distance. The cabin lights came back on after the object had left.

The above list is by no means inclusive of the sightings reported in the area. For example, the mother of the witness I reported two sightings of marginal quality. There were numerous others; but the investigation began three weeks after the primary sighting, and the signal-to-noise ratio was poor.

Conclusion

On the basis of available evidence, it is impossible to say whether or not the event reported is real.

Case 18
South Mountain
Spring 1967
Investigators: Low, Wadsworth

Abstract:

Several reports of lights in the sky traveling slowly and emitting sparks as they disappeared were attributed to hot air balloons set off as a scientific experiment by neighborhood boys.

Background:

One night in the spring of 1967 four hot air balloons were released by several college students. These balloons set off a small wave of UFO sightings. Accounts of some of the sightings were reported in local newspapers, and for several days the source of the objects was unknown except to the students who launched them. Because of the unexpected publicity, the students decided to come forth and give an account of the event to this project.

This report is intended primarily to examine the degree of correspondence between the reports of the event and the event itself. A description of the event based on an interview with the students is presented, followed by report summaries of a number of the sightings. It should be noted that the students were not attempting to make careful observations when they launched the balloons. Their accounts were somewhat general and lacking in details.

Description of Events as reported by Students

Four balloons of the type recently publicized in various news media and magazines were released. These balloons consisted of plastic dry-cleaners' suit covers, sealed at the top and held open at the bottom by crossed drinking straws attached to the edge of the opening. Hot air was generated by a cluster of birthday candles mounted along the straws where they crossed near the center of the opening.

The first balloon was launched at 9:15 p.m. There was no ground wind, and the sky was clear except for scattered patches of thin haze. This balloon did not travel far from the launching site. It went up a fairly short distance and then went out. The object appeared to the students to be larger than a star. Duration of the event was estimated at five to ten minutes.

By 10:00 o'clock, three more balloons were ready and were launched one after another. They appeared to maintain three different altitudes as they rose, and showed some flickering, growing dim and then brightening up again. The balloons quickly became unrecognizable as balloons and showed only as fire-colored lights. The plastic envelopes were faintly visible as dim shapes. The lights appeared the size of bright stars or larger.

One of the most obvious features of the event was the triangular formation that the balloons assumed upon gaining altitude. This triangle endured for some minutes; then upper level winds apparently began to take the balloons in different directions. The lower one drifted apart and went out. Duration of the entire event was estimated at 20 to 25 minutes.

Summaries of Observers' Reports:

1. Time: 9:15 p.m.
   Observers: mathematics professor and wife.
   Location: 0.25 mile WSW of launch site.
   Description: gold or orange-yellow light, larger than a star but smaller than a dime at arm's length, brighter than anything else in the sky; through binoculars, observers could see an area of "stronger density" adjacent to the light source.
   Direction and disappearance: object first seen at an elevation of 45° in the east; began moving north, receded toward the east and faded out.
   Duration: 5 minutes.

2. Time: 9:15 p.m.
   Observers: language professor and public school teacher.
   Location: 0.4 mile ENE of launch site.

Description: orange-yellow object larger than a star, smaller than a plane (which passed by at the time) but larger than the lights of the plane.
Direction and disappearance: object stopped, light varied and seemed to fizzle out, sparks dropped and light disappeared.
Duration: 10 minutes.

3. Time: 9:15 p.m.
Observers: two students.
Location: same as (2) above.
Description: gold-yellow object, little larger than a star, first thought it was a satellite.
Direction and disappearance: object was first seen slightly south of west and moving slowly eastward toward observers. Object came nearly overhead, dimmed, brightened, emitted sparks and went out.
Duration: 5 minutes.

4. Time: 10:00 p.m.
Observers: two women.
Location: 0.7 mile ENE of launch site.
Description: three lights in triangular formation; two on left were yellowish, one on right was reddish. Objects were about the size of a star when first seen, but grew larger as they moved toward the observers. Other people in the parking lot seemed not to notice the objects.
Direction and disappearance: Objects were first seen in southwest at about 45 to 60° elevation. They then seemed to move north, shifting from the triangle to a vertical line formation and rising. Observers left while objects were still visible. The objects seemed to have moved back to their original positions and become smaller.
Duration: 15 minutes.

5. Time: 10:05 p.m.
Observers: fine arts professor and wife.
Location: 0.7 mile SE of launch site.
Description: three red or pink lights in triangular formation at 45° elevation. Size and speed compared to Echo satellite.
Direction and disappearance: Objects first observed in northwest, then began to move southeast and shift from triangle to straight line formation. Movement continued till objects were approximately overhead and seemed to stop. Then one went south and went out, one north and went out, and one west and went out.
Duration: 15 minutes.

6. Time: 10:13 p.m.
Observer: chemical research assistant.

Location: 0.5 mile ESE of launch site.
Description: three lights like large stars in the form of a triangle. One appeared red, the others orange.
Direction and disappearance: objects were overhead and somewhat to the south when first seen. One moved to the southeast and disappeared in haze. One stayed overhead, then flickered, moved west, and blinked out. One arched away to the east and disappeared.
Duration: 5 minutes.

7. Time: 10:00-10:30 p.m.
Observer: man.
Location: 0.4 miles SE of launch site.
Description: three yellow-orange lights in a rough line formation. Appeared as dull glowing objects with haze around them. Observer thought they were small and low.
Direction and disappearance: objects were seen first in the northwest at an elevation of about 35°. Motion was southward, slow and haphazard. The first one continued to move south. The second two passed nearby overhead, seemed to move closer together, and drifted away to the southwest.
Duration: 5-10 minutes.

8. Time: 10:40 p.m.
Observer: astronomer.
Location: 1.0 mile SW of launch site.
Description: One object visible low in the east, yellow-orange and glowing continuously except several times when it dimmed. It was about 2nd or 3rd stellar magnitude, and 10°-15° above eastern horizon. Through binoculars it remained visible only as a point of light.
Direction and disappearance: Position when first viewed was about 10° north of east and 10-15° above horizon. Motion was very slow and difficult to determine, because of the lack of nearby reference stars.
Duration: 3-5 minutes.

9. Time: 10-10:15 p.m.
Observer: man.
Location: about 300 yards SE of launch site.
Description: two bright lights seen through the curtains of observers' apartment. From outside, they looked like blimps with fire at one end, and were one-quarter to one-half the apparent size of full moon. A third similar object appeared shortly after the first two.
Direction and disappearance: the first two appeared at 30-40° elevation in the northwest and drifted to an overhead position, where they separated and diminished with increasing altitude. The third behaved similarly.
Duration: 10-20 minutes.

Table 4

COMPARISON OF REPORTS IN TERMS OF DESCRIPTIVE CHARACTERISTICS

	STUDENTS' ACCOUNT		OBSERVERS' REPORTS	
LAUNCH TIME	9:15 p.m.	10:00 p.m.	9:15 p.m.	10:00 p.m.
SIZE	Larger than a star	Size of large star or larger	1. Larger than a star 2. Larger than a star 3. Larger than a star	4. Star 5. Echo satellite 6. Star 7. Size not given 8. 2nd or 3rd Magnitude star 9. ¼ or ½ diameter of full moon, (observer could see the plastic envelope as well as the light, and his size estimate referred to the whole balloon)
SHAPE	First visible as balloon; diminished to point source	First visible as balloons; diminished to point sources	1. Point source light (accompanied by area of density) 2. Point source light 3. Point source light	4. Point source light 5. Point source light 6. Point source light 7. Point source (dull glow) with haze 8. Point source light 9. Like a blimp with fire at one end
COLOR	Fire-colored	Fire-colored	1. Gold/orange-yellow 2. Orange-yellow 3. Gold-yellow	4. Yellow/red 5. Red or pink 6. Red/orange 7. Yellow-orange 8. Yellow-orange 9. "Fire"-colored
FORMATION OF OBJECTS	Single object	Balloons assumed triangular formation, then dispersed.		4. Triangular 5. Triangular 6. Triangular 7. Line 8. Only one object seen by observer 9. Objects close to observer; formation not noticed

Conclusions

A comparison of the event as described by the launchers with the reports of accidental witnesses reveals obvious similarities regarding size, shape, color, and relative positions of the objects. Taking into consideration the known inconsistencies inherent in most eye-witness testimony, the degree of similarity between the reports is noteworthy, especially since times of observations and locations of observers were not the same. Certain dissimilarities should be noted. For example, observer IX was located very near balloons. However, he was not able to identify the objects; nor did he mention the triangular configuration reported by other witnesses, probably because the objects seemed more scattered suggesting separateness rather than relatedness. It is interesting to note the tendency of observers to give more detailed accounts of the event than the launchers themselves gave.

The sightings all occurred within approximately one mile of the launch site. With two exceptions, the balloons were first observed in the direction of the launch site. The exceptions are sighting number 6, in which case they are nearly overhead when first seen; and number 8, when only one object remained visible. In three other cases the balloons were reported as being overhead or nearly so at some time during the observations. These three sightings (5, 7, and 9) along with number 6 are all located in the southeast quadrant of the sighting area, indicating that the balloons drifted southeast. It should be pointed out that the balloons also were moving relative to each other, and it was this motion that the students and most witnesses referred to in their accounts. The limited area of sightings is probably characteristic of cases involving these balloons, and could be considered along with the slow aimless drifting, the flickering, and the red-orange color as identifying evidence in future cases.

In summary, we have a number of reports that are highly consistent with one another, and those differences that do occur are no greater than would be expected from situational and perceptual differences. Many small discrepancies could be pointed out, especially with regard to estimates of distance and direction, but these are not great enough to affect the overall impression of the event.

It would be expected that a survey of witnesses' speculations about the nature of the objects would have shown much greater divergence, but this report is confined to observational data.

Case 19

South Mountain
Spring 1967
Investigator: Wadsworth

Abstract:

A project investigator was at the site of a predicted UFO landing. The landing did not occur.

Background:

This investigation was made in response to a unique sighting prediction based on alleged telepathic contacts with UFOs. The prediction came from a man who claims to have psychic abilities. He declared that his past predictions had been accurate, and he was confident that this one would produce positive results, specifically an UFO landing at a racetrack on a given day at 11:00 a.m.

On the night before leaving for the site, Wadsworth telephoned the predictor to get any additional information he might have. He confirmed the exact time and location of the predicted landing and stated that he had received "a very strong indication" that the event would occur. He assured us that we would not be disappointed. The purpose, he claimed, was "just to show us" that UFOs are real. He said that only one "saucer" would appear.

Investigation:

Wadsworth was met in the state capital city by two officers of the highway patrol. Patrol cars and a small aircraft were provided for the trip to the site.

Weather in the capital was clear; however, a squall front was moving into the racetrack area. When the party arrived at the racetrack at 10:15 a.m., the weather was still clear. The patrol plane was circling overhead. Wadsworth decided that the best place to wait would be the center of the large circular track. (There are two tracks at the raceway: one is straight and runs NW-SE; and adjacent to it is a large circular track which, as seen from the air, would be a possible target area.) Before landing the plane, the pilot directed the patrol car to the center of the circle by radio. The predictor had been very definite about 11:00 as the time for the event to occur. In his own words, the UFO would appear *exactly* at 11:00 a.m.

At 11:00 nothing unusual was noted. The front was still moving in; rain began at 12:00 noon. At 12:30 p.m. the group left the area.

Case 20

North Pacific
Spring 1967
Investigators: Craig, Wadsworth

Abstract:

Reports of "beeping" sounds emanating apparently from invisible aerial sources were identified with the calls of small owls.

Background:

Spring 1967 this project received word that a state Department of Civil Defense had been investigating an unidentified sound in an area of the state. Wadsworth telephoned the same day to obtain more complete information about the sound, and to determine whether it might be connected with UFOs.

The investigation was being conducted by the warning officer and communications coordinator for the state's Department of Civil Defense, who gave further information. He described the sound as a repetitious beeping signal of practically unvarying period and pitch that had been heard regularly from the same location for a period of several weeks, continuing for hours at a time without interruption. The most puzzling aspect of the sound was the lack of any visible source. Witnesses had approached the apparent location, only to find that the sound seemed to come from directly overhead. This location was at the top of a hill in a wooded area to which access was difficult. However, local interest in the sound was so high that many individuals had hiked into the area to hear it. The sound reportedly began at 8:00 p.m. PST each night, and continued until 3:00 or 4:00 a.m.

Other aspects that the Civil Defense official reported were: The sound had been heard for about three weeks. It had been heard as far as two miles away from its apparent source. A similar sound (believed by some to be from the same source) had been received on a police patrol car radio at 150 megacycles while the sound was being heard by persons in the above-mentioned area; visual UFO sightings had been reported in the general area of the sound during the same period. One sighting reported by two police officers and several FAA men occurred two days before the reported onset of the sound. A disc-shaped object was reportedly sighted passing overhead beneath an overcast ceiling of 1,000 feet. The sound did not alter perceptibly when people were in the area, even though they made noise, shone lights, or fired guns. When local time shifted from standard to daylight, the nightly time of onset also shifted an hour, indicating that the sound was oriented to real time, not clock time. The periodicity of the sound was approximately two beeps per second. Sometimes the sound source seemed to move as much as a quarter of a mile from its usual location in a few seconds, sometimes silently, sometimes beeping as it moved. One explanation for the sound that had been put forth was that it was the call of either a pygmy or a saw-whet owl, both of which are found in that area and emit calls similar to the reported sound.

A similar unidentified sound had been recorded elsewhere. Wadsworth took a tape recording of the sound under investigation and the other sound to an expert on bird calls. His opinion was that the latter was probably a saw-whet owl. The former, however, seemed unlike any bird or animal he had heard, although he could not be certain without knowing what distortions had been introduced by the tape recordings.

A decision whether to send out a field team was suspended until more could be learned about investigations already in progress. Any connection between the reported sounds and UFOs was speculation, and continued visual observations at the site of the sound had revealed nothing significant.

During the following week, significant new developments were reported. Sounds identical to that near the original location had been heard in other locations in the state.

The Civil Defense informant reported unusual animal reactions in some cases. Frogs, which were numerous and loud in the area, had all become silent 10-20 seconds before onset of the sound, suggesting that they might be sensing some kind of energy other than the audible sound. At other times, the cows and dogs in the area had suddenly shown marked excitement, and then become suddenly quiet. In one instance, this pattern had been repeated three times before the beeping began.

On another occasion, a man whose house was at the bottom of the hill where the sound seemed to originate had been frightened by the sound, which he said came suddenly down from the hill and continued beeping loudly just above his house. He was standing in the yard, and the sound was so eerie that he could "take it" for only a few minutes before going into the house.

The Civil Defense coordinator felt that he was at an impasse, and urged that a team from this project be sent to investigate.

Investigation

Spring 1967, Craig and Wadsworth went with three primary objectives: 1) to gather more information on the sound phenomenon and to experience it directly; 2) to obtain instrumented measurements, if possible; 3) to check for possible correlative visual sightings in the areas involved.

When the team arrived, they met with the Civil Defense coordinator and staff to plan the investigation. It was decided what area would be the best location for a thorough surveillance of the sound, and a base was set up in a barn about a mile below the hilltop where the sound was usually heard.

Stereo tape equipment was set up in the barn, and microphones were located about a quarter of a mile apart. The sound usually had been clearly audible at this location.

It was learned that, although the beeps had been loud in all kinds of weather, there was a considerably better chance of hearing them on a clear night. It was also reported that on some occasions the sound was very faint and of such short duration that no accurate location could be determined. It was not clear whether the occasions of fainter sound were due to distance or to a real drop in volume.

Equipment taken to the more inaccessible field site included: portable tape recorder; directional ultra-sonic translator; military infrared sniper scope; directional microphone audio detector ("snooperscope"); cameras loaded with infrared, ultraviolet, and conventional high-speed film; and two-way portable radios for communication with the operating base at the barn.

Shortly before the advance group reached the top of the hill (an hour's climb through steep, heavily forested terrain), the sound was heard. It lasted not more than 10 seconds and seemed to come from a direction different from its usual location. The team's subjective impression was that it sounded like a bird.

Throughout the night, and until 5:00 a.m., the sound was heard faintly eight or ten times for a few seconds each time. It did not seem to originate from directly overhead at any time, and the apparent direction and distance varied considerably. Part of this series was recorded on tape, but the sound was of low amplitude and brief duration. It was never heard at the main base below, so no high-quality tape was obtained.

Descriptions of an earlier observation had related that the sound had come from the top of a tall tree, then left the tree top and circled around it when someone climbed the tree. Although no bird had been seen in the darkness at the apparent source of the sound, and this description was similar in this respect to the farmer's account of the descent of the beeping source from the distant hill and its circling over his farm yard, such behavior certainly seemed owl-like. However, since the field team had heard only brief and distant emissions of the sound, they could not positively identify it.

Early the next evening, this team drove to a second site. The weather was rainy. Perhaps a dozen other cars were parked or cruising slowly by the area. The team heard no beeping sound during two hours of waiting.

The following morning, the team telephoned the county Sheriff's office, which had been handling the local investigation to ask whether the sound had been heard during the previous night. They were told that a bird had been shot by a farmer who lived adjacent to the second location. He had told the sheriff that, when the sound began the night before, he had gone out with a light and gun, shot the bird while it was beeping, and brought it in as evidence.

The owl was identified as a saw-whet by a local biology teacher. Despite this identification, some local persons expressed skepticism that the dead owl had been the source of sounds that they believed to be too constant in pitch and period to be generated by a bird. They questioned whether the farmer, who had been subjected to much harassment by the public, might not have produced the owl, hoping to put an end to these difficulties.

Tape recordings of the sound, made both before and during the project investigation, were later analyzed sonographically and compared with sonograms of recorded calls known to have been made by pygmy, saw-whet, and ferruginous owls. The original comparison was made with calls recorded in Peterson's Field Guide to Western Bird Calls. Later, other recordings of these calls were obtained from Cornell University's Laboratory of Ornithology. The comparisons showed the same sound structure, pitch, and period for the unidentified sound and for the saw-whet owl. Fewer overtones were displayed on the sonogram of the unidentified sound, but this difference probably was due to lack of sufficient amplitude and recorder frequency range limitations. It was concluded that the recorded unidentified sound was made by a saw-whet owl.

Conclusions

None of the reported visual sightings of UFOs in the vicinity was impressive enough to warrant more intensive investigation. While the project investigators could not be certain that owls accounted for all of the unidentified sounds reported from various areas of the state, they felt confident that the audible beeping was unrelated to visual sightings of UFOs, and that owls certainly accounted for most of the beeping sounds. The latter conclusion was based upon:

1. The correspondence between sonograms of the unidentified sound and of the beeping of a saw-whet owl;
2. Testimony that the dead saw-whet owl had been shot while making the beeping sound;
3. The fact that the locations and movements of the reported apparent sources were typical of those expected of owls.

The small size of the saw-whet owl (about six inches long) may account for the difficulty observers had in seeing it, thus allowing them to conclude that the sound came from a point in space that was not occupied by a physical object.

Case 21

South Mountain (location A)
Spring 1967
Investigators: Low, Rush

Abstract:

Operators of two airport radars reported that a target equivalent to an aircraft had followed a commercial flight in, overtaken it, and passed it on one side, and proceeding at about 200 knots until it left the radar field. No corresponding object was visible from the control tower. On the basis of witnesses' reports and weather records, explanations based on anomalous atmospheric propagation or freak reflection from other objects appear inadequate. The case is not adequately explained despite features that suggest a reflection effect (See Section III Chapter 6).

Background:

A radar traffic controller (Witness A) at an AF installation that serves as an airport for a nearby city (location A), telephoned the Colorado Project in the middle of May, 1967 to report an unexplained radar anomaly. The report was referred to Dr. Donald H. Menzel for comment, and Witness A and three other witnesses were interviewed at various times. The information so obtained is summarized in the next section.

Investigation:

Witness A, an air traffic controller of 20 years' experience, reported the following observations. At about 4:40 p.m., he and three other men were in the IFR (radar) room at the airfield. Two radars were in use: azimuth surveillance radar (ASR), used for early detection of arriving aircraft, and precision approach radar (PAR), used to monitor both azimuth and elevation of an aircraft approaching the runway (Fig. 2).

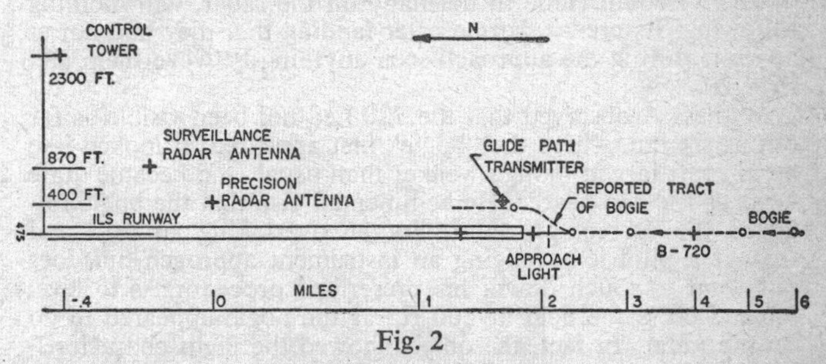

Fig. 2

ILS runway at the airfield, showing locations of radar antennas and tracks of aircraft and unidentified radar "bogie."

The controllers were monitoring the approach of a commercial Boeing 720. They got him onto the correct azimuth and glide path just as he broke through the 3,000 ft. ceiling about four miles from the radar receiver. Another commercial flight, a Viscount, showed on the surveillance radar about six mi. behind the 720. About the time the 720 appeared in the field of the precision radar, operated by Witness A, he noticed a very faint target on the elevation (glide path) screen about two mi. behind the 720. He adjusted the sensitivity of the instrument, and the unknown target became visible on the azimuth screen also. It appeared to be following the 720 on the glide path.

When the 720 had advanced about one mi., Witness A asked the operator of the surveillance radar, Witness B, whether he had the unidentified target; he did. Witness A then reported the object to the Viscount crew, about four mi. behind it. They saw nothing, though visibility under the overcast was 25-30 mi. He then reported the object to the visual control tower; but none of the three controllers there could see anything to account for it, even with binoculars. At this point, the departure scope man (the surveillance radar had duplicate screens for monitoring arrivals and departures) and the arrival data position man walked over to observe the precision scope. The target showed with equal clarity on both the elevation and azimuth screens. The unidentified object was overtaking the 720, and was about 0.25 mi. behind as the 720 passed the approach lighting system. At that point, the object pulled over, moved eastward, passed the Boeing on its right side, and continued on a parallel course at 200 ft. altitude and some 300 ft. east of the runway, until it passed out of the field of the precision scope. Unfortunately, no one thought to see whether the object appeared on the surveillance radar departure scope. At disappearance, it was about 1-1.5 mi. from the control tower. The controllers in the tower never saw anything to account for the target.

The Viscount came in normally on the radar, with nothing following. Its crew reported after landing that they had not at anytime during the approach seen anything between them and the 720.

Witness A observed that the 720 had not been visible as far out as six mi., where the "bogie" first appeared. It looked like an aircraft target, though weaker than usual, and became quite clear as it came nearer. He commented also that the bogie followed the correct procedure for an overtaking aircraft, and that, if a pilot is practicing an instrument approach but does not want to touch down, his prescribed procedure is to level off and cross the field at 200 ft., as the bogie appeared to do on the radar. In fact, the object showed the flight characteristics of a Century-series jet fighter (F-100, F-104, etc.), making an approach at a speed of 200-250 knots. However, such a jet makes a great deal of noise, and should have been heard even in the glass-enclosed tower.

Witness A was interviewed in detail when he first telephoned the project in Spring 1967, and questioned further on various aspects at several later dates. Other witnesses unfortunately were not contacted until Fall 1968.

Witness B, who had been monitoring the surveillance radar approach scope, was unable to recall details of the incident. He remembered only that it was "an odd thing"—a radar target, but nothing visual.

Witness C was a controller of 15 years' experience, 11 on radar, who had been in the radar room when the sighting occurred, and had watched it on the precision scope. He recognized the difficulty in remembering accurately after such a time interval, but felt that his memory for the key details was good. He had been deeply impressed by the incident, and had discussed it with Witness A and others on various occasions.

He confirmed the account of Witness A in almost all respects. He was not certain that the bogie had come in on the ILS glide path (which is indicated by a line on the elevation screen of the precision radar); it was following the Boeing and must have been on or near the glide path. Witness A had stated that the bogie overtook and passed the 720 at about the approach end of the runway. Witness C, however, recalled that the bogie had overtaken the 720 and flown alongside "like a wingman" (i.e., slightly behind and to the right of the 720) for one or two miles before touchdown. Then, about a half mile from the runway, it had "pulled up" and flown on ahead. The 720's approach speed was about 140 knots.

Witness C emphasized that the bogie target was indistinguishable from an aircraft. He said that, if the bogie had appeared ahead of the 720, he would not have hesitated to warn the 720 off the approach.

He noted also that the surveillance radar was an old, faulty instrument that sometimes missed targets that were known to be in the field.

Witness D was a controller in the tower during the incident. He remembered that the radar crew phoned about the bogie; the tower men looked and saw the 720 coming in, but nothing else, even with binoculars. The conditions were such that he was confident that no such aircraft as the radars indicated could have come in without the tower crew having seen it.

WEATHER

The report of the project's consulting meteorologist follows:

Following is a brief summary covering the weather situation near . . . [the airfield in location A] at and near 1640 MDT . . . [in the middle of] May . . . 1967:

SOURCES OF DATA

Hourly surface observations from—

. . . [Location A, location B, location C, location D, location E, location F]

Two and three hourly data from—

. . . [Location G, location H, location I] Winds aloft and radiosonde data for . . . [location D], at 12:00 noon and 6:00 P.M. MDT.

GENERAL WEATHER SITUATION

The general weather situation prevailing in . . . [the general area] was a condition of drizzle and fog with low ceilings at most all stations east of . . . [location H]. Amounts of precipitation were generally light but the drizzle and fog continued for many hours at most stations.

Shortly after noon colder air moved in from a northerly direction in a layer from 1000 to 5000 feet above the surface. At . . . [location D] the drop in temperature measured between the noon and 6:00 P.M. radiosondes was between 5° and 6° F. in this layer. This drop in cloud layer temperatures was accompanied by increasing winds near the surface. At 2:30 P.M. gustiness at . . . [location D] reached 30 knots. Similar increases in wind velocities began later at . . . [location A, location B, location E, and location J]. Some snow and snow pellets fell at various stations as this mixture of colder air took place.

MOST PROBABLE WEATHER AT 1640 MDT AT . . . [THE] AIRFIELD

Two layers of scattered clouds, at 900 and 2400 feet respectively, would have been moving rapidly from north to south in an air flow having surface winds averaging nearly 30 mph. It occurred at 1630 MDT. Gustiness of 8-10 additional miles per hour was occurring at this time. A layer of overcast cloudiness was estimated at 4000 feet above the station. Visibility was greater than 15 miles.

A condition of very light drizzle had ended at 1530 MDT and light snow pellets began at 1710 MDT. The differences in *surface* temperatures was only 1° (34 to 33) indicating that the greatest amount of change was taking place in the air at cloud level.

The snow pellets which began at 1710 MDT and intermittent snow showers continued past midnight. It is well known that water and ice surfaces mixed together inside clouds tend to intensify radar echo causing bright spots or bright lines to appear. The snow pellets would have produced an increased intensity of the radar echos in some small shower areas. Although snow pellets were not occurring at the station at 1640 MDT it is highly probable that some were in the vicinity.

Total amounts of precipitation were light. Only .03 inch was measured in the 24 hours ending at midnight.

At the same time that snow pellets and snow showers were observed at . . . [the airfield, location B] reported no precipitation.

SUMMARY

It is my opinion that fragmentary segments of two layers of scattered clouds moving at variable speeds beneath a solid overcast would have given a rapidly changing sky condition to any observer at or near the airport. Reflection of any lights could have caused greater or lesser brightness to the under surfaces of some of these scattered clouds. The strong gusty winds were not only capable of moving the clouds rapidly but could have carried some light substances, such as paper to an elevation similar to the lower cloud height. The shafts of snow pellets at a mile or more away from the base may have caused some distortion of visibility in directions concentrated to the west and northwest of the field.

HYPOTHESES

Anomalous targets on radar generally are caused by instrumental defects, birds, anomalous atmospheric propagation (e.g., mirage effects), out-of-phase echoes, or multiple reflections. Instrumental defects appear to be eliminated in this case, since the bogie was seen consistently on the surveillance radar and both the azimuth and elevation beams of the precision radar. The speed of the bogie, its radar intensity, and the course it followed all appeared inconsistent with a bird.

Neither did this anomaly show any of the typical characteristics of the "angels" caused by anomalous propagation; moreover, weather data indicate no inversion was present. Both witnesses A and C had had many years of experience with all the usual types of anomalies. The fact that they were mystified by the phenomenon and considered it worth reporting indicates that it was an uncommon effect.

Sometimes a distant, strong reflector may return a radar echo so long delayed that it arrives after a second pulse has been emitted. It will therefore appear at a spuriously short range. This possibility appears to be precluded by the different pulse frequencies of the surveillance and precision radars (1000 and 5500 per sec., respectively), and by the behavior of the bogie, which appeared to relate it to the Boeing 720.

There remains the possibility of multiple reflections. After reviewing a report of the incident, Menzel suggested that the bogie had been produced by reflection of radar energy from the 720 to a fairly efficient reflector on the ground, back to the 720, and thence to the radar receiver. The superfluous echo would have appeared on the line of sight from radar antenna to aircraft, and beyond the aircraft the same distance as that from aircraft to reflector. Menzel suggested that a structure involving a cube-corner — e.g., a steel dump-truck body — might act as a rather efficient reflector.

This hypothesis would explain some aspects of the observations. The bogie appeared about two miles behind the 720 when it was about four miles out, and gained on it at a rate roughly equal to the airplane's own ground speed of about 120 knots, as would be expected. This would imply that the reflector was about two miles ahead of the 720, which would place it about half a mile south of the approach end of the runway. The bogie then should have overtaken the 720 at that point.

Witness A said that it was about 0.25 mi. behind the 720 as the latter reached the approach light system; that would place the reflector approximately at the approach end of the runway. Witness C, however (a year and a half after the incident), stated that the bogie caught up with the 720 "one or two miles" before touchdown, flew alongside, and pulled ahead about a half mile from the runway. That would place the reflector about 0.5 to 1.5 mi. south of the runway, differing by as much as a mile from the location resulting from Witness A's account.

So far, so good. Men who were a bit excited, or trying to remember details after such an interval, might differ by a mile in their estimates, particularly since the range scale on the precision radar scope is logarithmic. Incidentally, half a mile from the runway the elevation of the ILS glide path was about 200 ft. — the elevation at which the bogie appeared to overfly the field.

However, a target produced by such a delayed reflection would not have appeared on the glide path. In elevation, the glide path was a line rising at an angle of 2.7° from the ILS transmitter 7,300 ft. south of the precision radar antenna. The line of sight from the radar to the Boeing four miles out thus intersected the glide path at a substantial angle, so the bogie reflection, seen on the radar line of sight, would have appeared about 0.25 in. below the line marking the glide path on the radar scope. It does not seem likely that an experienced controller would have failed to notice a discrepancy amounting to some 200 ft. in elevation that if not corrected would have been disastrous to an aircraft.

The shift of the unidentified object to the right as it overtook the 720 can be partially explained. If it is assumed that the bogie was a secondary echo from a reflector near the runway, then the bogie would have been always the same distance behind the 720 as the reflector in front of it, and would have appeared on the line of sight from the precision radar antenna to the 720. Since the antenna was about 400 ft. east of the runway, the bogie would have appeared projected to the west of the approach track. Its apparent course would have been a gradual swerve to its right.

However, the bogie would have nearly coincided with the radar image of the 720 as it passed low over the reflector; and immediately thereafter, as the 720 passed beyond the reflector, the bogie would have stopped its forward motion and moved laterally to the west. This hypothetical behavior contrasts sharply with the statements of witnesses A and C, both of whom insisted that the bogie moved over and passed the 720 on the right (east), and that it continued on that course, ahead of the airplane, until it left the radar field.

The case is therefore not satisfactorily explained. In general, the association of the unidentified target with the 720 and the lack of a visible counterpart suggest strongly that it was a radar artifact. Yet the details of its course can be reconciled with the reflector hypothesis only by discounting the accuracy of reports by observers who were intimately familiar with the context in which they were working.

Case 22
North Central
Spring 1967
Investigator: Craig

Abstract:

A weekend prospector claimed that a "flying saucer" landed near him in the woods, and that when he approached the object and touched it with his gloved hand, it soared away, its exhaust blast leaving a patterned burn on his abdomen and making him ill.

Events during and subsequent to a field search for the landing site cast strong doubt upon the authenticity of the report.

Background:

A 50-year-old industrial mechanic (Mr. A) claimed to have observed two UFOs while prospecting in the North Central area. The reported time of the sighting was about 12:12 p.m., CDT.

According to Mr. A, his attention was distracted by the squawking of nearby geese. He looked up and saw two disc-shaped objects descending together from the SW at an angle of 15°-20° above the horizon. One stopped 10-12 ft. above the ground; the other continued downward, and landed on the flat top of a rock outcropping 160 ft. from Mr. A. The objects had domes and were about 40 ft. in diameter. They had flown three or four diameters apart, keeping a constant distance. The first object hovered in the air (one of Mr. A's accounts says it hovered about 15 ft. above him) for about three minutes, then ascended in the same direction from which it had come, changing color from bright red to orange to grey and back to bright orange as it disappeared in the distance. It moved noiselessly, much faster than airplane speeds.

When Mr. A turned his attention to the landed craft, it, too, was changing color from glowing red to the iridescence of hot stainless steel. The craft had no markings. Intense purple light shone from apertures around the dome of the craft. Mr. A noticed wafts of warm air, a smell of sulphur, and a hissing sound from the craft. He sketched the object. After about 15 min. he noticed that a hatch on the side of the craft had opened. He could see nothing inside, because the light was too bright. He waited in vain for someone to emerge through the hatch.

About 30 minutes later, Mr. A approached the craft and heard human-like voices from within. Thinking the craft was of U.S. origin, he addressed the assumed occupants in English. When no response was heard, he tried Russian, German, Italian, French, and Ukrainian. The voices stopped. Panels slid over the hatch, through which Mr. A had noticed that the craft's walls were about 20 in. thick and honey-combed. After the hatch closed, Mr. A touched the craft with his gloved hand, burning the fingertips of his glove. The craft tilted slightly and started to spin rapidly. He was standing near a patterned ventilation or exhaust area on the craft's side. When the craft started moving, a blast from this opening burned his upper abdomen and set his shirt and undershirt afire. He tore off the shirts and threw them to the ground, stamping out the fire. His outer shirt was almost totally burned, but he retrieved the remains of his undershirt. A hole also was burned in the front of the top of the cap he was wearing. He was left with burns on his abdomen and sickened, apparently as a result of inhalation of vapors from the machine. The craft disappeared in the direction from which it came at a bearing of 255° (determined by Mr. A's compass) and at a speed estimated as far exceeding known aircraft capability.

Mr. A said he suffered headache, nausea, and cold sweats within minutes after the experience. He returned to his prospecting site (160 ft. away) and got his coat and prospecting equipment. He put the remains of his undershirt in his prospecting satchel. Feeling weakened and vomiting frequently he struggled to the highway to seek medical assistance. He was aware of a horrible odor associated with his breath.

He reached the highway and requested help from a constable of the Royal Canadian Mounted Police (RCMP) who was driving by. The constable thought Mr. A was intoxicated, and refused to help. Mr. A also failed to get help at the park headquarters and went back to his motel at Lake X. After several hours, he took a bus to Winnipeg. While waiting for the bus, he telephoned the *Winnipeg Tribune* to request assistance, asking, at the same time, he said, that they give his experience no publicity.

Mr. A was met by his son, who took him to hospital X for medical attention. The burns on his abdomen were diagnosed as superficial, and Mr. A returned home. He continued to complain of nausea, headache, offensive odor from his lungs, lack of appetite, and rapid weight loss.

Two days after the alleged event, Mr. A was attended to by a personal physician, whom he had not visited since Spring 1966. The following day he was taken to hospital Y to be checked for radiation trauma by the hospital's Department of Nuclear Medicine. A radiation pathologist found no evidence of the effects of radiation on the burned area, in his blood, or on Mr. A's clothing. He reported that the burn was thermal. A week after his sighting Mr. A was checked in the whole-body radiation counter at an Atomic Power Installation. This counter detects and measures gamma radiation from isotopes in the body. The test showed no count above normal background.

Mr. A said he lost a total of 22 lb. over the next seven days, but had regained his strength and some weight 11 days after his sighting.

Investigation:

The case involved close contact, and one of the most detailed descriptions of a material object of this type on record. The site at which the event allegedly took place had not been re-visited since the event, and held promise of providing tangible physical evidence that an unusual material object had actually been present. A project investigator left for city A as soon as word was received that Mr. A was physically able to search for the landing site. The investigator wanted to visit and examine the alleged site before it was disturbed by others.

Nearly two weeks after the event, when Mr. A was interviewed by the project investigator, he had regained sufficient strength to lead a search, which was planned for the following day. Mr. A displayed a rash on his neck and chest, which he associated with the alleged UFO exposure. He said the rash appeared two days earlier, 11 days after the sighting, and he had visited his physician the morning of the interview to have it checked. Mr. A had, on the same day, cooperated with authorities in a ground and air search which had not located the UFO landing site. Mr. A reluctantly agreed to lead another ground search, indicating that the new rash made him uncertain of his physical health.

Later, Mr. A led a party, including the project investigator, on a hike in the Canadian bush, ostensibly searching for the landing site which assertedly was about three miles north of a highway, which skirts the north shore of Lake X. The area searched was located 49°43′ ± 1′N, 95°19′ ± 1′W, in a forest reserve. A fire-watch tower stands between the highway and the area searched. The party began the search within a half mile of this tower, and never got more than two miles from it while wandering back and forth through an area within which Mr. A said the site had to be. Most of the area was covered by dense vegetation. Numerous beaver ponds, swamps, and rock outcroppings were contained in the area, the outcroppings rising as much as 40 ft. above the swamp level. It was on such an outcropping that the landing allegedly occurred.

This "search" impressed the investigator, as well as other members of the party, as being aimless. Mr. A expressed the desire to terminate the search after a few hours of hiking. The rest of the party felt a good effort had not yet been made, and pressed him to continue. In the early afternoon, when it seemed obvious that a "landing site" would not be found that day, the party returned to Lake X resort, where the investigator interviewed other people who were in the vicinity on the day of the alleged event.

Two youngsters who claimed they saw an UFO over the lake on the date in question gave a description suggesting that they may have observed a box kite or a balloon, but certainly not an object of the type described by Mr. A.

According to Conservation Officer Jim Bill, the fire lookout towers were manned on this date after 9 a.m. A ranger with Officer Bell indicated that the forest was dry at this time. Both rangers felt that a fire capable of burning a man would have started the forest burning. They commented that watchmen in the towers generally notice smoke immediately from even a small campfire, and felt that a small fire in lichen and moss, such as Mr. A said he tramped out when he threw his burning shirts to the ground, would have been seen by the watchman. They also believed objects as described by Mr. A would have been seen by the tower watchman, had they been present for even a fraction of the time Mr. A claimed. Watchtowers are 8′ x 8′. About six other towers are visible in the distance from the tower near the alleged landing site. Although a 35-40 ft. metallic saucer only ½-2 mi. away should have attracted the watchman's attention, nothing unusual was noted from the watchtower.

Weather Bureau information indicated the day of the reported sighting was mostly clear with broken clouds, in agreement with Mr. A's description.

The flight direction Mr. A gave for the UFOs would have brought them within about a mile of the golf course at Beach X, at an altitude of 4,000 ft. The course attendant said that there were hundreds of golfers on the course on this date, none of whom reported seeing an object such as Mr. A described.

The investigator sought other information supporting the claim that an unconventional flying object had been in the area on the sighting date. A check of several other UFO sighting reports in the region revealed that they had no relation to Mr. A's sighting, have occurred on a different day (except for the lake sighting already mentioned) in a different area.

Radar observers at three other locations (60 mi. NW of the claimed sighting, 85 mi. W, and 40 mi. E) reported noticing nothing unusual on the alleged sighting date.

With Mr. A's permission, the project investigator reviewed the case with his physician and with the other M.D.'s involved. Items of particular interest which were revealed to the investigator by Mr. A himself were (a) a rapid weight loss; (b) a lymphocyte count of 16% climbing later to 21%; and (c) the rash on Mr. A's throat and upper chest which developed 11 days after his reported sighting.

The claimed weight loss of 22 pounds in seven days, including 14 pounds the first three days, could not be verified. Mr. A's physician did not see the patient until two days after the alleged exposure and had not seen him during the previous year. There was no way to verify the weight claimed prior to the event. A medical consultant considered the claimed weight loss logically excessive for an inactive, fasting patient.

The lymphocyte percentages were not outside the limits of expected statistical variation of two routine counts of the same blood, and were therefore not considered to be significant.

The rash, which was not on the same body area as the original burn, looked like the normal reaction to insect bites. Mr. A said the rash appeared on the day he had gone on the site search with RCMP officers. In view of the great number of black flies in the area, the coincidence in date, Cpl. Davis' report that he was severely bitten while on the search, and the accessibility of the affected neck and chest area to flies when the shirt collar is not buttoned (it was Cpl. Davis' belief that Mr. A had worn his collar unbuttoned during the search), it seems highly probable that the rash was the result of insect bites and was not connected with the alleged UFO experience.

Comparison of recordings of separate accounts of Mr. A's UFO experience, as told to an APRO representative two days after the reported event and to the project investigator short of two weeks later, revealed minor variations, as would be expected in any two accounts of an involved experience. The inclusion in the account of a magnetic effect of the UFO developed during the first interview. The APRO representative asked Mr. A if the UFO had affected his compass. Mr. A first answered: "I couldn't tell you if the compass needle was affected. I hadn't looked before. It was kind of abnormal." Upon further discussion, the effect developed to a definite spinning of the needle, then a rapid whirling as the second object left the area. This latter description was repeated in subsequent accounts. It is hard to reconcile such a magnetic effect with the facts that Mr. A not only reported a definite compass reading for the direction of departure of the second UFO but also a definite reading of 140° for the direction of approach and departure of the first, which left while the second was still present.

The undershirt which Mr. A presented had been ripped apart in front, where it was burned. It also carried a patterned burn centered high on the back, the pattern matching, according to Mr. A, the pattern of the UFO's exhaust openings from which the burning vapors had spurted. Mr. A had been burned only on the abdomen, with slight singeing of the forehead. The reason for the presence of a patterned burn on the back of the undershirt was not obvious.

Mr. A was deemed very reliable by his employer. He had convinced representatives of the RCMP and RCAF, two of the several physicians involved, as well as his family, that he was telling the story of a real event. During the project investigator's interview, he seemed honest, sincere, and concerned. His presentation of his story was convincing. His wife and son verified his claim of an unusual odor coming from his body after his alleged UFO experience, indicating that the odor permeated the bathroom after Mr. A had bathed.

Analysis of Subsequent Developments:

1. The claimed finding of the site by Mr. A and an associate shortly over a month later.

The site was allegedly still obvious, with moss blown away in a circular pattern. Samples of soil and moss from the area, portions of the burned shirt, and a six-foot measuring tape which Mr. A had left behind were brought to city A. All three were radioactive. When sent to city B for analysis, they were found to be so strongly radioactive that the Radiation Protection Division of the Dept. of Health and Welfare considered restricting entry to the forest area from which they allegedly were taken. A careful check of the site by a representative of this department revealed that the perimeter of the "landing circle" and beyond were free of radioactive contamination. According to his report:

A thorough survey of the landing area was carried out, using a Tracerlab SU14, Admiral Radiac 5016, and a Civil Defense CDV 700 survey meter. One small area was found to be contaminated. This was located across the crown of the rock. There was a smear of contamination about 0.5 x 8.0 inches on one side of the crack. There was also some lichen and ground vegetation contaminated just beyond the smear. The whole contaminated area was no larger than 100 square inches. All water runoff areas were checked for possible contamination, but nothing was found.

No representative of an independent or official agency was present when the circular area alleged to be the landing site was rediscovered. In spite of an RCMP understanding with Mr. A that no evidence should be removed from the area should he relocate it, radioactive soil samples, (fortuitously selected from the small contaminated area), remnants of cloth, and the measuring tape were represented as having been removed from the area. Why the cloth remnants and the tape were radioactive was never explained. While these items could have been contaminated by contact with the soil samples, reports received by the project indicated that the items were in separate plastic bags, and major contamination would not be expected. The partially-burned undershirt had earlier been found not to carry radioactive contamination. The tape would have been left some 160 ft. from the landing circle, in an area found to be free of radioactive contamination.

Other individuals checked the site for radioactivity later. One of these was Mr. E. J. Epp of city A, who searched the site in Fall of 1967 and found no radioactive material. At the project's suggestion, he had the records of the Dept. of Mines and Natural Resources searched for mineral claims in the area filed by Mr. A. This was requested because of the possibility that Mr. A had deliberately misdirected the earlier searches in order to protect mineral claims. Such claims were filed by him, but not until later in the Fall.

The project never received a final report of the analyses of the soil samples taken by the Dept. of Health and Welfare. The origin of this material is therefore on open question.

The site presented did not match Mr. A's earlier description of it. An opening in the trees through which Mr. A said the UFO came and departed would have required the object to leave the landing circle traveling in a NNE direction, whereas Mr. A had said it departed to the WSW. Other aspects also differed from the original description.

2. Claimed recurrences (in the early Fall and other occasions) of the physiological reactions to the UFO experience.

Relation of these reported attacks with Mr. A's alleged UFO experience has not been established.

3. Commercial publication of Mr. A's story in a booklet.

This account differs in some aspects from Mr. A's original reports. In the booklet, for example, Mr. A is reported to have stuck his head into the open hatch of the "saucer" and observed a maze of randomly flashing lights inside the craft. In earlier accounts, Mr. A stated that he avoided going near the hatch and was unable to see inside it because of the brightness of the light coming from it. The account was chronologically jumbled, and showed a carelessness with fact.

4. A claimed visit to the site by Mr. A and another associate a year after the alleged sighting, at which time they discovered massive pieces of radioactive material in a fissure of the rock within the "landing circle." This material reportedly consisted of two W-shaped bars of metal, each about 4.5 in. long, and several smaller pieces of irregular shape. These items were said to have been found about 2 in. below a layer of lichen in the rock fissure. They were later analyzed as nearly pure silver. The results of the analyses of these pieces of metal were sent to the Colorado Project by Dr. Peter M. Millman of the National Research Council of Canada. The analysis of the report by Mr. R. J. Traill (Head, Minerology Section, NRC) showed that the two fragments each consisted of a central massive metal portion which was not radioactive. One of these was 93% and the other 96% silver. Both contained copper and cadmium, and had a composition similar to that found in commercially available sterling silver or sheet silver. The metal was coated with a tightly-adhering layer of quartz sand, similar to that used as a foundry sand. This also was not radioactive. The radioactivity was contained in a loosely-adhering layer of fine-grained minerals containing uranium. This layer could be removed readily by washing and brushing. The minerals were uranophane and thorium-free pitchblende, characteristically found in vein deposits. Mr. Traill's conclusion was:

> I would interpret the specimens as pieces of thin sheet silver that have been twisted, crumpled, partly melted, and dropped into, or otherwise placed in contact with, nearly pure quartz sand, while still hot. They have subsequently been covered with loosely-adhering radioactive material which consists of crushed pitchblende ore, much altered to uranophane and containing associated hematite. These naturally-occurring radioactive minerals are found typically in the uraniferous deposits of . . . [River X] area and in parts of . . . [camp X].

In view of the thoroughness of earlier searches of the site for radioactive material, it is improbable that the particles discovered a year later would have been missed had they been present when the earlier searches were made.

Conclusions:

If Mr. A's reported experience were physically real, it would show the existence of alien flying vehicles in our environment. Attempts to establish the reality of the event revealed many inconsistencies and incongruities in the case, a number of which are described in this report. Developments subsequent to the field investigation have not altered the initial conclusion that this case does not offer probative information regarding inconventional craft.

Case 23

North Central
Spring 1967
Investigators: Foster, Peterson, Wertheimer

Abstract:

Three couples hunting raccoons at night reported that an aerial object approached them, played a brilliant light on them briefly, then turned it off and flew away. Individual versions of the incident differed substantially as to motion, appearance, duration of sighting, and the object's identity. Investigation attributed the sighting to a prank by the crew of an airplane with a searchlight that had flown over the hunt area at the reported time.

Background:

Witness A reported the incident to an AFB two days afterward. A week later he wrote a report to NICAP, which sent a copy of his letter to the Colorado project. A telephone conversation with Witness A resulted in sending investigators to the area late in June.

Investigation:

The investigators interviewed seven witnesses and visited the site of the incident with one of them. They also visited the AFB to check on aircraft activity on the night of the incident.

Witnesses' versions of what had happened differed rather widely. For that reason, the situation as developed by the witnesses will be outlined, followed by a summary of the disparities in their stories.

Three couples were hunting raccoons on a ranch. Mr. A. was a professional man, Mr. B an administrator, and Mr. C a rancher. Witness D was another rancher who was keeping an eye on the hunters. "About 11:30 p.m." the men were about 0.5 mi. W of their truck, in which the women were waiting. They carried powerful flashlights that they turned on only briefly as needed.

All of the men and women saw a lighted aerial object approach as if gliding down toward them. When immediately over them, it turned a brilliant beam of light on the men for a short time, then turned it off and proceeded on its way. Witness D also saw the light.

However, the details of the individual accounts differed widely. (On some points, some witnesses did not comment.)

Five witnesses reported that the object came from the NW;

one from the N; and one from the E.

Three reported that it flew a straight course; two thought it turned 90° as it departed.

Three reported that it hovered while the bright light was on; two, that it kept moving.

All reported the light was blue, bluish-white, or white except D, who said it was yellowish.

One witness reported the object was about 50 ft. in diameter, alternately glowing dimly or brilliantly. Two reported several small red lights; one, small white and red lights; one, small blinking red, white, and green lights; one, no lights.

Four witnesses reported that the light from bright spotlight did not move over the ground. Two of the other three thought a second spotlight might have done so. All agreed that the beam was conical, emanating from a narrow source. Witnesses disagreed widely as to the location of the beam on the ground; each of those in the light path tended to think it was aimed directly at him.

Three witnesses reported a sound similar to that of a small airplane engine as the object approached; four noticed it some time after the bright light was turned on.

Total duration of the sighting was estimated by two witnesses as one to three minutes of the bright light; two to three minutes, one and a half minute, "a minute or so," a half minute, 30-45 sec., five seconds, and 15 sec., off briefly, then on again momentarily. Only one witness ventured a guess at the time the sighting occurred, "approximately 11:30 p.m."

One witness reported that he recognized the sound as that of a small twin-engine airplane, and thought he saw its outline as it departed. He suggested that the crew might have seen the hunters' blinking flashlights and turned the spotlight on them.

At the AFB, the investigators learned that on the date of sighting a rather slow twin-engine Navy airplane equipped with a powerful searchlight had departed at 10:34 p.m. on a course to the SE that would have taken him almost directly over the location of the sighting. The pilot was flying "visual," not on instruments. Further, an airman at the AFB reported that he had heard some conversation between the pilot and co-pilot before takeoff, indicating that they intended to use the searchlight to set off some UFO stories. Evidently the rancher's surmise was right: they had seen the blinking flashlights of the hunters and taken the opportunity to startle them.

Comment:

Unlike many comparable cases in which a mystifying apparition has generated widely different versions of the experience, this one was convincingly explained. It therefore affords an unusually good opportunity to study the reactions of witnesses to an unfamiliar and unexpected situation. The most obvious inference, already familiar to the legal profession, is that eyewitness testimony in such circumstances is inherently unreliable.

It is significant also that the only witnesses who recognized the object as an airplane were the two ranchers and the wife of one of them. They were in a familiar situation. The two couples from the city were on unfamiliar ground, were disoriented as to directions, and may have felt a bit of latent uneasiness that made them emotionally oblivious of this possibility. Witness A reported that, when the brilliant light came on, the rancher (Witness C) exclaimed to him: "My god, what's that?" A: "I don't know." C: "Do you suppose it's one of those flying saucers?"

Witness C, who said he had recognized the object as an airplane, commented in his interview: "It seemed to me the light came right out of the plane—after I got over tellin' it was a flyin' saucer!"

Mrs. C., who had been in the truck with the other women, commented in an interview: "We talked about it. First it was a plane—then I said, 'Was that a flying saucer?' and we just got to thinking . . ."

Case 24

North Eastern
Summer 1967
Investigators: Craig and Wadsworth

Abstract:

A 50-year-old general machine handyman and his son, 11, claimed to have seen and photographed a "flying saucer" close to their rural home. Neither the numbers on the backs of the two Polaroid photographs nor the focus of objects in the field of view were consistent with the account of the alleged sighting.

Background:

Two Polaroid photographs of a saucer-shaped UFO were said to have been taken by the witness about 12:15 p.m. EDT. The photographs showed windows or ports in both the upper and lower halves of the object. According to Mr. A's account, he was taking a picture of his 11-year-old son with his Model 800 Polaroid camera when a high-pitched humming noise attracted their attention. They looked in the direction of the noise, and saw an UFO about 60 ft. in diameter, some 500 ft. away, moving about 30 to 40 mph, at an altitude of 500-600 ft. Mr. A snapped two pictures during the 15-20 sec. before the object departed at a speed estimated to be 2,000 mph.

According to his account, Mr. A immediately took the pictures to a farm house, about 300 yd. from his home, to show the pictures, and learn if the neighbors also had seen the object. The neighbor, Mr. B., says that Mr. A arrived at their house about 12:30 p.m. ± 5 minutes, and the pictures were still "wet." None of the family had seen nor heard the UFO. At Mr. B's insistence the incident was made known to the public. Mr. A wanted to destroy the photos and not tell anyone else of the incident, for fear of ridicule. Mr. B., with A's reluctant permission, notified the state police and local newspapers of the incident and the existence of the photographs.

Investigation:

Although there are unexplained discrepancies in the story and pictures, project investigators were not able, on the basis of their investigation, to determine that the incident was a hoax. Mr. B was convinced the pictures were of a real object. Both Mr. A and his son's stories were generally consistent, and presented seriously with conviction. Neither witness was shaken from his original statement after hours of conversation and discussion. The suggestion that such pictures might result from deliberate deception brought only emphatic denial. Although Mr. A would not agree to lend the original pictures to this project for analysis, copies of the photographs were obtained.

In picture number one the UFO is in sharp focus but is dimly outlined against the sky because of overexposure. It appears to have three dark windows or ports on its lower section (which has the appearance of a pie tin) and a row of square dark windows of similar size, but more closely spaced, around its top portion (which resembled a lid of a frying pan, with a knob on top). A dark streak extends about half the distance along the ridge-like juncture of the top and bottom portions. This streak ends abruptly.

The image of the UFO in picture number one is just over three centimeters long. The top of a near-by automobile, the top of a ridge some 80 ft. from where Mr. A stood, and several trees and a bee-hive on the ridge are also visible in photo number one. The trees were not in focus.

Photo number two shows apparently the same UFO, somewhat more distant (a 2.8 cm. image), not in sharp focus, but with good contrast against the sky background. In this photo the UFO appears below a wire clothes line located seven feet from the camera. Tops of trees are visible in each bottom corner of the picture.

Both photos were taken within a few feet of Mr. A's house, number two from a position about 20 ft. from where he stood while taking number one. Photo number one was taken at a bearing of 100°, photo number two at 300°. The tree tops visible in photo number two are at distances of 40-65 ft. away from the camera. They are not the same trees that appear in photo number one.

Investigation Results:

1) *Polaroid photograph numbers.* Mr. A said the film had been in the camera several months, and only three pictures remained to be taken on the roll. He took number six, a picture of his son. Numbers seven and eight would then be the UFO photos. The numbers on the back of the UFO photos, however, were one and seven respectively.

2) *Disappearance of other photographs and photographic material.* Mr. A "could not find" the picture of his son, although Mrs. B said he had the three photos, including one of his son, when he arrived at the farmhouse at 12:30. Mr. A. said he "had thrown away" the negative back sheets of all photographs.

3) *Lack of other witnesses.* An object 60 ft. in diameter and at 500 ft. altitude would have been over a point less than 100 yd. from a major highway at the time the pictures were taken, and would have crossed over the highway on departure. The highway carries heavy traffic. A crew of gravel-company workmen would have been on their lunch break in the gravel pits over which the object was allegedly flying when it was photographed. No one reported seeing such an object, in spite of a radio appeal for other observers to identify themselves. No workmen in the gravel pit saw the object, although when questioned several of the workmen expressed the opinion that they are so accustomed to loud noises while they work that they would not have noticed the sound from an UFO as described by Mr. A. Neither Mr. B., who was on a tractor at 12:15, nor any of his family or crew saw the UFO.

The only response to the appeal for anyone who had seen UFO about noon on the date of Mr. A's sighting to identify himself came from youngsters. Project investigators checked what seemed the most significant of these reports but they had no relation to the object in Mr. A's photos.

One farmer did report that he and his brother, baling hay about one mile from Mr. A's home, (in the direction of claimed departure of the UFO), heard something that sounded like "many jet planes" about noon on this date. They commented on the sound to each other at the time, but did not see anything which could have generated this noise.

It seems probable that someone on the highway, or working in the vicinity, would have seen the UFO if it were as described.

Inquiries were made at radar installations at Youngstown, Ohio air terminal and with the FAA Cleveland Center. No observations of unidentified objects were made at either place.

4) *Position from which picture number two was taken.* To reproduce picture number two (minus the UFO), it was necessary for the photographer to lower the camera by kneel-

ing on the ground. Mr. A. said he merely stooped over a bit to take the second photo.

5) *Preliminary examination of the photographs by W.K.H.* Copies of Mr. A's photographs were sent to Dr. Hartmann for preliminary examination and evaluation. A summary of his response follows:

In picture number one, the object is in focus (showing square corners on portholes), while the background trees and beehive are out of focus. Since the trees and beehive are some 80 ft. away, they should have been in fairly sharp focus if the camera were focused for any distance close to or greater than 80 ft. Had the object been some 500 ft. away, as Mr. A claimed, and the camera focused essentially at infinity, the trees should be in sharper focus than the nearer car top. Photograph number one shows the car top in sharper focus than the trees, and the object in sharper focus than the car top.

In picture number two, the object is less sharp (portholes are blurred, not clearly square). The clothes wire also is somewhat out of focus, while the trees (40-65 ft. away in this case) are in sharper focus than in picture number one.

One possible interpretation of these observations is that the object, and the camera focal distance, was closer in picture number one than was the top of the car. The object would then have been five to ten feet away from the camera. Picture number two could have been made with the focus of the camera set at about 30 ft. while the object was enough closer to the camera to be noticeably out of focus.

If the object were five feet away its diameter was ten inches; if ten feet away, 20 in. Pictures duplicating Mr. A's could be produced with a 10-12 in. model, focusing the camera at five feet and 30 ft. for the first and second pictures, respectively, and suspending the model by fine thread or monofilament fishing line. (In photo number two the suspension could be either from the clothes line which appears in the picture or from a fishing pole.)

Conclusions:

The relative focus of objects in picture number one is not consistent with the claim that the UFO was a large object beyond the trees in the picture, but is consistent with an assumption that the UFO was pie pan sized. The other discrepancies in the account discussed here also contribute to the conclusion that these photographs would not merit further analysis even if the originals were made available for detailed study.

Case 25
North Eastern
Summer 1967
Investigators: Armstrong, Levine

Abstract:

Reports of noise, flashes, and power interruptions were attributed to power-line faults.

Background

A representative of APRO and NICAP phoned the project to report the following incident. On a Wednesday morning at 4:10 a.m., a man employed by an aircraft company reported that while driving in a northwest direction to work, he saw a bright light flashing to his rear. He turned his car around, and drove back to the location of the flashing light, and stopped at the intersection of two roads. He saw a ball he estimated to be two and one-half feet in diameter above trees to the northeast. He was frightened, and left the scene to report to the police. He said he saw the flash five times. The next day he stopped at the home of the woman on whose property the trees were located. She told him that she had seen the light.

The NICAP and APRO representative learned of the incident from the police. He interviewed both witnesses. He then looked about the scene of the sighting and discovered a place in some tall grass, about 30 inches high, where the grass had been flattened. The depression in the grass was circular and about six to ten feet in diameter. The grass was bent in a counter-clockwise direction. At 8:00 p.m., he took three Polaroid pictures of the area, one of which was a close-up of the depression. He reported that the close-up came out "white" and suggested radioactive fogging. On the basis of these reports, Armstrong and Levine went to this area.

Investigation

The investigators met with the APRO-NICAP man three days later at 11:00 a.m. The aircraft employee was not available, so they copied a tape recording of a statement he had given to the APRO-NICAP man.

The investigators then talked with the woman witness. She reported that she had been awakened at 4:40 a.m. on Wednesday by a noise she described as rumbling, crackling, or a "thunder sound," but she knew it was not thunder. Through a small crack in closed Venetian blinds, she had seen flashes of light that lit up her bedroom bright enough to read by. The light went on and off several times, and there were "nine or ten rumblings." She stopped watching, but could still hear the noise. The bright light lasted longer than lightning, but only a few seconds. She reported that the power had gone off at about 5:45 a.m. for about 45 minutes.

The investigators next examined the grassy depression. They found no radioactivity above background level. The depression was roughly circular, but there was little evidence of the grass lying counter-clockwise. The grass was of a kind that, if pushed down, stayed down for a long time. Foot tracks that had been made in it two days earlier were clearly visible. The investigators concluded that (1) there was no evidence of anything unusual about the depression, and (2) the depression could have been made at any time during the past week or longer.

They then spoke with a man who lived nearby. He reported having seen the light and heard the noise, which he said sounded like a power relay cutting out, between 4:30 and 6:00 a.m. He also noticed that light came from two places, a power pole with a transformer on it about 300 feet from his house, and an indistinct location down the road in the direction of the woman witness' house. A night-light in his room went out for 35 or 40 seconds when the noise and flash came, and all of these effects coincided in time. He noted that just before the sighting a heavy fog and rain had made the branches of the tree very heavy. He had attributed the noise and the flashes to the power transformers.

Conclusions

In view of the reported power interruptions and the heavy fog and rain, it is probable that all three of the witnesses' sightings were of flashing arcs associated with the power lines. The fog would enhance the dispersion of the light and lend a strange quality to it and would also facilitate high-voltage corona discharges.

Case 26
South Pacific
Summer 1967
Investigator: Craig

Abstract:

A 67-year-old security guard, on night duty at a lumber yard, reported firing six shots at a cigar-shaped UFO, and later, finding four of the flattened bullets which he said had fallen to the ground after ineffective impact with the UFO. Faced with police evidence, the guard admitted that the bullets were ones fired at a steel drum and that the "sighting" of the UFO was fictitious.

Background:

The witness reported firing six shots from his .38 caliber revolver at an 80-100 ft. long, cigar-shaped UFO which was hovering at about 50 ft. in the air at a distance of some 100 ft. The initial report of the incident was made at 3:50 a.m. PDT and the local police immediately made a preliminary investigation. At 8:00 a.m. on the same day, the witness reported finding four flattened slugs which he said he dug out of furrows in the asphalt surface.

The witness said that after being fired at, the object rose slowly at first, then sped out of sight in a westerly direction.

A bluish-green light, which surrounded the UFO, went out after the second shot. The object made no noise until it sped away, at which point the sound was comparable to that of an idling automobile motor.

Investigation:

A project investigator arrived at about 8:00 p.m. By this time, the witness had changed his story saying that he had made a mistake and was now sure that he had fired at a balloon. He said he shot at it only once, and that there was no visible effect, if in fact he hit it at all. The flattened slugs were ones he had saved from earlier target practice, and he had produced them on the spur of the moment, to embellish his UFO story.

Police investigation had showed that the furrows in the ground, from which the bullets had allegedly been retrieved, were made by bullets entering them at a 30-40° angle. It appeared more likely that the slugs were fired directly into the asphalt, and had not fallen to it as reported. However, the witness later asserted that he had made the furrows with a ball-peen hammer. In addition, police investigation had turned up a steel drum, with numerous holes and indentations on it from bullet impact. When presented with this evidence, the witness admitted having fired at the drum for target practice about a month before, and said that the slugs in question were some of those which had struck the drum.

There were no other reports of any unusual sightings in the vicinity on that day.

Conclusion:

In view of the witness' own admission that he had fabricated the story no further investigation or comment was deemed necessary.

Case 27
North Eastern
Summer 1967
Investigator: Rothberg

Abstract:

During a "flap" in the North East area, the project decided to study the feasibility of fielding an investigation in the area with maximum instrumentation. The objective was to obtain instrumented observations of UFO's and, if possible, to correlate sightings with nightly exposures made by an all-sky camera. Although UFO reports continued at high frequency during the feasibility study, less than 12 of 9,000 all-sky camera exposures contained images not immediately identifiable. Only two of these coincided in time and azimuth with a sighting report. Study of one negative suggests that the image is either that of a meteor whose path was at or nearly at a right angle to the focal plane or that an emulsion defect or impurity is responsible for the image. The other negative's image was identified as a probable aircraft.

Background:

During the summer of 1967, more than 80 sightings were reported in this North East area. The project decided to field an investigation in the area in the hope that the wave of sightings would continue and could be directly observed and measured by an array of instruments. The investigator was equipped with a car having a radio-telephone, still and motion-picture cameras, two U.S. Army infra-red detectors, and a Geiger counter. When on patrol the investigator was in frequent communication with a telephone answering service which had been retained to accept sighting reports and record them on Early Warning report forms. The number of the answering service was widely publicized throughout the region.

An all-sky camera (see Section VI, Chapter 10) was mounted in an undisclosed location, on the well-guarded roof of a local hospital dominating the area. It was hoped that if the frequency of reports was maintained, some of them could be correlated with all-sky camera exposures. The camera was operated during 17 nights. The camera made 9,000 exposures each covering a considerable area of the night sky over a period totalling some 150 hr.

Results:

No occasion arose in which it was possible to use any of the instrumentation with which the project investigator had been equipped.

One UFO was seized. It was a plastic bag made into a hot air balloon by mounting candles across its mouth and launching the device.

More than 100 sighting reports were filed, of which 50 were readily explainable as natural or man-made phenomena, 17 were judged to be identifiable, and 14 seemed to require further investigation. Attempts to acquire sufficient additional information regarding the last category were unavailing, so that no conclusion was drawn regarding them.

Study of the two all-sky camera negatives that contained images not immediately identifiable and that approximately coincided in time with reported sightings was undertaken by project experts and others. These were exposures made on two separate nights at 8:57 p.m. and 9:57 p.m. EDC.

The first frame contains a strong, elliptical spot. No adjacent frames show any image of similar intensity. Examination of the spot under 120X magnification shows near its center a minute defect or contamination that could have caused spurious development, but otherwise the spot shows the gradation of density normal to an exposure caused by light. The image's ellipticity could indicate motion of the light source during the exposure. Because the image appears on a single frame, it is regarded as either an emulsion or development defect or as caused by a meteor whose path was almost directly perpendicular to the focal plane of the camera.

The second frame contains a light trace resembling an airplane track and is identified as a probable aircraft. The sighting report that coincides in time with this exposure, however, is so fragmentary as to make impossible any firm identification of the object reported as being the trace shown on the film.

A third frame for 4 September at 00:32 EDT was also deemed worthy of further study by the field investigator, but project experts report that it and adjacent frames contain only the images of stars.

Conclusions:

This investigation was of particular importance because it offered an opportunity for study of UFOs at the time they were reported, and for measurement of their properties using sophisticated instrumentation, including the all-sky camera. The fact that even though scores of UFOs were reported during that time, the investigator could find nothing to examine with his instruments and nothing remarkable on thousands of all-sky camera exposures with the exceptions noted above is highly significant. We conclude that the expectation that it might be possible to place a trained, equipped investigator on the scene of an UFO sighting has a probability so low as to be virtually nil.

Case 28
South Pacific
Winter 1966 through Summer 1967
Investigators: Roach, Wadsworth

Abstract

Repeated sightings that began in late 1966 and recurred for many months, arousing widespread interest, were identified as a jet aircraft engaged in aerial refueling training practice.

Background

During late 1966, mysterious lights began to appear over the central part of an agricultural valley in the South Pacific. Local residents soon began to report them as UFOs, and the resultant publicity led eventually to investigation by NICAP and this project. These sightings, instead of reaching a peak and tapering off, continued for many months. By summer of 1967 interest was intense. Most of the sightings were witnessed from a site near a foothills town located at the eastern slope of the valley.

The key witness in the area was a resident (Witness I) of the town. He and his wife had observed, logged, and photographed UFOs on numerous occasions during the preceding months. He also coordinated an UFO surveillance network using Citizens Band radio which covered a radius of approximately 80 miles. As principal contact in the area, he provided background information that included names of witnesses, taped interviews, and photographic evidence. This material proved invaluable in preliminary assessment of the situation.

Sightings, General Information

The sightings fell into two groups: one (hereafter referred to as the primary group) was highly homogeneous and comprised approximately 85% of the total number of sightings. Objects in the primary group appeared as orange-white lights above the valley at night. These lights moved, hovered, disappeared and reappeared, and sometimes merged with one another. This report deals with the primary group of sightings.

Sightings from the smaller group will be reported separately, as they form a heterogeneous assortment that is clearly discontinuous with the primary group.

Photographs

The high frequency of primary-group sightings provided Witness I with numerous opportunities to take pictures with a tripod-mounted Rolleiflex camera. The resulting photographs, while providing no answers to *what* the objects were, did constitute firmer evidence than the unsupported testimony of witnesses.

Area Features

a. The ranch home of Witness I was located in the foothills east of the valley and 1800 ft. above the valley floor.

b. The view from the ranch was unobstructed from southeast to southwest. Foothills in the foreground obscured in the distant horizon from northwest to northeast.

c. Most observations from the home of Witness I were from the rear patio, which faced south with a full view of the unobstructed horizon as well as parts of the foreground foothills to the east and west. In most instances he, alone, made the observations.

d. Most sightings were to the southwest over the valley floor.

e. Area residents habitually sat outside at night during the summer because of the heat. This practice contributed to the frequency of sightings.

f. The recurrence of sightings excited the people in the area, thereby causing an increase in reports of low reliability.

Investigation

After detailed discussions with local NICAP people, including Witness I and his wife, project investigators decided to try to observe the UFOs themselves. On the night of 12 August they saw nothing unusual. On 13 August, however, the following events occurred:

At 10:30 p.m. a light appeared low in the southern sky, travelling approximately 10°/sec. After about 10 sec., more detail became visible and the object was identified as probably an aircraft with conventional running lights and an anti-collision beacon.

Meanwhile, another light had appeared to the east of the presumed aircraft, travelling west at a similar angular rate. This light was not obviously an aircraft, but appeared as a dull orange light that varied somewhat in intensity as it moved. The object could have been an aircraft. Witness I, however, said that it was exactly the kind of thing that had been reported frequently as an UFO. He was disappointed that it had not been as near and bright as he had observed on other occasions.

After about 15 sec., the UFO, which had been travelling horizontally westward, seemed to flicker and then vanished. The original object continued eastward, disappearing in the distance in a manner consistent with its identification as an aircraft. Duration of both observations was less than a minute.

On 14 August Wadsworth and Witness I drove to a village 20 miles south of the sighting area, where several sightings had been reported, and west and northwest toward towns A, B, and C. This area had been most frequently indicated by observers as the apparent location of the UFOs. However, interviews with area residents disclosed no significant information.

Another sky watch that evening by Wadsworth, Witness I and his wife (Roach had gone) yielded nothing unusual until midnight. At 12:00 a.m. and again at 12:42 a.m. on 15 August UFOs were observed. They hovered, moved horizontally, and vanished. They appeared as bright orange lights showing no extended size and varying in intensity. Wadsworth thought they might be low-flying aircraft on flight paths that produced illusory hovering, but they could not be identified as such. Witness I described the lights as "good solid sightings," typical of the recurrent UFO sightings in the area. One of the sightings was later confirmed in all essentials by two women, who lived nearby.

The Monday night sighting was reported by telephone to the base UFO officer at a nearby Air Force base. He stated

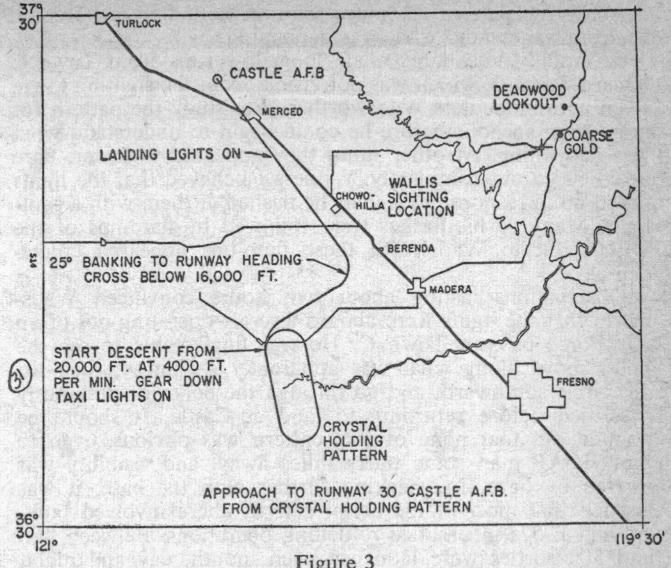

Figure 3

that no aircraft from that base had been in the air at the time of the sighting.

Project investigators then instituted a surveillance plan for the night of 15-16 August. About 9:00 p.m., Wadsworth drove to a fire lookout tower atop a mountain near the sighting area. This lookout, the highest in the area, afforded an optimum view over the entire valley. He carried a transceiver to communicate with Witness I in the town of sighting for coordination of sighting observations, and was accompanied by a local NICAP member. Also present were the resident fire lookouts at the station.

At midnight orange lights appeared successively over the valley in the direction of towns A, B and C (see map, figure 3). These lights, observed simultaneously by Wadsworth and Witness I, appeared to brighten, dim, go out completely, reappear, hover, and move about. Sometimes two of them would move together for a few moments and then separate. This behavior continued for an hour-and-a-half.

The mountain vantage point afforded a much more comprehensive view of the phenomena than did the valley town site. It was possible to observe a general pattern of movement that could not have been seen from below, because the north end of this pattern was over Town C, which was not visible from the sighting town. Even with binoculars Wadsworth had to study the pattern for more than an hour before he could begin to understand what was happening.

Essentially, the lights made long, low runs from Town C toward Town B, which was not visible from the sighting town. Even with binoculars Wadsworth had to study the pattern for more than an hour before he could begin to understand what was happening. At other times they appeared to hover, flare up, then go out completely. Witness I believed that the lights flared up in response to signals he flashed at them with a spotlight. Many of his flashes were followed by flare-ups of the UFOs, but to Wadsworth these flare-ups appeared coincidental.

Observations lasting about two hours convinced Wadsworth that the lights were aboard aircraft operating out of an Air Force base in Town C. He was finally able to see the lights move along what was apparently a runway, then lift off, circle southward, and go through the behavior previously described before returning to land at Castle. It should be pointed out that none of this pattern was obvious, even to the NICAP man some thirty miles away, and visibility was limited by haze. In checking further with the base, it was learned that most of the aerial activity there involved tankers and B-52s in practice refuelling operations. Between 400 and 500 sorties were launched each month, day and night. These planes carried large spotlights that were switched on and off repeatedly during training. This feature explains the flare-ups and the disappear-reappear phenomena, that had been observed from the town. The apparent hovering is accounted for by the fact that part of the flight pattern was on a heading towards the observer. The closing behavior followed by separation was the refuelling contact. Maps supplied by the AFB showed flight patterns consistent with these sightings as to the objects' locations, motions, and disappearance-reappearance-flareup behavior. (See fig. 3, p. 337) Since these objects were essentially identical to those seen the previous night, it was assumed that the UFO officer had been in error when he stated that no aircraft activity had originated at the Air Force base.

Summary and Conclusion

The sightings were of interest for two reasons. First, the phenomena were strange enough to defy simple explanation. Second, they were on a large enough scale to arouse widespread interest. Sighting frequency was high and did not decline with time.

However, the sightings were not individually spectacular, being essentially lights in the night sky. This case is an example of conventional stimuli (aircraft) that, by their unusual behavior, lighting, and flight paths, presented an unconventional appearance to witnesses.

Before the project investigation, observers had become loosely organized around Witness I, who logged sightings, taped interviews with witnesses, and obtained photographs of the objects. He also called on Los Angeles NICAP for further assistance. But one thing that apparently no observer did was to drive across the valley to the Air Force base while sightings were occurring. There may have been two reasons for this omission. First, Witness I had phoned the base on several occasions to report sightings, and had been erroneously but authoritatively informed that the sightings could not be accounted for by planes based locally. Second, few observers were seeking a conventional explanation that would dispel the intriguing presence of UFOs. Even when the sightings were identified by Wadsworth, Witness I was loath to accept the aircraft explanation. Thus a solution was not forthcoming from the local situation, which had reached a kind of equilibrium.

After examining the previously compiled information, project investigators decided a more direct approach was needed. The methods of inquiry and observations that they used resulted in the discovery of a pattern of behavior readily identified with aircraft activity originating from the local air base.

Case 29

North Eastern
Summer 1967
Investigators: Craig, Levine

Abstract:

Six to 16 bright lights, appearing and disappearing in sequence, were seen by several independent witnesses. Some witnesses reported seeing the outline of an object to which the lights were apparently attached. Investigation showed that the lights were ALA-17 flares dropped from a B-52 aircraft as part of an USAF aircrew training program.

Background:

At least 17 witnesses in ten independent groups reported seeing six to 16 bright objects or as many lights associated with a single object, in the northeastern sky at about 9:30 p.m. EDT. Most of the reports indicated that the lights were visible for 10-15 sec., although a few claimed durations up to five minutes.

The first report was made by a group of six teenagers who said they saw a noiseless "flying saucer" with six yellow lights 200 ft. in the air over the concession stand on the beach. They reported the object to be about 20-35 ft. across with a "round thing on the top and bottom."

Publication of this report was followed by numerous reports

of similar observations that had been made at the same time. These observations were from four different beaches, an airport, and a fishing boat off-shore. The reports varied in detail, but agreed that the sighting was sometime between 9:15-9:45 p.m.; several reports placed the time within five minutes of 9:30. They all agreed that the lights appeared in the northeast. Elevation angles that were indicated varied from 5-30° above the horizon. The lights were described as blinking on and off; some descriptions indicated that they appeared in sequence from left to right and blinked off in reverse sequence, right to left. Most observers saw five or six yellow lights in a roughly horizontal line, each light being comparable in brightness with the planet Venus. One private pilot observing from the ground at an airport saw a horizontal string of six to eight pairs of lights, one yellow and one red light in each pair. The array moved toward the horizon and seemed to get larger for five to seven seconds, stopping four to five seconds, then beginning to retrace the approach path before blinking out about four seconds later. While most observers saw only lights, at least one witness, in addition to the teenagers at the original beach, reported seeing a large disc-like object encompassing the lights. Other of the witnesses "had the feeling the lights were attached to an object."

Investigation:

Six witnesses in this northeastern area were interviewed directly, most of them at the locations from which they saw the lights. Others were contacted by telephone. The multiplicity of consistent reports indicated that unusual lights in the sky had indeed been seen; it was not certain whether they were separate lights or were lights on a single object.

Reports of these UFO sightings, when they had been telephoned to the nearest Air Force Base by observers, had been disregarded there. No unusual unidentified radar images had been recorded at the nearest FAA Center.

The observations as described did not resemble airplane activity or meteorological or astronomical phenomena. No blimps or aircraft with lighted advertising signs were in the vicinity of the sighting at the time.

Since reports of UFO sightings had been frequent in this region, the investigating team spent several late hours observing the sky in hopes of getting first-hand information about the lights or objects that had been seen. No UFOs appeared during the watches.

One of the witnesses to the original sighting, a high-school senior, reported seeing "that object" again on a subsequent evening. He guided the investigating team around a golf-course, describing a large saucer with surrounding windows which he had seen there just a few yards above his head. This report was judged to be a fabrication.

A few weeks after the project team returned to Colorado,

the NICAP Subcommittee Chairman, Raymond E. Fowler, learned that 16 flares had been dropped at 9:25 EDT on the night in question from a B-52 aircraft 25-30 mi. NE of the beach area. Information about the flare drop was furnished, at Mr. Fowler's request, by the Wing Information Officer.

The Strategic Air Command had initiated an aircrew training program for dropping ALA-17 flares on the day before with aircrews releasing as many as 16 flares per drop. The flares are released over controlled areas at 20,000 ft. or more. They burn with a brilliant white light, and are easily visible at distances in excess of 30 mi.

Conclusion:

In view of the close coincidence in time, location, direction and appearance between the flares dropped and the UFOs sighted on the same day, it seems highly likely that the witnesses saw the flares and not unusual flying objects. It also seems highly likely that the suggestion of an outline of an object as reported by a few witnesses was, in fact, a product of their expectation to see lights in the sky *on* something rather than floating about by themselves.

Case 30

South Pacific
Fall 1967
Investigator: Staff

Abstract:

A civilian employee at an AFB confirmed an earlier report that base personnel had made an UFO sighting, although official sources denied that such an event had occurred.

Background:

A rumor was relayed to this project by a source considered to be reliable, reporting in the fall, 1967, six UFOs had followed an X-15 flight at the AFB. It was suggested that motion pictures of the event should be available from the Air Force.

Investigation:

Before initiating a field investigation, Project members checked by phone with Base Operations for confirmation of the rumor. There was no log book record of an UFO report and no X-15 flight on that day. The last X-15 flight had been 8 days previously and the last recorded UFO report submitted to the base had been a month before.

The rumor persisted, however, with indications that official secrecy was associated with the event. If reports of the event had been classified, no record would appear on the operations log. Although there apparently was no association with an X-15 flight, a responsible base employee (Mr. A), who wished to remain anonymous, had reassured our source that there was a sighting by pilots and control tower operators. Mr. A had left the AFB for temporary duty elsewhere. His replacement, Mr. B, was unable to obtain details of the event but was quoted as saying that there apparently was something to it because "they are not just flatly denying it."

Mr. A was contacted by telephone at his temporary assignment by a project investigator. He said he actually did not know too much about the incident, since all the information had been turned over to the public information officer, who was the only one at the base who could discuss it. According to Mr. A the information had come to his desk; his action was to pass it on to the PIO.

Attempts to learn more about the reported event from the PIO were met with apparent evasion from that office. The Director of Information was reportedly unavailable when phoned. He did not return calls. On one attempt to reach him, the investigator indicated to a PIO secretary that he would prefer to replace the call when the Colonel was in, rather than to speak with a lieutenant who was available at that moment. The secretary's response was "Well, the Colonel is busy this year—but you'd still prefer to wait until next Monday?"

On Monday, the Colonel was again unavailable and once again did not return the call. A request was then made through the Pentagon for determination of whether or not an UFO event had in fact, occurred at the base on the day specified. A Pentagon officer transmitted a request to the base Director of Information that he telephone the project investigator and clarify this situation. This resulted in a telephone message, left by an assistant to the Director of Information, that there was no UFO event at that base on the day in question.

Mr. A was contacted later, after his return to the base, and asked for clarification of the incident. He responded only that the Director of Information had told him to "stay out of that."

Conclusion:

Although it is true that the report of this incident was never more than a rumor, it is also true that project investigators were not able satisfactorily to confirm or deny that an UFO incident had occurred. Attempts to investigate the rumor were met with evasion and uncooperative responses to our inquiries by base information.

Case 31

North Eastern
Fall 1967
Investigators: Ayer, Wadsworth

Abstract:

A woman and her children driving on a rural road at night saw a trapezoidal pattern of dim red lights over the road. As the car approached the lights, they moved off the road and disappeared between the trees. The possibility that the lights were on a microwave tower in the vicinity of the sighting is discounted by the witness' familiarity with the road and tower, her accurate account of accessory details, and other factors.

Investigation:

Interviews with the principal witness in the fall of 1967 brought out the following account:

A woman was driving north with her three young sons on a country road about 7:45 p.m., when her oldest boy, aged about ten, called her attention to about 18 extended dim red lights arranged in a trapezoidal pattern. They appeared about as high as the first cross-piece on a telephone pole, and as wide as the road—that is, about 15 ft., and hovered about 1.5 ft. above the road.

As soon as the woman saw the lights, she acelerated to try to catch them, and chased them up the road about 300 yd. until they vanished between two sugar maples on her left. The lights disappeared as if they had been occulted from right to left. The structure to which the lights were presumably attached was never visible.

After hearing the woman's report, a project investigator drove S on the road about 4:30 p.m. to check the landmarks. In addition to the two maples about 300 yd. north of the house where the lights were first seen, there was a third maple nearer the road and about 250 yd. further north, and a microwave tower about 500 yd. N of the third maple and somewhat W of the road. Such towers usually are well lighted at night. It appeared that, if the trees cut off the view of the top of the tower, the lower part would resemble the strange lights, provided that the number of lights agreed with those reported. The third maple would be responsible for the occultation.

Accordingly, both investigators returned to the road about 8:30 p.m. The first glimpse of the illuminated tower severely undermined the hypothesis. The tower carried only a red beacon at the top and four red lights halfway down, one on each leg of the rectangular structure.

A subsequent talk with the witness revealed that she had traveled back and forth along the road a great many times. She was quite familiar with the appearance of the tower, and denied emphatically that it was what she had seen, because the lights on the object were dim and extended, while those on the tower were "points with rays." Furthermore, there were too few lights on the tower.

Comment:

This witness impressed both investigators as an accurate and wide-awake observer who was quite capable of relating to known landmarks the behavior of an unexpected and unfamiliar sight with little distortion.

The sighting can be explained by the presence of the microwave tower. A further argument for the tower hypothesis depends on the fact that the road ran upgrade about 40 ft. in elevation between the witness' locations at first sighting and at disappearance. Thus, it appears that the light on top of the tower would have been seen low over this rise in the road, the lower lights on the tower being obscured.

The tower cannot therefore be regarded as a fully satisfactory explanation. The reported lights were seen just above the roadway; but at no point does the road run directly toward the tower. Further by the witness' account, the strangeness of the object was apparent to both her and her son, both of whom were very familiar with the road and the tower.

Case 32
South Mountain
Fall 1967
Investigators: Ayer, Wadsworth

Abstract:

The death of a horse was popularly believed to be related to UFO sightings, but professional investigation disclosed nothing unusual in the condition of the carcass. No significant conclusions could be derived from numerous reports of UFO sightings.

Background:

During the early fall, 1967, news of a series of events that were popularly held to be related filtered in to the Colorado project. One such event had been the death of a horse under allegedly mysterious circumstances a month before. This death had become associated in the public mind with recent UFO sightings in the area.

The horse, owned by a woman and pastured on her brother's ranch, had not come in for water one day and had been found dead two days later. It was reported that all the flesh and skin had been removed from his head and neck down to a straight cut just ahead of the shoulder, and that crushed vegetation, strange depressions in the ground, and dark "exhaust marks" had been found nearby. The owner of the horse was a correspondent for a local newspaper, and a spate of releases had rapidly inflated public interest in the case.

When, a few days later, word came through that a second dead horse had been found, amid persistent rumors of unreported UFOs, it was decided that project investigators should go to the area.

Investigation:

The area about the carcass had been trampled by several

hundred visitors. The investigators therefore considered it was not worthwhile to try to investigate anything at the site except the carcass. When they learned that no veterinarian had examined it, they called in a veterinarian, who examined the carcasses of both of the horses. His essential findings were:

The horse's carcass was extremely old for an autopsy, but there was evidence suggesting a severe infection in a hindleg that could have disabled or killed the animal. There was evidence also of a knife cut in the neck, possibly made by someone who found the horse hopelessly sick. Absence of nerve tissues and viscera was normal for a carcass dead several weeks.

Magpies and other birds ordinarily cannot peck through the skin of a horse, but will eat the flesh and skin if they can get into it. In this case, they evidently had taken advantage of the cut and removed all accessible skin and flesh from the neck and head before the carcass had been found.

The second horse carcass showed evidence that death had resulted from encephalitis.

It had been reported that a forest ranger with civil defense training had found a high level of radioactivity near the "exhaust marks." When questioned by an investigator, he said that his meter had indicated only "slight" activity two weeks after the carcass had been found. The investigators concluded that the activity he had measured on his simple survey instrument had been no greater than the normal background radiation they measured three weeks later.

Conclusions:

There was no evidence to support the assertion that the horse's death was associated in any way with abnormal causes.

Other Sightings:

The investigators then turned their attention to the numerous reports of UFO sightings in the same area. Many were vague or involved direct lights at night. Only the more interesting cases are reported here.

1) A service-station attendant and former aircraft gunner reported three sightings in ten years. The second, about 1962, occurred while he, with three companions, was driving west at 65 mph., about 3:30 a.m. They noticed on the slope of a nearby mountain a point of blue light that moved toward the highway and then turned parallel to it, pacing the car a few feet from the ground. It soon pulled ahead and vanished over the valley. Suddenly, the witness saw what he assumed was the same light appear in the middle of the road some distance ahead and approach at high speed, so that he ran the car off into the graded ditch to avoid collision. As the light approached, it grew to at least the size of his car. As it passed, it

shot upward a few feet, turned south, and disappeared.

In the spring of 1967, the same witness, with his wife, was driving west when he saw an object that resembled a box kite crossing the highway from the left. He associated it with a helicopter, although he was familiar with them and the apparition was silent. Thinking that it was some kind of aircraft that might land at the airport, he drove directly there. During this part of the trip, the object disappeared behind some buildings. When they arrived at the airport, it was nowhere in sight.

2) About 5:15 a.m., late summer, 1967, a couple were driving south when they saw two extended objects outlined with a dull glow, at an altitude of about 15°. One was directly south over the road, and the second was south-southwest. The objects moved northwesterly until they were apparently "directly over [the mountain]." There the second moved up beside the first and they hovered for several minutes before descending rapidly to the ground, where they merged with the vegetation and disappeared. The witnesses estimated that the minimum distance to the objects was one mile, and presumably was never very much greater; however, they hovered "directly over [the mountain]," which was at least 8 mi. away.

3) On an unrecalled date, late in the summer, 1966, about 5:30 a.m., two boys, ages 13 and 17, were traveling north when they saw an extended bright light in the road. The UFO kept ahead of them for about 20 mi., then disappeared.

4) At 10:15 p.m., early fall, 1967, the owner of the horse mentioned above, with her husband, was driving west. They saw three pulsating red-and-green lights pass over, moving generally southwest.

After five to ten minutes, the third object seemed to explode, emitting a yellow flash, then a second flash nearer the ground, and a puff of smoke that the witnesses observed for ten minutes. Several fragments were seen to fall to the ground after the second explosion.

The husband and wife disagreed as to the location. He said the wreckage should lie somewhere between the second and fifth hill south of a nearby town, but she said she saw the explosion over a brown hill ten miles east of the same town. The explosion was also seen by a farmer, and his times and bearings supported the husband's account. Ayer drove between the second and third and the third and fourth hills, and he flew over the region south of the fifth hill, but he saw nothing of interest.

The data on this sighting were sent to Major Quintanilla, who reported that no satellite re-entries had been seen or predicted at the reported time. This finding, however, did not preclude the unobserved re-entry of a minor fragment that had not been tracked.

5) Another couple reported several sightings, one of these, between 9:00 and 10:00 p.m., fall, 1967, considered by them

to be a "meteor." Its location was not given. This sighting was also reported to Major Quintanilla, but no satellite had been observed to re-enter on that day.

6) In the fall, 1967, "ten minutes before dark," two ranchers driving west saw a small cigar-shaped cloud, vertically oriented in a sky that had only one other cloud in it. The cigar was about the size of a thumb at arm's length, 20° above the "horizon" and 45° south of the road, that is, southwest of the point of first sighting. It was slightly boat-tailed at the bottom and its outlines were not sharp. The second cloud was obviously a cloud, at a slightly greater altitude in the south. The two men drove about three miles while the "cigar" tilted slightly toward the other cloud and moved slowly toward it. They stopped the car to observe more closely. Pointing toward the larger cloud, the "cigar" continued to approach it. After a few minutes the witnesses drove on, and a few minutes later the "cigar" melted into the cloud.

Summary:

None of these sighting reports were considered to be current or strange enough to warrant detailed investigation.

Case 33

North Eastern
Summer 1967
Investigators: Ayer, Wadsworth

Abstract:

Two teen-aged girls in a rural home reported that in the evening a large glowing object had hovered nearby and that several child-sized figures had been seen running about near the barn. Testimony of others in the area was inconclusive, in some respects supporting and in others weakening their account. No definite explanation was found, but the case is considered weak.

Background:

Preliminary information, elaborated by interviews of the witnesses, developed the following summary account:

Two fourteen-year-old girls in a second-story bedroom in the home of one of them were looking out a window about 9:00 p.m., when they saw a large glowing object above and beyond the barn, which was south of the house. During the next hour, the object moved up and down, left and right, and varied considerably in brightness. Both girls thought the object was between the barn and a hill no more than a few hundred yards beyond it. After about a half-hour they heard a sound, apparently from the barn, like the "put-put" made by a power mower when it fires but fails to start. Then three small figures ran from the barn and stopped by a mail box next to the adjacent road. They stood there for several minutes looking in the direction of the house and then ran across the road to stop under a large tree where they were partially hidden in shadow. Shortly afterward a car approached, the object blacked out, and the figures ran across the road, past the barn and disappeared into the shadows. After the car had passed, the object began to pulsate between a very bright white and a dull red. It also began moving diagonally from upper right to lower left. This was repeated a number of times before a second car, driven by the mother of the girl whose home they were in, approached the house. The object then became dim, as if reacting to the approach of the car. The mother was able to see the object dimly, and it remained dim throughout her observation. No attempt was made to get a closer look, and around 10:00 p.m. the observers went to bed, with the object still dim but visible. Nothing unusual could be found to account for the sighting.

Investigation:

INTERVIEWS OF WITNESSES

The two girls were interviewed in the home where the sighting had occurred. Conditions were unfavorable as other members of the family were present and asking them to leave would have been awkward. Because of the initial nervousness of the girls, and since they had already been interviewed separately by Ted Thobin of NICAP, a single interview was held with both girls. Their accounts were generally the same as told earlier to Thobin; however certain discrepancies in different versions will be pointed out: Both witnesses tended to be very general when asked to describe the sighting in a narrative manner. Thus it became necessary to ask direct questions in order to obtain details, so that it was difficult to avoid leading the witness. In general, the girls seemed to lack curiosity and interest in the sighting. They also seemed rather immature for fourteen-year-olds, and it is difficult to evaluate the reliability of their report.

RELATED TESTIMONY

Two neighbors were questioned in connection with the sighting. One lived about a quarter-mile south of the house where the sighting had occurred; i.e., in the general direction of the sighting. She had seen nothing unusual on the night of the sighting; however, she remembered that several fires were burning in a swamp area about one-half mile southeast of her house at the time of the sighting, and were tended by someone on a motor scooter. A check of the exact location of the fires relative to the UFO was inconclusive. The UFO was approximately S of the house, while the fires were 10-15° E of S. The motor scooter might account for the "put-put" sound. When asked about this, the girls stated that the sound had come from the barn, not beyond. It should also be mentioned that the neighbor who mentioned the fires did not see them even though she was much nearer than the girls. The fires were about forty feet lower than her house and sixty feet below the house where the girls were, obscured by moderately dense timber.

A second woman, who lived almost directly across the road from the observers' house, was originally considered a corroborating witness to the sighting. She had reluctantly admitted having seen the object, but emphasized that she did not wish to be involved. She told Ted Thobin that she had seen a bright white watermelon-shaped thing when she went out to take in the wash between 9:00 and 10:00 p.m. This, however, was after she had teased the girls about seeing "little green men." More detailed information sought by the project team was refused. Her husband said that he had taken garbage out around 9:30 p.m. that night and had seen nothing unusual.

Another two-witness report was received later from NICAP as a possible corroboration of the original sighting. An object described as a clam-shaped, glowing red UFO was sighted 15 September 1967 at 7:50 p.m. from a location less than a mile from the girls' sighting.

A sighting made by one of the girls and her mother two nights after the primary sighting was described as follows:

At 9:30 p.m., a bright star-like object was seen in the SE at 25° elevation, moving W at apparent aircraft speed. When directly S of their house (a later version said SW), the object abruptly stopped and remained motionless for several minutes. Then an airplane approached from the E, and the object took off toward the E, retracing its original course and passing above the plane to disappear from sight in the direction from which it had come. Total duration was several minutes.

RECONSTRUCTION OF SIGHTING

1. The object was first seen as the girls were looking up the road from an upstairs bedroom window. The bedroom light was out, and the only lighted room on that side of the house was the kitchen.

2. The object appeared as a bright white light that alternately dimmed and then brightened again, seeming to grow larger. One of the girls implied that this change of brightness was of several seconds periodicity; the other said that the object "blinked fast," and that it was mostly white.

3. Both girls had watched this for about half an hour when they heard a "putting sound" from the barn. This sound ceased almost immediately, and two or three figures ran from the barn and stopped by the mail box next to the road. At this point, there are discrepancies as to the number of figures and their behavior. One girl initially mentioned three figures; she said two stood by the mail box, one on either side, and then moments later all three appeared as they ran past the

barn and vanished into the shadows. NICAP's report indicated that the two figures who stood by the mail box dashed *across the road,* stopped under a tree, and then dashed back across the road, where for the first time a third figure was visible running with the other two past the barn. The version obtained by the project team at first did not mention the figures having crossed the road at all. When asked about this, the girls were vague; however, they agreed that, after the figures stopped by the mail box, they next appeared across the street under a tree. Neither girl remembered seeing the figures cross the road in either direction. Only general details of the figures were reported: height was estimated as about 4.5 ft. by comparison with the mail box; clothing seemed the same for all three—no details; the heads appeared disproportionately large.

4. After the figures had been momentarily observed across the road, a car approached from behind the observers, and three figures were seen running past the barn, where they vanished in shadow. The figures were seen as silhouettes against background light from the moon which was three days before full phase and from the luminous object. The witnesses could not remember whether the lights of the approaching car partially illuminated the figures. At the same time, the luminous object dimmed out. One girl said that it became so dim they could hardly see it. The other said its lights went out and did not come back on for five minutes. Thus there was a period during which little was seen, after which the object brightened as before.

5. Then, in addition to its changes in brightness, the object began to move diagonally from lower left to upper right. This motion was confined to several diameters of the object, perhaps two or three degrees according to sketches made by the girls.

6. Another discrepancy concerned the position of the object relative to the background. Originally, the girls had said that the object dropped down behind the barn several times, and also appeared sometimes against the background of trees. Upon closer questioning, using sketches, both girls indicated that the object was never actually below the horizon even when it seemed to drop down. This statement, if accurate, sharply reduces the quality of the sighting, because the original distance limits of a few hundred yards can no longer be relied upon, and size estimates—which are characteristically exaggerated—lose meaning. It should be mentioned that the size estimate given Thobin was likened to a VW automobile at 150 yd. The brightness was said to be equivalent to sunlight, but later changed to four times as bright as the moon. In reconstructing what was seen, these various estimates must be given low reliability.

7. Details for the latter part of the sighting are sketchy. Both girls continued to watch the object for 20 or 30 min., while it intermittently behaved as described. It is not clear

whether the display declined, but apparently it did. No further sound was heard or figures seen, and one of the girls stated that, by the time her mother returned home, about 10:00 p.m., the object was very dim though still visible. It was implied that the object dimmed in reaction to the approach of the car, but the girls were not clear on this later aspect of the sighting. They apparently were tired of watching, and after showing the object to the mother, they went to bed. The mother apparently had not noticed the object when she returned to the house, until the girls pointed it out to her. Evidently it was not conspicuous enough to attract her attention as she drove into the yard.

8. Nothing unusual was seen the next morning, and nothing was found to account for the sighting. The project investigators later searched the barn and the area beyond for burns, radioactivity, or other evidence, but found nothing significant.

9. At the time of the sighting, the girls did not associate the figures with the luminous object, or the object with UFOs. The figures were assumed to be children; the object was the mystery. Later the girls decided that, since no children of the size they had seen lived nearby, there might be a stranger implication.

Comment:

Essentially, this sighting was a two-witness event with additional low-weight corroboration. The lack of independent witnesses is a weakness for which the marginal corroboration cannot compensate. Though no physical evidence was discovered that could account for the sighting, the possibility of illusory elements and distortions of memory leaves serious doubts as to the accuracy of the account.

Case 34

North Atlantic
Fall 1967
Investigator: Levine

Abstract:

Information obtained in telephone interviews of officers of Canadian Naval Maritime Command and RCMP indicated that an object bearing several colored lights glided with a whistling noise into the sea. Search by boats and divers found no debris or wreckage.

Investigation:

On the basis of a report from James Lorenzen (APRO), project investigators telephoned several sources in the area.

A watch officer at the Naval Maritime Command stated that reports indicated that an object about 60 ft. long with four lights on it had gone whistling into the sea; it flashed when it hit, and a white light remained on the water afterwards. He stated that the original report had come from two teenagers, and that the Navy was searching for wreckage. No aircraft were reported missing in the area. He mentioned also that sightings had been reported throughout the year.

A corporal of the RCMP stated that the first report had come from five young people, 15-20 yr. old, who while driving near the shore had seen three or four yellow lights in a horizontal pattern comparable in size to a "fair-sized" aircraft, descending at about 45° toward the water. The witnesses had lost sight of the object for about ten seconds while passing a small hill; they then saw a single white light on the water about where they estimated the object should have gone in. They observed the light while they drove on about .25 mi., then reported the incident to the RCMP detachment.

Two officers and the corporal had arrived about 15 min. later, in time to see the light on the water. It persisted about five minutes longer. Ten minutes after it went out, the two officers were at the site in a rowboat; a Coast Guard boat and six fishing boats also were on the scene. They found only patches of foam 30-40 yd. wide that the fishermen thought was not normal tide foam; the tide was ebbing, and the white light had appeared to drift with it.

The site of the presumed impact was in between an island and the mainland, about 200-300 yd. offshore. Apparently no one actually saw anything enter the water. However two young women driving on the island reported that a horizontal pattern of three yellow lights had tilted and descended, and then a yellow light had appeared on the water. Another witness, about two miles from the site, saw a horizontal line of three red-orange lights descending at "aircraft speed," with a whistling sound like a falling bomb. He thought the object was like an aircraft. It disappeared behind some houses, and the sound ceased a second or two later.

The RCMP corporal stated that the light on the water was not on any boat, that Air Search and Rescue had no report of missing aircraft in the area, and an RCAF radar station nearby reported no Canadian or U.S. air operations in the area at the time, nor any unusual radar object. The night was clear and moonless. A search by Navy divers during the days immediately following the sighting disclosed nothing relevant.

Five days later the Naval Maritime Command advised the project that the search had been terminated. The watch officer read a report from the RCMP indicating that at the time in question a 60 ft. object had been seen to explode upon impact with the water.

The captain of a fishing boat that had been about 16 mi. from the site of the earlier reports, reported to the project that he and his crew had seen three stationary bright red flashing lights on the water, from sundown until about 11:00 p.m. The ship's radar showed four objects forming a six mile square; the three lights were associated with one of these objects. At about 11:00 p.m., one of the lights went straight up. The captain had judged that the radar objects were naval vessels and the ascending light a helicopter; he had attached no significance to these observations until he had heard on the radio of the sightings; he then reported the foregoing observations to the RCMP. However, since the position he reported for the objects was about 175 n. mi. from the original site, the two situations do not appear to be related.

No further investigation by the project was considered justifiable, particularly in view of the immediate and thorough search that had been carried out by the RCMP and the Maritime Command.

Case 35

South Pacific
Fall 1967
Investigators: Levine, Low, and others

Abstract:

The events began with a visual sighting about 8:00 p.m. of a stationary object with colored lights over the ocean. Missile-tracking radars were asked to look for the object; they immediately picked up many unidentified targets, most of them moving, and tracked them. Most moving targets permitted radar lock-on. They moved at speeds up to 80 knots, and sometimes returned very strong echoes. Several additional visual sightings were reported. Most sightings were made over the ocean, but some targets appeared to the east and north, over land. The radar targets were still being observed when the equipment was closed down about 2:30 a.m. Yet no aircraft were known to be in the area, and three flights of fighters sent in to investigate found nothing unusual.

An unusually strong temperature inversion provided favorable conditions for both visual and radar mirage effects. Mirages of ships below the normal horizon appear to account adequately for the stationary or slow objects. The higher, faster radar targets were consistent with birds, which tracking-radar operators had not had occasion to look for before. Similar radar observations were reported on two subsequent days.

Investigation:

Project Blue Book had notified the Colorado project of this interesting visual and radar sighting at AFB A. It was also reported that, in a test three nights after the sighting, it had been established that radars at the base could once again observe "bogies" similar to those sighted on the night of the original sighting. Project investigators and others visited the site on two different dates. On the later day, the following were present: R. T. H. Collis, Roy Blackmer, and Carl Herold of Stanford Research Institute; Marx Brook of New Mexico Institute of Mining and Technology; Roger Lhermitte of the

Environmental Science Services Administration; and Low and Levine of the Colorado project. On the first date Low and Dr. Robert Nathan of the Jet Propulsion Laboratory had visited AFB A.

Observers. The AFB A sightings were exceptional because of the high professional qualifications of the observers. Two were officials of the Western Test Range, each having had 17 yr. of experience as a naval aviator. One of them had 10,000 hr. as an air intercept and final approach controller; the other also had been an air intercept controller. A third, who was Range Air Control Officer on the night of the first sighting had had 11 yr. experience with ground and airborne electronics systems. Six others were radar operators employed by private contractors on the base, all of whom had had extensive experience in radar operation. They displayed impressive understanding of the sophisticated radar systems they were operating and good comprehension of radar engineering principles. Another witness was of the security force, without extensive technical training.

Radars. The following radars were involved in the sightings:

FPS-16 C-band tracking radar with 1.2° beam.

TPQ-18 C-band tracking radar with 0.4° beam.

GERTS X-band tracking and command radar usually used in beacon mode in which the radar transmission triggers a beacon carried by the vehicle being tracked but during the sightings used in skin-track mode, i.e., conventional radar operation in which the target is seen by reflected radiation from the transmitted pulse.

M33 X-band tracking radar.

ARCER L-band search radar.

Details of the sightings. 2000 to 2045 For one-half hour a missile range official observed from his home an object at azimuth 290°. He called another official, also at home three miles to the south, who confirmed the sighting at azimuth approximately 280° and altitude 10° to 15°. The second observer reported that the object seen through 7 × 50 binoculars, appeared the size of a large thumbtack, elliptical in shape having a red and green light separated by a distance about the wing span of an aircraft. But the object was stationary, and fuzzy like a spinning top.

2045 Observer two called Range Control Operations (located at an altitude of 900-1,100 ft.). The range control officer confirmed the visual observation. To him it appeared to have white, red, and green or blue colors that did not vary. They "looked like the running lights on a stationary object." He gave its bearing as 290°, range, several miles, altitude approximately 10,000 ft., and suggested that the object looked like a helicopter.

2045 FPS-16 radar in search mode locked on two strong targets, one moving around and one stationary. The stationary target appeared in the general direction of the visual sighting, but the optical position was not determined with sufficient accuracy to establish that this was a simultaneous optical-visual sighting. The original interpretation was a helicopter, with another assisting.

2100 The range control officer checked for possible air traffic in the AFB A area with several other air bases. All reported negatively.

2100 Using its FPS-16 in lock-on automatic mode, base D reported strong targets headed toward AFB A. Because of the narrow beam of the radar the targets were presumed to be in line.

2100 TPQ-18 radar at AFB A was brought into operation, and saw many targets. One, at 8 n.m. range, 4,000 ft. altitude, 290° azimuth, and 4°.6 elevation proceeded south at low speed. One strong target approached and went directly overhead. At one time, the TPQ-18 saw four targets. Base D saw as many as eight. AFB A and base D did not establish that they were looking at the same targets.

RADAR OBSERVATIONS

a. Dozens of targets were seen. Speed ranged from 0 to 80 k. with rapid changes in altitudes. The radars would lose their tracking "locks" on the objects, and then re-engage.

b. The target that went directly overhead produced an extremely strong 80 dB signal. Three persons went outside the radar shack, but were unable to see any object. On the TPQ-18 radar one of the strongest targets appeared to separate into eight objects after which it was necessary to switch to manual to gain control to separate the signal.

c. NORAD surveillance radar at AFB A operates at a frequency quite different from the tracking radars. It saw no targets, but its operator reported clutter or possible jamming.

d. Base D reported a target "bigger than any flat-top at three miles."

e. As the radar activity increased, the number of visual observations decreased.

VISUAL SIGHTINGS
(ONLY THE MOST INTERESTING ARE DESCRIBED)

a. Many objects were sighted, but they declined in frequency as the radar activity increased.

b. One visual appeared to move toward the observers so alarmingly that one of them finally yelled, "Duck."

c. One object, dull in color but showing red, white, and green, moved generally south and finally out of visual range.

d. Another, the color of a bright fireball, moved on a zig-zag course from north to south. Two radar operators reported,

"The radar didn't get locked onto what we saw. By the time the radar slaved to us, the object was gone visually, and the radar didn't see anything. . . . It looked like a fireball coming down through there. Like a helicopter coming down the coast, at low elevation. We got the 13-power telescope on it." Then it grew smaller and smaller until it disappeared. Duration 1.5-2 min. Moved only in azimuth. Brighter than a bright star. Like aircraft landing lights except yellower. This sighting occurred between 0100 and 0200 on the second night. A balloon was released about this time, and the winds were right to accord with the sighting; but the weather officer thought it could not have been a balloon, because the report did not indicate that the object rose, and a balloon would have risen at approximately 1,000 fpm.

f. Two other radar operators reported having seen an object that traversed 45° in a few seconds, "making four zigs and four zags," and then, after reappearing for one second, disappeared to the north.

2310 Air Defense Command scrambled the first of three flights of fighters to investigate the situation. The tape of the conversations with the radar sites and other bases gave evidence of considerable confusion at this time.

The fighters were handed off to AFB A Range Control by the FAA at a nearby city and controlled locally. Range Control tried to vector the fighters in on the bogies, but found it impossible to do so very systematically. By the time the second flight came in, the controllers were so busy with the aircraft that they no longer observed any unidentified targets. They did observe a moderate amount of clutter in the west and southwest quadrant. None of the fighter pilots saw anything. One pilot observed something repeatedly on his infrared detector, but only at distance. As soon as he would close in, the object would disappear. Another aircraft did "lock-on" to a target which was found to be a ship.

Weather. The weather officer reported that there was an inversion layer at 1,800-2,200 ft. (The unidentified targets generally were reported to be above the inversion). All observers indicated that the night was exceedingly clear. The project's consulting meteorologist reports:

> The following is a summary of weather conditions surrounding UFO visual and radar sightings near . . . [AFB A] between 7:30 P.M. and midnight on . . . [the date of the first sighting].

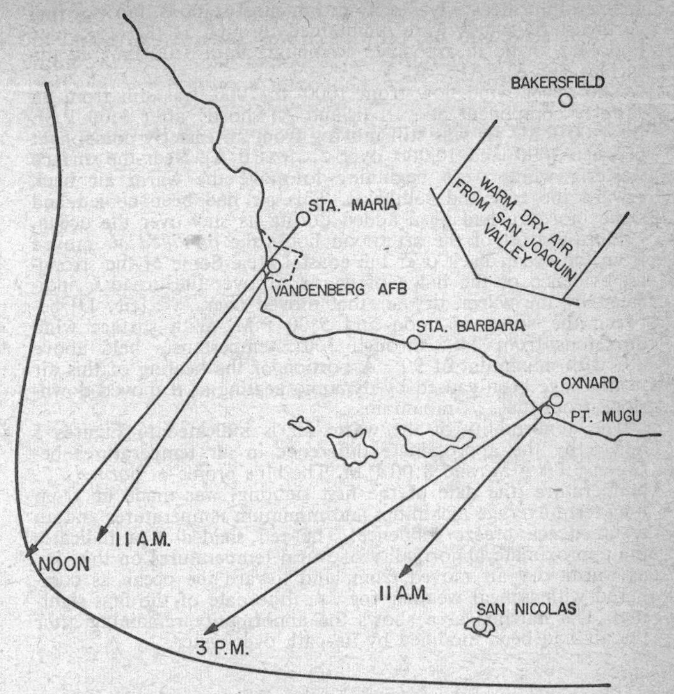

Figure 4

SOURCES OF DATA

Radiosonde and wind data from—

. . . [AFB A, island A, city A]

Surface weather observations surrounding the times of sightings from—

. . . [city B, C, D, E; AFB A, B, C; base D]

GENERAL WEATHER SITUATION

In a weather sequence which moved a trough line and a low pressure center southeastward from northwestern Utah to northwest Texas. . . . [the day prior to the first sighting], a dome of high pressure formed over the Great Basin and a surge of warm air moved from northeast to southwest. . . . Most of the surge of warm air moved southwestward from the southern part of the . . . Valley between midnight . . . [the day before the sighting] and 3:00 P.M. . . . [the day of the sighting]. Weather stations near the coast from . . . [city B] to . . . [city D] all showed abnormally warm temperatures at a time of day when ordinarily a sea breeze would have created a cooling influence.

THE OVER-OCEAN FLOW OF WARM DRY AIR

Using surface wind data from various coastal stations it is possible to reconstruct an approximate pattern of the forward edge of the warm, dry air which moved out over the ocean from a general northeasterly direction. For most stations, fairly strong northeasterly winds were maintained through 11:00 A.M. (see Fig. 4) with northeast winds continuing until 3:00 P.M. at the surface at . . . [AFB B].

The upper wind flow from 1000′ to 7000′ was still from an easterly component at . . . [island A] shortly after 3:00 P.M. By 4:00 P.M. air was still moving from an easterly component between 3000′ and 10,000′ over . . . [AFB A]. Near the surface westerly winds were beginning to move the warm air back toward the east and southeast. This air had been cooled and some moisture had been added during its stay over the ocean.

During most of the afternoon hours the *modified air* moved from the ocean back over the coastal area. Some of the strongest evidence of the bulge of warm air over the ocean is indicated by the warm, dry air that moved over . . . [city D] between the hours of noon and 5:00 P.M. With surface wind directions from 240° through 300°, temperatures held above 80° with maximum of 90°. A portion of the heating of this air would have been caused by dynamic heating as it moved downslope from the . . . mountains.

The abnormality of the warm air is indicated in Figures 5 and 6 by the approximate difference in air temperatures between 6:00 A.M. and 8:00 P.M. The blue profile of *normal* . . . temperature [the date of the first sighting] was made up from long term average maximum and minimum temperatures and an assumed sea breeze influence. The red shaded area indicates the approximate abnormality of warm temperatures on this day as warm, dry air moved from land toward the ocean as compared with typical weather for . . . [the date of the first sighting]. The hatched area shows the abnormality remaining after the air had been modified by its path over water.

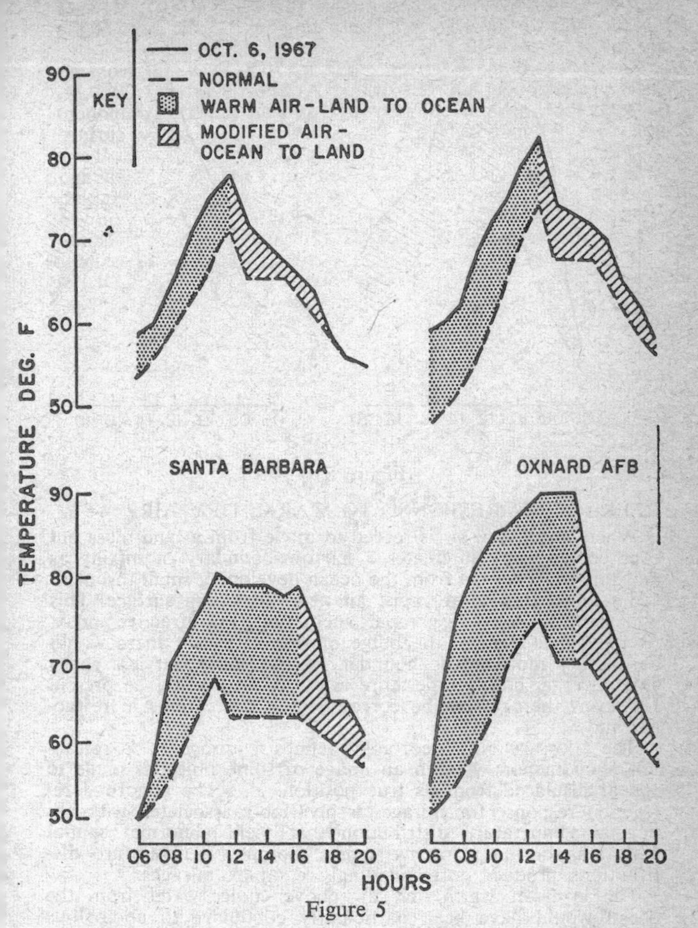
VANDENBERG AFB
SANTA MARIA
KEY
OCT. 6, 1967
NORMAL
WARM AIR-LAND TO OCEAN
MODIFIED AIR-OCEAN TO LAND
SANTA BARBARA
OXNARD AFB
TEMPERATURE DEG. F
90
80
70
60
50
06 08 10 12 14 16 18 20
HOURS

Figure 5

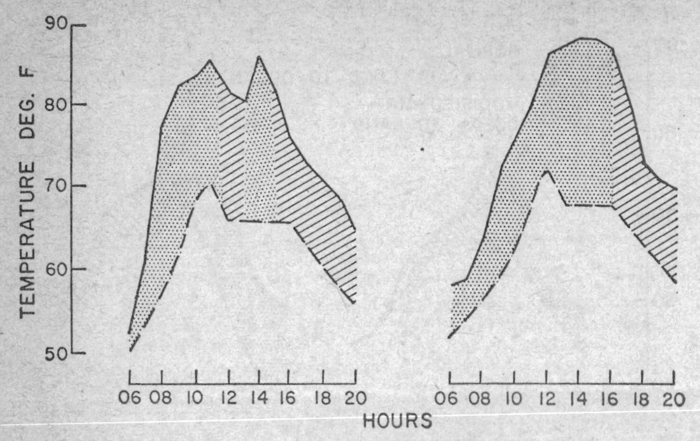

Figure 6

REFRACTION RESPONSE TO WARM, DRY AIR

When warm, dry air is forced to move from a land mass out over cooler water it creates a narrow boundary of mixing as moisture is picked up from the ocean developing small turbulent eddies of cooler, more moist air near the ocean surface. This is accompanied by very rapid fluctuations of refractive index. At the upper edge of the bulge of warm, dry air there would be another more difuse boundary where somewhat less sharp differences in both temperature and moisture would be present However, there would be corresponding fluctuations in refractive index.

The Glossary of Meteorology defines a mirage as "a refraction phenomenon wherein an image of some object is made to appear displaced from its true position. . . . The abnormal refraction response for mirages is invariably associated with abnormal temperature distribution that yield abnormal spatial variations in the refractive index. Complex temperature distributions produce correspondingly complex mirages."

The layer of warm, dry air above cooler water from the ocean would have been particularly conducive to anomalous propagation of any radar unit scanning the atmosphere at low angles. A somewhat less important segment of the air mass capable of producing anomalous propagation on the radar would have been the upper boundary of the bulge of warm dry air. The following is quoted from Battan's book on RADAR METEOROLOGY under the heading of Meteorological Conditions Associated with Non-standard Refraction. "There are various ways that the index of refraction can be modified to give rise to anomalous propagation. . . . When warm, dry air moves over cooler bodies of water, the air is cooled in the lowest layers, while at the same time moisture is added. In this way strong ducts are produced. These conditions are frequently found over the Mediterranean Sea as air blows off the African continent. Extreme anomalous propagation has been experienced in this region. For example, there have been days when centimeter radar sets have 'seen' ground targets at ranges of 400-500 miles, even though the horizon was at perhaps 20 miles. In conformance with meteorological terminology, superrefraction brought about by the movement of warm, dry air over a cool, moist surface may be called 'advective superrefraction.' By the nature of the processes involved, it can be seen that such conditions can occur during either the day or the night and last for long periods of time. The duration would depend on the persistency of the glow patterns producing the advection."

Figure 7 contains the wind and temperature profiles for . . . [island A] and . . . [AFB A] beginning with release times of 3:15 P.M. and 4:08 P.M. PST respectively on . . . [the date of the first sighting]. At . . . [AFB A] (shown by the solid lines of temperature, dew point, wind direction and velocity) dry air prevailed for all levels above the surface at 4:00 P.M. (For the *lowest point* on the profile, surface temperatures reported at 7:30 P.M. have been substituted). The vertical sounding of temperature, dew point, wind velocity and direction for . . . [island A] are indicated by the dashed lines in Figure 7. Temperatures even warmer than over . . . [AFB A] were re-

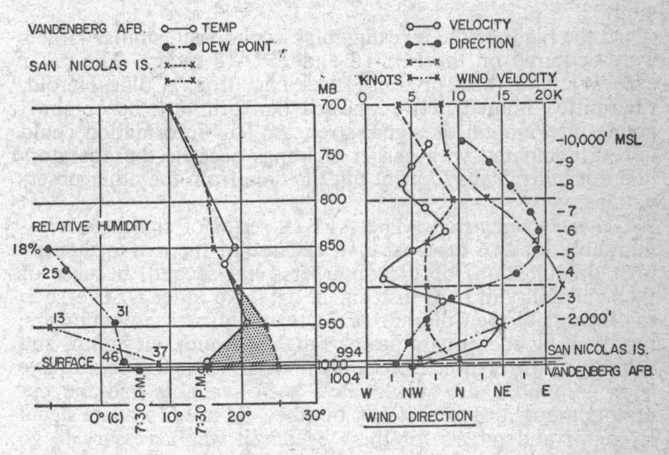

Figure 7

ported in the ascent above . . . [island A]. For emphasis, the area shaded in red indicates how much warmer the temperatures were over . . . [island A] than at . . . [AFB A] during the mid-afternoon hours. Ocean water temperatures between 58° and 59° were being reported, which is considerably cooler than the warm, dry air having temperature in the 80's as it moved from land to over the water.

CONCLUSION

It is the author's opinion that the surge of very warm, dry air may have caused a mirage and visual observations could have been correspondingly distorted in the vicinity of . . . [AFB A] between 7:30 P.M. and 8:30 P.M. It is more certain that the air mass conditions prevailing over the water continuing through at least midnight in an arc from south of . . . [AFB A] swinging eastward to the coastline could have produced anomalous propagation echoes on radar. Visibility observations were generally 12 miles or greater at all stations and no clouds were reported by the observer at . . . [AFB A] between 7:00 P.M. and midnight. . . . [base D] reported a few stratus clouds offshore in the Remarks Column beginning at 7:00 P.M. continuing through 11:00 P.M.

Evaluation and Conclusions:

Further radar tests. Three days after the first sighting, under weather conditions similar to the first day but with more wind, more coulds, and lower temperatures, the FPS-16 radar at . . . [AFB A] was operated to determine if similar targets could be seen again. Targets having the same general characteristics were acquired, but they were not as strong as the earlier sightings. Two other operators, working unofficially with a different radar, indicated that they observed "some of the same sort of stuff."

On the night of the investigators' second visit, similar targets were acquired on the FPS-16 and TPQ-18 radars. The radar experts among those present (Blackmer, Brook, Collis, Herold, Lhermitte) immediately requested that printouts be obtained giving information on signal strength. This information could not be compared with earlier sightings because the operators had not taken steps to print out the data from the other observations.

General conclusions. The AFB A series of sightings is remarkable for two reasons; first, because of the extraordinarily high qualifications of the observers, and second, because of the availability of hard instrument data. No other UFO case in the records of the Colorado project contains so many numbers, representing such quantities as range, azimuth, elevation, and velocity. Information from which signal strengths could have been computed also would have been available had the operators thought to print it out, but they did not. To relate signal strengths and ranges for these events, it was necessary to go back to the tape of the conversations and find the reports of signal strengths, which, when assigned precise times (fortunately, the tape contained good timing references), could be compared with the printouts of range, which also included timing references. Information on the visual sightings was, except for the high credibility of the observers, comparable to that in other reports of UFO sightings in the Colorado files: i.e., no reliably measured quantitative values were available from such sightings.

Mirage conditions. The detailed weather study by Loren Crow was not available at the time of the second trip to AFB A, so that it was not known at that time that the atmospheric conditions were in fact quite unusual. Fig. 7 of the Crow report indicates that at AFB A, although return air flow at the surface was well established by the late afternoon of the original sighting, the flow at 2,000 ft. was still from the northeast, so that a thin sheet of warm, dry air lay over the cool, moist air. This sheet of air extended southward almost to the island, where there was return flow from the surface to 3,000 ft., but easterly flow persisted from 3,000-10,000 ft. There were strong gradients of moisture and temperature at both stations. Crow has pointed out that the temperature and moisture contrasts probably were even greater than those shown, because the surface measurements were not made at the surface, but at some distance above it. Altogether the weather report indicates that conditions were very favorable indeed for optical mirage and scintillation and for anomalous radar propagation.

It should be noted that the incident that set off the entire sequence of events was an optical sighting at 8:00 p.m. It appears highly probable that the observer saw the running lights of a ship below the normal horizon, but made visible as a result of mirage. The conditions of such a mirage were present, but it must be pointed out that both the first two witnesses insisted emphatically that the object appeared at an elevation of about 10°. That is too high for a mirage of a ship's lights below the horizon. Hence, either their reports of the elevation angle were incorrect, or some other explanation must be found. However, even experienced observers tend to overestimate elevation angles.

A further fact is of interest, and that is that, in the Operations Control Center on the date of the second visit to AFB A, one of the operators of a search radar declared that he never saw any ships, that the shipping lanes were too far off the coast for ships to be seen by radar from that location, although the antenna was at an altitude of approximately 1,000 ft. He thereupon switched to his most distant range (80 mi.) and immediately a sprinkling of blips appeared at extreme range. They turned out to be ships, their identity conformed by their slow speed. Since there is no reason to suppose, from a quick study of weather conditions that night, that anomalous propagation had anything to do with the observation of ships, it must be concluded that they could be seen any time. The only reasonable explanation of the operator's statement that he never saw ships on the scope is that he had never looked for them. Both the original witnesses indicated that large ships never were seen visually from the coast, and that is undoubtedly correct, because they would be below the horizon. Computations show, however, that, under mirage conditions, the running lights of ships would be visible at 80 mi. range the radars had indicated.

Some of the visual sightings obviously were not of ships.

However, they were impossible to evaluate on the basis of the limited and subjective descriptions given. In this connection, it is significant to note the importance of quantitative instrument observations or records in such investigations. The visual objects could not be evaluated with much confidence, for lack of definitive evidence; but abundant quantitative radar records made it possible to identify most of the radar targets beyond serious doubt.

Birds. The behavior and characteristics of the unidentified radar targets appeared to be consistent with the hypothesis that most of them were birds. Individual birds would produce signal strengths consistent with those observed. (The targets observed the night of the second visit to AFB A, according to calculations made by Dr. Lhermitte, yielded a radar cross section of approximately 10 $cm.^2$). The velocities and coherent tracks of the targets also suggested consistency with the bird hypothesis.

In view of the remarkable inversion conditions on the date of the original sighting, it is highly probable that *some* of the radar targets were effects of anomalous propagation (radar mirages). Temperature and moisture gradients were quite sufficient to produce echoes from atmospheric discontinuities.

At first, even the radar experts were puzzled by the radar data, because the remarkably strong echo signals returned by some of the moving targets suggested much larger objects than birds. Their confusion was resolved when it became apparent from comparisons of range data and concurrent signal strengths that the very strong signals were always associated with targets at close range. A radar echo declines in strength proportionally to the fourth power of the distance of the target from the antenna, so that even a small target at unusually short range can produce a very strong signal. Also, the pulse power of the tracking radars was much greater than that of the more familiar search radars, and they were normally used to track relatively distant rockets. Consequently, their use in the unaccustomed search mode drew attention to the deceptively strong signals from very near targets.

No attempt had been made during the sightings to associate ranges and signal strengths. Had someone asked, "When you get an 80-dB signal, what range do you read?" the evening probably would have ended differently. Future radar operating procedures might very well provide that, when unidentified targets are causing concern, ranges and signal strengths be correlated. Apparently no formal procedure existed at the time of the sightings for use in identifying unusual radar targets such as insects, sidelobe echoes, anomalous echoes from object on the ground, etc. In the absence of such a procedure, the operators involved in this case handled the situation reasonably.

Comments:

Some comments in a leter from Mr. Collis are particularly pertinent:

> I think that the . . . incident could be a landmark case in the whole area of UFO studies. It combines so many factors. Firstly, the incident involved a whole complex of associated events, which were reported by the most respectable observers. It combined multiple radar and multiple optical sightings. It occurred very recently and a substantial amount of recorded data is available—i.e., the TPQ 18 radar records and the meteorological data. At least in part, the radar echo phenomena were repeatable and were observed by design on subsequent occasions. It was sufficiently strange to cause interceptor aircraft to be sent off to investigate it in the heat of the moment, and also to cause the local and visiting experts considerable perplexity even in the cool light of day. We thus have a wonderful opportunity not only to study the physical nature of the incident but also to study the psychological implications of such incidents.
>
> It would seem that most of the inexplicability of the events in this case (and possibly in many others) arises not from the facts themselves, (i.e., the specific sightings, etc., at any given instant) but in the interpretation made and significance attached to them when they were considered in inappropriate juxtapositions. The way in which this was done at the time under operational pressures and even subsequently provided, in my opinion, a most important object lesson.

It does indeed! The lesson is that the "flap" could have been avoided if the radar operators had been acquainted with the kinds of targets they might pick up in search mode, especially during anomalous atmospheric conditions. It is unlikely that such a "flap" will occur again at AFB A in such circumstances; but it can happen elsewhere unless this experience is communicated through appropriate operating procedures or in some other manner, to other operators of powerful tracking radars.

Case 36

South Mountain
Fall 1967
Investigator: Wadsworth

Abstract:

Four independent witnesses saw a glowing, rapidly moving object that was evidently a "fireball" meteor.

Investigation:

A University Professor in the South Mountain area supplied statements from four apparently independent witnesses of an aerial event for possible interest.

1. About 9:05 a.m., a man on a golf course six miles east of the city saw a glowing yellow and blue-green cylindrical object cross the sky northward at high speed.

2. About 9:00 a.m., a commercial pilot flying about six miles southeast of the city saw a glowing yellow and blue-green cylindrical object travelling northward on a descending path at very high speed. It exploded or deteriorated in midair as it approached the White Mountain area. He judged it was a meteor.

3. About 9:00 a.m., a rancher and mine-mill worker, north of town, saw a very bright object travelling at high speed northward on a descending path. It exploded in the air.

4. About 10:00 a.m. a mining assayer driving west on the highway six miles east of town saw a cylindrical object glowing a metallic blue-green as it passed in front of him, travelling northward at high speed.

Sighting Features:

The four sightings are summarized in Table 5. The preponderance of similar features indicates a single event. Only in the fourth sighting is there some reason for doubt. The dis-

Sighting	Time, Location	Shape, Color Size	Speed, Path	Duration, Distance, Disappearance	Other
1	9:05 a.m. 6 mi. E of city	Cylinder Brilliant yellow body surrounded by blue-green welding color 200 ft. long 3 ft. diam.	Very fast Northward descending toward White Mt.	2-3 sec. 1 mi. Vanished on course toward base of mountains	Short tapered tail
2	9:00 a.m. 6 mi. SE of city	Cylinder Bright yellow core, blue-green shell ---	Very fast Northward descending 45° toward White Mt.	--- 1 mi. Exploded or deteriorated in air	Short tail Thought it was meteor
3	9:00 a.m. N of city	--- Glowing (no specific color) ---	Very fast Northward descending	--- Appeared quite far away (couldn't estimate)	---
4	10:00 a.m. 6 mi. E of city	Cylinder Metallic blue-green glowing 4 ft. long	Very fast Northward straight toward White Mt.	2-3 sec. 150 ft. ahead of car ---	May have had a tail or exhaust

Table 5

crepancies in distance and size are hardly significant because such estimates are characteristically inaccurate. Further, these are consistent in that the ratios of size to distance estimated by witnesses I and II are roughtly similar. These two witnesses were very near each other, and their accounts are similar except for the one hour discrepancy in time. However, witness I was prompted to report his experience by hearing a report of witness IV's experience on the radio, and so may have been influenced by it.

The time discrepancy of one hour has not been accounted for. The preponderance of evidence indicates an error in the time reported by witness IV, but is just as possible that two meteoric fragments came in on similar patterns an hour apart.

Reports of the first and fourth sightings were sent to Dr. Charles P. Olivier of the American Meteor Society, who stated that both accounts showed "every indication of being rather typical daylight fireball reports."

Comment:

It is concluded that probably a single event was witnessed by four observers, and that the object was a "fireball" meteor.

Case 37
South Eastern
Fall 1967
Investigators: Craig, Ahrens

Abstract:

Law enforcement officers in several communities reported seeing, chasing, and being chased by unidentified bright objects in the early morning hours on four successive days. One object was reportedly detected by a ground radar unit while the object was being pursued by two men in a small aircraft. Pictures had been taken. Lengthy interviews of observers, including participants in the airplane pursuit, established clearly that the pursued object was the planet Venus. Jupiter was also involved in some of the reports.

Background:

Initial reports of an UFO sighting suggested that it was an event with unsurpassed UFO information content: A large bright object was seen, that approached as close as 500 ft., and was pursued by reliable observers in different communities; it had been seen repeatedly on successive mornings, and might be expected therefore to reappear while an investigator was on the scene. The pilot of a light aircraft had reportedly seen the object rise from the river below while ground observers were watching it, and had pursued it in vain as it sped away from him; FAA traffic control radar had allegedly reported that returns from both the aircraft and the unidentified object had appeared on the radarscope during the chase. Photographs allegedly had been taken which showed both a bright object near the horizon during a pre-dawn chase and an apparently solid "sombrero"-shaped object photographed in a wooded section of the same general area by a 13-year-old boy in the afternoon.

The main observers of the pre-dawn phenomenon were law enforcement officers on duty in 11 communities in the central part of the state. Police officers, sheriff's officers, and highway patrolmen were involved, sometimes in radio communication with each other during a sighting and pursuit. The object fled from and then pursued police cars at speeds up to 70 mph, and came close enough to one police car to light up the interior of the car so brightly that wristwatches could be read. It also changed color and shape while under observation.

Investigation:

The most detailed reports, as well as the airplane chase and the photographs, centered around a town of 11,000 population, Town A. These reports were investigated by the project team. Reports from the other towns generally fit into the same pattern, and were assumed to arise from the same type of observation. Each aspect of the reports was investigated in turn.

Radar Confirmation:

Recorded conversation between the pilot and the Flight Control radar operator, indicated the pilot was chasing an UFO, which he said had risen from the river area below and was now moving away from him. The radar operator said he had a target on the scope, which he assumed to be the plane. He also said he had a second target, seen intermittently for a duration of about one minute. The pilot was heading at 110°, directly toward the object. This direction seemed to be consistent with the assumption that the second target was the chased UFO. The time was 5:30-5:58 a.m., EDT.

The pilot said the object was about 1,000 ft. above him, apparently over a small town, Town D. On first contact with the Flight Control, the Cessna was at an altitude of 2,500 ft. climbing as it chased the UFO. The pilot said the object was a very bright light, which he could not catch. He could not match its altitude or speed. He said the object moved toward the ground at times, but maintained an altitude above them at all times. It moved away when they chased it, and came back when they turned.

The radar operator said at the time that the target on his screen was heading at 110°, but he didn't know whether his target was the airplane or UFO. Later, thinking about his experience he left word at the radar tower that he wasn't at all sure he had seen a second target. Contacted later by phone, the operator stated that he never did identify the plane, much less a second object. He had one steady target, which he assumed to be the aircraft, since it disappeared when the pilot said he was at 2,500 ft. and returning to the airport. The intermittent target painted only on two sweeps in about a minute. This was on an ASR-5 radar (which would make 10 or 12 sweeps per minute). It was early in the morning, the operator was somewhat tired at the time, according to his own words. He was quick to point out that the "intermittent target" was not a "good paint," and could well have been a ghost return.

Ground Observation:

Of the numerous law enforcement officers associated with the reports, one of the police lieutenants, a veteran of 11 years on the force, was asked to describe the sightings. He had participated in all the sightings reported from his town. His account of the event follows:

(First Observation)

A. The object was the closest the first night we saw it. We first noticed it at 4:36 a.m., EDT Friday, October 20. At first, I thought it was a new street light we had never seen before, but as we got closer, it began moving away. We followed the object, which was then a bright red, football-shaped light, for about eight miles out into the country. It appeared to be as big as the moon in the sky. We lost sight of it, and headed back into town.

This object, whatever it was, caught up with us as we approached the city limits. The other officer started making a pretty scared sound and pointing out behind us. That is when I turned around and saw it.

It lit the police car enough inside to make the hands on your wristwatch visible. The whole surroundings were lit up. I radioed in that we were being followed by a flying object. I didn't know what it was, but it was following us. I could see the object in the rear-view mirror, but when we stopped the car and I got out, it veered away and disappeared behind the trees.

After we returned to town and got a third officer to come out with us, the object had started climbing and had gotten about twice the height of the tree line. We observed the object for about 20 minutes. It changed from bright red to orange, then to real white-looking. The object then appeared to change its shape from round to the shape of a giant four-leaf clover.

Our radio operator contacted the officers in Town C. In a few minutes they radioed back, and said they had the object in sight. It was to the east of us, apparently hovering over Town B. From Town C, it was to the west and appeared to be between Town A and Town B. We had it between the two of us.

I started back into town, and then is when it started moving south at a very high rate of speed.

(QUESTION: You said earlier that it crossed over the top of the police car. Did it get directly overhead?) No, sir, I didn't mean it came directly over the car. It came over the wooded area, over the top of the trees, and appeared right behind the car. I would say it was maybe 500 feet behind us and maybe 500 or 600 feet high, roughly guessing. When I did stop the car and jump out, I did see it when it went back.

(QUESTION: What direction were you travelling when the

object reappeared behind the car?) The car was headed in a westward direction.

(QUESTION: In what manner did the object finally disappear this first night that you saw it?) We watched it until it climbed and took a position in the sky. It climbed to such a height that it appeared to be a star, and that is where it was hanging when I got off duty at 7 o'clock and went home. It was still visible, and looking like a star at that time.

(Second Observation)

B. Although the object was reported from another town on the morning of [Day 2], it was not seen that morning in [Town A], but it was seen here [on days 1, 3, 4, and 5].

Sunday morning, [Day 3], I believe it was about ten minutes till two, or ten after two, when we got a phone call from a gentleman . . . who was on the outskirts of town. He said an object had followed him down the highway. We went out to look for it, and two objects were clearly visible. This was the first morning that two objects were spotted. You can't see the higher object until the other comes to view, then there appears this other object directly over it. It appears to be 5,000 to 6,000 feet above the lower object. The second object is as bright as the first, but higher and smaller.

(QUESTION: In what manner did these objects eventually disappear?) The sky was clear. When I left at 7 o'clock the two objects were still hanging in the sky—way up high.

(QUESTION: Were they staying about the same distance apart?) Yes. Maybe they had driften off some, but not too much. About 8:30 or a quarter to nine, after the sun had come up, these objects were still visible, and I showed them to my parents at that time. The objects were still there when I went to bed.

The lower object looked like a piece of floating tin foil, it looked flat, with a bent place in it. The higher object was round, and stationary in one place—it was not bobbing and floating like the other one.

(Third Observation)

C. Monday, Day 4. This is the morning the airplane went up.

Other people had already spotted it when we went out. The first object was in view. It was bright, star-like. While we watched it, the second object appeared through the trees—down and to the left of the first object. This was about a quarter to five.

The pilots scrambled to the airport, and went up after the object. We guided the pilots in to the object—they had gone past it when they were looking for the object, and, after they got back into range, we told him where to look. He said there were hundreds of objects up there—they were stars, I guess. I turned the police car lights on to show the direction of the object. When I turned him directly into it, he said he had it in sight—he saw it. I thought he didn't see it, because he flew under it.

The object bobbed and moved upward, but did not move to the side as it was pursued by the plane. I thought, if it tried to escape the plane, it would move to one side or the other, but it just moved upward.

(QUESTION: Did the object appear to get dimmer or smaller, as if it might be moving away from you and the airplane?) No, it didn't appear to get dimmer. I couldn't tell that it was moving away from the airplane.

(QUESTION: How did this object finally disappear?) Again, it was still hanging in the sky at 7:30, above the city hall.

The Airplane Chase of the UFO:

The pilot, who flies forest service patrol for the County Forestry Commission and had some 4,000 hrs. flying time, and a companion, formerly with the County Sheriff's Department, took off in a Cessna aircraft shortly after 5 a.m., in an effort to catch the object sighted from the ground. They were in radio contact with the [Town A] airport, and through the airport with the sheriff's officers and others on the ground with walkie-talkies, as well as with the radar operator at the Flight Control Center.

The pilot and his associate were interviewed by project investigators, who wanted particularly to know if they themselves had actually observed the object's rising from the river area below them, as the pilot stated it had in his recorded radio conversation, or if the statement was a mere repetition of the claim of ground observers.

The pilot said when they first started looking for the object, they were looking low, near the ground. One light they spotted proved to be a yard light. They couldn't find the object at first. Ground observers then got word to them that it was behind them—they had passed it. They turned back, still looking low, when the word came "It's above you." They had seen a light above before, but hadn't paid any attention to it, apparently assuming it was a star. Now they did see the object, and started chasing it. "When we flew directly toward it, it backed off, decreasing in size until it was only about the size of the head of a pencil. We went up to about 3,500 ft., but it kept moving higher and away from us."

The pilot was strongly impressed with the great decrease in the size of the object as it "receded" from the plane. When he first spotted the object, it appeared to him one-half to two-thirds the size of the moon. It decreased to a fraction of its original size. He said he was awakened about 5 a.m., and they landed the plane, after giving up the chase, about 6 a.m. He said the color of the object was a constant brilliant white. As they gave up the chase and returned to [Town A], the object moved back to about its original position, and was still there when he landed.

Reports from other towns:

1) Town E, sighting early Sunday, Day 3

As reported in local newspapers, a highway patrolman at a state patrol station near [Town E] spotted two UFOs—one ice blue and about a mile high and the other one a yellow rectangle-shaped object with a red side which was about 100 yd. above the trees.

Another [Town E] patrolman there said he chased a ball of light down a road just outside [Town E]. The object was traveling above tree-top level. According to the patrolman's report,

"It was a good distance in front of us, pulling away, so we turned around to come back to town. The object turned on us and followed. It gained on us and was going about 75 mph. After the object caught up with us, it pulled into the sky, emitting a beam of bluish light that illuminated the roadway."

Newspaper accounts stated also that a [Town E] police officer said a dark blue ball chased him and then hovered over [Town E] until daybreak. (The implication is that this experience involved a different officer than the one just mentioned; however, this might be another reference to the same experience.)

2) *Additional Reports*

A patrolman of [Town F] police department summarized reports of sightings on [Day 1] as follows. This summary is included as an example of the extent of the UFO activity [in this area]. All objects described were noiseless.

UFO Report 0505 hours, Day 1

Lt. A, [Town A] Police Department, reported that Patrolman B and Patrolman C, [also of Town A] Police Department, reported sighting a sphere-shaped object approximately 25 ft. in diameter, red, white flashing red, green and white lights, traveling south from [Town L].

[Town D] Police Department reported an object as above traveling south from [Town D]. Patrolmen D and E, [Town G] Police Department, reported sighting four objects described as above traveling northeast. Patrolmen F and G of [Town G] Police Department reported an object described as above traveling east from [Town G]. Patrolman G from [Town G] Police Department followed the object east . . .

The County Sheriff's Office reported sighting an object described as above traveling east.

[Town H] Police Department reported an object described as above traveling west.

[Town J] Police Department . . . reported an object described as above traveling east from [Town J].

[Town K] Police Department reported an object traveling west.

[Town L] Police Department reported two objects—one traveling south and one traveling east.

Relevant Information

During the period [days 1-5] Venus had a magnitude of −4.2; Jupiter's magnitude was −1.5. Venus rose about 2:50 a.m. local standard time. Jupiter rose about 40 min. earlier, the time difference varying a few minutes each day. The tremendous brightness of Venus made its appearance spectacular, and it had been the cause of numerous UFO reports across the country for weeks prior to these dates.

The moon which was full 15 days later, was shining in the western sky during the early morning hours. The bright star Capella also could be seen to the west (northwest) during the early morning hours.

Analysis of the UFO Observations

The fact that the UFO's reappeared *each day* during early morning hours suggested immediately that the sightings might be related to the earth's rotation. Timing with the appearance of Jupiter and Venus to the east, and the fact that most reports showed the UFO or UFOs to be to the east, made the investigators suspect immediately that the appearance of Venus, plus suggestion and unfettered imagination, might account for most, perhaps all, of the UFO reports in this series. Sleepiness and fatigue also could have been significant factors, since some police officers involved had been working double shift.

Initial checks showed the radar confirmation of the presence of the UFO to be so tenuous as to be essentially non-existent.

The airplane pilot revealed that he had not actually observed the UFOs "rising from the river area," but had merely repeated the claims of ground observers that it had done so. His description of the chase fits nicely with the hypothesis that he was chasing a planet. The apparent recession of the object, with apparent diminishing size, could be accounted for by his rising above a haze layer which, by dispersion of light, caused a magnified appearance of the planet when he was at a lower altitude (See Section VI, Chapter 2). All reports indicated a heavy mist or haze did exist over the river area each morning when the UFOs were observed.

When the investigators suggested to the pilot that he might have been chasing the planet Venus, and explained the reasons for its unusual appearance, the pilot felt that this might possibly have been the case.

As for ground observations, besides daily reappearance, the fact that the object or objects each day eventually took a position in the sky and looked like stars was taken as confirmation that the UFOs indeed were planets. The positions they eventually "took in the sky" were the positions known to be occupied at the time by Venus and Jupiter. The police observers were shown the planet Venus during late morning hours. (Venus was quite visible during the day during this period, but was noticed only if one knew precisely where to look.) They all agreed that the appearance was the same as their UFO after it "took its position" after sun-up.

Conclusion:

The conclusion that the reported UFOs were misinterpretations of sightings of planets, particularly of Venus, seems not only tenable but imperative.

Photographs:

The series of photographs taken during a pre-dawn chase showed a light near the eastern horizon, and was not of special interest. The other pair of photographs, showing an apparently solid object, shaped much like the outline of a sombrero, suspended over a clearing in the woods, was taken by a lone 13-year-old boy who had taken his Polaroid camera into the woods to hunt UFOs. His hunt had been successful, and he got two pictures of the object before it flew away. His pictures apparently were taken with the sun shining directly on the camera lens, diffusing light onto the film and causing the UFO image to appear in very poor contrast with the background.

The photographs were examined by Dr. W. K. Hartmann who commented that while the lack of contact made the appearance consistent with the claim that the object was at a considerable distance, the poor quality of the photographs prohibited significant quantitative tests. The photographs themselves were thus not of high enough quality to allow determination of the size or distance of the object photographed. It is believed that the object photographed had no relation to the object pursued in the pre-dawn activity.

Conclusions:

It seems quite clear that the UFO excitement was caused primarily by the planet Venus.

The case serves to illustrate the extreme elaboration which can develop from misinterpretation of a natural and ordinary phenomenon. Suggestion, coupled with common visual effects which are not familiar to or understood by the observer (see Section VI, Chapters 1 & 2), frees the imagination, to produce the kinds of observations described in this case.

The case also illustrates the *appearance* of motion of a stationary distant object, particularly that caused by the motion of the observer; the magnifying effects of haze scattering and near-horizon observation; and scintillation of a light near the earth's horizon.

The rapid attrition of supporting information which the initial UFO sighting reports included also is demonstrated impressively in this investigation. The case illuminates the inadequacy of current education regarding fundamental astronomy and atmospheric physics.

Case 38
North Eastern
Fall 1967
Investigators: Ahrens, Craig

Abstract:

Over 800 sightings of UFOs were claimed in the North East region. The sightings, most of which could be attributed to aircraft lights and stars, were largely stimulated by individuals engaged in UFO "research." No evidence was offered to support claims of close sighting of manned saucers, footprints, and saucer "nests."

Background:

Sightings of UFOs were reported almost every night at a small town, location B, seven miles SW of location A. The sightings were purportedly made by dozens of persons, some of whom allegedly had seen 50 or more UFOs, many of them in a single night. A total of over 800 sightings, was claimed in the vicinity by Mr. A, local resident and observer, and Mr. B, who claimed to be investigating on behalf of a civilian UFO research organization. Besides getting radio and newspaper publicity for the events, these individuals had arranged public meetings to discuss UFOs. At one such meeting, Dr. J. Allen Hynek, two Air Force representatives from a nearby airfield, and four news representatives were present, along with several dozen interested local people.

Most sightings were of the moving-light-in-the-sky type. A notable exception was the report by two boys, aged 10 and 12, that they observed at close range a "flying saucer" in which they saw two occupants. Another exception involved a report by a 55-year-old woman residing a few miles from location B. She stated that she had observed a large glowing light behind her house. The next morning, she found a "saucer nest" in the cattails where she had seen the light, according to her account. In another locality, Mr. A claimed to have taken a photograph of a strange footprint, as yet undeveloped.

Investigation:

Project investigators interviewed 12 witnesses, and spent a part of each of three nights on a hill on the outskirts of location B, the locale of most of the reported sightings. Discussions with persons familiar with the situation brought out the following facts:

1. The region has a high density of commercial airplane flights, at both high and low altitude.
2. A charter air service operating out of the airport at location A has four planes equipped with the relatively new stroboscopic anti-collision light. On these planes, this light is mounted on top of the tail fin and can be seen in all directions other than directly below. The light emits 50-60 seven-second flashes/min. at an intensity of 2×10^6 candlepower. Its use is under the control of the pilot. Mr. Allen Hayes, operator of the charter service said that his planes frequently fly around the area at night. Many private planes land at location A; a route of several commercial lines pass over this area also. Mr. Hayes felt certain that anti-collision lights on his and other planes were responsible for many of the local UFO reports.
3. The sheriff's office advised that the Asplundh Tree Expert Company had perhaps been flying helicopters at night along the power lines for an electric and gas corporation checking for corona discharge along the lines and sparking from lines to vegetation. Since aerial observation of such an operation could conceivably result in UFO reports, the information was checked. It was found that although this company uses helicopters to spray defoliants along the power lines, the work is done during daylight hours, and had not been conducted within the past two months.
4. Local state police were interested in the UFO reports. State Trooper Eisenberg had responded to a call from Mr. A, had found him and several youngsters with blankets over their heads, peering from under the blankets to look for UFOs. The trooper observed with them for a time, watched their excitement as they saw "another one," which he also observed. Trooper Eisen-

berg was certain he and the others were looking at an airplane.

5. Mr. John Levy, Assistant Manager of location A's Chamber of Commerce and occasional reporter for a newspaper in a nearby city, said he went out one evening to observe the UFOs with Mr. A, Mr. B, and the interested local youngsters. While he was there, the others saw three "UFOs," two of which he could identify as airplanes by the sound of their motors. Mr. A has insisted that they were noiseless and therefore not airplanes. (No noise was heard when the plane lights were first sighted). The third "UFO" was silent, and looked to Mr. Levy like a satellite.

During the investigators' observations, only airplanes and stars were seen. The first two nights were overcast with intermittent snow flurries. On the third night the sky was clear. A project investigator accompanied Mr. A, Mr. B, and one of their friends to the hill outside of location B for observation, while the other investigator remained at the hotel to receive incoming telephone calls.

During the early evening, two calls were received which reported that an UFO was being observed at the time, still hanging in the sky. The UFO he now described was the bright star Sirius. After the suggestion that this might be the case, he phoned back to agree that he had been looking at Sirius. One caller was a high school teacher who had reported earlier a light-in-the-sky sighting that might have been an airplane.

The sky observation party returned to location A later in the evening. The project investigator reported that when Sirius rose over the distant trees as he and the others were watching on the hill, his companions also immediately called Sirius one of the UFOs. They watched it change color, particularly when it was low in the sky. Only after some time did they agree that this "UFO" was a star.

A few minutes later, a phone call reported another sighting. Mr. B spoke to the woman, and, after short conversation, excitedly handed the phone to a project investigator, declaring: "The woman is seeing an object which is spewing out green, white, and red beams . . ." Additional comment indicated the object had emitted glowing red globs and was now hovering near the woman's home. The location described again was that of Sirius. The woman was told there that the star should appear relative to the constellation Orion, and was asked if it possibly could be this bright star she was observing. She did not accept this as a possibility, and relayed information to her daughter for checking, before going into a discussion of other UFO activity in the area. After this review, she was again asked about the hovering object she had originally reported. Her response was, "Yes, I guess we've been bamboozled again. I guess that it is just the star."

Investigation of UFO reports that involved other than lights in the sky revealed the following:

1. The "strange foot print" which reportedly was photographed by Mr. A (photo still in camera) was described and sketched by him. The sketch was the size and shape of a bear track.
2. A daylight search of the small swamp where the "saucer nest" in the form of a 30-ft. diameter area where "cattails had been squashed down and found to lie in a clock-wise spiral pattern" revealed no evidence of existence of such a "nest." This search took place several weeks after the event, and it could be argued that the "nest" had been disturbed in various ways to make it no longer obvious.

The woman who made this report is employed in local government service, and impressed interviewers as sincere and intelligent. According to her testimony, she told her sons (aged 16 and 22) the night of the observation, about seeing the glowing object behind the house during their absence. They were incredulous and she did not tell anyone about finding the "saucer nest" the next morning until some three weeks later, after the report was circulated that the boys had seen a saucer with occupants. The 16-year-old son of this woman said he had never gone out to look at the saucer nest, even after his mother reported its existence.

With frequent prompting from Mr. B, the 10 and 12-year-old boys in location B told project investigators the story of their sighting. A tape recording of an earlier account by the boys was not entirely consistent with the new account and the taped accounts suggested that the mode of questioning itself was developing the story.

According to the boys, they saw a large saucer-like object which hovered between a tavern-restaurant and an adjacent house across the street from the younger boy's home. The object tilted up, and they saw two occupants by a window on its near side. Instrument control panels with red and white lights were visible through the window. The object disappeared after about two minutes, moving upward before vanishing suddenly.

There were no other observers. The reported event happened on the main street of this small town (location B) at about 9:30 p.m. Three dogs were said to have been howling strangely because of the object's presence. The 12-year-old looked at his watch during this sighting to see what time it happened, according to his account. Discrepancies in the report, resemblance of the reported object and occupants with those pictured in a TV serial, and the prior association of the boys with Mr. A and the group of youngsters he influenced created serious doubts that the described event was real.

After the visit of the project team, a reported discovery of four mysterious clearings on a densely wooded hillside near location A was presented in the magazine section of the local newspaper as tangible evidence that "saucers" had landed or hovered there. In circular or elliptical areas, from 100-150 ft. in diameter, the trees had all fallen. Some were uprooted, others broken off near ground level. Strange lights were reported to have been seen over the wooded area several months earlier.

A copy of the magazine, showing photographs of the areas of forest damage, was sent for comment to Mr. C. A. Shields, Director, Division of Administrative Management, United States Forest Service. He sent our request to Dr. Carl E. Ostrom, Director, Timber Administrative Management Division, who offered several possible explanations as accounting for the circular patches of damage: 1) A tornado touching down briefly at several places in the forest; 2) Islands of damage caused by heavy ice or snow. This kind of damage occurs to red and jack pine in the Northern Lake States; 3) Patch-like infestations of *Fomes annosus,* a root rotting organism that destroys supporting roots even though the trees remain green; and 4) Pine root-collar weevil, an insect that partially girdles the stem just below the ground line, giving rise to patches of timber collapse.

Dr. Ostrom considered the most likely explanation to be 2) above, perhaps superimposed on stands already weakened by 3) or 4). This area occasionally receives heavy ice and snow storms.

The claimed connection between the areas of forest damage and UFO sightings was extremely nebulous. Since there are natural, ordinary explanations for such patches of damage, it seems most logical to attribute the damage to them.

Conclusion:

The lights-in-the-sky UFO reports apparently were caused by the suggestion and influence primarily of two individuals. Most, if not all, of these reports can be attributed to airplanes and stars.

One housewife testified that she and her husband saw what appeared to be airplanes, except that they were soundless. Yet, she could not believe there could be that many airplanes in the sky around location B on a given evening. On the other hand, she was quite willing to believe there could be that many flying saucers from outer space around her city.

This case stands out as an extreme example of the extent to which UFO excitement can be generated by one or more individuals in an ordinary community, where ordinary events are occurring.

Those reported sightings involving more than lights-in-the-sky were made by people who also were members of or close to the group activity stimulated by Messrs. A and B. There appeared to be little convincing evidence that these sightings involved objects that were physically real.

Case 39
South Pacific
Fall 1967
Investigator: Craig

Abstract:

A businessman reported that his automobile had been stopped by an UFO he observed while driving alone in a rural area. The case was checked as a possible source of information regarding electromagnetic effects of UFOs. Comparison of the magnetic pattern of the automobile body with that of another car of similar make and model showed the businessman's car had not been exposed to a strong magnetic field. The case, therefore, apparently did not offer probative information regarding UFOs.

Background (as received from members of a NICAP affiliate):

In Fall of 1967, a business executive was driving alone in a 1964 Chrysler convertible in a remote region of the South Pacific area, when at 3:30 or 4:00 a.m. his car stopped, the lights went out, and the radio went dead. He reported feeling strong pressure exerted from above, pressing down on his head and shoulders. He then saw, through a break in the fog in which he had been driving, an unidentified object that moved over his car and hovered over the highway ahead. It now lit up the roadway and area about him. The object was about 30 ft. in diameter, saucer-shaped, red-orange in color, and hazy in outline. Its altitude was estimated at 160 ft. The object had rotating lights, and wobbled as it moved and hovered. The witness viewed the object for about 90 sec. before it took off into the fog ahead. His headlights and radio then came back on, and he was able to re-start the car. It ran unevenly for a few seconds, sounding as if one or two cylinders were not firing. It then operated normally.

The witness was extremely frightened by the experience. He drove immediately to the nearest town, even though it was a short distance off his route home. He said he had an urgent desire to be where there were other people. He met a milkman, and told him of the experience. No cafe was open, and the milkman directed him to another town, on the witness' original route, where he could get a cup of coffee. He stopped at the cafe and related his experience to a waitress there, who knew him.

He afterward decided, for business reasons, it should not become known that he had reported seeing an UFO, and he told his story to NICAP and project investigators only after firm assurances that he would not be identified.

Investigation by NICAP:

NICAP investigators checked the witness' car for evidence of unusual residual effects. They found the clock had stopped at 3:46 a.m., and was still stopped (the witness said the clock had been running O.K.). They found the paint loose and easy to rub off a spot on the hood, and a strange pitting in both paint and glass. A radiation check on the car showed beta-gamma readings of .01 to .02 mr/hr, which seemed slightly higher to them than readings similarly taken on another car owned by the witness. They felt also that stereotapes which were in the witness' car at the time of stoppage by the UFO had lost fidelity, particularly in the low notes. They also noted areas of unusual optical distortion in the back window as if it had been damaged by its exposure to UFO effects.

Investigation by Colorado Project:

The witness' description of his UFO experience was tape-recorded, and his car examined. The witness then drove the project investigator to the UFO site in the Chrysler and he re-enacted his experience of five days earlier.

The witness was an apparently successful businessman in his forties, seemingly proud of his achievements and particularly proud of his family. His story was basically as told earlier, except for distance to the object and estimated size of the object. He now estimated the object as probably 55 ft. in diameter, and passing 50 or 75 ft. over his automobile. He still described it as a flowing orange-red object, with noticeable fluttering and rotation.

The automobile was a metallic-silver 1964 Chrysler convertible. The witness bought it as a used car in 1965.

Several areas were noted where the paint was extremely thin, particularly along body ridges and on an area about six by 12 in. on the left side of the hood. Pitting of the paint was evident in this and other areas of the hood. The pitting of the paint was fairly extensive; it appeared to the investigator to be the result of long-term corrosion. On the whole, the paint condition was not unusual for a four-year-old car. As for the thinness of paint, an automobile dealer has pointed out that it is not unusual to receive a car from the factory with a spot almost entirely missed in the painting operation.

The back window, which was said to have been only three months old, did exhibit areas of sharp distortion. Its appearance was almost identical with that of the back window in another 1964 Chrysler convertible that was examined later on a used car lot. Perhaps the witness' window was newer than the one with which it was compared; but it had been subjected to summer use in an area where temperatures of 120° or more are common.

No radioactivity above normal background was found on or in the car.

The clock was stopped at 3:46. The witness had not noticed the stopped clock until the NICAP representatives mentioned the significant agreement with the time of his UFO sighting. He was not certain the clock had been running the day before the UFO experience, but though it probably was. He was sure it "used to run." Since the automobile clock is spring driven, and only wound by electric current (it continues to run if the line to the battery is disconnected), electromagnetic effects which might conceivably stop cars and car radios would perhaps not be expected to stop such a clock.

The AM radio operated normally. The FM was not operative five days later, but hummed loudly across the entire tuning range. The witness said he normally had good reception from several FM stations in this area. According to his story, he had tired of listening to recorded tapes and had switched on his radio (probably FM) shortly before the UFO sighting.

The project investigator was particularly concerned to determine whether the magnetic signature (characteristic magnetic pattern) of the Chrysler body had been altered as by subjection to a strong magnetic field. A Brunton pocket transit was used for a crude test for magnetic signature change. Readings were recorded for selected spot samplings of points on the hood, left fender, and trunk deck. These readings later were compared with readings at corresponding points on a 1964 Chrysler convertible in Boulder, Colo. The readings were as follows, for points indicated on the sketch (top views shown):

front

A H P Q R S T U V WX Y Z AA

B I

C J

D K

E L hood and left fender

F M

N

G O ←chrome strips, separating hood from fender---------------→

↓ ↓

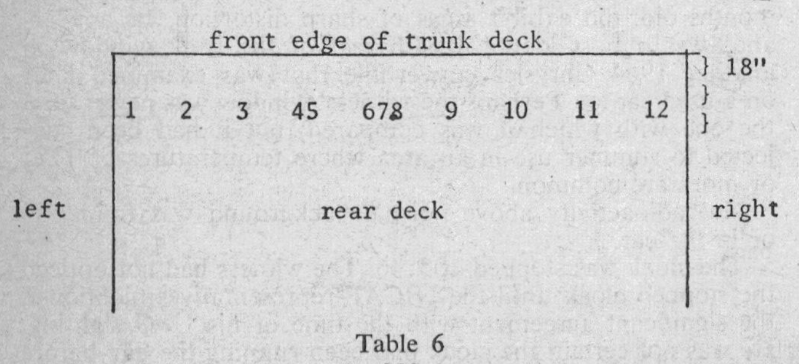

Table 6

Table 7

Comparative Magnetic Signature Readings for Two 1964 Chrysler Convertibles

Position	*Car X*	*Car B*	*Position*	*Car X*	*Car B*
A	0	20	U	320	320
B	60	60	V	300	310
C	110	90	W	330	280
D	70	100	X	40	40/80*
E	95	80	Y	30	10
F	70	70	→		
G	40	80	Z	345	340
H	330	330	AA	340	340
I	300	300	1	0	300
J	290	—	2	60	110/0*
K	285	285	3	110	**
L	290	290	4	80/20*	**
M	300	300	5	0	0/180*
N	340	—	6	355	290
O	355	350	7	15	240/310*
P	345	310	8	0	0
Q	20	0	9	270	270
→			10	293	260
R	345	340	→		
S	340	335	11	0	0
T	320	320	12	100	100

Note: The numbers given are raw transit readings taken with the car, in each case, headed at a magnetic bearing of 160°. The readings were taken by pointing the main transit sight to magnetic north, and reading the compass while holding it next to the car body at the designated point. Since the transit is designed to read the bearing of a sighted object, and the sight is aimed north in these measurements, the readings shown are the 360° complements of compass-needle bearings. Because comparative readings for two cars made the same year at the same factory were all that were of interest, the data were compared without correction.

Some points of sharp change in magnetic orientation may have displayed that change because of structure beneath the hood. However, the comparison car did show readings very similar to those of the witness' car throughout, including corresponding points of sharp change. Even with this crude check, it appears reasonably certain that his Chrysler had experienced no reorientation of its magnetic signature, as one might expect if the car had been subjected to a strong magnetic field.

* When two numbers are shown, a very small variation in front-to-back distance gives markedly different compass readings.

** A visible dent was present in this area on car B. Magnet readings were sporadic around the dented area.

Miscellaneous Comments:

The milkman told the NICAP people that the witness had told him about the UFO about 3:30 or 3:45 a.m., on the date of the reported sighting. Both he and the cafe waitress said the witness was scared, but not intoxicated when they talked with him.

The witness claimed that his experience had made him both religious and a UFO believer. He was afraid to return to the site of his experience, and said he would avoid this area in the future. In attempting to re-enact his experience at the site, he experienced moments of apparent illness or dizziness, for which he apologized, and waited briefly to regain his composure. Three NICAP people and the Colorado investigator were with him when he returned to the site. When they suggested that they leave in the opposite direction for their return to the city, while he would return in his Chrysler to his home, he asked them to accompany him to the highway intersection 2.6 mi. away, as he did not want to be in the area alone.

There are serious discrepancies in the witness' story. The most serious involves the distance and location of the object. NICAP people previously had asked him to show how big the object appeared by indicating how much of a ruler held 24 in. away would have matched the diameter of the object. His response was 9.5 to 10 in. When describing the event to the CU investigator in his house, the witness said the object filled his whole windshield, and was 50 or 75 ft. away. During the reenactment at the site, he decided the object had not come directly overhead, but had come in from the right side, hovering over the road at a point he indicated by the positions of approaching cars and trucks. This point was measured to be 0.2 mi. away. He said the object was as wide as the road (33 ft.). At the indicated distance, such an object would subtend less than an inch on the ruler held 24 in. away. He was then asked to sketch on his windshield with a wax pencil the outline of the object as he had seen it. (His car was parked where he said it had been stopped.) He sketched a football shape four inches long. His eyes were 18 to 20 in. from the windshield while he sketched.

His description of the object was extremely vague.

The highway ahead at the point of reenactment was bearing about 110°. When he arrived with the investigators at the site, however, he was not sure which straight section of highway he had been on when he saw the UFO. He decided the 110° section must be it. Had he chosen the section on the other side of a curve just passed, the highway bearing would have been almost directly east.

Conclusion

Because of the vagueness of the witness' description of the "object," the wide inconsistencies in his estimates of its size and distance, the fact that no one else observed the alleged event, and the fact that the car body did not show evidence of exposure to strong magnetic fields, more detailed investigation of this event as a source of evidence related to the electromagnetic effect on automobiles did not seem warranted.

Case 40
South Mountain
Fall 1967
Investigator: Ayer

Abstract:

A light witnessed and photographed from a mountain slope was analyzed by rough photometry and reference to a map of the area. It was attributed almost certainly to headlights of a surface vehicle in the valley.

Background:

Two young college men decided to watch for UFOs over a valley from the flank of a mountain peak. In the evening, they drove off a highway east of city A, north on a road about 0.75 mi. past a ranch access road, then turned east on a dirt road about 0.5 mi. up the slope of a mountain. There they set up their camera on a tripod. It was a Yashica-D with 80-mm lens, 2.25 by 2.25-in. frame, loaded with Eastman Tri-X film. The moon was high and the sky clear.

About 1:20 a.m., a white light appeared in the valley to the west, apparently above the valley floor but below the line of lights that marked a well travelled highway on the valley floor. About 1:30 a.m., while the light was still stationary, two photographs were taken with exposures of 40 and 80 sec. Later the light moved northward at both low and high speeds, then returned to its starting point. Its apparent path is shown in Fig. 8.

Investigation:

The latest, unpublished Geological Survey map indicates that the altitude of the camera site was about 7,800 ft. From this and other known altitudes, it was deduced that the line of sight to the UFO intersected the valley floor about seven miles from the camera. The camera position was almost due east of city B, which lies in a valley between a mountain to the south and other mountains to the north. These features can be approximately identified on the photographs. They indicate that the bearing of the UFO from the camera was 290°.

The positions and lengths of the star tracks, corrected for the camera motion apparent on the longest exposure, indicate that the first exposure was roughly three times as long as the second, and that the reported exposure times were approximately correct. A vertical microdensitometer tracing of the region to the right of the edge of the disc of the UFO spot on the 80 sec. exposure indicated substantial illumination of the valley floor, suggesting that the light was on a vehicle on the ground.

The eye usually can distinguish two objects having an angular separation less than one minute of arc, or about ten feet at seven miles. This limitation would explain why the boys saw only one light, even though the source may have been a pair of headlights. Application of Rayleigh's criterion for resolving power to the camera lens indicates that if of excellent quality it could have resolved headlights at any stop opening greater than f/12; presumably it was used wide open.

However, the two headlight images would have been only 8.6 μ apart on the camera film. Tri-X film is rather coarse-grained; the manufacturer's specifications indicate that it cannot register separate image details, even with poor efficiency, unless they are at least 15 μ apart. Contrast effects between bright headlights and the dark background would further reduce the resolution on the film. It seems clear that a pair of headlights could not have been distinguished from a single light in the photographs. A horizontal densitometer trace showed three shallow peaks of unequal height, but the separation of the two greater ones was roughly ten times the expected value for headlights. The shallowness of the peaks suggested they might be artifacts.

The intensity of the unknown source was determined approximately from the geometry of the situation and the density of the image of the source on the film. If we call the intensity of the source I, the light flux from the source into the camera lens F, the area of the lens opening A, and its distance from the source R, then $F = IA/R^2$. Absorption and other losses in the lens reduce this flux by a factor T, estimated as 0.8. The remaining light flux falls on an image spot of area at the film. Therefore, if J is the illumination at the image, $Ja = TIA/R^2$.

The lens opening is assumed to have been f/3.5, or 2.28 cm. diameter. The diameter of the image spot on the 40-sec. negative was determined from a densitometer trace as 0.4 mm. The density of the image spot, corrected for background, was 3.2. The H-D curve published by Eastman for Tri-X film with antihalation base, developed seven minutes in D-76 at 86 F., shows only the toe and straight section. If the exposure is determined by a linear extrapolation of the straight section, a minimum value of the illumination results, namely 4.0 meter-candles.

If the preceding equation for the intensity I of the unknown source is solved with these data, $I = JaR^2/TA = 197{,}000$ candlepower. However, this equation has assumed implicitly that the unknown source was radiating uniformly in all directions. Since headlight beams are concentrated in the forward direction, the result above must be reduced by the ratio of the solid angle effectively filled by the headlight beam to that of the full sphere. Since the distribution of light in the beam is not uniform and depends on the individual headlight design and condition, no accurate correction of this result is possible. It can only be noted that the solid angle effectively filled by a headlight is roughly .05 to 0.1 of the full sphere, reducing the computed source intensity to an estimated 10,000 to 20,000 candlepower. Further uncertainties occur as to whether the assumed headlights were pointing directly toward the camera, and in estimating the source distance, lens stop used, and illumination of the film.

Maximum intensities of the high beams of automobile headlights lie in the range 15,000 to 50,000 candlepower. The re-

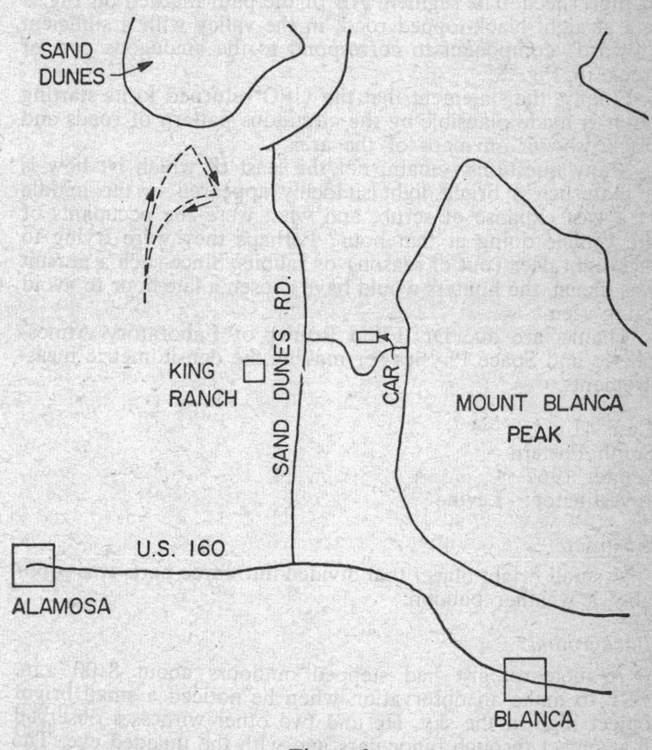

Figure 8

sults of the photometric computation of the source intensity therefore are compatible with automobile headlights, though subject to broad uncertainties.

The following hypothesis can now be advanced: a vehicle, probably 4-wheel driven, moved in the valley along a path similar to that shown in Fig. 8. No wheeled vehicle can move cross-country in the valley because of the ubiquitous stiff vegetation: but a map of the area shows crude roads or sand tracks that approximate the path described by the boys. These roads are blocked by barbed-wire fences along the section lines. Stopping to open take-down gates in these fences accounts for the interrupted progress of the UFO. The fading of the original light is explained by the change in direction of the vehicle, and the appearance of a red color by the coming in view of a tail-light.

The UFO was reported to have moved toward the boys at high speed. The segment AB of the path marked on Fig. 8 is a straight black-topped road, in the valley with a sufficient "toward" component to correspond to the analogous part of track in Fig. 8.

Finally, the statement that the UFO returned to its starting point is made plausible by the circuitous pattern of roads and tracks shown on maps of the area.

Many questions remain, not the least of which is: how is it that such a bright light suddenly appeared in the middle of a vast expanse of scrub, and what were the occupants of the vehicle doing at that hour? Perhaps they were trying to jack-light deer (out of season) or rabbits. Since such a pursuit was illegal, the hunters would have chosen a late hour to avoid being seen.

Thanks are due Dr. Elmo Bruner of Laboratory Atmospheric and Space Physics for making the densitometric measurements.

Case 41
South Eastern
Winter 1967
Investigator: Levine

Abstract:

A small bright object that divided into three parts was probably a weather balloon.

Background:

A meteorologist had stepped outdoors about 8:00 a.m. EST to make an observation when he noticed a small bright object high in the sky. He and two other witnesses observed that object through binoculars and with the unaided eye. The object was observed five minutes against clear sky, and then approximately seven minutes through thin cirrus clouds.

The object split into apparently three pieces when it was directly overhead. These three objects were observed for a short period; then two of them disappeared. The object had moved through an arc of 30° in about 12 min.

During the sighting, the High Altitude Control at an ARTC center indicated that they could not detect the UFO on radar.

A radiosonde balloon had been launched by the U.S. Weather Bureau 45 mi. west of the sighting at 6:25 a.m. EST. The balloon persisted until 7:59, when it was at an altitude of 30,600 m. and a slant range of 85,100 m. east. The horizontal range of the balloon was about 45 mi. The winds aloft at 80,000 and 90,000 ft. were from the east and inconsistent with the reported direction of motion. The winds at lower altitude were generally from the west, and therefore consistent with the eastward drift of the balloon.

If the observed object was at an altitude of 100,000 ft. the observed angular displacement of 30° in 12 min. implies a speed of about 20 mph. This is comparable with the reported wind speeds at similar altitudes: 80,000 ft., 20 knots; 90,000 ft., 8 knots; 100,000 ft., 6 knots.

Conclusion:

The Weather Bureau stated that when such a balloon bursts, it splits into several parts which quickly disappear; then a parac is deployed. This action fits the appearance of the UFO. The coincidence in time and location suggests that the witness had observed the balloon.

Case 42
North Central
Fall 1967
Investigators: Craig, Ahrens, staff

Abstract:

A state trooper, on duty since 5 p.m., was cruising the outskirts of his small midwestern town alone at 2:30 a.m. He reported a saucer-like object landed on or hovered over, the highway 40 ft. in front of him. The object departed straight upward at high speed. The trooper could not account for a 20-min. period during which he assumed he must have been near the UFO. No evidence was found that a physical object had been present as claimed. Psychological assessment of the trooper, carried out with his approval and cooperation, also failed to provide evidence that the reported object was physically real.

Background:

A state trooper, cruising alone about 2:30 a.m. in his squad car, had a feeling of uneasiness that something unusual was nearby. At 1:00 a.m. and at about 1:35 a.m. he had checked the cattle at the local sale barn, and found them behaving strangely — bawling and kicking the chutes. After

2:00 a.m. he was checking various facilities along Highway A, and near its intersection with Highway B noticed red lights to his right, which he thought were perhaps on a truck stopped on Highway B. He passed the intersection, then turned around and returned to B, to check the presumed truck. The patrolman switched his headlights to bright and stopped the police car as his headlights struck the source of red light, that he thought was some 40 ft. ahead (later measured to be 150 ft.). The red lights were blinking. They appeared now to be shining from windows of a saucer-shaped object, hovering 6-8 ft. above the highway, tilted at an angle of about 15° from the horizontal. The object glowed brilliantly, and started rising, emitting a siren-like sound, the trooper reported. It rose gradually, with some side-wise fluttering, and emitted a flame-colored material from its under side. With his head out the open car door, the trooper said he watched the object move nearly overhead, then move upward rapidly, shooting out of sight. After a quick check of the site by flashlight, he returned directly to the troop barracks, where he was surprised to find the time to be 3:00 a.m. As he turned his car around on Highway A, he had noticed that the time was 2:30 a.m. and it seemed to him that no more than ten minutes could have elapsed before he reached the troop barracks. He felt that perhaps he had not been conscious during a period of approximately 20 min. while he was observing the UFO. He had a feeling of paralysis at the time, and felt strange, weak, sick, and nervous when he returned to the troop barracks, according to his report.

In describing the object later, the trooper said it had a row of oval portholes around its periphery, each port about two feet across. The light was glowing from inside the object. He could see nothing through the red-lighted ports as the lights blinked off except a black line moving up and down. Below the portholes, he described a cat-walk around the object. The surface of the object appeared to him like polished aluminum, and was quite bright in reflected light. The night was reported to be clear, calm, and moonless.

Investigation:

His superior officer declared that the trooper was dependable and truthful. His chief was convinced that this report of an UFO sighting was not the result of hallucination or dishonesty. He had checked the area the next morning. Among ordinary litter beside the road, beneath the point that the trooper said the object hovered he found a small piece of metallic-appearing material which he did not recognize. This material, less than one centimeter long and paper thin, was offered as possible residue left by the UFO. The chip of material was black on one side, while the other surface had the bright appearance of aluminum paint. A portion of this material was analyzed semiquantitatively. Its major constituents were iron and silicon. Since the relation of the material to the reported UFO was so tenuous, no further effort was made to determine its specific origin, for it could plausibly be accounted for in terms of ordinary corroded earthly waste.

The site area was checked for radioactivity, no evidence of which was found. No other evidence that an unusual object had landed on or hovered over the site was found.

His superior officer said the trooper had been given a polygraph examination at the trooper's request by an experienced operator at an official agency. The polygraph reportedly showed no indications that the UFO report was other than truthful.

The trooper said he had served with the U.S. Marines. With his approval, a series of psychological assessment tests were administered by project personnel and psychologists at the University of Colorado Center for Student Life Programs. In addition, a test utilizing partial hypnotic techniques was conducted by Dr. R. Leo Sprinkle, Professor of Psychology, the University of Wyoming. The latter test was conducted in an effort to determine whether or not hypnotic techniques might have value in developing otherwise inaccessible information about UFOs. During this session, new information was added to the trooper's account of his UFO experience; however, the authenticity of the reported experience remained unestablished. Dr. Sprinkle expressed the opinion that the trooper believed in the reality of the events he described.

Tests administered were the Rorschach, Thematic Apperception Test, Sentence Completion, Word Association, Wechsler Adult Intelligence Scale, and Minnesota Multiphasic Personality Inventory. Results of these tests were evaluated by Mr. R. Dean Land, Counselor, and Dr. Robert H. Fenner, Assistant Director for Clinical Services, of the University of Colorado Center.

Conclusion:

Evaluation of psychological assessment tests, the lack of any evidence, and interviews with the patrolman, left project staff with no confidence that the trooper's reported UFO experience was physically real.

Case 43

South Central
Fall 1967
Investigators: Ayer, Wadsworth

Abstract:

Confused reports by teenagers of strange lights were attributed to assorted lights on flat countryside and possibly aircraft.

Background:

At approximately 10:30 p.m. 5 December 1967, six teenagers returning home from a basketball game detoured in order to drive by a cemetery to frighten themselves. As they approached the cemetery, they saw through the trees a blinking light in the sky beyond. They pulled off the road just past the cemetery, where they had an unobstructed view. The object, low on the eastern horizon, was moving northward with an up-and-down motion. It appeared to be flashing different colors or rotating, or both. The most similar conventional object with which it could be compared would be an aircraft with flashing beacon. This, however, was ruled out by the witnesses because of its up-and-down motion. As soon as they saw it moving north, they turned around and followed, hoping to obtain a better look. Although an accurate estimate of distance could not be made, the witnesses believed the object to be less than two miles away, and heading in a direction they could follow by using country roads.

The remainder of the story is not clear, as individual accounts are highly inconsistent with one another. Generally, witnesses agree that they "followed" the object for several miles, losing sight of it two or three times as they turned down different roads. Finally, they came to a location from which lights, attributed to the original object, were seen off to their left, apparently in a field. Later this location could not be determined as four different possibilities were indicated by the witnesses and no one was certain. Lights were seen in the "field," some like car lights, some (or one) green or blue-green; a dim structure is mentioned, and finally spotlight beams or revolving beams. The structure mentioned turned out to be an extremely marginal perception, leaving essentially lights and little more.

The dramatic element in accounts written by the witnesses seems based on *interpretation* of the lights as UFO phenomena, rather than on definite evidence. A much less dramatic picture of what they had seen emerged from questioning the witnesses. For example, one witness said that three independent "objects" were possibly involved: the object first sighted, the light which was "followed," and the light(s) in the field. He saw only lights, no structure, and was not sure of what they were. Three others held similar views, except that they were less certain of the sequence of events. The language used in the various reports suggests that they were verbalizing their impressions during sightings and had opportunity to standardize certain descriptive terms.

In addition to written accounts, individual maps showing the areas and locations of various events were obtained through questioning of the witnesses. Wide discrepancies and inconsistencies are apparent in these items.

Two of the witnesses, a girl and her boy friend, produced

the most elaborate descriptions and the most dramatic reports. They also appeared to be prone to exaggerate perception of anything fearful or unconventional. The boy had studied UFOs for quite some time, and took them extremely seriously. He was obviously upset about the "experience," and showed very little objectivity about the occurrence. The girl, who drew an elaborate sketch of what she had "seen" in the field, later admitted that she had not actually seen such an object. She said that her sketch was more on the imaginative side and was what the lights *suggested* to her. As to structure, she said that what she actually saw was so dim she had to look to one side to see it. At the height of the excitement, both witnesses thought the object rose up and was coming at them. None of the other witnesses saw this motion, even though all were looking at the same thing. There was, however, general agreement that a bright light like a searchlight seemed to shine in their direction, whereupon they rapidly departed.

Investigation:

Certain important factors were noted during attempts to reconstruct the incident.

First, the area was examined in the daytime during unsuccessful attempts to pin down the location of the final incident. The terrain is monotonous — flat farmland with scattered scrub growth. The few hills are so low and rounded that one would prefer to call them swells or rises. It was immediately clear that one could easily become disoriented in such an area, especially at night.

The same area was examined at night. Again, one feature stood out. Lights were visible in all directions. These were widely scattered, and were of various colors, intensities, and degrees of scintillation. Some were in clusters, some alone. When witnesses were questioned and returned to the area of the sighting, it became clear that no "site" could be agreed on.

Thus we have six conflicting stories as evidence. There is disagreement over what was seen, where it was seen, and what the witnesses themselves did at the time. There is agreement that a flashing light was followed and lost several times, and that lights seen in a field, were presumed to be the original light and watched until a bright light or lights shown at the observers, whereupon they became frightened and left.

As a tentative explanation, one of the possible sites was found to contain a farm with yard light and outbuildings with blue-green and various other lights. The yard light could be seen discontinuously from locations between the cemetery and the farm. Thus this light, which was bright white and scintillated dramatically when viewed from several miles away, could have been "followed" via various routes by automobile. As one approached more closely, the greenish lights became visible below and to the right of the yard light. A car in the vicinity of the farm might account for the "searchlight" effect reported by witnesses. This, however, is not a completely satisfactory explanation, mainly because the yard light would have been easily recognizable as such by anyone who approached closely. Possibly this light was switched off by the time the witnesses reached the location. Another flaw in this explanation is the northward motion of the original object. This was reported by all witnesses, and does not sound like illusory motion caused by involuntary eye movement.

Conclusions:

At this point we leave the original object as unidentified. The evidence is not sufficient to rule out aircraft, despite statements by witnesses to the contrary.

Additional Sighting:

The only other sighting reported in the area was made by a local radio announcer. He saw an object with red and green flashing lights in the sky northwest of the station at dusk on the same evening as the sighting by the teenagers. The object looked like a small plane; but it was moving very slowly, suggesting a strong headwind. After watching for two minutes, the announcer went into the station and thought no more about the matter until he heard of the other sighting.

Case 44
North Central
Winter 1967
Investigator: Wadsworth

Abstract:

Witness driving on highway at night reported having seen a dim shape and a pattern of colored lights above an underpass. From the farther side of the underpass, it appeared to have moved away opposite to the direction he was traveling. No field investigation was made.

Background:

The witness, a med student, telephoned the project 23 February 1968. He reported that, while driving from city A to city B on U.S. highway A and approaching an underpass 34 mi. from city B about 10:00 or 11:00 p.m., he saw directly above his side of the highway a pattern of lights almost in a vertical line. Two red lights were at top and bottom, and a "blue or green" between them. The lights appeared to be stationary directly above the underpass. Just before he entered the underpass, he saw a white light beside the blue/green.

He stopped about ¼ mi. beyond the underpass to look for the lights, thinking they should be overhead, and saw the pattern, now horizontal instead of vertical, low in the ENE, "like a struggling goose in the wind." He thought it was ½-1 mi. away, and perhaps 200 ft. up. He could not recall how it had disappeared.

Arriving at home he went to his apartment and went to bed. He had a strange feeling that "they" were still with him, and he slept poorly. He felt that "they" had communicated, wanting him to go on a trip with them; feeling of great friendship, buddies. He had "told" them he would go, but was not ready yet, too much to do, responsibilities etc.

Afterward, he could not concentrate on his med studies, lost interest, and "felt pressure building up." He acknowledged that he had been considering psychiatric help but wanted to contact the CU project first; he was concerned that psychiatry might interfere with our investigation. Wadsworth reassured him on this point, but explained that we could not offer any personal assistance. Because of the evidence of emotional disturbance predating the sighting, as well as the lack of supporting witnesses or other basis for further investigation, no field study was made.

Commenting on this case, the project's consulting psychiatrist observes: "Unequivocal statements concerning the emotional state of the witness in this, or any other case, cannot be made in the absence of intensive psychological testing and a psychiatric interview. The witness' statements suggest that he was under severe pressures at the time of the UFO sighting in connection with his studies, his marriage, and other factors in his life situation. One would suspect that at the time these pressures were at the very least producing a severe anxiety attack in the witness. It is conceivable that he was on the verge of a more serious mental disturbance. The fact that the witness states that he feels that he would like to consult a psychiatrist indicates his awareness that the solutions to his problems are to be found within himself rather than in the outside world or in the UFO."

Case 45
South Mountain
Winter 1967
Investigators: Ahrens and Levine

Abstract:

A lighted object seen at night by several people was found to have been a plastic hot-air balloon.

Background:

It was reported to the CU project that several persons at Castle Rock had seen an illuminated transparent object drifting over the town about 6:00 p.m. Mainly because the principal witness insisted that the object appeared to be about 75 ft. long, project investigators went to the scene.

Investigation:

The principal witness, interviewed the following evening, reported that, while he was outdoors in the early evening, he noticed several lights in the sky that were focussed toward him. He made out a transparent object about 75 ft. long by 20 ft. wide. In a circle underneath it were about twelve lights; he judged them to be much brighter than car headlights, though they did not blind him. He estimated the object to be about 25 ft. above the ground, which it illuminated. The object appeared empty; he could see through it. At first it was stationary; then it began to drift northward over the town. He followed in his truck, stopping at a service station to tell the men there of the "flying saucer." They later reported having seen slow-moving lights that dropped several fiery objects as they disappeared north of the town.

The investigators then visited the owner of the service station, and while there heard a radio report that a local teenage boy had launched a plastic hot-air balloon at about the time of the sighting, from a location about a block upwind of the principal witness' location. They learned by further inquiry that the balloon had been a polyethylene suit bag about two by three feet, with balsa cross-members supporting six small candles and a cup of lighter fluid. Several persons at the launching saw the balloon drift over the principal witness' location.

Conclusions:

The investigators concluded that the object of the sighting reports had been the balloon, despite the witness' exaggerated estimate of its dimensions.

Chapter III Photographic Case Studies (Cases 46–59)

Case 46
McMinnville, Oregon
11 May 1950
Investigator: Hartmann

Abstract:

Witness I reportedly saw a metallic-looking, disk-shaped UFO. She called her husband, they located their camera, and he took photographs of the object before it disappeared in the distance.

Background:

Time: 7:45 p.m. PST (1,2); 7:30 p.m. (3).

Position: Approx. 10 mi. SW of McMinnville, Ore. on the farm of the witnesses: 123 19′ 50″ W, 45 06′ 15″ N (7).

Terrain: Rolling farm country, elv. 210 ft.; houses several hundred meters apart (7).

Weather Conditions: Dull with an overcast at about 5,000 ft. (2, confirmed by the photos).

Sighting, General Information:

The sighting occurred in the back yard of a farm about 0.2 mi. S of the "Salmon River Highway" (U.S. 99W (7). Witness was feeding rabbits in the back yard,. S of the house and E of the garage when the object was first sighted 1, 2, 3, 6). apparently toward the NE (6). Witness II was apparently in the house at this moment, as three of the accounts (2,3,6) refer to Witness I calling to him and running into the house to fetch him from the kitchen, although one account (1) states that they had "been out in the back yard," and "both . . . saw it at the same time."

As far as Witness I could remember 17 yr. later (6), the rabbits gave no indication of disturbance.

Immediately after they both saw the object, apparently as it was still in a NE direction, moving slowly toward the W (6), they thought of their camera (1,2,3,6). Witness II ran to the car, thinking it was there, but Witness I remembered it was in the house and brought it (1,6). Witness II took the camera, which was already loaded. The roll of film had been purchased during the winter and already had two or three shots on it (4).

At this time "the object was coming in toward us and seemed to be tipped up a little bit. It was very bright—almost silvery—and there was no noise or smoke" (1).

Witness II explained that he took the first picture, re-wound his film as fast as possible and then as the object gathered speed and turned toward the northwest, he had to move rapidly to his right to get the second picture. Both were snapped within thirty seconds, he estimated (1). According to another early reference: "[Witness II] elaborated, 'There wasn't any flame and it was moving fairly slow. Then I snapped the first picture. It moved a little to the left and I moved to the right to take another picture.' " (3). Plates 23 and 24 show the two photographs in the sequence taken. During this interval the object was moving quite slowly, apparently almost hovering, and it apparently shifted both its position and orientation in a complex way, changing direction and tipping just before it moved away, as indicated in Plate 25 (2,6). However, Witness I described it as "not undulating or rotating, just 'sort of gliding' " (2). The UFO accelerated slowly during or just after the second photograph and moved away rapidly toward the west (2). Witness I ran into the house to call her mother-in-law, got no answer, and returned outside just in time to see the UFO 'dimly vanishing toward the west' (2).

Investigation:

The witnesses described the object as "very bright—almost

silvery" (1); "brightly metallic, silver or aluminum colored, with a touch of bronze . . . appeared to have a sort of superstructure . . . 'like a good-sized parachute canopy without the strings, only silvery-bright mixed with bronze'" (2); silvery on top but with more bronze on the bottom, the bottom being different (but, this being seventeen years later, Witness I was unsure whether it was darker) . . . shiny but not as bright as a hub cap . . . resembling a dull, aluminum-painted tank (which Witness I pointed out to the writer in our interview) . . . "awful pretty" (6). The rather bright, aluminum-like, but not specular, reflecting surface appears to be confirmed by analysis of the photos (see below). There was no noise, visible exhaust, flames, or smoke (1,3,6).

When the object tipped up, exposing its under side to the witnesses, they felt a gust of wind which they thought may have come from the UFO. "'. . . there was a breeze as it went overhead . . . which died down later'" (2). In the interview with the writer, Witness I stressed this, remarking the wind was "about to knock you over," though Witness II (interviewed separately) remarked that it made only a "very little" breeze as it was getting ready to fly off (6).

As to size, speed, and distance, the witnesses were reluctant to hazard a guess (1,2), as Witness II had no way of knowing its size (2), although one of the references quotes Witness II as estimating a diameter of "20 or 30 ft." (3), and Witness I compared its appearance (though not explicitly its size) to a parachute canopy (2,6).

As to the origin of the UFO, Witness II remarked both at the time and in 1967 that he thought it was a secret U.S. craft (1). "'. . . you hear so much about those things . . . I didn't believe all that talk about flying saucers before, but now I have an idea the Army knows what they are'" (3).

Witness II recalls finishing his roll of film on Mother's Day (4) and had it developed locally (1). Witness II mentioned his observation and showed the pictures to a few friends. He did not seek publicity about the pictures, admitting that he was "'kind of scared of it'" (2,3), and "afraid they would get in trouble with the 'government' and be bothered by the publicity" (2). However, McMinnville *Telephone Register* reporter Bill Powell learned of the sighting from two McMinnville bankers, Ralph and Frank Wortman, and followed up the story (1,2). He found the negatives "on the floor under a davenport where the Witnesses' children had been playing with them" (2). The *Telephone Register* broke the story Thursday, 8 June 1950 with a front page article containing the two pictures and Editor's Note:

> ". . . in view of the variety of opinion and reports attendant to the saucers over the past two years, every effort has been made to check Trent's photos for authenticity. Expert photographers declared there has been no tampering with the nega-

tives. [The] original photos were developed by a local firm. After careful consideration, there appears to be no possibility of hoax or hallucination connected with the pictures. Therefore the *Telephone Register* believes them authentic . . ." (1).

Various McMinnville residents, including the bankers Wortman, offered to sign affidavits vouching unreservedly for the reputation and veracity of the witnesses (1,2,4).

On Friday and Saturday, 9 and 10 June, the Portland, Ore., and Los Angeles newspapers carried the story (2,3). *Life* magazine carried the pictures the following week (4). The witnesses accepted an invitation to appear on a television program "We the People," in New York (6). Witness I remarked that they were encouraged by the people responsible for this show to make statements they (the witnesses) regarded as inaccurate. The witnesses, however, did not make such statements, but told only what they saw (6).

While in New York, the witnesses were to receive their negatives from *Life* magazine, but were informed that the negatives were temporarily misplaced (6). *Life* promised to return them by mail to Oregon, but apparently never recovered them (6). With the cooperation of *Life* the Colorado project discovered that in 1950 the negatives had been in the possession of International News Photo Service later merged with United Press International. The project located the original negatives and was permitted to examine them.

As mentioned above, various reputable individuals volunteered to attest to the witnesses' veracity. They appear to be sincere, though not highly educated or experienced observers. During the writer's interview with them, they were friendly and quite unconcerned about the sighting. Witness II was at work plowing his field and did not even get off his tractor. From interviews throughout this district one gained the impression that these were very industrious farm people, not given to unusual pranks.

Two inferences appear to be justified: 1) It is difficult to see any prior motivation for a fabrication of such a story, although after the fact, the witnesses did profit to the extent of a trip to New York; 2) it is unexpected that in this distinctly rural atmosphere, in 1950, one would encounter a fabrication involving sophisticated trick photography (e.g. a carefully retouched print). The witnesses also appear unaffected now by the incident, receiving only occasional inquiries (6).

The over-all appearance of the photographs, in particular the slightly underexposed land foreground and properly exposed sky, is consistent with the reported time 7:30 PST (sunset being roughly a few minutes after 7:15, and twilight lasting until after 8:45). There could be a possible discrepancy in view of the fact that the UFO, the telephone pole, possibly the garage at the left, and especially the distant house gables (left of the distant barn) are illuminated from the right, or east. The house, in particular, appears to have a shadow under its roof that would suggest a daylit photo, and combined with the eastward incidence, one could argue that the photos were taken on a dull, sunlit day at, say, 10 a.m. But accepting the UFO makes scarcely less sense than arguing that the witnesses staged a hoax at 10 a.m. and then claimed the photographs were taken at 7:30. Densitometry of the original negatives shows that the sky itself is brighter toward the west, as expected. It seems possible that, half an hour after sunset, the cloud distribution could result in a dull illumination preferentially from the NE (certainly there will be skylight from above).

Reality of physical object. As stated previously, it is unlikely that a sophisticated "optical fabrication" was performed. The negatives had not been tampered with.

Further, a geometric test was performed to determine whether the object shown in Plate 24 in approximate cross section was the same object photographed in Plate 23 at a different angle. The apparent inclination, i, can be determined from the ratio of the axes of the apparent ellipse in Plate 23.

$$\sin i = b/a \qquad (2)$$

Measures on several copies of photo 1 (the UPI print, an enlargement thereof, and two magazine reproductions) gave $\sin i = 0.368$, and

$$i = 21^\circ.6 \pm 0^\circ.1 \text{ (est. P.E.).} \qquad (3)$$

Plate 26 shows enlargements from UPI print with lines of sight superimposed on the Plate 24 "cross section" at 21°.6. The way in which these lines cut the image is in perfect agreement with the appearance of the object in Plate 23. Judging from the apparent position of the pole it is likely that the object has simply tipped, without rotation, between the two photos.

The lighting is also consistent with that in the rest of the photo. Both photographs, therefore, show real objects and that the object in Plate 23 is a view of the same object in Plate 24, seen in different perspective.

Asymmetry of UFO. It will be noted in Plate 26 that the UFO is distinctly asymmetric. The "pole" is off center and inclined, and there appears to be a difference in the profiles of the right and left sides (Plate 24), the left having a more pronounced notch defining the flange. The shading of the object also indicates a more distinct flange on the left in Plate 24. The asymmetries are judged physical, not optical effects.

Absence of rotation. The top of the "pole," barely visible in photo 1, is off center to the left by the same amount as in photo 2. This would be rather improbable if the object were rotating, and supports Witness II's statement that it was not rotating. This is a rather strong argument against a fabrication using a necessarily (for stability) spinning model similar to a "frisbee," especially in view of the fact that only 2 exposures were made in the middle of an intact roll of film.

Angular size of object. From measurements of recent photos (6) the photos were scaled and the UFO diameters estimated to be:

Plate 23: 1°.4
Plate 24: 1°.3.

The P.E. is probably about 0°.1, but the object subtends a smaller angle in photo 2, consistent with the allegation that photo 2 was made as the UFO was beginning to depart.

It follows immediately that the distance-diameter relation is determined, and a map of the locale (based on ref. 7) is shown in Fig. 1 with the azimuths, angular sizes, and example, that the object was less than a meter in diameter and over the driveway.

Psychological reaction. I judge it reasonable that as the object allegedly drifted to the left, in danger of being lost to sight behind the garage, that the observer should step unconsciously to his right, as the photos show he did, although one might expect the observer even more reasonably to step forward, to get in front of the garage. The reason for the first response may have been that the second would put the observer close to the house, where the object might be lost to sight if it moved back to the east, while by moving away from the garage, one moves toward the open yard SE of the house. In summary, the movement of the observer is consistent with the alleged observation.

Possibility of fabrication. The above tests all appear to be consistent with the witnesses' testimony. The possibility of optical fabrication seems remote. A model thrown into the air by hand appears an unlikely possibility because of the evidence for absence of rotation.

Another possibility can be considered, however. The object appears beneath a pair of wires, as is seen in Plates 23 and 24. We may question, therefore, whether it could have been a model suspended from one of the wires. This possibility is strengthened by the observation that the object appears beneath roughly the same point in the two photos, in spite of their having been taken from two positions. This can be determined from irregularities, or "kinks," in the wires. The wires pass between the camera positions and the garage (left). We know from the change in orientation of the object that it moved, or was re-oriented by hand, between exposures. The possibility that it is a model hanging beneath a point on the wire suggests a further test: Is the change in distance of the object in Plates 23 and 24 equal to the change in distance from the wires? Measures of the disk indicate that it is about 8% further away in Plate 24. Measures of the irregularities in the wires indicate that they are further away from the camera in Plate 24. The amount of the latter increase from the wires (measured by the separation of rather ill-defined "kinks") is less certain than the distance increase from the disk, but it is measured to be about 10%. These tests do not rule out the possibility that the object was a small model suspended from the nearby wire by an unresolved thread.

Given the foregoing analysis, one must choose between an asymmetric model suspended from the overhead wire, and an extraordinary flying object (See Table 1).

Photometric analysis. Although it is often stated that a *single* photograph of an object contains no information on the distance, this is not strictly true. Atmospheric extinction and scattering, combined, serve to reduce contrast as distance increases, an effect perhaps best appreciated by artists. The shadowed bottom of the UFO in Plate 23 has a particularly pale look, suggestive of scattering between observer and object, and if such scattering is detectable, it may be possible to make some estimate of the distance involved.

Table 1

Summary of Possible Interpretations

Interpretations	*Rejected*	*Comments*
Optical fabrications		
Double exposure	X	UFO darker than sky background
Retouch; drawn image	X	Negatives unretouched
Multiple copies, recopying	(X)	Overly sophisticated
Physical fabrications		
"Frisbee"-type model in flight	X	No rotation
Model suspended from wire		Under same part of wire in each photo
Extraordinary Flying Object		Photometry suggests large distance

The luminance, or apparent surface brightness at distance r of an object of intrinsic luminance B_o (r = 0) is

$$B = B_{sky}\,(1 - e^{-\beta r}) + B_o\, e^{-\beta r}, \qquad (4)$$

where β is the scattering coefficient. The first term represents scattered light; the second, extinction. Since all measures must be based on the witnesses' two photographs, we will determine β for the given day from the photographs themselves. Normalizing all brightnesses (measured from the film and assuming that the images measured fall on the linear portion of the gamma curve) to that of the sky near the horizon, i.e. on a line within a few thousand feet of the ground, where the UFO is constrained to be by the reported cloud height and probably nearness to the camera, we have

$$B = 1 + e^{-\beta r}\,(B_o - 1). \qquad (5)$$

Notice that if an object is sufficiently far away, its brightness equals the sky brightness (in physical terms, the optical depth $T >> 1$).

Given the brightness of an object at zero distance, B_o, and the observed brightness B, one may solve for the distance r. The first necessary step is to determine the scattering coefficient β. The original negatives were subjected to densitometric analysis, and Table 2 lists observed values of B. "Hill 2" lies at a distance of about 2.2 km (7). The photometry indicates that B = .685 for the distant hill, but the foreground foliage gives B_o = .403. This gives

$$= 0.289 \text{ km}^{-1},$$

or optical depth T = 1 at r = 3.5 km, (6)

which appears consistent with the appearance of the photos.

At this point the theory was checked against objects of known distance. For example, the roof of the distant barn ("B" in Fig. 1) has B = .506. If one assumes that its intrinsic brightness equals that of the foreground garage, then B_o = .495, so that r = 0.073 km.

Table 2

*Values of B for Objects Photographed**

Based on densitometry of original negatives; aperture 75μ x 75μ

Object	*Plate 23*	*Plate 24*
UFO "Pole"	1.07	
Illuminated right side	1.29	1.23
Illuminated left side	(1.35)	1.05
Shaded bottom	.675	
Garage roof	.489	.501
Shadows under eaves	.396	.426
Metallic tank:		
Illuminated	.86	.91
Shaded bottom	(.48)	(.40)
Foreground underbrush	.417	.389
Barn (roof)	.511	.501
Hill		
1	.63	.59
2	.71	.66
House		
Illuminated wall	(.77)	(.77)
Shadow	(.44)	(.52)
Sky		
Upper right	1.29	1.26
Upper left	1.51	1.62
Horizon	1.00	1.00
Unexposed edge of film	.32	.34

Measures in parentheses have lower weight

* B values are normalized to horizon sky brightness

The true r is about 0.32 km, and our error is a factor 4. One can resolve the discrepancy by assuming the barn roof was slightly (7%) darker than the garage roof.

Again, one can check the theory on the distant "Hill 1." $B = .610$ and $B_o = .403$ as measured in the foreground foliage. This gives $r = 1.5$ km. The true r is in the range 1.3 to 1.9 km, depending on the part of the hill observed, and the error is negligible.

A third check, more comparable to the UFO problem, is the distant house ("H" in Fig. 1). Unfortunately the densi-

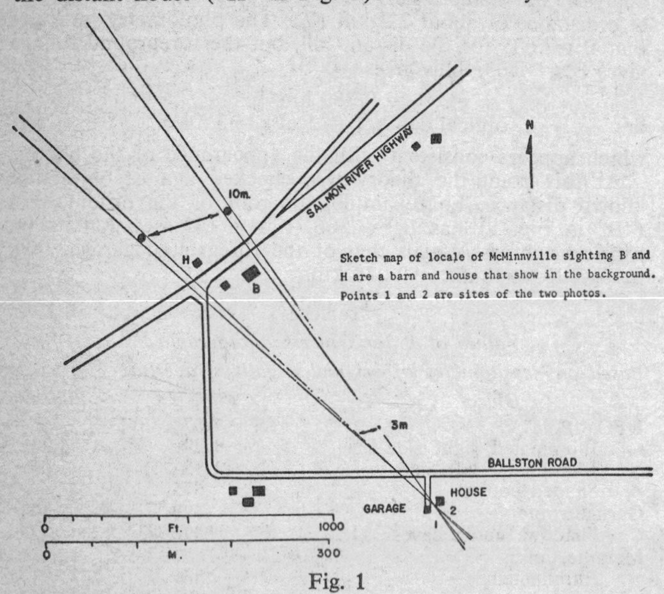

Sketch map of locale of McMinnville sighting B and H are a barn and house that show in the background. Points 1 and 2 are sites of the two photos.

Fig. 1

tometer did not clearly resolve the illuminated white facade from the intervening branches; however, supplementary measures with enlargements indicate that the facade brightness should be only slightly more than 1.00, e.g. $B \simeq 1.02$, and $B_o \simeq 1.04$, which means that the apparent brightness nearly equals sky brightness and hence is very insensitive to distance and gives no good solution. There are shadows visible on the house on the white surface under the eaves. Measures indicate $B = .48$. B_o for the shadows on this white surface, illuminated by the ambient illumination, should be intrinsically measurably brighter than the shadows under the dark wooden garage eaves and under the tank beside the garage ($B_o = .41$), but not as much brighter as the white illuminated surface is brighter than the darker wood. (If there were no ambient illumination, all shadows would be intrinsically black; $B_o = 0$). An estimated value is $B_o = .43$. This gives a distance or $r = 0.32$ km, only 14% less than the measured distance of 0.37 km. Naive use of $B_o = 0.41$, known to be too low, would have given $r = 0.44$ km, 19% too great.

It is concluded that by careful consideration of the parameters involved in the case of recognizable objects in the photographs, distances can be measured within a factor-four error. This justifies the assumption that we are on the linear part of the gamma curve. If such a good measure could be made for the UFO, we could distinguish between a distant extraordinary object and a hypothetical small, close model.

At this point we must be explicit about the geometry of the situation. We represent the environment as in Fig. 2. We assume that the UFO is within a homogeneous scattering layer with $\Upsilon = 1$ at 3.5 km. If the UFO were far away and at an altitude greater than the characteristic dimension of the layer (C in Fig. 2), it would be large and extraordinary in any case. If it is relatively close, $r \simeq 1$ km, the assumptions are justified. Our objective is to distinguish between cases A and B in Fig. 2. The sky brightness, to which all the brightness

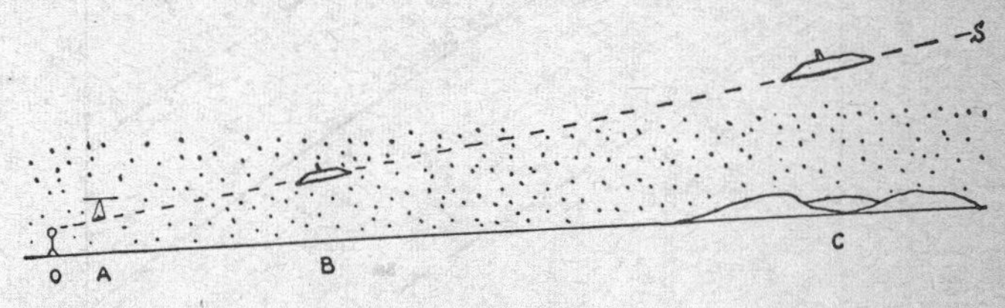

Fig. 2

values are normalized, must be the sky brightness at the horizon, since this is the value characteristic of long path length through the scattering layer.

For the solution of the UFO distance, we have two independent solutions from two independent observations: the illuminated and shadowed surfaces of the UFO. As was remarked above, it is the shadowed surface in particular that looks pale and hence suggests large distance.

Immediately from Table 2 we see that B = 1.21 describes the part of the UFO, while the illuminated part of the nearby dull aluminum-painted tank $B_o = .885$. Since, as the UFO recedes, B must approach 1.00. We thus know that 1.21 is the minimum intrinsic brightness of the UFO surface, i.e. $B_o \geq 1.21$. Thus the UFO in any interpretation is known to have a brighter surface than the foreground tank. Thus, the photometry at once confirms the witnesses' report that the UFO was shiny, like a fresh, aluminum-painted surface, but not a specular surface.

The question is, how bright is the surface intrinsically, and what surface properties would be consistent with both the observed illuminated and shadowed side? Fig. 3 shows two families of solutions, one for the illuminated top surface and one for the shaded bottom side. Solutions for the latter have an uncertainty introduced by the difficulty of measuring the true shadow intensity on the tank. The distance is given as a function of the assumed increase in brightness over the value for the illuminated or shaded side of the aluminum-painted tank, respectively.

Fig. 3 graphically illustrates the problem. For example, if the object is a model suspended from the wire only a few

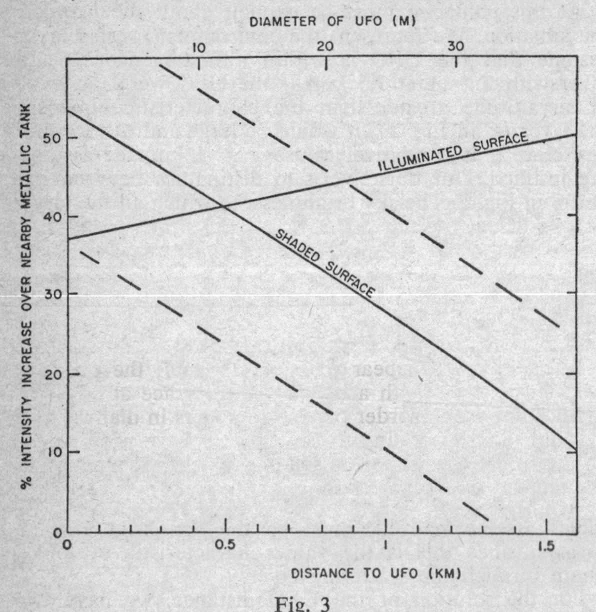

Fig. 3

meters away, its surface is some 37% brighter than that of the tank, and the shaded side is probably more than 40% brighter than the shadow on the tank. But this is nearly impossible to maintain in the face of the photometry. Although the distant house's surface is roughly twice as bright as the tank's surface, its shadows can be only a few percent brighter, intrinsically, than those on the tank. This is basically the problem that was suggested by initial inspection of the photos: the shadowed side of the UFO appears to be so bright that it suggests significant scattering between it and the observer.

The upshot is that if the top and bottom surfaces of the UFO are made out of essentially the same material, i.e. with the same albedo, the photometry indicates that the UFO is distant, at roughly $r = 1.3 \pm 0.4$ km (est. P. E.). The witnesses referred to a slightly different hue of the bottom side of the UFO: they said it was more bronze than the silvery top side. We have assumed this change in tint had negligible effect on the photometry, although the implication is that the bottom has slightly lower albedo. If so the UFO would be still more distant.

There is one last possibility for fabrication which has not been ruled out. Suppose the object is a small model with a pale grey top and a bright white bottom (e.g. an aluminum pie pan sealed on the bottom with white paper). Could this account for the apparent lightness of the bottom, shaded side of the UFO?

It is difficult to defend this idea in the face of the photometry. Our analysis of the house indicated that its shaded white surface had an intrinsic brightness of 0.43, which is very close to the value measured for the shaded part of the aluminum-painted tank. Yet hypothetical fabrication requires a surface on the shaded bottom of the model that is of intrinsic shaded brightness 0.68, considerably brighter than the shaded part of the white house. In other words, the photometry appears to indicate that a *very* white surface on the bottom of a small model would be required to match the appearance of the photographs.

To the extent that the photometric analysis is reliable, (and the measurements appear to be consistent), the photographs indicate an object with a bright shiny surface at considerable distance and on the order of tens of meters in diameter. While it would be exaggerating to say that we have positively ruled out a fabrication, it appears significant that the simplest, most direct interpretation of the photographs confirms precisely what the witnesses said they saw. Yet, the fact that the object appears beneath the same part of the overhead wire in both photos can be used as an argument favoring a suspended model.

Conclusion:

This is one of the few UFO reports in which all factors investigated, geometric, psychological, and physical appear to be consistent with the assertion that an extraordinary flying object, silvery, metallic, disk-shaped, tens of meters in diameter, and evidently artificial, flew within sight of two witnesses. It cannot be said that the evidence positively rules out a fabrication, although there are some physical factors such as the accuracy of certain photometric measures of the original negatives which argue against a fabrication.

Case 47

Great Falls, Montana (lat. 47° 30′ and long. 111° 18′)
15 August 1950 (see below)
Investigator: Hartmann

Terrain: Within the city limits but near the northwestern outskirts of Great Falls, near the Missouri River and the Anaconda Copper Company, and approximately three mi. NW of Malstrom AFB (then, Great Falls AFB). *Weather Conditions:* At 5:30 a.m., MST (15 August 1950) the weather was partly overcast with middle altocumulus and altostratus clouds; the surface wind was SW, 16 knots. A cold front lay just north of the Canadian border, extending several hundred miles EW; it moved south and passed over Great Falls in the afternoon. The upper winds were reported W-WNW 250° 280°, 6 knots at 9,000 ft. on the previous evening. Temperatures were of the order of 20°C, dew point 9°C, and there was a slight inversion of 2°C in the 666-636 mb layer. The local half-hourly surface weather observations for 15 August 1950 at the Municipal Airport Weather Station showed that the surface wind increased to readings between 25 and 28 mph between 9:00 a.m. and 12 noon, and that it reached 37 mph at 1:12 p.m., and then stayed between 25 and 30 mph until almost sunset. The surface wind direction was constantly SW from 10:00 a.m. until 4:00 p.m. The sky was clear (visibility, 60 mi.); the temperature was 77° at 11:27 a.m., and reached a maximum of 83° at 4:27 p.m. The barometer fell slightly from 30.05 in. Hg. at 9:30 a.m. to 29.98 in. Hg. at 3 p.m., then steadied, and finally rose again after dark.

Abstract:

Witness I, general manager of a Great Falls baseball team, and Witness II, his secretary, observed two white lights moving slowly across the sky. Witness I made 16mm. motion pictures of the lights. Both individuals have recently reaffirmed the observation, and there is little reason to question its validity. The case remains unexplained. Analysis indicates that the images on the film are difficult to reconcile with aircraft or other known phenomena, although aircraft cannot be entirely ruled out.

Background:

At 11:25 a.m. (5 August or 15 August) Witness I, general manager of the Great Falls Electrics, a baseball team, was making an inspection of the baseball stadium (1,3) with his secretary, Witness II. In virtually all early publications (e.g., 3,5) the date for this is consistently given as 15 August 1950. However, Dr. Roy Craig of the Colorado project notes early correspondence between Witness I and Project Blue Book that raises an uncertainty about the date. A letter dated 9 January 1953, from Great Falls AFB (renamed Malstrom AFB later) to Project Blue Book, conveying results of a reinterrogation which had been requested by Blue Book, states:

> "(Witness I's) version of the incident is as follows:
> 'On about the 5th or 15th of August, 1950, I, as manager of the Electrics, a local baseball team, walked to the grandstand of the local stadium here in Great Falls, Montana. It

was approximately 11:30 a.m. and my purpose was to check the direction of the wind in preparation for the afternoon's game.' "

A subsequent undated Blue Book review of the case, dated late 1956, carries the case dated "5 or 15 August, 1950." Dr. Craig determined by checking Great Falls newspaper records that no home game was scheduled for 15 August, and, in fact, the witness' team played that evening in Twin Falls, Idaho. Mrs. LaVern Kohl, Reference Librarian, Great Falls Public Library, determined, at Dr. Craig's request, that the baseball team played no home games in Great Falls between 9 and 18 August, 1950. The 15 August sighting date is therefore certainly open to question.

Accounts of the incident give essentially the following information:

As was his habit, Witness I looked NNW to the smokestack of the Anaconda Copper Company in order to ascertain the wind direction. (1, 2, 3) Directly in line with the stack, he saw two bright lights stationary in the sky (1). After a few seconds, he decided they could not be airplanes (1), directed his secretary's attention to the objects, and ran to his car which was 50-60 ft. away (1, 2, 3). Her observations were reported in Blue Book files to be identical to Witness I's (1). At his car he took five to eight seconds to load his motion picture camera with Eastman Kodachrome, daylight-type (1). The camera was a Revere turret-type, 16mm. magazine loader, with a F.1.9 telephoto lens with a 3 in. focal length. He set the diaphragm at F.22 and the focus at infinity. Film speed was 16 frames per second (2). From the time of sighting until he began filming, approximately 30 seconds elapsed (3). At a point near his car (1), he began "panning" his camera slowly from right to left (2). During this time the lights had moved from a stationary position toward the SW and they continued to the SW until they faded away (1, 2, 3). The first frames were not made until the object was already in the SW (3). (See Plate 27 and Fig. 4).

According to the initial Air Force report of 6 October 1950, Witness I described two disk-shaped lights having a bright, clean, "aluminum quality" (2). He thought that the objects were about 50 ft. in diameter, 3 ft. in depth and about 50 yds. apart (2). In a subsequent written statement quoted in the Blue Book report of 9 January 1953, he described them as being "like two new dimes in the sky" (1) and said they may have made whistling or whooshing noise (2).

According to the initial report of 6 October 1950, Witness I described a definite spinning motion (2). While in a stationary position "an occasional vibration seemed to momentarily tilt them, after which they would instantly correct their level plane to its seemingly balanced position. The two objects made an abrupt flight in an arc motion at very high speeds" (1). In late 1952 he estimated the speed as being over 400 mph. (1). The Air Force report of 1950 quotes his first estimate of the speed as about 200 mph (2).

Witness I thought they were between 5,000 and 10,000 ft. in altitude and at an elevation angle of 30°-35° above the horizon and within 0.75 mi. (2) or 2-2.5 mi. (1) from him (1,2). Measurements of the motion picture film (3) indicate that in the first available frames, the lights were at an elevation of about 15° and slowly descending (3).

In 1953 this witness reported that the sighting lasted for 3.5 minutes (1). The 1950 Air Force report says that he

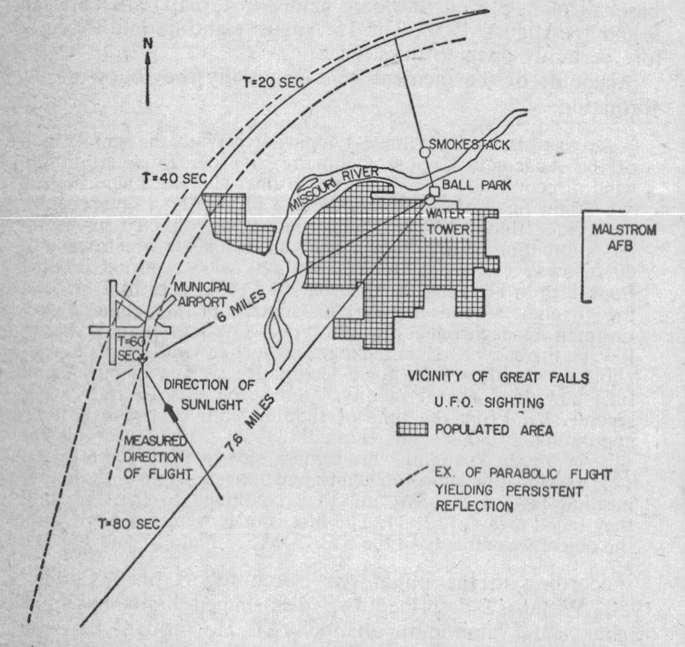

Attempt to reconstruct the Great Falls sighting as reflections off two airplanes. Arguments listed in the text constrain any involved airplanes to approximately the geometry shown and suggest that no bright reflection would be obtained from the aircraft during the filming. Nonetheless, the arguments against the aircraft hypothesis are inconclusive and the explanation depicted here can be described as tenable. (Adapted from diagrams by *Baker,* ref. 3).

Fig. 4

reported that the objects were observed a total of about 30 sec. by him and about 7 sec. by Witness II (2). The apparent discrepancy probably refers to the fact that Witness I made about 20 sec. of film. The reference to Witness II seeing the lights for 7 sec. is unexplained. It would appear that about 30 sec. to a minute elapsed from the moment of the sighting (over the smokestack to the north) until he began filming (3). Eight seconds of that time were spent preparing the camera (2). He actually filmed the event for 16 sec. and possibly more (see next paragraph) (3). A Douglas Aircraft Co. report of April 1956 states that the objects hovered at a point above a water tower for "a while" and then flew out of sight with a swooshing sound (1). This may refer to hovering prior to the filming; the film indicates steady motion.

The first 10 to 20 frames on the extant film show the objects at their brightest and largest. Witness I alleges that about 30 frames preceding these show the lights as disk-like objects with rotary motion visible, but that these frames were missing when the film was returned by the Air Force (see below). Throughout the sequence, the two images stand out from the sky background because of their intensity, sharpness, and constant relative orientation, one preceding the other in a smooth progression across the sky and behind the water tower. There is a slow fading and dwindling in size. In the film, the lights do not hover or decelerate near the tower. According to a photogrametric analysis of the film (3), the lights disappear completely from view by the end of the 16 sec. film. A later analysis (3) indicates that although the images are fading by the final frames (fading out by #225), they fade out suddenly enough at the end that they "were not isotropic constant-luminosity reflectors" (e.g. balloons).

At all times the two images present elliptical shapes which the analysis (3) concludes, "is due exclusively to the movement of the camera" (panning right to left), but my own measurements (see below) suggest that, except for a few frames, the ellipticity is present because the reflecting source is not circular. The ellipticity is most clearly seen in the first frames, where the objects appear larger.

Witness I had his film processed and showed it to various interested friends and service clubs (3,4). Witness II never saw this film (4). (No mention of the sighting was recorded in either of the Great Falls newspapers prior to 12 September 1950). Witness I was frequently mentioned in the newspapers in his role as baseball manager, however (4). A newspaperman affiliated with the *Great Falls Leader* was the link in reporting the sighting to officials (4). Witness I submitted the film to Air Force ATIC officials who at that time were investigating UFO's (3). It was analyzed there, and also by the U.S. Navy (3). The initial Air Force report is dated 5 October. Ruppelt (5) reports that:

> "(he) had sent his movies to the Air Force back in 1950, but in 1950 there was no interest in the UFO so, after a quick viewing, Project Grudge had written them off as the 'reflections of two F-94 jet fighters that were in the area.'

"In 1952, at the request of the Pentagon, I reopened the investigation. . . ."

After the original, apparently cursory study of the film in 1950, the Air Materiel Command Headquarters in a written statement to Witness I concluded with the following example of military obfuscation: ". . . our photo analysts were unable to find on it anything *identifiable* of an unusual nature. *Our report of analysis must therefore be negative.*"

According to Ruppelt (5) the 1952 ATIC investigation "quickly confirmed that the objects were not birds, balloons, or meteors." The conclusions were that, assuming the objects to be at a distance too great to be resolved, they moved too fast and were too steady to be birds, but moved too slowly to be meteors. Airplanes were the only tenable alternative (see below). The objects were described by Ruppelt as of "unknown" origin. Mr. Al Chop, employed by ATIC at that time and contacted in 1955 by Baker (3), "recalls that the analysis was considered inconclusive," confirming Ruppelt's account.

When the film was returned from the Air Force, according to Witness I, about the first 30 frames had been removed (3). If so, they were never recovered. According to him, as described by Baker (3), "the first 30-odd frames showed larger images of the UFOs with a notch or band at one point on the periphery of the objects by which they could be seen to rotate in unison while on the rest of the film the objects show up only as unarticulated bright white dots."

The film was purchased by Green-Rouse Productions, Sam Goldwyn Studios, Hollywood, and was made part of a documentary feature-length movie released by United Artists in 1956.

Dr. R. M. L. Baker, Jr., of Douglas Aircraft Co., borrowed a 35mm. reprint of the film from Sam Goldwyn Studios in 1955 for the photogrammetric analysis reported in reference (3).

While studying the problem of reassessing old, "classic" cases, Dr. Roy Craig of the Colorado Project interviewed several of the principals in the case in 1967. Dr. Craig reported (4): (1) that Witness I had a file of correspondence with the Air Force but could not locate a letter in which, he asserted, the Air Force admitted deleting some of the film; he could not remember any information (such as his own discussion in the United Artists' film) about the two airplanes in the vicinity; (2) that Witness I distinctly remembered seeing a single light, rushing outside with Witness I to photograph it, and noting that its appearance was quite different from an airplane, she remembered seeing only one object; (3) that some individuals who reportedly saw the film before it was lent to the Air Force agreed that not all was returned, but several other of these individuals disclaimed having seen the film at all.

Witnesses

1. According to the 1950 report of the Air Force interrogator, Witness I went to Montana State University in 1935 and graduated in 1938 with a BA in journalism. Since 1941 he has resided in Great Falls. During the war he served in the Army Air Forces from June 1943 to October 1945, attaining the rank of Corporal and was editor of a newspaper at Great Falls AFB. He has been married since 1940. At the time of this UFO sighting, he was general manager of the Great Falls baseball club, and was a radio sports commentator. He is regarded as a reliable, trustworthy, and honest individual and is highly respected in the community.
2. Witness II, 19 years of age, was employed as Witness I's secretary at the time of the sighting. She impressed the Air Force interrogator as being a "fairly reliable individual and of good sound judgment."

Analysis

In view of the detailed published analysis by Dr. Baker (3) I will limit this discussion to a summary of his results and some new results of our study.

A test not carried out by Baker has a bearing on his conclusions and thus will be described first. If the clear ellipticity of the images on the film were the result of resolution of disks oriented parallel with the ground, then the apparent inclination i, measured by the minor and major axes, b and a, would be equal to the altitude angle α. That is,

$$i = \text{arc}\sin\frac{a}{b} = \alpha$$

The b and a values were measured on a number of the frames, the first frames (the larger images) giving the best measurements. Table 3 shows the results.

In spite of the rather large uncertainties in the i measurements, especially in the later frames, the meaning of the table is clear: the flattening of the recorded image is not nearly enough to be explained by the foreshortening of a horizontally-oriented ellipse. As does Baker, I infer that the object probably is not really resolved; rather, it is a bright source with an angular size somewhat less than the maximum measured in the first frames (0.00151 radians). Since the measured apparent i stays constant while the angular size drops to 0.6 this value by the last measured frames, the true image size must be only slightly less than the apparent size and some of the rounding may be due to halation. Baker concludes that the ellipticity is due to camera panning motion; however, the relative consistency of the "i" values, plus the clear case of camera motion in frame 2, greatly exceeding the flattening in the other frames, indicates to me that there was a true and constant ellipticity or flattening. The true or intrinsic value must be "flatter" than the 59° indicated by Table 3, and could, of

Table 3

INCLINATION VERSUS ALTITUDE

Frame No. (See Ref. 3)	Inclination		Altitude
	i_1 (1st UFO)	i_2 (2nd UFO)	
1	64°	58°	15°
2	image blur due to camera motion		
3	57	59	
16	63	55	14°
32	57	58	
48	48	56	
64	55	52	
80	68	61	
96	58	63	
112	51	75	
128	50	52	13°

course, even be 14° (i.e., consistent with a horizontal disk).

With the conclusion in mind that the angular diameter was less than 0.00151 radians, consider the possible explanations of the film:

If the 15 August date were correct, the objects were not balloons or airborne debris because they are moving into the wind. They are disappearing to the SW, and Baker's analysis indicates a well determined azimuth heading of 171°, while the wind was out of the southwest (3).

The objects, as reported, were not birds because of the disk shape and general strangeness to both witnesses; the objects filmed are very unlikely to have been birds because of the linearity of the path and uniformity of the images over 16 seconds, with absence of any variation in photometry or shape that could be attributed to flapping (usually 5-13 strokes/sec.), changes in orientation, or changes in direction.

The objects were not meteors, since their angular rate of travel was so slow, and they were filmed for at least 16 sec., yet they left no trail, made no audible or visible explosions or fragmentation, and were not reported elsewhere across Montana and other northwestern states. The great bolide of 25 April 1966, for example, though it was visible for about 30 sec., underwent marked brightness variations and at least two explosions, left a marked trail indicated on all photos, and was seen by thousands of persons.

Past investigations have left airplanes as the principal working hypothesis. The data at hand indicate that while it strains credibility to suppose that these were airplanes, the possibility nonetheless cannot be entirely ruled out.

There are several independent arguments against airplane reflections. (1) Short-term variations in image size (correlated with brightness), time scale ca. 1 sec., are typically not more than ± 5%. *A priori* considerations of aircraft stability and empirical observations by Baker indicate that it is very unlikely that two aircraft could maintain such constant reflections over not only the 16 sec. and the 20° azimuth arc photographed but also the minimum of 50 sec. visually observed. I have confirmed this by studying aircraft visually in the vicinity of Tucson airports; in at least a dozen cases none has been seen to maintain a constant or unidentifiable reflection as long as 16 sec.

(2) Assuming that 15 August was the correct date, Air Force investigators found that there were two F-94 jets in the vicinity and that they landed only minutes after the sighting, which could well have put them in circling path around Malstrom AFB, only three miles ESE of the baseball park. However, Witness I reported seeing two planes coming in for a landing behind him immediately following the filming (3), thereby accounting for those aircraft.

References

1. Supplemental report of 9 January 1953, which was in response to an order from Project Blue Book for more information. This report contains an approximately one-page typewritten statement by the chief witness.

2. Investigating Officer's report of 6 October 1950, containing summary of information per provisions of Air Intelligence Requirements Memo number four.

3. Baker Jr., Robert M. L. "Photogrammetric Analysis of the 'Montana' Film Tracking Two UFOs," *Douglas Aircraft, Inc.*, March 1956. (Also published in *J. Astronaut, Sci.*, 15, No. 1, 1968. Includes:

3a: 1950—Interrogation of pilots of reported F-94's by Project Bluebook, probably identical to 2.

3b: 1950—Two sources of weather data: "weather maps," and half hourly surface observation by Weather Bureau at Great Falls Municipal Airport.

3c: 1955—Telephone conversation; R. M. L. Baker to witness I, March.

3d: 1955—Correspondence; R. M. L. Baker to Col. D. M. Hamilton, Commanding Officer, Malstrom AFB, November.

4. Craig, Roy, Private communications—see also Dr. Craig's discussion of this incident in Section III, Chapter 1.

5. Ruppelt, Edward J. *The Report on Unidentified Flying Objects,* New York: Doubleday; Ace, 1956.

Case 48

Barra Da Tijuca, Brazil (Coast of Brazil near Punta da Marisco; near Rio de Janeiro)

7 May 1952

Investigator: Hartmann

Abstract:

This case has been presented as one of the strongest and demonstrably "genuine" flying saucer sightings. It contains an obvious and simple internal inconsistency, which is pointed out by D. H. Menzel and L. G. Boyd.

Background:

This sighting is described in considerable detail in "A.P.R.O. Special Report No. 1" (Fontes, 1961; ref. 1). According to this description, the two witnesses, one a press photographer and the other a reporter of *O Cruzeiro* magazine, were on a "routine job for their magazine." Dr. Fontes, a Brazilian representative of A. P. R. O., quotes a television discussion of the case by Fenando Cleto, described as a "high ranking employee of the Bank of Brazil" and a leading Brazilian UFO private investigator (ref. 1):

> At 4:30 PM, [Witness II] suddenly spotted an object approaching in the air at high speed. He thought at first it was an airplane he was facing [see photo no. 1]. . . . There was still something strange, he realized. That "plane" was flying *sideways.*"
>
> He shouted, "What the devil is that?" [Witness I] had his Rolleiflex at hand and [Witness II] yelled, "Shoot . . ."
>
> [Witness I] grabbed his loaded camera and got five pictures in about 60 seconds, thus obtaining the most sensational photographic sequence of a "flying disc." [Two of these photos are reproduced in Plates 28 and 29, kindly supplied by APRO].

Investigation:

Dr. Fontes' report (1) continues with Mr. Cleto's account of Brazilian Air Force analysis of the photos. Mr. Cleto stated that he had been "authorized" by Brazilian Air Force officials to show some of the Air Force documents on the case. Mr. Cleto stated that certain diagrams provided by the Air Force "demonstrated . . . the absolute impossibility of a hoax" by virtue of distances and altitudes depicted. These dimensions exceeded the limits for a small model thrown by hand. Dr. Fontes also states that the graphic analyses and photographs constitute "absolute photographic evidence that the unconventional aerial objects called UFOs or 'flying saucers' are real."

Diagrams, apparently hand-lettered, are presented in reference 1 as based on "results obtained by the Air Force's top photography experts who did the analysis of the photos, including also the data, calculations and estimations obtained in the methodical and exhaustive technical investigations made at the spot where the pictures had been taken." Among their tests, the Air Force analysts made photographs of a hand-thrown wooden model (later confusing the case because of resulting local rumors that men had been seen photographing obvious models). However, no satisfactory justification is given for the distances from observer to disk, indicated on the diagrams as being on the scale of several kilometers.

In general, the Colorado project has avoided cases outside North America because of the difficulty of obtaining first hand evidence. It is not instructive to go into further detail about the history of the Barra da Tijuca case, because the information is third-hand and channeled through individuals we have not interviewed. (Experience has shown that this is usually unsatisfactory). Nonetheless, this case contains elements that must be taken into account in any general discussion of the UFO problem.

In spite of this case's presentation as one of the most convincing of all, with "*official documents* . . . perspective studies and mathematical calculations . . . cold, scientific facts" (Fontes emphasis), the case contains an obvious internal inconsistency that has still not been adequately explained. Menzel and Boyd (2) pointed out that on one of the photos, the disk is clearly illuminated from the left, while the hillside below appears to be illuminated from the right. They flatly label the case as a hoax.

Plates 28 and 29 show two representative frames of the series of photos. Plate 29 is the photo in question; the lighting of the disk is easily verified. Plate 30 is an enlargement of the hillside, and the palm tree as well as certain clumps of foliage appear to be illuminated from the right, in accord with Dr. Menzel's observation.

Dr. Fontes acknowledges this criticism, but states that "The solution is very simple. There are two broken leaves in the tree and one of them is in an inclined position while the other has fallen over the tree itself. These leaves are responsible for the 'wrong' shadow on the tree." This however, does not account for the additional clumps of foliage that also suggest the "wrong" lighting.

A map included in the Fontes report shows the Barra da Tijuca region. It appears from this map that the hills range clockwise from NW to SSW of the camera, while the sea stretches from WNW to SW. At 4:30 p.m. in May the sun, seen from this point near latitude 24° S, would be in the NW. The analytic diagrams based on the Air Force results show the sun at elevation 27½° and show the UFO approaching from the direction of the sun, then moving off to the right. This would seem to be in accord with the photos: Plate 28 appears to be backlighted *and* there would be hills to the right of the sun. However, the map is not explicit enough to determine which hills are shown, and the lighting of the hills suggests they may be the ridge SSW of the camera (far left of the sun).

There is not enough information available to suggest whether the Air Force, in attempting to duplicate the photos with a model at the site, discovered or considered this problem.

Conclusion:

The objection raised by Dr. Menzel is supported by our independent enlargement of one of the frames (kindly provided by APRO).

This case is presented as an example of photographs which have been described as incontrovertible evidence of flying saucers, yet which contain a simple and obvious internal inconsistency.

Sources of Information

1. Fontes, O. T. *APRO Special Report No. 1—The Barra da Tijuca Disc,* (October, 1961).
2. Menzel, D. H. and L. G. Boyd. *The World of Flying Saucers,* Garden City, N. Y.: Doubleday, 1963.

Case 49

Tremonton, Utah
2 July 1952 (Wednesday)
Investigator: Hartmann

Abstract:

Witness I accompanied by his wife (Witness II) and their two children saw and made motion pictures of a "rough formation" of apparent point sources "milling around the sky." The visual observations and film are not satisfactorily explained in terms of aircraft, radar chaff, or insects, or balloons though the films alone are consistent with birds. Observations of birds near Tremonton indicate that the objects are birds, and the case cannot be said to establish the existence of extraordinary aircraft.

Background:

Time: About 11:10 MST ("MST" appears in early AF documents, ref 4).

Location: Seven miles north of Tremonton, northern Utah (41°50′N; 112°10′W)

Camera Data: 16mm Bell and Howell Automaster; magazine load; 3 in. f.1. telephoto lens on turret mount; f/8 and f/16; Kodachrome Daylight film; hand held; 16 f.p.s.

Direction of sighting: First seen in east, moved out of sight to west.

Weather conditions: Cloudless deep blue sky. Sun at altitude 64.5°, azimuth 131° (Naval Observatory—ref 4).

Weather data from Corinne, Utah, about 18 miles south of the site, were obtained by Baker (1): Max. temp: 84°. Min. temp. 47°. No precipitation. A high pressure cell from the Pacific Northwest was spreading over northern Utah during the day. "The pressure at Tremonton would have a rising trend, the visibility good, and the winds relatively light."

Witness I, with his wife and two children (ages 12, 14) were en route from Washington, D.C. to Portland, Ore., driving north on State Highway 30 seven miles north of Tremonton (1.4a; refs. 2 and 3 incorrectly state the witness was in transit to Oakland, Calif.). The witness's wife called his attention to a group of "bright shining objects in the air off towards the eastward horizon" (1).

Sighting, General Information:

Approximately five weeks after the events, Witness I sent the following account to Project Blue Book (11 August; NT4-28/8310/177283; ref. 4a):

> Driving from Washington, D.C. to Portland, Ore., on the morning of 2 July my wife noticed a group of objects in the sky that she could not identify. She asked me to stop the car and look. There was a group of about ten or twelve objects—that bore no relation to anything I had seen before—milling about in a rough formation and proceeding in a westerly direction. I opened the luggage compartment of the car and got my camera out of a suitcase. Loading it hurriedly, I exposed approximately thirty feet of film. There was no reference point in the sky and it was impossible for me to make any estimate of speed, size, altitude or distance. Toward the end one of the objects reversed course and proceeded away from the main group. I held the camera still and allowed this single one to cross the field of view, picking it up again and repeating for three or four such passes. By this time all of the objects had disappeared. I expended the balance of the film late that afternoon on a mountain somewhere in Idaho (See Plate 31).

This letter serves as the principal descriptive document in the Air Force file (4). According to a chronology by Col. W. A. Adams, Chief, Topical Division, Deputy Director for Estimates, Directorate of Intelligence, in a letter dated 8 Sept., 1952 (4), the next contact with Witness I was an intelligence officer's interview on 10 Sept., 1952.

In this second deposition, as recorded by the Air Force Intelligence officer, the witness establishes the following facts: "No sound heard during observation. No exhaust trails or contrails observed. No aircraft, birds, balloons, or other identifiable objects seen in air immediately before, during, or immediately after obeservation. Single object which detached itself from group did head in direction opposite original course and disappeared from view while still travelling in this direction.

The witness used a "camera [without tripod] pointed at estimated 70° elevation and [panned] arc from approximately due east to due west, then from due west to approximately 60° from north in photographing detached object . . .

"Sun was approximately overhead. Objects were at approximately 70° above terrain on a course several miles from the observer . . . Bright sunlight, clear, approximately 80°, slight breeze from east northeast approximately 3 to 5 m.p.h.

[In the witness's] opinion: . . . Light from objects caused by reflection. Objects appeared approximately as long as they were wide and thin [sic]. [All of them] appeared to have same type of motion except for one object which reversed its course. Disappeared from view by moving out of range of eyesight . . . Observer facing north [during bulk of observation]."

The key witness had been in the Navy 19 years with service as a warrant officer and had over 1,000 hours on aerial photography missions (4b). Baker states the witness had 2,200 hours logged as chief photographer. The witness graduated from naval photographic school in 1935 (4b). He "does considerable ground photography" and "it is believed [he] could be classified as an expert photographer" (4b). Intrigued by his experience, the witness later accepted an "appointment as special Adviser to NICAP," acting in a private capacity (4, quoted from NICAP's "The UFO Investigator").

Investigation:

In 1955 R. M. L. Baker's analysis of the case, (1) gives substantially the same account, with the additional information: "When he got out, he observed the objects (twelve to fourteen of them) to be directly overhead and milling about. He described them as 'gun metal colored objects shaped like two saucers, one inverted on top of the other.' He estimated that they subtended 'about the same angle as B29's at 10,000 ft. (about half a degree, i.e. about the angular diameter of the moon)."

This data is a substantial addition to that recorded above. I have been unable to find any record of these statements in the Blue Book file supplied to the Colorado project (an inch-thick stack of nearly unsorted documents). The essence of Witness B's early deposition describes entities or "objects," apparently reflecting, bright, circular or spherical, at considerable distance. The indication of both his testimony and the film that he photographed captured (unresolved) objects nearly overhead, including one that retraced its motion above him, giving no suggestion that the objects could ever have been as large as half a degree even at close approach, or that Witness I ever clearly saw metallic construction saucer-shaped profiles. The witness's original letter of 11 August offers the film "for whatever value it may have in connection with your investigation of the so-called 'Flying Saucers,' " a phrasing which does not suggest he was convinced of the existence of extraordinary metallic craft at that time. Baker (private communication, 31 May 1968) indicates that the description in question was given in interviews about 1955. His memory may have become "set" by this time, or affected by events such as the witness's service as a NICAP advisor in the interim.

The film contains about 1200 frames (1), i.e. about 75 sec. After roughly 20 or 25 sec., the Witness decided he was somewhat over-exposing the film, and changed the stop from f/8 to f/16, trying to increase contrast (4a). The objects were milling around, often in groups of two or three travelling together among the others. The films indicate that the objects fluctuated markedly in brightness.

The witness had the film processed and submitted it to his Navy superiors (1). The letter from the witness to Hill Air Force Base, Ogden, Utah, 11 Aug. 1952, transmits the film to the Air Force (4c). The Air Force ATIC Blue Book team was advised, and the variability of the objects suggested airplanes, but this idea was ruled out because the witnesses heard no engine noise, and a large distance would have indicated impossible speed (10 mi. indicated 1300 mph—ref 1). Balloons were rejected due to the large number of objects, the random milling, and the departure of one object in opposite direction from the others.

A favorite hypothesis was birds, but there was no strong evidence in its favor, and it was believed the objects were too far away (hence too fast).

Ruppelt (2) reports that after several weeks, "the Air Force photo lab at Wright Field gave up. All they had to say was, 'We don't know what they are but they aren't airplanes or balloons, and we don't think they are birds.' " Baker (1) quotes Mr. Al Chop (who was with ATIC) confirming Ruppelt's account: the ATIC group was convinced they were not airplanes, but could not rule out that the camera might have been slightly out of focus and that the objects were soaring birds.

The films were then forwarded at the request of the Navy to a group of Navy photo analysts at Anacostia, who had some ideas about how to study the films. The Navy group concluded that the UFOs were intelligently controlled vehicles and that they weren't airplanes or birds. They arrived at this conclusion by making a frame-by-frame study of the motion of the lights and the changes in the lights' intensity. The analysts stopped short of identifying the objects as interplanetary space craft (2) although this implication was evidently present.

These conclusions were presented to the Robertson panel, which was meeting at this time (early 1953). Ruppelt reports (2) that there was some criticism of the Navy analysts' use of the densitometer, and that one of the panel members raised the possibility that while the key witness "thought he had held the camera steady . . . he could have 'panned with the action' unconsciously, which would throw all of the computations way off. I agreed with this, but I couldn't agree that they were sea gulls." The panel members' favored explanation of what was seen was white gulls which are known to inhabit the Great Salt Lake area. Ruppelt (2) concludes that he personally watched sea gulls later in San Francisco, circling in a clear sky. "There was a strong resemblance to the UFO's in the Tremonton movie. But I'm not sure that this is the answer."

R.M.L. Baker, Jr. made an independent analysis in 1955 under the auspices of Douglas Aircraft Co. He ruled out airplanes and balloons for reasons similar to those of the Air Force. In addition he argues against anti-radar chaff (bits of aluminum foil) or bits of airborne debris because of the persistence of non-twinkling "constellations," the small number of objects, and the differential motions. Soaring insects, such as "ballooning spiders" are unsatisfying as an explanation, as the objects were observed a short time from a moving car, indicating a considerable distance, and there were no observed web streamers.

Baker points out that since the tendency of the observer would be to pan *with* the object, not against its motion, the derived velocities are *lower* limits (unless the key witness panned with the group, not the single object). Thus the suggestion of panning could compound the difficulty with the bird hypothesis. Baker concluded that "no definite conclusion could be obtained" as the evidence remains rather contradictory and no single hypothesis of a natural phenomenon yet suggested seems to completely account for the UFO involved.

Menzel and Boyd (3) dismiss the objects as birds. Their conclusion, however, is phrased in a way inconsistent with the facts: "The pictures are of such poor quality and show so little that even the most enthusiastic home-movie fan today would hesitate to show them to his friends. Only a stimulated imagination could suggest that the moving objects are anything but very badly photographed birds." This gives the totally wrong impression that the objects are difficult to identify merely because of poor photography. The objects may be birds though unresolved because of distances, but the images are small and relatively sharp, and lack of a clear identification cannot be ascribed to poor photography. (The films we have analyzed are those shown to the Robertson panel, which evidently did not consider the solution as being so obvious as is implied by Menzel and Boyd.)

The Tremonton case came at a time when members of several official groups were privately concerned with the serious possibility that "flying saucers" might exist in fact (cf.2). The Navy report (4), released by the U.S. Naval Photographic Interpretation Center (the earliest known copy is stamped "Dec. 5, 1952"), was prepared by a group inclined to accept unknown aircraft. For example, the report contains under "Discussion" the following statements:

> In the analysis conducted, no attempt is made to explain the phenomena nor are the comments tempered by knowledge of present day science . . . Comments are as seen, as analyzed, and as computed; and as such, are partly at variance with the natural phenomena theories.

It is inferred in the Navy report that the objects are intrinsic light sources, not reflected light sources. This "opinion . . . is based on the time they can be viewed continuously on the film, approximately 90 sec., and on the angle through which they can be photographed, approximately 60°. It is felt that if these images were reflected light, blinking would occur." This inference ignores the fact that the objects *were* "blinking," i.e. erratically changing brightness, a fact pointed out in a list of questions which the report was designed to answer.

The velocity was treated in the Navy report by analyzing the final part of the film, assuming the camera was stationary and the objects moving perpendicular to the optical axis. " . . . the only unknown in the determination of the velocity is the distance from the observer to the object. This was arbitrarily set at five miles." Though it is celarly stated that this is an assumption, this treatment apparently led to misunderstandings, as we will show.

The findings of the Navy report were summarized in a list of comments including the following statements.

1. It appears to be a light source rather than reflected light.
2. No bird known to be sufficiently actinic . . .
9. Velocity was computed to be 3780 mph for a shift of 1mm per frame if the object is five miles from the observer.

The sentences immediately following the last quote show that the actual measurements show an average displacement not of 1mm per frame, but of "0.1729mm" per frame. It is then stated that "on this basis the mean velocity is 653.5 mph." Again, it is still *assumed* that the distance is 5 miles.

This result, properly interpreted, is quite compatible with that of Baker (1), who gives 670 mph for 5 miles distance. At ten miles, the speed would be some 1,300 mph; however, Ruppelt (2) in 1956 states, "Had the lone UFO been 10 miles away it would have been traveling several thousand miles an hour." This incorrect judgment is attributed by Ruppelt to the Air Force analysts, but may represent an incorrect reading of the Navy report.

In February 1953, the month after the Robertson panel meetings, there was correspondence within Project Blue Book on the wording of a press release on Tremonton. Ruppelt (4) suggested that it be stated that "the images were caused by surfaces having good light reflective qualities, such as sea gulls . . ." He noted that though many experts "firmly believed the objects to be sea gulls or balloons," the Air Force could not prove that they were. Apparently, no complete release of its Tremonton analysis was made.

As much as the intrinsic ambiguity of the images, it was apparently (1) the existence of a report intimating intelligent control (however inappropriately), (2) ill-advised statements that very high speeds might be involved, (3) the allegation that it could be and had been proved that spacecraft were involved, and (4) lack of serious response to his challenge made the Tremonton film a "classic" among flying saucer devotees.

An example of the distortion of the case in the popular press is an account in comic-book form, a copy of which is included in the Blue Book file that (while accurate in most other respects) shows the key witness photographing a series of large, disk-shaped objects of, one would judge, several degrees apparent size. Such subtle distortion makes the gull explanation seem absurd, and abets popular misconceptions.

Analysis:

Angular size, distance, and velocity. The angular size of the objects has been determined by Baker's microscopic measurements: (1) The angular diameters of images range from 0.0016 to 0.0004 radians (5.5 to 1.5 min. of arc). Assuming a "bird-size" reflecting circle of 8 in. diameter, these results would give distances of 415 - 1,670 ft., respectively. Their larger sizes are undoubtedly due to "flaring" and consequent overexposure of the images, substantiated by Chop's report (1) that they were very dense, "burned right down to the celluloid backing," and the Air Force analysts' report (4) that when the objects dimmed sufficiently, they faded out entirely with no dark dot or silhouette being visible.

Therefore, the minimum distance compatible with the bird hypothesis is estimated to be about 2,000 ft. At this distance, the hypothetical bright reflecting 8 in. breast would subtend about 1.2 min. of arc, and a 2 ft. wingspan, 3.6 min., or about 0.1 the angular diameter of the moon. The human eye's resolving power is 1 to 3 min. of arc (1). As the camera was pointed about 70° elevation during the filming, it is doubtful that the objects ever exceeded these apparent sizes or that a better visual observation was obtained. The dimensions given are compatible with several gulls known in the region, such as the California and Herring gulls (1, 5). Many of these gulls have breasts much more highly reflecting than their wings. Consequently the fact that the wings were not resolved either visually or photographically is not surprising, since they were at the margin of resolvability. This problem would be all the more likely if the "gulls" were smaller or further away.

As noted above, the Navy's and Baker's angular velocity measurements give similar values. Baker's measurements of the single object, where it is reported and assumed that the camera was stationary, gave values of 0.01 to 0.07 radians per sec. Variations were attributed to camera jiggling. Values averaged over two sequences were 0.031 and 0.039 radians/sec. These correspond to linear transverse velocities (at 2,000 ft. distance) of 14-95 mph, with the averaged values being 42 and 53 mph. Since the objects were at a high elevation angle, the transverse velocity probably approximates the total velocity. Taking into account an additional positive or negative uncertainty due to possible residual panning motion, the indicated range of velocities is compatible with the bird hypothesis.

Baker also measured relative angular velocities of the objects in the cluster with respect to each other, finding values ranging from zero to 0.0065 radians per second. At 2,000 ft. distance, this corresponds to 0 to 13 fps or about 0 to 9 mph.

"Flaring" and light variations. As indicated by the Robertson panel (2), the Navy conclusion that no bird could reflect enough light to cause such images was unsubstantiated. While there was no periodic variation reminiscent of wing flapping, the "flaring" of the objects and their intermingling and erratic motions suggest soaring birds. One gains the impression that sometimes the two to four objects in one of the sub-constellations flare almost simultaneously, suggestive of grouped birds wheeling in flight. (This is difficult to establish visually, as the film was scratched and the image jerky. In this regard I performed no quantitative test.)

Conclusions:

In favor of the hypothesis that the Tremonton objects were birds, probably gulls, we have the following arguments: (1) White gulls are known to be present in the area. (2) Bird-sized objects at a distance of 2,000 ft. would be on the limits of visual resolution, moving at about 45 to 55 mph east to west, with relative motions up to 9 mph; (3) Such motions are independently supported by the testimony that the objects overtook and were first sighted from a moving car traveling toward the NW. The objects were kept in sight until the car was stopped, and nearly a minute and a half of film exposed. (4) Baker points out that the departure of a single object from the group is typical of a bird seeking a new termal updraft. (5) Variations in motion and brightness suggest wheeling birds. (6) The bulk of informed opinion among those who studied the film, both in and out of the Air Force, is that birds were the most probable explanation.

Arguments against gulls include the following: (1) The distances and velocities cited are on the margin of acceptability. If the gulls were slightly closer, they should have been clearly identified since their angular size would exceed 3 min. of arc; if they were slightly further away, their velocity would become unacceptably high. This argument is considerably weakened by noting that somewhat smaller birds could be unresolvable but slow. (2) Arguments have been raised that the weather conditions would not be conducive to thermal updrafts that would allow long, soaring flights of birds. This is not a strong argument, however, since there is insufficient data concerning weather conditions. (3) No clear, periodic flapping is observed on the film. This is not critical, since there *are* erratic brightness fluctuations, and since the objects were evidently below the limits of resolution. (4) The strongest negative argument was stated later by the witness that the objects were seen to subtend an angle of about 0.5° and were then seen as gun-metal colored and shaped like two saucers held together rim to rim, but the photographs and circumstances indicate that this observation could not have been meaningful.

Although I cannot offer an expert ornithological opinion, it appears to me that the Tremonton objects constitute a flock of white birds. The data are not conclusive, but I have found nothing in the detailed Blue Book file incompatible with this opinion. The objects are thus provisionally identified as birds, pending any demonstration by other investigators that they could not be birds. There is no conclusive or probative evidence that the case involves extraordinary aircraft. On 23 August 1968 after completion of the above report, I had occasion to drive through Utah and made a point of watching for birds. The countryside near Tremonton is grassy farmland with trees, streams, and meadows. It was within 30 mi. of Tremonton that I noticed the greatest concentration of bird activity. A number of large gulls were seen, some with white bodies and dusky-tipped wings (rendering the wings indistinct in flight) and some pure white. About 10 mi. south of Tremonton and again about 20 mi. north of Panguitch (in southern Utah) I saw flocks of white or light birds at once distinctly reminiscent of the key witness's films. The birds milled about, the whole group drifting at about 20 or 30 mph (I noticed no surface wind) and subtending 10° to 20°. The individual birds (in the second case) were not quite resolvable, yet appeared to have some structure. Sometimes pairs would move together and sometimes individuals or pairs would turn and fade out as others became prominent. As suggested by the key witness they appeared to require a telephoto lens for photography. They were not prominent, but distinctly curious once noted — a group of white objects milling about in the sky. (The only proof that my second group of objects, which I observed from a considerable distance, were indeed birds, was that I saw them take off.) These observations give *strong evidence that the Tremonton films do show birds,* as hypothesized above, and I now regard the objects as so indentified.

Sources of Information

Baker, Robert M. L., Jr. *Analysis of Photographic Material,* Douglas Aircraft Co., 1955.

Menzel, D. H. and Boyd, L. G. *The World of Flying Saucers,* Garden City, N.Y.: Doubleday, 1963.

Peterson, R. T. *A Field Guide to Western Birds,* Boston: Houghton-Mifflin.

Project Blue Book files

a. Correspondence: Key witness to U.S.A.F., 11 August 1952.

b. Interview between A.F. Intelligence Officer and key witness, 10 September 1952.

Ruppelt, E. J. *The Report on Unidentified Flying Objects,* Garden City, New York: Doubleday; Ace Books.

Case 50
Fort Belvoir U. S. Army Facility, Va.
September 1957
Investigator: Hartmann

Abstract:

A black ring that became obscured by an opaque white cloud, reportedly witnessed by about 15 persons and photographed by the principal witness, is identified as the by-product of an "atom bomb simulation demonstration" on the army base.

Background:

Time: Approx. 9 a.m.
Position: Looking NNE past building T741, Fort Belvoir, Va.
Terrain: Gently rolling hills with scattered technical buildings, residential areas, and woods.
Weather Conditions: Exact date unknown; hence weather conditions unavailable. Photographs show scattered cloud cover.

Sighting, General Information:

Private X, who worked as a draftsman with Post Engineers (1), has given the following account of the visual and photographic sighting. He was in one of several buildings facing on a parking lot flanked by buildings T741 and T742 (1, 3). Someone from the outside called for the men to come out and see the curious object approaching overhead. Pvt. X and several others came out in time to see a dark, ringshaped object approaching in the north. He ran to his car in the parking lot and got his Kodak Brownie camera (1, 2, 5).

Pvt. X thought the black ring "seemed solid," as opposed to being "like smoke" (2), although he also stated that it was not metallic, shiny, or dull, but very black with no reflection (1). He estimated that the ring was about 60 ft. in diameter and five to six feet thick (2, 5). He felt that it moved systematically faster than the clouds (1), and was "high above the treetops," but below the clouds (2). It did not stop or hover, but moved continuously (1) and horizontally (2). Standing in one spot as well as he can recall (1), Pvt. X took six photographs of the UFO (Plates 32-37). Between taking the second and third, the black ring began to be "engulfed in smoke" (2), though Pvt. X does not remember seeing how this happened; he believes he was distracted by winding the film of his camera at that time (1). Sources 1, 2, and 5 are in agreement with regard to the circumstances and description of the UFO (All three references resulted from interviews with Pvt. X.)

The duration of the sighting was estimated at not more than five minutes (1), with perhaps 30-60 sec. required for the black ring to become enveloped by smoke.

Roughly 15 men saw the phenomenon, and at least two photographed it (1). Pvt. X did not know any of these men personally, as he had recently been assigned to work in this building. Efforts to locate other witnesses were unsuccessful. After watching the cloud for a while the men returned inside without waiting to see what became of it. There was a feeling at this time that perhaps the object represented some kind of secret test (1, 2, 5).

Investigation:

Pvt. X believed that the object was connected with some sort of test or experiment and that it perhaps should not have been photographed. As a result he made no inquiry or report at Fort Belvoir and did not have his photographs developed until a month after the incident when he had returned home (1, 2, 5). He notes, "I was only a private in the Army . . . the only thing mentioned was that it was strange and maybe someone was experimenting so we didn't tell anybody that we even took these pictures . . . I didn't want to get in trouble so when I came home I had the pictures developed then" (2).

Pvt. X had changed his residence five or six times since the photos were made and the original negatives have been misplaced. He still has the camera, a Brownie Holiday, purchased in 1957 (1). He showed the photographs to various friends, whose reaction was typically a mixture of joking and scoffing. Finally, in the spring of 1966, he showed them to a friend who sent the photographs to NICAP with an inquiry. Dr. James McDonald became interested in them in mid-1966 and called them to our attention. In view of the excellent photographic material we gave them a high priority.

With regard to the sighting Pvt. X has been an intelligent and interested advisor. His suggestions for locating other witnesses indicated a sincere attempt to be helpful in shedding light on the affair.

Photographic analysis. A preliminary analysis was carried out on this case on the basis of which it was regarded by us as potentially interesting. The early tests are briefly described as examples of the kind of analysis which allowed us to classify UFO reports as potentially important, verifiable, and/or explicable.

Consistency with observer's report. The photographs all overlap on a large tree whose complex foliage shows no parallax whatsoever, verifying Pvt. X's statement that all photographs were taken from one spot. This was later determined to be in the middle of the parking lot near Pvt. X's building.

By overlapping and "blinking" the six exposures, motions of the background clouds could be followed from Plates 34-37. The numbering of the photographs was found to be consistent with the motion of the clouds. A montage showing the object and cloud motions in the six frames is shown in Fig. 5. It is significant that the relative spacings of *both*

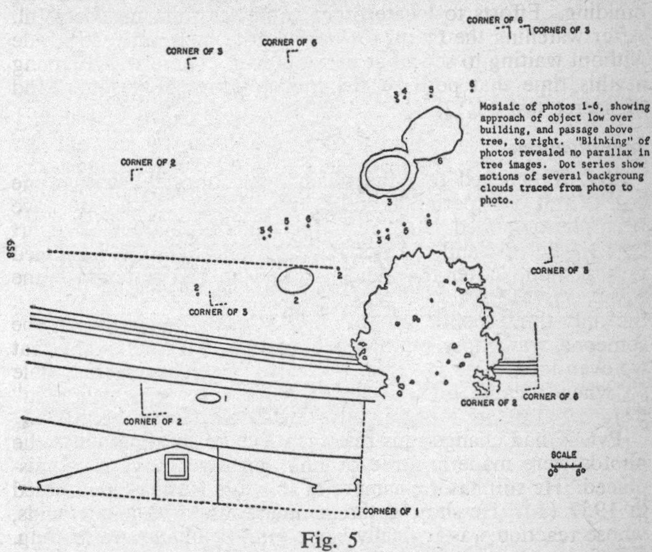

Fig. 5

UFO and cloud positions are the same; this is an argument against a fabrication created by sketching an object on six photographs, because such a fabrication would require a certain sophistication on the part of the artist.

The relatively long pauses after exposures 1 and 2, and the sudden burst of exposures 3 and 4, followed by the somewhat slower pair 5 and 6, are judged to be psychologically consistent with the sudden observation that the remarkable black ring was being enveloped, even more remarkably, by a white, misty cloud before exposure (3).

Geometric and physical tests; Inclination vs. altitude. If a flat disk or ring moves with its plane parallel to the ground (the mode of flight usually associated with "flying saucers"), the observed inclination angle (observer-center-rim) should equal the observed altitude. One initial hypothesis was that these photos could represent optical fabrication with an image drawn in on photographs made earlier. It was important to test the geometric consistency of the images with tests more sophisticated than might be expected of a hoaxer. Table 4 shows the results of these measures.

Table 4

Inclination vs. Altitude

Photo	*Inclination*	*Altitude*	*Pitch Angle*
1	19.9°	16°	4°
2	42.0	31	11
3	46.8	47	0
4	48.1	48	0
5	49.0	49	0
6	49.1	51	2

Only in Plate 33 does there appear to be a significant departure from level flight. From the apparent attitude of the ring in this photo it is judged to be out-of-level not only in the vertical plane of UFO observer, but in the vertical plane perpendicular to this. Nonetheless, it is concluded that the ring and disk-cloud can be described as oriented essentially horizontally, with some "wobble"-like perturbations.

Distance vs. angular size. If the linear diameter of the UFO is D and the angular diameter δ, and if its vertical height is Z and its altitude α, then (if δ is small),

$$\frac{\sin \delta}{\sin \alpha} = \frac{D}{Z}$$

if the UFO moves along a path roughly parallel to the ground. One has a subjective impression, both from the testimony and from the photos, that this was the motion in this case. Table 5 shows the results of measures of this sort (made with a millimeter scale on prints). It is concluded that within tolerances of 7%, the object did move on a path roughly parallel with the ground, although it may have been slowly rising and expanding.

Table 5

$$\frac{D}{Z} = \frac{\sin \delta}{\sin \alpha}$$

Photo	$\frac{\sin \delta}{\sin \alpha}$
1	.181
2	.170
3	.141
4	.147
5	.146

Illumination properties. Another item of evidence against an optical fabrication is the subtle consistency between the illumination of the cloud and the laws of physics. In Plate 34 when the cloud is first forming, it is tenuous. The optical depth is low, so that we can still see the dark ring inside quite clearly. The sunlight is coming from the upper right. If the optical depth is low, the sunlight must pass through the cloud with only moderate diminution. Hence, no strong shadows can be formed on the "dark" side of the cloud, as is shown by the photograph.

Plates 35 through 37, the cloud develops and becomes opaque. The dark ring becomes invisible, and a cumuloform structure can be seen. In Plate 37, the cloud is quite white and opaque, like a dense cumulus cloud. The optical depth is great; the sunlight must be absorbed and shadows must form. This is also shown by the photograph.

It is unlikely that had the prints been fabricated by using airbrush, the artist would have thought, even intuitively, to establish this consistency. This test, like the others, leads to the conclusion that the data are consistent with a real object becoming enveloped first in a tenuous, then in an opaque, cloud.

The fact that the six photos overlap lends interest to the case, relative to cases with markedly different backgrounds in allegedly continuous photo sequences. The rather subtle discovery of the cloud motions in the sky background confirmed that the photos were definitely taken in the order reported. The fact that the UFO spacings were consistent with the cloud spacings gives no support to the hypothesis of an optical fabrication with a drawn-in-image. The psychological consistency of the spacing of exposures adds credibility.

Finally, and perhaps most significant, the UFO was moving with a vector motion approximately equal to the background cloud vector motion; i.e. the directions and angular velocities were about the same. This at once suggested that the whole apparition was drifting with the wind, a conclusion consistent with the appearance of the smoky cloud.

Estimate of dimensions of UFO. Since the approximate velocity and height of the background clouds and the time intervals between photos are known, one can derive an approximate distance, hence size, for the UFO as a function of the UFOs height by using the observed cloud and UFO angular velocities. Although the exact date is unknown and therefore weather data were unavailable, we need only order-of-magnitude data, since the UFO dimensions are *a priori* quite unknown. A geometric model and estimated parameters were used in this way to estimate the diameter and distance of the ring. The observation that the UFO drifts smoothly and in approximately the same direction and with the same angular velocity as the clouds makes reasonable an assumption that the UFO is at an appreciable fraction of the height of the clouds, and large and high enough to be out of the region of ground eddies.

With these assumptions, using 20 mph as the wind velocity at cloud height, and various reasonable values for cloud height and time intervals, the assumption that the object was higher than one-tenth the cloud height, allows a rough estimation of the ring diameter as 30-600 ft. Once again, the conclusion was that all the data are compatible with a large, unusual, real object.

The case had come originally through Dr. James McDonald from NICAP. Although we made no effort to publicize it, it was described in a magazine article by Ralph Rankow (1967). Rankow presented it as a complete mystery, but his article generated a letter from Jack Strong, graduate student at the University of Wisconsin, who said that he had been present at bomb demonstration tests at Ft. Belvoir, and described clouds from such tests. At this time the suggestion was not taken very seriously, as none of those involved imagined that such a phenomenon would be produced by an explosion.

Sergeant-Major A. M. Wagner, interviewed at Ft. Belvoir, immediately identified the pictures as showing a cloud produced by "atomic bomb simulation demonstrations" which were frequently carried out at Ft. Belvoir for visiting officials and military cadets. This identification was made without mention of such a hypothesis. Before the geometry of the situation was discussed, Sgt-Major Wagner showed a map of the base and the location of the bomb demonstration site. It was clear that the ring and cloud in the photographs were drifting radially away from this site (see Fig. 6).

Sergeant-Major A. Husted further confirmed this and described the technique of the explosion. Five 55-gal. drums of gasoline, diesel fuel, TNT, and white phosphorus are arranged in a circle and detonated. The blast throws up a fireball enveloped in black smoke. The top of the mushroom cloud is a stable vortex ring, which ultimately drifts away. Depending on the weather and explosion conditions, this ring sometimes never forms at all and at other times forms a perfect, persistent circle. According to Sergeant-Major Husted, the white phosphorus produces a white smoke that eventually envelopes the black vortex produced by the diesel fuel. He estimated that the vortex occasionally held together as long as 40 min.

Strong, who believes he witnessed the same vortex that was photographed in this case, makes the following remarks: "I recall that the ring could be seen to revolve rapidly up to the time that the developing cloud had obscured details. By 'revolve' I mean, of course, motion about the centerline of the vortex [not around the vertical axis]. I don't recall the direction of this revolution, whether upward or downward through the center . . . This rapid rotation, along with the calmness of the air, probably had a lot to do with the great stability and symmetry of the vortex."

Photographs of one of the tests were obtained through Sergeant-Major Husted. Plates 38, 39, and 40 were made by Sergeant First Class James O'Dell and show the early stage of such a test, up to production of the independent black vortex.

The dimensions of the ring are estimated from the O'Dell photographs to be as follows: diameter $\sim$ 200 ft. for the fire-

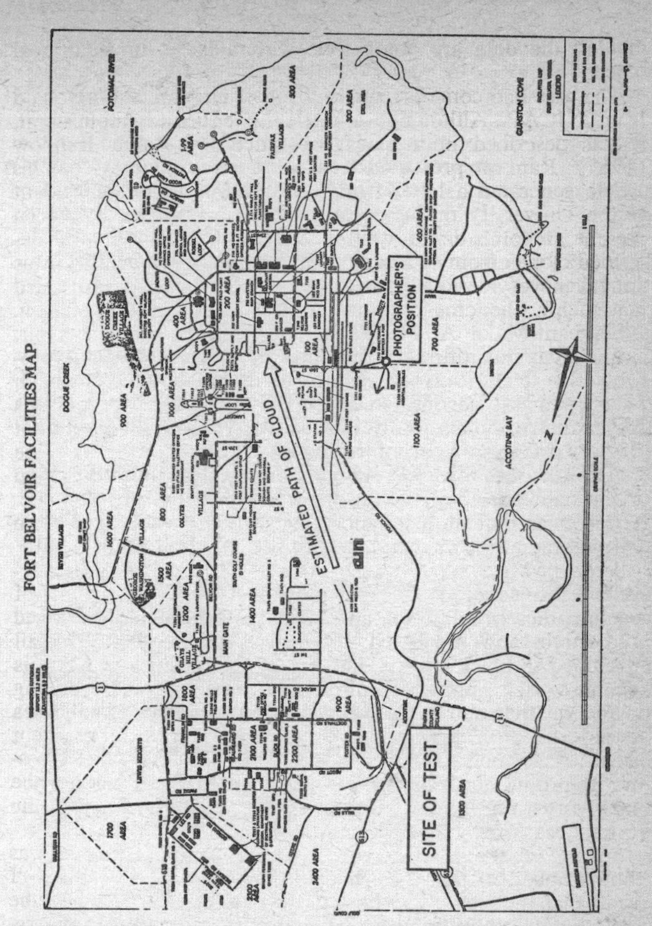

Geometry of Ft. Belvoir sighting superimposed on a map of the base. Arrows from photographer's position show directions of photos 1 and 6.

Fig. 6

ball in Plate 38, and 260-300 feet outside diameter for the ring in Plate 40. From the angular diameters of about 6° in Plates 32-37, and the estimated line-of-sight distance of 5,000 ft., a diameter of about 500 ft. is derived by the time the ring was passing near the witness. These figures are consistent with the expected expansion of the ring, and with the estimates made from the photographs (Plates 32-37) alone.

There are, on the other hand, some indications of possible

fabrication of the photographs. Upon close inspection, Plate 33 reveals a set of radial scratches or striations around the outer and inner borders of the black ring. Each mark is of length comparable to the width of the ring; the pattern is reminiscent of iron filings near a magnet. It is conceivable that these marks represent a retouching of the original vortex ring to make it appear more regular and thus more puzzling. It is also conceivable that these are a natural step in the formation of the white cloud. In view of the positive identification of the entire event and consequent irrelevance to UFOs, this question was not pursued further.

Conclusions:

In the light of identifications both by officials at Fort Belvoir and other technically competent observers familiar with the event, this case is considered positively identified as an atomic bomb simulation demonstration of the type commonly carried out at Fort Belvoir during this period.

The fact that this case did not come to light until nine years after it occurred because the witness was afraid of ridicule or possible reprimand for military security breaches testifies to the reality of the "hidden data" problem in UFO studies.

Sources of Information

1. Hartmann, W. K. (24 May 1967), Telephone interview with Pvt. X.
2. NICAP file on Ft. Belvoir incident, consisting of correspondence and interviews with Pvt. X.
3. Hartmann, W. K. (21 Dec. 1967), Interviews with staff personnel, Ft. Belvoir, Va.
4. Klass, Phillip J. (1967), Miscellaneous correspondence with Hartmann regarding Ft. Belvoir incident.
5. Rankow, Ralph. "The Ring-Shaped UFO," *Flying Saucers,* No. 4, (Fall, 1967).
6. Correspondence between Dr. James McDonald and Jack Strong, University of Wisconsin.

Case 51
Vandenberg Air Force Base, Calif.
5 December 1963
Investigator: Hartmann

Abstract:

During a daytime launch of a Thor-Agena rocket, several tracking cameras independently recorded a bright, star-like object apparently passing the missile. The object has been conclusively identified as Venus.

Background:

Time: 1:54 p.m., PST
Location: Complex 75-1-1, Vandenberg AFB, Calif.
Camera data: UFO clearly shown in films from site TS10, with a 16mm Mitchell camera using a 12 in. lens (frame rate:

24 FPS). Two identical cameras with 6 in. lenses did not show the UFO. Certain other films are also alleged to show the UFO but were not examined.

Weather conditions: Deep blue sky with scattered thin clouds. On the film sequence that shows the UFO, the sky is clear, but from the other two sites, at that moment, thin clouds were present, through which the rocket was still clearly recorded.

Sighting, General Information:

The sighting was reported by R. M. L. Baker (1) as an example of an unidentified object with potentially discriminatory tracking data. Baker had received a copy of the tracking film through contacts at Vandenberg (2), and subsequently brought it to our attention.

Investigation:

The tracking camera films were supplied to the project by the U.S. Air Force, and a 16mm copy of the three sequences described above was examined. It was noted that at the moment the UFO is visible, the rocket was moving down in the sky on a southerly course toward the horizon. Clouds drifted upward across the screen as the rocket passed them. The UFO had a similar motion, suggesting that it might be fixed in the sky, rather than "moving up past the rocket." This, plus the fact that the smaller lenses under poorer conditions did not record the object, in turn suggested the possibility that the object might be Venus, which reaches sufficient brilliance to be seen by the naked eye in a clear, daylight sky. Plate 41 shows a sample frame.

Classified tracking data made available (3) predicted the altitude and azimuth of the rocket as seen from "radar site 1," near the launch pad. From certain considerations related to the film, we know the absolute time of the passage of the UFO to within a few seconds, and the predicted tracking data gives positions at similar intervals. Fig. 7 shows a plot of the predicted path of the rocket, seen from "site 1" compared to the actual position of Venus. It can be seen that the rocket should have passed within 2° of Venus within a few seconds of the time that the UFO was observed. The predicted data can be taken as very accurate, but the actual position of the camera site TS10, some 5,000 ft. east of the pad, was probably east of "radar site 1," so that parallax would shift the rocket's path to the right by probably not more than 1°.

Conclusion & Summary:

At precisely the time that the UFO was recorded, the missile was less than 2° from Venus, and Venus was thus within the camera frame. The UFO image has precisely the properties expected for Venus. This compelling evidence leads to the conclusion that the "UFO" was Venus.

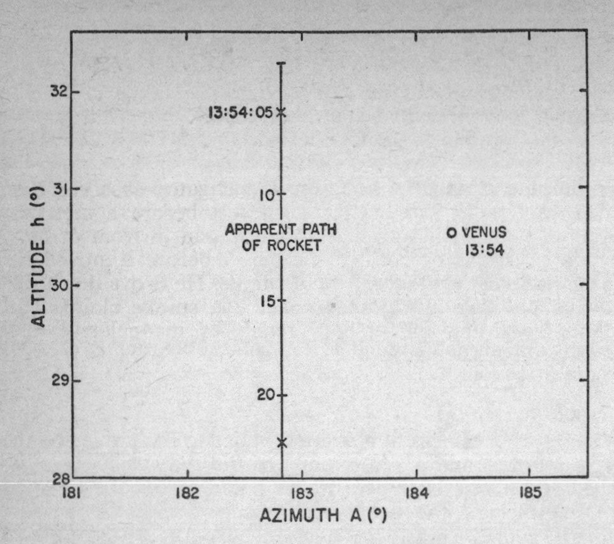

Computed position of Venus and path of rocket across the sky. The UFO sighting is known to be restricted to the time interval of about ±10 sec. around 13:54:09.

Fig. 7

We have heard many allegations, sometimes detailed and more often apocryphal, of UFO's being "observed," "tracked," or "photographed" during rocket tests at military bases. Many such "sightings" have been reported at White Sands Proving Ground in the last 20 years. In most reports there is insufficient detail to be checked. This case, before the films were located, had all the earmarks of such a report: an "object" was recorded on several different, independent cameras a mile or more apart. If assumed to have been near the rocket, the object would have been properly interpreted as very bright. A number of individuals had knowledge of the sighting, and therefore a number of rumors of an UFO passing near a rocket launched at Vandenberg could have been generated.

The analysis of this case leads to the suspicion, in the absence of better data, that most if not all such allegations may be based on similarly inconsequential circumstances.

Sources of Information

Baker, R. M. L., Jr. *An Introduction to Astrodynamics,* New York: Academic Press, 1967.

Interview with R. M. L. Baker, Jr. (W. K. Hartmann and Roy Craig, 21 September 1967).

Classified Air Force Documents.

Case 52
Santa Ana, Calif.
3 August 1965
Investigator: Hartmann

Abstract:

While he was on duty a Traffic Investigator observed that his two-way radio had been cut off just before a metallic-looking disk allegedly moved across the road in front of him. He took three photographs of the object before it moved off into the haze and emitted a ring of smoke. He drove down the road about a mile and photographed the smoke cloud. The evidence regarding the object's reality is inconclusive and internally inconsistent.

Background:

Date: 3 August 1965

Time: Approx. 12:37 p.m. PDT (Early reports give the time as 11:30 a.m. PDT. This was later corrected to 12:30 on the basis of studies of telephone pole shadows (6, 8). The observer had no watch (8).

Position: Myford Road, Santa Ana, Calif., approx. 0.3 mi. SW of the Santa Ana Freeway, ENE of the Santa Ana U.S.M.C. Air Facility and within the flight pattern of the El Toro Marine Corps Air Station.

Terrain: Flat farmland.

Weather Conditions: Ground observer: No wind, "some haze overhead" (1). G. W. Kalstrom, Meteorologist-in-Charge at the Los Angeles Airport, wrote "We do not have an observational report from Santa Ana at 11:30 AM . . . but from surrounding reports it would appear that the sky was hazy and the horizontal visibility was between 2½ and 5 miles . . . reduced by haze and smoke. Earlier in the morning there had been low overcast conditions but these clouds had apparently dissipated leaving considerable haze." (2). The photographs suggest considerable haze or smog. The investigator visited the site on 9 September 1967 and found heavy smog, apparently comparable to that shown in the witness' photographs, visibility was estimated at one to two miles.

The following analysis of weather conditions is an independent study by Loren W. Crow, consulting meteorologist, Denver:

SOURCES OF DATA

Hourly surface observations from—El Toro Marine Base, Long Beach, Los Angeles, Burbank, Ontario, March AFB, and Norton AFB, California.

Early morning radiosonde and upper wind observations from San Diego August 3, 1965, and Santa Monica, August 3, 1965.

GENERAL WEATHER SITUATION

The general weather situation during the forenoon hours of August 3, 1965 in southern California was made up of a stable air mass with onshore flow of air during the daylight hours and a low level inversion near the coast.

The air flow during the early morning hours was a light drainage wind from the land toward the coast. The inland stations of March Air Force Base and Norton Air Force Base near Riverside and San Bernadino respectively remained clear in the drier air over these stations. Ontario remained clear but visibilities were less than three miles between 6 a.m. and 11:40 a.m. with a mixture of haze and smoke.

Ground fog and fog formed in the moist air at Burbank, Los Angeles International Airport and El Toro Marine Corps Air Station during the hours of darkness just prior to sunrise. Overcast cloud cover with bases measuring from 300 to 600 feet were most common for near the coastal stations until after 8 a.m. when surface heating began to dissipate the cloud cover.

Between midnight and 4 a.m. the air flow at El Toro was from the east with velocities ranging from 2 to 4 mph. This was followed by a calm period lasting from 4:30 through 11 a.m. with only a brief period at 9 a.m. registering a velocity at 2 mph from the northwest.

At Long Beach the air flow was primarily from the east southeast between midnight and 6 a.m. It gradually shifted through southerly directions and developed an onshore flow beginning at 10 a.m.

The direction of air flow at Los Angeles International Airport was quite variable between midnight and 6:30 a.m. Velocities were generally less than 5 mph. with ten different directions being reported in this period. From 7 a.m. through midnight of the third, an onshore flow prevailed with the direction of flow being generally from 140° through 280°.

The dissipation of the fog and low cloud was directly related to the increase in surface temperature. Cloudiness would have disappeared earliest several miles inland from the coast and the cloudiness at any one point within 20 miles of the coastline would have gone from overcast to broken, then to scattered and finally to clear as heating took place near the earth's surface. Unfortunately, haze and smog increased and held surface visibilities to low values after the cloud cover had been dissipated by the warmer air.

The relationship between rising temperatures and the dissipation of cloud cover is well illustrated in the vertical cross sections shown in Figure 8 for the four stations nearest the coast. The time period covered by these cross sections is from 5 a.m. through noon. At the approximate time of the UFO sighting (11:30 a.m.), scattered clouds were still being observed at Los Angeles International Airport. Scattered stratus clouds at 1200 feet had been reported at the Long Beach airport at 11 a.m. but were not observed there at noon. The record does not indicate *when* they were last seen but their final disappearance would have been some time between 11 a.m. and noon.

MOST PROBABLE WEATHER NEAR SIGHTING POINT AT 11:30 a.m., August 3, 1967

By 11:30 a.m. on August 3, 1965, all overcast cloud cover

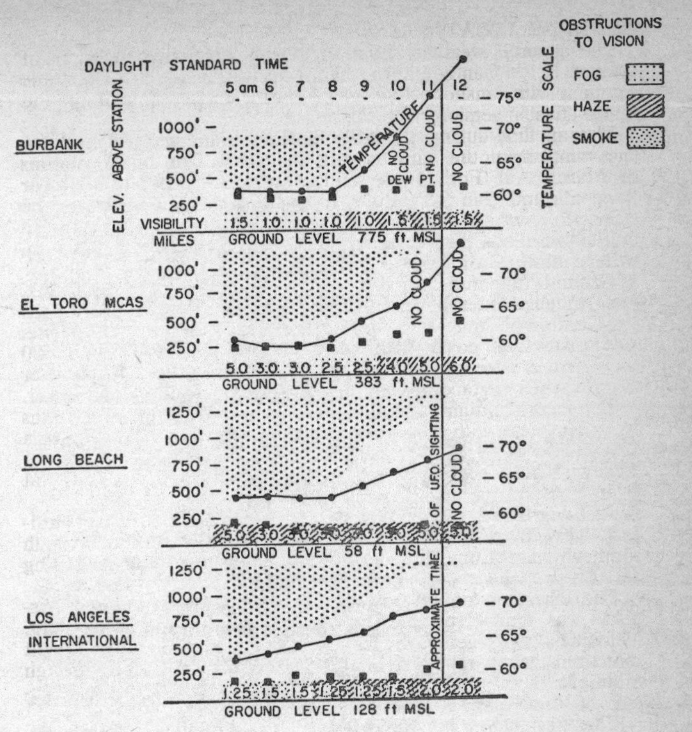

Fig. 8

would have been limited to over-the-ocean or a very narrow belt of land area nearest the coast where the onshore flow of air could carry it before the heated land surface would cause dissipation. At the forward (landward) edge of the cloud mass the cloud cover condition would change rapidly from overcast to broken to scattered to clear. The small cloud parcels making up the scattered condition could have seemed to appear and disappear rapidly. The disappearance would have been caused by the change of state from liquid water to vapor as mixing with the surrounding warmer air took place.

The forward edge of the scattered cloud condition would have been limited to the coastal side of the Santa Ana Freeway and probably was at a distance of 4 to 8 miles from the sighting point. Surface visibility reported at both Long Beach and El Toro Marine Corps Air Station at 11 a.m. was limited to 5 miles. Thus, any clouds which may have been sighted could only have had a rather vague outline as seen several miles away through the haze.

Sky conditions inland from the Santa Ana Freeway are believed to have been totally cloud free at this time.

Sightings, General Information:

Setting. On 3 August 1965 the witness, Traffic Inspector Tech 2 for the Orange County Road Department, Calif. (1) was driving SW on Myford Road in his official car, a Ford van bus (8, 9), inspecting overhanging growth along the roadside. He proceeded SW on Myford Road, turned around and drove slowly NE, at about 5 mph along the right-hand shoulder of Myford Road, about 0.3 mi. SW of the Santa Ana Freeway (3).

Radio disturbance. At approximately 12:30 p.m. PDT (estimated N.E. ±10 min.) the witness began trying to contact Orange Co. Road Maintenance headquarters by radio. According to the witness, about three words were received by base station "8" on East Fruit St. after which "The radio went completely dead (1)." An Air Force investigator later recorded notes that the witness stated "that he had attempted to use his two-way radio once or twice just before he sighted the UFO and could neither transmit nor receive any signal although the radio panel lights indicated that the radio was operational. Detailed questioning indicated that this definitely occurred before the UFO sighting and not during the UFO sighting (5)."

Both the witness' supervisor (4), and the Road Maintenance Superintendent were in vehicles (3, 7c, 14h). The superintendent was located about 0.5-1.0 mi. from the witness on the Santa Ana freeway, and states that he heard the witness trying to contact station "8." He heard the transmission begin, but after about three or four words there was a complete, sudden, sharp cutoff. He stated that the sudden cutoff was unlike normal radio interference or disturbance. The cutoff he heard could not have been produced by simply switching off the truck radio (7c). The Santa Ana FCC Facility reported no UHF or VHF interference on this day (5).

Visual and photographic sighting; description of object. The witness states:

> At this time, I became aware of the UFO, however I thought it was a conventional aircraft . . . The UFO moved from my left to in front of me and momentarily hovered there. At this time I grabbed the camera (semi-automatic-Model 101 Polaroid), from the seat of the truck and took the first photograph through the windshield of the truck.
>
> The object then moved slowly off to the northeast. I then snapped the second picture through the right door window (window closed). This is when I saw the rotating beam of light emitting from the center of the UFO on the bottom side. [See below-WKH]
>
> The UFO positioned itself to another angle of view and I snapped the third picture through the same side window as in picture two . . .
>
> As the UFO traveled, it maintained a relatively level altitude (150 ft.) in relation to the flat terrain, however the UFO acted similar to a gyroscope when losing its stability. The UFO continued moving away slowly gaining altitude, tipped its top

toward me slightly. It seemed to gain stability, then it increased its velocity (speed) and altitude more rapidly leaving a deposit of smoke-like vapor.

The smoke-like vapor was blue-black in color and circular in shape as though it had emitted from the outer ring of the UFO. This doughnut shaped vapor ring remained in the area in excess of thirty seconds. The UFO disappeared in a northern direction toward Saddleback Mountain (this is known on the maps as Santiago Peak and Modjeska) (1).

Plates 42, 43, 44 show the three photographs in the order mentioned above. Although the above reference does not mention it, a fourth photograph (Plate 45), of the smoke cloud, was later produced by the witness. The earliest document mentioning this photograph is a report by the witness and a NICAP investigator (2), and a letter by a local member of NICAP (3), both dated 25 September 1965.

On the basis of more detailed questioning, as reported in the referenced documents, it has been possible to construct the following more detailed account of the alleged visual and photographic sighting.

The camera mentioned is standard equipment for Orange Co. Road Department officials, and has the following characteristics: F. L. 114 mm., variable aperture from f8.0 to about f42, picture format 3¼ x 4¼ in., shutter speed "unknown but variable," and black-and-white film, speed ASA 3000 (4). The camera is described as fully automatic, utilizing a built-in light meter which automatically adjusts shutter speed and aperture. The only controls are a black-and-white or color select and a shutter release button (4).

Doubts as to whether or not the witness could have observed the UFO, stopped his vehicle and taken three photographs within 15-25 sec. were resolved by testing such a camera. It was determined that an experienced man could easily take three photographs within 12 sec. (5).

In reconstructing the incident two years later an investigator, accompanied by the witness and several others in an identical truck and with an identical camera, concluded that with the seat in the appropriate position, the UFO in the first photograph would have been obliterated by the top of the windshield as seen through the camera's snap-up viewfinder, but not through the camera's lens. The witness then remarked that he had not sighted through the viewfinder but "shot from the hip (8)."

According to the witness, he picked up his camera, shot the first photograph through the front windshield, then slid two feet to the right and slightly to the rear in the front seat (6), and shot the two other photos through the closed right window. From the second to the third photograph, the UFO has moved to the left (approx N) and the witness has shifted correspondingly to the right, apparently to keep the object in sight and centered in the window.

The UFO then assertedly continued on in this direction, diverging to the right from Myford Road by about 25° (i.e. heading 65°) and fading in the distance due to the smog (14).

The witness told a Colorado project investigator that he is not sure if he saw the "smudge" of smoke before he started on down the road (7a). He thinks he restarted the truck before proceeding, but does not recall definitely that he ever switched off the engine (3). He believes that he did not see the UFO again after he became aware of the smoke (7a). Answering the NICAP report form question, "How did the object(s) disappear from view?" the witness replied: "Left the area—northerly direction (1)."

The appearance of the UFO can be judged from the photographs as well as from various accounts and interviews. The apparent angular size, judged from the first photograph, was about 2°.4. The witness estimated a diameter of 30 ft., thickness of eight feet (1, 4), and distance of about ⅛ mi. (1, 4), which corresponds to angular diameter 3°.5. The object was also described on the NICAP report form as equivalent to a dome at arm's length, i.e. about 2°.6 in angular diameter.

The object was sharply defined, with a reflecting surface of "dull gray" color, with the sun "reflecting from different portions of it as it wobbled (1)." It did not change color (1). It made no sound, although the witness noted that nearby helicopters from the Marine Corps Air Facility could be heard, and that their noise could have drowned out sounds the UFO might have made (1). The AF investigation report described the color as "silver or metallic except for dark areas which appeared to be either whitish or metallic such as that which could indicate light reflection from a relatively slow-moving propeller or rotating blade. In Plate 43 there is a faint indication of such a line running from the center outward at a relative bearing of about 280°. Officials in the G-2 office at El Toro stated that the light line was clearly visible in the original (Plate 45) (see Fig. 9)." Heflin refers to this feature as a "light beam" in an accompanying sketch (1).

Asked if the bottom of the UFO appeared to have any type of structures, openings, or what might appear to be landing gear housings, the witness replied, "No! The only thing I saw on the bottom of the craft was a white beam of light emitting from the center and sweeping in a circle to the outer edge of the craft. The movement of the beam was similar to the sweep of a radar scope beam (1)."

A number of statements attribute a wobbling, unsteady motion to the UFO: The "object oscillated and/or wobbled (1);" it "moved slowly off to the northeast . . . positioned itself to another angle of view . . . traveled further northeast and

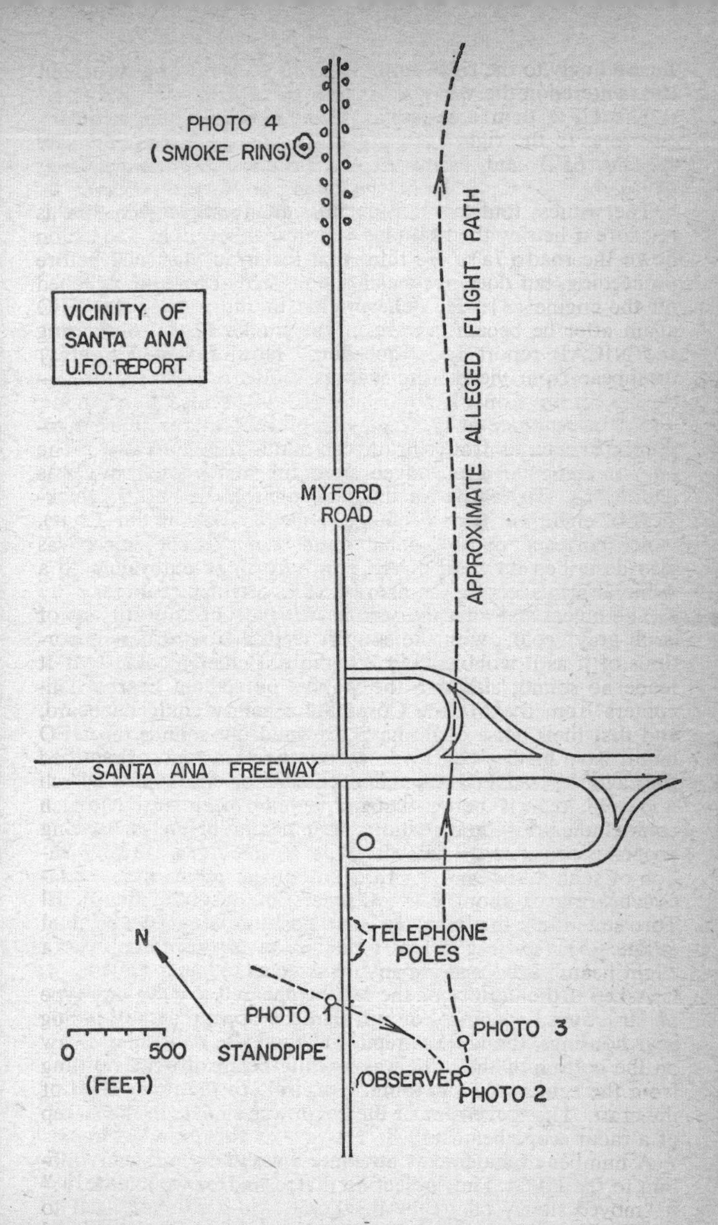
PHOTO 4
(SMOKE RING)
VICINITY OF
SANTA ANA
U.F.O. REPORT
MYFORD
ROAD
APPROXIMATE ALLEGED FLIGHT PATH
SANTA ANA FREEWAY
TELEPHONE
POLES
N
PHOTO 1
STANDPIPE
PHOTO 3
OBSERVER
PHOTO 2
0
500
(FEET)

Fig. 9

showed the upper portion of the craft (1);" it "momentarily hovered (1);" it "acted similar to a gyroscope when losing its stability . . . continues moving away slowly gaining altitude, tipped its top toward me slightly . . . seemed to gain stability, then increased its velocity . . . and altitude more rapidly (1)." On the NICAP report sheet, the witness suggests an airspeed of "300 mi. per hr. est. (1), which apparently refers to the rapid departure of the UFO.

The report to NICAP states that the interval during which the disc-shaped UFO was visible was "20 seconds max. (1)." The AF report notes: "Observer estimated total period of observation to be about 15 sec. Based on a test of observer's ability to measure time, it is believed the duration of sighting would be closer to 25 seconds (4)."

The witness drove about a mile NE on Myford Road in the direction of the smoke ring, which would have taken him through an underpass beneath the Santa Ana Freeway (7a). He had seen the ring before crossing under the freeway (14), and the implication of his statements is that he began driving in that direction in order to get a better look at the distant "smudge." He "drove his car quite some distance closer to where the object had been—got out of his car and pointed the camera right up at the smoke ring (3)." At approximately the location indicated, on the left (NW) side of Myford Road, stands a row of orange trees with overhead telephone wires, consistent with the fourth photograph (Plate 46): apparently the observer was looking to the NW over these trees at this point (7b). The UFO had departed at an azimuth about 25° to the right of Myford Road, (i.e. about 65°); the smoke ring had drifted to the left (NW) across the road (14). (See Fig. 9). The NICAP correspondence contains the following remarks: "You will notice that the smoke ring picture shows a rather cloudy sky, and perhaps the finishing of the photo may have something to do with it (3)."

In an interview at the site 16 January 1968, the witness pointed out not only the above angles, but also that the smoke "smudge," as seen from the first position, had an elevation angle judged to be 8°. This gives an altitude of about 700 ft. The witness stated that the ring was larger in linear dimensions than the UFO had been although he did not actually see it expand. When he left, it was still there, in the process of breaking up as the toroid expanded and dissipated (14).

After the sighting. The smoke ring was estimated to have "remained in the area in excess of thirty seconds (1)." Having described the smoke cloud and the disappearance of the UFO, the witness declared in his narrative, "At this time I contacted the Santa Ana Base Radio Station and asked them if they could now copy my transmission. They replied the copy was clear (1)."

The witness made no mention of his experience over the

radio (7c). Later that afternoon, at the end of the working day he returned to the office, and showed his supervisor only the first three photographs, not the "smoke ring (7c)." Another person states that the witness took him aside to show him the fourth photo, which he had left in the truck, but recollects that the witness probably did not show it to the others. He recalls that the witness said that "three were enough for one day" and that his story was already incredible enough (7g).

Radar results. ". . . A check made by the Marine Corps investigators indicated that no UFO was observed on the Marine Corps Air Facility radar at the time of the reported UFO observation (5)."

The "Facility" referred to by the Air Force investigator is a relatively small base within direct sight of the Myford Road site, but contains only a sporadically used training radar installation. Marine officials interviewed 15 January 1968, were unable to determine whether radar was in service 3 August 1965.

The Air Force investigator may have intended to refer to the surveillance radar, used in Air Traffic control at El Toro M.C. Air Station. Dr. J. E. McDonald and the Colorado investigator examined this radar, which has a four second sweep time and MTI filtering of ground clutter, such that only moving targets are displayed. It was quite clear that a UFO such as reported by the witness, though it would show up on the El Toro screens, would not be remarked by the routine operators. In the first place, it would appear as ground traffic; trucks on the Santa Ana freeway were clearly visible. Second, the entire area traversed during the first three photographs constitutes merely one radar "blip" diameter. Third, even if the UFO took off at moderate speed, it would probably be interpreted (if noticed at all) as a light aircraft. We were informed that no action would be normally taken unless it approached or endangered commercial or military aircraft, in which case only the larger aircraft, not the "light aircraft," would be contacted.

Numbering and sequence continuity of photos. Since Polaroid film packs carry numbering on the back, important confirmation for the Santa Ana case could be found if any of the witness' associates could testify that the four photos were in a continuous sequence. Generally, none of them could recall noting the numbers. The witness, however, testified in 1968 (14) that the pictures had *no* numbers on the back. J. E. McDonald therefore corresponded with the Polaroid Corporation and received the reply that "the numbers indicating picture sequence . . . have never been omitted by deliberate design. If the Type 107 film pack in question does not have these numbers, a rare oversight in film manufacture is responsible (15)." However, the witness demonstrated to NICAP investigators from county road department records that there was film in use during the period of the sighting that lacked sequence numbers (15).

Chronology of Subsequent Events and Interviews:

3 August to 14 September 1965. A friend "convinced the witness that they should try to sell the photographs to *Life* Magazine (5)." With the witness' consent he called *Life* the afternoon of the sighting, (7g) and later sent the photos to the Los Angeles office of *Life* (5, 12). According to the Air Force account, the Los Angeles office expressed interest and advised sending the photos to New York (5, 9); the photos were sent by the witness's friend and returned two weeks later "without written comment . . . at about the same time the Los Angeles office telephoned the witness to say that the main office had declined to utilize the material 'because it was too controversial' . . . (5)" The NICAP account differs slightly: "After a period of one week the pictures were returned with a letter stating that the subject was too controversial to publish, however, they did state that the pictures were the best they had seen so far (1, 5)."

During the first few days copies of the photos were requested by various of the witness' friends (5), and the witness let them take the originals to a photo service where copies were made (12).

"Time passed and apparently more copies of the pictures were made and handed out to various friends of friends, until most of Santa Ana was saturated with the UFO pictures (5)."

The witness loaned the original photos to his sister to show to a friend (9, 12), who took them to an amateur photographer (6, 12), who in turn made copies that were "poor but were not cropped (12)." According to the Air Force account, "one of these pictures was obtained by a druggist who then apparently showed it to a friend, a customer who worked for the Santa Ana Register (5)."

Possible Air Force Involvement in August, 1965. A document (10) entitled "Photo Analysis Report 65-48" was supplied to us by Blue Book. It carries the curious date "14 August 1965." The photographs were not public at this time, nor did the Air Force appear to be actively involved, since their first interview with the witness was on 23 September. One possibility is that this is a typist's error and should have read 14 October 1965, 12 days before the report was quoted in public as the Air Force analysis of the case.

This raises the possibility, then, that without the knowledge of any of the principals, the Air Force was involved in the case less than two weeks after it happened.

Officials of Project Blue Book informed the Colorado project in March 1968 that this question had been raised before, and that the Photo Analysis Report was in error, and that month should have read October.

15-18 September 1965. On 15 September the witness was interviewed by a reporter Frank Hall from the *Santa Ana Register* (9). According to Hall's recollection two years later the witness brought his three prints to the paper on the next day. These prints, the witness said, were not originals, but Polaroid copies of the originals which had been made by the witness' close friend (7d). They were good copies in the sense that they filled most of the frame; the second showed the "rotating light beam (7d)." It is not clear which copies these were. On Friday, the newspaper staff visited the site (7d).

The Air Force chronology states that on or about 18 September the *Santa Ana Register* borrowed the three original prints from the witness, returned them to him, and published an article with one UFO picture on 20 September 1965 (5). This account is compatible with the reporter's recollection, except that he believes the photos were not originals.

Chief photographer of the *Santa Ana Register* gives a similar account of the meetings with reporters (3): "The first photographs I saw . . . were copies of the originals . . . To me the photos looked clear, with all parts of the picture being in focus from the windows and [rear-view] mirror to the UFO and then farther on down the road to the cars . . . As far as I could tell the photos were authentic and had not been altered in any way whatsoever."

During the newspaper interviews, the reporter recollects, the witness suggested a polygraph test, but wanted the *Register* to pay the cost. The newspaper management, however, refused (7d). The Marine report carries this account: "During the interview with the *Register* reporter, the question was asked whether [the witness] would submit to a polygraph examination, concerning the UFO. He stated that he would . . . only if the *Register* or someone put up $1,500.00 with no results guaranteed. [The witness] feels that from his experience as an investigator [sic] that the polygraph is not reliable enough and that if the examination turned out negative, it would endanger his job (9)." It is difficult to choose between these two accounts.

18 September 1965. The witness was "prevailed upon to allow the *Santa Ana Register* to make six sets of negatives from the original Polaroid prints. He watched while negatives were being made. These were cropped (12)." The NICAP chronology (12) dates this as 18 September. The reporter however, spoke of these pictures as the Polaroid copies, not the original prints (7d). Thus it is not at all clear that the *Register* negatives were made from the *original* Polaroid prints, although the witness insists that the negatives were made from his originals (14).

On the same day the El Toro Marine Air Station investigator then interviewed the witness at his residence (9,5).

20 September 1965. The *Santa Ana Register* carried an

account of the witness' story with the first photo (5,1,12). *The Bulletin,* in Anaheim, also published at least one photograph (12). The Los Angeles NICAP Subcommittee first learned of the case on this day (12).

Two of the three photos were released by the *Register* to UPI (5).

The witness lent his prints to the Marine Corps investigator (12), who confirms that he did so without hesitation and without verifying the investigator's credentials or asking for a receipt (5). According to NICAP (12), these were the original prints. The Marine advised the witness "not to talk about his sighting (12)."

Among numerous telephone calls, the witness says he received two of special interest: one from a man who identified himself as a colonel attached to NORAD, the other from a man who identified himself as a representative of the Boeing Airplane Co. (5,12). The first caller allegedly asked the witness "to refrain from further comment until they have an opportunity to discuss the matter with him. A tentative date for the discussion [was] set for September 22—but no more was ever heard from the 'colonel' (12). The other man identified himself as an "engineer with the L.A. office of Boeing Aircraft . . . not representing Boeing, but personally interested, [he] asked that his name not be mentioned or the fact that he had phoned. He also suggested that it might be better if [the witness] did not talk about the case (12)." These calls are described in the same way in the Air Force report (5), though in less detail. Source (1) also describes the "NORAD" call, placing it between 18 and 25 September.

20 September to 21 September 1965. The witness received a number of calls in this period, in addition to the two described above. These included apparent hoax calls and two bomb threats (5). A letter came from a vice-president of McDonnell Aircraft, St. Louis requesting technical information (7f).

21 September 1965. The *Santa Ana Register* "reported that [the witness] had been 'muzzled' by the government. Dale Kindschy of the Public Affairs Office at NORAD's Colorado Springs headquarters said "We can find no one in our organization who contacted [the witness]. This wouldn't normally be in our scope anyway." Col. D. R. Dinsmore, Air Force public information officer in the Pentagon, said, "We have not yet confirmed that [the witness] was contacted by one of our people, but it would be normal procedure if they had (12)."

The fourth (smoke ring) photograph. The witness mentioned the fourth (smoke ring) photo to very few people up to this point in the chronology. The witness indicated the UFO merely left the area, toward the NE. One reporter recalls his saying that it went off to the right of the road (7d). The Marine report, apparently based on the interview of 18 September (although not prepared and dated until 22 September) says merely that "the object accelerated eastward toward the Saddleback mountains . . . he lost sight of the object due to the haze and distance (9)." The report carries only the first three photos. It would appear unlikely that the Marine report would have omitted an incident so remarkable as the "smoke ring cloud" had it been mentioned during the interview of 18 September, or during the transfer of the photographs on 20 September.

22 September 1965. The Marine Corps G-2 investigators returned the original prints (5) and obtained a signed receipt of return (12).

Later in the evening according to the witness, (source 12 places it two or three hours after the photos were returned) "two men, claiming to be from NORAD, arrived at the witness' home and asked to borrow the original Polaroid prints. They showed identification cards identical in appearance to those shown to him by the El Toro Marines. The witness turned the photos over to them. These three original Polaroid prints have never been returned (12)."

The Air Force account of the witness' version of this incident on 23 September is substantially the same, except that the witness mentioned only one visitor: ". . . on the evening of 22 September a man in civilian clothing visited his house, flashed an identification card, and announced that he was 'an investigator from the North American Defense Command.' [The witness] said that he did not examine the man's credentials closely but recalled that the man's I.D. card was in a special cardcase about 4″ x 5″ and that the single I.D. card appeared to consist of two sections—the upper half being orange or pink in color, and the lower half being blue or blue-green in color in the dimness of the porch light. [The witness] stated that he gave the original prints of the photographs to this man, again without receipt (he being a trusting soul), and assumed that he would eventually get the pictures back."

On 15 January 1968, the witness insisted that there had been two men (14).

The original photographs are unrecovered. The fourth "original" was lent to a NICAP investigator and eventually misplaced. A later investigation by NORAD resulted in a denial that any official of theirs had visited the witness. The witness' description of the I.D. card was likened to a gasoline credit card (11).

Some time on 22 September apparently in the evening after the photos had been surrendered, a NICAP member interviewed the witness. Neither this investigator nor any other NICAP member ever saw the three original photos.

Comment on the "NORAD visitors." The fact that on the day following the alleged visit of the NORAD officers, an Air Force investigator would leave with the clearly recorded impression (5) that only one man had visited the witness is of special interest. Further, a NICAP report dated 25 September 1965, signed by the witness declares that "*a man* with a brief-case later called . . . and said *he* was . . . and that *he* would like to see . . . [The witness] agreed to loan the pictures to *him* providing *he* would . . . (2, my emphasis W.K.H.)."

An attempt to clarify this on 15 January 1968 (14) was made by asking the witness in essence "Why it is that you are now clear on there having been *two* NORAD visitors, while on the very next day the Air Force man came away with the idea that *a* man came up and flashed *his* card . . .?"

He immediately replied in effect that only one man showed his card. He repeated that there were two men, in their early thirties, but that one stood back while the other did most of the talking. Since two independent reports from the next three days clearly indicate one visitor, while the witness has since insisted there were two, the "NORAD episode" is still regarded as open to serious question.

J. E. McDonald (15) has found an additional discrepancy concerning the "NORAD visitors." In 15 January 1967, discussions with Dr. McDonald and the Colorado investigator, the witness repeated that the I.D. cards shown him had no photographs of the bearers, although he described them as like those of personnel from El Toro Marine Corps Air Station. McDonald has learned from official sources that all I.D. cards carried photographs at this time. Indications are that if the two visitors did exist in fact, they were imposters.

25 September 1965. A letter dated 25 September to NICAP in Washington, D. C. accompanying supplementary notes contained the first NICAP reference to the smoke ring photograph: "One item of interest is, that [the witness] retained what he calls his ACE IN THE HOLE. A fourth picture. This picture shows clearly the vapor ring that was left by the UFO. [The witness] asked me to keep this information in confidence the night of the interview, however, if nothing came of the mysterious phone call asking [the witness] not to speak, then I would be allowed to pass on this information with a copy of the picture (2)."

A Los Angeles NICAP official wrote to NICAP headquarters: "You will see that there is a *fourth* photo—the smoke ring. I don't know what [the witness'] motive was in holding this picture back in the beginning. Perhaps he thought it was unimportant—and as time went on and the furor began, he hesitated to complicate the situation further and cause more problems for himself. He seems to be sick of the publicity and this weekend is moving and getting a new telephone number."

"Blaring headlines (12)" in most local newspapers announce "AIR FORCE LAUNCHES COUNTY UFO PROBE."

Further comment on the fourth (smoke ring) photograph. We have already seen that [the witness] was allegedly somewhat hesitant in showing the smoke ring photo when he returned to the road department office on 3 August and that he did not mention the smoke ring in early talks with the Marines or the *Santa Ana Register*. During the early NICAP interview the presence of a fourth photo was not recorded, although the ring was apparently mentioned. During the Air Force interview, the witness not only did not mention the smoke ring or fourth photo, but gave a somewhat different description of the disappearance of the UFO. The Air Force account states: "Just after taking the third picture . . . [the witness] heard a vehicle approaching from the rear. Concerned that he might have parked in an awkward position, he turned around to see if there was enough road clearance for the vehicle to pass him. Noting that he was on the shoulder of the road, he immediately turned again to look at the UFO but found that it had 'disappeared into the haze' (5)." This is the only account that mentions a diversion by another vehicle. It has been suggested by a NICAP member that this was probably a falsehood. On 5 June 1967 (7a) the witness said he had been advised by NICAP to withhold information from the Air Force to this end. An attempt was made to check this discrepancy in more detail on 15 January 1968 (14) by asking if the incident about the approaching vehicle had been manufactured as a cover for the fourth photo, and the witness denied that he had fabricated any of the testimony to the Air Force. He did not remember any passing vehicle, however (14).

27 September 1965. The witness sought advice from County District Attorney, Kenneth Wililams, regarding the harassment resulting from the UFO report and publicity (12).

4 October 1965. NICAP headquarters received a preliminary report from their photo analyst, Ralph Rankow, supporting the authenticity of the sighting.

A Saturday in mid-October (7f). The witness, a geodetic engineer, and two NICAP investigators visited the alleged site of the smoke ring photo and "identified the part of the tree appearing in the lower left corner of the picture (7f)." Additional measures and photographs were taken for the purpose of establishing the geometry of the sighting (12).

Clearly, the first allegation is of extreme importance, since the existence of such a peculiar vortex smoke ring *above Myford Road,* if it could be established from photo four, would be strong evidence in favor of the UFO report. As can be seen in Plate 45, very few physical details (part of a tree and a wire), are available to confirm the Myford Road location of Plate 45. With this in mind, on 15 January 1968 J. E. McDonald, R. Nathan, the Colorado investigator, questioned one of the NICAP investigators in detail about the identification of the tree. It became quite clear that the witness had taken them to the site, and that they had come away convinced by the gross geometry that this was indeed where photo four had been made. This is easy to do: having picked one of the several trees as the one in the photo, one can pick the "spot" within a few feet, using the parallax of the tree and wire (Plate 46). However, it was also clear that the NICAP men and the geodetic engineer had not carried out the extremely critical procedure of comparing the tree, *branch by branch and twig by twig* with that on the photograph, and that on geometric grounds it could *not* be said that it was absolutely certain that the photograph was made on Myford Road. As the NICAP man has pointed out (7f), "trees along the road have since been trimmed back," and it is no longer possible to perform this test.

17 October 1965. The U.S. Air Force released an official statement disputing the UFOs dimensions as estimated by the witness (12), reading in part: "The . . . evaluation . . . is based on enlargements made from copies of the original prints. Although it is not possible to disprove the size of the object from the camera information submitted, it is the opinion of the Air Force that the following is the true case. The camera was probably focused on a set distance and not on infinity as the terrain background was blurred . . . The center white stripe on the road and the object . . . have the same sharp image. Therefore it is believed that the object was on the same plane as the center white stripe (or closer) to the camera and could not possibly be the size quoted in the report. Using the width of the road as a factor, the size of the object was estimated to be approximately one to three feet in diameter and 15 to 20 feet above the ground (3)."

The statement appears to be based on, and quotes almost directly from, an internal U.S.A.F. "Photo Analysis Report 64-48" requested by Project Blue Book (10). The only significant additional information in the analysis is a final paragraph describing an experiment to reproduce the Santa Ana photos. "A test was conducted by the FTD Photo Analyst and Photo Processing personnel with the results shown on the attached photos . . . The object seen in the photographs was a 9″ in diameter vaporizing tray, tossed in the air approximately 8 to 12 feet high at a distance from the camera of approximately 15 to 20 feet. The result of the test shows a surprising similarity between the object on the test photography and the object on [the witness] photography (10)."

On 27 October 1965, Maj. Hector Quintanilla, Jr. of Project Blue Book, told the *Santa Ana Register*, that the Air Force had "classified it as a photographic hoax on the basis of extensive photo analysis (12)." Ralph Rankow, NICAP's photo analyst immediately announced strong disagreement with the Air Force analysis.

1 November 1965. On the basis of analysis by Rankow and Don Berliner (an aviation magazine photographer in Washington, D. C.) NICAP issued a press release calling the Air Force "hoax" classification "an insult to the intelligence of the public . . . [The witness] holds a responsible position and has suffered considerable embarrassment upon being accused of being a hoaxer, without evidence . . . We welcome independent analysis of the photographs by a qualified expert . . . Our own photographic advisers have found no evidence of trickery, but if some one else can find such evidence, we would like to settle the matter, one way or the other (12)."

9 December 1965. The *Santa Ana Register* quotes a letter from Air Force Col. William E. Poe to Rep. Alphonzo Bell (R-Santa Monica, Calif.) stating "We have not classified the photograph as a hoax (12)."

According to the witness, on 11 October 1967, during the period when our own investigation was beginning, an officer in Air Force uniform came to the witness' home in the evening and presented his credentials. Mindful of past experience, the witness studied them carefully. They gave the name Capt. C. H. Edmonds, of Space Systems Division, Systems Command. The witness reported this encounter within a few days to NICAP; he was sure about the rank and spelling of the name (14).

The man allegedly asked a number of questions, including "Are you going to try to get the originals back?" The witness claims that the man appeared visibly relieved when the witness replied "No." The "officer" also assertedly asked what the witness knew about the "Bermuda triangle" (an area where a number of ships and an aircraft have been lost since 1800's) (14).

This alleged encounter took place at dusk on the front porch. During the questioning, the witness says he noted a car parked in the street with indistinct lettering on the front door. In the back seat could be seen a figure and a violet (not blue) glow, which the witness attributed to instrument dials. He believed he was being photographed or recorded. In the meantime, his FM multiplex radio was playing in the living room and during the questioning it made "several loud audible pops (14)."

In order to investigate this report, NICAP sent a letter to "Capt. C. H. Edmonds," Space Systems Division (the office from which the original Air Force investigating officer had come), but received no reply. Robert Nathan, an independent investigator, phoned and talked to people who remembered the original Air Force investigator of 1965 but could not identify "Edmonds." Robert J. Low of the Colorado project obtained from the Air Force data on officers of similar name. The list contained four "C. H. Edmonds," but none with the correct rank and spelling. All were of rather high rank and none should have had any connection with the Santa Ana case (14).

The significance of this report is still unclear but suggestive.

Other alleged inquiries. During an interview with the witness, 15 January 1968, he indicated that he believes his phone had been tapped, that many friends had reported they could not reach him on occasion, and that the phone company found that only *his* wires had been tampered with. He also stated that on three or four occasions his neighbors had advised him that men in military uniform had come to his door during the day, when he was not there.

Analysis:

Rather than recount in detail the long series of interviews, experiments, and questions that were involved in analyzing the Santa Ana case, only the value of the case in terms of the UFO problem and the possible reality of extraordinary flying objects will be considered here.

From the point of view of the Colorado study the principal question of concern is: *does a case have probative value in establishing the reality of unusual aircraft?* In a case like this, where both the observer and photographs *clearly* allege an extraordinary vehicle, a second question is, of course, automatically implied: does the case represent a fabrication or was the object a true unknown? But it is not in general our purpose to make a judgment on that question. We are concerned only with establishing evidence as to whether or not there exist extraordinary flying objects.

In that context, this case is equivocal.

In the course of my study I was able to simulate effectively the first three photographs by suspending a model by a thread attached to a rod resting on the roof of a truck and photographing it (Plate 47). Without assuming the truth or untruth of the witness' story this has led me to conclude that the case is of little probative value.

Conclusion:

The evidence for the reality of the UFO is not sufficiently strong to have probative value in establishing the existence of extraordinary flying objects. The strongest arguments against the case are the clouds in photo four and the inconsistent early records regarding the "NORAD" visitors. The photos themselves contain no geometric or physical data that permit a determination of distance or size *independent* of the testimony. Thus the witness' claims are the essential ingredients in the case. The case must remain inconclusive.

Although the authenticity of the UFO in this case is still open to question owing to internal inconsistencies in the early testimony, and inconsistency of the photographs and weather data, this case is still held to be of exceptional interest because it is so well documented. This is a result of early attention from the U. S. Marine Corps, the U. S. Air Force,

NICAP and the press. Regardless of the existence or non-existence of extraordinary flying objects, this case supplies good documentation of the dealings between our society and a man who claims to have seen one.

Sources of Information

1. NICAP report form and handwritten narrative, 22 September 1965.
2. File of miscellaneous documents supplied by NICAP including narrative report, 22 September through 17 December 1965.
3. File of miscellaneous correspondence supplied by NICAP including several narrative letters, 24 September 1965 through 11 January 1966.
4. Basic Report LAW AFR 200-2. Report to USAF based on interviews, 23 September 1965.
5. Narrative Report and Assessment. Report to USAF based on interviews, 23 September 1965.
6. Re-evaluation of shadow circumstances. Report to NICAP by NICAP investigator, 23 July 1966.
7. Hartmann, W. K. Miscellaneous telephone interviews and correspondence, 5 June 1965.
   a. Telephone conversation with witness, 5 June 1967.
   b. Visit to the site on Myford Road, Santa Ana, 9 September 1967.
   c. Telephone conversation and correspondence 28 September 1967; interview 16 January 1968.
   d. Telephone conversation 18 October 1967.
   e. Telephone conversation 22 November 1967.
   f. Correspondence 5 November 1967, and 25 November 1967.
   g. Phone conversation 11 January 1968.
   h. Interviews at El Toro Marine Corps Air Station, and others, 15 January 1968.
8. Nathan, R.
9. U. S. Marine Corps G-2 Investigation Report, El Toro Marine Air Facility, 22 September 1965.
10. Photo Analysis Report requested by Major H. Quintanilla for U. S. Air Force.
11. Letter from Chief of Staff, NORAD.
12. Chronology of Events, received by W. K. H. 18 November 1967. Prepared in 1967 and based on original NICAP files, 1965-67.
13. Crow, Loren W. Special report to Colorado project on weather conditions related to Santa Ana sighting, 4 December 1967.
14. Joint meeting in Los Angeles with witness and other interested parties, 15 January 1968; interview with the witness at Myford Road, 16 January 1968.
15. McDonald, J. E. Private communication; correspondence with Polaroid Corporation, 1968.
16. Vallee, J. and Vallee, J. *Challenge to Science*, Chicago: Regnery, 1966, pp. 30, 43.

Case 53

North Eastern
Summer 1965
Investigator: Hartmann

Abstract:

Two photographs of a bright disc with a reportedly invisible but (in Plate 48) opaque, reflecting, and (in Plate 49) glowing "appendage" can be easily produced by hand-holding an illuminated model. There is no probative evidence for an unusual phenomenon.

Background:

Time: 11:30, E.D.T. (1)
Locale: Backyard in populated area; hilly terrain (1, 2)
Weather: Hazy evening sky; bright moon; no wind noticeable (1).
Camera: Yashika 635 camera; Altipan 120 film (ASA 100); f:3, focus infinity, six-second exposures (3).

Sighting, General Information:

The key witness was aiming his camera upward at an angle of roughly 30°-45°, in a southwestern direction toward the top of a hill close to the house (2,5). As he prepared to take a time exposure, he noticed a "bright white," "self-luminous" object, "brighter than the moon or headlights" approaching from behind some trees on the horizon to the left (1). The object was seen nearly simultaneously by the key witness and his brother. The object moved "like an airplane would go" (5), "faster than a Piper Cub" (1), but then suddenly hovered. The key witness made a hurried exposure (Plate 48).

The object then drifted to the right, brightening somewhat (1). Again it hovered; the key witness had advanced the film and made a second exposure (Plate 49). Then the object "zoomed up" (1), or "rose at high speed and disappeared" (4), before a third exposure could be made. No sound was heard. (1) The object, described as a "big, disk-shaped light," uniformly white, not reflecting; without a clearly visible surface (5), "solid, flattened on bottom, was visible for about 30 sec.

The negatives showed an opaque, dark extension beneath the object in the first photo, and a bright, apparently transparent extension below in the second; the witnesses repeatedly stated that this was not visible to them at the time of the sighting (4, 5).

Investigation:

At the urging of friends the key witness presented the photos within a few days to the local newspaper. (3, 4). The newspaper staff made a careful study of the negatives, superimposing them, determining that there was no parallax in the horizon trees and no shift in position of the moon, but that the object was in two different positions.

Critique:

The similarity of the appendage of Plate 49 to a human arm and hand with knuckles, thumb, with shadows being consistently suggested is striking. Test photos (Plates 49, 50, and 51) simulating the originals were made in the following manner: A dish was held by a hand gripping a short handle which had been attached with tape to the bottom of the dish. The dish was illuminated by a flashlight and moved during the brief exposure. In the test simulation of Plate 48, the light was kept off the supporting arm, while in Plate 49 the light was played over the wrist and additional streaks were introduced by moving the illuminated hand across the field (after the dish had been removed). The test exposures illustrate the possibility of simile reproduction (Fig. 10) of: (1)

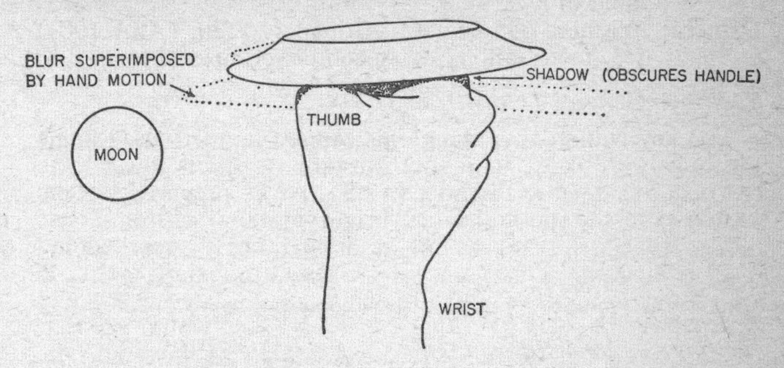

Fig. 10. Schematic diagram of Plate 51 and hypothetical reconstruction of Plate 48.

the glowing, blurred disk (plate or model), (2) the opaque appendage in Plate 48 (unilluminated arm supporting model); (3) the glowing appendage with hand-like features (illuminated hand); (4) the transparency of the glowing feature (removal of the arm during the time exposure); (5) non-detection of continuation of appendage in densitometry (duration of "UFOs" presence = small fraction of total exposure time).

Conclusion:

The photographs have little value in establishing an extraordinary phenomenon.

Sources of Information

1. NICAP Report form filled out by witnesses.
2. Correspondence between P. J. Klass and W. K. Hartmann.
3. Internal NICAP correspondence, kindly provided by NICAP.
4. Klass, P. J., *UFOs Identified,* New York: Random House, 1968.
5. Fuller, J. G., *Incident at Exeter,* New York: Putnam's, 1966.

Case 54
Gulfstream Aircraft, Huntsville, Ala. to Minneapolis, Minn.
11 March 1966
Investigator: Hartmann

Abstract:

An electronics specialist associated with the Marshall Space Flight Center, on a flight from Huntsville, Ala. saw and photographed an exceptionally bright, elliptical UFO. The object was lower than the plane and appeared to be at a great distance moving away from the plane. The object is inconclusively identified as a sub-sun on the basis of photographic evidence, though not all the testimony directly supports this.

Background:

Time: About 3:00 to 3:20 p.m. CST

Aircraft Position: En route nonstop from Huntsville, Ala. to Minneapolis, Minn. Altitude: 20,000 to 22,000 ft. Exact location unknown. (Source 1).

Weather Conditions: Partly cloudy below the plane; complete overcast above, with the sun not visible (1).

Photographic Data: Kodak Retina II, 35 mm Plus-X (2) black-and-white film (ASA 160); Xenon f2 50 mm lens (uncoated, perfect condition), focused on UFO during first exposure; exposure 1/500 sec at f16. Exposure meter General Electric PR-1, serial number J95126 (Source 1).

Sighting, General Information:

During a chartered Gulfstream Aircraft flight from Huntsville to Minneapolis, the witness, an electronics specialist for Marshall Space Flight Center observed from the rear left window an extremely bright object outside. Initially the object was estimated to be about 15° behind the plane in azimuth and 5° below. The photographs, Plates 52-55 indicate a much greater declination below the horizon. The initial direction of the object was believed to be southwest of the aircraft, based on an *assumed* northerly heading, and was observed for approximately 20 min. (All descriptive material, Source 1).

Fifteen months after the sighting the object was described by the witness in a letter dated 13 June 1967, as follows:

> Perfect ellipse with axes ratio of approximately 1:3, with the major axis horizontal (see Fig. 11). The edges were sharp and perfectly defined. Surrounding this ellipse was a brilliant halo which I noticed but did not study as much as I did the object. The brilliance made my eyes water and pain.
>
> [The color was] overall brilliant yellow-orange, very much like the sun . . . The UFO always appeared the same, except diminishing in size, perfectly outlined with a halo. No other detail was seen. It did not change its flight line . . . The UFO was southwest of the plane at first and disappeared northwest of the plane. I am here assuming the plane was always flying on a north heading . . .
>
> The distance could not be determined accurately, but I had a distinct impression at first that I was viewing something from ½ to 1 mile away. Also the camera rangefinder indicated a long distance but not infinity. I have had considerable experience in judging distance and elevations of airplanes and in photography. Later the UFO was much more distant, as shown in the film . . .
>
> The UFO was viewed under several different conditions. At first it was slightly behind the plane, lighting the inside of the

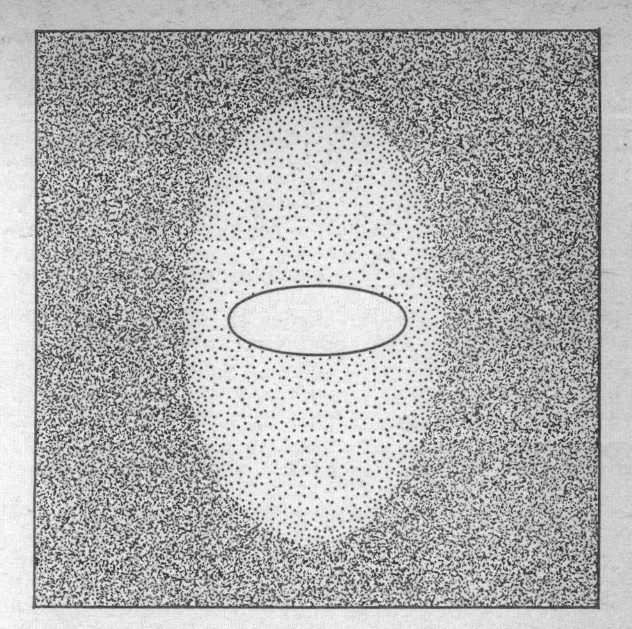

Fig. 11. Sketch of reported visual appearance of the UFO, after a sketch by the witness. The central horizontal ellipse was reportedly the brightest; the photos show only the halo.

plane. I moved my head to see if it would affect the image. I cupped my hands around my face and on the pane. Neither of these changed the view at all. For the first picture (Plate 52) I backed about four feet away from the window . . . so as to frame the UFO with the window frame. This was to add perspective. The other pictures were taken through the window while the camera was held close to it. One of the other frames shows a small section of the left wing . . .

I was immediately shocked at the appearance of the UFO. It seemed too definite in outline to be a reflection, sun dog, or ice crystal image of the sun, even if the sun had been shining. I have often seen such natural phenomena, since I have studied meteorology, but pay little attention to them. This was different. It was just too bright to be natural, I thought. Remembering the often reported sudden disappearance or speeding up of UFOs, I expected it to do likewise. But it did neither. I had waited a few minutes after seeing it before I realized it might stay long enough for a picture. After the first one, I took the other three at about 5-minute intervals. The situation was embarrassing. I felt I should be able to explain the UFO but could not since the sun was not shining. Furthermore, I could not arouse interest in any of the other six or eight passengers, who were playing cards. Only one man, an engineer, even bothered to look at it, explaining it as a "reflection."

The witness considered and rejected several explanations of the phenomenon. He had seen and launched several kinds of balloons and had seen skyhook balloons launched; he was sure that it was neither a balloon, a plane, or "any other object I have ever seen" (1). His background includes varied experience in radio repair and electronics. He holds a B.S. in electrical engineering and has worked at Marshall Space Flight Center (Redstone Arsenal) since 1958. The witness has been very cooperative and articulate in supplying supplementary information on the sighting.

Investigation:

Of several scientific colleagues with whom the witness discussed the sighting after his return on 12 March, "a few insisted that the light on the pictures was a sun dog or a weather balloon even though I had insisted the sun was not out" (1).

The witness "did not report it officially because of the way witnesses have been treated." After showing the film to various other colleagues, including "Ph.D.'s and highly specialized scientists," the witness contacted Dr. J. A. Hynek, and the case was subsequently brought to the attention of the Colorado project.

The similarity of the object to a sub-sun at once suggested an explanation. A photograph of a sub-sun provided by NCAR (Section III, Chapter 3, Plate 2) strengthened considerably the sub-sun hypothesis. Minnaert (3) describes this phenomenon as follows:

> This is to be seen only from a mountain or an airplane. It is somewhat oblong, uncolored reflection; the sun reflected not in a surface of water but in a cloud. A cloud of ice-plates, in fact, which appear to float extremely calmly judging from the comparative sharpness of the image.

Several objection and questions are raised by this hypothesis. The most serious objection is that (1) the witness stressed that the sky above the aircraft was so overcast that he could not see the sun. Considering the sub-sun hypothesis it is necessary to assume that the overcast was thin enough, especially during the first minutes of the sighting, to allow a bright image of the sun (even if diffused by overcast) to be produced by laminar ice crystals. A gradual increase in density of the overcast above the airplane would provide a natural explanation of the fading of the apparition and would not contradict the witness' belief in an overcast.

(2) The witness reported that the direction was initially southwest of the aircraft "15° behind" it, but that the UFO

disappeared to the northwest. During an interval of only 20 min. the azimuth of the sun, and hence of the sub-sun, could not change by such a large angle (though the motion of the sun would contribute a few degrees in this direction). These estimates were with respect to the plane and were based on the witness' *assumption* that the plane was flying *constantly* due north. Since the witness mentions that the initial southwest direction of the UFO was only 15° behind the plane, it is clear that "southwest" and "northwest" are not to be taken literally as 90° apart. Furthermore, Plates 53 and 55, which can be oriented by the wing, were made about 10 min. apart but indicate a shift in the UFO's position of not more than a few degrees. Therefore, a change in flight direction of 30° or less, would explain the apparent change in direction of the sub-sun. A change such as this would not necessarily be obvious, especially in overcast flying conditions. Since the course from Huntsville to Minneapolis is north-northwest, the view out of the left side would be west-southwest, the approximate direction of the sun at 3:00 p.m., supporting the sub-sun hypothesis.

(3) The object was described as a "sharp and perfectly defined" horizontal disk with a vertical "halo"; but, the photographs do not confirm the horizontal ellipse. Although the major axis of the ellipse was sketched nearly as wide as the halo, microscopic examination of the original negatives and high density prints (Plates 56 and 57) give no indication of a central bright ellipse. Only the halo was photographed. Although the inner part of the halo is overexposed and evidently saturated, masking a possible small central ellipse, photographic evidence suggests that any flattened central disk was not as well-defined or as large as the testimony might suggest. An indication that the inner isophotes do not have as large a vertical ellipticity as the outer isophotes is evidenced by the fact that the images on the last photographs, when the apparition was evidently fainter, are more rounded. This may account for the witness' impression of a horizontal, flattened inner core. In all respects, the photographs of the witness appear to be similar to the sub-sun photograph supplied by NCAR.

(4) The object was so extremely bright that it was reportedly capable of throwing the exposure meter off scale, illuminating the inside of the plane, and hurting the witness' eyes. These observations apparently refer to the initial sighting, before the apparition dimmed (Plates 54 and 55). One might question whether a sub-sun could appear so bright. A sub-sun is literally a reflection of the sun; that is, its brightness could approach that of the sun itself, if the reflector were efficient enough. Ambient light over a cloud deck is already

large, and a relatively small fraction of the sun's full brightness in an image reflected under especially good conditions could produce the reported effects.

(5) The apparent decrease of angular size would not be expected in a reflection of the sun. The witness interpreted this as a departure of the object: "Later the UFO was much more distant as shown in the film." The film shows only that the angular size of the "halo" and apparently the total brightness decreased. Since no clear, hard, disk-shaped core can be made out in the over-exposed central "halo," there is *no* photographic evidence for a decrease in angular size of a well-defined object or for an increase in its distance. The observed image sequence could have been produced by a gradual decrease in brightness; i.e., by obscuration of the overhead sun or by decreasing density or alignment of the reflecting ice crystals.

(6) The witness focused on the UFO and concluded that his rangefinder "indicated a long distance but not infinity." However, he "had a distinct impression at first that I was viewing from ½ to 1 mile away." These two statements are inconsistent. In conclusion it appears that there are no significant and accurate data on the distance of the object in view of the difficulty of accurate focusing on ill-defined or very bright objects and of the inaccuracy of the registration of distance on many camera rangefinders.

(7) Finally, we must remark that the witness does not believe that the object was a sub-sun, regardless of evidence presented in the above argument. In spite of this subjective response, one can judge the case only on the most objective data, i.e. the photographs and his most descriptive testimony. The witness makes no assertion that the object was artificial or solid.

Reflections appear to be ruled out as the witness cupped his hands around the window in order to study the moving object.

Summary and Conclusion:

In summary, the principal arguments in favor of the sub-sun hypothesis are: (1) The appearance is consistent with that of a sub-sun. (2) The azimuth is consistent, within the limits of the known direction of flight. (3) The elevation angle of the sun above the horizon must equal the declination of the sub-sun below the horizon; it is calculated to be approximately 30° ± 4°. Estimates of the declination, based on the known angular scale (photo height ca. 26°) and the estimated vanishing point of the clouds in the photographs (the horizon being out of the frame) place it in the range 28 to 33°. These figures are consistent.

The sub-sun hypothesis requires that the witness overstated the situation by insisting that "the sun was not out." An overhead cloud deck of not too great opacity may have led the witness to this assertion.

In spite of some questions raised by the testimony, the apparition can be inconclusively identified as a sub-sun. In view of the high degree of similarity of the photographed object with a sub-sun, it would be unwarranted to assert that this sighting constitutes evidence for an extraordinary or unknown phenomenon.

Sources of Information

1. Report of the witness to Colorado project (13 June 1967).

2. Correspondence and telephone conversations between the witness and Colorado project (June-July 1967).

3. Minnaert, M. *The Nature of Light and Colour in the Open Air,* N. Y.: Dover, 1954.

Case 55
N. M. (Aircraft flight from St. Louis to Los Angeles over N. M.)
22 April 1966
Investigator: Hartmann

Abstract:

The pilot and passengers of a commercial airliner sighted a bright cloud-like object that was in view for several minutes. The pilot speculated that it was a flare experiment launched from White Sands Proving Grounds. The most consistent evidence is in accord with this. However, the case has the interesting, if dubious, distinction of having apparently been confused later by extraneous photographs and testimony given by a sailor, who was a passenger, to a civilian UFO investigator.

Background:

During the evening twilight, about sunset, American Airlines Flight 387 from St. Louis to Los Angeles was passing over Farmington, N. M., at an altitude of 33,000 ft. (1). The pilot announced to the passengers that he had spotted an unusual object outside the aircraft. A preliminary account of the sighting is best reported in notes taken by Witness I immediately after the incident:

> . . . The pilot called our attention to an object off (at a great distance) from our left wing. It was early twilight. He said, "I have never seen anything like it before. Other planes in the area have also seen it nor can they identify it." We were at an altitude of approximately 33,000 feet and well above

all clouds. The pilot moved our plane much closer. The pilot said, "It is entirely too high to be a cloud." It appeared at first to be a very bright cloud but there was a long rosy cloud-like tail behind it. . . . Then later it appeared to solidify more and have a ring around it. It appeared in this form for perhaps only a minute then went back to the original form. After about seven minutes, it evaporated.

The pilot then said, "In all fairness we are now over New Mexico and it might be something from White Sands." He laughed. "If anyone reports seeing an unidentified flying object, I will deny seeing it."

In the seat next to me sat a young sailor from Cleves, Ohio, who took a picture of it and said he would send it to me.

Witness I's notes go on to relate two UFO incidents recounted to her by the sailor, Witness II.

Investigation:

A year after the flight to Los Angeles (17 April 1967) Witness I was queried by Mr. L. H. Stringfield, a private UFO investigator. She reported the following supplementary information:

> Persons sitting on the left . . . for the most part looked out of the window. On the right side a few persons stood to look out the left windows, then everyone settled back to magazines and newspapers in a surprisingly short time. I think (Witness II) and I were the only ones in our section (First Class) who watched it until it disappeared.
>
> The object, assuming it was a UFO, was covered by a jet-like vapor. To me it looked like a beautiful white cloud. . . . Either it was enormous and a great distance away or it was smaller and much closer than I realized. The cloud-like tail was rosy in color. It kept pace with us (10-15 minutes?) until it briefly solidified, then the vapor (cloud or whatever) stayed where it was and wafted away.
>
> The sun must have been dead ahead. We were flying west/southwest. . . . The pilot said, "Please look off the left wing-tip if you want to see a flying saucer" (or maybe he said UFO). . . . We were in perfectly clear blue sky in the early twilight above the clouds. I thought whatever we saw was an "escaped" cloud, but the pilot said it was impossible to have clouds at our altitude.

The sailor, Witness II, was contacted in April 1967 by Mr. Stringfield, to whom he related the additional information that the pilot had checked with the "control tower" and found there were two other aircraft within 100 mi. These were evidently the planes that reported the object. Witness II stated that he thought the American Airlines plane might have been over Utah. The object was off its left (southern) wing. He described the object, according to Mr. Stringfield's notes, as "brilliant white phosphorous light; oblong, without definite contour, moving parallel to ship, same speed; one and a half minutes in view; disappeared forward and up at tremendous speed; UFO seemed to advance and retreat in flight without any change of light intensity or color" (3).

Witness II reported to Mr. Stringfield that he took "about four" photos, two of which were submitted. He used sunglasses, described as sunglasses for an acetylene torch, as a filter in his photographs (3). He had earlier told Witness I (2) that the "photo" (singular) did not "turn out." However, he subsequently claimed to Mr. Stringfield that he had done this to avoid publicity and that, furthermore, "there was a top-secret mission involved and he (Witness II) could not talk about it" (quoted from ref. 4—not directly from Witness II).

Investigation:

On 16 January 1968, the Colorado project contacted the pilot of the airliner, who confirmed the event. He said that he saw one brilliant object which he thought was a sodium flare. This he reported to the FAA ARTC, which he said could not identify the object. The pilot said his position was over Farmington, New Mexico, and that the object was also seen from several aircraft north of him. He felt that the object was something fired from White Sands Proving Ground, about 300 mi. SSE of Farmington. It was the brightness of the object that led him to believe it was a sodium flare. He believed the flare was still in sunlight although the plane was already in shadow; he also recalled the tail extending from the object as described by Witness I.

It appears that an initially unidentified object was undeniably seen from Flight 387. The testimony consistently indicates that the object was distant and far above the commercial airliner; the pilot believed it was high enough to be illuminated after sunset. A quantitative, order of magnitude estimate of the distance can be based on the fact that the object appeared to "keep pace" with the aircraft for a matter of at least 1.5 min. (Witness II), or 10 to 15 min. (Witness I). That is, the parallax was negligible for, say, 10 min. (Witness II's testimony is given lower weight; see below). At approximately 500 mph, the plane would have moved through a baseline of the order 80 mi. during this interval. Had the object drifted through $\leq 20°$ parallax during this ten minutes, its distance would have been of the order ≥ 240 mi. This estimate is consistent with other sightings by other planes in a distance range on the order of 100 mi.

It should be noted that the position for optimum visibility of a high, illuminated cloud was at a considerable distance away, but not far to the west, so that the still-illuminated cloud was seen low in a twilight sky. A pilot more nearly beneath it might not have seen it during its few minutes of visibility.

The object described clearly had the appearance of a cloud. Witness I's sketch depicts a somewhat elliptical cloud (with traditional scallop-like outlines and a smoky tail extending upward to the right). The "ring" to which Witness I refers is shown in a second sketch as a streak or bar in front of the cloud. Because the object was suspected to result from an experiment launched from White Sands, the project requested information on this possibility from the Air Force. Col. Quintanilla, of Project Blue Book, informed us that (1) there was no record of any test on this date, (2) tests that could produce such phenomena (flares, etc.) were not rare in this southwestern area, and (3) systematic records of such scheduled tests are generally not preserved after three to six months. Verification of a flare experiment was therefore not possible.

The following data strongly suggest a high-altitude flare and/or rocket experiment: (1) large distance and altitude inferred by several witnesses and the order-of-magnitude calculation; (2) the tail, characteristic of exhaust train left by the vehicle carrying the "flare"; (3) bright light which attracted the pilot's attention; (4) rapid fading or "evaporation" in a matter of minutes (dissipation of emitted material or termination of illumination?); (5) pinkish color of tail suggests illumination by setting sun.

Highly inconsistent with these factors is a part of the testimony of Witness II. Other witnesses did not report the remarkable motions he described. His photographs, made with a Kodak 126 Instamatic with color film, (Plate 58) show not the cloud-like, slightly elliptical object of the other observers, but a highly flattened orangish ellipse with a sharp outline, against a black background. Witness I reported that Witness II took "a picture" of the cloud-like object, which he subsequently said did not come out. He reported four photographs and submitted two to Mr. Stringfield, who forwarded the negatives to the project. At this time, Witness II told Mr. Stringfield that he could not discuss the matter further because of a secret project. (If the implication is that he was associated with the project that produced the object, his presence on the commercial airliner would seem irrelevant; if another project is indicated, silence would be unnecessary.)

The photographer who prepared color prints from the two submitted negatives advanced a hypothesis that the photo was a fabrication. The blue-green object in the upper left (alleged to be the aircraft wing) was held to be a fluorescent light fixture; the orange ellipse, an electric lamp, seen from the side; and several other orangish light spots, reflections off a chair. The colors are consistent with this. This alleged wing appears to be entirely in the wrong position. (i.e., overhead; the top is defined by other scenic negatives on the film) for the wing of an American Airlines commercial airliner to be seen from the left side from a First Class seat. The "wing" is of brightness comparable to the reportedly very bright UFO. It appears that there is considerable support for the hypothesis that the photos in this case are extraneous.

Conclusion:

Evidence suggests that some type of man-made flare experiment or test was sighted by the pilot and passengers of American Airlines Flight 387, as the pilot speculated. The case was complicated by some inconsistent and apparently extraneous photographs for which there is evidence of fabrication.

Sources of Information

1. Notes by Witness I, 22 April 1966.
2. Correspondence between Witness I and L. H. Stringfield.
3. Notes by L. H. Stringfield on conversations with Witness II.
4. Colorado project notes on conversations with L. H. Stringfield.
5. Conversation between the pilot and Colorado project personnel.

Case 56
North Pacific
Winter 1967
Investigator: Hartmann

Abstract:

This case involves two photographs of a disk-shaped UFO. The apparent time interval between the photos is inconsistent with the eight-second reported interval (which was based on careful restaging of the alleged incident). The report must be listed as internally inconsistent and therefore is not satisfying evidence for an unusual phenomenon.

Background:

Time: 3:45-3:46 p.m. PST.
Location: Backyard of suburban residence.
Weather: Some rain earlier in the day, overcast (1). The observers reported wind as "north to south—16 mph" and "cloud cover at 2100 ft.," allegedly based on contact with the weather bureau (1). The weather bureau (2) data: for 3:40 p.m. ground winds were recorded as gusting up to 39 mph from the WSW with a squall line moving through; at 3:58 p.m. the winds were 14 mph from the SSW and clouds were scattered at 2100 ft.; broken at 2500 ft.; and overcast at 6000 ft. The conflict in reported wind direction between the witnesses' report and weather bureau may be due to their mis-

understanding the reported direction, "210°," (*from* the SSW).

Camera data: Polaroid "Swinger" camera.

Sighting, General Information:

Witnesses I, II, and III were in the backyard when Witness III reportedly saw a disk-like object hovering above them and pointed it out. He continued watching while Witness I ran indoors and got the camera. Witness II immediately took the camera and shot the first photo (Plate 59) as the object still hovered. His brother, Witness I tore off the exposed picture and held it as the Polaroid film developed.

At this point, the disk had begun to move. As soon as Witness II was able, he took a second picture (the last one on the roll) as the UFO moved off in the distance (Plate 60). The position from which this second photo was made was about five yards to the right of the previous photo. The UFO disappeared in the distance with a smooth motion.

The object was described as solid, of a definitely metallic, dull-grey color (3) estimated to have been as much as 25 ft. in diameter (1).

The witnesses took the photos to the local newspaper. The photos were later distributed by a wire service.

By restaging the entire sequence of events it was determined that the interval between the two photos was about eight seconds and not longer than ten seconds, the time required to make two rapid-sequence photos, and that the entire sighting lasted about 45 sec. This timing was held to be fairly accurate; i.e. to within about 25% (3).

Critique:

However, overlapping and blinking of the two prints indicated that, while the principal dark grey cloud mass beneath the disk in Plate 59 is probably the same as the mass over the church in Plate 60 it had considerably changed its form and the other clouds were not recognizably the same.

Parallax of the trees indicates a shift in camera position that is small compared to the distance to the tree. These reported positions were later measured to be about five yards apart, consistent with the photos. Plate 60 was reportedly taken from a position to the right of Plate 59 on a line nearly perpendicular to the direction of view in Plate 59. Since this position is not appreciably further from the trees, the considerable downward shift of the cloud is not related to parallax, unless the reported separation was incorrect in azimuth and in distance by a factor of about three.

Thus, the photos appear to be inconsistent with the testimony. The time interval and possibly the positions would have to be independently and simultaneously in error by factors of about three to explain the inconsistency between the photographed clouds and the testimony. In fact the downward (westward) motion of the main dark cloud, combined with the direction of winds aloft from the SW, inconclusively raises the possibility that the pictures were taken in reverse order from that reported.

The angular diameters of the object in Plate 59 and 60 are about 2°.7 and 0°.82, respectively. The elevation angles are about 24°.6 and 11°.0. If the boys' distance estimate of 0.5 mi. in Plate 59 were correct, the corresponding diameter of the craft would be 120 ft. (In Plate 60 at the estimated five miles, it would have to be about 380 ft., but we have already assumed that the five mile figure was erroneously large.) If one assumes a diameter of 50 ft. (compromising between the 25 ft. estimate and the 120 ft. result), the slant range distance would be 1100 ft. in Plate 59 and 3500 ft. in Plate 60; the corresponding altitudes above the ground would be about 460 ft. and 670 ft., indicating that the craft was not flying parallel to the ground.

Alternatively, if one assumed that the object was 12 in. in diameter, the slant ranges would be about 22 ft. and 70 ft.; and the altitudes would be about nine feet and 13 ft.

Conclusion:

Inconsistency between the reported eight-second interval and gross changes in cloud structure and position impair the usefulness of these photographs as evidence to establish the existence of "flying saucers" or other unusual phenomena.

Sources of Information

(1) Report form filed with Colorado Project.
(2) Telephone conversation with U. S. Weather Bureau, McNary Field, Salem; 6 June 1967.
(3) Interview with the three boys and the mother and father, 6 June 1967.
(4) Letter from the father to Colorado Project, 27 March 1967.
(5) Interview with Salem *Capital Journal* staff, 7 June 1967.

Case 57
Highwood Ranger Station, Alberta
3 July 1967
Investigator: Hartmann

Abstract:

The witness and two companions reportedly sighted and took two photographs of an object described as shiny, and approximately 25-ft. in diameter. The craft reportedly dropped a small object, which when recovered was reported to be composed of solder, aluminum, and magnesium. A report by the Royal Canadian Air Force implied substantial evidence that the sighting was authentic and that the object was, subject to certain assumptions, 40 to 50 in. diameter. Although the case was widely described, both in the press and by several investigators, as being exceptionally strong, examination of the original photographs and the circumstances indicates no evidence of probative value for the existence of unusual aircraft. Only the sworn testimony of the witnesses could be described as making this case more impressive than most others.

The key witness and his two companions were hiking east in the rugged mountain terrain when all three of them reported seeing an object approaching (1a, b, c).

The key witness is described as a salesman and one of his companions as a student ca. 16 years old (1, 3). Various individuals contacted by the project, either involved in or investigating the case, remarked on the "quizzical" nature of responses of the principals to certain situations (see below), questioning in particular the key witnesses' and companions' actions. Reference (2) describes the "two observers"—evidently the key witness and a companion as engaged in "gold prospecting." Reference (4) describes them as looking for a legendary lost mine.

Background:

Time: "At or about 6:30 P.M." (PDT?) (1a, 1b, 1c). Ref. 2 gives "approximately 1700 hrs."

Location: "Approximately 80 miles SW of . . . Calgary" (1); "approximately 30 miles W of Naton, Alberta" (2); "about 3 to 5 miles E of . . . Coleman-Kananaskis Highway" (1); "approximately 3 miles SSE of the Highwood Ranger Station" (2). Note: 80 mi. SW of Calgary would fall in British Columbia; it appears from the other data that the phrase should read approximately 50 mi. SW of Calgary.

Sightings, General Information:

According to the witnesses the object approached from east, and at a relatively close distance and passed out of sight behind some trees; it reappeared, hovered, and then was lost to sight to the south (1). There were scattered cumulus clouds with base level approximately 10,000 ft. above sea level (2, quoted from "Met Office"). The observers were at altitude approximately 5,000 ft. (2), where there were winds of 15 mph. (2).

When first sighted, the "craft" was at an altitude not more than 2,000 ft. and distance not more than 2 mi. (1a, b). It was gradually losing altitude (1a, b). According to the key witness in his deposition approximately eight months later (1a):

> It was traveling toward us gradually losing altitude, passed in front of us, and as it passed slightly out of view behind some trees, it then reappeared and hovered in open sky, and something of a much smaller size fell from the craft.

One of the witness's companions reports in his deposition (1b):

> It travelled towards us gradually losing altitude and at a distance of not more than ½ mile it hovered for moments, at which time some object was seen to fall from the craft. The fallen object was possibly one hundredth (.01) the size of the mother craft. At tree-top level the craft in question then disappeared from sight.
>
> I am not sure at this point whether it became invisible, or dissolved, or merely sped out of sight at such a great speed that it was hard for the eye to follow. At any rate, it was moving away from us at a great speed when it disappeared from sight.

Photographs:

The key witness took the two photographs in rapid succession (2), and stated (1a) "I . . . took two pictures of this strange craft and swear, to the best of my knowledge, that there were no other humans in that area and that there was no camera trickery involved." See Plates 61 and 62. The key witness was using an Olympus PEN EE. The slide format was 18 x 24 mm. (half the standard 35 mm. format). The film speed was ASA 64, set 7 ft. to infinity (2).

Investigation:

In the initial report to the Canadian Department of National Defence, dated "Sept. 67," the object was described as "circular, shiny, aluminum, approximately 25 feet in diameter. First observed 2,000 to 2,500 feet above the altitude of the observer, banked and descended much lower, disappeared behind the trees moving south at high speed" (2).

One of the key witness's companions, whose deposition is most detailed, states:

> No sound accompanied the sighting and no exhaust or colours of any kind were seen. What we saw was a disc-shaped object with a silvery tone to it, with a size that the Department of National Defence in Canada described to be 35 to 40 feet in diameter with a depth ratio of 4 to 1. My guess as to its size would put it as certainly no bigger than that.

(Note: The depositions referred to are signed and carry the proviso: "And I make this solemn declaration conscientiously believing it to be true, and knowing that it is of the same force and effect as if made under oath, and by virtue of The Canada Evidence Act.")

In the weeks following the sighting, the UFO report gained some publicity. A report containing the details was sent from the "Can Pers Unit, Calgary" to The Royal Canadian Air Force Headquarters, Ottawa, dated 7 Sept. 1967. Further data were received by the Canadian Air Force through a telephone conversation, 11-12 October 1967.

On 18 October 1957, a report was sent by the Defence Photographic Interpretation Centre of the Air Force to the Director of Operations of the Air Force. This report, by Major K. J. Hope (ref. 2), contained an analysis of the photographs.

The Canadian analysis was in the form of four tests. In "Exercise A" it was concluded that the cloud masses shown in the two photos were essentially the same, consistent with the quick succession of the photos and 15 mph. winds, and that *two* different photographs were taken on the site, consistent with very slight differences in foliage pattern in the trees. However, the possibility that the case involved "a photo montage combining a studio prepared UFO with each of two on-site shots" could not be "proved or disproved."

"Exercise B" used the camera characteristics to conclude that the fuzziness of Plate 62 could be due either to out-of-focus recopying or camera movement. The shutter speed of 1/25 sec. was consistent with, but did not prove camera motion.

"Exercise C" used meteorological data (clouds at about 5,000 ft.) to show that the alleged visibility of the objects at 2,000-2,500 ft. was credible.

"Exercise D" concluded that since the observation was made in a wilderness area that it was reasonable that no other reports had been obtained.

The Canadian report also concluded from the photographs that the object had a torus or possibly oblate ellipsoid shape, and that at about 2,000 ft. its diameter would have been 40-50 ft. and its thickness 11.5-14 ft. The two photos together indicated ascent or descent, in accord with the testimony.

The language of the report implies that since all tests were "passed," i.e., since the photos were in several ways consistent with the testimony, the case was very strong. Among the conclusions were the statements: "From statistical data supplied the object *has* a diameter of 40′-50′ and *has* a depth of 11.5′-14′ . . ." (WKH emphasis); "A review of all technical data, . . . indicated a very acceptable degree of compatibility. If the story and photographs are a hoax, then it is a well prepared one, that would require on the hoaxer's part knowledge of photography and possibly photogrammetry to support the written and verbal information. . . . Alternatively, the data supplied a most fortunate and lucky combina-

PHOTOGRAPHIC CASE STUDIES

LEGENDS AND PLATES

PLATE 1. Lenticular cloud photographed in Brazil. Photo courtesy APRO.

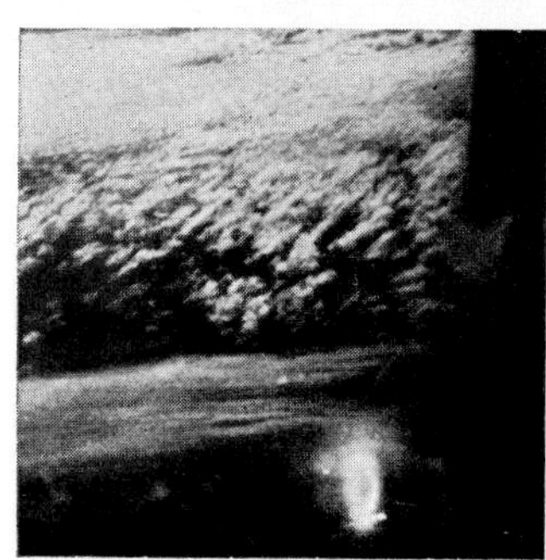

PLATE 2. Sub-sun. Photo courtesy NCAR.

PLATE 3. Time "trail" exposure of the moon. Photo by author.

PLATE 4. Reported "UFO" identified as a film defect. Palomar Mt. Photo courtesy Mrs. Z. Rungee.

PLATE 5. Reported "UFO" identified as a developing defect. Pinawa, Manitoba. Photo courtesy of the witness.

PLATE 6. Lens flare (upper right) caused by street lamp in photograph of Comet Ikeya Seki. Photo by author.

PLATE 7. "Physically fabricated" UFO photo made by hand-throwing a spinning model. Photo by author.

PLATE 8. "Physically fabricated" UFO photo—a suspended model. Photo by author.

PLATE 9. "Physically fabricated" UFO photo. Nighttime time exposure of a model held by hand and illuminated by flashlight. (Cf. Beaver, Pa., case.) Photo by author.

PLATE 10. "Optically fabricated" UFO photograph. Double exposure of elliptical lamp superimposed on a landscape. (Cf. El Guapo, Venezuela, case, APRO bulletin.) Photo by author.

PLATE 11. "Optically fabricated" UFO photograph. Cut-out drawing superimposed on a print and recopied. Photo by author.

PLATE 12. "Optical fabrication." Full moon in the midst of a sunset scene—a physical impossibility. Image of moon (behind the observer) was reflected in a sheet of glass through which photo was taken. Photo by author.

PLATE 13. Photograph taken from an orbiting spacecraft showing the luminous airglow layer above the earth illuminated by moonlight. At an oblique angle to the earth's surface the zodiacal light band is apparent as a conical band. The bright object near the apex of the zodiacal band is the planet Venus.

PLATE 14. The airglow layer photographed from a rocket. The earth's surface is not illuminated by moonlight in contrast with the photograph in Plate 13. Just beneath the airglow layer are many stars and the solid earth can be delineated by means of city lights.

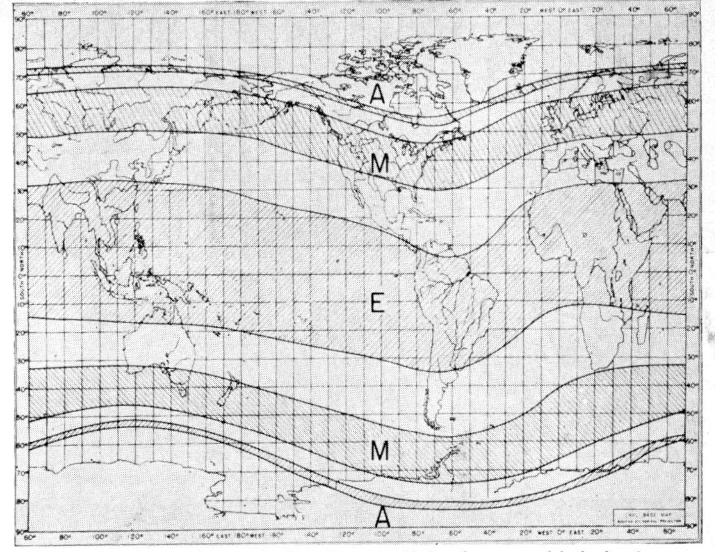

PLATE 15. Auroral zone inclined to parallels of geographic latitude.

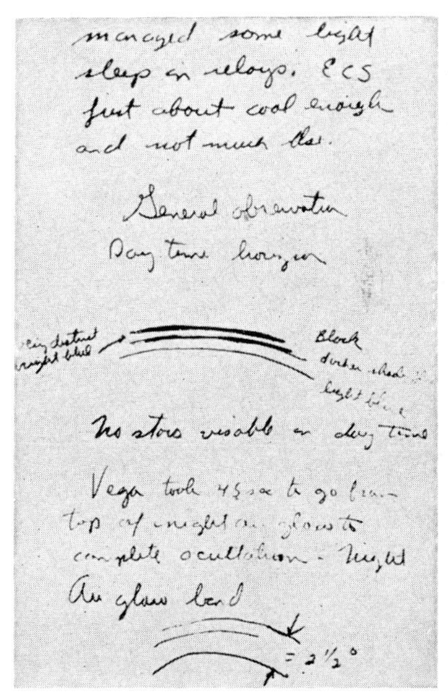

PLATE 16. Sketch made by Gemini 7 astronauts of an auroral arch below the airglow layer.

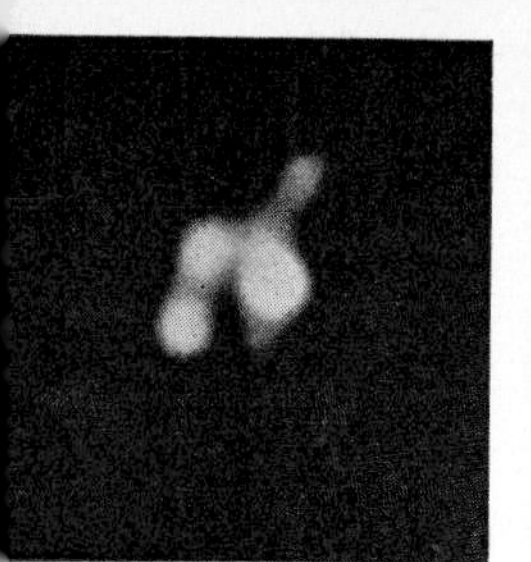
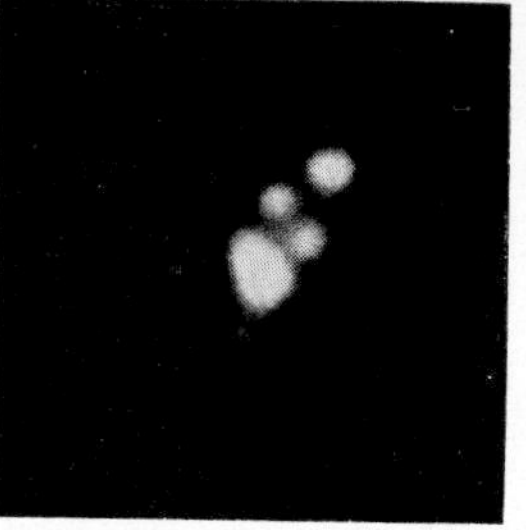
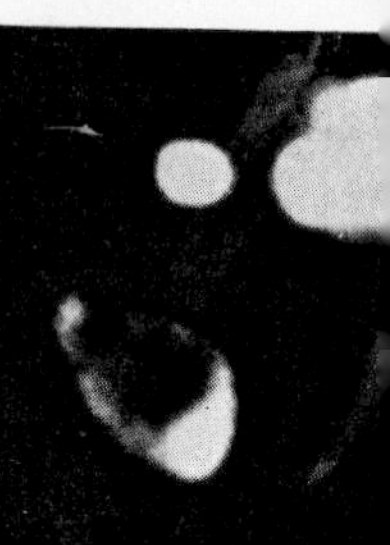

PLATE 17. A 100x (approx.) enlargement of Gemini 11. Frame 10, of Magazine 8. S66-54661. PLATE 18. A 100x (approx.) enlargement of Gemini 11. Frame 9, of Magazine 8. S66-54660. PLATE 19. Photograph of a Radar Evaluation Pod (REP) made by Gemini 5 astronauts.

PLATE 21. A spectacular photograph showing the rendezvous of GT-6 and GT-7.

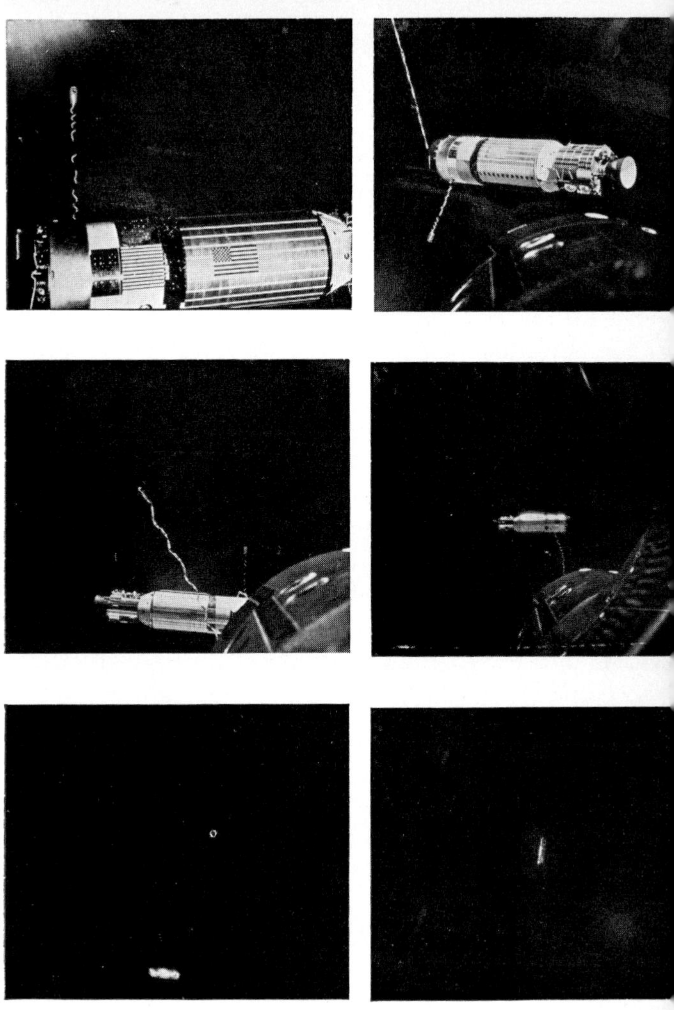

PLATE 20. The appearance of Agena as seen at distances varying from 25 to 250 feet.

PLATE 22. "Uriglow." Brilliant stars appeared when crystals formed from a urine dump at sunrise were illuminated by the sun.

PLATE 23. McMinnville photo 1. Photo courtesy U.P.I.

PLATE 24. McMinnville photo courtesy U.P.I.

PLATE 25. Approximate apparent path of UFO, as indicated by June, 1967. Photo by author at original site, June, 1967.

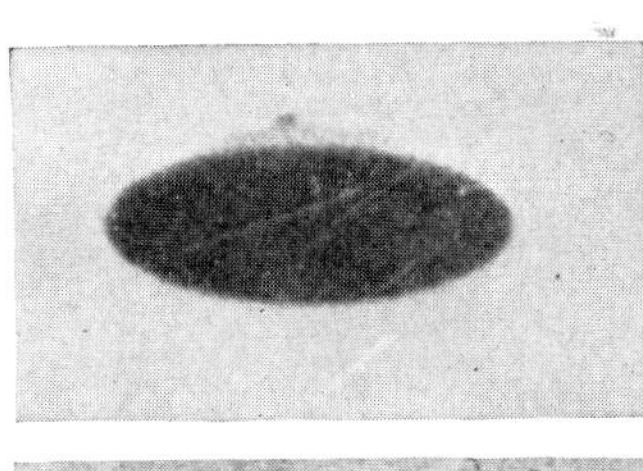

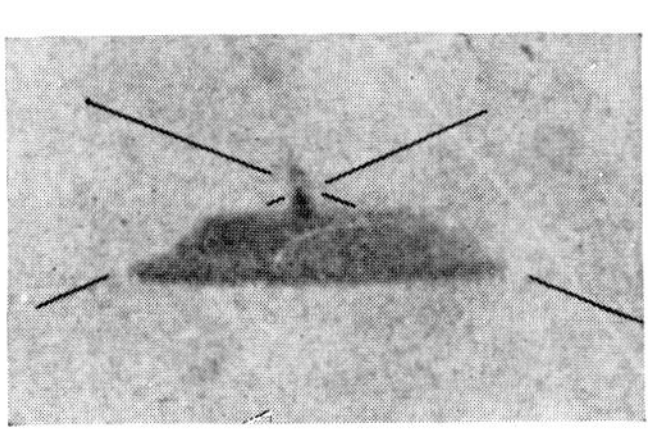

PLATE 26. Enlargements of UFO images from photos 1 and 2.

PLATE 27. Portion (about ⅓) of a frame (approx. no. 114) of the Great Falls motion picture. At bottom edge of frame are ventilator ducts on a nearby building.

PLATE 28. The first Barra da Tijuca photo, reportedly showing the disk approaching. Photo courtesy APRO.

PLATE 29. Barra da Tijuca photo 4. Lighting of the disk is clearly from the left, but details of the hillside suggest lighting from the right. (Cf. Plate 30) Photo courtesy APRO.

PLATE 30. Detail of Plate 29. The palm tree and clumps of foliage indicate shadows on the left with incident illumination from the right. Photo courtesy APRO.

PLATE 31. Typical frame from the Tremonton, Utah, movie. Black bars mark the top and bottom of the original frame.

PLATE 32. Ft. Belvoir photo 1. The army private who took the photographs was called from his building to see the approaching object, which appeared to be a black, non-reflecting ring.

PLATE 33. Ft. Belvoir photo 2.

PLATE 34. Ft. Belvoir photo 3.

PLATE 35. Ft. Belvoir photo 4.

PLATE 36. Ft. Belvoir photo 5.

PLATE 37. Ft. Belvoir photo 6.

PLATE 38. Detonation of "atom bomb simulation demonstration" at Ft. Belvoir. Photo courtesy of the witness.

PLATE 39. Black mushroom cloud produced by "atom bomb simulation demonstration" at Ft. Belvoir. Photo courtesy of the witness.

PLATE 40. Stable black vortex ring detaching itself from mushroom column in "atom bomb simulation demonstration" at Ft. Belvoir. Photo courtesy of the witness.

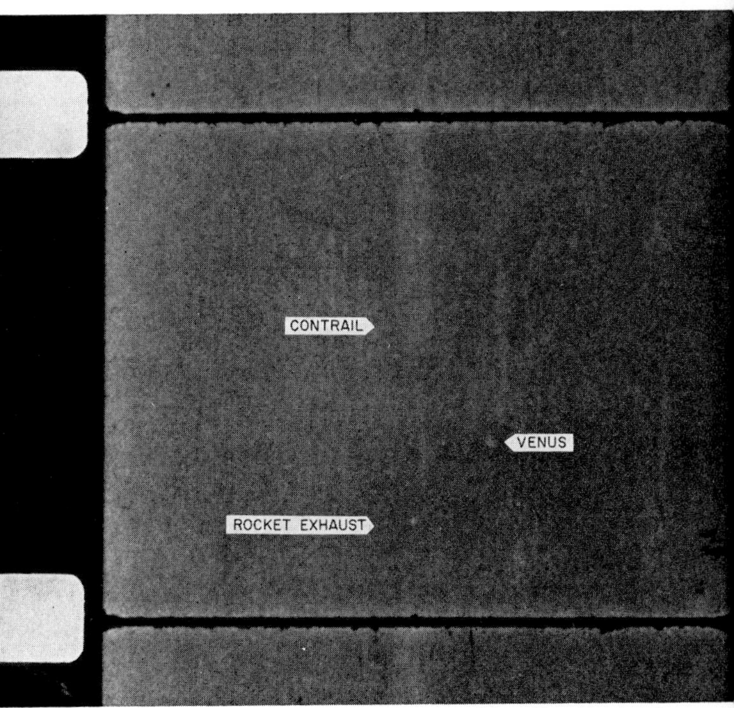

PLATE 41. Frame from the Vandenberg tracking film. Rocket is moving away and down toward southern horizon. Only the bright exhaust is visible. The UFO, identified as Venus, appears to move upward past rocket. Width of field approx. 2°.

PLATE 42. Santa Ana photo 1, looking NNE down Myford Road through front windshield of Heflin's truck. Santa Ana freeway about 0.5 km distant.

PLATE 43. Santa Ana photo 2, looking out right window of Heflin's truck.

PLATE 44. Santa Ana photo 3, looking out right window of Heflin's truck. Standpipe about 80 m distant.

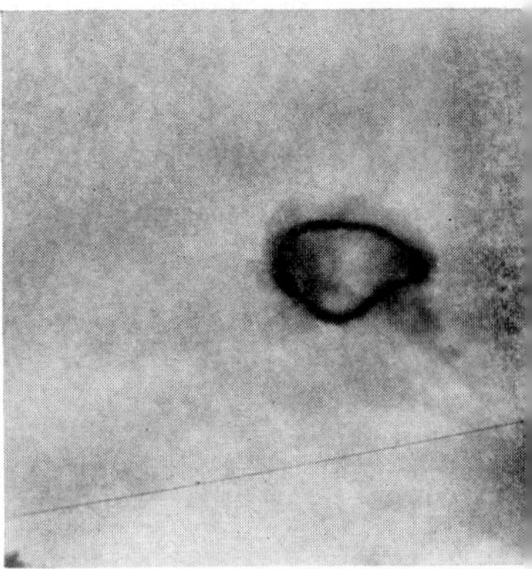

PLATE 45. Santa Ana photo 4, alleged to be looking NNW from middle of Myford Road, outside truck.

PLATE 46. Alleged site of photo 4, showing match with tree and wire. (Cf. Plate 45.)

PLATE 47. 4½ cm (1¾ in.) diameter Leica lens cap suspended on a fine thread a few inches outside van window, 16 January 1968. Copied from a Polaroid print.

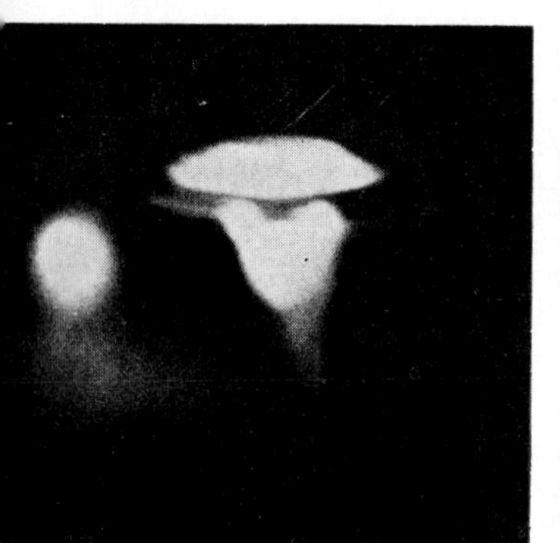

PLATE 48. The first of the two Case-53 photographs. Object reportedly approached from the left, then hovered. The moon is at the left.

PLATE 49. The second of the two Case-53 photographs. The moon is at the right.

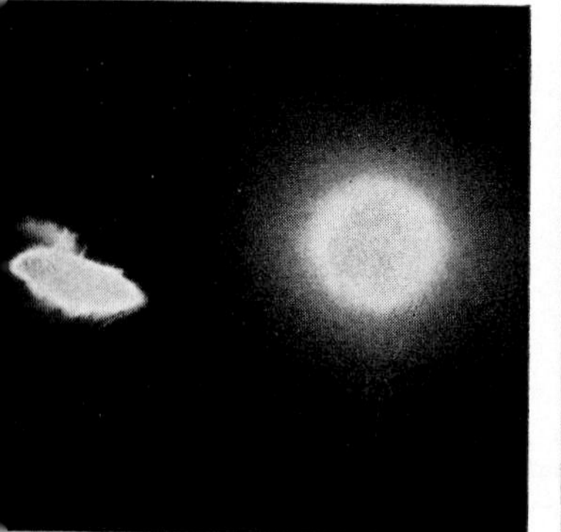

PLATE 50. Attempted simulation of Case-53 photo 1, made by holding an illuminated object (blurred by hand motion). Moon at right.

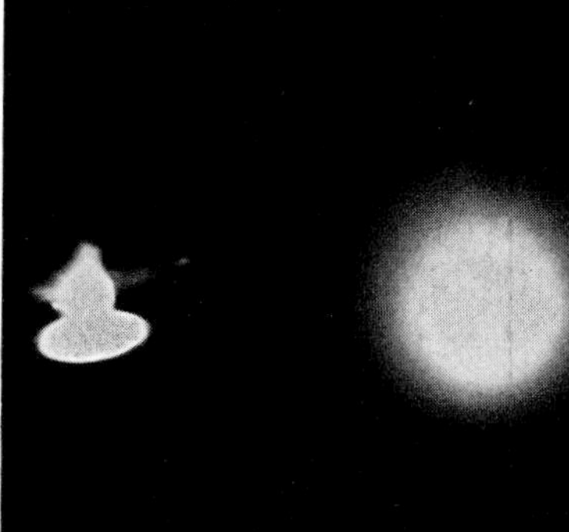

PLATE 51. Attempted simulation of Case-53 photo 2, made by holding a plate, illuminated by flashlight and blurred by hand motion. Moon at right.

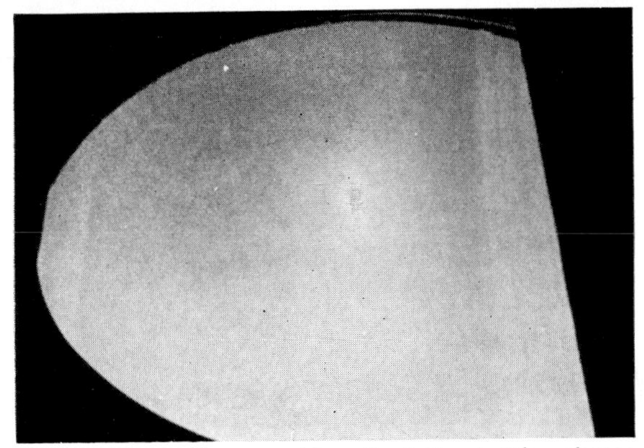

PLATE 52. Gulfstream Aircraft photo 1. The photos were made at about 5-minute intervals over a period of 20 minutes. Note reflection of window curtains.

PLATE 53. Gulfstream Aircraft photo 2. The negative was inadvertently creased when a book was rested on it prior to receipt by the Colorado Project. This accounts for the diagonal streak through the image. Aircraft wing in upper right.

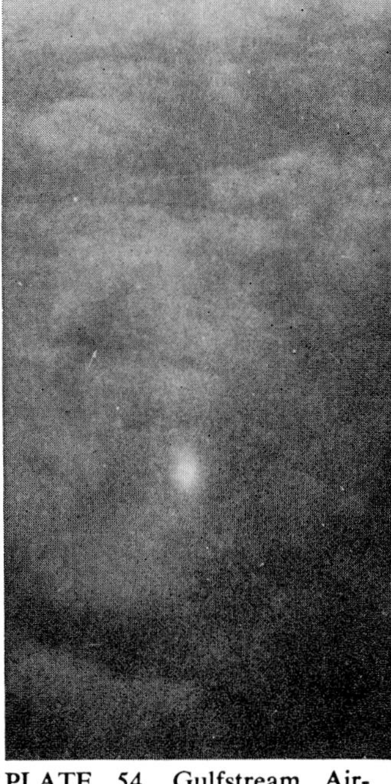

PLATE 54. Gulfstream Aircraft photo 3.

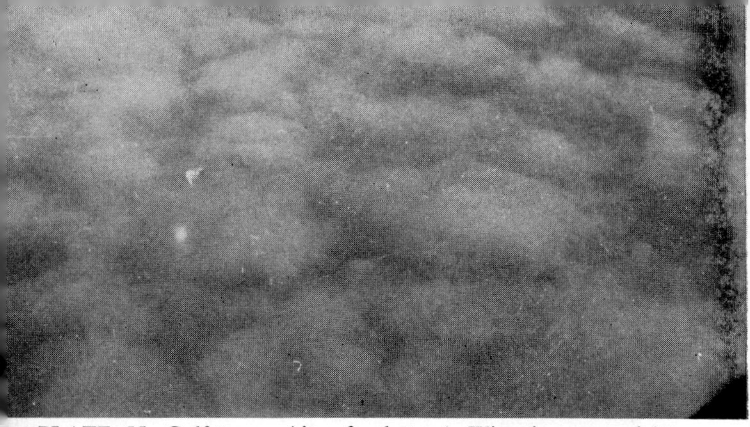

PLATE 55. Gulfstream Aircraft photo 4. Wing in upper right.

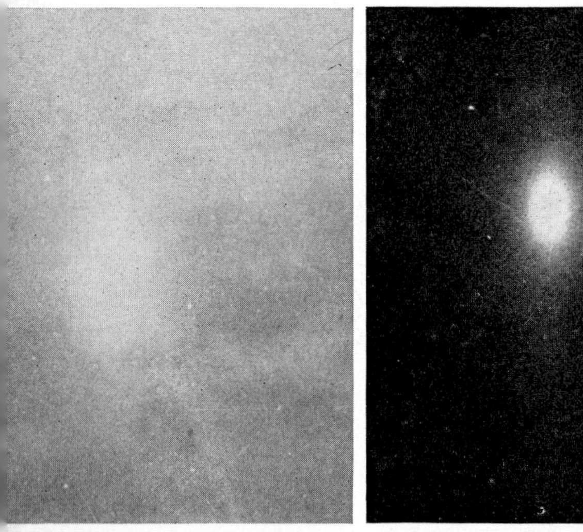

PLATE 56. Enlargement of Gulfstream Aircraft Plate 53, printed at low density to show the structure of the outer halo. Scale is defined by the pattern of film defects and the grain. (Cf. Plate 53.)

PLATE 57. Enlargement of Gulfstream Aircraft Plate 53, printed at high density to show the core of the bright object. While the core is overexposed, there is no evidence for the horizontal disk shown in Fig. 11 and reported visually. Scale is the same as Plate 56.

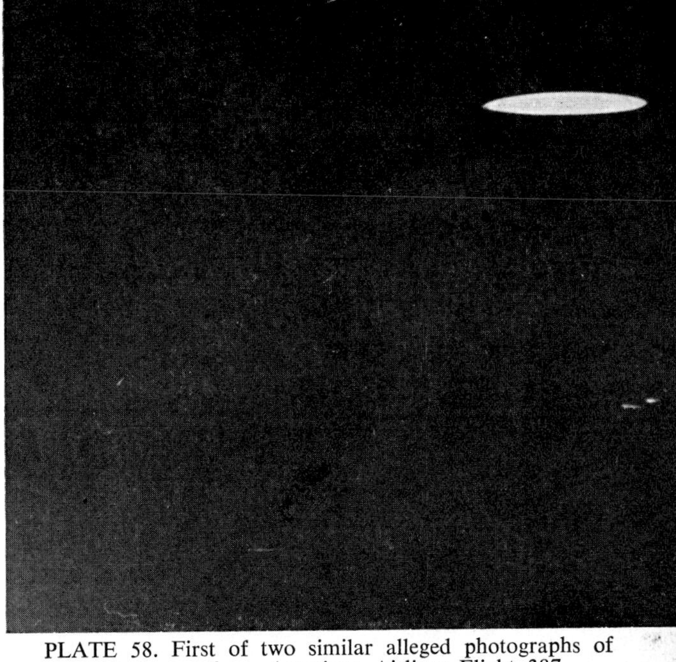

PLATE 58. First of two similar alleged photographs of object seen from American Airlines Flight 387.

PLATE 59. First photo of North Pacific UFO. Copyright Kenneth Baker 1967

PLATE 60. Second photo of North Pacific UFO.

PLATE 61. First photograph of alleged UFO photo by the witness.

PLATE 62. Second photograph of alleged UFO photo by the witness.

PLATE 63. The Sonora, California, UFO. Arrow shows small, bright source which drifts toward top of frame on motion picture footage.

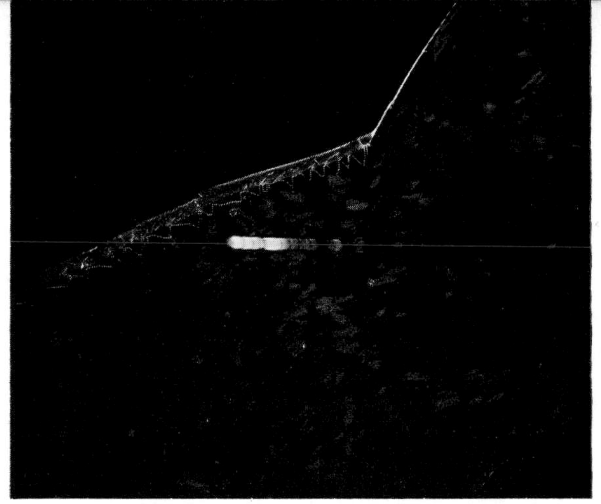

PLATE 64. Polaroid photo of a pattern of colored lights made by a 12-yr.-old boy in Lakeville, Conn.

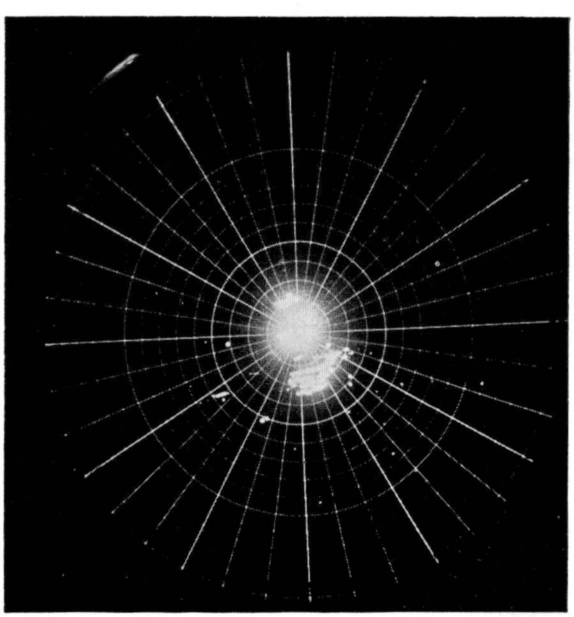

PLATE 65. Time lapse photograph of PPI. Diameter of area covered is 300 nautical miles.

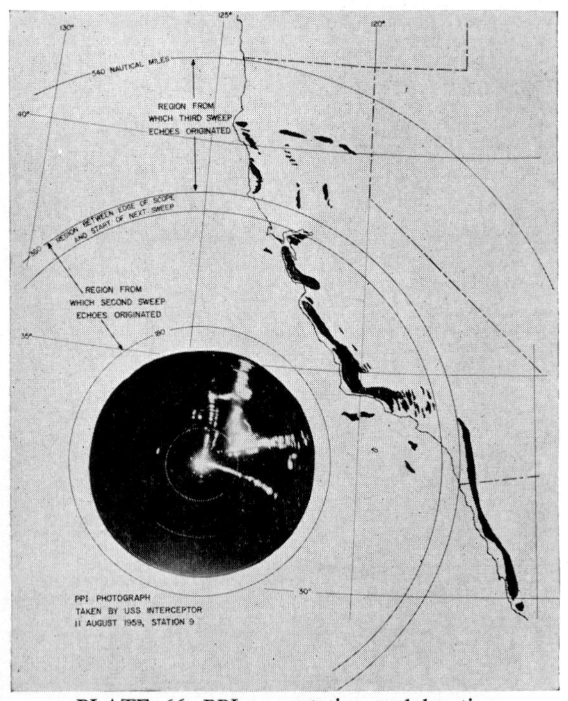

PLATE 66. PPI presentation and location of targets from which radar echoes were received during the occurrence of a strong elevated duct.

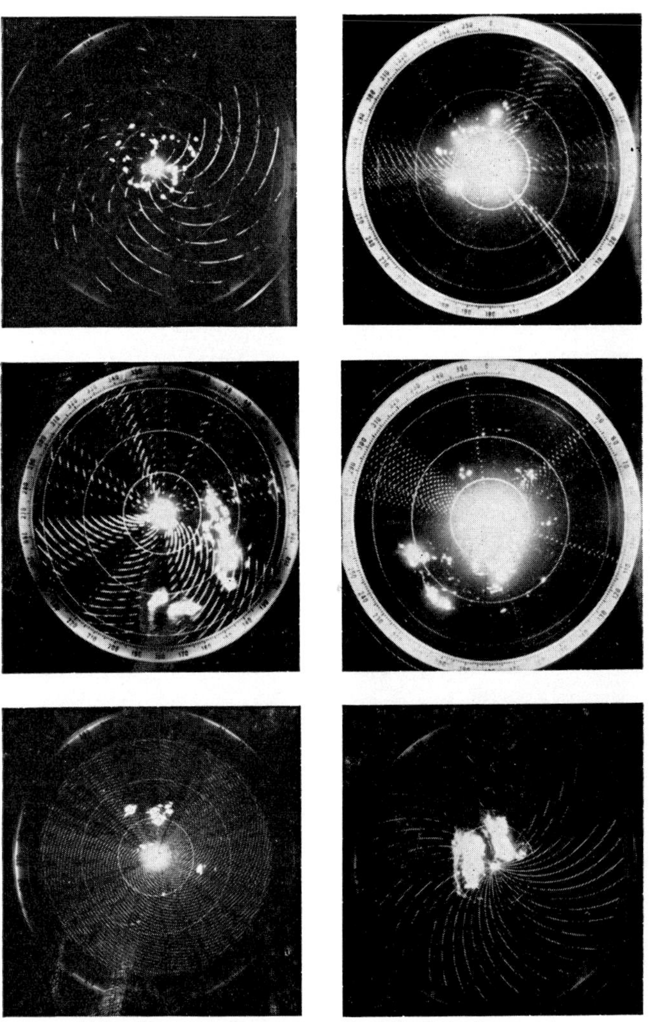

PLATE 67. Examples of radio interference.

a. stratiform precipitation

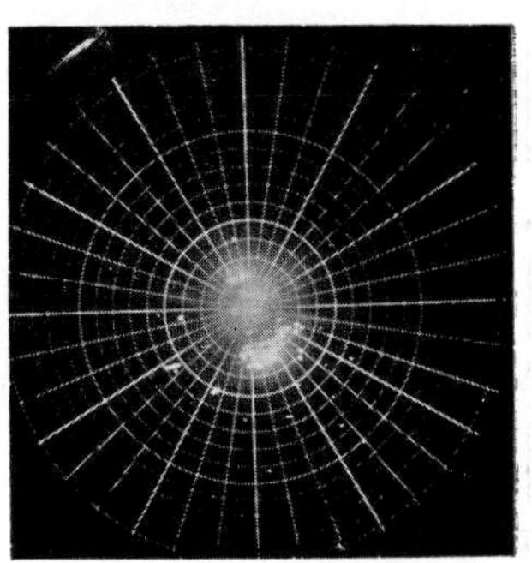

b. normal ground clutter

c. anomalous propagation

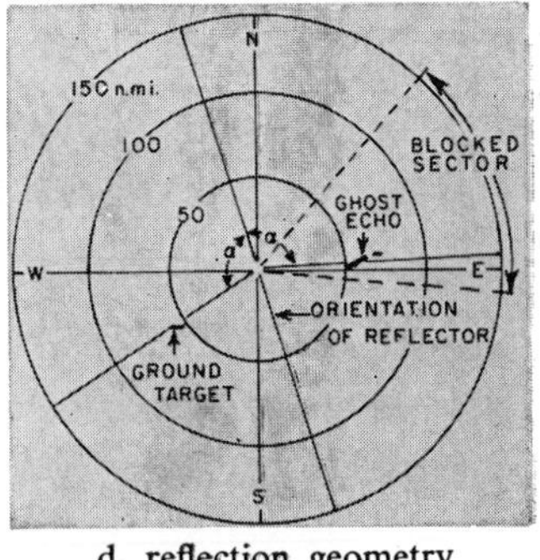

d. reflection geometry

PLATE 68. Reflection echo during anomalous propagation conditions.

THE FOLLOWING
ILLUSTRATIONS APPLY TO REFERENCES
IN APPENDIX Q.

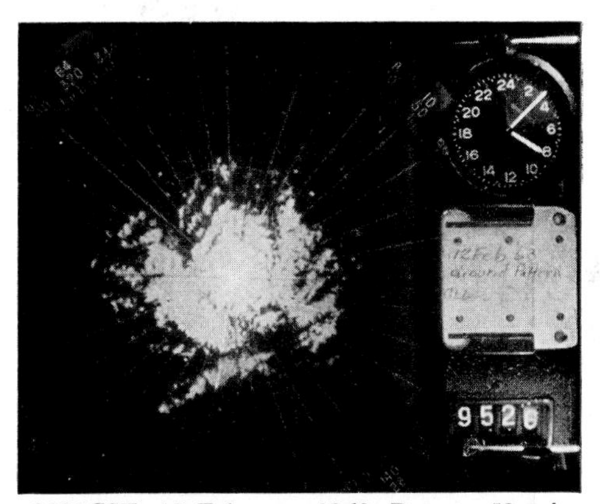

0808CST, 12 February 1963, Range: 50 mi.
Fig. 6 Normal Ground Pattern for AN/CPS-9 Radar located at CLL.

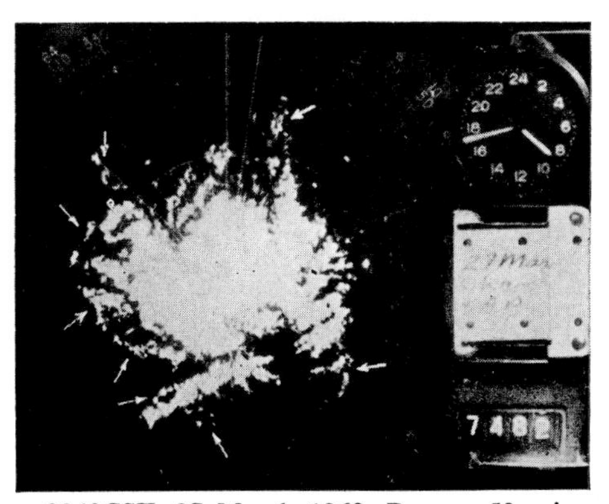

0843CST, 27 March 1962, Range: 50 mi.
Fig. 7 Expansion of Ground Pattern by Anomalous Echoes.

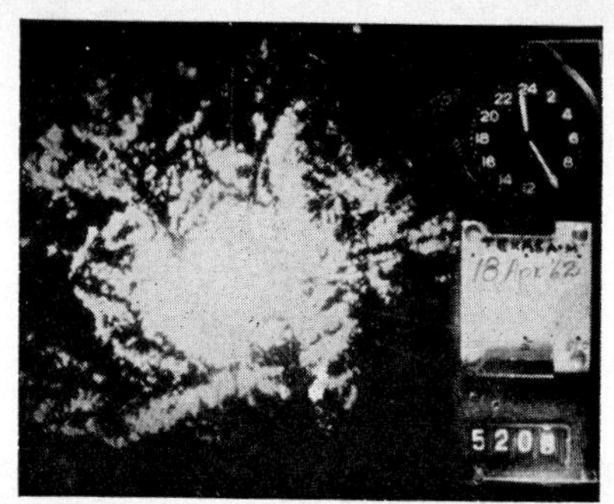

2320CST, 18 April 1962, Range: 50 mi.
Fig. 8 Expansion of Ground Pattern by Anomalous Echoes.

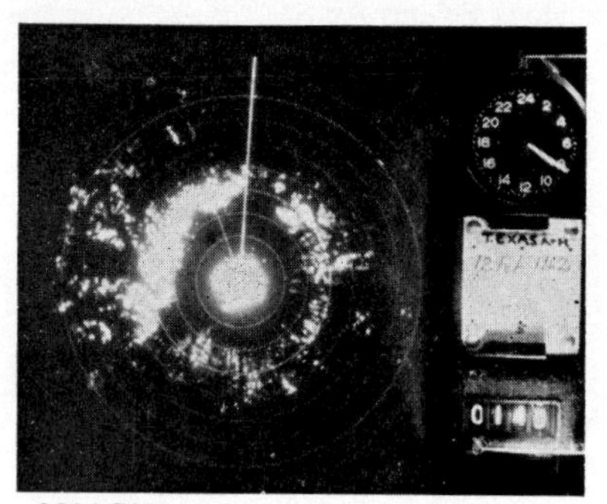

a. 0820CST, 7 May 1962, Range: 300 mi.
Fig. 9 Radial Pattern of Anomalous Echoes Associated with an Elevated Refracting Layer.

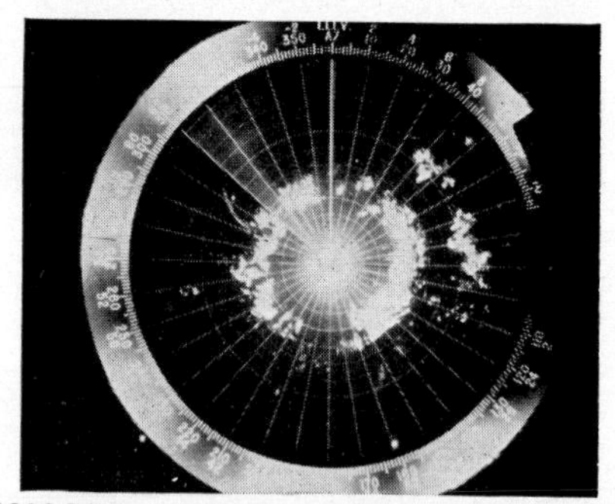

b. 0820CST, 12 February 1962, Range: 225 mi.
Fig. 10 Radial Pattern of Anomalous Echoes Associated with an Elevated Refracting Layer.

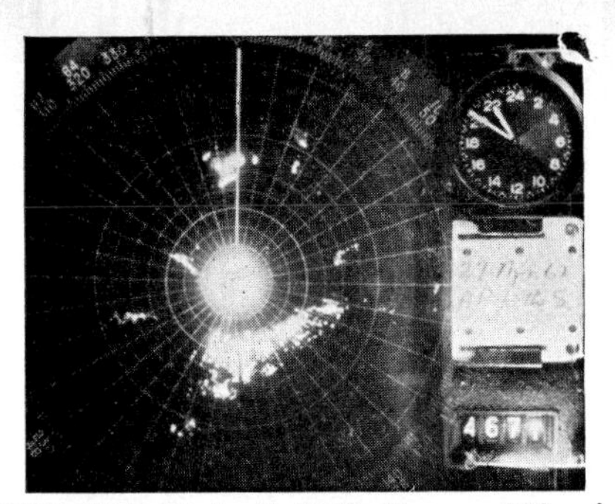

2250CST, 27 April 1962, Range: 300 mi.
Fig. 12 Anomalous Echoes Associated with the Formation of an Elevated Refracting Layer.

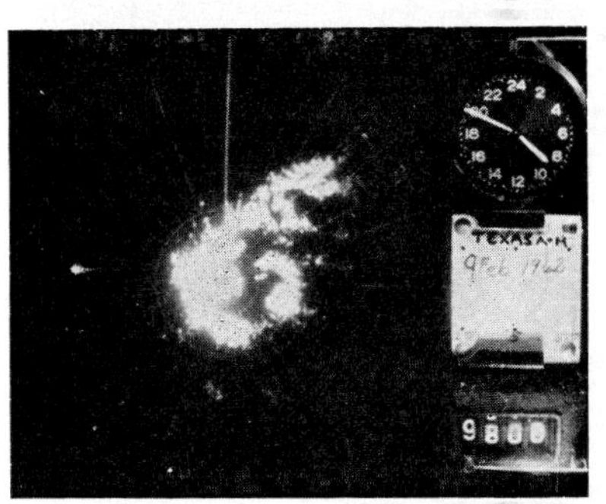

a. 0850CST, 9 February 1962, Range: 300 mi.
Fig. 13a Anomalous Echoes caused by a Strong Super-refractive Layer at the Surface.

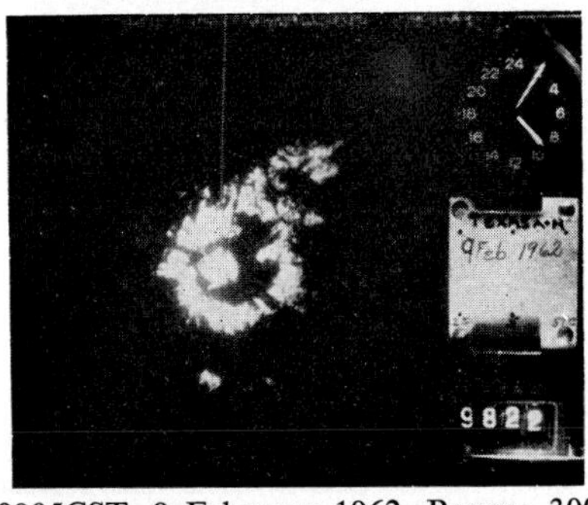

b. 0905CST, 9 February 1962, Range: 300 mi.

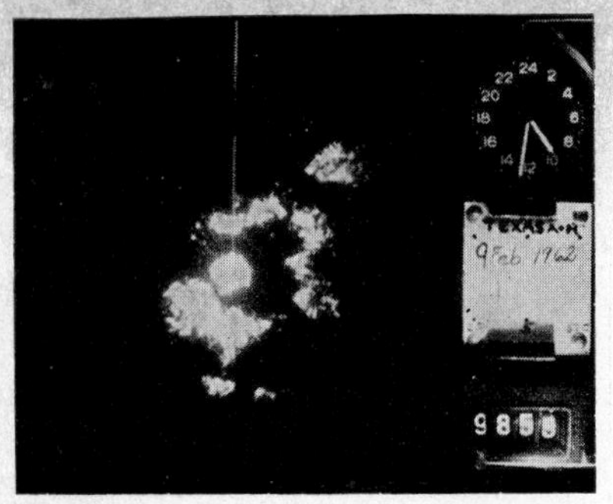

c. 0931CST, 9 February 1962, Range: 300 mi.

Fig. 13b & c. Anomalous Echoes caused by a Strong Super-refractive Layer at the Surface.

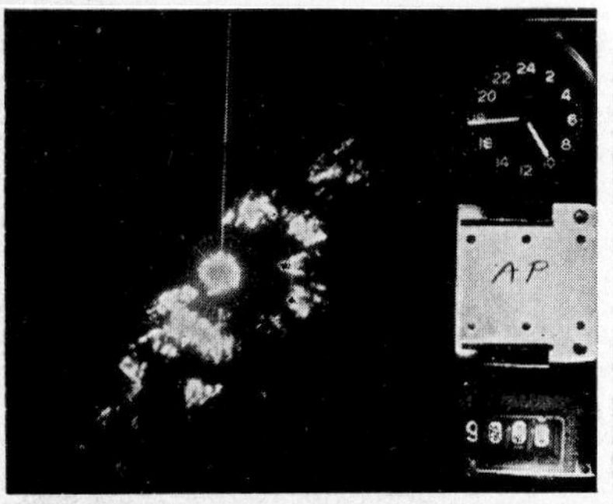

d. 0944CST, 9 February 1962, Range: 300 mi.

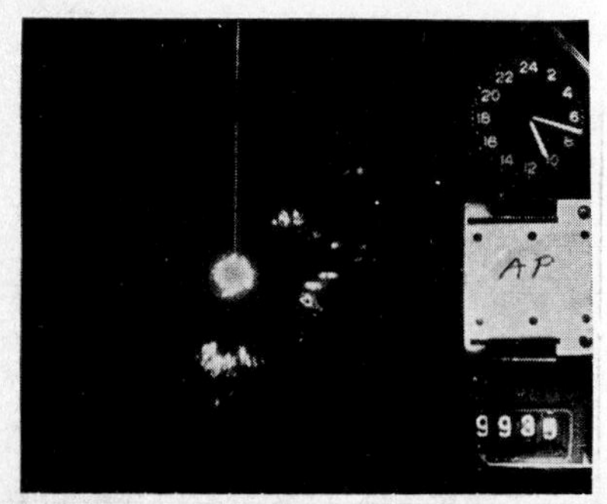

e. 1018CST, 9 February 1962, Range: 300 mi.

Fig. 13d & e. Anomalous Echoes caused by a Strong Super-refractive Layer at the Surface.

tion of circumstances to make a hoax realistic; . . . the four exercises . . . reasonably substantiate the observer's report, by both technical data and logic; . . . *Conclusion:* The findings arrived at above are supported by technical data. . . ."

At this time in the investigation (snow was already on the ground), one of the companions returned to the woods to locate the site and look for the object reportedly dropped by the UFO (3). He instructed friends to notify the authorities if he was not back within three days. (3) After one week, the key witness notified the local news media, instead of the police. When the companion emerged unscathed from the woods, he objected to the excitement and searches being conducted at that time by army and police (3). Dr. J. Allen Hynek, consultant to U.S.A.F. Project Blue Book, advised the Colorado project that a specimen or specimens brought out by the companion thought to be related to the sighting, were solder with particles of aluminum-magnesium alloy embedded in them (3).

Later investigators (3) questioned (without conclusive results) the motivation of the key witness in his handling of publicity, e.g., notifying the news media in preference to search authorities. Hynek, who later described the case (4) as being the closest he had come to fully documented, believable photographs, worthy of further investigation, studied the original slides in January, 1968. At this time, permission was obtained through a Montreal lawyer for the Colorado project to study the originals.

According to notes in the Colorado files (3), Hynek visited Calgary and interviewed the key witness and other persons involved in the case. This trip was made shortly after national disclosure of a photographic UFO hoax in Texas; Mr. Mike Adamson, of Calgary radio station CKXL arranged at this time for lie detector tests to be given to the key witness and other companions who were both anxious to take such tests. These tests were to be at the expense of CKXL.

However, in a misunderstanding, Dr. Hynek left Calgary before such a test could be performed, and the radio station personnel, to whom the test was worthless without Dr. Hynek's participation in the resulting broadcast, canceled the test.

Analysis:

The analysis by the Royal Canadian Air Force reported above, is regarded as technically valid, although I believe that the interpretation attaches unwarranted credence to the case. In particular, the statements that a hoax "would require . . . knowledge of photography and possibly photogrammetry to support the written and verbal information . . ." and that "it would require a most fortunate and lucky combination of circumstances to make a hoax realistic" are too strong. It should be remembered that if a hoax were involved, the written and verbal information would be prepared *after* the photographs were taken, in accord with what the photographer thought he had "recorded" on film.

Certainly, the "Calgary" photographs do not require photogrammetric knowledge or sophisticated photographic experience to produce. In fact, the rapid panning and blurring of the second photo, and the pitch of the disk toward the observer are characteristic of photographs of hand-thrown models. In my opinion, it is basically this problem that makes the "Calgary" photos of no probative value in establishing the existence of "flying saucers": the photographs cannot be distinguished from photographs of a hand-thrown model.

The R.C.A.F. report is reminiscent of the early U. S. Navy laboratory report on the Tremonton motion pictures: the report was prepared by a group that was inclined to believe in the existence of "flying saucers" and while the analysis was more or less valid, it did not warrant the conclusion, presented to the Robertson Panel, that possibly alien intelligent control was involved.

An important test passed by the photographs is that the background cloud patterns are identical, consistent with the statement that the photographs were taken in rapid succession. (The Salem case, for example, was classified as containing fatal internal inconsistencies when this test was not passed.)

Measurements of Plates 61 and 62 (on 8 x 10 enlargements) give angular diameters of 0°.98 and 0°.84, respectively. The key witness and his companion testified (attested to by the other companion) that the object was initially "no higher than 2,000 feet" (1a), and "first sighted at an altitude of not more than 2,000 feet" (1b), and losing altitude. The object had approached from a distance of "no greater than two miles" to "not more than one-half mile" when the pictures were made. A horizontal range of, say, 2,000 ft. would require an altitude of approximately 1,400 ft. to be compatible with the elevation angle of approximately 35° measured in the first photo. In the second photo, the UFO has dropped vertically downward to an elevation angle of about 14°, corresponding to an altitude of about 240 ft. These figures are consistent with the verbal testimony.

Using a line-of-sight distance of about 2,200 ft., the measured angular diameter of 0°.9 corresponds to a linear diameter of 35 ft. The distance uncertainty results in a diameter uncertainty of perhaps 40%. Thus, the *verbal* testimony, combined with the photographs, indicates a linear diameter of 35 ± 14 ft.

After examination of enlarged images, I see no evidence

to support the R.C.A.F. assertion that the object has a toroidal shape. Only the blurred image (Plate 62) is pitched up toward the observer, and a light zone not quite centered in the dark disk can be interpreted as a highlight, as opposed to a central hole.

Dr. Hynek reported to the project that Fred Beckmann, of the University of Chicago, had studied the original slides with a densitometer and concluded that the image was a "real," photographic image, and that there seemed to be some haze in front of the object suggesting considerable range (See the similar analysis of McMinnville, Ore., Case 46). However, in view of the shiny nature of the surface, the clear presence of bright highlights, and the relatively high contrast of distant ground details, it would be difficult, in my judgment, to get a clear indication of enough scattering between the observer and the UFO to indicate a distance of the order of only 2,000 ft.

Conclusion:

The tests which could be performed were consistent in all respects with the verbal testimony. The tests included: (1) Time spacing of the pictures; (2) compatibility of reported range and altitude with measured elevation angle; (3) compatibility of reported size with measured angular size and reported distance. Characteristics of the reported "craft," assuming the reported distance, would be diameter 35 $\pm$ 14 ft. and thickness 8 $\pm$ 3 ft.

In spite of the internal consistency of these results, it must be stated that the photographs are also consistent with a hand-thrown model and that there is insufficient information content to rule out this hypothesis. Therefore, the case cannot be said to contribute significant evidence in establishing the existence of unusual aircraft.

Sources of Information

1. Statutory Declarations, 28 February 1968
   a. By the key witness
   b. By the first companion
   c. By the other companion
2. Hope, Maj. K. J. (18 October 1967) "Photographic Analysis—Two Copy Colour Slides of Alleged UFO"
3. Notes on telephone conversations between Dr. Roy Craig (Boulder), Dr. J. A. Hynek, and others concerned with case. January-March, 1968.
4. Grescoe, Paul. *The Canadian Magazine*, 25 May 1968.

Case 58
Sonora and Camarillo, Calif.
1 November 1967 (Sonora); 27 December 1967 (Camarillo)
Investigator: Hartmann

Abstract:

Two objects photographed in unrelated incidents by Universal City Studios are judged to be real but of little probative value in establishing the existence of extraordinary flying objects. These objects can be attributed easily to airborne debris.

Background:

Time: 12:10-12:15 p.m. PST (S); 10:00 a.m. PST (C)

Location: On location near Sonora; Broom Ranch near Camarillo

Camera Data: 35 mm motion picture camera; 24 frames/sec; Eastman Color film processed by Techniscope; approx. f9; f.1. 30 mm (S) 100 mm (C);

Scene (from "A Man Called Gannon"): 59A-2, "A" Camera (S); 317A-5, "B" Camera (C).

Direction of view (both cases): eastward, elevation about 30° above horizon.

Weather conditions. Cloudless deep blue sky in both cases.

Sighting, General Information:

During the filming of a feature motion picture, "A Man Called Gannon," two lengths of footage, when developed, showed unidentified images drifting across the field of view. In neither case did any of the film crew or actors recall seeing an object. According to film company personnel, this was the strangest aspect of the case, because the cameramen habitually look for aircraft or contrails, especially in historical dramas. In situations where aircraft are filmed the scene is immediately reshot, and the footage showing inappropriate detail is rejected. However, in these two cases the images were discovered only during the editing, when the processed film was being viewed.

The first case, shot at Sonora, Calif., 1 November 1967, showed a small bright source drifting slowly toward the top of the screen (Plate 63) at the very beginning of a sequence, while the camera slate is still being shown. The slate is removed and the scene shows only deep blue sky and the drifting object, which leaves the upper margin near the left corner after roughly ten seconds, before any subsequent action starts. The object is below or near the resolution of the film and resembles a wide-angle shot of the moon, except that the camera was stationary and the object is drifting.

The second case involves film shot on the Broom Ranch near Camarillo 27 December 1967. During a dialogue sequence the camera was focused on the head and shoulders of an actor who was astride a horse. The horizon is out of the picture. At this time a pale, circular extended object, which appears to be an out-of-focus image of a point source or a small bright source, drifts across the screen from the right edge to the left edge in roughly 15 sec. (The image does not reproduce well in black-and-white.) The object definitely appears to pass behind the actor as it is not visible against several dark portions of his clothing. Again, the camera was fixed, although there is a sudden offset to compensate for a movement of the horse. The shooting of this scene will not be cut from the final motion picture.

Investigation:

At my request, Mr. William J. Wade, head of the camera department at Universal Studio used his standard depth-of-field tables to check the depth of field in each case. These tables are based on a circle of confusion of 0.002 in. diameter. In the Sonora case, the camera was focused quite close (after the slate is removed and the UFO has disappeared, an actor jumps into the foreground). For a 35 mm lens at f8, focused at 25 ft., the depth of field is 7 ft. 2 in. to infinity. Thus an object passing anywhere in the background would be in focus. This is consistent with the small, apparently unresolved, bright image. In the Camarillo footage, the longer focal-length lens had less depth of field. For a 100 mm lens at f8, focused at 20 ft. (the approximate distance of the actor) the depth of field is 16 ft. 1 in. to 27 ft. 2 in.; at 25 ft. it is 19 ft. 2 in. to 36 ft. 8 in. This restricted depth of field is consistent with the image being badly out of focus, assuming that the object passed at a distance greater than some 30 ft.

There is no reason to suspect that any fabrication is involved. The officials with whom I spoke were helpful and appeared genuinely puzzled. There has been no evidence of any attempt to capitalize on the event. Had the studio wanted to fabricate an UFO, the facilities were readily available to create a much more vivid result.

Conclusion:

It is concluded that real objects were photographed in both cases, consistent with the camera geometry. The information content of the films is so low that the cases are of little value in establishing the existence of "flying saucers." In addition, it strains credulity to argue that a single film crew would unknowingly and accidentally photograph rare, extraordinary objects on *two* occasions occurring 56 days and approximately 275 mi. apart.

Alternatively, it is easy to argue that both objects may have been some sort of wind-blown debris, either natural, such as a bit of milkweed-type plant debris, or artificial, such as a bit of white tissue. A two-inch diameter white object at about 50 ft. distance would be consistent with the observations. The camera crew, checking for aircraft, would not have seen anything. The object would be in focus in the Sonora case, out of focus in Camarillo. In the Sonora photographs the object would subtend an angle of only 0°.2 and show up as only a small bright source. During the shooting, the object would be unlikely to attract the attention of the camera crew, being neither "up in the sky" at infinity, nor in the region of focal interest.

Sources of Information

Personal visit by W. K. Hartmann to Universal City Studios, Universal City, Calif.; personal discussions with Howard Cristie, Producer, and William J. Wade, Head, Camera Department.

Case 59
Lakeville, Conn.
January 1967
Investigators: Ayer, Wadsworth

Abstract:

Many unidentified sightings, principally of lights at night, were reported in the Lakeville area over several months. Most, including a photograph, came from a boys' prep school. Some of the sightings probably were aircraft lights, but no generally applicable explanation is apparent.

Background:

Various reports had indicated a wave of UFO sightings in the Lakeville area from about Thanksgiving Day 1966 into the spring of 1967; these emanated chiefly from a boys' prep school near Lakeville. On 20 September 1967, while the CU investigators were in that area, they visited the school and also obtained copies of State Police reports on some of the sightings.

Investigation:

From the police reports and investigators' interviews, 20 September 1967 at the school, it developed that a teacher and at least seven students had seen an unidentified object or objects on various nights from 12 to 23 January, and that one student had taken a photograph of it. The teacher described it as an elliptical object with two pulsating red lights on the sides, moving south in the western sky. His sighting was on 19 January, about 9:55 p.m. on a clear, cold night. The boys gave essentially the same description as the teacher, except one who reported erratic motion and hovering in various parts of the sky on several occasions.

The investigators learned also that a 12-yr.-old boy who lived near the school had made a Polaroid photo of a pattern of colored lights that he had seen in the sky from the living room of his home on the evening of 24 January; but they were unable to interview the family or obtain the photo.

No practicable means of clarifying the visual sightings was available, so that the investigation reduced to examination of the photograph the student had made (Plate 64). The object was sighted about 9:00 or 10:00 p.m. on or about 23 January. According to the 17-yr.-old student, who was photographer for the school paper, others saw the object and called him; but it had disappeared when he arrived outside the dormitory with his camera equipment. He set up the camera on a heavy-duty tripod and aimed at the last observed position of the object. After about five minutes it reappeared, and he exposed the film for about seven seconds. The object was in view for about five seconds of the exposure, during which time it pulsated twice before it disappeared behind Indian Mountain. He immediately rewound the film, with only the one exposure on it, and developed. The exposed frame was torn in rewinding, apparently because it had become very cold and he did not wait for it to return to room temperature.

The object was seen in the western sky, north of Indian Mountain, moving south. The photographer described it as a "bright point of light" that blinked or pulsated irregularly. From his estimate of its location relative to the mountain, it was apparently a few hundred feet above the ground and at least 2.5 miles distant. The night was clear and very cold.

The camera was a Voightlander Ultramatic 35mm., with a 50mm. Skopar f/2.8 lens. A Glanz-Samigon monocular was attached to the lens to give 7X magnification (the student photographer had prepared the combination after earlier sightings). The optical combination had a focal length of 350mm., aperture f/8. The film was Kodak Tri-X, speed ASA 800; it was developed in D-76 diluted 1:1, at 68°-70° for 14 min., agitated ten seconds each half-minute for maximum contrast.

The Photograph:

The edges of the image parallel to the direction of motion are sharp, as confirmed by densitometer traces, indicating that the object was accurately focussed. Measurement of its diameter, together with the known focal length of the camera system, gives an angular diameter of about 7′ of arc, more than one-fifth the diameter of the moon. This observation conflicts with the photographer's description of it as a bright point. In explanation, he stated in a letter dated 22 October 1967: "Because of the relatively poor quality of the optical system I was using, the images on the film are rather crude representations of the UFO. It was actually a bright point of light. The lens and possibly the film have diffused the image somewhat into circular form." Nearly all of such diffuseness would have to be attributed to the lens system, as the film was capable of rendering detail well under 1′ of arc; and such serious aberration does not seem likely for the equipment he was using, if it was properly focussed. The photographer's judgment of the visual appearance of the object would have been influenced by its brightness and his state of accommodation, as well as his visual acuity.

The fact that part of the film frame is missing raises obvious questions as to authenticity. However, the rather jagged tear, with emulsion pulled off the film base in a sawtooth pattern, is characteristic of Tri-X film torn at a temperature of around 0°F. At room temperature it tears smoothly, leaving a nearly straight edge on both film base and emulsion. This observation obviously supports the statement that the film was accidentally torn while being rewound at low temperature.

It should be mentioned that the State Police report 25 January 1967 on the sightings at the school listed as exhibits "two photos of UFO taken on Jan. 19, 1967," at approximately 9:00 p.m. and approximately 9:10 p.m., both with five seconds exposure. The student photographer told the CU investigators that he had made only the one exposure.

If the photograph is indeed the image of a moving luminous disk, then it is a time-exposure showing a disk that was not uniformly bright over its area, and was either moving erratically or changing in brightness erratically, or both. However, these unsophisticated observations offer little basis for speculation as to the identity of the object or the authenticity of the photograph.

Dr. William K. Hartmann notes that "the image bears a strong resemblance to a slitless spectrogram of an annular emission-line source."

Section V

HISTORICAL ASPECTS OF UFO PHENOMENA

No study of UFO Phenomena would be complete without providing the historical and international context within which the present inquiry has been conducted. In the succeeding three chapters events leading up to 1947 are considered over the sweep of recorded history; the two decades of intensive UFO activity are reviewed; and the degree to which foreign countries are officially studying UFO phenomena is surveyed.

Chapter 1 UFOs in History / Samuel Rosenberg

In his summary of the work of the Colorado project, which appears as Section II of this report, Dr. Condon defines (at p. 13 supra) an UFO as follows:

> An unidentified flying object (UFO, pronounced OOFO) is defined as the stimulus for a report made by one or more individuals of something seen in the sky (or an object thought to be capable of flying but seen when landed on the earth) which the observer *could not identify as having an ordinary natural origin* . . . (emphasis—SR).

Dr. Condon's definition accurately mirrors the persistent, tantalizing inconclusiveness of all UFO reports, modern and ancient. In this chapter this definition will be applied to the past from which a sampling of "UFO reports" gathered from various books and records is readily forthcoming — so readily, in fact, that a report of all such sightings of mysterious objects which the observer "could not identify" would fill the entire space devoted to the project report as a whole.

The wealth of ancient "UFOs" is due to a basic fact about man's perception of his contemporary universe. A concentrated glance backward in time quickly reveals that throughout our recorded history (and presumably before that), mankind has always seen UFOs and reported "sightings" that remained unexplained even after examination by persons believed to be competent. Our earliest ancestor gazed earnestly into terrestrial and outer space to witness an infinite variety of phenomena and — understood virtually none of them. In fact, his entire universe, both "external" to himself, as well as "internal," was largely outside of his comprehension. He had only the most rudimentary pragmatic knowledge and was totally unable to explain factually or conceptually whatever he plainly saw. In short, to him *everything was UFO.*

This in no way prevented him from interpreting what he saw or utilizing his interpretations in a manner that seems to have been convenient to the needs of his contemporary society. A reminder of the social consequences of the ancient attitudes toward "things seen in the sky" may therefore be helpful in dealing with present-day reactions to UFO reports.

We know some of early man's UFO sightings as sun, moon, lunar halo, stars, constellations, galaxies, meteors, comets, auroras, rainbows, wind, rain, storm, tornado, hurricane, drought; others as sunrise, sunset, mirage, phosphorescence, lightning, etc, etc. In modern times, inductive scientists have given us rational explanations for a great many natural phenomena, or they have asked us to suspend judgments of the still vast unknowable, pending further investigation. But our inveterate impatience persists.

Perhaps the most persistent and dramatic early UFO sightings of the species that has with characteristic self-importance designated itself as *Homo sapiens* (intelligent man) were the "heavenly" lights he saw whenever he looked upward or outward into space. Without knowing what they were — and what wild guesses were made! — man was still able to use the moving points of light for his navigating, hunting or migrating orientations. But our ancestors could not endure living without immediate explanations for all of the natural phenomena that surrounded them. So, in the absence of scientific explanations for what they saw, they conjured up other interpretations equally satisfying to them: the poetic, the dramatic, the supernatural, the mythological, and even the nonsensical, or comic. Any explanation was better than none at all, because man, a part of nature, abhors a (mental) vacuum. Indeed the need to establish orientation by means of hastily improvised hypotheses or fantasies appears to be a fundamental, almost instinctual biological adjunct.

Bits of the vast accumulations of intuitive rationalizations concocted by early man while he waited impatiently for more accurate answers, still continue to satisfy our craving for poetry, drama and other imaginative story-telling. Francis Thompson wrote: "Man was able to live without soap for thousands of years, but he could never live without poetry." So for multimillenia we have had poetry and allegory and all sorts of remarkably ingenious supernatural fantasies standing in for crucially needed, verifiable factual truth. Sometimes the interim quasi-sciences have served us pragmatically and have led to positivistic science and to some degree of environmental control. But, on balance, it becomes painfully evident from reading history that hasty, premature, wrong explanations—however pretty or ingenious—have led only to more wrong explanations, to a crippling of correct analytical functioning, to the substitution of dogma for fresh research, to the stifling of debate, to punishment for dissent—and to frequent disasters.

There were always some isolated scientific experimenters who worked in many fields (usually in secret), but they did not make much headway against the politically entrenched supernatural theoreticians and their *MIFOs—mistakenly identified flying objects*. It was not until the end of the sixteenth century that emerging nationalistic power-politics and the new mercantile and manufacturing demands of Western Europe made scientific methods highly desirable and profitable.

Before that, for hundreds of thousands of years, most human procedures were based on magical interpretations of environmental phenomena. From remote times, magicians and astrologers were consulted before any political or military decisions were made; and justice was administered according to magical formulae. Until a moment or two ago in man's long history all natural phenomena were devoutly believed to be gods, angels, spirits, devils, fairies, witches, vampires, succubi and incubi; or omens of fortune, good and evil. What remains today as semantic residues, or charming fairy tales or myths, were once life-and-death formulations acted upon with the utmost seriousness. In many of the so-called "primitive" societies still extant, the magical interpretation of the world still prevails. Even today, most American newspapers print magical astrological predictions. In 1962, all governmental business in India was suspended on the day when, for the first time in several hundred years seven of the major planets were lined up in conjunction. All of India heaved a collective sigh of relief when that fruitcake day ended,

In their book *Lure and Lore of Outer Space,* Ernst and Johanna Lehner (1964) have compiled an illustrated review of the cosmos as it was understood and visualized by earlier cultures. The Lehners make it evident that the inventors of cosmic diagrams were convinced that their images of outer space were real and completely factual, Pseudo-explanations of the nature of the cosmos were at the very core of their religious and political ideologies; belief in them was mandatory and could be disputed only at the risk of imprisonment or death.

The Chinese evolved a celestial globe completely different from the Western concept in which our earth was surrounded by the *Four Supernatural Creatures* presiding over *The Four*

Quadrants of Heaven: the *Azure Dragon* over the East; *the Vermilion Bird or Phoenix* over the South; the *White Tiger* over the West; and the *Black Warrior,* or *Tortoise* over the North. These four quadrants are enclosed by the *Pa Kua* or *Eight Diagrams,* representing heaven, water, lightning, thunder, wind, clouds, mountains and earth. They are encircled by the 12 zodiacal animals which, in turn, are surrounded by the 28 *Kung,* or constellations of the Chinese Heaven: the Earth Dragon, the Sky Dragon, the Badger, the Hare, the Fox, the Tiger, the Leopard, the Griffon, the Ox, the Bat, the Rat, the Swallow, the Bear, the Porcupine, the Wolf, the Dog, the Pheasant, the Cock, the Raven, the Monkey, the Ape, the Tapir, the Sheep, the Muntjak, the Horse, the Deer, the Snake, and the Worm. (Lehner, 1964).

These were some of the UFOs seen by the ancient Chinese. The Egyptians following the universal rule of interpreting UFOs in terms of the technology of the time—depicted interstellar vehicles as "barges of the Sun" carried on the "star-studded back of *Nut, the Heavenly Vault.*" Later, cosmic UFOs 'seen' by the Greeks and the Romans (and inherited by us) resulted in a fascinating heavenly attic chockful of people, gods and goddesses, flora and fauna, mythological beasts, assorted seafood, furniture, equipment, and miscellaneous bric-a-brac. Here, from an American astronomical chart published in the 1830s, is a partial list of constellations that were visually extrapolated from a few randomly scattered points of light: *Peacock, Herschel's Telescope, Cameleopard, Bird of Paradise, Hadley's Quadrant, Sun Dial, King Charles' Oak, Phoenix, Andromeda, Perseus, Centaur, Water Snake, Dog, Lobster, Painter's Easel, Cross, Bear, Cow.* Most appropriately for this report, there were also three interstellar vehicles: *Argo Navis* (The Sailing Ship), *The Chariot,* and *Noah's Ark.* There are also other constellations in which Gods or Goddesses or beasts act as heavenly carriers: *Iris, the Goddess of the Rainbow,* for example, carried sinners to perdition.

The worship of the sun was endemic in antiquity. In nearly every religion the sun was the supreme deity and in some societies was even given the ultimate tribute of human sacrifice. To the Greeks he was *Helios;* to the Egyptians *Horus.* For a time, in the guise of the Persian God *Mithras,* he very nearly became the predominant deity of the Western world before Christianity finally prevailed. The Incas and most other American Indians regarded the sun as their principal deity and worshipped the dominant astronomical phenomenon that was blindingly visible to everyone, but never properly understood. The sun was a veritable UFO sighting of the first magnitude.

But the concept of the UFO sun as deity was not merely metaphorical. Its identity as god was declared to be irrevocably

Truth and Dogma and was backed up by courts of law, police and armies. In theocratic states, an avowed disbelief in the theological explanation of the relationship of the sun to our earth was tantamount to treason and punished as such. On 1 July 1968, the Catholic Church announced "that it might revise its censure of Galileo Gallilei for his heretical statement that, contrary to the official Catholic dogma, the sun did not revolve around the earth, but vice versa." (New York Times, 1968). The article in the Times appears cheek-to-cheek with another news story about some UFOs that turned out to be parts of Russian satellites that ignited as they re-entered the earth's atmosphere (see Section VI, Chapter 2). The juxtaposition of these two "news items" is not accidental: they are part of a persistent pattern of response to UFOs that have always been plainly visible to mankind—and misinterpreted.

In *The Rainbow,* Carl Boyer writes:

> Anaxagoras, the friend and tutor of Pericles, found a popular atmosphere in Athens which was hostile to natural science; and, when he asserted that the sun, far from being a divinity, was nothing but a huge white-hot stone, he was jailed for impiety. Anaxagoras also courageously questioned the divinity of *Iris, the Goddess of the Rainbow.*

It seems that Iris has been a major UFO for many thousands of years, with a highly charged emotional effect upon those who witnessed the phenomenon. Some like the Hebrews, were delighted to see the rainbow, because they interpreted it as a sign of God's forgiveness of the few survivors on Noah's Ark after He had destroyed all other life on earth. But to the highly sophisticated Greeks and Romans, the rainbow was a terrifying sight because Iris was regarded as the harbinger of evil tidings. It was her special mission to come down to earth, after the storming thunder and lightning rages of Zeus, to inform men of their transgressions and to execute the penalties imposed by the Deity. Iris was ominously present after the great deluge of Deucalion, when Zeus decided that mankind was unredeemable and must be totally eliminated. His "final solution" was to be an extreme coldness that would freeze all humans to death. It was Iris who was sent to inform Menelaus of the elopement of his daughter, Helen of Troy, an act that started the Trojan Wars. Iris announced the tempest that shipwrecked Aeneas. She severed the last slender thread that kept Queen Dido alive; and it was Iris who thereafter carried water from the River Styx and forced condemned sinners to drink. Shakespeare, steeped in Ovidian mythology, knew Iris well. In "All's Well" he called her "the distempered messenger of wet" and in "Henry VI, Part II," he had the Queen threaten the exiled Duke of Suffold: "For wheresoe'er thou art in this world's globe, I'll have an *Iris* that shall find thee out." There was no escape from the rainbow messenger and executioner.

The trepidations of the Greeks, the Romans, and the Elizabethan English were shared by primitive ufologists the world over. Africa tribal lore regarded the rainbow as a giant snake who, seeking a meal after the rain will devour whomever he comes upon. In the Americas, the rainbow was also a hungry god, fond of indiscriminately ingesting water, cattle, and tribesmen, especially the youngest members. The Shoshoni Indian believed that the sky was made of ice against which the serpent rainbow rubbed its back, causing snow in the winter and rain in the summer. It is not recorded whether the Shoshoni's heavenly serpent thus relieved some dorsal itch, but other primitive descriptions of the rainbow reveal a very thirsty god indeed: Plutarch describes Iris as having a head of a bull that drinks the water of rivers and streams, while Ovid also depicts her as distinctly bibulous. Other explanations of the rainbow include the hem of God's garments (Greenland); a hat (Blackfeet American Indians); a bowl for coloring birds (Germans); a camel carrying three persons, or a net (Mongol); and, in Finnish lore, a "sickle of the Thunder-God."

Homer may have been the champion literary projectionist of Greece. He too saw Iris either literally or figuratively as a serpent. The Great Visualizer of modern times, however, is beyond any doubt Professor Hermann Rorschach. That compulsive spiller of ink is surely the twentieth century's patron saint of visualization. The doctor of ink and blot has convinced psychologists that whenever we look at something that is disorderly, meaningless, amorphous, or vague, we immediately project upon something else. And that *something else* is an image withdrawn from our internal picture library and projected onto the shapeless blob placed before us. It seems that we cannot tolerate vagueness and insist on replacing it with *what we wish to see* or *what we dread seeing.*

Some experts insist, however, that we pretend to see something in order to be kind to the earnest psychologists who try to be helpful by showing inky messes to total strangers. During World War II, I was present as an observer when a brilliant young lieutenant was being tested. He did quite well until he was handed an enormous inkblot and asked to describe what he saw. He gazed at it dutifully for quite a while, then handed it back, and said: "It looks like an inkblot to me sir." He was disqualified for his flagrant anti-social response, of course, and it served him right! I also looked at the configuration, and there plainly visible was a lovely picture of an old woman dressed all in black, riding her monocycle down a deserted country road.

And, speaking of tests, in 1875, after conducting a long

series of experiments, the eminent physiologist Dr. Francis Galton published his discovery that a surprising number of "entirely normal and reliable" Englishmen he had tested habitually saw objects, colors, forms, and vivid kinaesthetic patterns involving mixed image and color not seen by others.

I offer these digressions with the suggestion that a great deal of work still remains to be done on the visualizing characteristics of the so-called "normal and reliable" people who have made "sightings" of all kinds. I do this not to challenge the validity of all UFO 'sightings,' but to call attention to the possibility that not very much is known about the nature of visualization. It has been generally assumed that if a man is a respected member of a respected profession (like a commercial jet-pilot) he is *ipso facto* free of any visualizing aberrations, and that he always sees the world and its phenomena as nakedly, as honestly as my young lieutenant saw it when he declined to play the inkblot game.

It is therefore hardly surprising that strange objects and phenomena of all kinds have been chronicled and reported for about 3,500 years, and for thousands of years previously as oral tradition in systems of religion, mythology, and folklore. The number of reports of "strange phenomena" have increased steadily with time, an increase caused by the great proliferation of journals and newspapers since their start in the seventeenth century. As the news media increased in number, they gathered and printed more and more reports of strange happenings that would otherwise have remained localized and been forgotten. The current great interest in UFOs has resulted in a ransacking of religious literature, mythology, as well as the old newspapers and journals for UFO-like sightings and their inclusion in the current UFO literature. With the help of another researcher, I have gone through many old sources in search of new significant "UFO" material, but have found that the ufologists have covered the ground quite thoroughly not hesitating to graft new interpretations on the old reports.

Led by the genius poet-investigator, Charles Fort (1874-1932), who for about 40 years assiduously gathered reports of "strange phenomena" from scientific journals and news media, the ufologists have ferreted out and compiled many hundreds of reports of "UFOs" that were seen before the age of aviation and rocketry.

The use of selected UFO books—with frequent spot checks of their sources and veracity—serves a double purpose. It enables us to read the "ancient reports" in them and—this is nearly as important—it permits us to see what the modern ufologist selects from the past and how he utilizes and interprets the evidence he has compiled.

Such compilations pose some serious problems for the reader not already convinced of the existence of UFOs. They inflict mental fatigue and anxiety after the reading of each "report" because one is inevitably led into the same brain-numbing round of unanswered questions: Does the alleged book or manuscript in which the report was found really exist? Where is it? Did the writer actually see the original document or is he quoting a secondary source? Is the version presented here a faithful copy of the original or an accurate translation? Is the "report" in question a factual honest report of something actually seen, or is it a poetic, metaphorical, religious, symbolical, mythical, political, fabrication made legitimately within its own social context, but one that is no longer viable or meaningful to us now? If the "strange phenomenon" was actually seen, then, we ask: "Was this "light," or "fiery sphere," "wheel of fire," or "flaming cross," or "cigar-shaped object" or "saucer" or "disk" seen by reliable witnesses? How reliable is the judge of their reliability? What did they actually see? Where did it come from? What was it made of? Who, if anyone or anything, was in it? And so forth, far, far, into the night. Inconclusiveness, the mental plague of ufology, invariably cancels out or suspends in mid-air the great majority of the fascinating reports and leaves the reader (*this* reader for sure) quite frustrated and disappointed.

It soon becomes clear that it would take years of fulltime research to track down and verify the thousands of "ancient" reports included in the nearly 1600 books and articles about UFOs. This means, then, that the general reader, who rarely ever bothers to verify what he reads, is merely given the option to trust or distrust the scholarly accuracy and motivations of the writers who offer him the impressive-looking lists of UFOs sightings. This becomes a very narrow choice indeed: one that is negotiable only in the arena of speculation provided by the writers who believe in UFOs. And, since to my knowledge, no one has written an impartial or objective book about ancient "UFO reports," the nature of the dialogue between an UFO author and his reader becomes that of a man convinced of the existence of UFOs and a reader whom he hopes to convert to his belief.

The strategy for UFO proselytizing is predictable. In book after book, the reader is assured that UFOs are not a sudden, modern manifestation but that there have been numerous reports of similar visitations "down through the ages." The author then proceeds to list the most impressive and authoritative-sounding of the "ancient UFO reports," stressing those that most closely resemble modern accounts of "spacecraft sightings."

He also seeks to create an aura of believability and respectability for UFO phenomena by quoting and re-interpreting "UFO reports from the Holy Bible," from ancient Roman authors like Pliny The Elder, from Shakespeare, from Hindu religious texts, from "ancient manuscripts found in monasteries," or as in one notable example, from a "papyrus manuscript found among the papers of the late Professor Alberto Tulli, former director of the Vatican Egyptian Museum."

This is a legitimate procedure, of course, and we know that many important scholarly discoveries have been made in church archives, (to take that example) because in many periods in history, the church did chronicle and preserve records of important events. But the presentation of such prestigious ecclesiastical material is used in UFO literature in order to bestow an aura of sanctity upon all UFOs, ancient and modern; i.e., to make them respectable by association.

Thus, for example, *The Flying Saucer Reader,* edited by Jay David (1967) self-described as "an anthology of the best and most authoritative of the incredible but undeniable phenomenon of UFOs," begins with "evidence" from Biblical times; and a chapter written by Paul Thomas in (1965) in which he declares that the famous "miracle of Fatima, Portugal" (13 October 1917) was actually a flying saucer that was mistakenly identified as the Virgin Mary. The book also includes excerpts from two books in which the authors describe their fluent communications with "extra-terrestrial beings" with the aid of: (1) a ouija board using a pencil taped to a water glass, and (2) "mental telepathy."

For the true-believing ufologist, the Holy Bible is a veritable treasure-trove of sacred and profane UFOs. In Chapter 13, verse 21 of the *Book of Exodus,* ". . . the Lord went before them by day in a pillar of fire, to give them light; to go by day and night." Ufologists regard this as evidence that God sent a spaceship to guide the Israelites during their 40-year journey to the Holy Land.

The image from *Exodus* is repeated in the *New Testament* in the "Star of Bethlehem": According to *St. Matthew,* (2,9) "and, lo, the star, which they saw in the East, went before them, till it came and stood where the young child was." Though not regarded as an UFO, but a "star," it also behaved like some UFOs that start and stop.

There are, also, many "fiery chariots," "angels with wings," and "cherubim" in the New and Old Testaments, all of which have been claimed by the occultistic modern ufologists as UFOs.

The selected list of "ancient" UFO reports that follows is taken mainly from various books written by contemporary ufologists. They are all writers who believe "flying saucers" really exist, and who offer various speculations on their origin, mode of "flight" and significance.

213 B. C. "In Hadria an 'altar' was seen in the sky, accompanied by the form of a man in white clothing. A total of a dozen such sightings between 222 and 90 B. C. can be listed, but we have eliminated many more sightings because we felt that they could best be interpreted as misinterpretations of meteors or atmospheric phenomena." (Vallee, 1965).

218 B. C. "In Amiterno district in many places were seen the appearance of men in white garments from far away. The orb of the sun grew smaller. At Praeneste glowing lamps from heaven. At Arpi a shield in the sky. The Moon contended with the sun and during the night two moons were seen. Phantom ships appeared in the sky." (Trench, 1966).

100 B. C. "Pliny mentions the strange shields in *Natural History* Volume II, chapter XXXIV: 'In the consulship of Lucius Valerius and Ganius Valerius (about 100 B. C.) a burning shield scattering sparks ran across the sky at sunset from east to west." (Green, 1967).

742-814 A. D. "During the reign of Charlemagne, spacecraft took away some of the earth's inhabitants to show them something of the way of life of space people. These events are described in the Comte de Gabalis' *Discourses.*" (Trench, 1966).

"However, when the space craft returned bringing back the Earth people they had taken away, the population were convinced that they were actual members of the spacecraft whom they regarded as sorcerers."

1270 A. D. Bristol England: "In *Otto Imperialia,* Book I, Chapter XIII, Gervase of Tillbury wrote about an aerial craft over a city. The craft caught an anchor in a church steeple and a occupant of the ship scampered down a ladder to free the device. The man was stoned by a crowd and asphyxiated in the earth's atmosphere. The 'demon's body' was said to have been burned." This story is to be found in several UFO books, and is quoted here from *Let's Face the Facts about Flying Saucers,* (1967) by Warren Smith and Gabriel Green, President of the Amalgamated Flying Saucer Clubs of America.

1561 A. D. "In Nuremburg, April 14, 1561, many men and women saw blood-red or bluish or black balls and circular discs in large numbers in the neighborhood of the rising sun. The spectacle lasted one hour 'and appeared to fall to the ground as if it was all on fire and everything was consumed amid a great haze.'" (Cited from a mediaeval text found in the *Annals of Nuremburg* by C. R. Jung.)

7 August 1566 A. D. "People saw a crowd of black balls moving at high speed towards the sun, they made a half turn, collided with one another as if fighting. A large number of them became red and fiery and there after they were consumed and then the lights went out." (Quoted by Dr. Jung from the *Annals of Basle.)*

6 March 1716 A. D. "The astronomer Halley saw an object that illuminated the sky for more than two hours in such a way that he could read a printed text in the light of this object. The time of the observation was 7:00 P. M. After two hours the brightness of the phenomenon was re-activated 'as if new fuel had been cast in a fire.' " (Vallee, 1965).

There are hundreds of astronomical "sightings of strange lights," to be found in the modern UFO books. For example, Jacques Vallee, quotes the following from the *Journal of Natural History and Philosophy:*

> I saw many meteors moving around the edge of a black cloud from which lightnings flashed. They were like dazzling specks of light, dancing and traipsing thro' the clouds. One of them increased in size until it became of the brilliance and magnitude of Venus, on a clear evening. But I could see no body in the light. It moved with great rapidity, and pasted on the edge of the cloud. Then it became stationary, dimmed its splendor, and vanished. I saw these strange lights for minutes, not seconds. For at least an hour, these lights, so strange, played in and out of the black cloud. No lightning came from the clouds where these lights were playing. As the meteors increased in size, they seemed to descend . . ."

This observation was made by John Staveley, an astronomer, at Hatton Gardens, London, on 10 August 1809 and reported in the *Journal of Natural History and Philosophy and Chemistry*. (Vallee, 1965).

1820. Francis Arago, in *Annales de chimie et de physique,* wrote "concerning observations at Embrun, France: 'numerous observers have seen, during an eclipse of the moon, strange objects moving in straight lines. They were equally spaced, and remained in line when they made turns. Their movements showed a military precision.' " (Vallee, 1965).

"Lights in the dark of the moon" are considered to be UFO spacecraft by many ufologists. Fort cites many, and here are some:

November 1668. A letter from Cotton Mather to Mr. Waller of the Royal Society dated "at Boston, November 24, 1712" (now in the Library of Massachusetts Historical Society, Boston) refers to "ye star below ye body of ye Moon, and within the Horns of it . . . seen in New England in the Month of November, 1668." (Lowes, 1927).

1783. In *Philosophical Transactions* (Volume LXXVII) for 1787, the great astronomer reports a "bright spot seen in the dark of the moon . . . which seen in the telescope resembled a star of the fourth magnitude as it appears to the natural eye." (Lowes, 1927).

1794. In *Philosophical Transactions,* 1794, a total of seven letters in Volumes XXVI and XXVII, reporting "lights in the dark portion of the moon." The principal sighting was communicated by the Astronomer Royal, the Reverend Nevil Maskelyne, on the "observations of Thomas Stretton, who saw the phenomenon in St. John's Square, Clerkenwell London. In another letter to the Royal Society, a Mr. Wilkins reports his "sighting" in terms exactly like those used by many who claim to have seen UFOs. "I was," writes Wilkins, "as it were, rivetted to the spot where I stood, during the time it continued, and took every method I could to convince myself that it was not an error of sight, including the testimony of one who passed and said it was a star." (Lowes, 1927). "I am very certain," he adds in his third letter, "of this spot appearing *within* the circumference of the moon's circle." Mr. Stratton declared that it was a "light like a star, as large as a star, but not so bright, in the dark part of the moon." (Lowes, 1927).

July 1868. In *Lo!* by Charles Fort, as quoted by Jacques Vallee (1965) "at Capiago, Chile, an aerial construction emitting light and giving off engine noise was interpreted locally as a giant bird with shining eyes, covered with large scales clashing to give off a metallic noise."

22 March 1870. "An observation was made aboard the 'Lady of the Lake' in the Atlantic Ocean. The object was a disk of light grey color. What appeared to be the rear part was surrounded by a halo, and a long tail emanated from the center. This UFO was viewed between 20° and 80° elevation for half an hour. It flew against the wind and Captain Banner made a drawing of it." (Vallee, 1965).

24 April 1874. "On the above date, a Professor Schafarick of Prague saw 'an object of such a strange nature that I do not know what to say about it. It was of a blinding white and crossed slowly over the face of the moon. It remained visible afterwards.'" (*Astronomical Register* XXIII, 206 quoted by Vallee, 19).

15 May 1879. "On the above date, at 9:40 p.m. from 'the Vultur' in the Persian Gulf, two giant luminous wheels were observed spinning slowly and slowly descending. They were seen for thirty-five minutes, had an estimated diameter of forty meters (130 feet) and were four diameters apart. Similar 'giant wheels' were seen the year after, again in May, and in the same part of the ocean, by the steamer 'Patna.'" Quoted by Vallee, (1965) from *Knowledge*, a journal.

This list of "strange phenomena" could easily be extended over hundreds of pages. The reader, if he wished, can consult the writings of Charles Fort (1941) and others. At the end of all this reading, he will probably find that the mysterious phenomena remain mysterious. He can then exercise his option to believe that the strange phenomena reported down through the ages are reports of extra-terrestrial visitors from planets whose civilizations are infinitely older and superior to ours. On the other hand, his curiosity may be aroused in quite a different direction. The citations of "ancient UFO reports" by the ufologists have one hauntingly familiar common characteristic: the authors are uniformly highly uncritical of the authenticity of these reports, so much so that their presentations of them falls well outside the boundaries of normal scholarly skepticism.

Let us take as an example one particular "UFO case history" given credence and awesome attention in books by Vallee, Green, Trench, Desmond and Adamski, Jessup, and Thomas. The report is an alleged "observation made in 1290 at Byland Abbey, Yorkshire, of a large silvery disk flying slowly, a classical one and [one that] can be found in a number of books" (Vallee, 1965). Each of these authors quotes it from one of his colleagues but none has taken the precaution of checking on the "manuscript scroll that was discovered several years ago (1953) in Ampleforth Abbey in England."

After deciding to check on the "Byland Abbey sighting on 1290," I backtracked through the various books and read the complete transcript of the "Ampleforth Abbey UFO sighting of 1290" as it is given in Desmond and Adamski's *Flying Saucers Have Landed* (1953):

> oves a Wilfred suseptos die festo sanctissorum Simon is atque Judae asseverunt. Cum autum Henricus abbas gratias redditurus erat, frater guidam Joannes referebat. Tum vero omnes eccuccurerunt et ecce *res grandis, circumcircularis argentea disco quodam haud dissimils,* lente e super eos volans atque maciman terrorem exitans. Quo tempore Henricus abbas adultavisse (qua) de causa impius de . . .

"Mr. A. X. Chumley," who supplied the information, gives the following translation:

> . . . took the sheep from Wilfred and roast them in the feast of SS. Simon and Jude. But when Henry the Abbott was about to say grace, John, one of the brethren, came in and said there was a great portent outside. Then they all went out and LO! *a large round silver thing like a disk flew slowly over them,* and excited the greatest terror. Whereat Henry the Abbott immediately cried that Wilfred was an adulterer, wherefore it was impious to . . .

Authors Desmond and Adamski comment: "What probably happened is that a flying saucer did, in fact, pass over Byland Abbey at the close of the thirteenth century and that the astute Abbott Henry seized the opportunity to admonish Wilfred for his carryings on, and the community for their lack of piety."

Then, in Paul Thomas's *Flying Saucers through the ages* (1965), we read the following: " . . . in Yorkshire, a flat shining disk flew over the monastery of Byland. (Translater's note: There are grave doubts on the genuineness of this. Two Oxford undergraduates admitted to me in 1956 that they forged this document for a joke — *but there is nothing to prove that they really did so!)* (emphasis—SR).

After wondering why the translator did not, in the nine years between 1956 and 1965, seek to verify the ancient manuscript by means of a visit, letter or phone call to "Ampleforth Abbey", I began my own investigation. The British Information Service in New York verified the existence of Ampleforth Abbey, now a Benedictine College, in York, England. Then, I cabled a friend, Mr. John Haggarty, in London, and asked him to verify the existence and contents of the "Byland Abbey manuscript." Haggarty cabled promptly:

HAVE CHECKED WITH COLLEGE STOP AMPLEFORTH
DOCUMENT A HOAX PERPETRATED BY TWO SIXTH FORM
BOYS IN LETTER TO TIMES (LONDON) REGARDS

Such a fabricated "UFO report" has been used for the greater glory of the new mythology in *Let's Face the Facts About Flying Saucers,* (Green, 1967).

The authors have offered their own enlarged and embellished version, of the "Byland Abbey sighting," complete with some nifty, monk-type dialogue (not in the original fabrication); and some 'inner thoughts' of the monks — also absent from the 'original.' They have even pinned the heinous crime of "sheep-hiding" on "Wilfred, the adulterer":

Brother John's Medieval Saucer

It was an early afternoon in October, A.D. 1250 (Jacques Vallee writes that it occurred in 1290), and the monks at Byland Abbey in Yorkshire, England prepared to celebrate the feast of St. Simon and St. Jude. Henry the Abbott had previously discovered that Brother Wilfred had hidden two fat sheep on the Abbey grounds. The abbott confiscated the sheep from Wilfred and their succulent carcasses were roasting over a roaring fire in the dining hall.

The brothers were in a jovial mood. "I wish thee would till the fields as willingly as thee would watch the mutton," one said to an eager friend.

"Black bread and cheese do not compare with mutton," answered his companion.

As the brothers assembled for their evening meal, they heard a noise in the doorway. Brother John stood in the doorway with a terror-stricken look on his face.

"What happened, Brother John?" inquired the abbott.

"I was walking towards the abbey from the fields and thinking about the roast mutton dinner. A strange noise overhead scared me. I looked up in the sky. A large silver plate is up there in the sky."

The monks forgot their dinners and dashed into the yard.

"There it is," shouted Peter.

"Mother of God!" said a brother.

Henry the Abbott and Brother John stepped from the dining room. A giant flying disk hovered in the sky and drifted slowly in the clouds. The monks were panic-stricken. They fell to their knees with shouts of "Judgement Day," and " 'tis the end of the world" punctuating their frantic prayers.

The shaken monks turned to Henry the Abbott for clarification. "What does the appearance of this mean?" they inquired.

"Wilfred is an adulterer and must be punished," snapped the abbott.

A second "spot-check," made of one of the more spectacular "ancient UFO reports," has produced some fascinating results. It is the "UFO legend" offered by Mr. Frank Edwards in his *Flying Saucers — Serious Business* (1966). In his opening chapter entitled "What Goes On Here?" Edwards, from a source not mentioned, gives us the following awesome account:

A chronicle of ancient India known as the *Book of Dzyan* is in a class by itself, not only because of its age, but because of a surprising account therein. The Book is a compilation of legends passed down through the ages before men were able to write, and finally gathered by the ancient scholars who preserved them for us.

They tell of a small group of beings who came to Earth many thousands of years ago in a metal craft which first went AROUND Earth several times before landing. "These beings," says the Book, "lived to themselves and were revered by the humans among whom they had settled. But eventually differences arose among them and they divided their numbers, several of the men and women and some children settling in another city, where they were promptly installed as rulers by the awe-stricken populace."

The legend continues:

"Separation did not bring peace to these people and finally their anger reached a point where the ruler of the original city took with him a small number of his warriors and they rose into the air in a huge shining metal vessel. While they were many leagues from the city of their enemies they launched a great shining lance that rode on a beam of light. It burst apart in the city of their enemies with a great ball of flame that shot up to the heavens, almost to the stars. All those in the city were horribly burned and even those who were not in the city—but nearby—were burned also. Those who looked upon the lance and the ball of fire were blinded forever afterward. Those who entered the city on foot became ill and died. Even the dust of the city was poisoned, as were the rivers that flowed through it. Men dared not go near it, and gradually crumbled into dust and was forgotten by men.

"When the leader saw what he had done to his own people he retired to his palace and refused to see anyone. Then he gathered about him those of his warriors who remained, and their wives and their children, and they entered into their vessels and rose one by one into the sky and sailed away. Nor did they return."

This would seem to be an account of an attempt by some extra-terrestrial group to establish a colony on Earth in the distant past. Like so many colonizing attempts by man, it appears to have ended in dissension and conflict. The most interesting portion of the story is the description of the great "lance that traveled on a beam of light," which bears a surprising resemblance to a modern rocket and its jet of flame. The effect of this so-called "lance" brings to mind a rather detailed picture of a nuclear blast and its catastrophic sequels. If this is a mental concoction of some primitive writer, it is at least remarkable. If it is a reasonably accurate piece of factual reporting, then it is even more remarkable. Since it is unverifiable, we must at this late date classify it as "interesting, but unproved."

This most impressive, goosepimply account of extra-terrestrial colonists who once waged nuclear war on our planet and then left has only one thing wrong with it — it is completely spurious.

To begin with, the so-called *Book of Dzyan* is not, as Edwards writes, "a compilation of legends passed down through the ages . . . and gathered by scholars who preserved them for us." The "Book or Stanzas of Dzyan" made their very first appearance in 1886 in the famous book *The Secret Doctrine,* written by the high priestess of Esoteric Theosophy, Madame Helene Petrovna Blavatsky (1831-1891). The stanzas are the basis of her preposterous Atlantean "Theory of Cosmic Evolution." An unauthorized biographer declares that: "the mysterious 'Dzyan manuscript' like the 'Senzar' language they were written in, seem wholly to have originated in Madame Blavatsky's imagination." (Roberts, 1931).

Madame Blavatsky's own account, and those of her disciples, or the origin and meaning of the "Dzyan Stanzas" quickly show that they were concocted for an "occult" audience with a very low threshold of mental resistance.

That the "Stanzas of Dzyan" exist only in Madam Blavatsky's *The Secret Doctrine,* or in commentaries written by her disciples is clearly stated in the foreword of the only separate edition of the "Stanzas" published by the London Theosophical Society in 1908:

> For the information of readers into whose hands these *Stanzas* may now fall, it is desirable to give some brief account of their source, on the authority of the Occultist Madame Blavatsky who translated and introduced them to the world of modern thought. The following particulars are derived from Madame Blavatsky's *Secret Doctrine* and *Voice of The Silence*; which Madame Blavatsky tells us form a part of the same series

of long-concealed manuscript treasures in which the *Stanzas of Dzyan* belong.

> *Book of Dzyan is not in the possession of any European library, and was never heard of by European scholarship:* nevertheless it exists and lies hidden, even from the enterprising war correspondent, *in one of the mysterious rock libraries that the spurs of the Himalayas may yet contain.* (emphasis—SR).

In her own inimitable style Madame Blavatsky adds: "In the Tsaydam, in the solitary passes of the Kuen-Lun, along the Altyn-Tag" [this "Tibetan" word sounds German: "Alten-Tag" or "olden days"—SR] whose soil no European foot has trod, there exists a certain hamlet lost in a deep gorge. It is a small cluster of houses, a hamlet rather than a monastery, with a poor temple on it, and only one old Lama, a hermit, living near to watch it. Pilgrims say that the subterranean galleries and halls under it contain a collection of books . . . too large to find room even in the British Museum" (Introduction to *The Secret Doctrine,* Madame Blavatsky).

The preface of the London Theosophical Society's edition of the "Stanzas" explains more about them:

> The *Stanzas of Dzyan . . . are written in a language unknown to philology,* if indeed the word "written" is applicable to ideographs of which they largely consist, and this associated with the use of a colour system of symbology.
>
> They are given throughout, in their modern translated version, as it would be worse than useless to make the subject still more difficult by introducing the archaic phraseology of the original with its puzzling style and words. The terms used were non-translatable into English, are Tibetan and Sanskrit, and . . . will frequently be a stumbling block unless reference is made to *The Secret Doctrine* where the commentaries on the text will generally be found to supply the meaning (London Theosophical Society, 1908).

A thorough search of the *Stanzas* in Madame Blavatsky's books and those of her commentators has failed to divulge the enthralling "legend from the Book of Dzyan" quoted by Edwards. Now since the *Stanzas* exists only in *The Secret Doctrine,* and they, in turn, exist only "in the imagination of Madame Blavatsky," then the question arises: Where did the additional long account of "extra-terrestrial colonists" — come from? It seems that Edwards had "been had" by one of his sources, and has innocently passed on to his readers a fabrication superimposed on a gigantic hoax concocted by Madame Blavatsky.

Then there is the "UFO sighting" *sometime "during the reign of Thutmose III, (1504-1450 B. C.),"* cited by Trench (1966):

> Among the papers of the late Professor Alberto Tulli, former director of the Egyptian Museum at the Vatican, was found the earliest known record of a fleet of flying saucers written on

papyrus long, long, ago in ancient Egypt. Although it was damaged, having many gaps in the hieroglyphics, Prince Boris de Rachewiltz subsequently translated the papyrus and irrespective of the many broken sections he stated that the original was part of the *Annals of Thutmose III, circa* 1594-1450 B.C. The following is an excerpt:

"In the year 22, of the third month of winter, sixth hour of the day . . . in the scribes of the House of Life it was found a circle of fire that was coming from the sky . . . it had no head, the breath of its mouth had a foul odor. Its body was one rod long and one rod wide. It had no voice. Their bellies became confused through it: then they laid themselves on their bellies . . . they went to the Pharoah, to report it . . . His Majesty ordered . . . has been examined . . . as to all which is written in the papyrus rolls of the *House of Life*. His Majesty was meditating on what happened. Now after some days had passed, these things became more numerous in the sky than ever. They shone more in the sky than the brightness of the sun, and extended to the limits of the four supports of the heavens . . . Powerful was the position of the fire circles. The army of the Pharoah looked on with him in their midst. It was after supper. Thereupon these fire circles ascended higher in the sky to the south. Fishes and volatiles fell down from the sky. A marvel never before known since the foundation of their land. And Pharoah caused incense to be brought to make peace on the hearth . . . and what happened was ordered to be written in the annals of the *House of Life* . . . so that it be remembered for ever."

As I read, reread, and compared the *"Tulli* Egyptian papyrus" (c. 1500 B. C.) with the *Book of Ezekiel,* written about 900 years later (c. 590 B. C.), I became aware of a number of striking similarities between the texts. The most celebrated and oft-quoted of the ancient "UFOs" is "Ezekiel's wheel of fire, *(Old Testament, Ezekiel, Chapter One, King James Version):*

1: Now it came to pass in the thirtieth year in the fourth month, in the fifth day of the month, as I was among the captives by the river of Chebar, that the heavens were opened and I saw visions of God.

4: And I looked, and behold a whirlwind came out of the north, a great cloud, and a fire infolding itself, and a brightness was about it, and out of the midst thereof as the color of amber, out of the midst of the fire.

5: Also out of the midst thereof came the likeness of four living creatures . . . they had the likeness of a man.

6: And every one had four faces, and every one had four wings.

10: As for the likeness of the faces, they four had the face of a man, the face of a lion . . . and the face of an eagle . . .

13: . . . their appearance was like burning coals of fire, and like the appearance of lamps: it went up and down among the living creatures, and the fire was the fire bright and out of the fire went forth lightning.

15: Now as I beheld the living creatures, behold one wheel upon the earth by the living creatures, with his four faces.

16: The appearance of the wheels and their work was like unto the colour of beryl; and they four had one likeness; and their appearance and their work was as it were a wheel in the middle of a wheel.

17: When they went, they went upon their four sides: and they turned not when they went.

18: As for their rings, they were so high they were dreadful; and their rings were full of eyes round about them four.

19: And, when the living creatures were, the wheels went by them: and when the living creatures were lifted up from the earth, the wheels lifted up.

20: . . . for the spirit of the living creatures was in them.

The Book of Ezekiel consists of 48 chapters, most of which are devoted to Jehovah's bitter complaints about the immorality of his own people; and his lengthy tirades against all of Israel's enemies, *especially the Pharoahs of Egypt.*

29, 1: In the tenth year, in the twelfth day, the word of the Lord came unto me, saying . . . Prophesy against . . . Pharaoh, King of Egypt.

The "Tulli papyrus" and *Ezekiel* show so many exact similarities of style, language and detail *in sequence,* that one wonders whether, despite its alleged time priority, the "Tulli papyrus" may be taken from the King James version of the *Book of Ezekiel.* Or, if the "Tulli papyrus" is genuine, and its translation by Prince de Rachewiltz is accurate, then the *Book of Ezekiel* may have been plagiarized from the *Annals of Thutmose III!*

A tabulation of the similarities follows:

Egyptian	Ezekiel
"the *House of Scribes*"	"the *House of Israel*"
"*was coming in the sky*"	"*the heavens were opened*"
"it was a *circle of fire*"	"always referred to as *wheel of fire*"
"*it had no head*"	"*heads with four faces*"—"*everyone had four faces*"
"*It had no voice.*"	"*I heard a voice that spake*"
"Their hearts became confused through it: then *they laid themselves on their bellies*"	"When I saw it, *I fell on my face.*"
"*His Majesty ordered . . . written in rolls*"	"*and God spread a roll before me and it was written . . .*"
"*towards the south*"	"*out of the north*"
"the *brightness* of the sun"	"and a *brightness* was about it"
"it was after supper"	"cause thy belly to eat."
This all takes place allegedly in Egypt during the reign of Thutmose III	"in the land of Egypt."
	"I am against Pharaoh, king of Egypt"
"*Fishes* and volatiles *fell down from the sky.*"	29:5, 3: "thee and all the *fishes: thou shalt fall upon the open fields.*"

These dozen sequential similarities are so remarkable and raise so many questions as to the authenticity of the "Tulli papyrus," that a cable was despatched to the Egyptian section of the Vatican Museum seeking more information about both the "papyrus" and the "de Rachewiltz translation." The reply follows:

> Papyrus Tulli not propriety [sic] of Vatican Museum. Now it is dispersed and no more traceable.
>
> The Inspector to Egyptian
> Vatican Museum
> (signed) Gianfranco Nolli
>
> Citta del Vaticano 25 Luglio 1968

Skepticism being the mother of persistence, we nevertheless decided to trace it as far as we could. Dr. Condon wrote Dr. Walter Ramberg, Scientific Attache at the U. S. embassy in Rome. Dr. Ramberg replied:

> . . . the current Director of the Egyptian Section of the Vatican Museum, Dr. Nolli, said that . . . Prof. Tulli had left all his belongings to a brother of his who was a priest in the Lateran Palace. Presumably the famous papyrus went to this priest. Unfortunately the priest died also in the meantime and his belongings were dispersed among heirs, who may have disposed of the papyrus as something of little value.
>
> Dr. Nolli intimated that Prof. Tulli was only an amateur "Egyptologist" and that Prince de Rachelwitz is no expert either. He suspects that Tulli was taken in and that the papyrus is a fake . . . .

Do these startling coincidences or downright hoaxes mean that all such "ancient UFO reports" are fabrications? No, it does not. But they do indicate that the authors of at least seven UFO books have attempted to build up the argument for the existence of UFOs with "case histories" taken from secondary and tertiary sources without any attempt to verify original sources, and that they orbit around each other in a merry UFO chase of mutual quotation. If any scientist or scholar had behaved similarly, he would have long since been hooted out of his profession. My conclusion: all accounts of "UFO-like sightings handed down through the ages" are doubtful — until verified.

There is a positive side to all of this, however. The low-grade controversy generated by "devout believers in the existence of UFOs" (book ad in The New York Times) has attracted a great deal of attention in the news media of the world. A lot of rubbish about UFOs has been printed, and the entire field of speculation remains chronically inconclusive, but attention has also been drawn to a profound question: Are we alone in the universe? Is there life on other planets? And indirectly all of this has led to support and interest in governmental space programs.

But what of UFOs, ancient or modern? The best proposition I know for evaluating any hypothesis was offered 40 years ago by Bertrand Russell in *Skeptical Essays:*

> There are matters about which those who have investigated them are agreed: the dates of eclipses may serve as an illustration. There are other matters about which experts are not agreed. Even when all the experts agree, they may well be mistaken. Einstein's view as to the magnitude of the deflection of light by gravitation would have been rejected by all experts twenty years ago. Nevertheless, the opinion of experts, when it is unanimous, must be accepted by non-experts as more likely to be right than the opposite opinion. The skepticism that I advocate amounts only to this: 1) that when experts are agreed, the opposite opinion cannot be held to be certain; 2) that when they are not agreed, no opinion can be regarded as certain by a non-expert; 3) that when they all hold that no sufficient grounds for a positive opinion exists, the ordinary man would do well to suspend his judgments. These propositions seem mild, yet, if accepted they would revolutionize human life.

The revolution is not yet, but as a very ordinary non-expert and a card-carrying skeptic, I will begin it by regarding no opinion as certain.

References

Blavatsky, H. P. *Stanzas of Dzyan,* London: London Theosophical Society, 1908.

———. *The Secret Doctrine,* London: London Theosophical Society, 1888.

———. *The Voice of Silence,* New York: E. B. Page, 1899.

Boyer, Carly B. *The Rainbow,* New York: Thomas Yosalef, 1959.

David, Jay. *The Flying Saucer Reader,* New York: New American Library, 1967.

Desmond, Leslie and George Adamski. *Flying Saucers Have Landed,* New York: British Book Centre, 1953.

Edwards, Frank. *Flying Saucers—Serious Business,* New York: Lyle Stuart, 1966.

Fort, Charles. *The Books of Charles Fort,* New York: Henry Holt & Co., 1941.

Galton, Francis. *Inquiries into Human Faculty and its Development,* London: J. M. Dent and Co., 1908.

Green, Gabriel. *Let's Face the Facts about Flying Saucers,* New York: Popular Library, 1967.

Hynek, J. Allan. *Christian Science Monitor,* (23 May 1967).

Lehner, Ernst and Joanna. *Lure and Lore of Outer Space,* New York: Tudor Publications, 1964.

Lowes, John Livingston. *The Road to Xanadu,* Cambridge: Houghton, Mifflin, 1927.

New Testament, King James Version, *Book of Matthew,* 1604.

Old Testament, King James Version, 1604.

Old Testament, King James Version, *Book of Ezekiel,* 1604.

Pliny, The Elder. *Natural History,* Vol. II, Chapter XXXVIV, Cambridge: Harvard Press, 1962.

Roberts, C. E. B. *The Mysterious Madame,* London: John Lane, 1931.

Russell, Bertrand. *Skeptical Essays,* New York: Norton and Co., 1928.
Thomas, Paul. *Flying Saucers through the Ages,* London: Spearman, 1965.
Trench, Brinsley Le Poer. *The Flying Saucer Story,* London: Spearman, 1966.
Vallee, Jacques. *Anatomy of a Phenomenon,* Chicago: Henry Regnery, 1965.
Wilkins, H. T. *Flying Saucers on the Attack,* New York: Citadel Press, 1954.

Chapter 2 UFOs: 1947-1968 / E. U. Condon

1. Initial Activity: Project Sign.

This chapter provides a concise historical account of the development of official and public interest in the UFO phenomenon, principally as it occurred in the United States from the initial sightings of Kenneth Arnold on June 24, 1947 to the present. It does not undertake to make a detailed study of the more famous of the past incidents, but merely to give a brief account of them as examples of the way in which interest in the subject developed.

The Kenneth Arnold sightings were accorded a large amount of newspaper publicity throughout the world. The most detailed account of the Arnold sightings is to be found in a book written and published by Arnold with the collaboration of Ray Palmer, a science fiction editor and author (Arnold and Palmer, 1952).

The Arnold sightings and the accompanying flurry of UFO reports occurred just before the Army Air Force was reorganized as the U. S. Air Force and made a part of the newly created Department of Defense.

In the first few months, the Army Air Force began to study UFO reports that came to its attention at the Air Technical Intelligence Center, (ATIC) located at Wright-Patterson Air Force Base near Dayton, Ohio. About the earliest formal action looking toward establishment of a study of flying saucers — the term UFO was not coined until later — was a letter dated 23 September 1947 from Lt. Gen. Nathan F. Twining, Chief of Staff of the U. S. Army to the Commanding General of the Army Air Force (Appendix R). This letter directs establishment of a study of UFOs. The new activity was given the code name, Project Sign, and assigned a priority 2-A in a letter dated 30 December 1947 from Maj. Gen. L. C. Craigie to the Commanding General of the Air Materiel Command (Appendix S).

Many of the attitudes which are held today began to be apparent almost at once, and many individuals in the public as well as in the military services began to adopt somewhat emotional positions. Some were ready to believe from the beginning that the UFOs were interplanetary or interstellar visitors, while others thought that UFOs were secret weapons of a foreign power, Russia being most frequently mentioned in this context. Still others tended to think that all UFOs were hoaxes or honest misidentifications of ordinary phenomena. Within the Air Force there were those who emphatically believed that the subject was absurd and that the Air Force should devote no attention to it whatever. Other Air Force officials regarded UFOs with the utmost seriousness and believed that it was quite likely that American airspace was being invaded by secret weapons of foreign powers or possibly by visitors from outer space. The time in question was just two years after the end of World War II. The period of difficult diplomatic relations between the United States and the U. S. S. R. had already started. Negotiations aimed at achieving international control of atomic energy had been under way for some time at the United Nations, but negligible progress was being made.

Four days after Arnold's sightings, an Air Force F-51 pilot saw a formation of five or six circular objects off his right wing while flying near Lake Meade, Nev. in the middle of the afternoon. That same evening near Maxwell AFB, Montgomery Ala., several Air Force officers saw a bright light that zigzagged across the sky at high speed and, when overhead, made a 90° turn and disappeared to the south. From White Sands Proving Ground in N. M. came a report of a pulsating light travelling from horizon to horizon in 30 sec. Reports poured in from many parts of the country.

On 4 July 1947 excitement was generated by the report of the first UFO photograph from Portland, Ore. This was later identified as a weather balloon, but only after the picture had been given newspaper publicity.

During World War II, the Navy had developed a plane designated as XF-5-U-1, and popularly referred to as the "flying flapjack," but this project had been abandoned. Nevertheless some thought that perhaps it was still being worked on and that this secret plane might be flying and giving rise to some of the UFO reports. This plane was never flown.

At the end of July 1947, the first tragedy associated with the UFO story occurred. It is known as the Maury Island Incident. Two Tacoma, Wash. "harbor patrolmen," declared that they had seen six UFOs hover over their patrol boat. A private citizen reported this to an intelligence officer at Hamilton AFB in Calif., claiming that he had some pieces of metal that had come from one of the UFOs.

As a result, Lt. Brown and Capt. Davidson flew from Hamilton to Tacoma and met the citizen in his hotel room at Tacoma. The citizen then told them that he had been paid $200 for an exclusive story by a Chicago publisher, but that he had decided the story ought to be told to the military. The two "harbor patrolmen" were summoned to the hotel room to relate their story to Brown and Davidson. In June 1947, the patrolmen said, they sighted the doughnut-shaped UFOs over Puget Sound about three miles from Tacoma. The UFOs were said to be 100 ft. in diameter with a central hole about 25 ft. in diameter. One appeared to be in trouble and another made contact in flight with it. According to the story, the disabled UFO spewed out sheets of light metal and a hard rocklike material, some of which landed at Maury Island. The harbor patrolmen went to the island and scooped up some of the metal. They tried to use their radio but found so much interference that they could not communicate with headquarters three miles away. While this was happening, the UFOs disappeared.

The next morning, one of the patrolmen said, he had been visited by a mysterious man who told him not to talk. Photographs were taken during the encounter with the UFOs, but the film was badly fogged, the patrolman claimed.

During the interview between the harbor patrolman and the Air Force officers, which occurred sometime after the event itself, Tacoma newspapers received anonymous tips about the interviews in the hotel room.

They returned to McChord AFB near Tacoma, and after conferring with an intelligence officer there, started the return flight to Calif. in the B-25 in which they had come. The plane crashed near Kelso, Wash. Although the pilot and a passenger parachuted to safety, Brown and Davidson lost their lives.

In the investigation which followed the "harbor patrolmen" admitted that the whole story was a hoax intended to produce a magazine story for the Chicago publisher. The alleged photographs could no longer be found. The men admitted that they were not harbor patrolmen. One admitted to having telephoned tips on the interviews with Air Force officers to the Tacoma newspapers. The Air Force officers had already decided that the story was a hoax, which was why they did not take with them the metal fragments alleged to have come from the UFO.

This case is presented in somewhat more detail in Ruppelt (1956). Another version of the same case is given in Wilkins (1954). *Life* acknowledged the UFO wave with an article "Flying Saucers Break Out over the U. S." in its 21 July 1947 issue. *Newsweek* covered the story under the headline "Flying Saucer Spots Before Their Eyes" in the 14 July 1947 issue.

The following year another case ended in tragedy when Capt. Thomas Mantell lost his life on 7 January 1948. He was attempting to chase an UFO near Louisville, Ky. This is the first fatality on record directly connected with an UFO chase (Ruppelt, 1955).

At 1:15 p.m. reports from private citizens were made to the Kentucky State Highway Patrol describing a strange, saucer-shaped flying object, some 200-300 ft. in diameter. Soon it was seen by several persons, including the base commander, at the control tower of Godman AFB, outside Louisville.

About this time a group of four F-51s arrived and the flight leader, Capt. Mantell, was asked by the base commander to have a look at the UFO. Three of the planes took up the investigation. Unable to see the UFO at first they followed directions from the control tower.

After a while, Capt. Mantell reported that he had found the UFO ahead of him and higher. He told the tower that he was climbing to 20,000 ft. The other two planes remained behind. None of the three planes had oxygen. The others tried to call Mantell on the radio, but he was never heard from again. By 4:00 p.m. it was reported that Mantell's plane had crashed and that he was dead.

Initially it was concluded that Mantell had been chasing Venus. The case was restudied by Ruppelt in 1952 with the assistance of Hynek, who concluded that the UFO was probably not Venus, because although the location was roughly appropriate, Venus was not bright enough to be seen vividly in the bright afternoon sky. Ruppelt's later study led him to the belief that what Capt. Mantell chased was probably one of the large 100 ft. "skyhook" balloons that were being secretly flown in 1948 by the Navy. Their existence was not known to most Air Force pilots. This explanation, though plausible, is not a certain identification.

Two other 1948 cases figure largely in reports of UFO sightings. On 24 July 1948 an Eastern Airlines DC-3, piloted by Clarence S. Chiles and John B. Whitted, was on a regular run from Houston, Tex. to Atlanta, Ga. At 2:45 a.m. they saw a bright light dead ahead coming rapidly toward them. They pulled to the left to avoid a collision. Looking back they saw the UFO go into a steep climb. The pilots described it as a wingless B-29 fuselage and said that the underside had a deep blue glow. Two other reports from the general vicinity at the same time gave a similar description.

On 1 October 1948, at 9:00 p.m. Lt. George F. Gorman of the North Dakota National Guard was approaching Fargo, N. D. in an F-51. The tower called his attention to a Piper Cub which he saw below him. As he prepared to land, suddenly what he took to be the tail-light of another plane passed him on his right, but the control tower assured him no other planes were in the area. Chasing the light, he got within 1,000 yd. of it. It had been blinking but suddenly became steady and started to move rapidly with the F-51 pursuit. There followed a complicated chase in which Gorman had to dive on one occasion to avoid collision. Suddenly the light began to climb and disappeared.

Some months later, 24 January 1949, the Air Weather Service provided ATIC with an analysis which indicated that Gorman had been chasing a lighted balloon. This explanation is not accepted by Keyhoe (1953), who says that although the Weather Bureau had released a weather balloon, it had been tracked by theodolite and found to have moved in a different direction from that in which Gorman had his UFO encounter.

In late July 1948 an incident occurred of which much is made by critics of Air Force handling of the UFO problem. The staff of Project Sign, on the basis of study of cases reported in the year since the original Arnold sightings prepared an "Estimate of the Situation." This is said to have been classified "Top Secret" although "Restricted" was the general classification applicable to Project Sign at that time. The intelligence report was addressed to Air Force Chief of Staff, Gen. Hoyt S. Vandenberg.

According to the unconfirmed reports, the "Estimate" asserted that the staff of Project Sign were convinced that the UFOs were really interplanetary vehicles. This report never became an official document of the Air Force, because Gen. Vandenberg refused to accept its conclusions on the ground that the Project Sign "Estimate of the Situation" lacked proof of its conclusion. Copies of the report were destroyed, although it is said that a few clandestine copies exist. We have not been able to verify the existence of such a report.

Some Air Force critics make much of this incident. As they tell it, the Estimate contained conclusive evidence of ETA, but this important discovery was suppressed by arbitrary decision of Gen. Vandenberg. We accept the more reasonable explanation that the evidence presented was then, as now, inadequate to support the conclusion.

Project Sign at ATIC continued its investigations of flying saucer reports until 11 February 1949 when the name of the project was offically changed to Project Grudge.

The final report of Project Sign was prepared and classified "Secret" February 1949, and was finally declassified 12 yr. later. It is a document of vii + 35 pages officially cited as Technical Report TR-2274-IA of the Technical Intelligence Division, Air Materiel Command, Wright-Patterson AFB, Ohio.

This report concludes with these recommendations:

> Future activity on this project should be carried on at the minimum level necessary to record, summarize and evaluate the data received on future reports and to complete the specialized investigations now in progress. When and if a sufficient number of incidents are solved to indicate that these sightings do not represent a threat to the security of the nation, the assignment of special project status to the activity could be terminated. Future investigations of reports would then be handled on a routine basis like any other intelligence work.

Reporting agencies should be impressed with the necessity for getting more factual evidence on sightings, such as photographs, physical evidence, radar sightings, and data on size and shape. Personnel sighting such objects should engage the assistance of others, when possible, to get more definite data. For example, military pilots should notify neighboring bases by radio of the presence and direction of flight of an unidentified object so that other observers, in flight or on the ground, could assist in its identification.

Of particular interest even today, as indicating the way in which the problem was being attacked in that early period are Appendices C and D of the report which are reproduced here as our Appendices D and T. Appendix C is by Prof. George Valley of the Massachusetts Institute of Technology who was at that time a member of the Air Force Scientific Advisory Board, attached to the Office of the Chief of Staff. Appendix D is a letter by Dr. James E. Lipp of the Rand Corporation, Santa Monica, Calif., to Brig. Gen. Donald Putt who was then the Air Force's director of research and development, which discusses Extra-Terrestrial Hypotheses. Historically it serves to show that the Air Force was in fact giving consideration to the ETH possibility at this early date.

A curious discrepancy may be noted: On page 38 of the paperback edition of Keyhoe's *Flying Saucers from Outer Space* (Keyhoe, 1954) there is given a two-paragraph direct quotation from the Project Sign report. However a careful examination of the report shows that these paragraphs are not contained in it.

2. Project Grudge. Early Magazine Articles and Books.

After 11 February 1949, the work at ATIC on flying saucers was called Project Grudge. It issued one report, designated as Technical Report No. 102-AC 49/15-100, dated August 1949, originally classified "Secret" and declassified on 1 August 1952. The report concerns itself with detailed study of 244 sighting reports received up to January 1949. Comments on individual cases from an astronomical point of view by Dr. Hynek predominate. About 32% of the cases were considered to have been explained as sightings of astronomical objects.

Another 12% were judged to have been sightings of weather balloons on the basis of detailed analysis of the reports made by the Air Weather Service and the Air Force Cambridge Research Laboratory. Some 33% were dismissed as hoaxes or reports that were too vague for explanation, or as sightings of airplanes under unusual conditions. A residue of 23% was considered as "Unknown."

Although the report was declassified in 1952, not many copies are in existence. We were supplied a copy by the Air

Force for our work on this project. The report is discussed in some detail by Ruppelt (1956). He implies that the investigations of the residue were incomplete and inadequate.

Examination of the record indicates that many of the reports were too vague for interpretation and that if anything, the Air Force investigators gave them more attention than they deserved. Two of the reports are reproduced here as a sample of the kind of material involved, and the kind of comment on it that was made by Air Force investigators:

Incident No. 40. 7 July 1947, 1600 hours, Phoenix, Arizona. One observer witnessed an elliptical, flat gray object, measuring 20-30 ft. across, flying 400-600 mph, spiraling downward to 2000 ft. from 5000 ft. then ascending at a 45° angle into an overcast. Observer ran into a garage where he obtained a Kodak Brownie 120 box camera, and snapped two pictures; one negative, and a print of the other, are contained in project files. The negative displays a small apparently flat object rounded on one end, and pointed on the other. The object appears to have a hole in the center. The image is in stark contrast with the background of clouds. From the print, the object appears to be jet black with sharp outlines. Four expert photographers concur in the opinion that the image is of true photographic nature. However, they disagree with each other as to the possibility of filming such an occurrence under the conditions described. Considering the object was gray as described, and at a distance of 2000 ft., it seems unlikely that it would appear pure black on the print. In subsequent correspondence to the reporter of this incident, the observer refers to himself as Chief of Staff of Panoramic Research Laboratory, the letterhead of which lists photography among one of its specialities. Yet, the negative was carelessly cut and faultily developed. It is covered with streaks and over a period of six months, has faded very noticeably. An OSI agent discovered that a letter by this observer was published by Amazing Stories magazine early this year. In this letter he stated that he had been interviewed by two Federal agents, had given them pictures of "flying discs" and that the pictures had not been returned. He requested the advice of the magazine as to how to proceed to sue the Government. This individual is aware of the whereabouts of these pictures, but has never requested their return. There are other undesirable aspects to this case. The observer's character and business affiliations are presently under investigation, the results of which are not yet known. Dr. Irving Langmuir studied subject photographs, and after learning of the prior passage of a thunderstorm, discounted the photographed object as being merely paper swept up by the winds.

AHC Opinion: In view of the apparent character of the witness, the conclusion by Dr. Langmuir seems entirely probable.

Incident No. 51. 3 September 1947, 1215 hours, Oswego, Oregon. A housewife observed twelve to fifteen round silver-colored objects at a high altitude. No further information was submitted, therefore no conclusion can be reached.

The Grudge Report contains these recommendations:

1. That the investigation of study of reports of unidentified flying objects be reduced in scope.

   a. That current collection directives relative to unidentified flying objects be revised to provide for the submission of only those reports clearly indicating realistic technical applications.

2. That Conclusions 1 and 2 of this report, with sufficient supporting data be declassified and made public in the form of an official press release.

3. That Psychological Warfare Division and other governmental agencies interested in psychological warfare be informed of the results of this study.

In accordance with the recommendations, a press release announcing the closing of Project Grudge was issued on 27 December 1949.

A fuller statement of Conclusions and Recommendations is given on page 10 of the Grudge Report and is quoted here in full:

A. There is no evidence that objects reported upon are the result of an advanced scientific foreign development; and, therefore they constitute no direct threat to the national security. In view of this, it is recommended that the investigation and study of reports of unidentified flying objects be reduced in scope. Headquarters AMC will continue to investigate reports in which realistic technical applications are clearly indicated.

NOTE: It is apparent that further study along present lines would only confirm the findings presented herein.

1. It is further recommended that pertinent collection directives be revised to reflect the contemplated change in policy.

B. All evidence and analysis indicate that reports of unidentified flying objects are the result of:

1. Misinterpretation of various conventional objects.
2. A mild form of mass-hysteria and war nerves.
3. Individuals who fabricate such reports to perpetrate a hoax or to seek publicity.
4. Psychopathological persons.

It is, therefore, recommended that Conclusions 1 and 2 of this report, with sufficient supporting data, be declassified and public in the form of an official press release. This action would aid in dispelling public apprehension, often directly attributable to the sensationalistic reporting of many of these incidents by the press and radio.

C. There are indications that the planned release of sufficient unusual aerial objects coupled with the release of related psychological propaganda would cause a form of mass-hysteria. Employment of these methods by or against an enemy would yield similar results.

In view of this the Psychological Warfare Division and other governmental agencies interested in psychological warfare should be informed of the results of this study. These agencies should then coordinate in and provide further recommendations for public release of material relative to unidentified flying objects as recommended herein.

The remarks under B. and C., originally dated August 1949, indicate that the Air Force was aware of the public relations problem involved in the UFO situation. The Air Force was also aware that public concern with the problem could be used in psychological warfare. This was just two years after interest in the subject had been generated by newspaper publicity about the Kenneth Arnold sighting. The same kind of problem in a slightly different form was an important consideration when the problem was again reviewed by the Robertson panel in January 1953.

Even in 1968 opinion remains sharply divided as to whether or not the Air Force should have done more or less to investigate UFOs.

By 1950 magazine and book publishers had discovered that money could be made in the UFO field. The first major magazine article appeared in the issue of *True* magazine dated January 1950. It was entitled "The Flying Saucers are Real," written by Donald Keyhoe. *True* magazine is an unusual place in which to announce a major scientific discovery, but that is what this article did: it unequivocally asserted that flying saucers are vehicles being used by visitors from outer space to scrutinize the earth. The 1950 Keyhoe article was the subject of a great deal of radio, television, and newspaper comment.

In the March 1950 issue, *True* extended its coverage of UFOs with an article entitled "How Scientists Tracked Flying Saucers," written by Commander R. B. McLaughlin, U. S. N. CDR McLaughlin came out on the side of Extra Terrestrial Hypothesis. Describing an UFO he had seen at White Sands, he declared, "I am convinced that it was a flying saucer, and further, these discs are spaceships from another planet, operated by animate, intelligent beings." *True* continued to established its position by publishing a collection of seven UFO photographs in its April 1950 issue.

More serious interest developed in the news media. The *New York Times* (9 April 1950) published an editorial entitled, "Those Flying Saucers—Are They or Aren't They," and the *U. S. News and World Report* (7 April 1950) carried a story relating the flying saucers to the Navy's abandoned XF-5-U project. Edward R. Murrow produced (9 September 1957) an hour-long television roundup on the subject. In its 26 June 1950 issue, *Life* published an article on "Farmer [X's] Flying Saucer" based on the photographs taken at the witness' farm near McMinnville, Ore. (see Section III, Chapter 3).

The first three books on flying saucers also appeared in 1950. The smallest of these was a 16-page booklet by Kenneth A. Arnold entitled, "The Flying Saucer as I Saw It." Next there appeared a book by the Hollywood correspondent of *Variety*, Frank Scully, entitled "Behind the Flying Saucers" published by Holt and Co., New York. In the fall of 1950, Donald Keyhoe's first book, "The Flying Saucers are Real" appeared, published by Fawcett Publications of Greenwich, Conn. It was essentially an expansion of his article in the January 1950 issue of *True*.

A new field for book publishing had been established: each year since 1950 has seen the publication of an increasing number of books on the subject.

In accordance with policy decisions based on the final report of Project Grudge, the activity was discontinued as a separate project and ATIC's investigation of UFO reports was handled as a part of regular intelligence activities. Then, on 10 September, 1951, an incident occurred at the Army Signal Corps radar center at Fort Monmouth, N. J. An UFO was reported seen on radar travelling much faster than any of the jet planes then in the air. Later it turned out that the radar operator had miscalculated the speed and the "UFO" was identified as a conventional 400 mph jet airplane.

Before this explanation was discovered, however, the case attracted the attention of Maj. Gen. C. P. Cabell, director of Air Force Intelligence. He ordered a re-activation of Project Grudge as a new and expanded project under the direction of E. J. Ruppelt (1956). Ruppelt headed the new project Grudge from its former establishment on 27 October 1951, and later under its new designation as Project Blue Book in March 1952, until he left the Air Force in September 1953.

Starting in November 1951, Project Grudge and later Project Blue Book issued a series of "Status Reports" numbered 1 through 12. Numbers 1 through 12 were originally classified "Confidential," while 10, 11, 12 were classified "Secret." All were declassified as of 9 September 1960 but copies were not readily available until 1968 when they were published by NICAP.

The story of the Fort Monmouth sightings is told in Special Report No. 1, dated 28 December 1951, and is quoted in part here both for its intrinsic interest and as representative of the way in which the investigations were reported:

> On 10 September 1951 an AN/MPG-1 radar set picked up a fast-moving low-flying target (exact altitude undetermined) at approximately 1100 hours southeast of Fort Monmouth at a range of about 12,000 yards. The target appeared to approximate-

ly follow the coast line changing its range only slightly but changing its azimuth rapidly. The radar set was switched to full-aided azimuth tracking which normally is fast enough to track jet aircraft, but in this case was too slow to be resorted to.

Upon interrogation, it was found that the operator, who had more experience than the average student, was giving a demonstration for a group of visiting officers. He assumed that he was picking up a high-speed aircraft because of his inability to use full-aided azimuth tracking which will normally track an aircraft at speeds up to 700 mph. Since he could not track the target he assumed its speed to be about 700 mph. However, he also made the statement that he tracked the object off and on from 1115 to 1118, or three minutes. Using this time and the ground track, the speed is only about 400 mph.

No definite conclusions can be given due to the lack of accurate data but it is highly probable that due to the fact that the operator was giving a demonstration to a group of officers, and that he thought he picked up a very unusual radar return, he was in an excited state, accounting for his inability to use full-aided azimuth tracking. He admitted he was "highly frustrated" in not being able to keep up with the target using the aided tracking. The weather on 10 September was not favorable for anomalous propagation.

Here is a quotation from the report of another sighting at Fort Monmouth made the next day:

On 11 September 1951, at about 1330, a target was picked up on an SCR-584 radar set, serial number 315, that displayed unusual maneuverability. The target was approximately over Havesink, New Jersey, as indicated by its 10,000 yard range, 6,000 feet altitude and due north azimuth. The target remained practically stationary on the scope and appeared to be hovering. The operators looked out of the van in an attempt to see the target since it was at such a short range, however, overcast conditions prevented such observation. Returning to their operating positions the target was observed to be changing its elevation at an extremely rapid rate, the change in range was so small the operators believed the target must have risen nearly vertically. The target ceased its rise in elevation at an elevation angle of approximately 1,500 mils at which time it proceeded to move at an extremely rapid rate in range in a southerly direction once again the speed of the target exceeding the aided tracking ability of the SCR-584 so that manual tracking became necessary. The radar tracked the target to the maximum range of 32,000 yards at which time the target was at an elevation angle of 300 mils. The operators did not attempt to judge the speed in excess of the aided tracking rate of 700 mph.

It is highly probable that this is an example of anomalous propagation as the weather on 11 September was favorable for this type phenomenon. The students stated that they were aware of this phenomenon however, it is highly probable that due to the previous sightings of what they thought were unusual types of aircraft, they were in the correct psychological condition to see more such objects.

Meantime the news media continued to give the UFO stories a big play. In August 1951, the incident now known to all UFO buffs as "The Case of the Lubbock Lights," attracted a great deal of attention (Ruppelt 1956).

In the closing months of 1951, Ruppelt arranged for the technical assistance of "a large well-known research organization in the Mid-West" for his reactivated Project Grudge. This organization was assigned the task of developing a questionnaire for formal interviewing of UFO sighters. It was also to make a detailed statistical analysis of the UFO reports on hand at that time and later.

At the beginning of 1952, public interest had reached a point at which the first of the amateur study organizations to function on a national scale was formed. This was the Aerial Phenomena Research Organization (APRO) of Tucson, Ariz., founded by Mrs. Coral Lorenzen. Its first mimeographed bulletin was mailed out to 52 members in July. In 1968 this organization claimed 8,000 members.

With the change of name from Project Grudge to Project Blue Book in March 1952 there soon followed a step-up in support and authority for UFO study at ATIC. The instructions to Air Force bases relative to the new level of effort are contained in Air Force Letter 200-5, dated 29 April 1952. Among other things it specifies that early UFO reports from the bases throughout the country are to be sent by telegram both to ATIC and to the Pentagon, followed by fuller reports to be submitted by air mail.

The big event of 1952 was the large number of reports of UFOs seen visually and on radar in the Washington, D. C. area during June and July. This was a big year for UFO reports elsewhere as well, the largest number on record having come to the Air Force during that year. Table 1 give the number of UFO reports received at Wright-Patterson for each month from January 1950 to the present. Inspection of Table 1 shows the great variation of reports that exists from month to month and from year to year. It is not known whether these fluctuations reflect a real actual variation in number of sightings by the public, or are largely the result made up of shifts in the propensity of the public to make reports. Attempts have been made to correlate the maxima with waves of press publicity, with oppositions of Mars, and with other events, but none have yielded very convincing evidence of a real association between the events. For an appreciation of the perils inherent in the statistical analysis of such data, the reader is referred to Section VI, Chapter 10 of this report.

On 19 August 1952 there occurred the case of Scoutmaster D. S. Desvergers in Florida, which Ruppelt, (1956) has called

Table 1

Number of UFO Reports Received each Month by Project Blue Book.

(Sum of those received from Air Force Bases and those received directly from the public.)

	J	F	M	A	M	J	J	A	S	O	N	D	Total
1950	15	13	41	17	8	9	21	21	19	17	14	15	210
51	25	18	13	6	5	6	10	18	16	24	16	12	169
52	15	17	23	82	79	148	536	326	124	61	50	42	1501
53	67	91	70	24	25	32	41	35	22	37	35	29	509
54	36	20	34	34	34	51	60	43	48	51	46	30	487
55	30	34	41	33	54	48	63	68	57	55	32	25	545
56	43	46	44	39	46	43	72	123	71	53	56	34	670
57	27	29	39	39	38	35	70	70	59	103	361	136	1006
58	61	41	47	57	40	36	63	84	65	53	33	37	627
59	34	33	34	26	29	34	40	37	40	47	26	10	390
60	23	23	25	39	40	44	59	60	106	54	33	51	557
61	47	61	49	31	60	45	71	63	62	41	40	21	591
62	26	24	21	48	44	36	65	52	57	44	34	23	474
63	17	17	30	26	23	64	43	52	43	39	22	22	399
64	19	26	20	43	83	42	110	85	41	26	51	15	562
65	45	35	43	36	41	33	135	262	104	70	55	28	887
66	38	18	158	143	99	92	93	104	67	126	82	40	1060
67	81	115	165	112	63	77	75	44	69	58	54	24	937
68	18	20	38	34	12	25	52	41	29				

the "best hoax in UFO history." It is also discussed in Stanton (1966) and Lorenzen (1962).

The scoutmaster was taking three scouts home about 9:00 p.m., driving along a road near West Palm Beach. He thought he saw something burning in a palmetto swamp and stopped to investigate, leaving the boys in the car. As he drew nearer he saw that the light was not from a fire but was a phosphorescent glow from a circular object hovering overhead. From it emerged a flare that floated toward him.

When, after some 20 min., the scoutmaster had not returned, the boys summoned help from a nearby farmhouse. A deputy sheriff was called. When he and the boys returned to the car they found the scoutmaster emerging in a dazed condition from the palmetto thicket. His forearms had been burned and three small holes were found burned in his cap.

In the investigation that followed some grass near where the "saucer" had been was found scorched at its roots but not on top. How this could have happened is not clear.

According to Ruppelt's account, the scoutmaster was an ex-Marine whose military and reformatory record led the Air Force investigators ultimately to write his story off as a hoax.

News media and the magazines continued to build up interest in the flying saucer stories. Table 2 is a partial tabulation of the treatment of the subject in the major magazines of America.

Table 2

Partial list of UFO articles in major U. S. magazines in 1952.

Magazine	*Title*	*Date*	*Page*
American Mercury	"Flying Saucer Hoax"	October	61 -66
Collier's	"How to Fly a Saucer"	4 October	50 -51
Life	"Have We Visitors from Outer Space?"	4 April	80 -82
	"Saucer Reactions"	9 June	20
New Republic	"New Saucer Epidemic"	18 August	49
Newsweek	"Korean Saucers"	3 March	44
	"Saucer Season"	11 August	56
	"Saucers Under Glass"	18 August	49
New Yorker	"Reporter at Large"	6 September	68
Popular Science	"Flying Saucers are Old Stuff"	May	145-47
	"How to see Flying Saucers"	September	167-70
	"Hollywood Builds Flying Saucers"	November	132-34
Reader's Digest	"Flying Saucers, New in Name Only"	July	7 -9
Time	"Those Flying Saucers"	9 June	54 -56
	"Blips on the Scopes"	4 August	40
	"Something in the Air"	11 August	58
	"Theology of Saucers"	18 August	62
	"Wind is Up in Kansas"	8 September	86

Project Grudge Report No. 6 reports the following concerning the public response to the 4 April articles in *Life:*

> During the period of 3 April to 6 April approximately 350 daily newspapers in all parts of the United States carried some mention of the article and some mention of the fact that the Air Force was interested in receiving such reports.
>
> It should be noted here that the conclusions reached by *Life* are not those of the Air Force. No proof exists that these objects are from outer space.
>
> ATIC received approximately 110 letters in regard to the article. The letters are divided among those that offer theories as to the origin of the objects as well as those reporting objects. The letters offering theories comprise about 20 per cent of the total. Although it cannot be stated that the theories are incorrect, a majority of them cannot be further evaluated since they have very little scientific basis. . . . The writers of these letters

ranged from mystics to highly educated individuals. . . . It has been reported that *Life* Magazine has received 700 letters in response to the article.

The subject was also beginning to attract journalistic attention in Europe, for example *France Illustration* of Paris published "Une Enigme Sous Nos Yeux" in its 5 May 1951 issue and "Soucoupes Volantes" on 4 October 1952.

Table 1 indicates that the number of UFO reports in 1952 was some eight times the number for the previous two years. The investigation, however, continued to give no indication of a threat to national security, and no "hard evidence" for the truth of ETH.

Blue Book Report No. 8, dated 31 December 1952, says that an astronomical consultant to the project had interviewed 44 professional astronomers as to their attitude on UFOs. He found their attitudes could be classified as

	Number
Completely Indifferent	7
Mildly Indifferent	12
Mildly Interested	17
Very Interested	8

The Air Force's astronomical consultant commented:

Over 40 astronomers were interviewed, of [whom] five made sightings of one sort or another. This is a higher percentage than among the populace at large. Perhaps this is to be expected, since astronomers do, after all, watch the skies. On the other hand, they will not likely be fooled by balloons, aircraft, and similar objects, as may be the general populace.

It is interesting to remark upon the attitude of the astronomers interviewed. The great majority were neither hostile nor overly interested; they gave one the general feeling that all flying saucer reports could be explained as misrepresentations of well-known objects and that there was nothing intrinsic in the situation to cause concern. I took the time to talk rather seriously with a few of them, and to acquaint them with the fact that some of the sightings were truly puzzling and not at all easily explainable. Their interest was almost immediately aroused, indicating that their general lethargy is due to lack of information on the subject. And certainly another contributing factor to their desire not to talk about these things is their overwhelming fear of publicity. One headline in the nation's papers to the effect that "Astronomer Sees Flying Saucer" would be enough to brand the astronomer as questionable among his colleagues. Since I was able to talk with the men in confidence, I was able to gather very much more of their inner thoughts on the subject than a reporter or an interrogator would have been able to do. Actual hostility is rare; concern with their own immediate scientific problems is too great. There seems to be no convenient method by which problems can be attacked, and most astronomers do not wish to become involved, not only because of the danger of publicity but because the data seems tenuous and unreliable.

3. The Robertson Panel.

Some persons in the Defense establishment began to worry about the trend of public interest in UFOs from a different viewpoint, namely, the possibility that the military communication channels might be jammed with sighting reports at a time when an enemy was launching a sneak attack on the United States. On the other hand, there was the possibility that an enemy, prior to launching such an attack, might deliberately generate a wave of UFO reports for the very purpose of jamming military communication channels. The Central Intelligence Agency undertook to assess the situation with the assistance of a Special Panel of five scientists who had distinguished themselves in physics research and in their contributions to military research during and after World War II. The panel spent a week studying selected case reports and examining such UFO photographs and motion pictures as were available at that time. In mid-January, 1953, the panel produced a report which was classified secret until it was partly declassified in 1966 (Lear, 1966). The report is still partially classified to the extent that the names of some of the members are deleted from the declassified record of the proceedings.

The late Prof. H. P. Robertson of the California Institute of Technology served as chairman of the panel. He had been a member of the Mathematics Department of Princeton University from 1928 to 1947 when he joined the faculty of Calif. Inst. of Tech. In academic work he distinguished himself by his research in cosmology and the theory of relativity. During the war he made important contributions to operation research of the Allied forces in London (Jones, 1968). After the war he served from 1950-52 as research director of the Weapons Systems Evaluation Group in the office of the Secretary of Defense and in 1954-56 was scientific advisor to the Supreme Allied Commander in Europe.

Prof. Samuel A. Goudsmit, with Prof. George Uhlenbeck, discovered electron spin while they were young students in Leiden, Holland, in 1925. Soon after that both came to the University of Michigan where they developed a great school of theoretical physics which contributed greatly to the development of research in that field in America.

Goudsmit is best known outside of academic physics circles as having been scientific chief of the Alsos Mission toward the end of the war. This mission was the intelligence group that was sent to Germany to find out what the Germans had accomplished in their efforts to make an atom bomb (Goudsmit, 1947; Groves, 1962; Irving, 1967). Most of the post-war period he has served on the physics staff of the Brookhaven National Laboratory on Long Island.

Luis Alvarez is a Professor of Physics at the University of California at Berkeley and vice-president of the American Physical Society (1968).* During World War II he was a member of the Radiation Laboratory at Massachusetts Institute of Technology where he made a particularly outstanding contribution in the development of a micro-wave radar system for guiding plane landings in heavy fog. The research then known as Ground Controlled Approach (GCA) was of decisive importance in the war. The location of the incoming aircraft is followed closely by the radar system on the ground whose operator instructs the pilot how to bring the plane onto the runway for a safe landing. In the latter part of the war he served under J. Robert Oppenheimer on the great team that developed the atom bomb at Los Alamos. In the post-war period, Alvarez has made many great research contributions in high-energy physics. At present he is engaged in using cosmic ray absorption in material of the Egyptian pyramids near Cairo to look for undiscovered inner chambers.

Lloyd Berkner, born in 1905, was an engineer with the Byrd Antarctic Expedition as a youngster in 1928-30. Most of the pre-war period he was a physicist in the Department of Terrestrial Magnetism of the Carnegie Institution of Washington. At the beginning of the war he became head of the radar section of the Navy's Bureau of Aeronautics, and for a time at the end of the war was executive secretary of the Research and Development Board of the Department of Defense. In 1949 he was special assistant to the Secretary of State and director of the foreign military assistance program. While in the Department of State he prepared the report which led to the posting of scientific attachés to the principal American embassies abroad. From 1951 to 1960 he was active in managing the affairs of Associated Universities, Inc., the corporation which operates Brookhaven National Laboratory, and toward the end of that period was its president. In 1960 he went to Dallas, Tex. where he organized and directed the new Graduate Research Center of the Southwest. During most of his life he was a member of the U. S. Naval Reserve, and rose to the rank of rear admiral. The concept of an International Geophysical Year, (1957-58)—the greatest example of international scientific co-operation that has yet occurred—was his brainchild.

Prof. Thornton Page has been professor of astronomy at Wesleyan University in Middletown, Conn. since 1958. During the war he did research at the Naval Ordnance Laboratory, mostly in connection with design of underwater ordnance and operations research on naval weapons. This year (1968) he is

**Alvarez was awarded the 1968 Nobel Prize for Physics.*

vice-president for astronomy of the American Association for the Advancement of Science. In astronomy he has worked mostly on the atomic spectra of planetary nebulas.

The panel has been criticized for not having spent more time studying its problem. But in January 1953, the subject only had a four and a half year history and it was really quite possible for a group of this competence to review the whole situation quite thoroughly in a week. The panel has also come under incessant fire from UFO enthusiasts because of its recommendations.

It might have been possible to put together other panels that would have performed as well, but it would not have been possible to choose one superior in scientific knowledge, background of military experience, and soundness of overall judgment.

The Robertson panel report was originally classified "Secret" and declassified in the summer of 1966. Because of its central importance to the UFO story, and especially because it has been the subject of many misrepresentations, we present here the text of its main conclusions, and in Appendix U the full text of the declassified report just as it was released to the public with the names of certain participants deleted.

> 1. Pursuant to request . . . the undersigned Panel of Scientific Consultants has met to evaluate any possible threat to national security posed by Unidentified Flying Objects ("Flying Saucers"), and to make recommendations thereon. The Panel has received the evidence as presented by cognizant intelligence agencies, primarily the Air Technical intelligence Center, and has reviewed a selection of the best documented incidents.
>
> 2. As a result of its considerations, the Panel *concludes:*
>
> a. That the evidence presented on Unidentified Flying Objects shows no indication that these phenomena constitute a direct physical threat to national security.
>
> We firmly believe that there is no residuum of cases which indicates phenomena which are attributable to foreign artifacts capable of hostile acts, and that there is no evidence that the phenomena indicates a need for the revision of current scientific concepts.
>
> 3. The Panel further *concludes:*
>
> a. That the continued emphasis on the reporting of these phenomena does, in these parlous times, result in a threat to the orderly functioning of the protective organs of the body politic.
>
> We cite as examples the clogging of channels of communication by irrelevant reports, the danger of being led by continued false alarms to ignore real indications of hostile action, and the cultivation of a morbid national psychology in which skillful hostile propaganda could induce hysterical behavior and harmful distrust of duly constituted authority.
>
> 4. In order most effectively to strengthen the national facil-

ities for the timely recognition and the appropriate handling of true indications of hostile action, and to minimize the concomitant dangers alluded to above, the Panel *recommends:*

a. That the national security agencies take immediate steps to strip the Unidentified Flying Objects of the special status they have been given and the aura of mystery they have unfortunately acquired;

b. That the national security agencies institute policies on intelligence, training, and public education designed to prepare the material defenses and to react most effectively to true indications of hostile intent or action. We suggest that these aims may be achieved by an integrated program designed to reassure the public of the total lack of evidence of inimical forces behind the phenomena, to train personnel to recognize and reject false indications quickly and effectively, and to strength regular channels for the evaluation of and prompt reaction to true indications of hostile measures.

Table 3 shows the number of cases studied by Project Blue Book in the years 1953-1965 and how the Air Force classified them.

So far as can be determined, little was done to implement the recommendations contained under 4a and 4b of the report of the Robertson panel. It would have been wise at that time to have declassified all or nearly all of the previous reports of investigations of flying saucer incidents such as those making up the bulk of the Project Grudge and Project Blue Book reports 1-12. In fact they were not declassified until 9 September 1960. Had responsible press, magazine writers, and scientists been called in and given the full story, or had a major presentation of the situation been arranged at a large scientific convention, such as at an annual meeting of the American Association for the Advancement of Science, they would have seen for themselves how small was the sum of all the evidence and in particular how totally lacking in positive support was the ETH idea. The difficulty of attempting to base a careful study on the anecdotal gossip which was the bulk of the raw material available for the study of UFOs would have been clear.

But secrecy was maintained. This opened the way for intensification of the "aura of mystery" which was already impairing public confidence in the Department of Defense. Official secretiveness also fostered systematic sensationalized exploitation of the idea that a government conspiracy existed to conceal the truth.

There are those who still cling to this idea of a government conspiracy to conceal a portentous "truth" from the American people. Soon after our study was announced a woman wrote me as follows:

Table 3

UFO Cases Classified by Categories by Project Blue Book, 1953–1959

Category:	1953	1954	1955	1956	1957	1958	1959
Astronomical	175	137	135	222	341	221	144
Aircraft	73	80	124	148	210	104	63
Balloon	78	69	102	93	114	50	31
Insufficient data	79	102	95	132	191	111	65
Other	83	58	65	61	120	93	75
Satellite	0	0	0	0	6	13	0
Unidentified	42	46	24	14	14	10	12
Astronomical:							
Meteors	70	92	79	88	179	168	100
Stars and planets	101	44	52	131	144	56	40
Other	4	1	4	3	18	7	4
Other:							
Hoaxes, etc.	15	6	18	16	37	29	14
Missiles, rockets	2	1	1	3	2	6	14
Reflections	4	6	4	3	2	7	11
Flares, fireworks	1	4	8	6	8	3	5
Mirages, inversions	3	3	4	1	5	2	4
Searchlights	8	6	14	9	12	8	5
Clouds, contails	6	3	2	1	9	5	3
Chaff, birds	4	10	3	7	3	7	1
Physical specimens	1	6	5	3	5	10	3
Radar analysis	15	7	1	3	27	3	8
Photo analysis	1	1	2	4	1	7	4
Satellite decay	0	0	0	0	0	1	0
Miscellaneous	1	7	4	0	9	5	3

UFO Cases Classified by Categories by Project Blue Book, 1960–1965.

Category:	1960	1961	1962	1963	1964	1965
Astronomical	235	203	136	85	123	246
Aircraft	66	77	68	73	71	210
Balloon	22	37	19	23	20	33
Insufficient data	105	115	94	59	99	66
Other	94	77	65	50	88	122
Satellite	21	69	77	82	143	152
Unidentified	14	13	15	14	19	16
Astronomical:						
Meteors	187	119	95	57	61	101
Stars and planets	45	78	36	23	55	135
Other	3	6	5	5	7	9
Other:						
Hoaxes, etc.	13	17	11	16	34	34
Missiles, rockets	12	13	9	13	7	10
Reflections	9	3	3	0	2	7

Table 3 (cont'd)

Flares, fireworks	7	4	3	3	7	4
Mirages, inversions	5	6	3	0	2	5
Searchlights	6	1	3	2	6	9
Clouds, contails	4	5	4	5	0	1
Chaff, birds	7	5	7	4	5	12
Physical specimens	7	4	15	3	3	3
Radar analysis	6	9	0	1	2	6
Photo analysis	6	3	2	3	6	12
Satellite decay	0	3	3	4	3	8
Miscellaneous	3	4	2	4	6	13

Since your committee is using moneys appropriated by the people, it is your duty to level with the citizens of this country and tell the truth. Don't bend facts to suit the Silent Group. People are intelligent. Have faith in the adaptability of our citizens to take the truth. The public didn't collapse under the facts of A bombs, H bombs and the L bombs. It took our space program in stride. It adopted the use of "miracle" drugs. We, as citizens, can manage to live with the truth about saucers. DO NOT knuckle under to the censorship boys. If you want a place in history that is honorable—report the truth to the public about UFOs, because millions of us already know and believe. I have seen "flying saucers." I have heard a man talk who has been to Mars and he can prove it, I'm sure. Of course the planets and stars are inhabited. Our government is acting like the small child who was punished for an act which endangered the lives of his brothers and sisters. Our government should be big enough to face facts as our citizens are able to face the facts. JUST TELL THE TRUTH. It is the easiest way and the only way.

Where secrecy is known to exist one can never be absolutely sure that he knows the complete truth. There is an ironic recognition of this fact in Lt. Gen Nathan Twining's letter of 23 September 1947 (See p. 884) in which he acknowledges that consideration must be given to "the possibility" that UFOs "are of domestic origin—the product of some high security project not known to AC/AS-2 or this Command."

We adopted the term "conspiracy hypothesis" for the view that some agency of the Government either within the Air Force, the Central Intelligence Agency, or elsewhere knows all about UFOs and is keeping the knowledge secret. Without denying the possibility that this could be true, we decided very early in the study, that we were not likely to succeed in carrying out a form of counter-espionage against our own Government, in the hope of settling this question. We therefore decided not to pay special attention to it, but instead to keep alert to any indications that might lead to any evidence that not all of the essential facts known to the Government were being given to us.

Although we found no such evidence, it must be conceded that there may be a supersecret government UFO laboratory hidden away somewhere of whose existence we are not aware. But I doubt it. I do not believe it, but, of course, I cannot prove its non-existence!

About half way through this study, a young woman on the editorial staff of a national magazine telephoned from New York to Boulder. She wanted my comment on a report that had come to her editor that the Colorado study was merely pretending to be a study of UFOs, that this was a cover story. What we were really doing, she was told, was to carry on a "Top Secret" study for the Defense Department's "Martian Invasion Defense Program (MIDP)," that is, a war plan for a response by our defense forces in the event of an invasion of Earth by the Martians. She wanted to know whether this was true!

I could only tell her, "If it were true, I think it would certainly be Top Secret; then I would not be at liberty to tell you about it. This being the case, if I tell you that it is not true, you do not have the slightest idea as to whether I am telling the truth or not."

Her problem was like that of the man who thought his wife was unfaithful. He set all kinds of clever traps to catch her, but he never got any evidence. From this he concluded that she was deucedly clever about her infidelity.

In 1953 the general level of suspicion and mistrust was pervasive. The new administration was re-opening old security cases. The whole system of security investigations was being elaborated. This was the peak year in the career of the late Senator Joseph McCarthy. This was the year that charges were made against the late J. Robert Oppenheimer, culminating in AEC denial of his clearance in the spring of 1954.

In this atmosphere all kinds of dark suspicions could and did take root and grow—including the belief—and the commercial exploitation of the pretended belief—that the government knew much about UFOs that it was concealing, or that the Government was woefully ignorant of the real truth.

In 1956 the National Investigations Committee for Aerial Phenomena was founded by Donald E. Keyhoe, a retired Marine Corps major. As its director he now claims that NICAP has some 12,000 members. Although organized for the purpose of studying UFO cases on an amateur basis, a large part of its effort has gone into promulgation of attacks on the government's handling of the UFO matter. In October 1953, Keyhoe's second book appeared, *Flying Saucers from Outer Space* and soon was found on best-seller lists. Of it, E. J. Ruppelt commented, "To say that the book is factual depends entirely upon how one uses the word. The details of the specific UFO sightings that he credits to the Air Force are factual, but in his interpretations of the incidents he blasts way out into the wild blue yonder." (Ruppelt, 1956).

Here is how Keyhoe links the conspiracy hypothesis with the ETH:

> Three years ago this proposal would have amazed me. In 1949, after months of investigation, I wrote an article for *True* magazine, stating that the saucers were probably interplanetary machines. Within 24 hours the Air Force was swamped with demands for the truth. To end the uproar the Pentagon announced that the saucer project was closed. The saucers, the Air Force insisted, were hoaxes, hallucinations, or mistakes.
>
> Later, in a book called *The Flying Saucers are Real* I repeated my belief that the Air Force was keeping the answer secret until the country could be prepared. Several times officers at the Pentagon tried to convince me I'd made a bad mistake. But when I asked them to prove it by showing me the secret sighting reports, I ran into a stone wall . . . (Keyhoe, 1953).

Another sensational book of this period was Harold T. Wilkins' *Flying Saucers on the Attack* (Wilkins, 1954). It is characterized by its publishers as "A book of facts that is more astounding and incredible than science fiction and which is an introduction to events that may dwarf our civilization. Has the invasion of Earth by beings from another world already begun? The most startling revelations yet made about mysterious visitors from outer space." Wilkins too professed to believe that the government was concealing these "astounding and incredible" facts from the people.

The late newscaster, Frank Edwards, found the Air Force's secrecy baffling and difficult to deal with. In *Flying Saucers — Serious Business* (Edwards, 1966) he recalled:

> Through the Washington grapevine, various friends in the news business had told me that the Pentagon was very unhappy because I continued to broadcast reports of UFO sightings. By late 1953 the news services had virtually ceased to carry such reports; if they were carried at all it was on a strictly local or regional basis. The major leak—and just about the only major leak in the censorship of UFO's—was my radio program.

Developments of this kind leave no doubt in my mind that a serious mistake was made in early 1953 in not declassifying the entire subject and making a full presentation of what was known, as recommended in the report of the Robertson panel.

Another major recommendation of the Robertson panel favored the launching of an educational program to inform the public about UFOs. If any attention was given to this proposal the effort was so slight that there was no discernible effect. But in any event such a program could hardly have been expected to be effective while the "aura of mystery" continued because of continued secrecy surrounding much of Project Blue Book's activities.

Much of the attack on the Robertson panel report centers on the fact that the report declared that a broad educational program should have two major aims, "training and 'debunking' ". Training would be broadly concerned with educating pilots, radar operators, control tower operators and others in the understanding and recognition of peculiar phenomena in the sky. The panel concluded that, "this training should result in a marked reduction in reports caused by misidentification and resultant confusion."

The word *debunking* means to take the bunk out of a subject. Correctly used, one cannot debunk a subject unless there is some bunk in it. Over the years, however, the word has ac- a different coloration. It now sometimes means presenting a misleading or dishonest account of a subject for some ulterior purpose. The critics of the Robertson panel insist that this latter meaning is what the group had in mind. That the earlier definition of *debunking* was what the panel meant is evident from the following statement explaining how the "debunking" would be carried out:

> The "debunking" aim would result in reduction in public interest in "flying saucers" which today evokes a strong psychological reaction. This education could be accomplished by mass media such as television, motion pictures and popular articles. Basis of such education would be actual case histories which had been puzzling at first but later explained. As in the case of conjuring tricks, there is much less stimulation if the "secret" is known. Such a program should tend to reduce the current gullibility of the public and consequently their susceptibility to clever hostile propaganda.

So far as we can determine, no official steps were ever taken to put into effect the training and "debunking" recommendations of the Robertson panel. A private effort was not to be expected, since such a program would not be commercially attractive and would conflict with books that were beginning to make money by exploiting popular confusion about the ETH and alleged government conspiracies.

In 1953, Donald H. Menzel, then director of the Harvard College Observatory published an excellent book (Menzel, 1953). It emphasizes the optical mirage aspects of the subject (Section VI, Chapter 3), and is generally regarded as "debunking" and "negative." Menzel's book never achieved a large enough market to be issued as a paperback and is now out of print.

By contrast, a book, by D. Leslie and George Adamski entitled, *Flying Saucers Have Landed* was published in 1953 (Leslie and Adamski, 1953). Best known for its full account of Adamski's alleged interview with a man from Venus on the California desert on 20 November 1952, it enjoyed widespread popularity in hardcover and paperback editions.

It is difficult to know how much of the UFO literature is intended to be taken seriously. For example, Coral Lorenzen's first UFO book was first published under the title, *The Great Flying Saucer Hoax,* but in the paperback edition it became, *Flying Saucers: the Startling Evidence of the Invasion from Outer Space,* subtitled "An exposure of the establishment's flying saucer cover-up." (Lorenzen, 1962, 1966).

The paperback edition contains an introduction by Prof. R. Leo Sprinkle of the department of psychology of the University of Wyoming. In this introduction, Prof. Sprinkle writes:

> Coral Lorenzen has been willing . . . to describe her fears about potential dangers of the UFO phenomena; to challenge sharply the statements of those military and political leaders who claim that citizens have not seen "flying saucers"; and to differ courageously from those who take a "head in the sand" approach . . . She realizes that censorship is probably controlled at the highest levels of governmental administration . . .
>
> It may be that the earth is the object of a survey by spacecraft whose occupants intend no harm to the United States. However, regardless of the intent of UFO occupants, it behooves us to learn as much as possible about their persons, powers and purposes. Mrs. Lorenzen realizes that her present conclusions may not all be verified, but she is also aware that it may be too late for mankind to react to a potential threat to world security. It is to her credit that she has avoided feelings of panic on one hand and feelings of hopelessness on the other. She has demonstrated a courageous approach: the continuation of the process of gathering, analyzing, and evaluating of information, and the encouragement of the efforts of others to come to grips with the emotional and political and scientific aspects of the UFO phenomena.

Her book is largely taken up with vivid accounts of UFO incidents that are alleged to be factual and to support the idea of ETA, of actual visits to Earth of extra-terrestrial intelligences. A sample of the kind of material presented is the following condensation of an incident in Brazil which is said to have occurred on 14 October 1957 (p. 64 et seq.).

On that evening Antonio Villas-Boas was plowing a field with a tractor when an UFO shaped like an elongated egg landed about 15 yd. away from him. The tractor engine stopped and Villas-Boas got out of the tractor and tried to run away when he "was caught up short by something grasping his arm. He turned to shake off his pursuer and came face-to-face with a small 'man' wearing strange clothes, who came only to his shoulder." He knocked the little fellow down and several more came to the aid of the first one. They "lifted him off the ground and dragged him toward the ship," which had a ladder reaching to the ground.

There follows a description of the interior of the ship and of the way in which the unearthly visitors talked with each other which "reminded Antonio of the noises dogs make, like howls, varying in pitch and intensity." He was forced to undress and to submit to various medical procedures, but then:

"After what seemed like an eternity to Villas-Boas the door opened again and in walked a small but well built and completely nude woman." There follows a description of her voluptuous, distinctly womanly figure.

"The woman's purpose was immediately evident. She held herself close to Villas-Boas, rubbing her head against his face. She did not attempt to communicate in any way except with occasional grunts and howling noises, like the 'men' had uttered. A very normal sex act took place and after more pettings she responded again . . . The howling noises she made during the togetherness had nearly spoiled the whole act for they reminded him of an animal."

Villas-Boas' clothing was then returned to him and he was shown to the UFO's door. "The man pointed to the door . . . then to the sky, motioned Antonio to step back, then went inside and the door closed. At this, the saucer-shaped thing on top began to spin at great speed, the lights got brighter and the machine lifted straight up . . ."

Meanwhile, back at the tractor, Villas-Boas consulted his watch and concluded that he had been aboard for over four hours.

Mrs. Lorenzen comments:

> The above is condensed from a 23-page report which was submitted to APRO by Dr. Olivo Fontes, professor of medicine at the Brazilian National School of Medicine . . . My own first reaction was almost one of scoffing until I began to add up some important factors:
>
> If an alien race bent on contact and possible colonization were to reconnoiter this planet, one of their prime tasks would be to learn if the two races could breed. To do this they would need a human subject. Either sex would be all right, but it would be much more efficient to pick a male by some means. If a human female subject were used, the chances of no conception, or conception followed by miscarriage, would be great due to the considerable nervous strain of removing that female subject from her familiar surroundings to a completely foreign location and alien companions, and then literally subjecting her to forcible rape. It should be quite well known, especially to an advanced culture, that the psychological makeup of women, especially where sex is concerned, is considerably more delicate than that of her male counterpart. The ideal situation, then, would be for the experimenters to pick their own female subject whose ovulation period would be known beforehand and

proceed exactly as the strange UFO occupants apparently did with Villas-Boas.

She says that it was not possible at that time to have Villas-Boas examined by a psychiatrist and that Villas-Boas has subsequently married and "does not care to dwell on the subject because of his wife's feelings in the matter. Preliminary examination by Dr. Fontes, however seems to assure us that Villas-Boas is stable, not a liar, and certainly not knowledgeable about certain information which he would have to have in order to concoct such a *logical* tale."

Mrs. Lorenzen's final comment is: "It is unnerving to me that, along with the thousands of sightings of flying, landed and occupied unconventional aerial objects, an incident such as the above could take place and not be objectively scientifically and logically analyzed because of *emotional predisposition!*" But in her account there is no indication of any corroboration: the story stands or falls entirely on the veracity of Villas-Boas.

Her book is a compilation of reported incidents of which the preceding is fairly typical. What is of particular interest for a *scientific* study of UFOs is that in many instances the investigations, like that of the Villas-Boas case in Brazil, are carried out by a person having an advanced degree and an academic position. The next one in the book describes the case of some men who were bow-hunting on 4 September 1963 near Truckee, Calif. One of them became separated from the others and was chased up a tree by some "robots" also called "entities," who belched out puffs of smoke which would cause the man to lose consciousness. She writes:

> He said he felt that the "robots" were guided by some kind of intelligence, for at times they would get "upwind" of him to belch their sleep-inducing "smoke."

After a harrowing night the man escaped and "dragged himself toward camp, finally collapsing on the ground from exhaustion."

In this case the APRO investigator who supplied the details to Mrs. Lorenzen was Dr. James A. Harder, associate professor of civil engineering at the University of California in Berkeley. Dr. Harder received his bachelor's degree from the California Institute of Technology, and his doctorate at Berkeley, served as a design engineer for the Soil Conservation Service, and served in the Navy during World War II. He was one of those who took part in a symposium on UFOs before the House Science and Astronautics Committee, sitting under the chairmanship of Congressman J. Edward Roush of Indiana (29 July 1968). In this congressional testimony, Dr Harder said:

> . . . there have been strong feelings aroused about UFOs, particularly about the extra-terrestrial hypothesis for their origin. This is entirely understandable, in view of man's historic record of considering himself the central figure in the natural scene; the extra-terrestrial hypothesis tends inevitably to undermine the collective ego of the human race. These feelings have no place in the scientific assessment of facts, but I confess that they have at times affected me . . .
>
> Indeed, there are flying saucer cultists who are as enthusiastic as they are naive about UFOs—who see in them some messianic symbols—they have a counterpart in those individuals who exhibit a morbid preoccupation with death. Most of the rest of us don't like to think or hear about it. This, it seems to me, accurately reflects many of our attitudes toward the reality of UFOs—natural, and somewhat healthy, but not scientific.

In the second Lorenzen book, a considerably more detailed account of the Truckee, Calif. incident than the first one is given including this comment:

> At present the preliminary interviews by a qualified psychiatrist have been made preparatory to either sodium amytol or hypnotic trance questioning. We feel that Mr. S [the man who was up the tree] may have information buried at a subconscious level which may shed considerably more light on the whole incident. We are reasonably certain that the whole incident took place and was a true physical experience, and therefore the trance questioning will not be done to attempt to discredit him in any way.

4. Regulations Governing UFO Reports.

Initially Project Blue Book operated under instructions set forth in Air Force Letter 200-5, issued 29 April 1952. This provided that telegraphic reports on UFOs were to be sent promptly both to Blue Book at Wright-Patterson and to the Pentagon, and followed by a more elaborate letter reporting the details. Experience showed that this procedure was unnecessary when applied to *all* UFO reports, so a simpler procedure was authorized in Air Force Regulation 200-2, classed under "Intelligence Activities" and continued in force with minor changes until it was superseded by AFR 80-17 on 19 September 1966 and AFR 80-17A on 8 November 1966. The new regulation classes the activity under "Research and Development" (Appendix B).

> This regulation establishes the UFO Program to investigate and analyze UFOs over the United States. Such investigation and analysis are directly related to Air Force responsibility for the defense of the United States. The UFO program provides for the prompt reporting and rapid reporting needed for successful "identification," which is the second of four phases of air defense—detection, identification, interception and destruction. All commanders will comply strictly with this regulation.

Critics of the Air Force have made much of paragraph 2c of AFR 200-2, entitled "Reduction of Percentage of UFO 'Unidentifieds'" which says:

> Air Force activities must reduce the percentage of unidentifieds to the minimum. Analysis thus far has explained all but a few of the sightings reported. These unexplained sightings are carried statistically as unidentifieds. If more immediate, detailed, objective data on the unknowns had been available, probably these, too could have been explained. However, because of the human factors involved, and the fact that analyses of UFO sightings depend primarily on the personal impressions and interpretations of the observers rather than on accurate scientific data or facts obtained under controlled conditions, the elimination of all unidentifieds is improbable.

Critics of the Air Force have tried to read into this paragraph an exhortation that investigation is to result in commonplace identifications at all costs, not excluding that of stretching the truth. But reasonable people will read this paragraph as a straight-forward instruction to Air Force personnel to take the job of investigation seriously, without making shortcuts, in an effort to arrive at an accurate understanding of as many UFO reports as possible. Honestly read, there is nothing in the wording which rules out ETH, that is, the possibility of identifying an UFO as a visitor from outer space is not excluded by the instructions given.

Critics have also attacked AFR 200-2 and the similar provisions in AFR 80-17 for the fact of its centralization of public relations in the Secretary of the Air Force Office of Information. The relevant section of AFR 80-17 states:

> B-4. *Response to Public Interest.* The Secretary of the Air Force, Office of Information (SAF-OI) maintains contact with the public and the news media on all aspects of the UFO program and related activities. Private individuals or organizations desiring Air Force interviews, briefings, lectures, or private discussions on UFOs will be instructed to direct their requests to SAF-OI. Air Force members not officially connected with UFO investigations will refrain from any action or comment on UFO reports which may mislead or cause the public to construe these opinions as official Air Force findings.

Critics have charged that this provision imposes censorship on UFO reports. But reasonable people will see in such a provision an arrangement designed to minimize the circulation of wild stories and premature reports before an investigation is completed. At the beginning of our study, we found certain elements of the news media extremely willing to give us their cooperation. One Denver newspaperman was willing to stand ready at all times to take us to various places in his private plane. In return he wanted us to give him a full account of what we were doing as we did it, before we had a chance to check and evaluate our field data. Of course, we could not accede to such an arrangement.

AFR 80-17 contains one exception, but one which is frustrating to newspapermen who are trying to build up a spot news story: It is Section 5c Exceptions:

> In response to local inquiries regarding UFOs reported in the vicinity of an Air Force base, the base commander may release information to the news media or public after the sighting has been positively identified. If the stimulus for the sighting is difficult to identify at the base level, the commander may state that the sighting is under investigation and conclusions will be released by SAF-OI after the investigation is completed. The commander may also state that the Air Force will review and analyze the results of the investigation. Any further inquiries will be directed to SAF-OI.

These provisions reflect the traditional conflict between authorities who are responsible for carrying out a careful investigation without premature and irresponsible publicity, and the representatives of the news media who wish to have a live story while the news is still hot. At such a time nothing can be more frustrating to a reporter than to be told that one has to wait for the completion of an investigation. It is also true that these rules could actually be used to keep the public from learning promptly about a real visitor from outer space if one should appear, but in practice the Air Force has not sought to "control the news" in this way, and the restraint required by the regulation has usually resulted in the release of more accurate information than was available before the promulgation of AFR 200-2.

Another regulation which includes UFOs in its scope and which has frequently been used as a basis for criticizing the Air Force's handling of UFO reports is Joint Army Navy Air Publication-146. For example, Frank Edwards (Edwards, 1967) commented that Air Force personnel are reminded of severe penalties for "making public statements without approval!"

JANAP-146 is not a classified document. It has been issued with various revisions over the years. The copy we have is JANAP-146 (E), the revision that is dated 31 March 1966. Its title is "Canadian-United States Communications Instructions for Reporting Vital Intelligence Sightings." It is issued in the United States by the Joint Chiefs of Staffs. In its Letter of Promulgation it says that it "contains military information and is for official use only," but it also explicitly says, "Copies and Extracts may be made from this publication when such are to be used in the preparation of other official publications."

On that basis a discussion of some of its contents is presented here.

Section 102a defines its scope in these words: "This publication is limited to the reporting of information of *vital importance* to the security of the United States of America and Canada and their forces, which in the opinion of the observer, requires very urgent defensive and/or investigative action by the U. S. and/or Canadian armed Forces."

Reports made from airborne or land-based sources are called CIRVIS report; those from waterborne sources, MERINT reports. The relevant section on security for CIRVIS reports is as follows:

> 208. *Military and Civilian.* Transmission of CIRVIS reports are subject to the U. S. Communications Act of 1934, as amended, and the Canadian Radio Act of 1938, as amended. Any person who violates the provisions of these acts may be liable to prosecution thereunder. These reports contain information affecting the national defense of the United States and Canada. Any person who makes an unauthorized transmission or disclosure of such a report may be liable to prosecution under Title 18 of the US Code, Chapter 37, or the Canadian Official Secrets Act of 1939, as amended. This should not be construed as requiring classification of CIRVIS messages. The purpose is to emphasize the necessity for the handling of such information within official channels only.

JANAP-146 lists the categories of sightings which are to be reported as CIRVIS reports as follows:

> (a) Hostile or unidentified single aircraft or formations of aircraft which appear to be directed against the United States or Canada or their forces.
> (b) Missiles.
> (c) Unidentified flying objects.
> (d) Hostile or unidentified submarines.
> (e) Hostile or unidentified group or groups of military surface vessels.
> (f) Individual surface vessels, submarines, or aircraft of unconventional design, or engaged in suspicious activity or observed in a location or in a course which may be interpreted as constituting a threat to the United States, Canada or their forces.
> (g) Any unexplained or unusual activity which may indicate a possible attack against or through Canada or the United States, including the presence of any unidentified or other suspicious ground parties in the Polar Region or other remote or sparsely populated areas.

The presence of item (c) in the list can be interpreted to signify that the presence of UFOs in the air space over and near the United States and Canada is officially regarded as information of *vital importance* to the security of the United States and Canada, but such an implication is totally misleading. The essenial thing about an UFO is that the observer does not know what it is. For this reason alone it *may* have defense significance. Since in military matters especially it is better to be safe than sorry, it is quite appropriate that observers be explicitly notified of their obligation to report UFOs, that is, *all* puzzling things, rather than take a chance on their not being significant.

Provision is made in JANAP-146 for prompt transmission of cancellation messages. If something has been seen, but is later identified by the sighter as having no defense significance, it is important that the defense headquarters be notified at once.

Air, sea and land surveillance activities are conducted continuously to guard against sudden hostile activities. JANAP-146 provides for the transmission of reports on suspicious circumstances to proper authorities for analysis and appropriate defense action. It would be most unwise that the military response to such circumstances be publicized, nor for that matter should the circumstances themselves be a matter of public knowledge.

5. *Orthoteny, the "Straight Line Mystery."*

The mid-1950s also produced an attempt to find statistical regularities or a "pattern" in UFO sightings. Aime Michel (1958), a French journalist who has studied and written about UFOs believed that he had found a pronounced statistical tendency for the places where UFOs are reported within a short time interval such as 24 hours to lie on a straight line, or more correctly, on a great circle on the earth's surface.

To describe this supposed tendency he coined the word "orthoteny" in 1954, deriving it from the Greek adjective "orthoteneis," which means stretched in a straight line

He first noticed what seemed to him a tendency for the locations to lie on a straight line with regard to five sightings reported in Europe on 15 October 1954. These lay on a line 700 mi. long stretching from Southend, England to Po di Gnocca, Italy.

Another early orthotenic line which has been much discussed in the UFO literature is the BAYVIC line which stretches from Bayonne to Vichy in France. Six UFO sightings were reported on 24 September 1944 in the location of the ends and along the line.

When Michel first started to look for patterns he plotted on his maps only those reports which he had described as "good" in the sense of being clearly reported Later he decided to plot all reports, including the "poor" ones, and found the straight line patterns in some instances.

A peculiarity of the supposed orthotenous relation is that the appearance of the UFOs in these various reports along a line may look quite different, that is, there is no implication that the sequence represents a series of sightings of the same object. Moreover the times of seeing the UFOs do not occur in the order of displacement along the line, as they would if the same object were seen at different places along a simple trajectory.

Continuing his work he found other cases of straight line arrangements for UFO reports in France during various days in 1954. At this time there were an unusually large number of such reports, or a French "flap." But not all reports fell on straight lines. To these which clearly did not he gave the name "Vergilian saucers" because of a verse in Vergil's Aeneid, describing a scene of confusion after a great storm at sea: "A few were seen swimming here and there in the vast abyss."

Without understanding why the locations of UFO reports should lie on straight lines, this result, if statistically significant, would indicate some kind of mutual relationship of the places were UFOs are seen. From this it could be argued that the UFOs are not independent, and therefore there is some kind of pattern to their "maneuvers."

The question of statistical significance of such lines comes down to this: Could such straight line arrangements occur purely by chance in about the same number of instances as actually observed? In considering this question it must be remembered that the location of a report is not a mathematical point, because the location is never known with great precision. Moreover the reports usually tell the location of the observer, rather than that of the UFO. The direction and distance of the UFO from the observer is always quite uncertain, even the amount of the uncertainty being quite uncertain. Thus two "points" do not determine a line, but a corridor of finite width, within which the other locations must lie in order to count as being aligned. The mathematical problem is to calculate the chance of finding various numbers of 3-point, 4-point . . . alignments if a specified number of points are thrown down at randow on a map.

Michel's orthoteny principle was criticized along these lines by Menzel (1964), in a paper entitled, "Do Flying Saucers Move in Straight Lines?" This triggered off a spirited controversy which included a number of papers in the *Flying Saucer Review* for 1964 and 1965 by various authors.

The most complete analysis of the question to be published to date is that by Vallee and Vallee (1966). They summarize their work in these words:

The results we have just presented will probably be considered by some to be a total refutation of the theory of alignments. We shall not be so categorical, because our data have not yet been independently checked by other groups of scientists, and because we have been drastically limited in the amount of computer time that we could devote to this project outside official support. Besides no general conclusion as to the non-existence of certain alignments can be drawn from the present work. The analyses carried out merely establish that, among the proposed alignments, the great majority, if not all, must be attributed to pure chance.

The point is that while the straight-line theory, as far as we can say, is not the key to the mystery, a body of knowledge has been accumulated and a large edifice of techniques has been built, and this development reaches far beyond the negative conclusion on the straight-line hypothesis.

As matters now stand, we must regard as not valid the work on orthoteny and "the straight-line mystery."

6. *The O'Brien Report and events leading up to it.*

In the years from 1953 to 1965, interest in UFOs or flying saucers continued to fluctuate. APRO had been founded in 1952, and NICAP was incorporated as a non-profit membership organization in 1956. In addition various local organizations flourished for a few years. Newspapers and magazines of large circulation seem not to have had a consistent policy toward the subject. More and more, but not always, they tended to make fun of flying saucer sightings. Not many of the press stories achieved national distribution by the wire services and many of those that did were handled as humorous features rather than as serious science.

As Table 1 shows, the number of UFO reports reaching Project Blue Book was well under a thousand for each of these years except for 1957 when the number was 1,006. Officers at Air Force bases and the small staff of Project Blue Book continued to investigate these reports to determine whether the things seen constituted a defense threat. In no case was a threat to national security discovered, a result consistent with that reached by the Robertson panel in 1953.

At the same time there continued to be published a considerable number of popular books and magazine articles. Most of these continued to insist that some UFOs really indicate the presence on Earth of visitors from superior civilizations elsewhere in the Universe.

Some of the books contain some rather startling assertions for which, however, no proof or corroboration is given. For example in *Spacecraft from Beyond Three Dimensions* (Allen, 1959) opposite page 98 is a full-page photograph showing two men holding hands with a miniature man about three feet tall, and carries the following caption, "A 'saucer crewman' very much like the moon man (or spirit) described by Swedenborg in his writings about the inhabitants of different planets of the solar system with whom, he stated, he had conversations. This photograph is from Germany (note trench coats and North European types), but the 'saucer crewman' is from a UFO that crashed near Mexico City; the corpses were sent to Germany for study. Was he based on Luna?"

The author of this book is employed by a major aircraft company in the Pacific Northwest. We got in touch with him, seeking more specific information about the alleged crash near Mexico City, and about the circumstances of sending saucer crewmen's corpses to Germany. Allen offered to give us additional information but only at what to us seemed to be an exorbitant price, considering that there was no indication of the validity of any of this story.

UFO enthusiasts are not one great happy family. They consist of a number of antagonistic sects marked by strong differences in their belief. Some of the schismatic tendencies seem to be related to personality clashes. One of the greatest points of difference between the groups is their attitude toward "contactee" stories.

Some writers, of whom George Adamski was a pioneer, have published detailed stories giving accounts of their conversations with visitors from Venus and elsewhere. Some have published accounts of trips in flying saucers, either involving high speed travel between points on Earth, or actual visits to other planets (Fry, 1966). Other writers heap scorn on those who believe in such contactee stories.

There is a particularly wide spectrum of attitudes to be found among UFO enthusiasts with respect to the late George Adamski. A periodical called *UFO Contact* is dedicated to his memory. The editor of *UFO Contact* is Ronald Caswell, 309 Curbers Mead, Harlow, Essex, England. It is published by IGAP, which is the acronym for "International Get Acquainted Program" at Bavnevolden 27, Maaloev, SJ, Denmark. According to an editorial announcement this organization was founded by Adamski in 1959. Of the periodical the editors say:

> His hope was that as many as possible would discover the truth of the present age and turn to face the time to come—to learn to accept, through conviction, the fact that we are all citizens of the Cosmos and children of the Cosmic Power whose Laws run through the entire cosmos. These Laws we can learn to comprehend through study and understanding of the "Science of Life" brought to our attention by the presence of friendly visitors from other worlds . . . We shall try to detect any and every move in the direction of that truth which we have accepted, but which is not yet officially accepted or recognized in broader circles:

1. People from other worlds in our system are visiting our planet.

2. People from other worlds are in contact with certain political and scientific circles in East and West.

3. People from all walks of life, official and unofficial, all over the world, have been contacted by people from other worlds; such contacts have been kept secret so far.

4. The philosophy brought to the world by Mr. George Adamski is considered an aid in helping to understand the truth of our origin and our future destiny.

The magazine will make no attempt whatsoever to fight anyone, in spite of any action which might be launched against it. Only the truth, whatever its guise, will be brought to bear, to allow each to decide for himself what he can and will accept in this wonderful world on his march forward to new experiences.

In sharp contrast, is the comment about Adamski in the second of the Frank Edwards' books (Edwards, 1967):

The first and foremost among them [the contactees] was a fellow named George Adamski. He was a man of meager scholastic attainments, but he made up for that shortcoming by having an excellent imagination, a pleasing personality and an apparently endless supply of gall.

George established the ground rules for the contactees which they have dutifully followed. He was the first—and he showed that there was considerable loot to be made by peddling tales of talking with space people. George instinctively realized that everything had to be pretty nebulous; he knew that details would be disastrous.

Prior to becoming associated with a hamburger stand on the road to Mt. Palomar, George had worked in a hamburger stand as grill cook. With this scientific background he wrote, in his spare time, a document which he called *An Imaginary Trip to the Moon, Venus and Mars*. He voluntarily listed it with the Library of Congress for copyright purposes as *a work of fiction*.

That was in 1949.

His effort did not attract many customers but it did attract the attention of a lady writer who saw gold in them there space ships. She made a deal with George to rewrite his epic; she was to furnish the skilled writing and he was to furnish the photographs of the space ships.

This lady brought the finished manuscript to me for appraisal and she brought with it a clutch of the crudest UFO photographs I had seen in years. I declined to have anything to do with the mess and she left my office in a bit of a huff.

In its revised form it told a yarn of how George had ventured into the desert of southern California, where he met a "scout ship" from which stepped a gorgeous doll in golden coveralls. She spoke to him with a bell-like voice in a language he did not understand, so they had to resort to telepathy, or something similar, to carry on their conversation. And then, as she prepared to leave him, she tapped out a message in the sand with her little boot. George realized that she wanted him to preserve this message (it was terribly important) and, having a pocket full of wet plaster of Paris (which he seemingly always carried with him on desert trips), George quickly made a plaster cast of the footprint with the message, which he eventually reproduced for the educational advancement of his readers, who were legion.

Of the numerous photographs which embellished the book let it be said that some of them could not have been taken as claimed. The others were crudely "simulated," as the Air Force put it charitably.

But for me the payoff was the alleged photograph of Adamski's "scout ship" in which he allegedly took a trip to Venus and returned. The picture as shown in his book was taken either on a day when three suns were shining—or else it was a small, object taken with three floodlights for illumination. After eight years of patient search I finally came to the conclusion that his space ship was in reality the top of a cannister-type vacuum cleaner, made in 1937. I doubt that many persons are traveling through space in vacuum cleaner tops.

Adamski communicated with me frequently. When he was questioned about the title of "professor" which he used, he explained that it was just an honorary title given to him by his "students," and that he never used it himself. George was evidently forgetful, for the letters he sent to me were always signed "Professor George Adamski."

But this congenial con man sold a jillion books to those who were eager to believe that somebody from space was crossing millions of miles of the trackless void for the dubious privilege of conversing telepathically with former hamburger cooks. Adamski toured this country on the lecture circuit; then he branched out into Europe, where he even arranged a private confab with the Queen of The Netherlands, a maneuver which stirred up quite a bit of comment for the Queen, very little of which was favorable.

The bogus professor followed his first book with another volume but it did not meet with the ready acceptance which the public had granted his first offering. For one thing, some of his "witnesses" to his alleged meeting with the golden girl from a distant galaxy had changed their minds about both George and his story. And perhaps more importantly, several other contactees had rushed into print with yarns of having ridden in space ships and of having conversed with the operators thereof.

The remainder of Frank Edwards' Chapter 7 deals with other contactee stories in a similar vein.

During this period the UFO literature became very large indeed. It would require too much space to deal with it in detail. An excellent guide to this material is provided by a bibliography published by the Library of Congress.

By the early 1960s the pattern for UFO books and magazine writing had become quite clearly established: the text consisted of a stringing together of many accounts of reported sightings with almost no critical comment or attempts at findings the validity of the material reported, mixed with a strong dash of criticism of the Air Force for not devoting more attention to the subject and for allegedly suppressing the startling truth about visitors from outer space.

On the evening of 3 September 1965 a number of sightings were reported at Exeter, N. H. which were made the basis of a brief article in the *Saturday Review* for 2 October 1965, and later of a book, *Incident at Exeter* by John G. Fuller (Fuller, 1966a). The following year Fuller wrote another book, *The Interrupted Journey* (Fuller, 1966b) which dealt with the case of Barney and Betty Hill, who claimed to have been taken aboard a flying saucer while driving through N. H. This story was told in condensed form in *Look* magazine.

Probably the greatest furor in 1966 was generated by the Michigan sightings early in March. These occurred near Dexter, Mich. on the night of 20 March and near Hillsdale, Mich, on the next night.

These sightings received a great deal of newspaper publicity. They were investigated for the Air Force by Dr. J. Allen Hynek, who suggested in a press conference the possibility that they might have resulted from burning swamp gas. This possibility has been known for years although it would be extremely difficult to obtain the kind of definite evidence that would make this possibility a certainty with respect to this particular case.

The swamp gas possibility has become the butt of a great many jokes and cartoons in the popular press. Although it is not established as a certainty, it seems to be quite genuinely a possibility. Here is the exact text of the Air Force press release that was issued as a result fo the study of these sightings:

> The investigation of these two sightings was conducted by Dr. J. Allen Hynek, scientific consultant to Project Blue Book; personnel from Selfridge Air Force Base, Mich.; and personnel from Project Blue Book office at Wright-Patterson Air Force Base, Ohio.
>
> In addition to these two specific cases, there has been a flood of reports from this area both before and after March 20 and 21. The investigating personnel have not had the time to investigate all of these. It has been determined, however, that in Hillsdale, over and above the sincere and honest reporting by the young ladies at Hillsdale College, certain young men have played prinks with flares. It has also been determined that the photograph released yesterday through press was taken on March 17 just before sunrise near Milan, Mich., and have nothing to do with the cases in question. The photograph clearly shows trails made as a result of a time exposure of the rising crescent moon and the planet Venus.
>
> The majority of observers in both the Dexter and Hillsdale cases have reported only silent glowing lights near the ground —red, yellow, and blue-green. They have not described an object. The only two observers who did describe an object have

stated that they were no closer than 500 yards—better than a quarter of a mile away—a distance which does not allow details to be determined.

Witnesses have described glowing lights—lights that seem to move but never far from a definite place or lights which suddenly disappeared and popped up at another place. The locale in both cases was a swamp. In both cases, the location of the glow was pinpointed—in Dexter it was seen between two distant groups of people and at Hillsdale it was seen in a swampy depression between the girls and the distant trees. It was in both cases a very localized phenomena. The swampy location is most significant.

A swamp is a place of rotting vegetation and decomposition. Swamps are not a province of astronomers. Yet, the famous Dutch astronomer, Minnaert, in his book, "Light and Colour in the Open Air," describes lights that have been seen in swamps by the astronomer, Bessel, and other excellent observers. The lights resemble tiny flames sometimes seen right on the ground and sometimes rising and floating above it. The flames go out in one place and suddenly appear in another, giving the illusion of motion. The colors are sometimes yellow, sometimes red, and sometimes blue-green. No heat is felt, and the lights do not burn or char the ground. They can appear for hours at a stretch and sometimes for a whole night. Generally, there is no smell and no sound except for the popping sound of little explosions such as when a gas burner ignites.

The rotting vegetation produces marsh gas which can be trapped during the winter by ice. When the spring thaw occurs, the gas may be released in some quantity. The flame, Minnaert says, is a form of chemical luminescence, and its low temperature is one of its peculiar features. Exactly how it occurs is not known and could well be the subject of further investigation.

The glowing lights over the swamps near Dexter and Hillsdale were observed for 2 or 3 hours, and they were red, green, and yellow. They appeared to move sideways and to rise a short distance. No sound was heard except a popping sound.

It seems entirely likely that as the present spring thaw came, the trapped gases, CH_4, H_2S, and PH_3, resulting from decomposition of organic material, were released. The chemistry book by Sienko and Plane has this to say: "In air, Phosphine PH_3 usually bursts into flame apparently because it is ignited by a spontaneous oxidation of the impure P_2H_4. The will-of-the-wisp, sometimes observed in marshes, may be due to spontaneous ignition of impure PH_3 which might be formed by reduction of naturally occurring phosphorus compound."

It has been pointed out to the investigating personnel by other scientists in this area that in swamps the formation of H_2S and CH_4 from rotting vegetation is common. These could be ignited by the spontaneous burning of PH_3.

The association of the sightings with swamps in this particular instance is more than coincidence. No group of witnesses observed any craft coming to or going away from the swamp. The glow was localized and Deputy Fitzpatrick described the glow from beyond a rise adjacent to the swamp as visible through the trees. He stated that the light brightened and dimmed such as stage lights do—smoothly and slowly—and this description exactly fits the Hillsdale sighting also. The brightening and dimming could have been due to the release of variable quantities of marsh gas.

The disappearance of the lights when people got close with flashlights or carlights would indicate that the glow seemed bright to dark-adapted eyes. The night was dark and there was no moon. The Hillsdale girls kept their rooms dark in order to see the swamp lights.

It appears very likely that the combination of the conditions of this particular winter (an unusually mild one in that area) and the particular weather conditions of that night—it was clear and there was little wind at either location—were such as to have produced this unusual and puzzling display.

On 28 September 1965, Maj. Gen. E. B. LeBailly, who was then head of the Office of Information of the Secretary of the Air Force, addressed a letter to the Military Director of the Air Force Scientific Advisory Board in which he said:

> The Air Force has conducted Project Blue Book since 1948. As of 30 June 1965, a total of 9,265 reports had been investigated by the Air Force. Of these 9,265 reports, 663 cannot be explained.

Continuing, he wrote:

> To date, the Air Force has found no evidence that any of the UFO reports reflect a threat to our national security. However, many of the reports that cannot be explained have come from intelligent and well qualified individuals whose integrity cannot be doubted. In addition the reports received officially by the Air Force include only a fraction of the spectacular reports which are publicized by many private UFO organizations.
>
> Accordingly, it is requested that a working scientific panel composed of both physical and social scientists be organized to review Project Blue Book—its resources, methods and findings —and to advise the Air Force as to any improvements that should be made in the program to carry out the Air Force's assigned responsibility.

As a result of this formal request, a group was set up under the chairmanship of Dr. Brian O'Brien which was known as the "Ad Hoc Committee to Review Project Blue Book." This group met on 3 February 1966 and produced a short report of its findings in March 1966.

The persons who served on this committee are as follows:

Dr. Brian O'Brien, now retired, received his Ph.D. in physics at Yale in 1922. He served as director of the Institute of Optics at the University of Rochester from 1946 to 1953, and as vice president and director of research of the American Optical Company from 1953-58, after which he became a consulting physicist. He served as chairman of the division of physical sciences of the National Research Council from 1953-61, as president of the Optical Society of America in 1951-53, and received the President's Medal for Merit in 1948.

Dr. Launor F. Carter, psychologist, received his Ph.D. from Princeton in 1941. After holding various teaching and research positions he became vice president and director of research of the Systems Development Corporation of Santa Monica in 1955. He has been a member of the Air Force Scientific Advisory Board since 1955.

Dr. Jesse Orlansky, phychologist, received his Ph.D. in 1940 from Columbia University. He has been a member of the Institute for Defense Analyses since 1960 specializing on problems of behavioral science research for national security.

Dr. Richard Porter, electrical engineer received his Ph.D. at Yale in 1937, after which he joined the staff of the General Electric Company, where he was manager of the guided missiles department from 1950-55. He has been a member of the Space Science Board of the National Academy of Sciences since 1958 and chairman of its international relations committee since 1959.

Dr. Carl Sagan, astronomer and space scientist, received his Ph.D. at the University of Chicago in 1960. Since 1962 he served as a staff astrophysicist of the Smithsonian Astrophysical Observatory in Cambridge, Mass., until the summer of 1968 when he joined the faculty of astronomy at Cornell University. He is a specialist in the study of planetary atmospheres, production of organic molecules in astronomical environments, origin of life, and problems of extra-terrestrial biology.

Dr. Willis H. Ware, electrical engineer, received his Ph.D. from Princeton University in 1951. Since then he has been head of the computing science division of the Rand Corporation in Santa Monica. He is a specialist on problems related to the applications of computers to military and information processing problems.

The report of this committee is brief. It is printed in full below:

I. *INTRODUCTION*

As requested in a memorandum from Major General E. B. LeBailly, Secretary of the Air Force Office of Information dated 28 September 1965 (Tab A), and SAB Ad Hoc Committee met on 3 February 1966 to review Project "Blue Book." The objectives of the Committee are to review the resources and methods of investigation prescribed by Project "Blue Book" and to advise the Air Force of any improvements that can be made in the program to enhance the Air Force's capability in carrying out its responsibility.

In order to bring themselves up to date, the members of the Committee initially reviewed the findings of previous scientific panels charged with looking into the UFO problem. Particular attention was given to the report of the Robertson panel which was rendered in January 1953. The Committee next heard briefings from the AFSC Foreign Technology Division, which is the cognizant Air Force agency that collates information on UFO sightings and monitors investigations of individual cases. Finally, sightings with particular emphasis on those that have not been identified.

II. *DISCUSSION*

Although about 6% (646) of all sightings (10,147) in the years 1947 through 1965 are listed by the Air Force as "Unidentified," it appears to the Committee that most of the cases so listed are simply those in which the information available does not provide an adequate basis for analysis. In this connection it is important also to note that no unidentified objects other than those of an astronomical nature have ever been observed during routine astronomical studies, in spite of the large number of observing hours which have been devoted to the sky. As examples of this the Palomar Observatory Sky Atlas contains some 5000 plates made with large instruments with wide field of view; the Harvard Meteor Project of 1954-1958 provided some 3300 hours of observation; the Smithsonian Visual Prairie Network provided 2500 observing hours. Not a single unidentified object has been reported as appearing on any of these plates or been sighted visually in all these observations.

The Committee concluded that in the 19 years since the first UFO was sighted there has been no evidence that unidentified flying objects are a threat to our national security. Having ar-arrived at this conclusion the Committee then turned its attention to considering how the Air Force should handle the scientific aspects of the UFO problem. Unavoidably these are also related to Air Force public relations, a subject on which the Committee is not expert. Thus the recommendations which follow are made simply from the scientific point of view.

III. *CONCLUSIONS AND RECOMMENDATIONS*

It is the opinion of the Committee that the present Air Force program dealing with UFO sightings has been well organized, although the resources assigned to it (only one officer, a sergeant, and secretary) have been quite limited. In 19 years and more than 10,000 sightings recorded and classified, there appears to be no verified and fully satisfactory evidence of any case that is clearly outside the framework of presently known science and technology. Nevertheless, there is always the possibility that analysis of new sightings may provide some additions to scientific knowledge of value to the Air Force. Moreover, some of the case records, at which the Committee looked, that were listed as "identified" were sightings where the evidence collected was too meager or too indefinite to permit positive listing in the identified category. Because of this the Committee recommends that the present program be strengthened to provide opportunity for scientific investigation of selected sightings in more detail and depth than has been possible to date.

To accomplish this it is recommended that:

A. Contracts be negotiated with a few selected universities to provide scientific teams to investigate promptly and in depth certain selected sightings of UFO's. Each team should include at least one psychologist, preferably one interested in clinical psychology, and at least one physical scientist, preferably an astronomer or geophysicist familiar with atmospheric physics. The universities should be chosen to provide good geographical distribution, and should be within convenient distance of a base of the Air Force Systems Command (AFSC).

B. At each AFSC base an officer skilled in investigation (but not necessarily with scientific training) should be assigned to work with the corresponding university team for that geographical section. The local representative of the Air Force Office of Special Investigations (OSI) might be a logical choice for this.

C. One university or one not-for-profit organization should be selected to coordinate the work of the teams mentioned under A above, and also to make certain of very close communication and coordination with the office of Project Blue Book.

It is thought that perhaps 100 sightings a year might be subjected to this close study, and that possibly an average of 10 man days might be required per sighting so studied. The information provided by such a program might bring to light new facts of scientific value, and would almost certainly provide a far better basis than we have today for decision on a long term UFO program.

The scientific reports on these selected sightings, supplementing the present program of the Project Blue Book office, should strengthen the public position of the Air Force on UFO's. It is, therefore, recommended that:

A. These reports be printed in full and be available on request.

B. Suitable abstracts or condensed versions be printed and included in, or as supplements to, the published reports of Project Blue Book.

C. The form of report (as typified by "Project Blue Book" dater 1 February 1966) be expanded, and anything which might suggest that information is being withheld (such as the wording on page 5 of the above cited reference) be deleted. The form of this report can be of great importance in securing public understanding and should be given detailed study by an appropriate Air Force office.

D. The reports "Project Blue Book" should be given wide unsolicited circulation among prominent members of the Congress and other public persons as a further aid to public understanding of the scientific approach being taken by the Air Force in attacking the UFO problem.

Soon after it was received by the Secretary of the Air Force, the report was referred to the Air Force Office of Scientific Research for action.

On 5 April 1966, the House Armed Services Committee held a one-day hearing on the UFO problem under the chairmanship of the Hon. H. Mendel Rivers of S. C. The transcript of the hearing is printed on pp. 5991-6075 of the "Hearings by Committee on Armed Services of the House of Representatives, Eighty-ninth Congress, Second Session."

During this hearing, Air Force Secretary Harold Brown made the first public announcement of the O'Brien Committee report. Secretary Brown commented: "Recommendations by the Board are presently under study and are expected to lead to even stronger emphasis on the scientific aspects of investigating the sightings that warrant extensive analysis."

He further said:

> Although the past 18 years of investigating unidentified flying objects have not identified any threat to our national security, or evidence that the unidentified objects represent developments or principles beyond present-day scientific knowledge, or any evidence of extra-terrestrial vehicles, the Air Force will continue to investigate such phenomena with an open mind and with the finest technical equipment available.

Later in his testimony he commented further on his own views about the O'Brien committee recommendation in these words:

> I believe I may act favorably on it, but I want to explore further the nature of such a panel, and the ground rules, before I go ahead with it. I don't want to have a group of people come in for just one day and make a shallow investigation. They have to be prepared to look into a situation thoroughly if they are to do any good.

Concluding his testimony he said, after pointing out that 95% of the reports are being explained:

> This does not imply that a large part of the remaining 5%, the unexplained ones, are not also of this character, but we simply have not been able to confirm this because we don't have enough information about these sightings. It may also be that there are phenomena, the details of which we don't understand, which account for some of the sightings we have not identified. In certain instances, I think a further scientific explanation is a possibility. Therefore we will continue to develop this approach.

Dr. J. Allen Hynek, UFO consultant to the Air Force since 1948, was also a principal witness. In his opening statement he said:

> During this entire period of nearly twenty years I have attempted to remain as openminded on this subject as circumstances permitted, this despite the fact that the whole subject seemed utterly ridiculous and many of us firmly believed that, like some fad or craze, it would subside in a matter of months. Yet in the last five years, more reports were submitted to the Air Force than in the first five years.

Despite the seeming inanity of the subject, I felt that I would be derelict in my scientific responsibility to the Air Force if I did not point out that the whole UFO phenomenon might have aspects to it worthy of scientific attention . . . Specifically, it is my opinion that the body of data accumulated since 1948 through the Air Force investigations deserves close scrutiny by a civilian panel of physical and social scientists and that this panel should be asked to examine the UFO problem critically for the express purpose of determining whether a major problem really exists.

In the discussion which followed, the Hon. William H. Bates, Congressman from Mass. returned to the question of visitors from outer space asking,

But Secretary Brown, you indicated no one of scientific knowledge in your organization has concluded these phenomena come from extra-terrestrial sources?

To which Secretary Brown replied,

That is correct. We know of no phenomena or vehicles, intelligently guided, which have come from extra-terrestrial sources. I exclude meteors, which do come from extra-terrestial sources.

Asked the same question, Dr. Hynek replied:

This is also my conclusion. I know of no competent scientist today who would argue the sightings which do puzzle intelligent people. Puzzling cases exist, but I know of no competent scientist who would say that these objects come from outer space.

Asked by Congressman L. N. Nedzi of Mich. about the relation of UFOs to extra-terrestrial visitors, Hynek said:

I have not seen any evidence to confirm this, nor have I known any competent scientist who has, or believes that any kind of extra-terrestrial intelligence is involved. However, the possibility should be kept open as a possible hypothesis. I don't believe we should ever close our minds to it.

Congressman Bates introduced into the record a letter received from Raymond E. Fowler, chairman of the NICAP Massachusetts Subcommittee, which with its numerous attachments occupies pp. 6019-6042 of the hearing record. In addition to his NICAP affiliation, Fowler describes himself as a "project administrative engineer in the Minuteman Program Office for Sylvania Electric Products, Waltham, Mass."

Fowler wrote the committee in part as follows:

I do want to put myself on record as supporting the claims and views of NICAP and others which indicate that congressional hearings on the matter of UFOs are long overdue.

I feel that the American people are capable of understanding the problems and implications that will arise if the true facts about UFOs are made known officially. The USAF public information program and policy, as directed by the Pentagon, of underrating the significance of UFOs and not releasing true, pertinent facts about UFOs is not only a disservice to the American people now but in the long run could prove to have been a foolish policy to follow. After years of study, I am certain that there is more than ample high-quality observational evidence from highly trained and reliable witnesses to indicate that there are machinelike solid objects under intelligent control operating in our atmosphere. The aerodynamic performance and characteristics of the true UFO rule out manmade or natural phenomena. Such observational evidence has been well supported in many instances by reliable instruments such as cameras, radar, geiger-counters, variometers, electrical interference, physical indentations in soil and scorched areas at landing sites, etc.

I am reasonably sure that if qualified civilian scientists and investigators are able to come to this conclusion, that the USAF, supported by the tremendous facilities at its disposal, have come to the same conclusion long ago. However, present official policy deliberately attempted to discredit the validity of UFOs and a wealth of data and facts are not being released to the public . . . It is high time that the real facts about UFOs are released. A public information program should be inaugurated that presents facts. I am urging you to support a full congressional open inquiry on the UFO problem.

Although Fowler's letter strongly implies that important information is being withheld, it does not affirm a belief that UFOs are extra-terrestrial visitors.

7. Initiation of the Colorado Project.

Responsibility for the implementation of the recommendation of the O'Brien report was assigned to the Air Force Office of Scientific Research (AFOSR) by the Secretary of the Air Force. In doing so, he gave them latitude for further study of the specific details of the recommendations and decision to depart from the exact formulation given in that report. As a result of study within that office, it was decided to concentrate the project in a single university rather than to make contracts with a number of universities.

Recommendation B was incorporated into AFR 80-17 which replaced AFR 200-2. This was made effective 19 September 1966.

The staff of the AFOSR studied the question of which University to invite to take on the study, and also took counsel on this question with a number of outside advisers. As a result of this inquiry in the late spring and early summer of 1966, they decided to ask the University of Colorado to accept a contract for the work, and in particular asked me to take on the scientific direction of the project.

This request was made to me on 31 July 1966 by Dr. J. Thomas Ratchford of the scientific staff of AFOSR, who was introduced by Dr. W. W. Kellogg, associate director of the

National Center for Atmospheric Research and at that time a member of the Air Force Scientific Advisory Board.

This request was unwelcome for a variety of reasons. I was planning to write a new book on the theory of atomic spectra and in fact had started on it. This was to replace one written more than thirty years earlier with Dr. G. H. Shortley (Condon and Shortley, 1935). Despite its age it has been the standard work in the field for all those years but naturally is now quite out of date. I had at last arranged things so that I could do this writing and regarded it as the most useful professional activity in which I could engage before retirement.

Although I knew only a small fraction of what I now know, I was aware that the UFO subject had had a long history of confused and ambiguous observational material making a truly scientific study extremely difficult if not impossible. This would make the subject unattractive not only to myself but to scientific colleagues on whom one would have to call for help. Moreover, all of them were engaged in scientific work that was more to their liking, which they would be reluctant to set aside.

I had some awareness of the passionate controversy that swirled around the subject, contributing added difficulty to the task of making a dispassionate study. This hazard proved to be much greater than was appreciated at the outset. Had I known of the extent of the emotional commitment of the UFO believers and the extremes of conduct to which their faith can lead them, I certainly would never have undertaken the study. But that is hindsight. It may nevertheless be of value to some scientist who is asked to make some other UFO study in the future to have a clear picture of the experiences of this sort which we had.

These objections were met by counter-arguments in the form of an appeal to patriotic duty. A good deal of emphasis was placed on the shortness of the task, then envisioned as requiring only fifteen months.

I objected to the selection of myself, mentioning the names of various scientists of considerable distinction who had already taken an active interest in UFOs. To this the reply was made that these individuals were essentially disqualified for having already "taken sides" on the UFO question.

After several hours' discussion along these lines, I agreed to discuss the matter informally with a number of colleagues in the Boulder scientific community and, in the event that enough interest was shown in such preliminary conversations, to arrange a meeting at which representatives of AFOSR could present the story to a larger group and answer their questions. From this would come an indication of the willingness of some of them to take part in such a project if it were set up.

At this stage there was also the question of whether the University should allow itself to be involved in so controversial an undertaking. Several members of the faculty had grave misgivings on this score, predicting that the University might be derided for doing so.

In preparation for the meeting with AFOSR staff which was set for 10 August 1966, Robert J. Low, then assistant dean of the graduate school, wrote some of his thoughts in a memorandum dated 9 August 1966 which he sent to E. James Archer, then dean of the graduate school, and T. E. Manning, vice president for academic affairs.

The Low memorandum has acquired undue importance only because a copy was later stolen from Low's personal files and given wide distribution by persons desirous of discrediting this study. Portions of it were printed in an article by John G. Fuller (Fuller, 1968) which misconstrues it as indicating a conspiracy on the part of the University administration to give the Air Force a report which would support its policies instead of those being advocated by NICAP.

Commenting on Fuller's article, Low wrote in July 1968,

> The suggestion that I was engaged, along with Deans Archer and Manning, in a plot to produce a negative result is the most outrageous, ridiculous and absurd thing I ever heard of. My concern in writing the memo, was the University of Colorado and its standing in the university world; it was a matter of attitudes that the scientific community would have toward the University if it undertook the study. It had nothing to do with my own personal outlook on the UFO question.

Nor did it represent official policy of the University, since it was, at most, a preliminary "thinking out loud" about the proposed project by an individual having no authority to make formal decisions for the administration, the department of physics, or any other university body. Indeed, one of the proposals Low makes in it runs exactly contrary to the procedure actually followed by the project. Low proposed "to stress investigation, not of physical phenomena, but rather of the people who do the observing—the psychology and sociology of persons and groups who report seeing UFOs." It should be evident to anyone perusing this final report, that the emphasis was placed where, in my judgment, it belonged: on the investigation of physical phenomena, rather than psychological or sociological matters. It should be equally obvious that, had the University elected to adopt Low's suggestion, it would have hardly chosen a physicist to direct such an investigation.

I will, for purposes of record, go a step further in this regard. If nevertheless the University had asked me to direct this study along psychological and sociological lines, I would have declined to undertake the study, both on the ground that I am not qualified to direct an investigation having such an emphasis, and because in fact the views in the Low memorandum are at variance with my own. But the fact is that I was not aware of the existence of the Low memorandum until 18 months after it was written. This was long after the project had been set up under my direction, and, since I knew nothing of the ideas Low had expressed, they had no influence on my direction of the project.

The 10 August meeting lasted all day. At the end, it seemed that there was enough faculty interest to go ahead with the task for AFOSR. During September 1966, details of the proposed research contract were worked out in conferences between Low and myself and the staff of AFOSR. The contract was publicly announced on 7 October 1966, with work to start as soon after 1 November as possible. Because of other commitments, I could devote only half-time to the work. After 1 February 1968, I devoted full time to the project.

The O'Brien report had stressed the importance of using psychologists as well as physicists on the staff. Dr. Stuart Cook, chairman of the department of psychology, accepted appointment as a principal investigator on an advisory basis but could devote only a small fraction of his time to the study because of other commitments. In a short time he made arrangements for the project to have the part-time services of three of his professors of psychology: Drs. David R. Saunders, William B. Scott, and Michael Wertheimer. Saunders had worked on machine statistics in relation to problems in educational psychology. Scott's field was social psychology. He made some useful initial contributions but soon found that his other duties did not permit him to continue. Wertheimer is well known as a specialist in psychology of perception. He worked with members of the field teams and has contributed a chapter to this report (Section VI, Chapter 1).

The initial staff also included Dr. Franklin E. Roach as a principal investigator. Roach is an astronomer who has specialized in the study of air glow and other upper atmosphere optical phenomena. He was at the time near retirement after a long career with the National Bureau of Standards and the Environmental Science Services Administration and so was able to devote full time to the project. His experience was valuable as including a wide range of working contacts with the astronomers of the world, and also as a consultant with the NASA program which brought him into working relations with the American astronauts.

Low was able to obtain a leave from his position as assistant dean and assumed full-time appointment as project coordinator. Besides administrative background, he brought to the project a wide general knowledge of astronomy and meteorology derived from some twenty years of work with Walter Orr Roberts on the staff of the High Altitude Observatory of the

University of Colorado, and later with the National Center for Atmospheric Research during its formative years.

Announcement of the project received a large amount of newspaper attention and editorial comment. This was natural in view of the long history of UFO controversy, even extending into Congress, which had preceded the setting up of the study. Possibly the most prescient of comments was an editorial in *The Nation* for 31 October 1966, which declared, "If Dr. Condon and his associates come up with anything less than the little green men from Mars, they will be crucified."

The project's investigative phase ended on 1 June 1968, and the task of preparing a final report of the project's multifarious activities began. The results of those labors are presented here.

It seems hardly likely, however, that we have said the last word on this subject. Indeed, as this report is prepared the Library of Congress has announced publication of *UFOs, an annotated bibliography*. Prepared for the Air Force Office of Scientific Research (OAR), and scheduled for publication in 1969 by the U.S. Government Printing Office, the bibliography contains more than 1,600 references to works on the subject of UFOs. It will be offered for sale by the Superintendent of Documents.

Private organizations or government sponsored groups may well undertake to do more work on UFO phenomena, either in the name of science or under another rubric.

Meanwhile, the Scientific Study of Unidentified Flying Objects was brought to a definitive close when, on 31 October 1968, this final report on its researches was turned over to the Air Force for review by the National Academy of Sciences and subsequent release to the public. We thank those of the public who communicated to us their experiences and opinions. However, as the study is now at an end, it would be appreciated if no more UFO material is sent to the University of Colorado.

References

Adamski, George. *Inside the Space Ships,* New York: Abelard-Schuman, 1955.

Allen, W. Gordon. *Spacecraft from Beyond Three Dimensions—a New Vista of the Entirety from which Emerges the UFO,* New York: Exposition Press, 1959.

Arnold, K. E. and R. Palmer. *The Coming of the Saucers: a Documentary Report on Sky Objects that Have Mystified the World,* Boise: K. A. Arnold, 1952.

Bloecher, Ted. *Report on the UFO Wave of 1947,* Copyright by Ted Bloecher, 1967 (no address).

Condon, E. U. and G. H. Shortley. *The Theory of Atomic Spectra,* New York and London: Cambridge University Press, 1935.

Edwards, Frank, *Flying Saucers—Serious Business,* New York: Lyle Stuart, 1966.

———. *Flying Saucers—Here and Now!* New York: Lyle Stuart, 1967.

Fuller, John G. *Incident at Exeter,* New York: G. P. Putnam's Sons, 1966a.

———. *The Interrupted Journey,* New York: Dial Press, 1966b.
———. "Flying Saucer Fiasco," *Look,* 32:58, (14 May 1968).
Goudsmit, S. A. *Alsos,* New York: Henry Schuman, Inc., 1947.
Groves, L. R. *Now It Can Be Told,* New York: Harper and Brothers, 1962.
Guieu, Jimmy, *Les Soucoupes Volantes Viennent d'un autre monde,* Paris: Fleuve Noir, 1954. English edition: *Flying Saucers Come from Another World,* London: Hutchinson, 1956.
Heard, Gerald. *The Riddle of the Flying Saucers,* London: Carroll and Nicholson, 1950.
House Committee on Armed Services, the transcript of the 5 April hearing occupies pp. 5991-6075 of the printed record of this committee for the second session of the Eighty-ninth Congress.
Keyhoe, Donald E. *The Flying Saucers are Real,* London: Hutchinson, 1950.
Irving, David. *The Virus House,* London: William Kimber, 1967.
Jones, R. V. "The Natural Philosophy of Flying Saucers," *Physics Bulletin 19,* (1968), 225-230, (reproduced as Appendix V).
Keyhoe, Donald E. *Flying Saucers from Outer Space,* New York: Henry Holt, 1953.
Lear, John. "The Disputed CIA Document on UFOs," *Saturday Review,* (3 September 1966), 45-50.
Leslie, Desmond and George Adamski. *Flying Saucers Have Landed,* London: Werner Laurie, 1953.
———. *Flying Saucers Have Landed,* New York: British Book Centre, 1953.
Lorenzen, Coral. *The Great Flying Saucer Hoax: the UFO Facts and Their Interpretation,* New York: William-Frederick Press, 1962. Paperback edition titled: *Flying Saucers: the Startling Evidence of the Invasion From Outer Space,* New York: New American Library, 1966.
McDonald, James. "Are UFOs Extraterrestrial Surveillance Craft?" talk given before the American Institute of Aeronautics and Astronautics, Los Angeles, (26 March 1968).
Menzel, Donald H. *Flying Saucers,* Cambridge: Harvard University Press, 1953.
———. "Do Flying Saucers Move in Straight Lines?" *Flying Saucer Review,* 10, 2, (1964), 3.
Michel, Aime. *The Truth About Flying Saucers,* New York: Criterion Books, Inc., 1956.
———. *Mysterieux Objets Celestes,* Paris: Arthaud, 1958. English edition: *Flying Saucers and the Straight-line Mystery,* New York: S. G. Phillips Co., 1958.
Ruppelt, Edward J. *The Report on Unidentified Flying Objects,* New York: Doubleday and Co., 1956.
Scully, Frank. *Behind the Flying Saucers,* New York: Holt, 1950.
Stanton, L. Jerome. *Flying Saucers—Hoax or Reality?* New York: Belmont Books, 1966.
Vallee, Jacques and Janine, *Challenge to Science—The UFO Enigma,* Chicago: Henry Regnery Co., 1966.
Wilkins, Harold L. *Flying Saucers on the Attack,* New York: Citadel Press, 1954.

Chapter 3 Official UFO Study Programs in Foreign Countries / Harriet Hunter

Over the years since 1947, there have been many UFO reports originating in countries other than the United States. In fact, although America dates modern interest in the subject from the summer of 1947, there were 997 UFO reports that reached the Swedish government from private citizens in that country during 1946. Paralleling the developments in America, there has been some open official interest on the part of governments of other countries, as well as amateur organizations devoted to the study of UFOs, and popular books published in other countries and in other languages than English.

We made efforts to learn about the activities conducted officially on the UFO subject by other governments, strictly from the viewpoint of determining whether scientists in those countries had a program of UFO study from a scientific point of view or whether they were recommending to their governments that UFOs be studied for their scientific interest.

There is always the possibility that other governments are carrying on study programs that are classified. No effort was made to learn anything that was not freely and openly available.

CANADA

Dr. Craig visited Dr. Peter M. Millman in Ottawa on 13 June 1968. Dr. Millman's major responsibility is as Head of Upper Atmosphere Research of the National Research Council of Canada, but he also manages the study of UFOs in Canada. Until the spring of 1968, the study of UFO reports had been handled by the Department of National Defence in Canada; it was transferred then to the National Research Council. Very few field investigations are carried out; emphasis is mostly on the maintenance of a central file of the reports that reach the government from the public.

According to Dr. Millman, the Defense Research Board of the Department of National Defence in Canada formed a committee in April 1952, giving it the name Project Second Storey. It reviewed the situation with respect to UFO reports to determine whether the government should undertake large-scale investigations of the reports. Dr. Millman, at that time with the Dominion Astrophysical Observatory, was chairman of the committee, which held regular meetings over a period of a year. During this period, the Committee developed interview techniques and filing procedures for sighting reports. It recommended that the situation did not warrant a large-scale official investigation of unidentified aerial phenomena.

Project Second Storey became inactive after 1953. Sighting report files were maintained thereafter by the Department of National Defence. Particularly puzzling events were investigated when it appeared that data results of scientific value might be found. As of 1968, the file (called the Non-Meteoritic Sighting File) is maintained in the Upper Atmosphere Research Section of the Radio and Electrical Engineering Division of the National Research Council in Ottawa. The file is open to public inspection, but witness names are held in confidence, unless they have given permission for their release.

In 1967 there were 57 reports and 37 in the first five months of 1968.

Dr. Millman has studied the files covering reports over a period of 20 years, concentrating his attention on the hard core of unexplained cases. He favors continuing compilation of reports on an international basis using uniform reporting forms in all countries.

Project Magnet, established in December 1950 was headed by Mr. Wilbert B. Smith of the Telecommunications Division of the Canadian Department of Transport who was officially authorized by the Deputy Minister of Transport for Air Services to make as detailed a study of the UFO phenomena as could be accomplished within the framework of existing Canadian establishments. The report issued by Mr. Smith did not represent the official opinion of the Department of Transport or the Second Storey Committee, and in this respect is not a part of the official study of UFOs in Canada.

ENGLAND

The UFO problem is handled in England by a division of the Ministry of Defence in London. Colorado project coordinator, Robert Low met with its director on a visit to London in August 1967. Sighting reports from the public are routed to the Ministry of Defence whose central switchboard operators direct them to this office. The Royal Air Force assigns one man to work with this office on UFO matters. In a letter to this project dated 9 June 1967, it was said ". . . our investigations of reported UFO sightings are of a limited nature and are conducted on a low priority basis. Moreover, the bulk of recent sightings have been established as either earth satellite vehicles, space debris in orbit or manifestations of meteorological or other natural phenomena."

SWEDEN

Official responsibility in Sweden for handling UFO matters has been assigned to the Research Institute of National Defence, Avdelning 2, Stockholm 80. Dr. Tage O. Eriksson is in charge of this activity. He was visited by Low during the summer of 1967, and the Colorado project has had additional correspondence with him.

Dr. Eriksson receives sighting reports and maintains a file of them. He has the responsibility of deciding whether a report warrants investigation. He told Low that almost all reports up to 1963 were investigated and we found to be caused by natural or man-made phenomena. Since then reports are not being routinely investigated.

Asked about published reports that the Swedish Air Force had investigated a case in which an UFO allegedly crashed in

Spitzbergen in 1955, Dr. Eriksson replied: "I can assure you that this is not the case. Neither the Air Force nor the Research Institute of National Defence has at any time taken part in an investigation of a crashed UFO in Spitzbergen or elsewhere."

SOVIET UNION

News stories appeared in the American newspapers in early December 1967 stating that the U. S. S. R. was establishing a governmental project to study UFOs (*New York Times* 10 December 1967).

According to these reports, the study was already under way under the direction of Prof. Feliks Zigel of the Moscow Aviation Institute and a retired Major General, Porfiry A. Stolyarov, of the Soviet Air Force. Condon wrote to Zigel to explore the possibility of cooperation between the reported Soviet and Colorado projects. Condon's letter was transmitted to Prof. Zigel as an enclosure with a letter from Dr. Frederick Seitz, President of the U.S. National Academy of Sciences, to Academician M. V. Keldysh, President of the Soviet Academy of Sciences for subsequent transmittal to Zigel. The letter was mailed on 16 January 1968; as of 31 October 1968, no answer had been received. One attempt was made to stimulate a reply by discussing the matter with a Soviet member of the staff of the Outer Space Affairs Group at United Nations headquarters. He said he would write informally to a member of the Russian space research team to find out what is being done. Nothing further has been heard from this source. The U. N. official was of the opinion that no UFO study was being conducted in the Soviet Union.

Low met with Mr. U. Bogachev, First Secretary of the Information Department of the Soviet Embassy in Washington to express additional interest in cooperation in the study of UFOs and was courteously received; no further contacts were initiated in view of the lack of a reply from Zigel.

Pravda for 29 February 1968 carried an article on UFOs signed by E. Mustel, corresponding member of the A. N. U. S. S. R., D. Marynov, president of the All-Union Astronomical and Geodetic Society, and V. Leshkovtsev, Secretary of the National Committee of Soviet Physicists. The article emphasizes that study of American sightings in the past has provided natural explanations for most of them.

It concludes with these statements:

> No one has in his possession any new facts that would substantiate the reality of "flying saucers." They are not seen by astronomers who attentively study the skies day and night. They are not encountered by scientists who study the state and conditions of earth's atmosphere. They have not been observed by the Air Defense Service of the country. This therefore means

> that there are no grounds for reviving the nonsensical long-buried rumors about secret trips to our planet by Martians or Venusians. . . .
>
> Because of the high incidence of reports on "unidentified flying objects" on the pages of our press and in television broadcasts, the "flying saucer" question was discused at the U. S. S. R. Academy of Sciences. The Bureau of the Department of General and Applied Physics of the Academy heard a report by Academician L. A. Artsimovich at a recent meeting about current UFO propaganda. It was characterized as "anti-scientific" and Artsimovich noted that "these fantasies do not have a scientific basis at all; the observed objects are of a well-known nature."

DENMARK

The project had no direct contact with the authorities in Denmark, but in response to an inquiry, Prof. Donald H. Menzel of Harvard received a letter dated 25 April 1968 from Captain K. G. Konradsen, writing for the Minister of Defense which says:

> Some years ago, the public showed considerable interest in unidentified flying objects, and reports on sightings which were presented either to the police or to military authorities were at that time thoroughly examined by the Danish Defence Research Board. The findings were, most reports being incomplete, that further investigation generally was impossible. In those cases, in which it was possible to investigate and reconstruct the observations, they turned out to be sightings of aircraft or of atmospheric or astronomic phenomena. In several cases the reports were intentionally false.
>
> Today, Danish civilian and military authorities do not consider unidentified flying objects of any special significance. No effort is made offically to inform the public of possible reported sightings. Of course, the newspapers from time to time bring news of "mysterious" and "supernatural" occurrences in the air, but special circumstances are necessary to bring about an official investigation . . .

OTHER NATIONS

The cooperation of the Department of State was enlisted to seek information about UFO programs of the governments of other nations. On 11 April 1968 the following airgram was sent to various American embassies over the signature of Secretary of State Dean Rusk:

> The University of Colorado, acting under contract to the U. S. Air Force, is desirous of being informed if host country Governments, or Universities, or other organizations acting as contractors thereto, have, or are conducting, any studies on UFOs. The University of Colorado is not interested in studies made by UFO hobby clubs or UFO buffs. If serious study has or is being given to this subject, the Department would appreciate being advised by May 15 if mission knows of the name of

the agency conducting the work, and whether it could be described as a substantial or only a modest effort.

Replies informed us that in Australia the Director of Air Force Intelligence maintains sighting files and is responsible for investigations should they be deemed necessary. In New Zealand there is an informal arrangement between the Air Force Meteorological Service and the Department of Scientific and Industrial Research to collect reports for six months and then decide on the next step.

In Greece a report file is maintained by the National Meteor Service of the Greek Ministry of National Defense.

Countries in which it is known that no governmental activity concerned with UFOs is being carried on are: Argentina, Austria, Belgium, Brazil, Colombia, Finland, France, Ireland, Italy, Japan, Mexico, Netherlands, Norway, Portugal, Spain, Switzerland, and Venezuela.

The project is indebted to Dr. Donald H. Menzel for much of the information presented in this chapter regarding official activity—or in most cases, inactivity—in foreign countries.

UNITED NATIONS

Since UFO reports are received from observers in all parts of the world, it has been suggested that UFO studies might be undertaken by the United Nations. Such suggestions have come from, among others, Prof. James E. McDonald of the University of Arizona, who has discussed the matter with the working staff of the U. N. Outer Space Affairs Group.

Subsequent reports in the press that the U. N. was taking up the matter of UFOs led to the issuance of a statement dated 29 June 1967 by C. V. Narashimhan, Chef de Cabinet. It follows:

> It is not correct that the Secretary-General requested Dr. McDonald to come to New York City to confer with him. Dr. McDonald wrote to the Secretary-General requesting an interview and the Secretary-General agreed to see him on 7 June. Unfortunately, on that day the Secretary-General was preoccupied with meetings of the Security Council and Dr. McDonald only saw the Chief of the Outer Space Affairs Group and his colleagues. It is also not correct to say that the Secretary-General personally believes in the existence of UFOs. I hope this makes the position clear.

Replying to another inquiry on 5 July 1967, Marvin Robinson, scientific secretary of the Outer Space Affairs Group, declared that "the United Nations Committee on the Peaceful Uses of Outer Space has never discussed the subject of unidentified flying objects nor requested any study or report on this subject."

Since confusion about possible United Nations interest in the UFO question continued, Condon wrote on 6 March 1968 to Peter S. Thacher, counsellor on Disarmament and Outer Space of the U. S. Mission to the U. N., and later visited him in New York. The confusion seems to have arisen from the fact that there are two different U. N. entities: the Committee on Peaceful Uses of Outer Space, and a subsidiary body called the Outer Space Affairs Group. It was the latter body with which McDonald met. In a letter dated 18 March 1968, Thacher writes:

> As to Dr. James McDonald's presentation, it is completely correct that he did *not* make any presentation at any time to the UN *Committee* on Peaceful Uses of Outer Space. The committee consists of 28 representatives of states members of the General Assembly and is the outgrowth of a committee which was originally created in 1959. Having been thoroughly involved in the work of the committee since its origin, I can assure you that at no time has any representative on the committee suggested serious consideration of UFOs, nor to my knowledge has there been any corridor suggestion along these lines of the sort that might take place before any formal proposals were made. . . .
>
> From informal conversation with members of the Outer Space Affairs Group I understand that Professor McDonald sought to convey a statement on the subject of UFOs to the Secretary-General and was referred to this group. . . . The letter from Professor McDonald was not given any circulation and would not have come to any attention outside of the secretariat if it had not been through your letter and my subsequent inquiry. Therefore, Professor McDonald can correctly say that he has submitted a statement to the Outer Space Affairs Group, but this action is of itself not very meaningful. . . .

Thus, from the available evidence it would appear that there is no active official interest in UFOs in the United Nations.

Section VI
THE SCIENTIFIC CONTEXT

The contributions in this section are by specialists who are eminent in their respective disciplines. They endeavor to supply as completely as possible the background of scientific knowledge in their fields as it is judged to be relevant to the study and understanding of UFO phenomena.

Chapter 1 Perceptual Problems / Michael Wertheimer

Perception plays a role in the report of any unidentified flying object. Someone perceives—i. e., sees, hears, feels, etc. —something, and it is his conclusion concerning what it was that he perceived that results in an UFO report.

This chapter is devoted to some well known principles of perception, with special reference to how they apply to the processes that result in UFO reports. Basic accounts of perception and further details on the matters considered here can be found in such standard texts as Bartley (1958), von Fieandt (1966), Dember (1960), Beardslee and Wertheimer (1958), Gibson (1950), Forgus (1966), and Boring (1942). Lively, brief introductions to general problems of perception have been written by Hochberg (1964) and Leibowitz (1965).

Our discussion in this chapter is organized around the physical, physiological, psychological, and social sequence of events that eventuates in UFO reports. This sequence of events usually begins with some actual distal physical event (an energy change or source some distance away from the observer), resulting in the transmission of energy to the observer's sense organs. The energy that arrives at the observer's sense organ, the proximal stimulus, is encoded into neural events, producing sensations which are combined into percepts and finally into cognition. By this process, the observer becomes aware that there are some particular phenomena having particular characteristics taking place in some location at some particular distance and direction from the observer.

A report eventuates from this sequence only if the observer's cognition is such as to produce in him the conviction that what he has experienced should indeed be reported.

Since most of the observations reported in connection with UFO phenomena are visual, we shall consider each of the foregoing steps in terms, primarily, of the processes of visual perception.

1. The Distal Event

An actual, physical event usually precedes the report of an

UFO. Chapter 2 of Section VI discusses in detail some of the distal events that could give rise to UFO reports. In section 4 below, reports that arise despite the absence of any stimulus exterior to the observer are considered. For the purpose of the present discussion, however, we need emphasize only the fact that the distal events that give rise to UFO reports always involve the transmission of some form of energy. As we have pointed out earlier, that energy is usually in the visible spectrum.

2. *Transmission Processes*

The energy is transmitted from the distal source and arrives at a sense organ, where it produces a proximal stimulus in the form of an energy change to which the sense organ is attuned. But the energy arriving at the sense organ is not an exact copy of the energy that left the distal source. It is attenuated and distorted, and often is an incomplete version of the original (Brunswik, 1956). If, like most energy sources, the transmitted or reflected light obeys the inverse square law, the energy arriving at the sense organ is far weaker than at the source. Further, the characteristics of the medium through which the energy is transmitted distort and disrupt the energy. For example, mist, ground fog, smoke, rain, snow, fog, dust, temperature inversions and discontinuities, and other atmospheric phenomena can cause gross attenuation. They can also distort the energy by selectively filtering out or modifying certain components.

Turbulence in the air and peculiar temperature inhomogeneities can produce major distortions in the transmitted energy before it becomes a proximal stimulus (Minnaert, 1954). Intensity, "shape," color, direction, and other attributes can all be grossly altered. Atmospheric turbulence phenomena can, for example, cause distant mountains seen across a heated desert to shimmer and to change their shape eerily in an amoeba-like fashion. Other well knows kinds of mirages, discussed in detail in Section VI, Chapter 4, are superior and inferior mirages resulting from sharp temperature inhomogeneities in the air.

Other modifications of transmitted energy occur when the energy passes through glass, plastic, the exhaust of a jet, over a heated surface, etc. before reaching the observer.

Frequently the transmitted energy is so modified by the characteristics of the medium through which it has been transmitted that the proximal stimulus is far from an exact replica of the energy that left the distal energy source.

3. *The Proximal Stimulus*

Aside from the foregoing phenomena of attenuation and

distortion, the proximal stimulus itself may be quite impoverished. It may be difficult to tell, from the proximal stimulus alone, what the characteristics of the distal object actually are (Brunswik, 1956). Ambiguity occurs, for example, in size and distance estimation. A nearby, small object will cast the same image on the retina as will a larger, more distant one. UFOs are frequently observed under conditions providing no frame of reference from which distance and size may be inferred. Without such a clear frame of reference, judgment of size and distance is extremely difficult or impossible. Thus, an unknown, vaguely defined object in the undifferentiated sky can appear to be of any size or at any distance, depending on the inferences made by the observer. If he assumes the object is the size of an automobile, he will infer its distance in terms of that size. But if he assumes that it is the size of a teacup, he will infer that it is much closer to him. Even if the object is within a few yards of the observer, distance and size judgments can be grossly inaccurate for lack of a frame of reference, because the retinal image alone does not typically (and especially in the case of UFOs) supply enough information to the observer to permit determining whether it has been cast by a huge, very distant object, by a medium-sized one at a moderate distance, or a small one close by.

A typical example of this ambiguity is found in the reports of witnesses to the re-entry of fragments of the Soviet statellite, Zond-4, on 3 March 1968 at about 9:45 p.m. EST. Three witnesses reported seeing a single object traveling at "tremendous speed" at an altitude of "not more than 2,000 to 5,000 feet." The witness quoted is the chief executive of a large U.S. city. Another group of witnesses to the same event reported that "it was at about tree-top level and was seen very, very clearly and was just a few yards away." They estimated that it was 170-200 ft. long. A private pilot saw more than one object moving at "very high speed" and estimated the altitude at 30,000 ft. An airline pilot and his crew reported the objects as "heading in a NNE direction at high rate of speed & above 60,000 feet altitude." The observers were actually looking at several pieces of satellite debris entering the atmosphere at an altitude of about 100 mi. and at a speed of about 18,000 mph (Sullivan, 1968).

Estimates of speed are just as ambiguous as estimates of size and distance, as the foregoing demonstrates. The retinal image, and the successive changes in it, can be the same for a small, near object moving slowly as for a large, distant object moving rapidly. Apparent speed depends upon relative displacement within a framework, rather than upon absolute displacement across the retina (Brown, 1931).

The characteristics of motion are also inherently ambiguous, especially if the moving object is unfamiliar. A proximal stimulus that is actually rising could be produced by an object rising and receding from the observer or one rising and approaching him. Its actual path could be perfectly horizontal, if it is above eye level and is approaching the observer. It could even be an object whose actual path is descending if the path is one that will eventually pass over the observer's head. Still other distal stimulus movements could produce the same proximal stimulus.

Changes in the size of the proximal stimulus are also ambiguous. They could be due to approach or recession of the object, or to changes in its size while remaining stationary. An object whose proximal stimulus is gradually growing can actually be receding from the observer, if the retinal image is growing faster than it would shrink because of recession alone.

Nor does the shape of the proximal stimulus unequivocally represent the shape of the distal object. Many different distal objects could cast the same shaped retinal image simply because at a given orientation they present the same cross-section. Conversely, except in the case of a sphere, a given distal object can produce many different shapes of proximal stimulation. Consider a flat disk. In different orientations to the observer, it could look like a vertical line, a horizontal line, a slanted line, a cigar-shaped object in various positions, a circle, or many forms of ellipses.

4. Neural Encoding: Sensation

It is clear from the preceding that what is physically available to the observer, the proximal stimulus, is by no means an exact, information-filled, unambiguous replica of the originating event, the distal energy source. The distortions we have considered so far are purely physical; precise instruments would register them in a way that is comparable to the way in which human sense organs register them. With our discussion of sensation, we enter the skin of the observer, and must consider physiological and psychological events that occur inside him.

When the proximal stimulus reaches the cells of a receptor that is sensitive to the energy contained in the stimulus, the cells transform the light, sound, heat, etc. into impulses carried along nerve fibers. The impulses travel from cell to cell into the center of the brain, the thalamus, and thence to the outer layer of the brain, the cerebral cortex. A sensation depends upon the messages arriving at higher sensory center in the brain in combination with other events simultaneously occurring in these centers.

What actually goes on in the sensory areas of the cortex depends on many things. Thus whether a dim light is actually seen is a function of how dark-adapted or light-adapted the eye is. If one comes into a dark movie theater from a bright, sunlit street, at first he can barely, if at all, make out the seats and the other people, but after some time in the dark, things that were previously invisible to him become visible. Conversely, if the eye has been in the dark for some time a moderately intense light will appear so bright as to be blinding, and it may be impossible to tell what the light source is, even though it would be readily recognizable to the light-adapted eye. Clearly the sensation produced by a particular proximal visual stimulus varies greatly with the state of adaptation of the eye.

Second, the observer's state of alertness can affect how and even whether he will sense a given stimulus. If he is drowsy, fatigued, tired, intoxicated, dizzy, ill, or drugged, he will be a less sensitive, less accurate, more error-prone instrument for detecting stimuli. Spontaneous discharges in the sensory centers of the brain may be interpreted by him as distal events, even though there may be no corresponding proximal stimulus. In addition to these physical conditions, states of extreme tension or anxiety can also produce not only reduced alertness but an enhanced tendency to misinterpret or distort sensations.

Third, concomitant sensory events can modify sensations. A loud noise, absorption in a book, concentration on a TV show, etc. can make one less likely to notice something else. In fact, one stimulus may actually inhibit the neural events produced by another. In a now-classic experiment, investigators recorded the bursts of neural activity in the auditory nerve of a cat whose ear was stimulated by clicks; when a caged rat was placed before the cat, impulses in the auditory nerve stopped, even though the clicks still continued at the same rate and intensity (Hernández-Peón, 1958).

Fourth, various sensory anomalies can modify sensation. A sizable proportion of the population is color blind to some degree; many persons are nearsighted, or farsighted, resulting in fuzzy contours, while astigmatism results in various shape aberrations. Then there are the phosphenes, or entoptic phenomena: visual sensations produced by pressure on the eyeball, or from such other conditions as spontaneous neural discharges within the eye. One can obtain brilliant, brightly-hued floating shapes intentionally by closing one's eyes and applying moderate continuous pressure to the eyelids with one's fingers—fascinating swirling abstract designs will result, with ever-changing brilliant colors.

Fifth, there are several kinds of afterimages, or images that persist after the stimulus originally producing them has ceased. In a positive afterimage the sensations are the same as those in the inducing stimulus, while in a negative afterimage they are reversed. If, in darkness, a bright light is flashed in the eye the afterimage of the light can be seen floating eerily about, moving as the observer's eyes move, for as long as a minute or more. The image can hover, dart here and there, and change apparent size, depending upon where one happens to cast it. The color typically changes as the image gradually fades. The color can range thorough the whole spectrum, and typically alternates between the color of the original light and its complement. Negative afterimages are more common than positive ones, and are produced by staring for a time at a particular place in the visual field. The characteristics of the negative afterimage are opposite to those of the inducing stimulus. Thus where the original stimulus was white, the afterimage is black; where it was black in the stimulus the image is white; where the stimulus was red the image is green; where the stimulus was blue the image is orange-yellow; and so on. Negative afterimages fluctuate like positive ones, fading in and out. The longer the inducing stimulus was stared at and the greater the contrast in the inducing stimulus, the longer the afterimage persists. The apparent size of afterimages, both positive and negative, depends upon the distance to the surface upon which they are projected: the farther away the surface, the larger the image appears to be.

5. Perception

Perception is the process of identifying the distal object. The observer interprets the neural inputs as due to some object, assigning it particular characteristics, such as distance, direction, shape, color, etc. The amount of interpretation that the observer must employ to arrive at the final percept depends in part upon the clarity, the lack of ambiguity of the input. Thus the letters on this printed page are reasonably clear and unambiguous; there is an ample frame of reference, and the distal stimulus is clearly structured: the observer can obtain a fairly accurate percept of what the distal stimuli actually are. But if the perceptual framework is impoverished, as is true of most conditions under which UFOs are reported, then the perceiver must engage in much more interpretation before he arrives at a percept.

Typically, perception results in a clear, categorical conclusion about characteristics of perceived objects, even if the input is logically, geometrically or optically insufficient to specify these characteristics unambiguously. For objects in the sky, again, especially unfamiliar objects, shape, size, distance, direction, speed are all basically indeterminate in the proximal stimulus, and yet the processes of perception work in such a way as to give each a particular value in any given case.

Apparent shape depends upon the orientation of the object to the observer. Size, distance and speed depends upon each other in a complex way: an observer's automatic assumptions concerning one of them determine to a large extent how he will perceive the others. Apparent direction of motion depends upon a reference frame; thus clouds, for example, will typically appear to be moving at right angles to a reference line such as the roof line of a house or the part of a window frame one concentrates on while looking through the window at the moving clouds.

Apparent motion can be induced in an actually stationary object in a number of ways. The moon may appear to be moving while the clouds partly covering it seem to stay stationary. The landscape may seem to move in a direction opposite to that to which the eye was previously exposed, as when one sits in a train which has just stopped, or looks at the hillside next to a waterfall after staring at the waterfall a while. Normally a single object in a completely unstructured field will soon appear to move, even though it is actually stationary. This phenomenon, autokinesis, is frequently studied by experimental psychologists who ask subjects to report on the appearance of a pinpoint of light in a completely dark room. A light going out typically seems to shrink as it does so. A light that goes on as another is going off can, under proper time and space conditions, be made to look as though the light that went off had moved to the place where the light went on.

The angular elevation, or apparent location above the horizon, of objects is generally not estimated very accurately at all. The difference from 0° or from 90° of angles near the horizon or near the zenith tends to be substantially overestimated. Anything that is more than 45° or even 30° above the horizon is often reported as overhead.

Colors are sometimes perceived by interpretation only. The dark-adapted eye is insensitive to color, yet the grass still is perceived as green, a banana as yellow. There are also phenomena of color contrast or color induction: a small piece of gray paper on a strong green background takes on a reddish tinge; on a strong blue background it will take on a yellowish tinge. The same piece of gray paper looks appreciably brighter on a black background than on a white one.

In general, for just about all perceivable characteristics, perception typically works in such a way that the percept, as the perceiver is aware of it, is considerably clearer, less ambiguous, and less vague than the actual physical proximal stimulus warrants.

6. Cognition

One's judgment, conviction or belief about the actual identity and meaning of something, that is, one's cognition of it, are very much affected by mental set, expectation and suggestion. Every observer is ready to perceive reality in a certain way. The observer's sets and expectations arise from his experiences, opinions, and beliefs, including those derived from suggestion. The observer who looks for faces in cloud patterns or leaf patterns can find them easily. Setting oneself to see the letter "e" on this page makes the e's more salient, more noticeable. You probably were unaware just now of the pressure of the shoe on your left foot until it was mentioned in this sentence. What one notices, pays attention to, responds to, and how one interprets it, what it means to one, are deeply affected by one's attitudes, past experiences, opinions, and beliefs (Bruner, 1947; December, 1960; etc.). The influence on cognition of all these internal factors is especially strong in impoverished stimulus situations such as those under which UFO reports typically are generated. The observer's personality, his rigidity, absolutism, skill in scientific thinking, interest and belief in UFOs, readiness and ability to consider alternative interpretations of what is perceived, etc. substantially affect the observer's conclusions, typically without his being aware of this influence.

7. The Report

Whether the observer makes a report, and, if so, to whom and in what form, varies with the individual and with the situation. A frightened observer, or one who is oriented toward authority, is more likely to make a report than one who is unconcerned, or who does not know to whom to make a formal report. Once the observer has decided to make a report, the way in which he is questioned can substantially affect its content. The amount of detail and even the details themselves, can be much affected by the manner and form of questioning by the recipient of the report. Open questions (e. g., "Tell me what you saw.") result in less distorted answers then do closed questions (e. g., "Did you see it for longer or shorter than ten seconds," or, "You don't mean to tell me that it actually hovered, do you?"); interviewer bias can greatly influence the respondent's behavior (Rosenthal, 1966). Testimony is known to be quite unreliable especially under the pressure of leading, direct questions, a hypercritical or incredulous interrogator, or one who insists upon details about which the witness' memory is fuzzy. Memory of the percept like cognition, is subject to the distorting effects of motivation, personality, set, suggestion, etc.

8. An Evaluation

UFO reports are the product of a long chain of events, from

distal stimulus through to the final reporting; at every link in this chain there are sources of distortion. Details of specific reports, are, by the very nature of the processes of human sensation, perception, cognition and reporting, likely to be untrustworthy. Thus any report, even those of observers generally regarded as credible, must be viewed cautiously. No report is an entirely objective, unbiased, and complete account of an objective distal event. Every UFO report contains the human element; to an unknown but substantial extent it is subject to the distorting effects of energy transmission through an imperfect medium, of the lack of perfect correlation between distal object and proximal stimulus, and of the ambiguities, interpretations, and subjectivity of sensation, perception and cognition.

References

Bartley, S. H. *Principles of Perception*. New York: Harper, 1958.

Beardslee, D. and M. Wertheimer, (Eds.). *Readings in Perception*. Princeton, N.J.: Van Nostrand, 1958.

Boring, E. G. *Sensation and Perception in the History of Experimental Psychology*. New York: Appleton-Century-Crofts, 1942.

Brown, J. F. "The visual perception of velocity," *Psychol. Forsch,* 14 (1931), pp. 199-232.

Bruner, J. S. and C. C. Goodman. "Value and need as organizing factors in perception," *J. Abnorm. Soc. Psychol,* 42 (1947), pp. 33-44.

Brunswik, E. *Perception and the Representative Design of Experiments*. Berkeley, Calif.: Univ. of California Press, 1956.

Dember, W. N. *The Psychology of Perception*. New York: Holt, 1960.

von Fieandt, K. *The World of Perception*. New York: Dorsey, 1966.

Forgus, R. H. *Perception: The Basic Process in Cognitive Development*. New York: McGraw-Hill, 1966.

Gibson, J. J. *The Perception of the Visual World*. Boston: Houghton-Mifflin, 1950.

Hernandez-Peon, R., H. Scherrer, and M. Jouvet. "Modification of electrical activity in cochlear nucleus during 'attention' in unanesthetized cats," *Science,* 123 (1956), pp. 331-332.

Hochberg, J. *Perception*. Englewood Cliffs, N.J.: Prentice-Hall, 1964.

Leibowitz, H. W. *Visual Perception*. New York: Macmillan, 1965.

Minnaert, M. *The Nature of Light and Colour in the Open Air*. New York: Dover, 1954.

Rosenthal, R. *Experimenter Effects in Behavioral Research*. New York: Appleton-Century-Crofts, 1966.

Sullivan, Walter. "Rocket Re-entry Termed UFO." *Denver-Post-New York Times,* 2 July 1968.

Chapter 2 Process of Perception, Conception, and Reporting / William K. Hartmann

1. Introduction

The preceding chapter outlined the sequence of events, physical, physiological, and psychological, by which perception of a phenomenon is combined with previous conceptions. In this chapter we will review some evidence on how this proceeds in fact, and on how the conceptions, sometimes after significant interpretation, produce a report.

The question underlying this discussion is this: Are misinterpretation and misreporting sufficiently common as to make credible the assertion that the entire UFO phenomenon, or at least the residual of unidentified cases, is the result of these processes (plus deliberate hoaxes)? The data show that this assertion is indeed credible, although, of course, we cannot prove that this accounts for the unidentified objects.

2. Perception: Objects and Phenomena in the Atmosphere

In practice, it has proven impossible and potentially misleading to try to tabulate all of the possible causes of UFO perception. There are simply too many. The very point that is emphasized by case after case is the incredible variety of circumstances that may cause one to perceive an apparition of high strangeness and conceive of it as an UFO, or even more specifically as a "flying saucer."

Minnaert (1954), Menzel (1953), and Menzel and Boyd (1963) have described in detail many objects and phenomena that are unfamiliar to most persons. We need not repeat their description here. However, simply to illustrate the variety of causes that can and have produced UFO reports, Table 1 briefly lists some of the possibilities.

We can be virtually certain that all of the causes in Table 1 have, at one time or another, produced perceptions that could not be identified by the observer. It is perhaps not surprising, therefore, that about 3,000,000 out of 125,000,000 adult civilian Americans have perceived phenomena that they classify as "Unidentified Flying Objects" (See Section III, Chapter 8). The question is whether a few of these reports are extraordinary.

Table 1

Examples of UFO-Related Objects and Phenomena

Meteorological	
Subsun	Gulfstream aircraft (Case 54)
Lenticular clouds	Cf. Section III, Chapter 3
Noctilucent clouds	"Glowing" clouds, often in peculiar shapes
Mirages	Examples cited by Menzel (1953), Menzel and Boyd (1963)
Sundog	Debris thrown into air without
"Dust devils," etc.	apparent support
St. Elmo's fire	Cf. Section VI, Chapter 7
Ball lightning	
Astronomical	
Meteors, fireballs	Cf. discussion of 1913 fireball, this chapter
Satellite reentries	Cf. discussion of Zond IV, this chapter.

Aurora	
Venus, other planets	
Experimental and Technological	
"Skyhook" balloons	Responsible for Mantell tragedy (Menzel and Boyd, 1963)
Other balloons	Certain, little-flown types have been disk-shaped
Test aircraft	
Rocket launches	Rockets & contrails have generated UFO reports
High-alt. projectiles	Have been used in flare and wind-study experiments (Cf. New Mexico aircraft (Case 55)
Bomb tests	Fort Belvoir, Va. (Case 50)
Contrails	
Refueling	Coarsegold, Calif. (Case 28)
Searchlight reflections	
Aircraft reflections	Great Falls, Mont. (Case 47)
Aircraft afterburner	
Aircraft seen at unusual angles	
Aircraft landing lights	
Flare experiments	
Physiological and Psychological	
Autokinesis	Perceived motion of objects known to be stationary
"Autostasis"	Perceived stopping of objects known to be moving
Entoptic effects	Generated within the eyeball
Motes on the cornea	Perceived as spots
Hallucination	
"Airship effect"	Perceived connection of separate sources (cf. this chapter)
"Excitedness effect"	Selection effect on reports (cf. this chapter)
Industrial Effects	
Detergent foam	
Biological	
Angel hair	
Airborn debris (e.g. milkweed)	Camarillo, Calif. (Case 58)
Birds, flocks of birds	Tremonton, Utah (Case 49)
Swarms of insects	
Luminous fungi on birds	
Fireflies	
Miscellaneous	
Hot-air balloons	UFO reports generated by toy balloons using candles to create hot air (Boulder, Colo., Case 18)
Kites	
Reflections off windows	Witness interprets reflection as object outside window
Material fixed or moving on window	As above
Deliberate hoaxes	

Table 1 raises a problem for the UFO investigator: in a given case, how unusual may a phenomenon be to be cited as explanation? Certain investigators have been widely criticized for constructing elaborate conditions to explain (or explain away) UFO reports. One should be guided by "Occam's Razor:" an explanation becomes less credible as the number of *ad hoc* assumptions increases. Table 1 is not a list by which every case can be explained, but it does suggest that even without alien spaceships and undiscovered physical phenomena, many strange things will be perceived.

As an example of the complexities of just one class of objects, which has been inadequately studied both within and outside the context of UFOs, consider meteoroidal bolides. Bolides have produced exceedingly spectacular and unusual displays, but it is not widely recognized that they probably include a variety of objects. There are cometary debris, thought to be fragile and with a high volatile content, leading to fragmentation in the atmosphere. Many of these, having drifted in from the outskirts of the solar system have a very high velocity. Asteroidal fragments, thought to be represented by the stony and iron meteorites, enter the atmosphere at intermediate velocities and may have a different mass distribution. Least known of all, there may be a group of low velocity objects that are debris blown off the moon by impacts or in some other way captured in the earth-moon system. There may even be other unknown sources of cosmic debris.

The slow bolides (entry speed $\doteqdot$ escape velocity) are of particular relevance and interest because of the part that the epidemic of slow, green fireballs played in the development of the UFO problem in 1948-49 (Ruppelt 1956; Menzel and Boyd, 1963), and because of the scattered reports in the astronomical literature of majestic slow fireballs (Chant, 1913; discussed below). As an example of the diverse data bearing on the UFO problem, consider the possibility of observing fragments blown off the moon. It is believed that interplanetary meteoroids striking the moon dislodge material amounting to some hundreds of times their own mass (Gault, 1964). Material totaling roughly the initial projectile's mass may escape the moon's gravitational field, probably in the form of particles much smaller than the original projectile (Gault, 1964). Ordinary meteors of mass 10^4 gm are of magnitude about -10 (Vedder, 1966), and we may infer that a fragment of such mass from the moon would produce a spectacular display as it enters the earth's atmosphere. That is, lunar-impacting projectiles of mass of the order 10^6 to 10^8 gm could be expected to throw out fragments that, entering the earth's atmosphere, could produce spectacular, slow fireballs. How often do such *lunar* impacts occur? Meteor fluxes have been thoroughly reviewed by Vedder (1966) and for the mass range given, the rate of lunar impacts is estimated to be in the range 10 to 10^{-1} per year. It is expected that many circumlunar particles would ultimately decay into the earth's atmosphere so that we may predict that every few decades, or even more frequently, spectacular slow fireballs of lunar origin should occur, and that groupings of these objects would appear over periods of weeks, since clusters of ejecta are thrown out by each lunar impact, to decay at different rates.

This illustration is chosen because the predicted characteristics match those of the "green fireball episode" and suggest that lunar debris may, indeed, be the explanation of those unusual bolides.

It is important to note that we have not yet even considered the possibility that any of the common or unusual causes in Table 1 may be badly reported, so that an investigator may become hopelessly confused.

Whoever believes that the UFO phenomenon represents revolutionary and fantastic events must take full account of the facts that (1) UFOs by definition include all phenomena unkown to the observer; (2) such phenomena are present in effectively infinite variety, so that even widely experienced investigators, not to mention inexperienced witnesses, may be unaware of them; and (3) such phenomena, even if accurately perceived, may be badly interpreted and reported by the observer.

3. Conception: The Re-entry of Zond IV Debris

It is remarkably common for astronomers, when queried about UFOs, to cite the misconceptions that accompany reports of meteors. Most astronomers have talked to witnesses who believe a prominent meteor landed "just behind the barn" or "just over the hill;" thus, they stress the limitations of verbal reports from average observers.

Project Blue Book has supplied us with exceptionally good data to illuminate this problem. On 3 March 1968 the news agency of the Soviet Union announced that the spacecraft "Zond IV" had been placed in a low "parking orbit" around the earth and would soon be launched into "outlying regions of near-earth space" (Sullivan, 1968). The mission was unsuccessful. At about 9:45 p.m. EST on 3 March, hundreds of American observers near a line from Kentucky to Pennsylvania saw a majestic procession of fiery objects with sparkling golden orange tails move across their sky. The spacecraft was disintegrating upon re-entry. Most observers saw two or three main pieces, while observers near the end of the path saw more. These objects were soon identified by NORAD as pieces of the

Zond IV probe or its rocket booster and this identification was finally confirmed 1 July 1968 (Sullivan, 1968).

This case put us in the rare and fortunate position of knowing exactly what was involved even before we began to investigate the many UFO reports that were generated.

In brief, many of these reports were quite good, but there is an admixture of spurious elements that are astonishingly familiar to students of the "flying saucer" literature. The latter vividly illustrate the problem of conception and interpretation, and shed light on the entire UFO phenomenon.

Consider the conceptions that may be generated if one perceives three bright point sources moving across the night sky at constant angular separation of, say, 5°. The most objective observer may report as directly as possible the percept: three point sources moving with a constant angular separation. But this is just one end of a spectrum. A less objective observer and, from our Zond IV data, a demonstrably more typical one may introduce subtle elements of interpretation. He may report three point sources *flying* with constant angular separation, or three *lights flying* with constant angular separation, or three *lights flying in formation*. These changes in conception may be subtle, but when the observer *reports* his conception to a second party, they may produce vividly different conceptions (especially if the second party is inclined to believe "flying saucers" exist). Further toward the other end of the spectrum, but less typical than the above examples, a highly unobjective observer may introduce totally spurious elements. He may report three *craft flying in formation*. He may, for example, conceive the idea that the three point sources are connected, since they maintain a constant pattern. He may even imagine a dark elongated form connecting them so that they become *lights on a cigar-shaped object,* or even *windows on a cigar-shaped object.*

This spectrum of the conceptions of observers is not based on mere theorizing. It is directly derived from the Zond IV observations.

Quantitative analysis of the observations is somewhat confused by their heterogeneity. The file supplied by Project Blue Book contains reports ranging from very complete accounts on official Air Force report forms to fragmentary records of telephone reports. In all, there are some 78 reports, but only about 30 detailed letters or forms attempting to give a complete description are appropriate for analysis. There are only 12 Air Force report forms from which one can study the variations in response to specific questions; e.g. angular size, velocity, etc.

Study of the file, some 30 complete reports produced counts of certain conceptions indicated in Table 2, listed in order of decreasing frequency.

The following remarks apply to the items in Table 2. Item

(1) shows that virtually all the reports that made reference to sound correctly agree that there was none. One witness (item 16) reported sound like a piece of tin hurtling through the air. We can be certain this is in error; this conception must have resulted from an unrelated noise or a hallucination due to a belief that there *ought* to have been a sound. Items (2) and (14) are somewhat misleading semantic errors. A better choice

Table 2

*Selected Conceptions Generated by Zond IV Re-entry**

Conception	*No. of Reports*
1. Report absence of any sound	20
2. Report "formation"	17**
3. Estimate altitude or distance < 20 mi.	13**
4. Suggest phenomenon may be meteor(ite) or satellite re-entry	12
5. Report straight, uniform motion	12
6. Indicate individual sources were of angular size $\gtrsim 7'$	10**
7. Report rocket- or cigar-shape, or "saucer" shape	7**
8. Report curvature or change of direction or motion	6**
9. Estimate altitude or distance at $< 10{,}000$ ft.	5**
10. Report cigar-shape or rocket-shape	5**
11. Report "fuzzy" outline	4
12. Report "windows"	3**
13. Describe lights (implying lights *on* something)	2**
14. Refer to exhaust	2**
15. Report sharp, well defined outline	2**
16. Report noise	1**
17. Report reaction of animal	1**
18. Report vertical descent	1**

* Based in effect, on about 30 relatively complete reports out of a total file of 78.

** Conceptions that are to greater or lesser degree erroneous.

of word than "formation" would have been "pattern" or "constellation." "Formation" and "exhaust" imply guided vehicles. One observer even described one object as "pursuing" another; it "looked as if it was [sic] making an attempt to shoot the other one down." (3) and (9): As is usually the case with meteor reports, the object was conceived of as being much closer than in fact. This presumably results from the average observer's unfamiliarity with the concept of watching objects a hundred miles away. (4): A number of observers correctly considered meteoritic phenomena. A smaller number flatly identified the apparition as a re-entry of some sort and a few even indicated that they gave it scarcely a thought until they later heard of the excitement generated through radio, and newspapers! (5) and (8): Most observers described an essentially linear path, but a smaller number reported changes in direction. A few even ruled out a meteoritic phenomenon on this basis. Most of the reports of change in direction must be subjective, perhaps an autokinesis effect, but some are thought to result from observers' own motion in vehicles. (7): This includes all descriptions typical of "flying saucers," and (6), (7), and (10) together indicate a strong tendency to conceive of a *shape* even though the phenomenon involved virtual point sources. Most observers indicated that the fragments were about 3-4 min. of arc in diameter, just within the resolving power of the normal human eye. Reports of a "cigar-shape" apparently stem from a subjective tendency to connect the string of sources and from popularization of this concept in the UFO literature. This important phenomenon I will call the "airship effect;" it is demonstrably present even in reports as far back as 1913, and in Cases 34 and 37. Items (11) and (15), which seem to indicate merely the inadequacy of the report form's question (The edges of the object were: Fuzzy or blurred? Sharply outlined?) in the case of a nearpoint source with an ill-defined tail. Items (12) and (13) illustrate serious misconceptions, apparently due to unconscious *assumption* that there was a vehicle. Item (17) refers to a report that a dog was noted to become upset and to huddle, whimpering, between two trash cans. According to her own testimony, the witness was quite excited and the dog presumably detected this.

The Air Force report forms comprise a smaller set of more homogeneous data, since the questions are standardized. A range of conceptions are illustrated by the 12 report forms plus 5 highly detailed accounts, and are summarized in Table 2. The angular size, a relatively objective measurement, is fairly consistently estimated. The size, distance, and velocity estimates are hopelessly misconceived, as we have already seen, since the observers had no objective way of determining any of these (without realizing that a re-entry was involved). The estimates appear to be influenced by prior conceptions of and familiarity with airplanes. Typical errors exceed a factor of ten. Only four of the 12 respondents correctly noted that they could not estimate the speed. Of 17 observers, four chose to describe a "formation," and two, "windows."

An effect important to the UFO problem is demonstrated by the records: the excited observers who thought they had witnessed a very strange phenomenon produced the most detailed, longest, and most misconceived reports, but those who by virtue of experience most nearly recognized the nature of the phenomenon became the least excited and produced the briefest reports. The "*excitedness effect*" has an important bearing on the UFO problem. It is a selection effect by which the least accurate reports are made more prominent (since the observer becomes highly motivated to make a report), while the most accurate reports may not be recorded. In the case of Zond IV the two most lengthy unsolicited reports described the apparition as a cigar-shaped craft with a row of lighted windows and a fiery tail, while the correct identifications as a re-entry were short, in some cases recovered only by later solicitation of reports.

In summary, we conclude that all of the following factors demonstrably confuse reports of unidentified phenomena and make subsequent investigation difficult: (1) Objects are conceived of in terms of familiar concepts, such as aircraft. This produces misconceptions of distance, speed, shape, etc. (2) At least during the last decade conceptions have been heavily influenced by the "flying saucer" concept in movies, TV, and periodicals. Reports of "saucer-shape," "cigar-shape," and physiological reaction are probably a consequence. (3) Due to the nature of certain cases, certain questions on prepared questionnaires or report forms become ambiguous or meaningless. (4) The "excitedness effect" biases reports toward those containing more exotic conceptions. (5) The "airship effect" causes some observers to conceive of a shape surrounding light sources.

It is scarcely short of amazing, and certainly suggestive, that the seemingly straightforward Zond IV incident produced a high percentage of the very phenomena that have puzzled students of the UFO problem. Table 3 lists a selection of such reports. We have, in fact, reports of (1) a cigar-shaped object with windows and a flaming exhaust, (2) a vehicle or craft that passed low overhead in utter silence, (3) psycho-physiological response of dread, or in another case, an urge to sleep, and, (4) abnormal behavior of a nearby animal. To the extent that the argument for "flying saucers" rests on the strangeness of such observations, it is thereby weakened.

Of course, the important question in a case such as the Zond IV re-entry is not the quality of the worst observations, but rather whether the observations taken together did define and clarify the phenomenon. My own judgment is that, together, the reports *would* suggest a re-entry to anyone who was familiar with such a phenomenon. This results primarily from the vividness of this particular case, and the attendant diagnostic features: a bright bolide slowly disintegrating into many fragments, each attended by a train. Nonetheless, it must be said that only a fraction, about a quarter, of the reports point directly in this direction while about another quarter are misleading and the remainder insufficiently detailed to be diagnostic. A reporter or investigator coming upon the case in innocence would be hardput to distinguish the good from the bad reports.

Table 3 demonstrates that a large part of the UFO problem is a semantic one. One may point out that an accurate reconstruction of this incident would have been, after all, possible from the bulk of reports; but to generate a UFO case we need only (say) one to four witnesses to agree on and express misleading conceptions and other witnesses to be silent or (more commonly) non-existent.

Table 3

Selected Descriptive Comments on Zond IV Re-entry

Nature of the object:

"[I heard on] news . . . it was space junk. Never. It came down then went forward in perfect formation. So how can gravity be defied?"

"Suggestions: 1. Cylinder type rocket with two thrust rocket engines and one rocket engine in front for guiding purposes. 2. Meteor broken into three main parts. 3. Space or aeronautical craft."

"Observer does not think the objects were either satellite debris or meteors because they had a flat trajectory."

"Didn't attach much importance to the object because I thought it was a re-entry."

"Thought it looked like something burning up in space. . . . Thought it looked like a burn-in."

"I wasn't aware that I had seen anything unusual until the local TV newscast . . . advised of many other sightings of same for miles around."

"Neither I nor my fiancee sighted any connecting lines [among the bright sources]. If there were connecting lines, it would have formed the fuselage of a B-52 only about thirty to forty times bigger."

"Could not see actual object."

Appearance of object:

"All . . . observers saw a long jet airplane-looking vehicle without any wings. It was on fire both in front and behind. All observers also saw many windows. . . . If there had been anybody in the UFO near the windows I would have seen them."

"It was shaped like a fat cigar, in my estimation. . . . It appeared to have rather square shaped windows along the side that was facing us. . . . It appeared to me that the fuselage was constructed of many pieced or flat sheets . . . with a 'riveted together look'. . . . The many 'windows' seemed to be lit up from the inside."

[It could be compared to] "ordinary saucer inverted without protrusion on top; elongated a little more than a saucer. Protrusion on bottom midline and about 50% of bottom so covered."

"No flame was visible but . . . quantity of golden sparks. . . . In my opinion it was a solid rocket type vehicle with three lights or three oval saucer type vehicles."

"Object had red and blue lights."

"Observed an unidentified object. . . . It was long and narrow with a light in front and in back there was a streaming tail. . . . The object was dark black, trail was yellow gold."

"Fiery orange, long and narrow."

"Definite disk shaped."
"It was like two disk-shaped lights in some planned position."
"Tail appeared as metallic sparks."

"Formation Flight:"

"They flew in a perfect military formation."
When asked if they could be meteorites, [witness] replied, "It would be the first time I ever saw meteorites fly formation."
"It appeared as if one object was in pursuit of the other. One object seemed to be traveling at a higher or greater speed than the one pursuing it. The pursuing object . . . looked as if it was making an attempt to shoot the other one down."

Distance and dimensions:

"It was at about treetop level and was seen very, very clearly, just a few yards away."
A pilot "estimated each [tail] was about 0.5 mile in length."
"We saw two orange lights tailing [sic] about two yards apart."
Observer "felt that it would have hit in the wooded area south of (her city)."

Response and reaction:

"I really wanted to see a UFO. I remember saying aloud . . . 'This is no natural phenomenon. It's really UFOs, I . . . made an attempt to communicate with them. I had a flashlight . . . [and] signaled . . . in Morse code. . . . No visible response elicited. . . . After I came into the house I had an overpowering drive to sleep. . . . My dog . . . went over between the two trash cans . . . and whimpered and lay on the drive between the cans like she was frightened to death. . . . High frequency sound inaudible to us?"
"Frightened my eleven year old son, who was out with his telescope."

Hearsay:

"I heard there were [72] grass fires in this area on the day following this sighting. I would think there might be a possible connection."

4. *Conception: Re-entry of Titan 3 C-4 Debris*

An incident less widely observed than the Zond IV re-entry gave the writer an opportunity to compare his personal observation of the re-entry of satellite debris with verbal reports solicited from his community. The results are similar to those of the case described above.

On 28 September 1967, at 9:53 MDST I noticed from Tucson, a bright, orange-red stellar object drifting across the northern sky toward the northeast at a rate of about 40′ of arc per sec. Though initially of about zero magnitude, it suddenly dissappeared, giving the impression of a jet plane cutting off its afterburner. However, the object suddenly reappeared, then repeated the performance several times. During the last few degrees of the trail, some 5°-10° above the horizon, there appeared to be a disintegration into several barely resolved fragments. A second or two later, another object appeared and followed the first one down to the last 4° of the trail. Meanwhile, a faint milky-white train which had been left by the first object brightened for about 10 sec., then faded, twisted, and broke up in a period of about 6 min.

The tell-tale features of a satellite re-entry were present: the object was too slow for a meteor, had the brightness fluctuations and color of a burning object, fragmented, moved eastward and left a train that was distorted by high altitude winds. A later check through the Colorado project indicated that re-entry of certain fragments of Titan 3 C-4 satellite 1965-82KD, had been estimated to occur at about 6:00 a.m., MDST, on 29 September 1967 (see also King-Hele and Quinn, 1966). Earlier, the satellite had exploded in orbit, and the fragments were spread out along the orbit, so that sporadic decays near the predicted time were not unexpected; the observation of a second fragment a few seconds (some tens of miles) behind the first was consistent with this. Hence, the identification is regarded as virtually certain.

Rarely does the investigator himself have an opportunity to see the "UFO" being described. In order to take advantage of this opportunity to compare my own observations to the conceptions and semantics generated, I solicited observations through a local newspaper.

Fifteen reports were received from the Tucson area by telephone. The reports ranged from quite accurate to quite misleading. The most misleading of the 15 was from an articulate woman who was to all appearances an astute observer. She clearly reported that the object fell *between her and some mountains* a few miles away, appearing in front of (south of) the mountains and below their crests. (This conflicts with other reports of observers located north and west of the mountains, as well as the known identity of the object.) Other misconceptions reported included: (1) red and green flashing or rotating light (possibly confusing the object with an aircraft that was near the witness?); (2) much bigger than a star, could see a round shape; (3) motion toward the west (confusion with another object?); (4) "Looked like it was coming down right at me. It scared me. It was like it was right over me—like a fat airplane—with a big window." This is a repetition of the "airship effect" in which the observer conceives of a light as an aperture in a black, unseen, larger form.

The writer had concluded (before the Zond IV results were available) that roughly a quarter of the reports were accurate and articulate enough to be definitive, roughly a quarter contained seriously misleading elements, and the rest were sufficiently inarticulate or whimsical to be of no great value (It was "real red, like, you know, and pretty . . . It turned [sic] a beautiful white streak . . ."). A report made by an investigator arriving later would have depended on which conceptions he heard or adopted. The right selection would have cleared up any problem; the wrong one might have created a seemingly inexplicable and possibly celebrated UFO report.

5. Conception: The Great Fireball of 9 February 1913

C. A. Chant (1913a), in a 71-page report, gives a detailed account of the spectacular meteoric display of 9 February 1913. The series of disintegrating bolides passed from Saskatchewan ESE over the Great Lakes and over the New Jersey coast. Several "waves" of clustered objects were seen, noise was heard at least 50 mi. from the sub-bolide point, and ground shocks were reported. Other remarkable sporadic meteors were seen in various scattered locations around the world for a period of some days. Chant deduced that the height of the path, which followed the earth's curvature, was about 26 mi. and that the geocentric velocity was in the range 5-10 mi/sec. M. Davidson (1913) reanalyzed Chant's data, plus observations from Bermuda, and concluded that the object had a height of some 46 mi. over Ontario, and Chant (1913b) subsequently inferred that they reached perigee over Ontario, but were not destroyed, moving out into a new orbit when seen from Bermuda.

The phenomenon appeared rather like the Zond IV reentry. It is well-described in the "extended extracts" from letters published by Chant. Clusters of stellar-like objects passed overhead, with tails several degrees long and accompanied by smaller, fainter objects. It is a subjective judgment, possibly influenced by some editing of the letters by Chant, that the 1913 reports are on the whole more objective than those of this decade. There are probably two reasons for this: (1) In 1913 the demarcation between "educated" persons, from whom Chant was likely to receive letters, and "uneducated persons," was greater. (2) In 1913, there was no widely known conception (i.e. pre-conception of mysterious saucer-shaped aircraft or spaceship (although several reports refer to the object as an airship). Further, the 1913 reports (as published) tend to be more descriptive; the word "meteor" is used in a non-generic sense simply to mean a bright object passing across the sky. There is little attempt among the correspondents to infer what the objects were.

Chant himself indicates that the reports varied in quality due to the process of conception and interpretation: "The reader . . . will . . . see that intelligent people can differ widely in describing a phenomenon, and will be able to appreciate the difficulty I have had in discriminating between very discordant observations." He presents reports of nearly 150 witnesses.

The "airship effect" is clearly present. Consider these reports: (1) "The series of lights travelled in unison and so horizontal that I could think only of a giant flying machine. The lights were at different points, one in front, one further back, and a rear light, then a succession of small lights in the tail." (2) "They . . . did not seem to be falling as meteors usually do, but kept a straight course . . . above the horizon. Our first impression was that a fleet of illuminated airships of monstrous size [was] passing. The incandescent fragments themselves formed what to us looked like the illuminations while the tails seemed to make the frame of the machine. They looked like ships travelling in company." (3) "The meteor resembled a large aeroplane or dirigible, with two tiers of lights strung along the sides." (4) The witnesses "reported that they had seen an airship going east. The heavens were brilliantly illuminated, and with the passage of the meteors a shower of stones was seen to fall." (This last element is not mentioned elsewhere and appears to be spurious.) (5) "I took it for an aeroplane with both headlights lit, and as it came nearer the sparks falling behind it made it appear still more like one. However after a minute or a minute and a half I could see it was a meteor. . . . It was very low, apparently just above the hills. (6) "My brother shouted to me, 'An airship!' And I said, 'Mrs. M—'s chimney is on fire! It looked that near. . . . To the eye they were little above the housetops." (7) ". . . a voice from a group of men was heard to say: 'Oh, boys, I'll tell you what it is—an aeroplane race.' "

We have already noted in the Zond IV case that the angular size, a relatively objective estimate, was consistently measured. In this case the description of the noise is remarkably consistent, perhaps because of the ready availability of a charming simile. Here are five consecutive descriptions of the noise: (1) ". . . a heavy noise like a clap of thunder at a distance;" (2) ". . . a low rumble which at first made me think it was a buggy going along the road from church;" (3) ". . . like thunder, loud at first and rumbling every two or three seconds;" (4) ". . . like a horse and rig going over a bridge;" (5) ". . . like a wagon passing over a rough road."

There was more difficulty with conceptions such as angular elevation and distance. As usual, the latter was grossly underestimated. (1) ". . . midway between the horizon and the sky . . ." (2) ". . . midway between the earth and the sky . . ." (3) They travelled no faster than a crow flies." (4) ". . . never have I [seen] so many heavenly bodies moving at one time, or any moving so slowly or in so low an altitude." (5)

"They looked to pass about one mile south and at an elevation of about 300 feet." (6) ". . . I saw [it] for about half a minute. In that time it seemed to go about 150 yards." (7) "The position in the sky of the first one seemed very low, so low that at first I thought it was a rocket." (Skyrockets, of the fireworks type, were a common analogue).

Many more reports could be cited, illustrating comparison with familiar objects (kites, funnels, ships in formation), in some cases misleading, even though the reports taken together present a relatively clear picture. We again can conclude that a substantial number of misleading reports will be introduced in observations of unusual phenomena.

6. *Additional Remarks on Percepts and Concepts*

The "airship effect" and "excitedness effect" apply to the Eastern Airlines case of 1948 (better known as the Chiles-Whitted case). This will serve as an example of the difficulties of establishing any concrete evidence for "flying saucers" when one is forced to distinguish percepts and concepts of a few witnesses in older cases.

Briefly, pilot Chiles and co-pilot Whitted reported flashing by them in a few seconds a "wingless aircraft with no fins or protruding surfaces, [which] was cigar-shaped, about 100 ft. long, and about twice the diameter of a B-29 Superfortress. It seemed to have two rows of windows through which glowed a very bright light, brilliant as a magnesium flare. An intense dark-blue glow like a blue fluorescent factory light shown at the bottom along the entire length, and red-orange flames shot out from the rear to a distance of some fifty feet" (Menzel, 1963).

This case has been one of the mainstays in the arguments for "flying saucers" and NICAP has described it as the "classic" cigar-shaped object (Hall, 1964). Hynek, as consultant to the Air Force, and Menzel and Boyd account for it as a fireball (Menzel, 1963).

The present discussion provides definitive evidence that fireballs can be described in *just* the way reported by Chiles and Whitted. The investigator is faced with the perfectly conceivable possibility that Chiles and Whitted, suffering from the "airship effect," became excited and reported a misconception—a cigar-shaped object with windows and flames—just as a fraction of witnesses to spectacular fireballs are now known to do.

A second example from my own experience illustrates the difficulties of transforming perceptions into conceptions (and explanations). During the course of the Colorado project investigation, I was sitting in the left side of an airliner, just behind the wing. As I looked out over patchy clouds, I saw an object apparently passing us in the distance, flying the other way. It came out from under our wing, not far below the horizon, and drifted slowly behind us until, because of the window geometry, I could no longer see far enough behind to observe it. It moved like a distant airliner, but was a grey, ill-defined disk, with major axis about a third of the apparent size of the moon. It was darker than the clouds, but lighter than the ground. It appeared to be a disk-shaped, nebulous "aircraft," flying smoothly in an orientation parallel to the ground.

I was sufficiently shaken by this to pull out some paper and begin making copious notes. During this operation I glanced out again and this time saw clearly a distant airliner, slightly above the horizon this time, but moving in the same way. There was no question that *this* was an airliner, for in spite of its having the same angular size as the disk, I could clearly see its wings and tail. Just then, the pilot banked to the right, raising the left wing, and suddenly the distant plane became a grey, nebulous disk. It had passed behind the distorting exhaust stream of the jet engine, which was suspended and obscured under the wing. The first disk, or plane, had flown directly behind this stream, whose presence had slipped my mind.

In summary, an investigator of UFOs is in effect asking for all the records of strange things seen, and he must be sober in recognizing the tremendous variety of sources of distortion and misconception. Each case of misconception may involve its own processes of error, but perhaps common to all such cases is an easy tendency to "fix" on an early conception of a percept, by a process that is analogous to that of the "staircase" optical illusion in which one conceives of the staircase as being seen either from "above" or "below." Another example is the common difficulty in looking at aerial photographs. One may conceive of the relief as being seen either "positive" or "negative." Once the conception occurs it is difficult to dispel it. If you see a star at night from an airplane but conceive of it as an object pacing the aircraft at only 300 yd. distance, it is easy to retain this conception. As R. V. Jones (1968) has pointed out (reviewing his wartime intelligence investigative experience in the context of the UFO problem), "witnesses were generally right when they said that *something* had happened at a particular place, although they could be wildly wrong about *what* had happened." (WKH emphasis).

7. Reporting

"Reporting" means the process of transmission of the observation—from the observer to a journalist, Air Force investigator, the police, etc., and from there to the public. Reporting, we have found, is one of the most crucial factors in the UFO problem. My own conclusion has been that one must not form a judgment of any case from the popular literature.

Suppose, for example, that the pilot of my airliner had not banked the plane wing, and I had not learned the explanation of the grey, nebulous, elliptical object. I would have submitted my report, not of a "flying saucer," but of an object I could not identify. Assuming that the story got out, it is highly probable that because of its clear news value ("COLORADO PROJECT INVESTIGATOR SEES DISK"), it would have been publicized before anyone established that the jet exhaust had produced the phenomenon. Such a story, brought to public attention by newspapers and magazines, would stir more pressure on public officials and contribute to the illogical but widespread feeling that where there is so much smoke there must be *some* fire. A later solution would not be so widely publicized.

Ruppelt (1956) discusses another example that occurred in actual fact. The famous Maury Island Hoax, which even today stirs interest, was widely publicized. The story was sensational, in that it involved alleged fragments of a saucer that had been seen to explode. Two Air Force investigators on the case were killed in an accidental plane crash. The case was later clearly identified as a hoax. Ruppelt remarks,

> The majority of writers of saucer lore have played this sighting to the hilt, pointing out as their main premise . . . that the story must be true because the government never openly exposed or prosecuted either of the two hoaxers . . . the government had thought seriously of prosecuting the men, (but) it was decided, after talking to the two men, that the hoax was a harmless joke that had mushroomed. . . . By the time the facts were released they were yesterday's news. And *nothing is deader than yesterday's news*. (WKH emphasis).

Many writers in our culture, from fanatics and hypocrites to sincere reporters, are not, after all, committed to complete investigation and understanding of the subject, but to telling and selling a good story. Unfortunately there is a selection effect: if a "flying saucer" story is investigated *too* completely, and is found to be a misperception or a hoax, its interest and sales value are reduced.

Examples of journalists' distortion and slanting, conscious or unconscious, abound: misinformed amateurs quoted as authorities, repetition of hearsay evidence, and naive selection of data are examples of such dubious reporting. The UFO literature is full of the following sort of ill-advised criticism of non-believers: Edwards (1966) describes a case in which a world famous astronomer and authority on galactic structure, and two colleagues, reported that they had seen a "circular, luminous, orange-colored" light pass overhead too slowly to be a meteor. Noting that on the following day the Air Force, rechecking their files, found that the case was explained by two Vampire jets and a jet trainer on a routine training flight at 20,000 ft., Edwards then concludes with the remark, "If a professional astronomer really were incapable of telling *one* circular object from *three* jet planes at 20,000 feet, how reliable would his work be regarding an object 40 million miles away?" Aside from the facts that the "explanation" was not the astronomer's responsibility and that the latter figure misrepresents the scale of that astronomer's work by a factor of a billion, this concluding statement certainly shed no real light on the UFO problem, but rather creates a state of mind that may aid acceptance of the author's later remarks.

Jones (1968) illustrates well the problem of forming a reliable judgment from diverse reports of individuals on a single phenomenon. During the war, a British and an American physicist had the task of establishing from sailors' reports the German pattern of mine-laying at sea. One of them went on a field trip and discovered that reported ranges and bearings were unreliable; only the question of whether the mine was to the port or starboard was reliably answered. With this discovery, he solved the problem while his counterpart became bogged in a mire of meaningless data. The point is that by actual field interviews one may get some idea of what happened, but under no circumstances, simply because a witness says (or is reported to have said) that he saw a cigar-shaped object, should one assume that a cigar-shaped object was really there.

This well known rule applies in many other fields of investigation. Jones states: "I have made this discursion into some of my war experiences because it is relevant to the flying saucer story in that it illustrates the difficulty of establishing the truth from eyewitness reports, particularly when events have been witnessed under stress. I do not, of course, conclude that eyewitness reports must be discarded; on the contrary, excluding hoaxers and liars, most witnesses have genuinely seen something, although it may be difficult to decide from their descriptions what they really had seen."

There is still another problem: even if reliable reports are prepared, communication among investigators is so poor that the reports may not be read. Scientific journals have rejected careful analyses of UFO cases (apparently in fear of initiating fruitless controversy) in spite of earlier criticism (in the journals' own pages!) that the problem is not discussed in the scientific literature. Even at the most responsible levels, communication is poor. The House Committee on Science and Astronautics, in its 29 July 1968 hearings, received accounts of allegedly mysterious cases that already were among the best-explained of those studied by the Colorado UFO Project.

In order finally to demonstrate the very poor manner in which the UFO problem has been presented in the past, primarily in the popular literature, consider two imaginary accounts that could be written of the Zond IV re-entry, one by a sensationalizing, but perhaps sincere reporter, and one by a more sober investigator. Of course each reporter can back up his story with taped interviews and sketches.

A fantastic cigar-shaped object that entered the earth's atmosphere from space on 3 March 1968 is unidentified. Although some Air Force officials attempted to pass it off as a satellite re-entry, examination of the *official Air Force* papers indicates a reluctance to identify it with any known spacecraft.

The absurdity of the satellite explanation is proved by the reports of the witnesses who got the best look at the object. Witness after witness described the object as cigar-shaped, with a row or rows of windows and a flaming exhaust. Several others mentioned saucer-shaped lights visible as the craft flew overhead. Many observers, who apparently did not get such a good look at the mysterious craft, merely described a strange formation of lights.

There is little doubt that the craft came from space. The probability that it was under powered flight is raised not only by the exhaust but also by several observers who saw it change direction.

This event, witnessed by hundreds, in many states provides one of the best proofs yet that some kind of strange airships have invaded our atmosphere.

Although there was some preliminary uncertainty in Air Force circles as to the nature of the bolide of 3 March 1968, after several days study of the reports it became clear that the event was a satellite re-entry. This was confirmed some months later.

While the re-entry was confirmed by the bulk of the actual observations, it was badly misinterpreted by several excited witnesses, who wrote the longest reports and described the object as cigar-shaped. There was a tendency for some observers to interpret the string of disintegrating meteors as windows in a dark craft. Still others interpreted the yellowish tails of the objects as exhausts. Such misconceptions were widely scattered but in the minority.

Entering the atmosphere, the satellite grew incandescent and began to disintegrate into dozens of pieces, each moving at its own speed because of drag. Autokinesis effects were not uncommon among the ground observers, as the objects appeared as slowly moving light sources in the dark sky.

8. *Reports: The Credible Number of "Flying Saucers"*

Most readers of this report will perhaps be convinced that alien spaceships or some other unknown phenomena can be involved in only a very small percentage of all UFO reports or perhaps in none. Yet there is a curious tendency on the part of many students of the problem to imply that the sheer number of reports somehow proves that there must be some physical reality involved. For example, J. E. McDonald (1968) argues before the House Committee on Science and Astronautics, in a one-paragraph statement on witness credibility: ". . . It seems tedious to enlarge here on those obvious matters. One can be fooled of course; but it would be rash indeed to suggest that the thousands of UFO reports now on record are simply a testimony to confabulation, as will be better argued by some [selected cases]." Jones, who argues against the probability of any substantial number of flying saucers, says: "There have been so many flying saucers seen by now, if we were to believe the accounts, that surely one of them must have broken down or left some trace of its visits. It is true that one can explain the absence of relics by supposing . . . fantastic reliability . . ."

It would seem to me that if one begins by studying both witness reliability and selected cases, and if one thereby realizes that it is quite conceivable and probable for the great bulk of reports to be simple mistakes and fabrications, then arguments invoking the enormous number of reports become irrelevant. We are concerned by only a small "residual" of puzzling reports.

This raises another approach to the UFO "residual" reports. We could attempt to answer the question: what is the maximum frequency of spaceships that could actually have penetrated our airspace and still leave us with such meager evidence as we have for their existence? Obviously if a 30-ft. metal disk hovered over the Capitol for some hours, we would have a multitude of photos, video tapes, and other hard evidence from different observers in different positions.

Some measure of public reaction to spectacular and unfamiliar celestial phenomena can be gained from study of fireball reports. Six spectacular fireballs were studied to this end using analyses by C. P. Olivier of the American Meteor Society (1962, 1963, 1967) and reports in *Sky and Telescope*. Among these, the longest duration was only 31 sec. for the 25 April 1966 object; yet even for an object of such short duration, a number of photographs were made. In other cases, dust trains of duration up to 17 min. were photographed and widely reported. The Zond IV observations are also applicable. These data permit estimates of the frequency of both visual and photographic reports.

The fireballs were brighter than the full moon in most cases. Often they appeared not as point sources, but as a disk about half the size of the moon. Some of them were bright enough to attract the attention of persons indoors; some of them were accompanied by thunder-like explosions. All attracted national publicity. In short, they are remarkable enough to have attracted attention and photographs, and are thus considered comparable to hypothetical, well-observed "flying saucers" in public response.

The analysis must take into account the number of inhabitants in the area of visibility as well as the duration of visibility. We may call the product of the number of inhabitants times the duration, the "exposure" of the phenomenon. We can ask how the total number of actual witnesses is related to the exposure.

For short-period durations (a few minutes) it is reasonable to expect that the number of witnesses (a fraction of the number of inhabitants) would be proportional to the exposure. This can also be assumed about the number of detailed reports recovered by investigators who solicit them, and about the number of photographs. In the fireball and Zond IV cases there are data giving number of witnesses, number of recovered reports, or number of photographs. Thus, if N is the total number of inhabitants, and t is the duration of the event (sec.), we have a first-order theory of the form

$$\text{no. witnesses} = N_w = C_w N t,$$
$$\text{no. recovered reports} = N_r = C_r N t,$$
$$\text{no. recovered photographs} = N_p = C_p N t.$$

It is possible to identify the proportionality constant, C from the reports mentioned above. Derived values are listed in Table 4. The constant 1/C has dimensions man-sec/witness (or /report, /photographer). For example, the Air Force files on Zond IV yield 78 reports for a two-minute phenomenon visible from a region inhabited by an estimated 23,000,000 persons, giving 3.5×10^7 man-sec to generate one report.

It is clear that the number of photographs generated will depend on the duration of the phenomenon in a more complex way than indicated in our simple equation, since with durations longer than some limit, more witnesses will have time to obtain a camera. In this approximate and first-order treatment, this complication is neglected.

Application of Table 4 can be illustrated by the fireball reports. The original data suggest about 500 reports in five years for these very bright objects. We assume that the average fireball is visible roughly 10 sec. These figures allow us to solve the equation (cited above) for the number of inhabitants through whose skies pass fireballs in five years. If it takes 6×10^6 man-sec. to generate one report (Table 4), then the fireballs must have been exposed to about 300,000,000 people. This figure is expected to be accurate to something better than an order of magnitude. That is, every citizen of the United

States evidently has such a fireball in his sky about once every few years (whether or not he is outside and sees it). This is in good accord with known data—Vetter's (1966) estimate of the flux of meteors of magnitude −15 is one every three to four years over an area of the size of the United States.

The question before us is how many of the UFO reports could correspond to real objects in view of the available data. Is a "residual" of even 2% of the cases reasonable? We have three relevant statistics: (1) National Opinion surveys indicate that roughly 5 x 10^6 persons of the total U. S. population believe they have seen UFOs in 20-year interval since they were first reported. If 2% of these represent really strange un-

Table 4

Response to Unusual Aerial Objects*

Fireball Date	Location	$1/C_W$	$1/C_r$	$1/C_p$
17 November 1955	France		6.0 x 10^6	
16 January 1961	California	5.0 x 10^4		
23 April 1962	New Jersey		1.5 x 10^6	6.0 x 10^9
25 March 1963	Maryland		9.1 x 10^5	
9 December 1965	Michigan		5.3 x 10^6	$\leq$ 1.2 x 10^{10}
25 April 1966	New York	3.1 x 10^3	5.4 x 10^6	$\leq$ 4.0 x 10^8
3 March 1968	(Zond IV)		3.5 x 10^7	
Adopted value		10^4	6 x 10^6	5 x 10^9

* These figures are understood to apply only to short-duration sightings, since, obviously, by extending the duration one cannot obtain more witnesses than the number of inhabitants.

knowns, we should have 1 x 10^5 witnesses. (2) There have been roughly 15,000 recovered cases, representing perhaps 45,000 individuals' reports. A 2% residual would give 900 reports of unknowns. (3) The project study suggests that the "residual" photographs of unidentified numbers of the order of 20.

Combining these three statistics with the three constants from Table 4 we derive three independent estimates of the total number of citizens exposed to the "high-strangeness residual UFOs" in the last 20 years; viz., 2 x 10^7; 1 x 10^8; and 2 x 10^9. It can be seen that accuracy is no better than an order of magnitude. However, taking 200,000,000 persons as a representative value, the implications are clear. The results suggest that merely to generate the 2% residual, every person in the country has had an UFO visible above his horizon once in the last 20 years.

Of course, since most man-hours in this country are spent indoors, or asleep, or paying no attention to the sky, it is not surprising that very few people have reported seeing such craft. But taking into account the array of automatic surveillance equipment operating in this country, it *does* border on the incredible that the "hard" evidence should be so scanty. The statistic is similar to the five-year statistic for bright fireballs, and although the "evidence gathered over an arbitrary five-year time span for the existence of bright fireballs" is similar to that gathered over 20 years for "flying saucers" the "fireball evidence" is perhaps more convincing: it includes detection by automatic survey cameras, large numbers of witnesses per incident, and more reliable witnesses. To accept as many as 2% residual cases as examples of extraordinary aircraft, then, is to accept that an UFO could fly around the country in such a way as to be *potentially* visible to, or in the sky of, every citizen for 40 sec. without being positively recorded or conclusively reported.

9. Conclusions

As we have already stated, some students of the UFO problem have used the argument, either directly or by implication, that where there is so much smoke there must be some fire, i.e. that *some* of the UFO reports must involve truly extraordinary phenomena such as alien spaceships or unknown meteorological effects. This chapter is addressed to the question: is it conceivable and defensible that all of the UFO reports could result from mistakes, illusions, unusual conditions, and fabrications?

The answer appears clearly affirmative, although we claim no proof that all reports can be so explained. We have looked at a three-stage process: a *perception* is received of some unusual apparition; a *conception* is created by interpreting the percept and combining it with prior concepts; a *report* is eventually made to an investigator or on some public document. Each step introduces possibilities for error.

The number of phenomena and combinations of phenomena that can produce unusual percepts is so enormous that no investigation can begin with an *a priori* list of explanations and expect to match one to each case. The variety is effectively infinite and it must be realized that in effect the investigator is asking for a report each time an unusual percept is generated. Obviously, this will be frequent.

Our data demonstrates beyond question not only that weird and erroneous concepts are widely formed, but also that these erroneous concepts are often precisely those that show up in the UFO phenomenon. Perhaps as a result of their popularization in the UFO literature, the phenomenon feeds on itself to a certain extent.

Finally, the reporting processes are demonstrably such that very low signal-to-noise ratio is generated. That is, certain social forces conflict with clear, concise, and thorough presentation of UFO reports. Sarcasm is employed at the expense of logic. A whole body of literature exists by virtue of the sensational aspects of the problem.

In conclusion, it appears that the number of truly extraordinary events, i.e. sightings of alien spaceships or totally unknown physical-meteorological phenomena, can be limited to the range 0-2% of all the available reports, with 0 not being excluded as a defensible result.

References

Chant, C. A. "An Extraordinary Meteoric Display," *J. R. A. S. C., 7,* (1913a), 145.

———. "Further Information Regarding the Meteoric Display of Feb. 9, 1913," *J. R. A. S. C., 7,* (1913b), 438.

Davidson, M. "The American Meteor Display of Feb. 9, 1913," *J. R. A. S. C., 7,* (1913), 441.

Edwards, Frank. *Flying Saucers, Serious Business,* New York: Lyle Stuart, 1966.

Gault, D. E., E. D. Heitowit, and H. J. Moore. *The Lunar Surface Layer,* ed. J. W. Salisbury and P. E. Glaser, New York; Academic Press, 1964.

Hall, R. *The UFO Evidence,* Washington, D. C.: NICAP, 1964.

Jones, R. V. "The Natural Philosophy of Flying Saucers," *Phys. Bull.,* (July 1968), 225. (See Appendix V).

King-Hele, D. G., and E. Quinn. "Table of Earth Satellites Launched in 1965," *Planet. Sp. Sci., 14,* (1966), 817.

McDonald, H. E. "Statement on Unidentified Flying Objects," to House Committee on Science and Astronautics, 29 July 1968.

Menzel, D. H. *Flying Saucers,* Cambridge: Harvard Univ. Press, 1953.

Menzel, D. H., and Lyle G. Boyd. *The World of Flying Saucers,* Garden City, N. Y.: Doubleday, 1963.

Minnaert, M. *Light and Colour in the Open Air,* New York: Dover, 1954.

Ruppelt, E. J. *The Report on Unidentified Flying Objects,* Garden City, N. Y.: Doubleday, 1956.

Sullivan, Walter. *New York Times,* 2 July 1968.

Vedder, J. F. "Minor Objects in the Solar System," *Space Sci. Rev., 6,* (1966), 365.

Chapter 3 Psychological Aspects of UFO Reports / Mark W. Rhine

Scientists investigating the phenomena of unidentified flying objects have been faced with an unusual dilemma: in the absence of any "hard data" to evaluate, such as a fragment from an UFO or an actual visitor from outer space, the scientist is confronted with the question of abandoning the entire investigation or of relying on eye-witness reports, a notoriously unreliable source of information. The scientist is most comfortable with data which can be replicated and validated by repeated experiment and which his colleagues can confirm.

One way out of such a dilemma is, of course, to deal only with "hard data" and to reject eye-witness reports, with the rationalization that such reports are liable to distortion, cannot be "proved," or are apt to come from "crackpots." Such an attitude is as harmful to the pursuit of truth as is that which is uncritically willing to accept *any* eye-witness report. An open-minded investigator, honestly endeavoring to understand UFO phenomena, cannot dismiss eye-witness reports, which to date represent the only information he has. Neither can he accept such reports without scrutiny, for there are many possibilities for error and distortion. An initial attitude of "benevolent skepticism," as suggested by Walker (1968) in his excellent article on establishing observer creditability, seems appropriate to the evaluation of eye-witness observations.

Perception is an extraordinarily complex process by which people select, organize, and interpret sensory stimulation into a meaningful picture of the world (Berelson, 1964). Perception is more than just raw sensory data; it compromises the selection and interpretation of this data, and it is just in this evaluation of sensations that distortions are likely to occur which may render one person's perception of an event quite different than his neighbor's. There are three broad sources of error in reporting which are of significance to UFO research: 1) real stimuli which are misidentified (see Section VI, Chapter 1 and 2); 2) unreal stimuli perceived as real; and 3) deliberate falsification.

1. *Errors resulting from misidentification of real stimuli*

Optical illusions and the fact that the mind is apt to "play tricks" are well known. The moon on the horizon appears larger than when it is higher in the sky. A stick in the water seems to be bent. Guilford (1929) showed that a small stationary source of light in a dark room will appear to move about (the autokinetic effect). "Floaters" in the lens of the eye are perceived as "spots" in the air. The following lines look to be of different lengths:

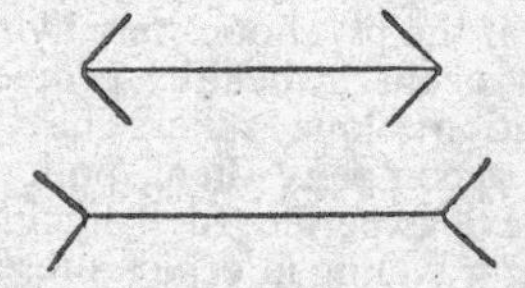

Measuring shows them to be exactly the same length.

These are perceptual distortions which are experienced by everyone. Other distortions may be peculiar to the individual because of his own psychological needs. It is common knowledge that "beauty is in the eye of the beholder." Poor children are more apt to overestimate the size of coins than are rich children (Bruner, 1947). Bruner showed that coins marked with a dollar sign were rated larger in size than equal coins marked with a swastika (Bruner, 1948). The psychological literature is full of reports of similar distortions of size, distance, and time and their relationship to individual emotional characteristics (Erikson, 1968; Forgus, 1966; Vernon, 1962). The concept of *perceptual defense* is used by psychologists to characterize the unconscious tendency of people to omit perceiving what they do not want to perceive (Erikson, 1968). Volunteers were more apt to recognize emotionally neutral words than emotionally laden words when they were briefly flashed on a screen (McGinnies, 1958).

All the above errors in perception occur in "normal" people in everyday situations. Some types of perceptual distortions are known to occur to normal people under extraordinary circumstances. Pilots, under the influence of rapid acceleration, diving, etc. may incur perceptual problems because of physiological changes which must be taken into account in evaluation of their sightings (Clark, 1957). In some delirious or toxic states (for example, resulting from pneumonia, drug ingestion, alcohol withdrawal), the patient will misidentify a stimulus. The example of a patient calling the doctor or nurse by the name of some friend or relative is quite common. Emotionally disturbed persons are more apt to misperceive than are more balanced individuals, but it should be emphasized that numerous distortions can afflict even the most "normal" individual and unwittingly bias his reports.

2. *Errors resulting from perception of unreal stimuli as real*

Such errors may be the result of psychopathology, as with the hallucinations of the psychotic. Unable to distingush his inner productions from outer reality, he reports them as real. Anyone who has awakened abruptly from a dream not knowing where he is or whether or not he has been dreaming will recognize this feeling, which in the psychotic persists in the waking state, as if the psychotic were living in a waking dream. Such states may occur in healthy people under conditions of sensory deprivation: lone sailors have reported imaginary helmsmen who accompany them, poliomyelitis victims living in iron lungs have experienced hallucinations and delusions, often resembling traveling in vehicles resembling the respirator. Pilots may show detachment and confusion, (Clark, 1957) and long-distance truck drivers may develop inattention, disorientation, and hallucinations (McFarland, 1957). Radar operators show serious lapses of attention (Mackworth, 1950). Such possibilities must be considered in evaluating the reports of isolated people. Isolation experiments have shown the development of hallucinations in normal subjects. For an extensive review of this subject, see Ruff (1966). Such errors may also occur in children, in suggestible people, in persons of low intelligence, and in those subject to visions.

3. *Deliberate falsification*

People with serious character pathology may lie for many reasons: fame, notoriety, attention, money. They constitute a problem not only to UFO research but to the courts. An example of this type of person is the man who confesses to a crime which he did not commit.

4. *The crowd effect*

The above examples suggest some of the many sources of distortion in the perceptions of individuals. Put two or more individuals together, and the possibilities for distortion multiply. "Mass hysteria" is a familiar concept. Charles Mackay (1967) wrote a lengthy volume in 1841 entitled *Extraordinary Popular Delusions and the Madness of Crowds* in which he recounted many of the popular follies through the ages. Two incidents are of particular interest to UFO investigators because they show clearly the role of crowd psychology in times of imminent disaster: one is the great London panic of 1524 in which thousands left the city to avoid a great flood which a fortune-teller predicted and which, of course, never occurred; the other concerns an epidemic plague which afflicted Milan in 1630; the populace attributed the disaster to the Devil (the germ theory was still several centuries off), and one individual, brooding over the calamity until "he became firmly convinced that the wild flights of his own fancy were realities," related being swept through the streets in an air-borne chariot, accompanied by the Devil. Mackay notes in his foreword that "the present [volume] may be considered more a miscellany of delusions than a history—a chapter only in the great and awful book of human folly which yet remains to be written, and which Porson once jestingly said he would write in 500 volumes." One wonders if future historians may laugh as readily at our concerns about UFOs as we can about the London panic or the attempts to explain the plague of Milan.

Sharif (1935) demonstrated in a classic experiment the influence people have on one another's perceptions. He had a group of people observe a stationary light (such as Guilford used) in a darkened room. Although stationary, the light appeared to move, and in a different direction to each observer. The members of the group were able to eventually reconcile the initially divergent perceptions, and to agree in what direction the light was "moving." Such ability to check out one's impressions with others and to get feedback is a healthy mechanism and accounts for one of the ways in which we confirm our perceptions. The unavailability of this mechanism may account for some of the misperception that occurs under conditions of sensory deprivation.

Although "feedback" from others is usually a healthy mechanism leading to a correction of misperceptions, under certain conditions it may lead to an exaggeration of faulty perceptions and to "mass hysteria." One of the best known examples in recent times was the "invasion from Mars" in 1938, when Orson Welles' radio broadcast of a science-fiction drama had thousands of listeners from coast-to-coast in a state of panic because they believed the Martians were really invading the earth and that the end of the world was at hand. Cantril's study (1966) of this incident, subtitled *A Study in the Psychology of Panic,* makes fascinating reading. He feels the anxieties of the times, the economic depression, and the imminent threat of war set the stage for the panic. He examines the psychological factors which made some people believe the broadcast to be true, whereas others regarded it as fiction or were able to ascertain what was happening (by checking other stations, phoning the police or newspapers, etc.). The believers seemed to have a "set," preconceived notion that God was going to end the world, that an invasion was imminent, or had some fanciful notions about the possibilities of science. When they heard the broadcast, they immediately accepted it as proving what they had already believed, and tended to disregard any evidence which might disprove their immediate conclusions. Others showed poor judgment in checking out the show, using unreliable sources of confirmation and accepting their statement that the broadcast was real. Others, with no standard of judgment of their own, accepted without question what the radio said. Cantril concludes (p. 138) that this susceptible group is characterized by:

> a certain feeling of personal inadequacy. The individual is unable to rely on his own resources to see him through . . . [he] believes his life and fate are very largely dependent on some focus beyond his control, or on the whim of some supernatural being. All this adds up to an intense feeling of emotional insecurity, one which is likely to be augmented as the situation surrounding the individual appears more and more threatening . . . [he] will be highly susceptible to suggestions when he is face-to-face with a situation that taxes his own meager self-reliance . . . whatever critical ability a person may normally

have, it is ineffective if in any given situation his emotional securities are so great that they overwhelm his good judgment. Such situations are likely to be those where the individual himself or something dear to him are threatened.

Another relevant study in social psychology is *The June Bug: A Study of Hysterical Contagion* (Kerckhoff, 1968). This is an account of a mysterious illness, manifested by nausea and a generalized rash, which afflicted some of the workers in a southern textile mill and was popularly attributed to the bite of an insect. The insect turned out to be non-existent and the symptoms were considered to be "hysterical." Only workers from one division of the factory were afflicted; the authors attributed the epidemic to the frustration and strain of a work situation (peculiar to the division in which the afflicted employees worked) from which there was no socially legitimate way to escape.

The June Bug contains an extensive review of the literature of "hysterical contagion," which is defined as "the dissemination of symptoms among a population in a situation where no manifest basis for the symptoms may be established," and where "a set of experiences or behaviors which are heavily laden with the emotion of fear of a mysterious force are disseminated through a collectivity . . . [it is] inexplicable in terms of the usual standards of mechanical, chemical, or physiological causality." Smelser (1963) is quoted as defining a hysterical belief as one "empowering an ambiguous element in the environment with a generalized power to destroy."

The possibility of hysterical contagion must be kept in mind in the evaluation of some UFO sighting reports.

The psychiatric literature on UFOs should be mentioned briefly. In comparison with the vast popular literature, the psychiatric literature is surprisingly scant. The only extensive work of which this author is aware is a volume by the late Swiss psychoanalyst, C. G. Jung, entitled *Flying Saucers: A Modern Myth of Things Seen in the Skies* (1959). Noting the tendency to welcome news about "saucers" and to suppress skepticism Jung raises the interesting question "why should it be more desirable for saucers to exist than not?" He feels that their appearance since World War II is a reflection of the anxieties of a nuclear age, in which man possesses the capability of actually destroying the world. Saucers may represent man's anxiety that the end of the world is here, or may represent a superhuman source of salvation. Historically, man's anxiety and his quest for salvation have been projected in many legendary and religious forms, but in an era of rapid technological and scientific advance including space flight, it is not surprising to find "scientific" rather than religious imagery. Other authors have mentioned the anxieties of the nuclear age and the personal search for magic as contributing to some of the belief in UFOs (Meerloo, 1968).

5. *Medical and psychological techniques*

It is clear that there are many factors which may influence perceptions and reporting. The investigator must be aware of possible sources of subjective interpretation by witnesses which may complicate the problem of arriving at the truth about UFOs. How can the investigator minimize such subjective error? Walker's recommendations on establishing observer creditability are excellent. He examines in detail the anatomic, physiologic, and psychological factors influencing perception and their many aberrations, and recommends a detailed medical, ophthalmological, and a neurological examination, and in those individuals who show no organic impairment, a full psychiatric interview. The testimony of any observer who shows no significant medical or psychological conditions which might distort perception or interpretation must gain in creditability. I would suggest that, in addition to Walker's detailed recommendations, the use of psychological testing (especially projective tests such as the Rorschach and the Thematic Apperception Test) be used when recommended by the psychiatrist. A psychiatric interview, if made a routine part of the evaluation of observers, should carry no social stigma.

Two adjuncts to the psychiatric evaluation must be mentioned. The polygraph (lie detector) may occasionally be used where deliberate falsification is suspected. The test is useful, but not fool-proof. The use of hypnosis has been reported in at least one of the popular accounts of UFO sightings to establish the "truth" of the observations (Fuller, 1966). Statements made under hypnosis are gradually acquiring greater legal acceptability (Katz, 1967; Bryan, 1962), but the fact remains that neither the evidence adduced from the use of a polygraph nor that obtained by hypnotic techniques can be relied upon as probative. Hypnosis has nothing to contribute to the routine evaluation of the creditability of the eye-witness. While it may occasionally be useful as a source of information, it cannot be used as a way of *proving* that the witness is telling the truth. Sometimes hypnosis can aid in bringing to conscious awareness, material that has been repressed. But persons who cannot distinguish their fantasies from reality will, under hypnosis only reveal more of the same fantasies. Their productions under hypnotic trance will demonstrate only that their reports are "real" to them, even though they may not in fact have any basis in objective reality. Wolberg (1966) states:

> It is essential not to take at face value memories and experiences recounted in the trance. Generally, the productions elabo-

rated by a person during hypnosis are a fusion of real experiences and fantasies. However, the fantasies in themselves are significant, perhaps, even more than the actual happenings with which they are blended. Asking a patient to recall only real events or to verify the material as true or false, reduces but does not remove the element of fantasy.

In addition to the evaluation of individual observers, it would seem wise in future investigations to make use of sociologists and psychologists in those cases where more than one person has made a sighting, to rule out the possibility of hysterical contagion, as well as to contribute to our knowledge of this condition. There should be opportunity to investigate both people who sight UFOs and those who do not.

This chapter raises more questions than it answers. There are many interesting psychological questions: Why have some fervid "believers" in UFOs never seen one? Why do some persons who see an UFO regard it as simply an unidentified aerial phenomenon, while others are sure it is a "space vehicle"? Why do some refuse to accept evidence that what they saw was really an airplane, weather balloon, etc., while others readily accept such explanations? The answers to such questions must await future research. It was not the purpose of the project to explore the psychology of UFO sighters, but rather to explore the nature of the UFOs themselves.

References

Berelson, B. and G. A. Steiner. *Human Behavior,* New York: Harcourt Brace and World, Inc., 1964.

Bruner, J. S. and C. C. Goodman. "Value and Need as Organizing Factors in Perception," *Journ. Abnormal Soc. Psychology,* 42, (1947), 33-44.

Bruner, J. S. and L. Postman. *An Approach to Social Perception,* in *Current Trends in Social Psychology,* ed. Dennis, Pittsburgh: University of Pittsburgh Press, 1948.

Bryan, W. J. *Legal Aspects of Hypnosis,* Springfield, Ill.: Charles C. Thomas, 1962.

Cantril, H. *The Invasion from Mars: A Study in the Psychology of Panic,* New York: Harper Torchbooks, 1966.

Clark, B. and A. Graybiel. "The Breakoff Phenomenon: A Feeling of Separation from the Earth Experienced by Pilots at High Altitude," *Journ. Aviation Medicine,* 28, (1957), 121-126.

Eriksen, C. W. *Perceptual Defense,* in *Psychopathology of Perception,* ed. Paul Hoch and Joseph Zubin, New York: Grune and Stratton, 1968.

Forgus, R. H. *Perception,* New York: McGraw-Hill, 1966.

Fuller, J. G. *The Interrupted Journey,* New York: The Dial Press, 1966.

Guilford, J. P. "Autokinesis and the Streaming Phenomenon," *American Journ. Psychology,* 40, (1929), 401-417.

Jung, C. G. *Flying Saucers: A Modern Myth of Things Seen in the Skies,* New York: Harcourt, Brace and Co., 1959.

Katz, J., J. Goldstein, and A. M. Dershowitz. *Psychoanalysis, Psychiatry and the Law,* New York: The Free Press, 1967.

Kerckhoff, A. C. and K. W. Back. *The June Bug: A Study of Hysterical Contagion,* New York: Appelton-Century-Crofts, 1968.

Mackay, C. *Extraordinary Popular Delusions and The Madness of Crowds,* New York: The Noonday Press, 1967.
Mackworth, N. H. "Researches on the Measurement of Human Performance," *Medical Research Council Special Report Series 268,* London: Her Majesty's Stationery Office, 1950.
McFarland, R. A. and R. D. Moore. "Human Factors in Highway Safety: A Review and Evaluation," *New England Journ. Medicine,* 256, (1957), 792-799.
McGinnies, E. "Emotionality and Perceptual Defense," *Psychol. Review,* 57, (1958), 373-376.
Meerloo, J. A. M. "The Flying Saucer Syndrome and The Need for Miracles," *Journ. Am. Medical Assn.,* 203, (18 March 1968), 170.
Ruff, G. E. *Isolation and Sensory Deprivation,* in *American Handbook of Psychiatry,* Vol. III, ed. Arieti, New York: Basic Books, 1966.
Sherif, M. "A Study of Some Social Factors in Perception," *Arch. Psychology,* 27, (1935), 187.
Smelser, N. J. *Theory of Collective Behavior,* New York: The Free Press, 1963.
Vernon, M. D. *The Psychology of Perception,* London: University of London Press, 1962.
Walker, S. "Establishing Observer Creditability: A Proposed Method," *Journ. Astronautical Sciences 15,* (March-April, 1968), 92-96.
Wolberg, L. R. *Hypnotherapy,* in *American Handbook of Psychiatry,* ed. Arieti, Vol. II, (1966), 1475.

Chapter 4 Optical Mirage / William Viezee

1. Introduction

An optical mirage is a phenomenon associated with the refraction of light in the gaseous (cloud-free) atmosphere. During mirage a visible image of some distant object is made to appear displaced from the true position of the object. The image is produced when the light energy emanating from the distant source travels along a curvilinear instead of a rectilinear path, the curvilinear path, in turn, arises from abnormal spatial variations in density that are invariably associated with abnormal temperature gradients.

The visible image of the mirage can represent shape and color of the "mirrored" object either exactly or distorted. Distortions most commonly consist of an exaggerated elongation, an exaggerated broadening, or a complete or partial inversion of the object shape. Frequently, mirages involve multiple images of a single source. Under special conditions, refractive separation of the color components of white light can enhance the observation of a mirage. Atmospheric scintillation can introduce rapid variations in position, brightness, and color variations of the image.

When both the observer and the source are stationary, a mirage can be observed for several hours. However, when either one or both are in motion, a mirage image may appear for a duration of only seconds or minutes.

Although men have observed mirages since the beginning of recorded history, extensive studies of the phenomenon did not begin till the last part of the 18th century. Since that time, however, a large volume of literature has become available from which emerges a clear picture of the nature of the mirage.

The comprehensive body of information presented here is based on a survey of the literature, and constitutes the state-of-the-art knowledge on optical mirages. The report provides a ready source of up-to-date information that can be applied to problems involving optical mirages.

No claim is made that *all* existing pertinent writings have been collected and read. The contents of many publications, especially of those dating back to the last part of the 18th Century and the beginning of the 19th Century are evaluated from available summaries and historical reviews. Also, when a particular aspect of the mirage phenomenon is considered, the collection of pertinent literature is discontinued at the point where the state-of-the-art knowledge appears clearly defined. The collected volume of literature covers the period 1796 to 1967.

In essence, the literature survey yields the following principal characteristics of the mirage: (1) Mirages are associated with anomalous temperature gradients in the atmosphere. (2) Mirage images are observed almost exclusively at small angles above or below the horizontal plane of view; mirages, therefore, require terrain and meteorological conditions that provide extended horizontal visibility. (3) A mirage can involve the simultaneous occurrence of more than one image of the "mirrored" object; the images can have grossly distorted forms and unusual coloring. (4) Extreme brightening and apparent rapid movement of the mirage image in and near the horizontal plane can result from the effects of focussing and interference of wavefronts in selected areas of the refracting layer.

Only minor shortcomings appear to be evident in present knowledge of mirage phenomena. Ultimately, a unified theory is desirable that can deal with both the macroscopic and microscopic aspects. Currently, the behavior of light refraction on a large scale is represented by means of rays while the finer details are treated with the wave theory. More observations are needed that deal with the microscopic optical effects of the mirage. The finer details that arise mostly from fosussing and interference are not commonly observed. They require close examination of areas that are highly selective in time and place.

2. *Cross Section of Surveyed Literature*

The contents of this report are based on a survey of literature on atmospheric refraction in general and on optical mirages in particular. The survey began with the review of such basic sources of information on atmospheric optics as *Meteorologische Optik,* by Pernter and Exner, *Physics of the Air,* by Humphreys, *The Nature of Light and Colour in the Open Air,* by Minnaert, and *The Compendium of Meteorology.* These sources present historical summaries, and their contents are to a large extent based on literature surveys. Key references mentioned in these sources were examined and a large volume of literature was subsequently collected by following successive reference leads. Pertinent information on atmospheric scintillation was obtained from several sources, in particular from *Optical Scintillation; A Survey of the Literature,* by J. R. Meyer-Arendt. A cross section of the collected literature is listed below. Because of the wide range of aspects covered, the literature is listed in the following categories: (1) papers on optical mirage the contents of which are mostly descriptive, (2) papers that propose theoretical models of atmospheric refraction or optical mirage, (3) papers that compare theory and observation, (4) papers that are concerned with the application of terrestrial light refraction to meteorology, surveying, and hydrography, (5) papers that present average values of terrestrial refraction based on climatology, and (6) papers on atmospheric scintillation. Within each category, publications are arranged chronologically.

In Category 1, descriptive accounts of mirages go back in time to 1796, when Joseph Huddart observed superior mirages near Macao. (Earlier accounts can be found in *Meteorologische Optik.)* Numerous recent observations of abnormal atmospheric refraction can be found in *The Marine Observer.* The two "classical" observations most frequently quoted as having "triggered" a long series of investigations on optical mirage are the observations of Vince and Scoresby. Vince (1798) from a position on the sea shore observed multiple images of ships, some upright and some inverted, above the ocean horizon; Scoresby (1820) observed elevated images of ships and coastal lines while navigating near Greenland. Both observations were carefully documented and results were read before bodies of the Royal Society.

Proposed theories of the mirage (category 2) are basically of three types, that are best represented by the respective works of Tait (1883), Wegener (1918), and Sir C. V. Raman (1959). Tait (in his efforts to explain the observations by Vince and Scoresby) considers a vertically finite refracting layer having a continuous change in refractive index, and formulates the ray paths for a plane-stratified atmosphere. Wegener (motivated by mirage observations made during his stay in Greenland) replaces Tait's finite refraction layer with a "reflecting" surface—*i.e.,* a surface of discontinuity in the refractive index—and formulates the ray paths for a spherically stratified atmosphere. Raman questions the use of geometric optics in the theory of the mirage and shows by means of physical optics that the upper boundary of the refracting layer resembles a caustic surface in the vicinity of which focussing and interference are the major mirage-producing effects. All three theories quite accurately describe various mirage observations.

Comparisons made between observation and theory (category 3) indicate that the two are compatible—*i.e.*, abnormal light-refraction phenomena are associated with anomalous atmospheric-temperature structure. Many investigations (category 4) are concerned with determining the effects of light refraction on optical measurements made in such fields as surveying and hydrography. Corrections for refraction based on average atmospheric conditions have been computed (category 5). Of specific interest to meteorologists are the attempts to develop inversion techniques for obtaining low-level temperature structure from light-refraction measurements (category 4). The temperature profiles that can be obtained do not have the desired resolution and accuracy. During the last decade, literature on atmospheric scintillation has become extensive due to its importance to astronomy, optical communication, and optical ranging. A selected number of recent papers are presented in category 6.

The publications categorized below represent a cross section of the various endeavors that have resulted from the Earth's atmosphere having light-refraction properties. The body of information is fundamental to the contents of this report. In addition to the listed literature, many other sources of information on atmospheric optics were consulted in its production. They are referenced throughout the text, and are compiled in a bibliography at the end of the report.

Category 1 (Descriptive Accounts)

1. Huddart, Joseph, "Observations on Horizontal Refractions Which Affect the Appearance of Terrestrial Objects, and the Dip, or Depression of the Horizon of the Sea," *Phil. Trans.* Vol. 87, pp. 29-42 (1797).
2. Vince, S., "Observations on an Unusual Horizontal Refraction of the Air; with Remarks on the Variations to Which the Lower Parts of the Atmosphere are Sometimes Subject," London *Phil. Trans.,* Part 1, pp. 436-441 (1799).
3. Wollaston, William Hyde, "On Double Images Caused by Atmospheric Refraction," *Phil. Trans.,* Vol. 90, pp. 239-254 (1800).
4. Scoresby, William, "Description of Some Remarkable Atmospheric Reflections and Refractions, Observed in

the Greenland Sea," *Trans. Roy. Soc. Edinburgh,* Vol. 9, pp. 299-305 (1823).
5. Parnell, John, "On a Mirage in the English Channel," *Phil. Mag.,* Vol. 37, pp. 400-401 (1869).
6. Forel, F. A., "The Fata Morgana," *Proc. Roy. Soc. Edinburgh,* Vol. 32, pp. 175-182 (1911).
7. Hillers, Wilhelm, "Photographische Aufnahmen einer mehrfachen Luftspiegelung," *Physik. Zeitschr.,* Vol. 14, pp. 718-719 (1913).
8. Hillers, Wilhelm, "Einige experimentelle Beiträge Zum Phänomen der dreifachen Luftspiegelung nach Vince," *Physikalische Zeitschrift,* Vol. 15, p. 304 (1914).
9. Visser, S. W. and J. Th. Verstelle, "Groene Straal en Kimduiking," *Hemel en Dampkring,* Vol. 32, No. 3, pp. 81-87 (March 1934).
10. Meyer, Rudolf, "Der grüne Strahl," *Meteorologische Zeitschrift,* Vol. 56, pp. 342-346 (September 1939).
11. Science Service, "Mirage in Desert May Explain How Israelites Crossed Red Sea Unharmed," *Bull. Am. Met. Soc.,* Vol. 28, p. 186 (1947).
12. Ives, Ronald L., "Meteorological Conditions Accompanying Mirages in the Salt Lake Desert," *J. Franklin Institute,* Vol. 245, No. 6, pp. 457-473 (June 1948).
13. St. Amand, Pierre and Harold Cronin, "Atmospheric Refraction at College, Alaska, During the Winter 1947-1948," *Trans. Am. Geophys. Un.,* Vol. 31, No. 2, Part 1, (April 1950).
14. Ten Kate, H., "Luftspiegelungen," *Hemel en Dampkring,* Vol. 49, No. 5, pp. 91-94 (1951).
15. Ewan, D., "Abnormal Refraction of Coast of Portugal," *The Marine Observer,* Vol. 21, No. 152, p. 80 (April 1951).
16. Mitchell, G. E., "Mirage in Gulf of Cadiz," *The Marine Observer,* Vol. 21, No. 152, p. 81 (April 1951).
17. Illingsworth, J., "Abnormal Refraction in the Gulf of St. Lawrence," *The Marine Observer,* Vol. 22, No. 156, pp. 63-64 (April 1952).
18. Markgraf, H., "Fata Morgana an der Norseeküste," *Wetterlotse,* Vol. 47, pp. 200-204 (November 1952).
19. Ten Kate, H., "Fata Morgana." *Hemel en Dampkring,* Vol. 50, No. 2, pp. 32-34 (1952).
20. Heybrock, W., "Luftspiegelungen in Marokko," *Meteorologische Rundschau,* Vol. 6, No. 1/2, pp. 24-25 (January/February 1953).
21. Ruck, F. W. M., "Mirages at London Airport," *Weather,* Vol. 8, No. 1, pp. 31-32 (January 1953).
22. Ainsworth, P. P., "Abnormal Refraction in Cabot Strait, Gulf of St. Lawrence," *The Marine Observer,* Vol. 23, No. 160, pp. 77-78 (April 1953).
23. Kebblewhite, Alexander W. and W. J. Gibbs, "Unusual Phenomenon Observed from East Sale," *Australian Meteorol. Mag.,* Melbourne, No. 4, pp. 32-34 (August 1953).
24. Menzel, Donald H., "Lenses of Air," Chapter 16 of

Flying Saucers (Harvard Univ. Press, Cambridge, Mass., 1953).

25. Nelson, Robert T., "Mirages and Chlorophyl," *Better Farming,* (Summer 1953).
26. Richard, R., "Phénomène Optique Remarquable," *La Meteorologie,* 4th Ser., No. 32, pp. 301-302 (October/December 1953).
27. Vassy, E., "Quelques Remarques sur un Phénomène de Mirage du Disque Solaire," *La Meteorologie,* 4th Ser. No. 32, pp. 302-303 (October/December 1953).
28. Williams, A. E., "Abnormal Refraction in North Atlantic Ocean," *The Marine Observer,* No. 166, pp. 208-210 (October 1954).
29. Jezek, __________ and Milan Koldovsky, "Totalni reflexe na inversnich vrstvach pozorovana s Milesovsky dne 18, listopadu 1953," *Meteorologicke Zpravy* (Prague), Vol. 7, No. 1, pp. 11-12 (February 1954).
30. Baines, J. P. E., "Abnormal Refraction off Cape Town," *The Marine Observer,* Vol. 25, No. 167, pp. 31-34 (January 1955).
31. Ashmore, S. E., "A North Wales Road Mirage," *Weather,* Vol. 10, pp. 336-342 (1955).
32. Ballantyne, J., "Abnormal Refraction in North Atlantic Ocean," *The Marine Observer,* Vol. 26, No. 172, pp. 82-84 (April 1956).
33. Durst, C. S. and G. A. Bull, "An Unusual Refraction Phenomenon seen from a High-Flying Aircraft," *Meteorological Magazine,* Vol. 85, No. 1010, pp. 237-242 (August 1956).
34. Collin, P., "Abnormal Refraction in Gulf of Aden," *The Marine Observer,* Vol. 26, No. 174, pp. 201-202 (October 1956).
35. Baker, R. E., "Abnormal Refraction in Red Sea," *The Marine Observer,* Vol. 27, No. 175, pp. 12-15 (January 1957).
36. Gabler, Horst, "Beobachtung einer Luftspiegelung nach oben," *Zeitschrift für Meteorologie* (Berlin), Vol. 12, No. 7, pp. 219-221 (1958).
37. Ives, Ronald L., "An Early Report of Abnormal Refraction over the Gulf of California," *Bull. Am. Meteorol. Soc.,* Vol. 40, No. 4 (April 1959).
38. Rossman, Fritz O., "Banded Reflections from the Sea," *Weather* (London), Vol. 15, No. 12, pp. 409-414 (December 1960).
39. Gordon, James H., "Mirages," Report, Publication 4398, Smithsonian Institution, Washington, D.C., pp. 327-346, 1959 (Pub. 1960).
40. O'Connell, D. J. K., "The Green Flash and Kindred Phenomena," *Endeavor* (July 1961).
41. Zamorskiy, A. D., "Optical Phenomena in the Atmosphere," *Priroda* (Nature), Moscow, No. 8, pp. 62-66 (Translation), (1963).
42. Ives, Ronald L., "The Mirages of La Encantada," *Weather,* Vol. 23, No. 2 (February 1968).

Category 2 (Proposed Theories)

1. Tait, Professor P. G., "On Mirage," *Trans. Roy. Soc. Edinburgh,* Vol. XXX (1883).
2. Förster, Gustav, "Beitrag zur Theorie der Seiten-refraction," *Gerlands Beitrage sur Geophysik,* Vol. 11, pp. 414-469 (1911).
3. Hillers, Wilhelm, "Bemerkung über die Abhängigkeit der dreifachen Luftspiegelung nach Vince von der Temperaturverteilung," *Physikalische Zeitschr.,* Vol. 14, pp. 719-723 (1913).
4. Hillers, Wilhelm, "Ueber eine leicht Beobachtbare Luftspiegelung bei Hamburg und die Erklärung solcher Erscheinungen," *Unterrichtsblätter für Mathematik und Naturwissenschaften,* Vol. 19, No. 2, pp. 21-38 (1913).
5. Hillers, Wilhelm, "Nachtrag zu einer Bemerkung über die Abhängigkeit der dreifachen Luftspiegelung nach Vince von der Temperaturverteilung," *Physik. Zeitschr,* Vol. 15, pp. 303-304 (1914).
6. Nolke, Fr., "Zur Theorie der Luftspiegelungen," *Physik, Zeitschr.,* Vol. 18, pp. 134-144 (1917).
7. Wegener, Alfred, "Elementare Theorie der Atmosphärischen Spiegelungen," *Annalen der Physik,* Vol. 57, No. 4 pp. 203-230 (1918).
8. Wurschmidt, Joseph, "Elementare Theorie der Terrestrischen Refraction und der Atmosphärischen Spiegelungen," *Annalen der Physik,* Vol. 60, pp. 149-180 (1919).
9. Hidaka, Koji, "On a Theory of Sinkiro or Japanese Fata Morgana," *Geophys. Mag.,* Vol. 4, pp. 375-386 (1931).
10. Meyer, Rudolf, "Die Entstehung Optischer Bilder durch Brechung und Spiegelung in der Atmosphäre," *Meteorologische Zeitschrift,* Vol. 52, pp. 405-408 (November 1935).
11. Schiele, Wolf-Egbert, "Zur Theorie der Luftspiegelungen," Spezialarbeiten aus dem Geophysikalischen Institut und Observatorium, Leipzig Universitat Veroffentlichungen Zweite Serie, Band VII, Heft 3 (1935).
12. Brocks, Karl, "Die terrestrische Refraction in polytropen Atmosphären," *Deutsche Hydrographische Zeitschrift,* Vol. 2, No. 5, pp. 199-211 (1949).
13. Haug, Odd, "On the Theory of Superior Mirage," Norway Meteorologiske Institutt, *Meteorologiske Annaler,* Vol. 3, No. 12 (1953).
14. Ozorai, Zoltan, "Mirages on Wave Surfaces," *Idö jaras,* 58 (3):143-153 (May/June 1954).
15. Raman, Sir C. V. and S. Pancharatnam, "The Optics of Mirages," *Proc. Indian Acad. Sci.,* pp. 251-261 (May 1959).
16. Raman, Sir C. V., "The Optics of Mirages," *Current Science,* Vol. 29, No. 8 (August 1959).
17. Baldini, Angel A., "Formulas for computing Atmospheric Refraction for Objects Inside and Outside the Atmosphere," Research Note No. 8, Task 8T35-12-001-01, U. S. Army Engineer, Geodesy, Intelligence and

Mapping Research and Development Agency (9 January 1963).

18. Kàbelač, Josef, "Atmosphärenmodelle and astronomische sowie parallaktische Refraction," *Studia Geophysica et Geodaetica,* Vol. 11, No. 1, pp. 1-20 (1967).

Category 3 (Theory and Observation)

1. Fujiwhara, S., T. Oomari and K. Taguti, "Sinkiro or the Japanese Fata Morgana," *Geophys. Mag.,* Vol. 4, pp. 317-374 (1931).
2. Futi, H., "On Road Mirage," *Geophys. Mag.,* Vol. 4, pp. 387-396 (1931).
3. Wegener, K., "Bemerkungen zur Refraction," *Gerlands Beiträge zur Geophysik,* Vol. 47, pp. 400-408 (1936).
4. Kohl, G., "Erklärung einer Luftspiegelung nach oben aus Radiosondierungen," *Zeitschrift für Meteorologie,* Vol. 6, No. 11, pp. 344-348 (November 1952).
5. Nakano, T., "Mirage in the Toyama Bay," *J. Meteorol. Res.* (Tokyo), Vol. 6, No. 1/3, pp. 67-70 (March 1954).
6. Hasse, Lutz, "Über den Zusammenhang der Kimtiefe mit meteorologischen Grössen," *Deutsche Hydrograph Zeitschrift* (Hamburg), Vol. 13, No. 4, pp. 181-197 (August 1960).
7. Trautman, Ernst, "Über Luftspiegelungen der Alpen, gesehen vom Bayerischen Wale," *Mitteilungen des Deutschen Wetterdienstes,* Vol. 3, No. 21 (1960).
8. Cameron, W. S., John H. Glenn, Scott M. Carpenter, and John A. O'Keefe, "Effect of Refraction on the Setting Sun as Seen from Space in Theory and Observation," *The Astronomical J.,* Vol. 68, No. 5 (June 1963).

Category 4 (Application to Meteorology, Surveying, and Hydrography)

1. Maurer, Von J., "Beobachtungen über die irdische Strahlenbrechung bei typischen Formen der Luftdruckverteilung," *Meteorologische Zeitschrift,* pp. 49-63 (February 1905).
2. Johnson, N. K. and O. F. T. Roberts, "The Measurement of Lapse Rate of Temperature by an Optical Method," *Quart. J. Roy. Meteorol. Soc.,* Vol. 51, pp. 131-138 (1925).
3. Brunt, D., "The Index of Refraction of Damp Air and Optical Determination of the Lapse Rate," *Quart. J. Roy. Meteorol. Soc.,* Vol. 55, pp. 335-339 (1929).
4. Brocks, Karl, "Eine Methode zur Beobachtung des vertikalen Dichte und Temperaturegefalles in den bodenfernen Atmosphärenschichten," *Meteorologische Zeitschrift,* Vol. 57, pp. 19-26 (1940).
5. Fleagle, Robert G., "The optical Measurement of Lapse Rate," *Bull. Am. Meteorol. Soc.,* Vol. 31, No. 2 (February 1950).
6. Freiesleben, H. C., "Die strahlenbrechung in geringer Höhe über Wasseroberflächen," *Deutsche Hydrograph-*

ische Zeitschrift (Hamburg), Vol. 4, No. 1-2, pp. 29-44 (1951).
7. Freiesleben, H. C., "Refraction Occurring Immediately above the Water Surface," *International Hydrographic Review,* Vol. 28, No. 2, pp. 102-106 (1951).
8. Brocks, Karl, "Eine räumlich integrierende optische Methode für die Messung vertikaler Temperatur-und Wasserdampf gradienten in der untersten Atmosphäre," *Archiv für Meteorologie, Geophysik und Bioklimatologie,* Vol. 6, pp. 370-402 (1953).
9. Bourgoin, Jean-Paul, "La refraction terrestre dans les basses couches de l'atmosphère sur l'inlandsis Groenlandais," *Annales de Geophysique,* Vol. 10, No. 168-174 (April/June 1954).
10. Yates, H. W., "Atmospheric Refraction over Water," Report 4786, Naval Research Laboratory, Washington, D.C. (July 1956).
11. Hradilek, Ludvik, "Untersuchung der Abhängigkeit der Lichtbrechung von den Meteorologischen Bedingungen auf dem Beobachtungstandpunkt," *Studia Geoph. et Geod.,* Vol. 5, pp. 302-311 (1961).
12. Sparkman, James K., Jr., "Preliminary Report on an Optical Method for Low-Level Lapse Rate Determination" in "Studies of the Three Dimensional Structure of the Planetary Boundary Layer," Contract Report, Univ. of Wisconsin, Dept. Meteorology, 232 pp; see pp. 69-79 (1962).

Category 5 (Average Values of Terrestrial Refraction)

1. Link, Frantisek and Zdenêk Sekera, "Dioptric Tables of the Earth's Atmosphere," *Publications of the Prague Observatory,* No. 14 (Prometheus Press, Prague, 1940).
2. Brocks, K., "Die terrestrische Refraction," *Annalen der Meteorologie,* Vol. 1, pp. 329-336 (1948).
3. Brocks, K., "Die Lichtstrahlkrümmung in den unteren 500 m der Atmosphäre," *Annalen der Meteorologie,* Vol. 5, pp. 47-57 (1952).
4. Brocks, Karl, "Die Lichtstrahlkrümmung in Bodennahe," *Deutsche Hydrographische Zeitschrift* (Hamburg), Vol. 13, No. 4, pp. 181-197 (August 1960).
5. Saunders, M. J., "Refraction Angles for Luminous Sources Within the Atmosphere," *AIAA J.,* Vol. 1, No. 3, pp. 690-693 (March 1963).

Category 6 (Optical Scintillation)

1. Ellison, M. A., "Why Do Stars Twinkle?" *J. Roy. Astron. Soc. Canada,* Vol. 46, No. 5, pp. 191-194 (September/October 1952).
2. "Transaction of the Conference of the Research on the Twinkling of Stars," English Translation, prepared by Translation Services Branch Foreign Technology Division, WP-AFB, Ohio.
3. Portman, Donald J., E. Ryznar, and F. C. Elder, "Visual Resolution and Optical Scintillation over Snow, Ice, and

Frozen Ground," Research Report III, Part II, U.S. Army Materiel Command, Cold Regions Research & Engineering Laboratory, Hanover, N.H. (October 1965).
4. Carlon, Hugh R., "The Apparent Dependence of Terrestrial Scintillation Intensity upon Atmospheric Humidity," Technical Report CRDLR 3324, U.S. Army Edgewood Arsenal, Chemical Research Development Laboratories, Edgewood Arsenal, Maryland 21010 (November 1965).
5. Hudson, Craig, C., "Experimental Evidence of a Twinkling Layer in the Earth's Atmosphere," *Nature,* Vol. 207, No. 4994 (July 17, 1965).
6. Meyer-Arendt, Jurgen R., and Constantinos B. Emmanuel, "Optical Scintillation; A Survey of the Literature," Technical Note 225, National Bureau of Standards, U.S. Dept. of Commerce (April 1965).
7. Kucherov, N. I., ed., "Optical Instability of the Earth's Atmosphere," Translated from Russian, Israel Program for Scientific Translations, Jerusalem (1966).
8. "Optical Effects of Atmospheric Turbulence," Compilation of the Results of Research Performed at the Electro-Optical Laboratory, Autonetics Division, North American Aviation, Inc. (March 1967).

3. *Basic Physical Concepts and Atmospheric Variables Involved in Light Refraction*

A. General

In a vacuum or in a medium of constant density, the energy from a light-emitting source travels along a straight line. Consequently, a distant observer sees the light source at its exact location. In a medium of variable density, such as the earth's atmosphere, the direction of enegry propagation is deflected from a straight line; i.e., refracted. Refraction causes an observer to see a distant light source at an apparent position that differs from the true position by an angular distance the magnitude of which depends on the degree of refraction, i.e. on the degree of density variation between the observer and the light source. Changes in the direction of energy propagation arise principally from changes in the speed of energy propagation. The latter is directly related to density.

A clear picture of what causes refraction is obtained by means of Huygen's principle which states that each point on a wavefront may be regarded as the source or center of "secondary waves" or "secondary disturbances." At a given instant, the wavefront is the envelope of the centers of the secondary disturbances. In the case of a travelling wavefront the center of each secondary disturbance propagates in a direction perpendicular to the wavefront. When the velocity of propagation varies along the wavefront the disturbances travel different distances so that the orientation of their enveloping surface changes in time, i.e., the direction of propagation of the wavefront changes.

Practically all large-scale effects of atmospheric refraction can be explained by the use of geometrical optics, which is the method of tracing light rays —i.e., of following directions of energy flow. The laws that form the basis of geometrical optics are the law of reflection (formulated by Fresnel) and the law of refraction (formulated by Snell). When a ray of light strikes a sharp boundary that separates two transparent media in which the velocity of light is appreciably different, such as a glass plate or a water surface, the light ray is in general divided into a reflected and a refracted part. Such surfaces of discontinuity in light velocity do not exist in the cloud-free atmosphere. Instead changes in the speed of energy propagation are continous and are large only over layers that are thick compared to the optical wavelengths. It has been shown (J. Wallot, 1919) that, in this case, the reflected part of the incident radiation is negligible so that all the energy is contained in the refracted part. Since in the lower atmosphere, where mirages are most common, absorption of optical radiation in a layer of the thickness of one wavelength is negligible, Snell's law of refraction forms the basis of practically all investigations of large-scale optical phenomena that are due to atmospheric refraction (Paul S. Epstein, 1930).

B. Optical Refractive-Index of the Atmosphere

The optical refractive index *(n)* is defined as the ratio of the velocity *(v)* at which monochromatic (single wavelength) light is propagated in a homogeneous, isotropic, non-conductive medium, to the velocity (*c*) of light in free space, i.e., $n = c/v$. In free space, i.e., outside the earth's atmosphere, $n=1$. Thus, in the case of a monochromatic light signal travelling through a given medium, $c/v > 1$. In case the light signal is not monochromatic and the velocities *(v)* of the component waves vary with wavelength (λ), the energy of the signal is propagated with a group velocity u where $u = v - \lambda(dv/d\lambda)$. The group refractive index is given by $c/u = n - \lambda(dn/d\lambda)$ (Jenkins and White, 1957). In the visible region of the electromagnetic spectrum the dispersion, $dn/d\lambda$ is very small (see Table 1) and a group index is nearly equal to the index at the mean wavelength.

For a gas, the refractive index is proportional to the density ρ of the gas. This can be expressed by the Gladstone-Dale relation:

$$n - 1 = k\rho \equiv k\frac{P}{RT} \qquad (1)$$

Table 1

DEPENDENCE OF OPTICAL REFRACTIVE-INDEX ON ATMOSPHERIC PRESSURE, TEMPERATURE AND WAVELENGTH

(a) Pressure Dependence

Conditions: 5455 A, 15°C	
P, mb	n
1,000	1.000274
950	1.000260
900	1.000246

(b) Temperature Dependence

Conditions: 5455 A, 1013.3 mb	
T, °C	n
0	1.000292
15	1.000277
30	1.000263

(c) Wavelength Dependence

Conditions: 1013.3 mb, 15°C	
λ, A	n
4,000	1.000282
5,000	1.000278
6,000	1.000276
7,000	1.000275
8,000	1.000275

where k is a wavelength-dependent constant, P and T are the pressure and temperature, and R is the gas constant. The refractive index of a mixture of gases, such as the earth's atmosphere, is generally assumed to obey the additive rule, that is, the total value of $n - 1$ is equal to the sum of the contributions from the constituent gases weighted by their partial pressures. When the atmosphere is considered as a mixture of dry air and water vapor,

$$(n - 1)P = (P - e)(n_d - 1) + e(n_v - 1)$$

or

$$n = n_d - \frac{e}{P}(n_d - n_v)$$

where P denotes the total pressure of the mixture, e the partial water vapor pressure and the subscripts d and v refer to dry air and water vapor, respectively. Using Eq. (1), the refractive index n of the moist air at any temperature T and pressure P can be written

$$n - 1 = \frac{PT_o}{TP_o}\left\{n_d - 1 - \frac{e}{P}(n_d - n_v)\right\}$$

where n_d and n_v are the refractive indices at P_o and T_o. For $\lambda = 5455$A° (about the center of the visible spectrum), at $P_o = 1013.3$ mb (760 mm Hg) and $T_o = 273$°K, $n_d = 1.000292$ and $n_v = 1.000257$, so that

$$n - 1 = (78.7 \times 10^{-6})\frac{P}{T}\left(1 - 0.12\frac{e}{P}\right)$$

For $P = 1013.3$ mb, maximum values of e/P (air saturated with water vapor) for a range of tropospheric temperatures are as follows:

T(°K)	273	283	288	293	298	303
e/P	0.006	0.012	0.017	0.023	0.031	0.042

It is evident that in problems related to terrestrial light refraction the effects of humidity on the atmospheric refractive index are negligible. It is of interest to compare the formula for the optical refractive-index with that for radio waves in the centimeter range. The latter can be written

$$(n - 1) = (77.6 \times 10^{-6})\frac{P}{T}\left(1 + \frac{4810}{T}\frac{e}{P}\right)$$

The formula for the optical refractive index can be written

$$n - 1 = k \frac{P}{R_d T}$$

where R_d = gas constant for dry air. By introducing k as a function of wavelength (Johnson, 1954), a final expression for the optical refractive-index in the atmosphere can be written as.

$$n - 1 = A + \frac{B}{\sigma_{o_1}^2 - \sigma^2} + \frac{C}{\sigma_{o_2}^2 - \sigma^2}. \qquad (2)$$

where the σ_{02} are resonance lines and σ is the wavenumber in inverse microns (i.e. $1/\lambda$). The latest equation is (Edlén, 1966):

$$(n_a - 1) \times 10^6 = (77.49_7) \pm 0.01_3) \frac{P_a}{T} Z_a^{-1} \left[0.30600_7 + \frac{88.2581}{130 - \sigma^2} + \frac{0.5868}{38.9 - \sigma^2} \right]$$

where n_a is the refractive index of dry air containing 0.03% CO_2, P_a is the partial pressure of dry air, and Z_a^{-1} is the inverse compressibility factor for dry air (Owens, 1967). Z_a^{-1} is very close to unity: for P_a = 1013.25 mb, T = 288.16°K (15°C), $Z_a^{-1} - 1 = 4.15 \times 10^{-4}$. The standard value of Z_a^{-1} is assumed, i.e., the constant is

$$77.49_7 \times 1.1000415 \simeq 77.5_3.$$

Table 1 gives the range of n for various ranges of atmospheric pressure, temperature, and wavelength. The listed values are of sufficient accuracy for a discussion of optical mirage. For a more recent version of Eq. (2) and differences in n smaller than 10^{-6} reference is made to the detailed work by Owens (1967).

Table 1 shows that the optical refractive index of the atmosphere is a relatively small quantity and that its largest variations with temperature, pressure and wavelength are of the order of 10^{-5}. Such small changes in the refractive index correspond to relatively small changes in the direction of optical-energy propagation. Hence, an optical image that arises from atmospheric light refraction cannot be expected to have a large angular displacement from the light source.

C. Snell's Law of Refraction

Snell's law, formulated for the refraction at a boundary, may be stated as follows: the refracted ray lies in the plane of incidence, and the ratio of the sine of the angle of incidence to the sine of the angle of refraction is constant. The constant is equal to the ratio of the indices of refraction of the two media separated by the boundary. Thus, Snell's law of refraction requires that:

$$\frac{\sin\phi}{\sin\phi'} = \frac{n'}{n}$$

Where Φ and Φ' are the angles of incidence and refraction respectively in the first and second medium, while n and n' are the corresponding values of the refractive index (see Fig. 1).

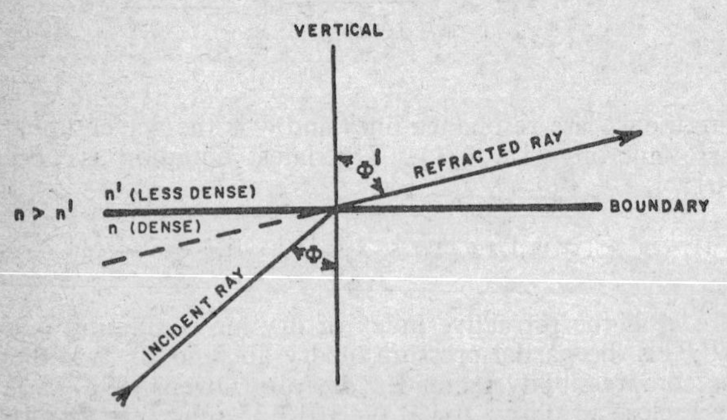

Fig. 1 Snells Law of Refraction

The angle of refraction (Φ') is always larger than the angle of incidence (Φ) when $n > n'$, and the direction of energy propagation is from dense-to-rare. The critical angle of incidence (Φ_c) beyond which no refracted light is possible can be found from Snell's law by substituting $\Phi' = 90°$. Thus,

$$\sin\phi_c = \frac{n'}{n}$$

For all angles of incidence $>\Phi_c$ the incident energy is *totally reflected,* and the angle of reflection equals the angle of incidence (Goos and Haenchen, 1947).

Mirages arise under atmospheric conditions that involve "total reflection." Under such conditions the direction of energy propagation is from dense-to-rare, and the angle of incidence exceeds the critical angle such that the energy is not transmitted through the refracting layer but is "mirrored." The concept of total reflection is most rigorously applied by Wegener in his theoretical model of atmospheric refraction (Wegener, 1918).

Snell's law can be put into a form that enables the construction of a light ray in a horizontal layer wherein the refractive index changes continuously. Introducing a nondimensional rectangular Φ,z coordinate system with the x-axis in the horizontal, $\tan \Phi = dx/dz$, where Φ denotes the angle between the vertical axis and the direction of energy propagation in the plane of the coordinate system. Snell's law can now be applied by writing.

$$\tan \phi = \frac{\sin \phi}{\cos \phi} = \frac{\sin \phi}{\sqrt{1-\sin^2\phi}} = \frac{dx}{dz}$$

and

$$\sin \phi = \frac{n_0 \sin \phi_0}{n}$$

where n_o and Φ_o are initial values. Substitution gives

$$\frac{dx}{dz} = \frac{n_0 \sin \phi_0/n}{\sqrt{1 - \frac{n_0^2 \sin^2 \phi_0}{n^2}}} = \frac{n_0 \sin\phi_0}{\sqrt{n^2 - n_0^2 \sin^2 \phi_0}} \qquad (3)$$

When the refractive index n is expressed as a continuous function of x and z, the solution to the differential equation (3) gives a curve in the x, z plane that represents the light ray emanating to the point (n_o,Φ_o). For example, when n^2 decreases linearly with z according to $n^2 = n^2_o - z$. Eq. (3) can be integrated in the form

$$x = \int \frac{n_0 \sin \phi_0}{\sqrt{n_0^2 \cos^2 \phi_0 - z}} dz$$

For an initial refractive index n_o and an initial direction of energy flow Θ_o, integration between 0 and z gives.

$$x = n_0^2 \sin 2\theta_0 - 2n_0 \sin \theta_0 \sqrt{n_0^2 \cos^2 \theta_0 - z}$$

This equation represents a parabola. Hence, for a medium in which n changes with z in the above prescribed fashion, the rays emanating from a given light source are a family of parabolas.

When the ordinate of the nondimensional coordinate system is to represent height, z must represent a quantity az', where z' has units of height and a is the scale factor.

By introducing more complicated refractive-index profiles

into Eq. (3), the paths of the refracted rays from an extended light source can be obtained and mirage images can be constructed. Tait and other investigators have successfully used this method to explain various mirage observations.

Application of Eq. (3) is restricted to light refraction in a planestratified atmosphere and to refractive-index profiles that permit its integration.

D. Partial Reflections from Atmospheric Layers

The theory of ray tracing or geometrical optics does not indicate the existence of partial reflections, which occur wherever there is an abrupt change in the direction of propagation of a wavefront. An approximate solution to the wave equation may be obtained for the reflection coefficient applicable to a thin atmospheric layer (Wait, 1962):

$$R \cong \left| \frac{\sec^2 \phi}{2} \int_{Z_1}^{Z_2} \left[\frac{dn}{dz}\right] e^{-2ik_0 \cos\phi Z} \, dz \right|$$

where R is the power reflection coefficient, Φ the angle of incidence, Z is height through a layer bounded by Z_1 and Z_2, and K_0 is the vacuum wavenumber $K_0 = 2\pi/\lambda$. The equation is generally valid only when the value of R is quite small, say $R < 10^{-4}$.

This result can be applied to atmospheric layers of known thickness and refractive index distribution; the most convenient model is that in which dn/dz = const. for $Z_1 \leqq Z \leqq Z_2$ and dn/dz = 0 everywhere else. Although some authors have argued that the reflection coefficient using this model depends critically upon the discontinuity in du/dz at the layer boundaries, it can be shown using continuous analytic models that the results will be the same for any functional dependence so long as the transition from dn/dz = 0 to dn/dz = const. occurs over a space that is not large compared to the effective wavelength. The effective wavelength is defined as $\lambda \sec\Phi$. For the simple linear model, R is given by

$$R \cong \left[\frac{\Delta n}{2} \sec^2\phi \, \frac{\sin\alpha}{\alpha}\right]^2$$

where $\alpha = K_0 \cos\Phi h$, Δn is the total change in n through the layer, and h is the thickness of the layer, $h = Z_2 - Z_1$. For large values of h/λ, and hence large values of α, the term $\sin \alpha/\alpha$ may be approximated as $1/\alpha$ for maxima of $(\sin \alpha)$. Since h/λ is always large for optical wavelengths, e.g. $h/\lambda \cong 2 \times 10^4$ for a layer 1 cm thick, the power reflection coefficient may be approximated by

$$R \cong \left[\frac{\Delta n}{4\pi}\left(\frac{\lambda_0}{h}\right)\right]^2 \sec^6\phi$$

Atmospheric layers with $\Delta n \cong 3.0 \times 10^{-6}$ and h = 1 cm are known to exist in the surface boundary layer, e.g. producing inferior mirage. For visible light with a "center wavelength" of 5.6×10^{-5} cm (0.56μ), λ_0/h is thus 5.6×10^{-5}. R then becomes

$$R \cong 1.6 \times 10^{-20} \sec^6 \phi.$$

This is a very small reflection coefficient, and light from even the brightest sources reflected at normal incidence by such a layer would be invisible to the human eye. The situation may be different at grazing incidence or large $\emptyset$; for a grazing angle of 1°, $\emptyset = 89°$, $\sec^6\emptyset \cong 3.54 \times 10^{10}$, and

$$R \cong 5.6 \times 10^{-10}, \quad \emptyset = 89^\circ$$

The critical grazing angle, Θ_c, for a total reflection for the thin layer under discussion in given by $\Theta_c \cong \sqrt{2\Delta n}$, which yields a value of 0.007746 rad or 26.6′. Substituting $\emptyset = 89°$ 33.4′ in the equation for R gives

$$R \cong 7.4 \times 10^{-8}, \quad \phi = 89^\circ\ 33.4'$$

Since the human eye is capable of recording differences at least as great as 3.5×10^{-8} (Minnaert, 1954), partial reflections of strong light sources may occasionally be visible. The theoretical treatment discussed here shows that as the critical angle for a mirage is exceeded there should be a drop in reflected intensity on the order of 10^{-7} 10^{-8}, so that instead of a smooth transition from totally to partially reflecting regimes, there should be a sharp decrease giving the impression of a complete disappearance of the reflection. This is in agreement with observation. The theory also indicates that faint images produced by partial reflection of very bright light sources, e.g. arc lights, may be seen at angles somewhat larger than the critical angle for a true mirage.

E. Spatial Variations in the Atmospheric Index-of-Refraction.

As dictated by Snell's law, refraction of light in the earth's atmosphere arises from *spatial variations* in the optical refractive-index. Since $n = f(P, T, \lambda)$ according to Eq. (2), the spatial variations of $n(\lambda)$ can be expressed in terms of the spatial variations of atmospheric pressure and temperature. Routine measurements of the latter two quantities are made by a network of meteorological surface observations and upper-air soundings. When the optical wavelength dependence of n is neglected, Eq. (2) takes the form (for $\approx\lambda$ 5455 A, and

$$n - 1 = (78.7 \times 10^{-6}) \frac{P}{T}$$

the gradient of n is given by

$$\nabla n = (78.7 \times 10^{-6}) \left(\frac{1}{T} \nabla P - \frac{P}{T^2} \nabla T\right)$$

Optical mirages are most likely to form when atmospheric conditions of relative calm (no heavy cloudiness, no precipitation or strong winds) and extended horizontal visibility (<10 miles) are combined with large radiative heating or cooling of the earth's surface. Under these conditions the vertical gradients of pressure and temperature are much larger than the horizontal gradients, i.e., the atmosphere tends to be horizontally stratified.* Thus,

$$\nabla n = \frac{\partial n}{\partial z} = (78.7 \times 10^{-6}) \left(\frac{1}{T} \frac{\partial P}{\partial z} - \frac{P}{T^2} \frac{\partial T}{\partial z}\right)$$

or

$$\frac{\partial n}{\partial z} = (78.7 \times 10^{-6}) \frac{P}{T^2} \left(\frac{-g}{R_d} - \frac{\partial T}{\partial z}\right)$$

$$\boxed{\frac{\partial n}{\partial z} = (78.7 \times 10^{-6}) \frac{P}{T^2} (-3.4^{\circ}\text{C}/100 \text{ m.} - \frac{\partial T}{\partial z}}$$

Thus, the spatial variation in the refractive index, i.e., light refraction, depends primarily on the vertical temperature gradient. When $\partial n/\partial z$ is negative and the direction of energy propagation is from dense to rare, the curvature of light rays in the earth's atmosphere is in the same sense as that of the earth's surface. Equation (4) shows that $\partial n/\partial z$ is negative for all vertical gradients of temperature except those for which the temperature decreases with height > 3.4°C/100 m. No light refraction takes place when $\partial n/\partial n = 0$; in this case $\partial T/\partial z = -3.4°$ C/100 m. which is the autoconvective lapse

* When horizontal gradients in the refractive index are present, the complex mirage images that occur are often referred to as Fata Morgana. It is believed, however, that the vertical gradient is the determining factor in the formation of most images.

rate, i.e., the vertical temperature-gradient in an atmosphere of constant density. Table 2 gives the curvature of a light ray in seconds of arc per kilometer for various values of $\partial T/\partial z$ near the surface of the earth (standard *P and T*). When ray curvature is positive, it is in the same sense as an earth's curvature.

Table 2

CURVATURE OF LIGHT RAYS FOR VARIOUS VALUES OF VERTICAL TEMPERATURE-GRADIENT AT STANDARD CONDITIONS OF PRESSURE (1013.3 mb) AND TEMPERATURE (273°K)

$\frac{\partial T}{\partial z}$ (°C/100m)	CURVATURE OF LIGHT RAYS ("/km)
-3.4	0
-1.0	5.3
-0.5	6.4
0	7.5
+6.9	22.7
+11.6	33.0

From Table 2 it is evident that two types of vertical temperature variation contribute most to the formation of mirages; these are temperature inversions [$(\partial T/\partial\ )>O$] and temperature lapse rates exceeding 3.4°C/100m (the autoconvective lapse rate). Superautoconvective lapse rates cause light rays to have negative curvature (concave upward), and are responsible for the formation of inferior mirages (e.g., road mirage). The curvature of the earth's surface is 33″/km, and thus whenever there is a sufficiently strong temperature inversion, light rays propagating at low angles will follow the curvature responsible for the formation of prominent superior mirages.

F. Meteorological Conditions Conducive to the Formation of Mirages

The strength and frequency of vertical temperature gradients in the earth's atmosphere are constantly monitored by meteorologists. The largest temperature changes with height are found in the first 1,000 m above the earth's surface. In this layer, maximum temperature gradients usually arise from the combined effects of differential air motion and radiative heating or cooling.

The temperature increase through a low-level inversion layer can vary from a few degrees to as much 30°C during nighttime cooling of the ground layer. During daytime heating, the temperature can drop by as much as 20°C in the first couple of meters above the ground *(Handbook of Geophysics and Space Environments,* 1965). Large temperature lapses are generally restricted to narrow layers above those ground surfaces that rapidly absorb but poorly conduct solar radiation. Temperature inversions that are due to radiative cooling are not as selective as to the nature of the lower boundary and are therefore more common and more extensive than large lapses. Temperature inversions can extend over horizontal distances of more than 100 km. Large temperature lapses, however, do not usually extend uninterrupted over distance more than a couple of kilometers.

At any given location, the frequency of occurence of large temperature lapses is directly related to the frequency of occurrence of warm sunny days. Fig. 2 shows the *average* distribution of normal summer sunshine across the United States (Visher, 1954). More than seventy percent of the possible total is recorded in a large area extending from the Mississippi to the West Coast. Consequently, low-level mirages associated with large temperature lapses may be rather normal phenomena in this area. Distribution for summer and winter of the frequency of occurence of temperature inversions $\leq$150 m above ground level are shown for the United States in Fig. 3 (Hosler, 1961). The data are based on a two-year sampling period. Figure 4 shows the distribution across the United States of the percentage of time that the visibility exceeds 10 km (Eldridge, 1966). When Figs. 3 and 4 are combined it is seen that large areas between roughly the Mississippi and the West Coast have a high frequency of extended horizontal visibility and a relatively high frequency of low-level temperature inversions. These meterological conditions are favorable for the formation of mirages. On the basis of the climatic data shown in Figs. 2, 3, and 4 it can be concluded that at some places a low-level mirage may be a rather normal phenomenon while in other places it may be highly abnormal. An example of the sometimes daily recurrence of superior mirage over the northern part of the Gulf of California is discussed by Ronald Ives (1968). Temperature inversions in the cloud-free atmosphere are often recorded at heights up to 6,000 m above the ground. These elevated inversions usually arise from descending air mo-

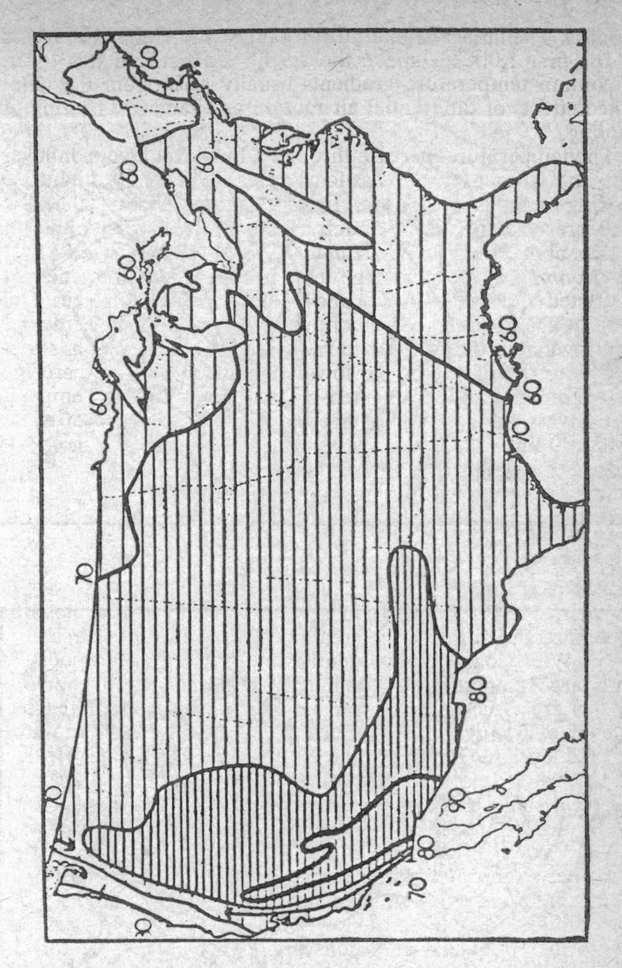

Fig. 2 Distribution of normal summer sunshine (Percentage of Possible Total)

tions, although radiative processes can be involved when very thin cirrus clouds or haze layers are present. Narrow layers of high-level temperature inversion, e.g., 4°C measured in a vertical distance of a few meters, extending without appreciable changes in height for several tens of kilometers in the hori-

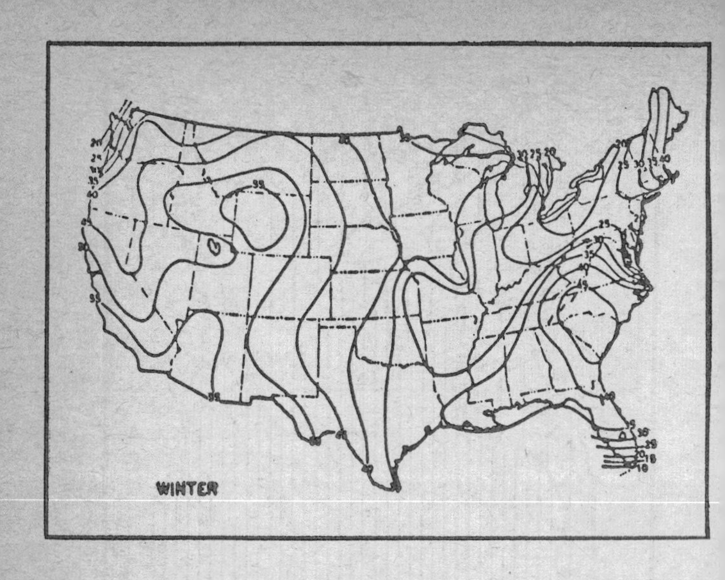

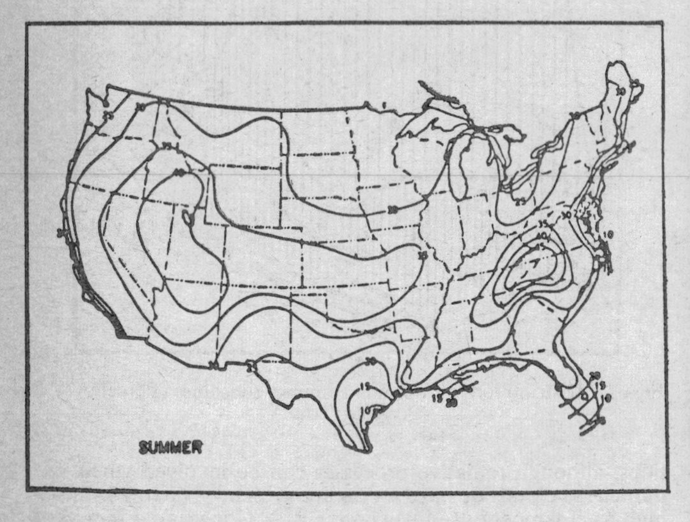

Fig. 3 Distribution of inversion frequency (Percent of Total Hours) for summer and winter

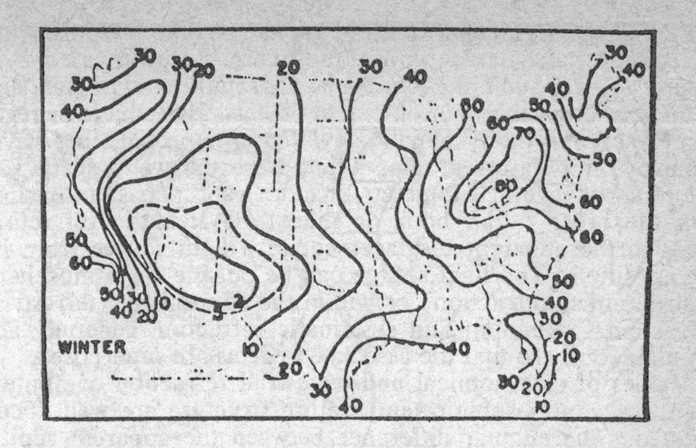

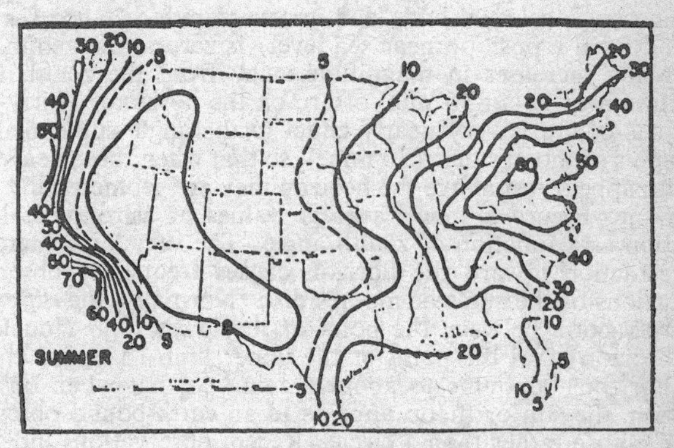

Fig. 4 Distribution of percentage of time the visibility is less than 10 km for summer and winter

zontal direction have been encountered (Lane, 1965). Such inversions are conducive to mirage formation when they are accompanied by extended visibility in the horizontal as well as in the vertical. A climatology of such inversions can be obtained from existing meteorological data.

4. *Visual Characteristics of Light-Refraction Phenomena in the Cloud-Free Atmosphere*

A. GENERAL

Light refraction as it occurs in the earth's atmosphere can be divided into *random* refraction and *systematic* or regular refraction (Meyer-Arendt, 1965). Random refraction is due to the small-scale (meters or less), rapid (seconds) temperature fluctuations associated with atmospheric turbulence, and is responsible for such phenomena as the scintillation of stars and planets, and the shimmer of distant objects. Systematic or regular refraction is the systematic deviation of a propagating wavefront by temperature gradients that are extensive in space (on the order of several kilometers or more) and persistent in time (on the order of an hour or more). Systematic refraction leads to the apparent displacement of a light source from its true position. The light source can be outside the atmosphere (astronomical refraction) or within the atmosphere (terrestrial refraction). Random and systematic refraction generally act simultaneously so that the associated effects are superposed.

Values of astronomical and terrestrial refraction computed for *average* atmospheric temperature structure are well documented. The angular difference between the apparent zenith distance of a celestial body and its true zenith distance (as observed from a position near sea level) is zero at the zenith but gradually increases in magnitude away from the zenith to a maximum of about 35 min. of arc on the horizon. Thirty-five minutes of arc is very nearly equal to the angle subtended by the sun's or moon's disc (30 min.), so that when these heavenly bodies appear just above the horizon they are geometrically just below it. Figure 5 shows average values of astronomical refraction as a function of zenith angle. The very large increase in refraction toward the horizon causes frequently observed distortions of the sun's or moon's disc. Normally, the *differential* refraction between the point of the lower limb (touching the horizon) and the point of the upper limb (30 min. above the horizon) amounts to about 6 min., so that when on the horizon, the sun or moon appears to an earth-bound observer as an ellipse rather than a circle. Recent observations indicate that the setting sun or moon as seen from outside the earth's atmosphere also appears flattened due to refraction (Cameron, *et al*, 1963). *Under abnormal atmospheric temperature conditions, the differential refraction can be so large that the rising or setting sun or moon appears in grossly distorted form* (O'Connell 1958).

Terrestrial-refraction angles have been computed as a function of zenith angle and altitude of the luminous source (Link and Sekera 1940; Saunders, 1963). Depending on height, refraction angles computed with reference to sea level vary from ≤ 5 sec. of arc at a zenith angle of 5° to ≤ 12 min. of arc at a zenith angle of 86°. Above 42 km refraction is negligible.

The importance of the seemingly small astronomical and terrestrial refraction on visual observations can be evaluated as follows. Resolving theory and practice have established

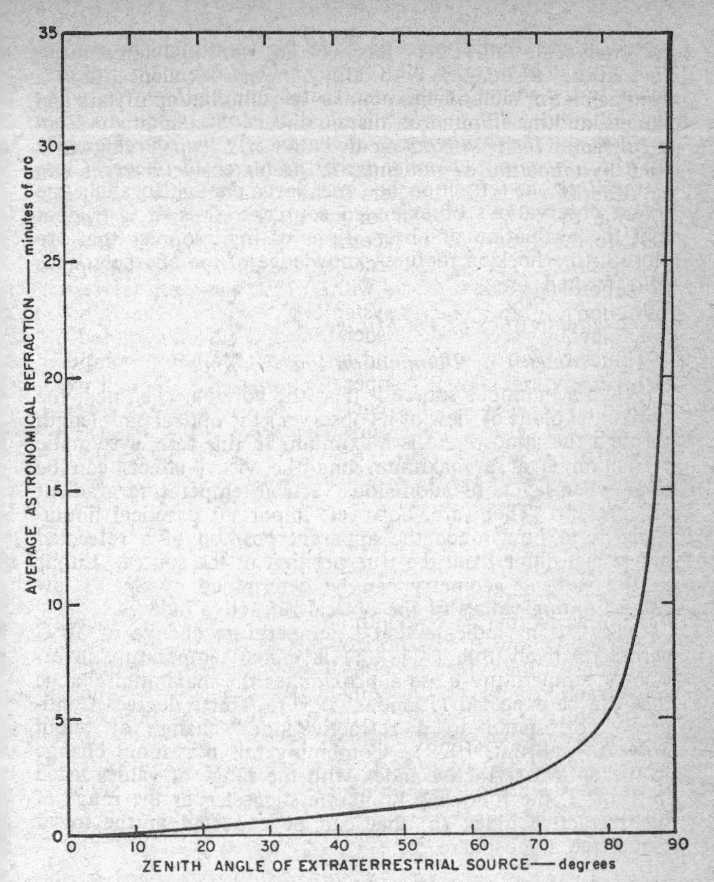

Fig. 5. Astronomical refraction vs. zenith angle corresponding to standard atmosphere

that the human eye (which is a lens system) cannot resolve, separate clearly, or recognizably identify two points that subtend an angle to the eye of less than 1/16° = 3.75 min. (Tolansky 1964; Minnaert, 1954). Under standard atmospheric-temperature conditions, angular deviations due to astronomical and terrestrial refraction that are larger than 3.75 min. occur when distant light sources are less than about 14° above the horizon (zenith angle larger than about 76°). Hence, the effects of systematic atmospheric refraction on visual observations of a distant light source (point source) which is less than about 76° from the zenith can be considered negligible because the average human eye cannot clearly separate the source from its refracted image. *However, when the luminous point source is located at about 14° or less from the horizon, the location and appearance of the source as seen by a distant observer are those of its refracted image.* Close to the horizon, refraction becomes large enough to affect the visual observations of extended sources. Thus, it is evident that the evaluation of observations of light sources that are close to the horizon requires knowledge of the characteristics of refracted images.

B. Characteristics of the Mirage

1. *Geometry of Illumination and Viewing*

When a luminous source is near the horizon, (i.e., near the horizontal plane of view of its observer) the optical path length through the atmosphere is maximum. In this case, systematic refraction is at a maximum and the visual effects can be large when layers of anomalous vertical temperature gradient are present. There are, however, important practical limitations as to how much the apparent position of a refracted image can differ from the true position of the source. Limits in the viewing geometry can be determined by Snell's law using limiting values of the optical refractive index.

Observations indicate that a temperature change of 30°C across relatively thin (<1 km) layers of temperature inversion or temperature lapse approximates the maximum change that can be expected (Ramdas, 1951). Thirty degrees Centigrade correspond to a refractive-index change of about 3×10^{-5} (Brunt, 1929). Combining this maximum change in the optical refractive index with the range of values listed in Table I, the following limits are suggested as the range of the refractive index *(n)* that can be expected in the lower cloud-free atmosphere.

$$1.00026 \leq n \leq 1.00029$$

Substitution of the upper and lower limit into the equation for total reflection gives

$$\sin\Phi c = \frac{1.00026}{1.00029} = 0.999970$$

and

$$\Phi c = 89.5°$$

Hence, when a horizontal layer or boundary across which n has the assumed maximum variation of 1.00029 to 1.00026 is illuminated by a light source (direction of propagation from dense to rare), the angle of incidence has to exceed 89.5° (½° grazing angle) in order to get total reflection and a possible mirage image. *For all practical purposes, 0.5° can be considered as the near-maximum angle of illumination that will allow for formation of a mirage.* When the refractive index *decreases* with height across the boundary and illumination is from below, the mirage image appears at a maximum angular distance of about 1° above the true position of the light source as illustrated in Fig. 6a. *Hence, one degree of arc must represent about the maximum angular distance that can be expected between the true position of the light source and its refracted image.* When the image appears above the true position of the source, the mirage is referred to as a *superior* mirage. When the refractive index increases with height and illumination is from above, an *inferior mirage* appears, i.e., the image lies below the true position of the source as shown in Fig. 6b. In terms of vertical temperature gradient, the superior mirage is associated with an inversion and the inferior mirage with a large temperature-lapse.

It is evident that *the presence of a layer of large temperature-gradient is necessary but not sufficient for mirage formation. A remaining requirement is the presence of light that illuminates the layer at grazing incidence.* The incident light can originate from a physical source such as sun, moon, or planet, or it can be skylight or sunlight reflected from the ground.

Whether the mirage is observed or not depends on the position of the observer with respect to the light source and the refracting layer. The planar geometry involved in a mirage observation can be illustrated by applying Eq. (3):

$$\frac{dx}{dz} = \frac{n_o \sin \phi_o}{\sqrt{n^2 - n_o^2 \sin^2 \phi_o}}$$

to a rectangular coordinate system in which the abscissa coincides with the ground. For simplicity it is assumed that $n^2 = n^2 - z$ (i.e., the refractive index, n, decreases with height), so that the solution to Eq. (3) represents a family of parabolas of the form

$$x = n_o^2 \sin 2\theta_o - 2n_o \sin \theta_o \sqrt{n_o^2 \cos^2 \theta_o - z}$$

(In applying Eq. (3) z represents az' where z' has units of height and a is the scale factor). The family of parabolas, sketched in Fig. 7, can be thought of as representing the light

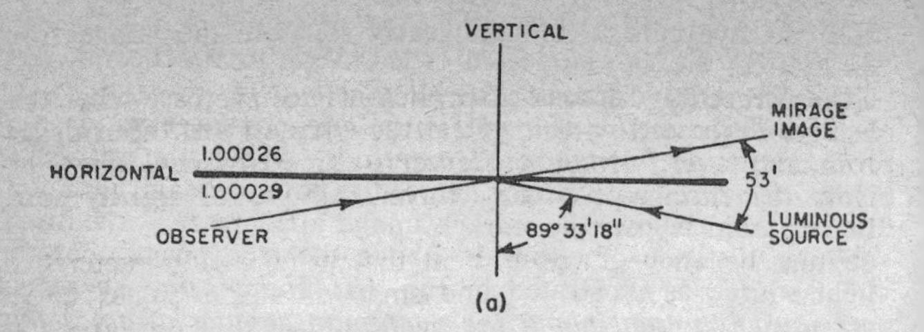

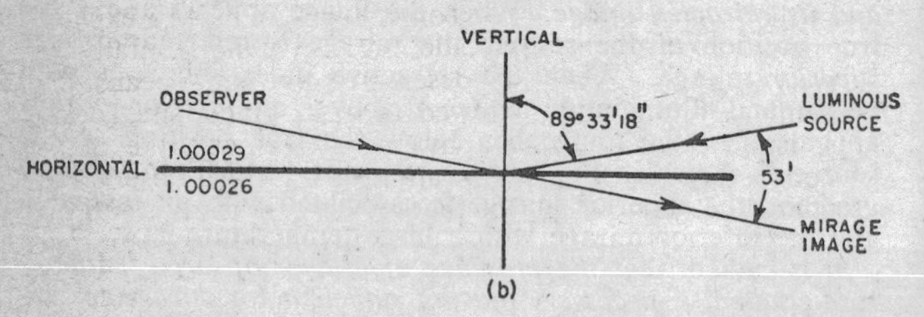

Fig. 6 Limiting angular viewing geometry of (a) superior mirage, (b) inferior mirage

rays from a point source located at the origin of the co-ordinate system. Using the upper and lower limit of the optical refractive index, $n_o = 1.00029$ and $n = 1.00026$, the largest horizontal distance (D) is covered by the light ray for which $\theta, = 89.5°$ (angles are exaggerated in Fig. 7). All mirage images must be observed within this distance (see Fig. 7). D can be expressed in terms of the height (H) of the refracting layer as follows. For each member of the family of parabolas, z is maximum at the point where $(dz/dx) = 0$, i.e., at the point ($z = n_o \cos^2 \theta_{o}$, $X = n^2{}_o \sin 2\theta,$). Since each member is symmetric with respect to this point also,

$$\frac{D}{H} = \frac{2n_o^2 \sin 2\ (89.5^o)}{n_o^2 \cos^2\ (89.5^o)} = 4 \tan 89.5^o$$

Hence, D = 500H, i.e., all mirage images in this particular case are observed within a distance from the light source that is about 500 times the thickness of the refracting layer. For example, when the thickness of the refracting layer is 10 meters, no mirage observations of a particular object are likely beyond a distance of 5 km. At about 5 km an image of the object may appear at an elevation of about 0.5°, while within 5 km images may appear at increasingly lower elevation angles until the eye can no longer clearly separate the image from the source.

The preceding discussion applies only to the case where the observer is located within, or at the boundary of, the mirage-producing layer. If the observer is some distance above or below the mirage-producing layer, mirages of much more distance objects may appear.

From the above, it is evident that principal characteristics of the optical mirage are the small elevation angles under which the phenomenon is observed ($\leq 1°$) and the large distance (tens of kilometers) between observer and "mirrored" object that are possible. The geometry of the mirage explains why many observations are made on or near horizontally extensive, flat terrain such as deserts, lakes, and oceans and frequently involve images viewed through binoculars (oases, ships, islands, coastal geography). Furthermore, the above geometry illustrates that the duration of a mirage observation is critically dependent on whether or not the source and observer are in relative motion. For example, when the light source is moving in such a way that the angle of illumination, θ_0, oscillates around the critical angle, a stationary observer located at A in Fig. 7 may see a mirage image that alternately appears and disappears. On the other hand, when the observer is moving relative to the source (from A to B in Fig. 7), the mirage image can change elevation, thereby creating an illusion of motion.

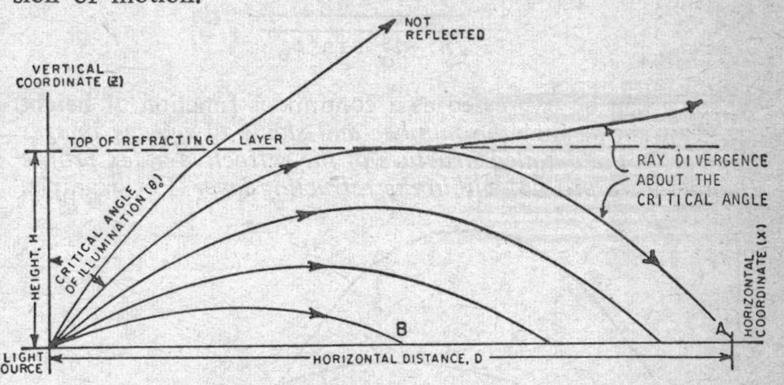

Fig. 7 Portrayal of light rays as family of parabolas ($n^2 = n^2_o - z$, $n_o = 1.00029$, $n = 1.00026$, $\theta_o = 89.5°$)

2. *Number and Shape of Mirage Images*

It has been recognized that systematic refraction of the light from a single source can lead to *multiple* mirage images the shapes of which can be complicated. The early observations by Vince (1798) and Scoresby (1820) included sightings of completely or partially inverted images of a single distant ship. From a coastal position on the English Channel, John Parnell (1869) observed *five* elevated images, all in a vertical line, of a lighthouse on the French Coast. All five images had different shapes. During their observations in Spain, Biot and Arago (1809) observed up to four elevated images of a distant (161 km) light signal. The images disappeared and reappeared intermittently and at times joined to form a narrow vertical column of light which subsequently separated into two parts, the lower part appearing red and the upper part appearing green. The above observations resulted from abnormal atmospheric light-refraction the observed images were distant, and in most cases detailed descriptions were made with the aid of binoculars.

Practically all theoretical and experimental investigations of optical mirages (e.g., Wollaston 1800; Hillers 1914; R. W. Wood 1911) have been concerned with demonstrating the number and shape of observed images. Tait's theoretical treatise and Wollaston's laboratory experiment can be considered classical examples. Tait's terrestrial-refraction model represents a horizontally stratified atmosphere, and a vertically finite refracting layer with a continuous change in refractive index. Under these assumptions the paths of light rays are represented by the solution to the differential equation:

$$d\chi = \frac{n_o \sin \phi_o}{\sqrt{n^2 - n_o^2 \sin^2 \phi_o}} \, dz$$

where n can be expressed as a continuous function of height (z). Tait shows that *the number and shape of mirage images depend on the detailed structure of the refractive-index profile (temperature profile) within the refracting layer*. For example,

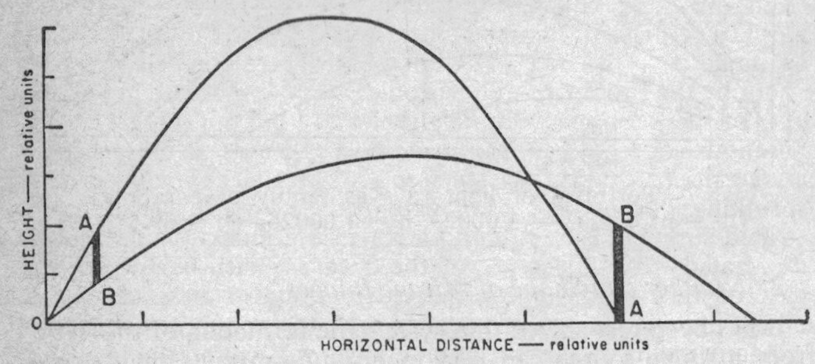

Fig. 8 Classical explanation of image inversion (AB to BA) by the crossing of light rays.

the elevated mirage image of a distant object becomes inverted when the refraction index in the upper part of the refracting layer decreases more rapidly with height than in the lower part. This "classical" explanation of image inversion is illustrated in Fig. 8. Shown are the paths of two light rays obtained from solving Eq. (3) for $n^2 = n^2_o - z^2$. Thus, the refractive-index gradient $(\partial n/\partial z)$ in the upper part of the refracting layer is much larger than in the lower part. When the observer's eye is placed at the origin of the $X_{,z}$ coordinate system, *observed image-inversion arises from the crossing of light rays.*

Apparent vertical stretching (elongation, towering) of a luminous object due to refraction is illustrated in Fig. 9. For the

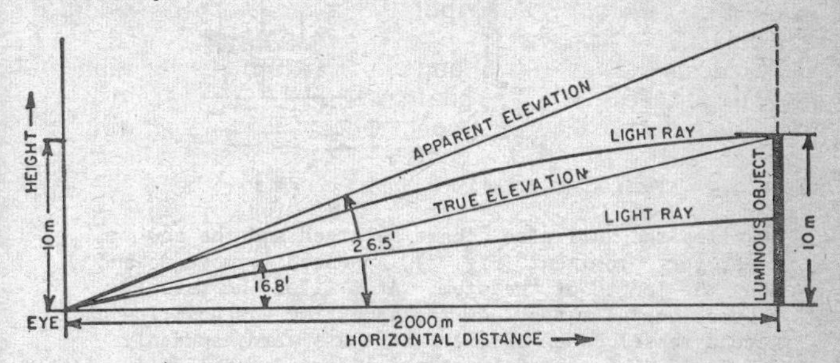

Fig. 9 Elongation of luminous object due to light refraction.

sake of clarity, height and elevation angles are exaggerated. A horizontal refracting layer is assumed that is 10 meters thick and through which the refractive index (n) decreases with height (z) from 1.00029 to 1.00026 according to the relation $n^2 = (1.00029)^2 - z^2$. Hence, the refraction of a light ray increases with height. It can be shown that a 10-m-high luminous object placed at a horizontal distance of 2 km subtends an angle of approximately 26.5′ at the origin. In the absence of the refracting layer the object would have subtended an angle of 16.8′. The apparent vertical stretching is brought about by the refractive-index profile; i.e., the increase in "bending" of the light rays with height elevates the upper part of the luminous source. *Vertical stretching can lead an observer to underestimate the true distance to the luminous object.* Vertical shrinking (stooping) of an extended object can be demonstrated similarly by assuming a refractive-index profile that is associated with a decrease of the gradient with height. In the case of vertical shrinking, the true geometric distance to the object involved is usually smaller than the apparent distance.

Many examples of image inversion, vertical stretching, and shrinking due to abnormal atmospheric refraction are given in *The Marine Observer.*

S.S. Bristol City. Captain A. L. Webb, O.B.E. Sydney (C.B.) to Swansea. Observers, the Master and Mr. R. Whitman, 3rd Officer.

18th September, 1952, 2000 G.M.T. A vessel approaching end-on at 15 miles, with hull just visible, appeared to have elongated masts and funnel (Fig. 1). At

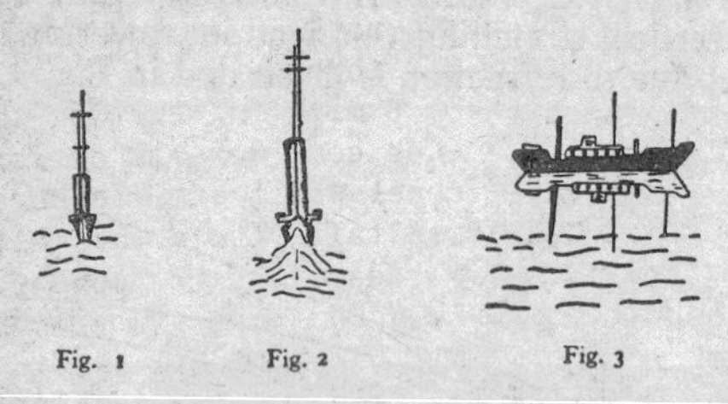

Fig. 1 Fig. 2 Fig. 3

10 miles the hull also became enlarged and the bow wave, very prominent (Fig. 2), appeared to move up and down the length of the stem. At 5 miles the vessel resumed normal shape. At the same time and position a second vessel, when 10 miles to the s'ward, suddenly developed an inverted image which lasted for 15 min before disappearing (Fig 3). A few minutes later the wake appeared, very prominent, resembling heavy surf which lasted another 10 min (Fig. 4). Before passing

Fig. 4 Fig. 5

out of view the vessel appeared to take on a "block" shape (Fig. 5), only resuming its normal shape at brief intervals as the vessel dipped in the slight swell. Sea Temp. 53°F, air temp. 52°, wet bulb 50°. Calm sea, slight swell.

Position of ship: 48°32'N, 44°50'W.

Note. This observation is also one of superior mirage and in Fig. 3 the inverted image is clearly seen. In Figs. 1 and 2 the vertical extension and distortion known as looming is well marked.

(Reproduced from *The Marine Observer,* Vol. 23, No. 161, p. 143, July 1953)

South Atlantic Ocean

S.S. Tenagodus. Captain W. Broughton. Cape Town to Algiers. Observers, Mr. J. J. Diston, Chief Officer, and Mr. J. F. Gristwood, 2nd Officer.

2nd March, 1955, 1730-1800 L.T. About one hour after leaving Cape Town abnormal refraction was noticed around the horizon from SW. through N. to E. A large tanker, 8 miles distant on the port beam, was considerably distorted; the funnel was greatly elongated and appeared taller than the masts, and swayed occasionally. The radar scanner appeared suspended well above the ship. On the starboard bow, 28 miles distant, a hill 280 ft high at Ysterfontein Point was observed to have an inverted image. A few minutes later there were three inverted images; these gradually telescoped until the hill appeared as a block. Temperatures: air 66°F, sea 59°. Slight sea, low swell.

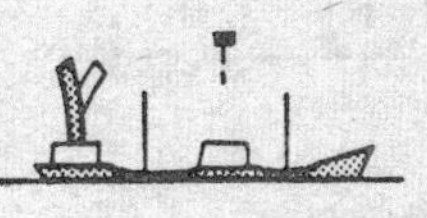

Position of ship: 33°49'S., 18°16'E.

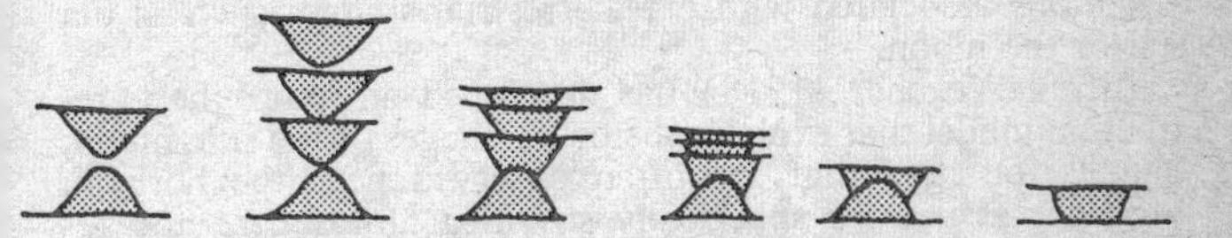

(Reproduced from *The Marine Observer,* Vol. 26, No. 172, April 1956)

Tait's theoretical approach, the emphasis on the refractive-index profile, is basic to many other theoretical investigations of the mirage. For example, Wilhelm Hillers (1913) shows how two refracted images of a single light source can be formed when the profile in the refracting layer is such that the refracted rays are circular. Figure 10 shows the geometry of this special case. The refracting layer lies above the observer and the distant light source. Refraction below the refracting layer is assumed negligible, i.e., light rays are rectilinear. When the light rays penetrating the refracting layer are circles concentric about M, two separate rays emanating from the light source reach the observer's eye and all rays intermediate and outside these two fail to be tangent to a concentric circle. Con-

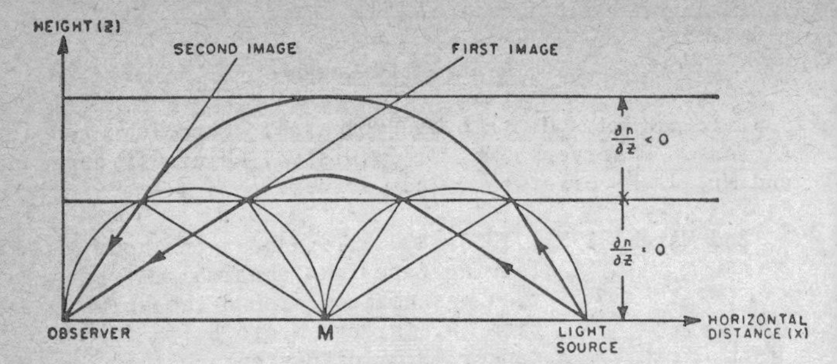

Fig. 10 Geometry of special case in which refraction gives two separate images of a single light-source.

sequently, the observer views two separate images. An example of three observed images of a distant hill is shown in the figure on page 631 in an excerpt from *The Marine Observer*.

Tait's approach cannot be applied indiscriminately to all mirage phenomena because integration of Eq. (3) is restricted to a selected range of refractive index profiles. Furthermore, the effect of the earth's curvature is excluded so that only mirage phenomena associated with not-too-distant objects can be considered. Hence, Tait's model cannot explain mirage observations associated with extraterrestrial sources such as the sun or the moon.

Alfred Wegener (1918) has developed an atmospheric-refraction model that explains distorted images of the sun, moon, planets, or stars that are often observed near the horizon. Wegener assumes a spherically stratified atmosphere and reduces the refracting layer to a refracting boundary or surface of total reflection. Wegener demonstrated that when the refracting boundary lies above the observer and the sun is on the horizon, the boundary refracts the solar light rays in such a way that the observer views two separate images of the solar disc, a flattened upper image and a distorted lower image. Fig. 11 shows the successive form of two images for a setting sun or moon in the presence of a 7° temperature-inversion layer 50 m above the observed as computed by Wegener. The degree of deflection of the incoming light rays and consequently the degree of distortion of the solar disc depends on the refractive-index change or temperature change across the reflecting boundary. When the temperature change is small, only a single distorted image of the solar disc appears. When the change across the boundary is very large only the flat upper part of the "split" solar image is seen, so that the setting sun appears to vanish above the horizon. When the atmosphere is highly

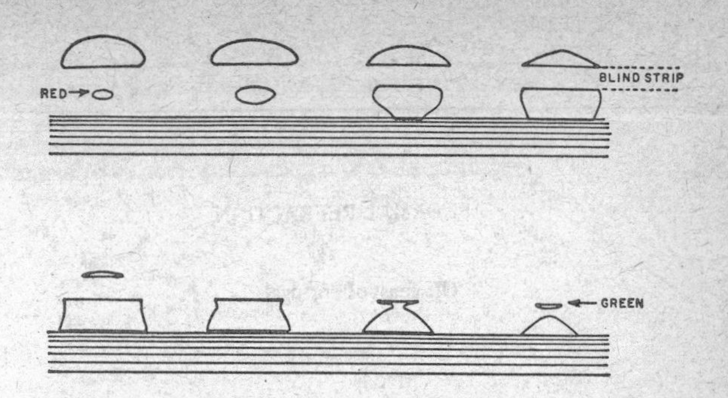

Fig. 11 Successive images of setting sun or moon during conditions of mirage

stratified, i.e., when several horizontal refracting boundaries are present, the setting sun can appear like a Chinese Pagoda or like a stack of discs. The refracted images of the setting sun computed by Wegener's model agree closely with those photographed and described by D. J. K. O'Connell (1958) in connection with a study of the green and red flash phenomena.

Wegener's model is not restricted to luminous sources outside the earth's atmosphere. It can be applied to distant terrestrial objects such as mountains from which emitted light rays are at grazing incidence to the top of the refracting boundary. Wegener's model of atmospheric refraction illustrates the characteristics that are basic to many spectacular rising or settings of sun, moon, or planet. Following are three accounts of such abnormal atmospheric-refraction phenomena as given in *The Marine Observer*.

The atmospheric-refraction models of Tait and Wegener quantitatively explain the basic characteristics of the most commonly observed mirage-images. Other theoretical investigations are available that discuss various special aspects. For example, the theory of the superior mirage by Odd Haug explains the appearance of up to four images from a single source. Wilhelm Hillers treats the special case of a lateral mirage, i.e., the refraction of light when the refractive-index gradient is horizontal, as may be the case along a wall heated by solar radiation. Koji Hidaka and Gustav Forster discuss the theory of refraction when the surfaces of constant density in the atmosphere are somewhere between horizontal and vertical. Together, these theoretical models explain adequately the varying ways in which a mirage image can appear to an observer. Currently, there is no *single* model with a numerical solution to all aspects of the mirage.

ABNORMAL REFRACTION

Off coast of Portugal

M. V. *Australind*. Captain J. F. Wood. Port Said to Bremen. Observer, Mr. D. Ewan, Chief Officer.

27th April, 1950, 0546-0549 G.M.T. The accompanying sketches picture the sequence of shapes assumed by the sun as a result of refraction. After

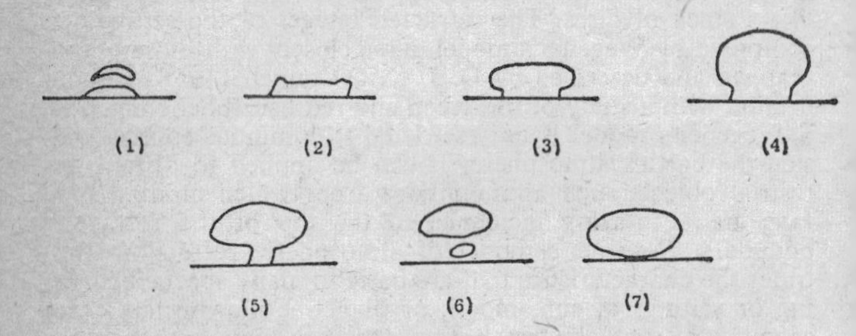

clearing the horizon the sun slowly regained its normal proportions and at an altitude of $1\frac{1}{2}°$ no refraction was apparent. No land was visible near the phenomenon. Wind N, force 4. Barometer 1020·3 mb., air temp. 58°F. Sky cloudless.

Position of ship: Latitude 38° 04′N., Longitude 9° 24′W.

(Reproduced from *The Marine Observer,* Vol. 21, No. 152, p. 80, April 1951)

ABNORMAL REFRACTION
North Atlantic Ocean

O.W.S. *Weather Recorder*. Captain A. W. Ford. At Ocean Weather Station A. Observer, Mr. J. Ballantyne, 3rd Officer.

5th May, 1955, 2220–2240 G.M.T. Towards sunset abnormal refraction was observed, and for a while two suns were visible. A false sun was seen for half its

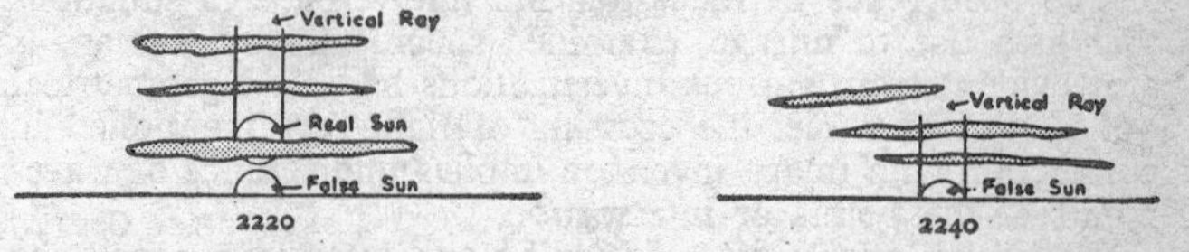

diameter on the horizon, and touching the real sun above. The real sun was partly obscured by cloud. The false sun persisted for 3 or 4 min after the real sun had set. A vertical ray with reddish coloration extended to about 4° above the real sun.

(Reproduced from *The Marine Observer*, Vol. 26, No. 172, April 1956)

ABNORMAL REFRACTION
English Channel

M.V. *Timaru Star*. Captain H. W. McNeil. London to Curaçao. Observer, Mr. N. Johnson, 3rd Officer.

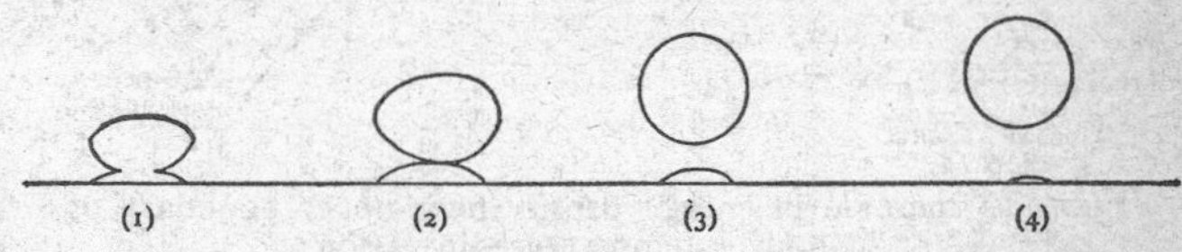

4th January, 1956. While proceeding down the English Channel at 0800 G.M.T., shortly after sunrise, the sun was observed to have a distorted appearance (sketch 1). By 0810 while the sun continued to rise a false " sun " began to set. Two minutes later there was a distinct gap between the true sun and the false and by 0814 the false sun was no longer visible. In the area of the rising true sun the sky was clear and a bright orange in colour. A phenomenon similar to sketch 2 was observed at sunset on the same day.

Position of ship: 50° 05′N., 02° 04′W.

(Reproduced from *The Marine Observer*, Vol. 27, No. 175, p. 13, 1957)

3. *Effects from Focussing and Interference*

A recent theoretical and experimental investigation of the optical mirage is presented by Sir C. V. Raman (1959). Sir C. V. Raman demonstrates that multiple, inverted images of a single object can arise from interference and focussing of the incident and reflected wavefronts near the boundary of total reflection. Raman's work, which is entirely based on wave theory, suggests the interaction of wavefronts within a refracting layer as a mechanism in mirage formation.

The occurrence of focussing and interference in situations that give rise to mirage, examined specifically by Raman, is also evident from various investigations based on geometrical optics. For example, the crossing of light rays mentioned in connection with image inversion implies interference of wavefronts at the points of intersection.

The visual effects from focussing and interference must be considered in particular when plane-parallel radiation (radiation from a very distant source) is incident on a layer of total reflection. In this case, there is a constant crossing of light rays within a relatively narrow region of the refracting layer, as illustrated in Fig. 12 (for the sake of clarity, height and elevation angles are exaggerated). In Fig. 12, a circular collimated light-beam of diameter A is incident on the lower

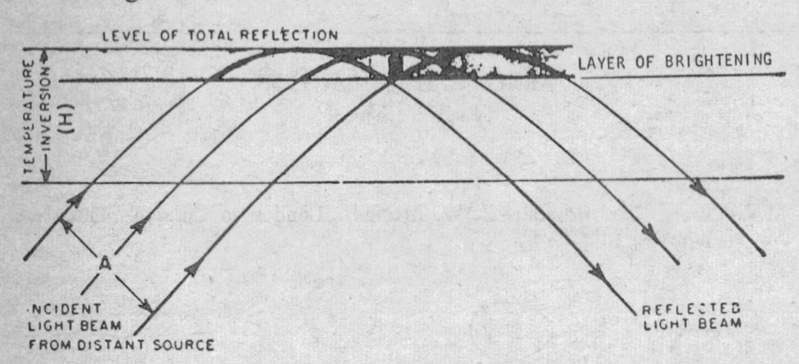

Fig. 12 Increase in energy density near upper boundary of high-level temperature inversion

boundary of a temperature-inversion layer at angle equal to or exceeding the critical angle for total reflection. Interference of the incident and reflected wavefronts occurs in a selected layer near the level of total reflection. This layer, shaded in Fig. 12, has a maximum thickness B, which is dependent on A. In the absence of absorption, the amount of radiant energy, flowing per unit time through πA^2 equals that flowing through πB^2. When B is less than A, the energy density at B is larger than at A, so that the brightness of the refracted light beam increases in the layer of interference.

An example of the ratio of A to B can be given with the aid of Eq. (3). It is assumed that the optical refractive index through the inversion layer varies from $n_0 = 1.00029$ to $n = 1.00026$ according to $n^2 = n^2_0 - z$. When the angle of incidence is near the critical angle for total reflection ($\theta_0 \cong 89.5°$), the light rays within the inversion layer are parabolas and the level of total reflection coincides with the upper boundary of the inversion layer. Under these conditions, it can be shown that

$$\frac{B}{A} = \frac{A}{16H}$$

where H is the thickness of the temperature-inversion layer. When the diameter A of the incident light beam is less than 16H, B is less than A and a brightening or focussing occurs near the top of the inversion. When the angle of incidence of the light beam is larger than the critical angle, ~ 89.5°, the level of total reflection lies below the upper boundary of the inversion layer. In this case, brightening can still occur near the level of total reflection, but the restrictions on the required beam-diameter become rather severe. The above example, based on a special case, demonstrates that sudden brightening can be encountered near the upper boundary of a refracting layer *when optical mirages are associated with a refracting layer that is thick with respect to the diameter of the incident light beam from a distant source and when the angle of incidence is near the critical angle.*

Observations of the brightening phenomenon must be considered rare in view of the selective location of its occurrence within the temperature-inversion layer and the requirement of plane-parallel incident radiation. Upper-level inversions seem most likely to produce the phenomenon. Some photographs showing apparent brightening of "spike" reflections on the edge of the setting sun are shown in O'Connell (1958, c.f., p. 158).

Microscopic effects due to interference of wavefronts within the area of brightening are illustrated in Fig. 13. Wavefronts are indicated rather than light rays. Unless absorption is extremely large, light rays are normal to the wavefront. A train of plane-parallel waves is assumed incident on the lower boundary of a refracting layer in which the refractive-index decreases with height. When the angle of incidence equals the critical angle, the incident waves are refracted upon entering the refracting layer and are totally reflected at the upper boundary. The crests and troughs of the waves are indicated by solid lines and dashed lines, respectively. At the upper

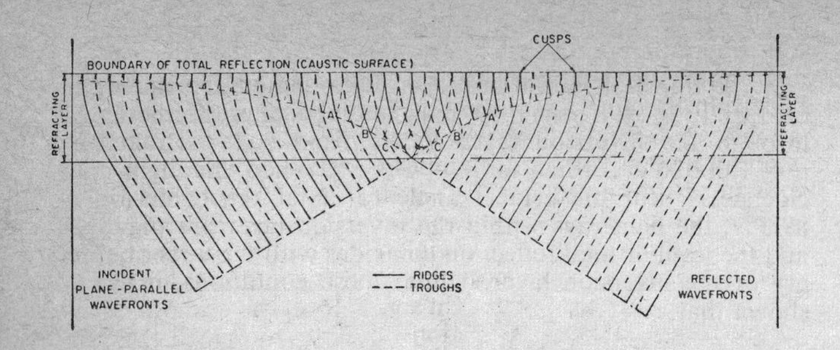

Fig. 13 Simplified construction of wavefronts in region of interference and focussing

boundary, the wavefronts of the incident and reflected waves converge to a focus. The focus is called a cusp. The upper boundary of the refracting layer resembles a caustic, i.e., an envelope of the moving cusps of the propagating wavefronts. Because of the focussing of wavefronts, a large concentration of radiant energy is usually found along the caustic (see Raman, 1959). In the area where the incoming and outgoing wavefronts interact, destructive interference is found along AA′ and CC′ (troughs meeting crests), while constructive interference is found along BB′ (incident and reflected waves have similar phase). Hence, brightness variations can be expected in the interference layer, as demonstrated by Sir C. V. Raman (1959). To what extent the microscopic effects from interference and focussing can be observed under actual atmospheric conditions of mirage is not known. Undoubtedly, the proper relation between refracting layer and distant light source must be combined with an observer's position near the upper boundary of the refracting layer. If the dark and bright bands in the area of interference can be observed, the observer could easily get the impression that he is viewing a rapidly oscillating light or a light that is drawing near and moving away at rapid intervals. Nighttime observations by airplane are most likely to provide proper evidence of this effect.

Currently, the focussing and interference effects are the least explored and consequently the least discussed of the various aspects associated with optical mirage.

4. *Refractive Separation of the Color Components of White Light (Color Separation)*

Due to the wavelength dependence of the optical refractive index, systematic refraction of white light leads to a separation of the composing colors. *Visible effects of color separation are most frequently associated with astronomical refraction.* In this case, the light enters the atmosphere at an upper boundary where n approaches unity for all wavelengths. At an observation site near sea level n is a wavelength-dependent, so that from the upper boundary of the atmosphere to the observation site the individual color components are refracted at different angles. The basic composing color of white light may be assumed to be red (24%), green (38%), and blue-violet (38%); the red is refracted less than the green, while the green is refracted less than the blue-violet. The visual effects of color separation depend on the zenith angle of the extraterrestrial light source. When a white light source is more than 50° above the horizon, the color separation is simply too small to be resolved by the eye. Close to the horizon it can be observed only in the case of very small light sources. The principle of color separation in astronomical refraction is illustrated in Fig. 14. The light from an extended source enters the top of the atmosphere and is separated with respect to color in the order red, green, blue, and violet. A bundle of light rays of diameter D can be selected for which all colors, upon refraction, converge at O. Hence, an observer at O sees the entire color mixture as white. When the extended source has a diameter larger than D, an area rather than a single point of color blending is formed. However, when the diameter of the source becomes less than D, the point of color convergence, O, recedes from the location of the observer. Now the observer begins to see a gradual refractive separating of color such that red tends to lie below green, and green tends to lie below blue-violet (see Fig. 14).

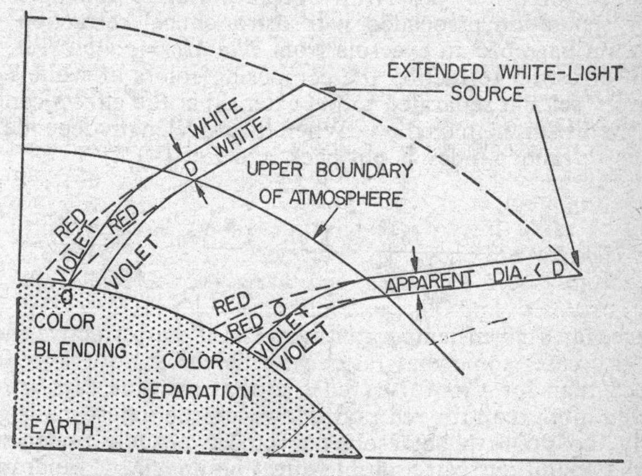

Fig. 14 Refractive color separation as a function of zenith angle

The diameter of the light beam from a given extraterrestrial source *decreases* with respect to an earth-bound observer, with increasing distance from the zenith, as illustrated in Fig. 14. Thus, when the zenith angle increases, the *apparent* diameter D of the light source decreases rapidly to a minimum value on the horizon. Hence, the chance of having a light source of diameter less than D is greatest on the horizon. *Therefore, color separation is observed most frequently on the horizon, when the light source is reduced to a bright point like a star or a minute portion of the solar or lunar disc.* A prominent example of the visible effects of color separation is the so-called Green Flash. This phenomenon is sometimes observed when the sun disappears in a clear sky below a distant horizon. The last star-like point can then be seen to change rapidly from pale yellow or orange, to green, and finally blue, or at least a bluish-green. The vividness of the green, when the sky is exceptionally clear, together with its most instant appearance and extremely short duration, has given rise to the name "green flash" for this phenomenon.

The same gamut of colors, only in reverse order, occasionally is seen at sunrise. The observations of the Green Flash require an unusually clear atmosphere such that the sun is yellowish, and not red, as it begins to sink below the horizon. A red setting sun means that the blue and green portions of the spectrum are relatively strongly attenuated by the atmosphere and hence indicates that conditions are not favorable for seeing the greenish segment. Thus, the meteorological conditions required for observing color separation are even more stringent than those required for observing optical mirages. Examples of color separation associated with astronomical refraction are given on page 639 in excerpts from *The Marine Observer*.

In terrestrial refraction the composing colors of white light are very seldom separated to the extent that the effects can be observed with the naked eye. When the wavelength dependence of the refractive index is put back into Eq. (4),

$$\frac{\partial n}{\partial z} = 77.5\left(1 + \frac{5.15 \times 10^{-3}}{\lambda^2} + \frac{1.07 \times 10^{-4}}{\lambda^4}\right)10^{-6}\,\frac{P}{T^2}\left(\frac{-3.4^\circ\mathrm{C}}{100\ \mathrm{m}} - \frac{\partial T}{\partial z}\right).$$

Hence, for a given temperature inversion, the refractive index (n) decreases somewhat faster with height (z) for $\lambda = 0.4\mu$ (blue) than for $\lambda = 0.7\mu$ (red), so that the blue rays are refracted more than the red rays. However, the difference is generally too small to be resolved by the eye. Only under very special conditions can a visible effect be imagined. For example, when a 100-m-thick inversion layer is assumed to be associated with a $\Delta T = 30°C$, the change of the refractive index for light and red light is respectively, $\Delta n\ (0.4\ \mu) \approx 3.01 \times 10^{-5}$ and $\Delta n\ (0.7\ \mu) = 2.93 \times 10^{-5}$. When the optical refractive indices at the lower boundary of the inversion are $n_o(0.4\ \mu) \approx 1.000282$ and $n_o\ (0.7\ \mu) \approx 1.000275$ (corresponding to $P = 1013.3$ mb and $T = 15°C$), values at the upper boundary are $n_o(0.4\ \mu) \approx 1.000252$ and $n(0.7\ \mu) \approx 1.000246$. When white light is incident at the lower boundary of the inversion at an angle Φ_o such that

$$\frac{1.000246}{1.000275} > \sin \Phi_o > \frac{1.000252}{1.000282}$$

then the blue rays are totally reflected by the inversion layer but the red rays are transmitted. Hence, for $\Phi_0 \approx 89°\ 33'\ 30''$ the blue rays are totally reflected, and for $\Phi_0 \approx 89°\ 33'\ 54''$ the red rays are totally reflected. The visible effects of color separation that can arise when Φ_0 fluctuates from $89°\ 33'\ 30''$ to $89°$

SETTING OF THE PLANET VENUS
Indian Ocean

S.S. *Strathnaver*. Captain I. M. Sinclair. Australia to London. Observer, Mr. J. C. Vint, Supernumerary 2nd Officer.

6th December, 1957 at 2105 S.M.T. The accompanying sketch illustrates the

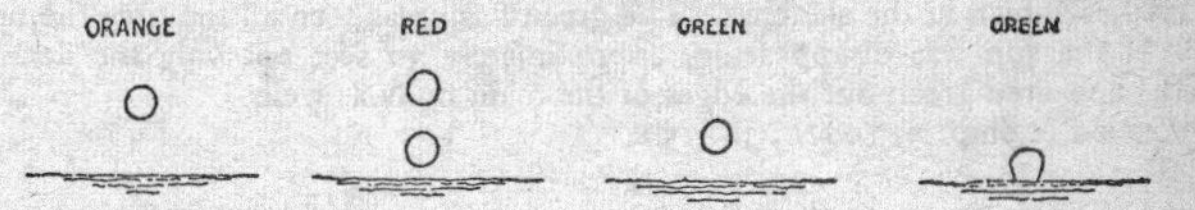

changes observed in the planet as it was setting. Prismatic binoculars were used to observe the phenomena.

Position of ship: 01° 40′N., 84° 32′E.

Note. The phenomena seen at the setting of the bright planets Venus and Jupiter vary considerably on different occasions and are always interesting. Sometimes no double images occur. When they are seen, they may be of the same or different colours. The green colour is not always seen before the instant of setting, as it was in this observation.

(Reproduced from *The Marine Observer*, Vol. 28, No. 182, p. 194, Oct. 1958)

GREEN FLASH

South Atlantic Ocean

M.V. *Drina*. Captain F. J. Swallow. Las Palmas to Buenos Aires. Observer, Mr. W. M. Wheatley, Chief Officer.

28th January, 1956. At sunset the sun, when half a diameter above the horizon, became lemon-coloured, although the shape remained normal. The final visible segment of the sun turned to a vivid electric blue. Visibility excellent. The sky after sunset was colourful with great clarity of cloud shapes and colours. Cloud 3/8 Cu and Ac.

Position of ship: 18° 28′S., 38° 28′W.

Note. The name of this phenomenon at sunset or sunrise is the " green flash ", green being the colour most usually seen. It would not be practicable to name it according to the colour observed, as these comprise various shades of green and blue, also purple or violet. We have had more observations of blue, purple or violet flashes in recent years. While these colours are admittedly much less frequently seen than various shades of green, it does appear that they are not as rare as was formerly supposed; a probable explanation of this is that more observers are now watching for the phenomenon.

Red Sea

M.V. *Gloucester*. Captain D. A. G. Dickens, R.N.R. Jeddah to Suez. Observer, Mr. R. E. Baker, Chief Officer.

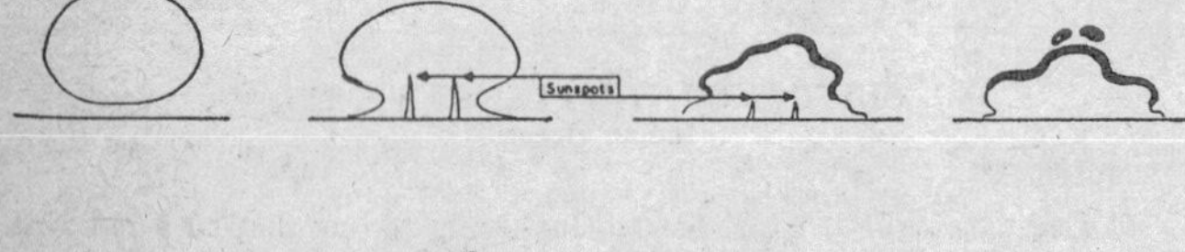

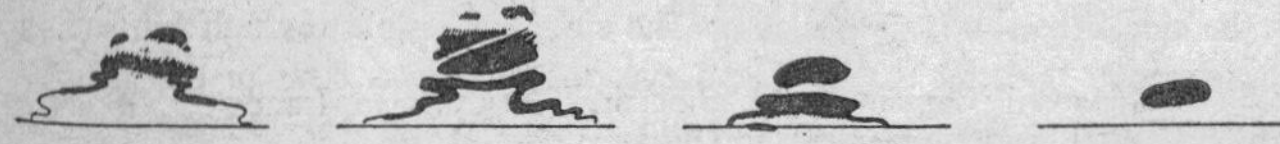

19th February, 1956. Abnormal refraction was observed as the sun set, apparently shaped as shown in the sketches. The green flash was seen all the time the upper half of the sun was disappearing, approximately 30 sec; not only the detached pieces appeared green but the edges of the main body as well.

Position of ship: 22° 08′N., 38° 25′E.

North Pacific Ocean

S.S. *Pacific Northwest*. Captain F. H. Perry. Panama to Los Angeles. Observer, Mr. W. P. Crone, 4th Officer.

29th January, 1956. Half a minute before setting at bearing 262° Venus appeared to turn bright red, becoming orange again just before setting. At the moment of setting at 0345 G.M.T. there was an emerald green flash of 1 sec duration. This observation was made with the aid of binoculars. Cloud 2/8.

Position of ship: 24° 55′N., 112° 44′W.

(Reproduced from *The Marine Observer*, Vol. 27, No. 175, p. 15, Jan. 1957)

GREEN AND RED FLASHES

South Pacific Ocean

M.V. *Cambridge*. Captain P. P. O. Harrison. Wellington to Balboa. Observers, the Master, Mr. P. Bower, Chief Officer, and Mr. L. Money, 4th Officer.

2nd May, 1957. When the sun rose at 0700 S.M.T. a green flash was plainly seen. There was a bank of cumulus whose base was one sun's diameter above the horizon and as the sun disappeared behind the cloud a red flash occurred lasting fully 3 sec.

Position of ship: 38° 51′S., 175° 10′W.

(Reproduced from *The Marine Observer*, Vol. 28, No. 180, p. 77, April 1958)

SETTING OF THE PLANET JUPITER

Gulf of Mannar

S. S. *Sirsa*. Captain N. Maguire. Rangoon to Cochin. Observer, Mr. J. Richardson.

3rd December, 1950, 1755 G.M.T. Jupiter on setting showed a red spot on the side nearest to the horizon. The spot was visible through binoculars and telescope but not to the naked eye. The sky was clear in the vicinity and the phenomenon was visible from the time that the planet was 20 above the horizon.

Position of ship: 7° 40′ N, 77° 47′ E.

Note. When abnormal refraction is present the light of stars or planets near the horizon tends to be elongated into a short spectrum with the red nearest the horizon and the green and blue farthest from the horizon. Many varieties of phenomena result, especially in the case of the bright planets Jupiter and Venus; these are more often seen with binoculars than with unaided vision. At times the planet may appear double, one red and one green, or the colour of the planet may change from red to green. In cases of extreme refraction the planet may be seen to "swim" about with a lateral motion, accompanied by changes of colour, usually from red to green, with momentary returns to the normal colour of the planet. The green flash of sunrise or sunset is an example of the same thing; the uppermost green image of the sun's limb is visible for a fraction of a second after the sun has set.

(Reproduced from *The Marine Observer*, Vol. 21, No. 154, p. 214, Oct. 1951)

35′ 54″, are illustrated in Fig. 15. It is assumed that the white-light source is far away so that the incident rays are near parallel. For $\Phi \approx 89° 33' 30''$ the blue rays are totally reflected by the red rays penetrate the upper boundary of the inversion. When Φ_0 varies from 89° 33′ 30″ to 89° 33′ 54″ the red rays are alternately transmitted and totally reflected. Hence, an observer near A may see an elevated image that is alternately bluish and white, while an observer at B may see a reddish image that disappears and reappears. The small fluctuation in Φ_0 can be produced by atmospheric turbulence or short-period changes in the lower boundary of the inversion. Color changes from red to green that frequently occur when distant lights are observed can be similarly explained. In general, visible color separation is the result of a combined action of random and systematic atmospheric refraction.

Thus, unusual color effects that can be observed with the unaided eye can be associated with mirage phenomena. Occurrence of these effects, however, must be considered unusual in view of the special set of circumstances required for their development.

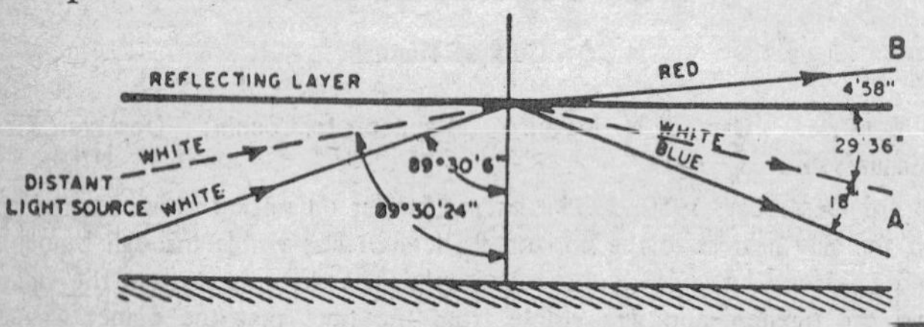

Fig. 15 Geometry of illumination and viewing for a special case of refractive color separation

5. *Effects from Atmospheric Scintillation*

Scintillation defines the *rapid* variations in apparent brightness, position, or color of a distant luminous source when viewed through the atmosphere. If the object lies outside the earth's atmosphere, as in the case of stars and planets, the phenomenon is termed astronomical scintillation; if the luminous source lies within the atmosphere, the phenomenon is termed terrestrial scintillation.

Scintillation occurs when small-scale (meters or less) inhomogeneities at atmospheric density interference with a propagating wavefront for a short duration of seconds or minutes. Such inhomogeneities are generally associated with turbulence and convection. Turbulence convection are most apparent in atmospheric layers close to the earth's surface where they develop under proper conditions of solar heating, wind velocity, and terrain. However, they can occur also at high levels in the atmosphere. Scintillation has been found associated with atmospheric layers near the tropopause (30,000 to 40,000 feet).

Rapid fluctuations in brightness (scintillation in its strictest sense) are observed most frequently. The reason for this may be that, on the average, the time interval between moments of nearly maximum brightness is around 1/10 of a second, a value that coincides with the frequency to which the human eye is most sensitive. Higher frequencies of scintillation do occur (30 to 50 per second), but their significance is restricted to measurement made by means of optical equipment such as telescopes. The apparent brightness fluctuations of a distant source may be so intense that an observer sees the light source as "flashing on and off."

Fluctuations in position are often referred to as "shimmer," "dancing," or "wandering," and involve the apparent jerky or continuous movement of an image about a mean point. Observations of this phenomenon are not as common as observations of intensity fluctuations. Under standard atmospheric conditions, position changes vary from 1″ to 30″ of arc, and such displacements can hardly be observed with the naked eye. Only under abnormal atmospheric conditions are apparent position changes manifest. Their occurrence is most probably in the case of point sources, i.e., sources having no apparent diameter. Position changes of a planet like Venus or Jupiter do occur, but actual observations are limited to very unusual atmospheric conditions when the changes in direction of the planet's light rays are so large as to be of the same order of magnitude as the apparent diameter (0.5 to 1.0 minutes of arc).

In the case of an extended luminous source, a slow or rapid "pulsation" can be observed. This contraction and expansion of the image usually results in apparent changes of the image size. Occasionally, pulsation of the solar or lunar limb can be observed during setting or rising.

In general, the effects of scintillation are minimum when the luminous source is viewed near the zenith, and maximum when the source is viewed near the horizon. When terrestrial light sources are involved, the scintillation increases with distance and is highly dependent on the meteorological conditions.

The many detailed discussions of scintillation encountered in the literature are primarily concerned with the application of optical instruments to astronomy, optical communication, and optical ranging. In this case, all light sources viewed through the atmosphere exhibit effects of scintillation irrespective of their position with respect to the zenith. When observations are made with the unaided eye, the above-mentioned effects of scintillation are manifested only when the observation concern objects close to the horizon (at low elevation or "low in the sky"). Under these conditions, the *most spectacular visual effects can be expected when the effects of scintillation (random refraction) are superposed on any visual image that arises from regular atmospheric refraction.*

The following section on aerosol particles has been contributed by Mr. Gordon D. Thayer of ESSA:

C. Light scattering by aerosol particles

An apparent optical image formed by light scattered out of a beam by a thin haze layer may be mistaken for a mirage. The theory of optical propagation in a scattering, attenuating atmosphere is well covered by Middleton (1952), an excellent reference containing much material on vision and the visibility of objects seen through the atmosphere.

The luminance or brightness, B, in e.g. lumens/m^2, of an extended object or optical source is invariant with distance except for losses due to scattering or absorption along the propagation path. Except under conditions of heavy fog, clouds, or smog, absorption is small compared to scattering, and may be neglected. If the scattering coefficient per unit length, O, is constant, attenuation of a light source of intrinsic brightness B is given by

$$B = B_0 e^{-\sigma R},$$

where R is the distance of range travelled by the light from the source to the point of observation. The portion of brightness lost by scattering out of the path is given by

$$B_s = B_o \ (1 - e^{-\sigma R});$$

this loss represents light that is scattered in all directions by the molecules of air and aerosol particles present in the propagation path. Secondary scattering is neglected.

The quantity σR is often called the optical depth of an atmospheric layer, although it is a dimensionless quantity. Thus for thin layers where σR is small, the scattered light flux, F, in e.g. lumens, is

$$F_s \cong \sigma R F_o ,$$

where F is the light flux incident on the layer.

The intensity, I_s, or light flux per unit solid angle, of the light scattered from a small volume of air, v, is the product of the incident light flux, F_o, the volume scattering function, $\beta'(\Phi)$, and the average thickness of the volume. The scattering angle, Φ, is defined in Fig. 16. The intensity of light scattered at an angle Φ with respect to the incident beam is usually

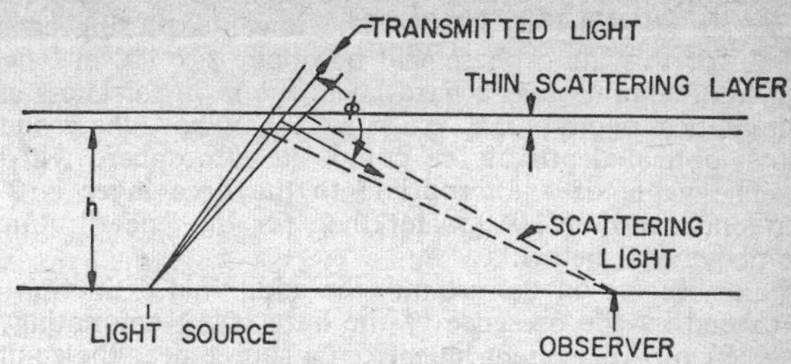

Fig. 16 Geometry of light scattering

defined in terms of the incident illuminance, E, or flux per unit area in e.g., lumens/m^2 on an element of volume dv. This results in

$$dI(\phi) = E\beta'(\phi)\, dv, \qquad \text{hence, } I(\phi) = \int_V E\beta'(\phi)dv,$$

which, in the case of a small scattering volume where E and $\beta'(\Phi)$ may be considered nearly constant over the entire volume, reduces to $I(\Phi) \cong E_o\beta'(\Phi)v$.

The units of $\beta'(\Phi)$ are typically lumens scattered per unit solid angle per unit volume per lumen incident light per unit area; $I(\Phi)$ then is expressed in candles, a unit of light intensity equal to one lumen per steradian. The volume scattering function is normalized by

$$2\pi \int_0^\pi \beta'(\phi) \sin \phi \sin \phi d\phi = \sigma;$$

hence for an isotropic scatterer, for which $\beta'(\Phi)$ = const. $= \beta'_o$, $\beta' = \frac{\sigma}{4\pi}$. The volume scattering function relative to an isotropic scatterer is conveniently defined as

$$f(\Phi) \equiv \frac{4\pi}{\sigma} \beta'(\Phi)$$

The relative volume scattering function for very clear air has maxima at $\Phi = 0°$ and $180°$, $F(\Phi) \cong 3.3$ and 1.7 respectively, and a minimum of $\Phi = 90°$, $f(\Phi) \cong 0.5$. Industrial haze, or smog, has a strong maximum at $\Phi = 0°$, $F(\Phi) \cong 8$, and a minimum at $\Phi = 120°$ to $160°$, $f(\Phi) \cong 0.2$, with a weaker secondary maximum at $\Phi = 180°$, $f(\Phi) \cong 1.3$.

As an example of a scattering situation, consider a very clear atmosphere with a total vertical optical depth of 0.2; this is about twice the optical depth of a standard atmosphere of pure air (Middleton, 1952). The linear scattering coefficient, Φ, for this atmosphere will be about $2 \times 10^{-5} m^{-1}$ near the ground. Assume that a haze layer one m in thickness and with an optical depth of 0.02 exists at 100 m above the ground; the total optical depth of the composite atmosphere will be 0.22. The value of σ appropriate to the haze layer is $2 \times 10^{-2} m^{-1}$, a factor of 10^3 greater than for the "clear" atmosphere above and below.

To an observer on the ground, the additional extinction of light caused by the presence of the haze layer, amounting to only 1.6% of the incident light from a source near the zenith, would not be perceptible except possibly very close to the horizon. However, light scattered out of an intense beam by the haze layer could be easily visible. Assume that a fairly powerful light source is aimed straight up from the ground; taking as typical values, e.g., for an automobile sealed beam unit, an intensity, I_o, of 3×10^4 candles (30,000 candlepower) and a beam width of 6°, the light flux incident on the layer at $h = 100$ m is

$$F_o = 236 \text{ lumens},$$

neglecting attenuation in the air below the layer. The beam solid angle, w_o, is 7.85×10^{-3} steradians. The incident illuminance, E_o, on the layer is

$$E_o = \frac{F_o}{A} = \frac{I_o}{h^2} = 3 \text{ lumens/m}^2$$

where the illuminated area, $A = w_o h^2$, is $78.5 m^2$. The scattering volume, v, is $78.5 m^3$ since the layer is one meter thick, and the intensity of the scattered light is

$$I(\phi) \cong E_o \frac{\sigma}{4\pi} f(\phi) v$$
$$\cong 3.75 \times 10^{-1} f(\phi) \quad \text{(candles)}.$$

If an observer is located 100 m from the light source, he will observe the scattered light at a distance of ~140 m and a scattering angle Φ, of 135°. The apparent source of the scattered light will appear to be elliptical, roughly 4° wide and 3° high, and will present an area normal to the observer, A_n, of $62.6 m^2$. The value of $f(\Phi)$ for a strongly scattering medium at $\Phi = 135°$ is about 0.2; therefore the light scattered toward the observer is

$$I_s \cong 7.5 \times 10^{-2} \text{ candles},$$

and the apparent brightness, B_s, of the scattering volume will be

$$B_s = \frac{I_s}{A_n} \doteq 1.2 \times 10^{-3}\ c/m^2$$

A fairly dark, moonless night sky has a background brightness, B_b, of about 10^{-3} c/m²; the scattered image would therefore have a total brightness of $\sim 2.2 \times 10^{-3}$ c/m² and a contrast against the night sky of $\epsilon = B_s/B_b \cong 1.2$. At this background brightness data given by Middleton (1952) show that the contrast required for 50% probability of detection for an object of 3°—4° diameter is about 5.7×10^{-2}; thus the image hypothesized in this example would have a brightness about 20 times greater than the minimum detectable, and would no doubt be easily visible as a pale, glowing, elliptical object.

In contrast, the air immediately above and below the haze layer with $\sigma = 2 \times 10^{-5}\ m^{-1}$ and $f(\phi) \cong 1.1$ at $\phi = 135°$ would yield a scattered brightness of only about 6.6×10^{-6} c/m² per meter thickness. The contrast against the night sky of the light scattered from the beam above or below the layer would therefore be on the order of 7×10^{-3}, which is not detectable with a background brightness of 10^{-3} c/m² according to Middleton (1952).

Increasing the background brightness to 10^{-2} c/m², corresponding to a bright, moonlit night, would decrease the contrast of the scattered image to 1.2×10^{-1}, which is about six times the minimum detectable contrast at that background brightness and the image would therefore still constitute a fairly obvious (object). Perception of light scattered from the rest of the beam under this increased background brightness with $\epsilon \cong 6.6 \times 10^{-4}$, would be out of the question.

The level of background brightness for which the contrast of the image in this example would be reduced to the point where there is only a 50% probability of detection by an observer looking in the right direction is roughly 10^{-1} c/m²; this value corresponds to the brightness of a clear sky about ½ hour after sunset.

Thus, scattering of light from sources of small beam width by localized haze layers in the lower atmosphere may cause the appearance of diffuse, glowing patches of light, moving with movement of the light source, that could easily be interpreted as a UFO by an observer unfamiliar with such phenomena. Data given by Middleton (1952) show that with common light sources and under average nighttime sky conditions, the main beam of light could easily be imperceptible by scattered light, while at the same time the light scattered from a haze patch or layer would be easily visible to an observer; thus the source of the UFO-like image would not be apparent.

6. *Evaluation of the State-of-the-Art Knowledge*

During the last decade, active interest in optical mirage appears to have waned. The reasons for the apparent decline are believed to be two-fold. Firstly, on the basis of simple ray-tracing techniques, the mirage theories satisfactorily explain the various large-scale aspects of observations. Thus, no disturbing contradictions between theory and observation have been found. Secondly, although atmospheric refraction remains of great interest to astronomy, optical communication, and optical ranging, the phenomenon of the mirage has so far failed to demonstrate a major use.

At the present time, there is no *single* theoretical model that explains *all* the aspects, both macroscopic and microscopic, of the mirage phenomenon. The absence of such a model must stand as evidence that shortcomings remain in current knowledge. These shortcomings are most eloquently discussed by Sir. C. V. Raman (1959), who suggests and actually demonstrates that any approach to explain the phenomenon must be based on wave-optics rather than ray-optics. The theory of wave-optics as applied by Sir. C. V. Raman, suggests the presence of some intriguing aspects of the mirage that arise from the interference and focussing of wavefronts in selected regions of the refracting layer. Raman's experimental studies reveal that when a collimated pencil of light is incident obliquely on a heated plate in contact with air, the field of observation exhibits a dark region adjacent to the plate into which the incident radiation does not penetrate, followed by a layer in which there is an intense concentration of light and then again by a series of dark and bright bands of progressively diminishing intensity.

Further theoretical and experimental investigations are warranted in order to determine to what extent the brightening and brightness variations that arise from interference and focussing can add unusual effects to observations of phenomenon associated with abnormal refraction in the atmosphere.

7. *Conclusions*

When an unusual optical phenomenon is observed in the atmosphere, its positive identification as a mirage cannot be made without a physically meaningful description of what is seen and a complete set of meteorological and astronomical data. The required "hard" data are practically never available for the specific place and time of observation, so that the descriptive account remains the only basis for identification; in this case, successful identification depends on a process of education. Thus, the casual observer of an optical phenomenon can establish the likelihood that his observation is a mirage only by being aware of the basic characteristics of mirage and the physical principles that govern its appearance and behavior.

The conditions required for mirage formation and the principal characteristics of mirage images, as described in this report, are summarized below. The summary presents a set of standards by which to interpret the nature of an optical observation in terms of a specific natural atmospheric phenomenon.

A. METEOROLOGICAL CONDITIONS

Optical mirages arise from abnormal temperature gradients in the atmosphere. A temperature decrease with height (temperature lapse) exceeding 3.4°C per 100 m or a temperature increase with height (temperature inversion) is most commonly responsible for a mirage sighting.

Large temperature lapses are found in the first 10 meters above the ground during daytime. They occur when ground surfaces are heated by solar radiation, while during nighttime they can occur when cool air flows over a relatively warm surface such as a lake. When the temperature decreases with height more than 3.4°C per 100 m over a horizontal distance of 1 kilometer or more, an observer located within the area of temperature lapse can sight an inferior mirage near the ground (e.g., road mirage, "water" on the desert).

Layers of temperature inversion ranging in thickness from a few meters to several hundred meters may be located on the ground or at various levels above it. In areas where they are horizontally extensive, an observer can sight a superior mirage that usually appears far away (beyond 1 kilometer) and "low in the sky." The strength of the inversion determines the degree of image-elevation; the stronger the inversion, the higher the image appears above the horizon. Layers of maximum temperature inversion (30°C) are usually found adjacent to the ground.

Calm, clear-weather conditions (no precipitation or high winds) and good horizontal visibility are favorable for mirage formation. Warm days or warm nights during the summer are most likely to produce the required temperature gradients.

B. GEOMETRY OF ILLUMINATION AND VIEWING

The geometry of illumination and viewing in the case of optical mirage is determined by the spatial variations of refraction index that occur in the cloud-free atmosphere, and by Snell's law of refraction, which relates these variations to changes in the direction of propagating wavefronts. The spatial variations in refractive index are associated with layers of temperature inversion or temperature lapse. Variations of 3×10^{-5}, corresponding to temperature changes of 30°C, are considered near maximum.

As a consequence of Snell's law and the small changes in the atmospheric refractive index, an optical mirage develops only when a temperature-inversion layer or a layer of large temperature lapse is illuminated at grazing incidence. The requirement of grazing incidence implies that the source of illumination must be either far away, i.e., near the horizon, or very close to or within the layer of temperature gradient. Therefore, both terrestrial and extraterrestrial sources can be involved. Because of the distance factor, the actual source of illumination may not be visible. Its location, however, must always be in the direction in which the mirage image is observed, i.e., observer, image and "mirrored" source are located in the same vertical plane.

Another consequence of Snell's law and the small spatial changes in refractive index is that noticeable refractive effects are not likely beyond an angular distance of approximately 14 degrees above the horizon and that a superior mirage image is not likely beyond an angular distance of 1 to 2 degrees above the horizon. Hence, mirages appear "low in the sky" and near the horizontal plane of view. An optical image seen near the zenith is not attributable to mirage.

Because of the restricted geometry between observer, mirage image, and source of illumination, the observed image can often be made to disappear abruptly by moving to higher or lower ground. Furthermore, when mirage observations are made from a continuously moving position, the image can move also, or can move for a while and then abruptly disappear.

C. SHAPE AND COLOR

A mirage can involve more than one image of a single object. Observations of up to four separate images, some inverted and some upright, are encountered in the literature. When multiple images occur they all lie in a single vertical plane or very close to it.

The apparent shape of a mirage can vary from clearly outlined images of an identifiable object such as a distant ship, landscape, or the sun or moon, to distorted images that defy any description in terms of known objects (e.g., Fata Morgana). Apparent stretching either in the vertical or in the horizontal plane is common.

During daytime, a mirage can appear silvery white ("water" on the ground), or dark when projected against a bright sky background, or it can reflect the general color of the land or seascape. Distinctly colored images ranging from red and yellow to green and blue are observed when unusual conditions of mirage occur near sunrise or sunset (e.g., Red and Green Flash) or, at night, during rising or setting of the moon or of a planet such as Venus.

In the presence of atmospheric turbulence and convection, the effects of scintillation become superimposed on the large-scale mirage image. When scintillation occurs, extended mirage images appear in constant motion by changing their shape and brightness. When the image is small and bright, as may be the case at night, large fluctuations in brightness and under unusual conditions in color can give an illusion of blinking, flashing, side to side oscillation, or motion toward and away from the observer. The effects associated with scintillation can dominate the visual appearance of any bright point-object in the area between the horizon and approximately 14 degrees above the horizon.

D. PRESENT UNCERTAINTIES

The theory of ray optics adequately explains such observed large-scale aspects of the mirage as the number of images, image inversion, and apparent vertical stretching and shrinking. However, if the interference and focussing of wavefronts within the refracting layer are as fundamental in mirage formation as purported by Sir C. V. Raman, the ray-tracing technique may have to be replaced by the theory of wave-optics.

Sir C. V. Raman's application of wave-optics to mirage suggests that under special conditions of illumination, the upper boundary of an atmospheric temperature inversion could exhibit a large concentration of radiant energy due to focussing of wavefronts. Also, interference of wavefronts could produce alternating layers of high and low brightness. Under what conditions and to what extent these brightness effects can be observed in the atmosphere is not known. Relevant observations have not been encountered in the literature, although some unusual observations of the green flash made under mirage conditions (O'Connel, 1958) could possibly have been caused by the enhancement of brightness in an inversion. The visual effects from focussing and interference of wavefronts must be considered as the least explored aspect of mirage.

Benson, Carl S., "Ice Fog: Low Temperature Air Pollution," Geophysical Inst., Univ. of Alaska (November 1965).

Brocks, K., *Vertikaler Temperaturgradient und terrestrische Refraction, insbesondere im Hochgebirge.* (Verlag von Dietrich Reimer Andrews & Steiner, Berlin 1939).

Dietze, Gerhard, *Einführung in die Optik der Atmosphäre* (Akademische Verlagsgesellschaft, Geest & Portig K.-G., Leipsig 1957).

Eldridge, Ralph G., "Climatic Visibilities of the United States," *J. Appl. Meteorol.*, Vol. 5, No. 3 (June 1966).

Epstein, Paul S., "Geometrical Optics in Absorbing Media," *Proc. Nat. Acad. Sci.*, Vol. 16, 37-45 (1930).

Epstein, Paul S., "Reflections of Waves in an Inhomogeneous Absorbing Medium," *Proc. Nat. Acad. Sci.*, Vol. 16, No. 10, 628-637 (October 1930).

Goos, F. and H. Haenchen, "A new and fundamental experiment on total reflection," *Ann. Physik,* Vol. 6, No. 1, pp. 333-346 (1947).

Handbook of Geophysics and Space Environments, Chapter 13, Air Force Cambridge Research Laboratories, Office of Aerospace Research, USAF (1965).

Hosler, Charles R., "Low-level inversion frequency in the contiguous United States," *Monthly Weather Rev.*, Vol. 89, No. 9 (September 1961).

Humphreys, C. E., *Physics of the Air* (McGraw-Hill Book Company, Inc., New York 1940).

Jenkins, F. A., and H. E. White, *Fundamentals of Optics,* 3rd Ed. (McGraw-Hill Book Company, Inc., New York 1957).

Johnson, John C., *Physical Meteorology* (Published jointly by the Technology Press of M.I.T. and John Wiley & Sons, Inc., New York 1954).

Lane, J. A., "Some investigations of the structure of elevated layers in the troposphere," *J. of Atmos. and Terres. Phys.*, Vol. 27, pp. 969-978 (1965).

Middleton, W. E. Knowles, *Vision Through the Atmosphere,* University of Toronto Press, 1952.

Minnaert, M., *The Nature of Light and Colour in the Open Air* (Dover Publications, Inc., 1954).

Neuberger, Hans, *General Meteorological Optics,* in *Compendium of Meteorology* (American Meteorology Society, Boston, Mass., 1951).

O'Connel, D. J. K., *The Green Flash and Other Low Sun Phenomena,* Vatican Observatory (North Holland Publishing Company, Amsterdam; Interscience Publishers, Inc., New York, 1958).

Owens, James C., "Optical Refractive Index of Air: Dependence on Pressure, Temperature and Composition," *Applied Optics,* Vol. 6, No. 1 (January 1967).

Pernter, J. M. and Felix M. Exner, *Meteorologische Optik,* (Wien und Leipzig, Wilhelm Braumüller, K. U. K. Hof- und Universitäts-Buchhändler, 1910).

Ramdas, L. A., "Micro-Climatological Investigations in India," *Archiv. für Meteorologie, Geophysik und Bioklimatologie,* Ser. B, Vol. 3 (1951).

Sears, F. W., *Optics* (Addison-Wesley Press, Inc., Cambridge, Mass., 1949).

Tolansky, S., *Optical Illusions* (Pergamon Press, New York, 1964).

Visher, S. S., *Climatic Atlas of the United States* (Harvard Univ. Press, Cambridge, Mass., 1954).

Wallot, S., "Der senkrechte Durchgang elektromagnetischer Wellen durch eine Schicht räumlich veränderlicher Dielektrisitäts konstante," *Ann. Physik,* Vol. 60, pp. 734-762 (1919).

Wood, Robert W., *Physical Optics,* 3rd ed. (The MacMillan Company, New York, 1934).

Chapter 5 Radar and the Observation of UFOs / Roy H. Blackmer, Jr. with contributions by R. J. Allen, R. T. H. Collis, C. Herold, R. I. Presnell

1. Introduction

This chapter covers studies of radar capabilities and limitations as they may be related to the apparent manifestation of unidentified flying objects. The studies were carried out by the Stanford Research Institute pursuant to a contract with University of Colorado (Order No. 73403) dated 23 June 1967, under sub-contract to the U.S. Air Force.

The preceding chapter of this report, entitled "Optical Mirage—A Survey of the Literature," by William Viezee, covers optical phenomena due to atmospheric light refraction.

As they became available other information and interim results of these studies were informally communicated to the University of Colorado study project in accordance with the referenced contract.

The purpose of this chapter is to provide a basic understanding of radar, the types of targets it can detect under various conditions, and a basis upon which specific radar reports may be studied. Studies of specific UFO incidents were performed by the Colorado project (see Section III, Chapter 5).

At first consideration, radar might appear to offer a positive, non-subjective method of observing UFOs. Radar seems to reduce data to ranges, altitudes, velocities, and such characteristics as radar reflectivity. On closer examination however, the radar method of looking at an object, although mechanically and electronically precise, is in many aspects substantially less comprehensive than the visual approach. In addition, the very techniques that provide the objective measurements are themselves susceptible to errors and anomalies that can be very misleading.

In this chapter we will consider how the radar principle applies to detection of targets that may be or appear to be UFOs, and attempt to establish the criteria by which such apparent manifestations must be judged in order to identify them. Since we make no assumptions regarding the nature of UFOs we limit ourselves to describing the principles by which radars detect targets and the ways in which targets appear when detected. In a word, we can only specify the nature of radar detection of targets in terms of physical principles, both in regard to real and actual targets and in regard to mechanisms which give rise to the apparent manifestation of targets. It is hoped that these specifications will assist in the review of specific instances as they arise. Even in cases where radar may identify target properties that cannot be explained within the accepted frame of understanding of our physical world, the authentic observation of a target having such properties will shed little or no light on its nature beyond the characteristics observed, and it will therefore remain unidentified.

2. *Radar Systems*

RADAR is an acronym for RAdio Detection And Ranging. It is a device for detecting certain types of targets and determining the range to the target. The majority of radars are also capable of measuring the azimuth and elevation angles of targets.

Radars operate on three fundamental principles:

1) that radio energy is propagated at uniform and known velocity;
2) that radio energy is normally propagated in nearly straight lines, the direction of which can be controlled or recognized; and
3) that radio energy may be reradiated or "reflected" by matter intercepting the transmitted energy.

Basically radar consists of a transmitter that radiates pulses of electromagnetic energy through a steerable antenna, a receiver that detects and amplifies returned signals, and some type of display that presents information on received signals.

Radar systems can be separated into three general categories:

1) operational systems,
2) special usage systems and
3) experimental and research systems. These include fixed and portable ground-mounted systems, airborne, and shipborne systems.

Many types of radars are specifically designed to perform specialized functions. In general, radars provide either a tracking or a surveillance function. The surveillance radar may scan a limited sector or 360° and display the range and azimuth of all targets on a PPI (plan position indicator). Tracking radar locks onto the target of interest and continually tracks it, providing target coordinates including range, velocity, altitude, and other data. The data are usually in the form of punched or magnetic tape with digital display readout. Air traffic control, ship navigation, and weather radars fall into the surveillance category; whereas instrumentation, aircraft automatic landing, missile guidance, and fire control radars are usually tracking radars. Some of the newer generation of radar systems can provide both functions, but at this time these are very specialized systems of limited number and will not be discussed further.

In addition to the above general applications, each of the radar systems have special selective functions for various purposes. For example, some radar systems are designed so that they can track moving targets. Signals from stationary targets such as the ground, buildings, or even slow-moving objects are excluded from the display. This simplifies the display and makes it possible to track aircraft even though they are moving through an area from which strong ground clutter signals would otherwise mask the echo from the aircraft.

In addition to the many radar types, the radar operator has at his disposal many control functions enabling system parameters to be changed in order to improve the radar performance for increasing the detectability of particular types of targets, thereby minimizing interference, weather, and/or clutter effects. These radar system controls can modify any one or any combination of the following characteristics:

- Transmitter output power
- Pulse repetition rate
- Sensitivity time control
- Transmitted pulse width
- AGC response time
- IF receiver bandwidth
- Transmitter operating frequency
- Antenna scan rate
- Polarization control of radiated and received energy
- Skin or transponder beacon tracking
- Receiver RF and IF gain
- Display control functions
- Numerous signal processing techniques for clutter suppression, weather effects, moving target indication, false alarm rate, and threshold controls.

The radar operator himself is an important part of radar systems. He must be well trained and familiar with all of the interacting factors affecting the operation and performance of his equipment. When an experienced operator is moved to a new location, an important part of his retraining is learning pertinent factors related to expected anomalies due to local geographical and meteorological factors.

Two other groups of persons also affect the performance of the radar system. They are the radar design engineer and the radar maintenance personnel. The designer seeks to engineer a radar which achieves the performance desired, in addition to being a system which is both reliable and maintainable. Highly trained maintenance technicians routinely monitor the system insuring that it is functioning properly and is not being degraded by component system failures or being affected by other electronic systems that could cause electrical interference or system failure.

During the past 30 years, radar systems design has considerably improved. Radars manufactured today are more complex, versatile, sensitive, accurate, more powerful, and provide more data-processing aids to the operator at the display console. They are also more reliable and easier to maintain. In the process, they have become more sensitive to clutter, interference, propagation anomalies, and require better trained operating and maintenance personnel. Furthermore, with the increased data-processing aids to the operator, the more difficult becomes his target interpretation problem when the radar systems components begin gradually to degrade or when the propagation environment varies far from average conditions. The more sophisticated radar systems become, the more sensitive the system is to human, component, and environmental degradations.

3. *Radar Fundamentals*

Radar detection of targets is based on the fact that radio energy is reflected or reradiated back to the radar by various mechanisms. By transmitting pulses of energy and then 'listening' for a reflected return signal, the target is located. The period of time the radar is transmitting one pulse is called the pulse length and is generally measured in microseconds (millionths of a second) or expressed in terms of the length from the front to the back edge of the pulse. (A one microsecond pulse is 984 ft. long, since radio waves, like light travel 186,000 statute mps.) The rate at which pulses are transmitted is called the pulse repetition rate. When pulses are transmitted at a high rate, the receiver listening time between pulses for return echoes is reduced as well as the corresponding distance to which the energy can travel and return. This means that the maximum unambiguous range is decreased with increasing pulse repetition rate. More distant targets may still return an echo to the radar after the next pulse has been transmitted but they are displayed by the radar as being from the most recent pulse. These so-called multiple trip echoes may be misleading, since they are displayed at much shorter ranges than their actual position.

Other important operating characteristics of a radar are its transmitted power and wavelength (or frequency). The strength of an echo from a target varies directly with the transmitted power. The wavelength is important in the detection of certain types of targets such as those composed of many small particles. When the particles are small relative to the wavelength, their detectability is greatly reduced. Thus drizzle is detectable by short wavelength (0.86 cm.) radars but is not generally detectable by longer (23 cm.) wavelength radars.

The outgoing radar energy is concentrated into a beam by the antenna. This radiation of the signal in a specific direction makes it possible to determine the coordinates of the target from knowledge of the azimuth and elevation angle of the antenna. The desired antenna pattern varies with the specific purpose for which the radar was designed. Search radars may have broad vertical beams and narrow horizontal beams so that the azimuth of targets can be accurately determined. Height finders on the other hand have broad horizontal beams so that the height of targets can be accurately determined. In either case the radiating and receiving surface of the antenna is usually a section of a paraboloid.

A circular beam may be described as a cone with maximum radiation along its axis and tapering off with angular distance from the center. The beam is described by the angle between the half power points (the angular distance at which the radiated power is half that along the axis of the beam). In the case of non-circular beams two angles are used, one to describe the horizontal beamwidth, a second to describe the vertical beamwidth. Later in this report the detection of targets by stray energy outside the main beam will be discussed.

The size of the beam for a given wavelength depends on the size of the parabola. For a given size parabola the longer the wavelength, the broader the beam.

When the radiated energy illuminates an object, the energy (except for a small amount that is absorbed as heat) is reradiated in all directions. The amount that is radiated directly back to the radar depends on the radar cross-section of the target. Differences between geometrical cross-section and radar cross-section are related to the material of which the object is composed, its shape, and also to the wavelength of the incident radiation. The radar cross-section of a target is customarily defined as the cross-sectional area of a perfectly conducting sphere that would return the same amount of energy to the radar as that returned by the actual target. The radar cross-section of complicated targets such as aircraft depends on the object's orientation with respect to the radar. A jet aircraft has a much smaller radar (and geometric) cross-section when viewed from the nose or the tail than when viewed broadside.

Equations relating the various parameters are given, in varying degrees of complexity, in textbooks on radar. In their simplest form the equations for average received power are:

For point targets (birds, insects, aircraft, balloons, etc.)

$$P_r = \frac{P_t G^2 \lambda^2 \sigma}{(4\pi)^3 R^4} \quad (1)$$

For plane targets (earth's surface at small depression angles)

$$\bar{P}_r = \frac{P_t G^2 \lambda^2 \Theta \, c\tau\sigma}{(4\pi)^3 \, R^3 \, 2} \quad (2)$$

For volume targets (precipitation)

$$\bar{P} = \frac{P_t G^2 \lambda^2 \quad \theta\psi \, c\tau \, \eta}{(4\pi)^3 \, R^2 \, 2} \quad (3)$$

Where:

P_r = average received power
P_t = transmitted power
G = Antenna gain
λ = wavelength
σ = radar cross-section
R = range of target
Θ = horizontal beamwidth of antenna
c = velocity of radio waves
τ = length of transmitted pulse
Ψ = vertical beamwidth of antenna
η = reflectivity per unit volume

These equations show that the intensity of echo signal varies according to whether the target is a point, a relatively small area, or a very large volume such as an extensive region of precipitation. The echo signal intensity of point targets varies inversely with the fourth power of the distance from the radar to the targets. The intensity of area targets varies with the cube of the distance, and that of large volume targets, with the square of the distance.

Figure 1 illustrates how the radar beamwidth and the cross-section area or volume of the target interact to give these different variations with range of the returned signal. In Fig. Aa, the point target has a radar cross-section σ. In Fig. Ab there may be a number of targets with radar cross-section σ over an area with dimensions of half the pulse length and the beam width at range R. Replacing σ in equation (1) with this new expression for radar cross-section cancels one R in the denominator giving the R^3 relationshiþ. When the target is many σ's

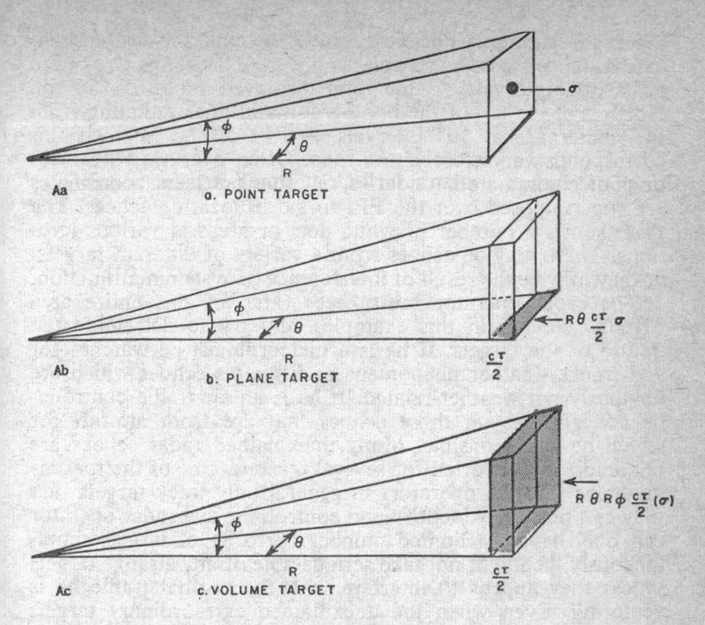

Fig. 1 Radar cross sections of various types of targets

spread over a volume with dimensions determined by range, horizontal and vertical beamwidth, and half the pulse length (Fig. Ac) R appears in the numerator twice, thus cancelling an R^2 in the denominator of equation (1).

Because of differences in variation with distance of the return signal from various types of targets it is apparent that with combinations of targets the point targets might not be detectable. For example, an aircraft cannot be detected when it is flying through precipitation or in an area of ground targets unless special techniques are used to reduce the echo from precipitation or ground clutter.

Information on signals returned to the radar by a target may be presented to an operator in a number of ways; by lights or sounds that indicate there is a target at a selected location; by numbers that give the azimuth, elevation angle, and range of a selected target; or in 'picture' form showing all targets within range that are detected as the antenna rotates. The latter form of presentation is called a Plan Position Indicator (PPI). Plate 65 shows a photograph of a PPI. This photograph is a time exposure equal to the time for one antenna revolution. The center of the photograph is the location of the radar station. Concentric circles around the center indicate distance from the station. In this case the range circles are at 10 mi. intervals, so the total displayed range is 150 mi. North is at the top of the photograph and lines radiating from the center are at 10° intervals. A PPI display such as this corresponds very closely to a map. Often overlays with locations of cities, state boundaries, or other pertinent coordinates are superimposed over the PPI to aid in locating echoes. The plate shows a number of white dots or areas at various locations. These may be echoes from a variety of different targets, or they may be the result of interference or system malfunction.

The radar operator must keep watch of this entire area (70,650 sq. mi. in this example) and try to determine the nature of the targets. If he is a meteorologist he watches for and tracks weather phenomena and ignores echoes which are obviously not weather-related. If he is an air traffic controller he concentrates on those echoes that are from aircraft for which he is responsible. Many unexplained radar echoes are not studied or reported for several reasons. One of the reasons might be that the operators in general only track targets that they can positively identify and control. Since a radar operator can only handle a limited number (6 to 8) of targets simultaneously, he might not take serious note of any strange targets unless they appear to interfere with the normal traffic he is vectoring. Even when the unexplained extraordinary targets are displayed, he has little time available to track and analyze these targets. His time is fully occupied observing the known targets for which he is responsible. In addition, the operator is familiar with locally recurring strange phenomena due to propagation conditions and suspects the meteorological environment as being the cause. In general, the operator seldom has a way in which to record the displayed data for later study and analysis by specialists.

In addition to the tracking of various targets he must also be aware of the possibility of malfunction of the radar.

4. *System Reliability*

Two types of failures occur in a radar system: those that are catastrophic and those that cause a gradual degradation. In spite of good maintenance procedures, there will be system component failures that occur due to external events such as ice or wind loading, rain on the cabling and connectors, bugs and birds in the feed structure. The operator is not always immediately aware of such failures. He is usually located in a soundproofed and windowless room remote from the transmitter, antenna, and receiving hardware. The operator has available to him only the console display and readout equipment. Catastrophic systems failure is usually self-evident to the operator. When the transmitter power tube fails, or the antenna drive unit fails, the operator is aware of this immediately on his PPI display. But when the gain in a receiving tube decreases, or the system noise slowly increases due to a component degradation, or the AFC in the transmitter section begins to go out of tolerance over a period of days causing increased frequency modulation or "pulse jitter" in the transmitted pulse, time may elapse before the operator becomes aware of the slowly deteriorating performance. Reduced sensitivity or the increased reception of extraneous targets from ground clutter or nearby reflecting structure is often evidence that the radar system is deteriorating.

It can be considered that a major system component of a typical radar might be subject to catastropic failure every 250 to 2,000 hours of operation (5 to 36 average failure-free days) and that graceful degradations of components occur continually. Possible failure thus becomes one of the first causes to be considered in analyzing unusual radar sightings. The next factor will be possible unusual propagation effects to which the radar is subject. Analysis of extraordinary sightings is further handicapped by the fact that the displayed data of the sighting usually are not recorded and that any explanations must frequently be based upon interpretations by the operators present at the time of the sighting. The point is that the operator, the radar, and the propagation medium are all fallible parts of the system.

5. *Relationships between Echoes and Targets*

There are five possible relationships between radar echoes and targets.

These are:

a) no echo—no target;
b) no echo—when a visual object appears to be in a position to be detected;
c) echo—unrelated to a target;
d) echo—from a target in a position other than that indicated;
e) echo—from a target at the indicated location.

The first and last possibilities are indicative of normal function. Possibility b) becomes of importance where there is an object that is seen visually. Then, from knowledge of the types of targets that are detectable by the radar, some knowledge of the characteristics of the visual object could be obtained.

The situations c) where there is an apparent echo but no target are those when the manifestation on the PPI is due to a signal that is not a reradiated portion of the transmitted pulse but is due to another source. These are discussed in a subsequent section of this chapter.

Situations where the echo is from a target *not* at the indicated location d) may arise due to one or a combination of the following reasons. First, abnormal bending of the radar beam may take place due to atmospheric conditions. Second, a detectable target may be present beyond the designed range of the radar and be presented on the display as if it were within the designed range, for example, multiple-trip echos from artificial satellites with large radar cross-sections. Third, stray energy from the antenna may be reflected from an obstacle to a target in a direction quite different from that in which the antenna is pointed. Since the echo is presented on the display along the azimuth toward which the antenna is pointed the displayed position will be incorrect. Finally, targets could be detected by radiation in side lobes and would be presented on the display as if they were detected by the main beam.

Possibility e) listed above encompasses the broad range of situations where there is a target at the location indicated on the display system. Of primary concern in this case is the identification of the target.

The possible relationships listed above show that radarscope interpretation is not simple. To attempt to identify targets, the operator must know the characteristics of his radar; whether it is operating properly; and the type of targets it is capable of detecting. He must be very aware of the conditions or events by which echoes will be presented on the radar in a position that is different from the true target location (or in the case of interference by no target). Finally, the operator must acquire collateral information (weather data, transponder, voice communication, visual observations or handover information from another radar before he can be absolutely sure he has identified an unusual echo.

6. *Signal Sources*

Sources of electromagnetic radiation that may cause real or apparent echoes on the radar display include both radiators and reradiators. Some sources, such as ionospheric electron backscatter, the sun, and the planets, are not considered, since they can be detected only by the most sensitive of research radars. As a radiator the sun does emit enough energy at microwave wavelengths to produce a noise signal. This signal has been used for research purposes (Walker 1962) to check the alignment of the radar antenna. Radio sextants have been built which track the sun at cm. wavelengths by Collins Radio Co. Since this signal is quite weak it is unlikely it would be noticed during routine operation of a search radar.

Reradiators include objects or atmospheric conditions that intercept and reradiate energy transmitted by the radar. Objects range in size from the side of a mountain to insects. Atmospheric conditions include ionized regions such as those caused by lightning discharges and inhomogeneities in refractive index caused by sharp discontinuities in temperature and moisture.

Table 1 lists some radiators and reradiators. This list is incomplete since continuing development of new types of radars or improvements due to evolutionary growth of existing radars results in new types of targets becoming detectable.

Table 1

1. Precipitation
2. Aircraft
3. Birds and Insects
4. Satellites, Space Debris, and Missiles
5. Ionization Phenomena or Plasmas
6. Balloons
7. Chaff, "Window," and "Rope"
8. Smoke
9. Distant Ground Return and "Angels"
10. Radio Frequency Interference

The signal sources listed have relatively unique sets of characteristics although in many cases there is some overlap. For example, a fast flying bird with a tailwind could have ground speeds comparable to a light aircraft with a headwind. At comparable range, however, the signal intensity would be quite different unless the bird were in the main beam and the aircraft in a side lobe. This section will discuss the typical characteristics and behavior of the return signals and the auxiliary information needed to confirm or reject them as the sources of a given echo will be mentioned. For example, as mentioned above, knowledge of wind speed is necessary to determine the air speed of a target.

In the discussion of detectability of the various signal sources

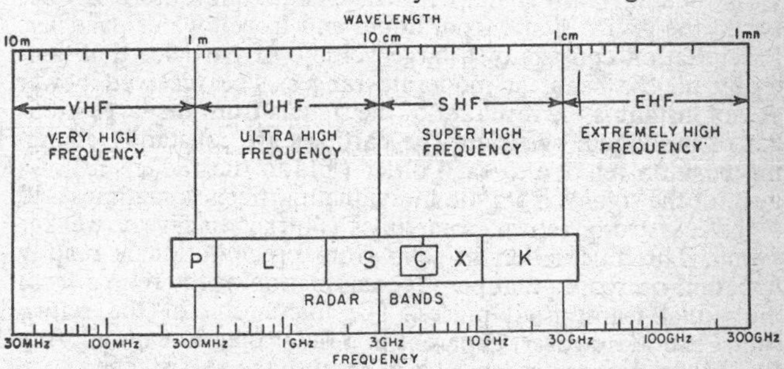

Fig. 2 Common designation of frequency bands

some specific frequency bands may be mentioned. Figure 2 illustrates the relationships between wavelengths and frequency in the various bands and shows specific radar bands within the frequency and wavelengths spectrum.

Precipitation

In the 1940's when radar technology advanced to the point where wavelengths less than half a meter began to be feasible, precipitation became a radar-detectable target. Ligda (1961) states that the first radar storm observation was made on 20 February 1941 in England with a 10 cm. (S band) wavelength radar. Since that time, radar has been widely used for meteorological purposes and special meteorological radars have been designed and constructed specifically for precipitation studies (Williams, 1952; Rockney, 1958). Many radars designed for purposes other than weather detection were found to be very adequate as precipitation detectors. Ligda (1957) studied the distribution of precipitation over large areas of the United States using PPI photographs from Air Defense Command (ADC) Radars during the period 1954 to 1958 and during 1959 studied the distribution of maritime precipitation shown by PPI photographs from radars aboard ships of Radar Picket Squadron I stationed off the west coast of the United States. Later programs concurrent with several of the meteorological satellites (Nagle, 1963; Blackmer, 1968) have also utilized data from ADC and Navy radars. Thus radars designed for other specific missions are often capable of detecting precipitation and an understanding of the characteristic behavior and appearance of precipitation is essential if the radar operator is to interpret properly the targets his radar detects.

Detailed studies have been made of characteristics of radar returns from precipitation. In a review of the microwave properties of precipitation particles Gunn and East (1954) discuss variations in return signal with wavelength and differences between the return signal from liquid and frozen water particles. Precipitation consists of a large volume of particles that generally fill the beam at moderate ranges. The received power at any instant is the resultant of the signals from the large number of individual particles. The particles are constantly changing position relative to each other (and to the radar site). As a result the signals from the individual particles sometimes add to give a strong return, sometimes subtract to give a weaker signal. This fluctuation in echo from precipitation is readily apparent on scopes that permit examination of the return from individual transmitted pulses. The fluctuation of the return signal is not, however, apparent to a radar operator monitoring the PPI or a search radar. This is because the persistence of the cathode ray tube used for PPI displays averages or integrates a number of pulses. Of importance to a radar operator concerned with interpreting the PPI is the variation of signal intensity with wavelength, with pulse length and with precipitation type. Particles that are large compared to the wavelength are more readily detectable than those that are small compared to the wavelength. Light drizzle may be barely detectable at short ranges while severe thunderstorms with large raindrops are detectable at ranges of 300-400 mi. When there is large hail falling from a severe thunderstorm the return signal may be quite strong.

Radar-detected precipitation may be in a variety of forms from very widespread continuous areas of stratiform precipitation of sufficient vertical extent to nearly cover the PPI of a long-range (150 n.mi.) search radar to only one or two isolated small sharp edged convective showers. The former is likely to persist for many hours, the latter for only a fraction of an hour. Between these two extremes there are many complex mixtures of convective and stratiform precipitation areas of various sizes. One of the distinguishing features of precipitation echoes is their vertical extent and maximum altitude. Usually precipitation echoes extend from the surface to altitudes up to 60,000 ft., although a more common altitude of tops is 20,000-40,000 ft. Further, isolated small volumes of precipitation seldom remain suspended in the atmosphere. The initial echoes from showers and thunderstorms may appear as small targets at moderate altitudes but subsequently grow rapidly. For example, Hilst and MacDowell (1950) examined the initial echoes from a thunderstorm. Horizontal measurements were made with a 10 cm. radar and the vertical measurements were made with a 3 cm. radar. Their first measurement showed a small horizontal area and a vertical extent from 11,000-18,000 ft. Presumably measurements a short time earlier would have shown smaller dimensions. Subsequently there was rapid growth to an area of 200 sq. mi. and a vertical extent from the surface to about 30,000 ft. The importance of this large vertical extent is that such an echo on the PPI of a search radar with a narrow beam can be present at a variety of ranges; that is, the beam will not be below the target at short ranges or above it at long ranges as would be the case with targets of limited vertical extent.

Since precipitation is less detectable at longer wavelengths and showers may have a quite short lifetime, it is possible that on rare occasions precipitation targets could confuse the radar operator. Consider for example a search radar operating at wavelengths of greater than 20 cm. in an environment where short-lived showers were occurring. A study by Blackmer (1955) using photographs from a 10 cm. radar showed a peak in echo lifetimes of 25-30 min. while the mean lifetime was 42 min. Also using data from an S band radar, Battan (1953) found a mean echo duration of 23 min. with the greatest number having lifetimes of 20.0-24.9 min. At longer wavelengths with short lifetimes, it is not impossible that an intense shower would be detectable only in the brief period during which it was producing hail, because a long-wavelength radar might not detect small precipitation particles but could detect hail. Water-coated hail acts as a large water sphere and thus gives very strong return signals even at long wavelengths. Geotis (1963) found that hail echoes are very intense subcells on the order of 100 M. in size. When a number of short-lived showers or long-lived showers that were detectable only when hail is falling, are within range of a long-wavelength radar, the PPI display could show over a period of time, a brief echo at one location, then an echo at a new location for a short period, etc. This might be interpreted as a single echo that was nearly stationary for a short period then moving abruptly to a new position.

One of the characteristics of precipitation echoes is that their motion is very close to that of the wind direction and speed. This wind velocity may not be the same as that observed at the radar site if the distance to the precipitation is great. Occasions have also been noted when precipitation echoes within a relatively small area have shown differences in motion due to being moved by different wind directions at various levels.

In general, however, precipitation is a relatively well behaved radar target and except for rare instances its extensiveness and orderly movement readily identifies it to the radar operator monitoring a PPI display.

AIRCRAFT

The term aircraft includes a wide variety of vehicles from unpowered sailplanes to the most advanced military jets with speeds several times that of sound. A target such as an aircraft has a very complex shape that is many times the wavelength of the incident radar energy. As the energy scattered from different parts of the aircraft adds or subtracts from other parts, the signal returned to the radar fluctuates. Fluctuations in the echo can also result from changes in the angle at which the aircraft is viewed. That is, when an aircraft is viewed broadside, its radar (and visual) cross-section is much larger than when viewed from the nose or tail. Skolnik (1962) reports a 15 dB change in echo intensity with an aspect change of only ⅓ of a degree. High frequency fluctuations due to jet turbines (Edrington, 1965) and propellers (Skolnik, 1962) have also been reported .These fluctuations are on the order of 1000 cycles per second and would not be apparent on a PPI.

Although aircraft echoes fluctuate due to aspect and propulsion modulations, there is a general correlation between size of aircraft and the amount of signal returned to the radar. An indication of the relative detectability of several aircraft as given by the Air Force (1954)is F-86 = 0.46, B-45 = 0.75, B-17 = 1.0, B-29 = 1.2. The numbers mean that, if on a given radar a B-17 was just detectable at 100 mi., an F-86 would be just detectable at 46 mi.

The radar cross-sections of components of a large jet aircraft was measured with a 71 cm. radar (Skolnik 1962) and maximum values in excess of 100 m^2 were found. The fuselage of the large jet when viewed from the front or rear had a cross-section of about one-half square meter. Smaller aircraft would have much smaller radar cross-section of about one-half square meter. Smaller aircraft would have much smaller radar cross-sections and light aircraft or sailplanes of fiberglass or wooden construction could have extremely small radar cross-sections.

Another type of fluctuation in echo signal from aircraft and similar point targets is due to the nature of radio wave propagation. When a radar wave is propagated over a plane reflecting surface there will be reflections from that surface to a target in addition to the direct path from the radar to the target. Figure 3 illustrates the geometry of beam distortion due to such a plane reflecting surface. In Fig. 3a an idealized beam pattern in free space is shown. When a reflecting surface such as the ground or sea surface is introduced a portion of the beam will be reflected from the surface as in Fig. 3b. A target will thus be illuminated both by a direct wave and a reflected wave. The echo signal from the target back to the radar travels over the two paths so that the echo is composed of two components. The resulting echo intensity will depend on the extent to which the two components are in phase. Areas along which the two components are in phase resulting in a stronger signal lie along lines of angular elevation of $\frac{2\lambda}{4h_a}, \frac{3\lambda}{4h_a}, \frac{5\lambda}{4h_a}, \ldots$ (λ = wavelength and h_a = antenna height). The two components are out of phase and nearly cancel each other between the maxima. The resulting beam pattern thus consists of a series of lobes as presented schematically in Fig. 3c. As an aircraft flies along it will progress through the regions of maxima and minima, and the signal will fluctuate from near zero in the minima to a value near twice the free-space intensity in the maxima.

The foregoing assumes a plane, perfectly reflecting surface. Since the surface in the vicinity of a radar station is generally

Ea

a. FREE SPACE BEAM PATTERN

Eb

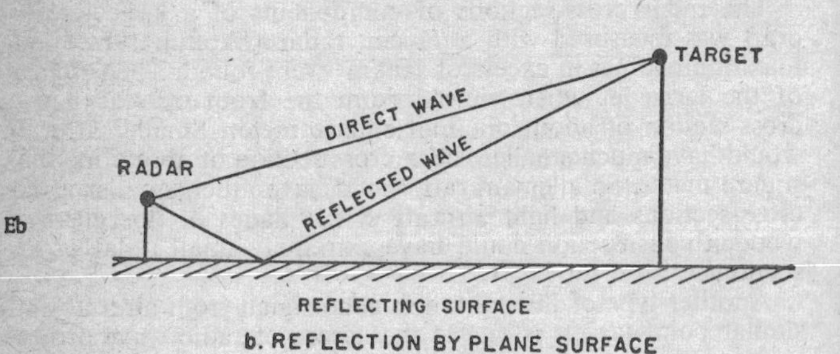

b. REFLECTION BY PLANE SURFACE

Ec

c. BEAM PATTERN WITH PLANE REFLECTING SURFACE

Fig. 3 Distortion of radar beam due to plane reflecting ground surface

not a plane and its reflecting qualities vary the situation is much more complex than the idealized case.

The effect of these fade areas is to cause aircraft targets to sometimes disappear and then (if the target has not reached a range such that the return signal is no longer detectable) to reappear. With a number of aircraft flying about it is not inconceivable that the fadings and reappearances of the several aircraft would be difficult to keep track of and could be misinterpreted as a smaller number of targets that were moving quite erratically.

Considering the whole spectrum of vehicles that travel in the atmosphere, there may be speeds as low as zero (hovering helicopter) or speeds exceeding Mach 3.0 Correspondingly, altitudes vary from the surface to 50,000-60,000 ft. (in some cases above 100,000 ft.) Different types of aircraft, however, are limited in their range of speeds and altitudes. A hovering helicopter cannot suddenly accelerate to three times the speed of sound. Neither can a supersonic jet hover at 60,000 ft. A characteristic of an aircraft echo on a PPI is therefore its relative uniformity of movement. To monitor this movement allowance must be made for fades. The direction of movement also will be quite independent of wind direction at flight level.

BIRDS AND INSECTS

Possibly the earliest observation of a radar echo from a bird was made by R. M. Page (1939) of the Naval Research Laboratory in February, 1939. It was made with an experimental 200 MHz. radar (the XAF) on the *U.S.S. New York* near Puerto Rico. Bird echoes, as reported by Lack and Varley (1945), were observed on a 10 cm. coast-watching radar set near Dover during 1941. Visual checks confirmed both of these early detections by radar as being returns of individual birds. Numerous bird observations by radar have been made since, especially of bird migrations as is evidenced in a bibliography compiled by Myres (1964), listing 89 papers, and a text written by Eastwood (1967). Radar cross-sections (σ) have been measured of birds in a fixed position suspended in a nonreflecting sling and of birds in flight. The values obtained, shown in Tables 2 and 3, vary with species, aspect, and radar wavelength.

Because of the inverse-fourth-power variation with range, a bird at short range in the main beam can give a radar echo comparable in intensity to that from an aircraft in the main beam at a long range. For example, if a pigeon with a broadside radar cross-section of 100 cm^2 were flying within the radar main beam at a range of 10 mi., it would produce as strong a signal to the radar as a jet aircraft with a σ value of 10^6 cm^2 (100 m^2) flying within the radar main beam at a range of 100 mi. However, if the aircraft were flying in a side-lobe 40 dB less powerful than the main beam in which the bird is flying both would produce equal intensity signals at the same range. If the side lobe were 30 dB down, a bird in the main beam at 10 mi. would look like an aircraft at 17.8 mi., and if the side lobe were 20 dB down, the bird at 10 mi. would look like an aircraft at 31.6 mi.

Theoretically the maximum detectable range as dictated by the amount of radar signal returned from birds can be calculated. However, verification is not easy due to the difficulty of spotting a bird and establishing that it belongs to a particular blip on a radar scope. This is particularly difficult in the presence of sea clutter as experienced during an experiment conducted by Allen and Ligda (1966) at Stanford Research Institute. During an experiment conducted by Konrad (1968), individual birds were released from an aircraft flying over water at 5,500-6,000 ft. from 8-10 n.mi. from the radars

Table 2

SUMMARY OF BIRD RADAR CROSS-SECTION DATA

(from Konrad, Hicks, and Dobson 1968)

Radar Band	Points at point/sec)	Mean radar Cross-section (cm^2)	Median radar cross-section (cm^2)	Root-mean-square fluctuations in cross section (cm2)	Mean-to-median ratio, p
		Grackle			
X	230	16	6.5	24	2.4
S	230	27	13	31	2.2
UHF-VV*	230	0.73	0.58	0.6	1.3
UHF-VH†	230	0.37	0.15	0.7	.
		Grackle			
X	116	15	7.2	21	2.1
S	116	23	11	32	2.2
UHF-VV	116	0.41	0.32	0.5	1.3
UHF-VH	116	0.03	0.015	0.04	
		Sparrow			
X	129	1.9	1.0	2	1.9
S	129	15	11	11	1.4
UHF-VV	129	0.025	0.02	0.02	1.3
UHF-VH	129				
		Sparrow			
X	233	1.3	0.60	2	2.2
S	223	12	11	5	1.1
UHF-VV	233	0.020	0.02	0.01	1.1
UHF-VH	233				
		Pigeon			
X	160	15	6.4	28	2.3
S	160	80	32	140	2.5
UHF-VV	160	11	8.0	7.0	1.3
UHF-VH	160	1.2	0.7	1.4	

*VV, Transmit vertical polarization and receive vertical polarization.
†VH, Transmit vertical polarization and receive cross-polarized or horizontal component.

After separation of the aircraft from the bird in the radar scope, each individual bird was automatically tracked for periods up to five minutes, so that the target observed was positively identified as a bird. Flocks of birds have been detected to ranges of at least 51 n.mi. as reported by Eastwood and Rider (1965).

Table 3

VARIATION OF RADAR CROSS-SECTION WITH ASPECT

(from Konrad, Hicks, and Dobson 1968)

Radar Band	Aspect*	Radar cross-section σ (cm^2)
	Starling (Sturnus vulgaris)	
X	Head	1.8
X	Broadside	25.0
X	Tail	1.3
	Pigeon (Columba livia)	
X	Head	1.1
X	Broadside	100
X	Tail	1.0
	House sparrow (Passer domesticus)	
X	Head	0.25
X	Broadside	7.0
X	Tail	0.18
	Rook (Corvus frugilegus)	
X	Broadside	250
	Turkey buzzard	
X	Unknown	25 to 250
	Duck and chicken	
UHF†	Head	600
UHF†	Tail	24

*For the cross-section measurements of the starling, pigeon, sparrow, and rook, the birds were suspended from a tower with their wings folded; the radar elevation angle was 18°. Measurements of the turkey buzzard were made when the bird was in flight; measurements of the duck and chicken were made when the birds were standing or squatting. †400 megacycles.

Very few birds fly over 13,000 ft.; most fly below 5,000 ft. In a survey conducted by Farrari (1966) of USAF reports of bird-aircraft collisions during 1965, 27% of all collisions were under 100 ft., 28% between 100-2,000 ft., 21% between 2,000-3,000 ft. and 24% above 3,000 ft. If it can be assumed that the probability of a bird-aircraft collision is equally likely at all altitudes (which may not be fully valid due to climb and descent) this should be somewhat of a representative figure of the height of flight for birds. There was one reported bird-aircraft strike at 17,000 ft. and a few sightings above 20,000 ft., however the number of birds flying at these altitudes appears to be extremely small.

Eastwood and Rider (1965) reported a rather complete analysis of the height of flight of various birds observed by radar at the Marconi Research Laboratory in England. Their findings agreed very closely with the above; about 90% of all birds were below 5,000 ft. Birds fly higher at night and during the spring and fall migration periods. A plot of the average altitude distribution over the year is shown in Fig. 4. All of these figures are probably applicable as height above the general terrain; i.e., at 5,000 ft. above mean sea level, 90% of the

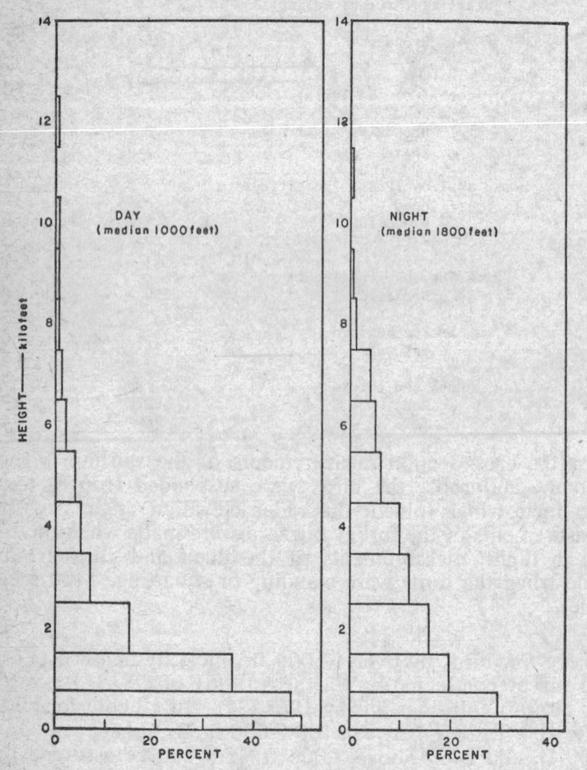

Fig. 4 Average altitude distribution of birds over the year (from Eastwood and Rider 1965)

birds would fly at altitudes below 10,000 ft.m.s.l. The amount of cloud cover also affects the height at which birds fly. Diagrams included by Eastwood and Rider (1965) clearly indicate a marked tendency for higher mean altitudes to be flown in the presence of complete cloud cover.

Target airspeed is another means for identifying a bird. It can be obtained vectorially from a knowledge of the wind velocity and the radar-measured target velocity. Houghton (1964) determined the airspeed of a limited sampling of the birds by visually identifying each through a telescope aimed by tracking radar, Fig. 5. In all cases the wind speeds were less than 5 knots. Target air speed cannot invariably distinguish between a helicopter, a slow moving aircraft and a bird flying

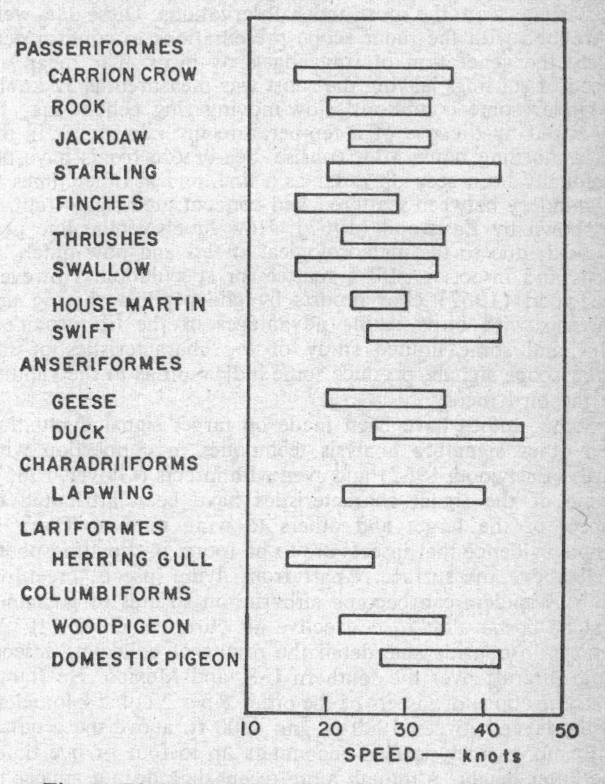

Fig. 5 Bird airspeed chart (from Houghton 1964)

in a high wind without precise knowledge of the wind at the bird altitude.

Flocks of birds sometimes produce rings on a radar scope which expand from a numhber of fixed points. These have been called "ring angels" and were first attributed to birds by Ligda (1958). Visual confirming observations were lacking at that time. Later, Eastwood, Isted and Rider (1962) verified that radar ring angels were definitely caused by the dispersal of starlings (Sturnus vulgaris) from their roosts at sunrise. After several radar scope observations were studied, it became possible to pinpoint the centers of the rings and the approximate locations of the roosts. A number of observers equipped with radio telephones were stationed at each location and signaled the precise moment of emergence of the successive flocks of starlings from the roost under observations. These data were correlated with the radar scope presentations to confirm definitely the generation of ring angels by birds. The mean air speed of starlings leaving the roost was measured as 37 knots.

Under some conditions, slow-moving ring echoes may be produced by the rise of a temperature inversion layer in the early morning hours after sunrise. Sea-breeze fronts have occasionally been seen on radar as a line, and at other times as a boundary between scattered and concentrated signal returns as shown by Eastwood (1967). How much of the line produced is due to the meteorological effects and how much by birds and insects is still a matter for speculation. However, Eastwood (1967) cites reports by glider pilots sharing upcurrents with birds taking advantages of the lift provided. This and some limited study of the characteristics of the radar scope signals, produce some indication as to the validity of the bird theory.

Some studies have been made on target signal fluctuation and other signature analysis techniques in connection with birds (Eastwood, 1967) and even with insects (Glover, 1966). Some of the signal characteristics have been attributed to aspect of the target and others to wing motion. There is ample evidence that insects are to be found in the atmosphere well above the surface. Apart from flying insects, creatures such as spiders can become airborne on strands of gossamer and be borne aloft in convective air currents. Glick (1939) reports in considerable detail the results of collecting insects from aircraft over the southern U.S. and Mexico. He found concentrations of insects of the order 1 per 2 cubic kilometers in the layer between 1000 ft. and 4000 ft. above the ground, with more widely spaced encounters up to four or five times the latter height. Although more recent data do not appear to have been collected, it is common for sailplane pilots to experience many types of insects impinging on the canopy or the leading edges of the wings at altitudes exceeding 10,000 ft. above terrain. Less commonly, birds feeding on insects carried aloft by thermals are observed at similar altitudes.

The radar cross-sections (σ) of the various insects listed in Table 4 (measured at wavelengths of 3.2 cm.) range from 0.01 cm^2 to 1.22 cm^2 for all but the locust which has a maximum σ value of 9.6 cm^2. The ability of any given radar system to detect radar cross-sections of these low values is a function of its design, its current performance, and the ability of the operator. Ultra-sensitive radar systems such as the MIT Lincoln Laboratory radars at Wallops Island, Va. have reported minimum detectable cross-sections at 10 km. of 6 x $10^{-4}cm^2$ for the X-band, 2.5 x 10^{-5} cm^2 for the S-band, and 3.4 x 10^{-5} cm^2 for the UHF radars (Hardy, 1966). The X-band radar is two orders more sensitive than required to detect the listed insects at a range of 10 km. and probably is functioning close to the limit of detectability. The majority of other radar systems in general use today are less sensitive. Some are not able to detect insects in the lower range of σ values. Tabulation of a large number of radar system characteristics has been published in classified documents by RAND. Major radar parameters for some airborne sets are listed in an article by Senn and Hiser (1963).

Insects are commonly found at surprisingly high altitudes. Swarms of butterflies and other insects are found in summer on 14,000-ft. mountain peaks in the Rockies. A few insects have been reported at over 25,000-ft. altitudes in the Himalayas.

Verification of insects as causing a particular blip on a radar scope is even more difficult than birds. However, this was accomplished as reported by Glover, et al (1966). Single insects were released from an aircraft and tracked by radar at altitudes from 1.6 to 3.0 km. and at ranges up to 18 km. Experiments of this sort and other studies involving clear atmosphere probing with high-power radars (Atlas, 1966; Hardy, 1966 and 1968) have led to valid conclusions that most of the dot echoes are caused by insects or birds.

Attention has been given by Browning (1966) to the determination of the velocity characteristics of some clear-air dot angels. A 5.42 cm. pulse Doppler radar with a 1° beam elevated at 30° and rotating at 4 rpm was used in the study. A series of radar soundings spaced about half to one hour apart were obtained at 500 ft. altitude intervals up to 3000 ft. using range-gating techniques. Temperature, humidity and wind data were collected simultaneously with the radar soundings.

Three kinds of angel population were distiguished according

Table 4

SUMMARY OF INSECT RADAR CROSS-SECTION DATA MEASURED AT 3.2 CM (from Hajousky et al, 1966)

Insect	Body Length MM	Body Diameter MM	σL cm²	στ cm²
Diptera				
Range Crane Fly-Timpula Simplex	13	1	0.30	0.02
Green Bottle Fly-Lucilia Ceasar	9	3	0.25	0.10
Hymenoptera				
Honey Bee (worker)-Apis Mellifera	13	6	1.00	0.30
California Harverter Ant-Pogonomyrmex Californicus	13	6	0.04	0.02
Coleoptera				
Convergent Lady Beetle-Hippodamia Convergens	5	3	0.02	0.01
Twelve-spotted Cucumber Beetle-Diabratica Duodecimpunctata	8	4	0.14	0.05
Lepidoptera				
Army Worm Moth-Cirphis Unipuncta	14	4	1.22	0.12
Alfalfa Caterpillar Butterfly-Colias Eurytheme	14	1.5	0.65	0.02
Orthopter				
Blue Winged Locust-Trimeratropic Dyanipennis	20	4	9.60	0.96
Aranedia				
Spider (unidentified)	5	3.5	0.10	0.06

to their mean deviation from the swarm velocity, their average vertical motion, their maximum relative velocities and their σ values. Atmospheric inhomogeneities or the presence of plant seeds appeared to be ruled out because of the small back-scattering cross-sections of individual angels (less than approximately 0.1 cm^2), their discreteness in space and velocity, their often quite large mean deviations (up to 4 m sec^{-1}) from a uniform velocity, and the fact that the only major upward velocities occurred after sunset, at a time when the lapse rate was becoming increasingly stable. The same data suggest insects as the likeliest cause.

Some of the larger man-made objects in space (such as the Echo 1 and Echo II metallized balloons, Pegasus, and large boosters) have large radar cross-sections and can be detected by search radars. For example, Peterson, (1960) found that occasionally the radar cross-section of Sputnik II approached 1000 m². Such space objects at altitudes of around 120 mi. and with speeds of around 18,000 mph could appear as multiple trip echoes if they were detected on a search radar.

Fig. 6 illustrates the possible appearance of the track of a satellite on the PPI of a search radar. The figure assumes a

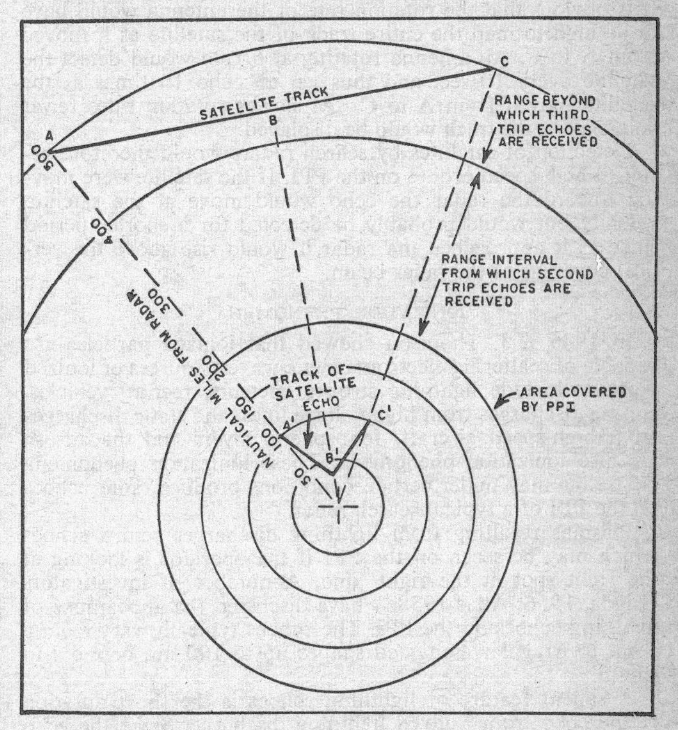

Fig. 6 Track of multiple trip satellite echo on a PPI

satellite at 120 n. mi. altitude moving radially at a distance of 500 n. mi. from a radar with an unambiguous range of 200 mi. (The elevation angle of the satellite would be about 8° which is within the vertical coverage of many search radars.) When the satellite is at point A the echo is displayed on the PPI at point A′, 400 mi. less than the actual range. As the satellite moves to point B its range closes to less than 450 mi. so the echo moves to within 50 mi. on the PPI. From B to C the range of the satellite opens to 500 mi. so the echo moves out to 100 mi. again. An interesting feature of this example is that while the actual path length from A to C is 500 mi. the length of the echo track is only 140 mi. Thus, if the satellite was moving at 18,000 mph the echo would move only 140/500 x 18,000 or 5,040 mph. At the speed of 18,000 mph the satellite would move 5 mi/sec and take 100 sec. to move from A to C. It is obvious that the rotation rate of the antenna would have to be high to map the entire track of the satellite as it moved from A to C. An antenna rotating at 6 rpm would detect the satellite every 10 sec. and thus get an echo 10 times as the satellite moved from A to C. At slower rotation rates fewer points along the track would be displayed.

Detection of satellites by search radars would therefore result in high-speed echoes on the PPI. If the satellite were moving toward the radar the echo would move at the satellite velocity but would probably be detected for a shorter period since as it approached the radar it would rise above the vertical coverage of the radar beam.

IONIZATION PHENOMENA

In 1906 J. J. Thomson showed that ionized particles are capable of scattering electromagnetic waves. Sources of ionized particles include lightning strokes, meteors, reentry vehicles, corona discharges from high voltage lines, and static discharges from high-speed aircraft. Ionospheric layers and the aurora are also ionization phenomena. These ionization phenomena or plasma may under certain conditions produce radar echoes on the PPI of a typical search radar.

Plasmas resulting from lightning discharges return echoes which may be seeen on the PPI if the operator is looking at the right spot at the right time. A number of investigators (Ligda, 1956; Atlas 1958a) have discussed the appearance of lightning echoes on the PPI. The echoes typically vary from a point to irregular elongated shapes up to 100 mi. or more in length.

A salient feature of lightning echoes is the short duration of the echo from a given lightning discharge. Since the echo lasts about 0.5 sec., it will be evident only on one scan.

The radar cross-section of the ionized column of plasma produced by lightning has been estimated by Ligda (1956) to be 60 m^2 depending on ion density within the plasma and

* However search radars are beamed to low altitudes above the horizon and so would miss satellites when at high altitudes.

on the wavelength of the radar illuminating the plasma. Electron densities of 10^{11}/cc are required for critical (100%) reflection of 3 cm. radar energy; only 10^9 electrons/cc are required with a 30 cm. radar. Thus, longer wavelength radars are more apt to detect lightning than the shorter wavelength radars. There is another factor which aids lightning detection at longer wavelengths. The longer wavelength radars detect less precipitation than the shorter wavelength radars. Therefore, a lightning discharge inside an area of light precipitation might be hidden within the precipitation echo on the PPI of a 3 cm. radar, while a 23 cm. radar might detect the lightning-produced plasmas but not the precipitation.

Confirmation that short-lived (one scan) echoes were caused by lightning was based on the fact that there were visual lightning discharges in the area from which the radar received the echoes. Atlas (1958a), however, estimated (from echo intensities and dimensions) that discharges may occur that are radar detectable, but are not visible to the eye. Whether or not there is visible lightning in the area of these short echoes, there will undoubtedly be precipitation areas in the vicinity. The exact distance from precipitation that lightning may occur has not been adequately studied. It is known that the probability of radar detection of lightning is greatest when the radar beam intercepts the upper levels (ice crystal regions) of thunderstorms. In a mature thunderstorm the ice crystal blowoff or anvil may extend many tens of miles downwind of the precipitation area. Atlas (1958a) illustrates a lighting echo some 10 to 20 mi. ahead of the precipitation echo but within the anvil cloud extending downwind from the storm.

In addition to short duration lightning strokes there is the longer-lived "ball lightning." Ritchie (1961) mentions the controversy surrounding ball lightning and also some of its alleged characteristics such as sliding along telephone wires, fences, or other metallic objects. Radar detection of ball lightning under these conditions is difficult since echoes of the metallic objects and the ground would tend to mask ball lightning near the surface.

Since search radars can detect echoes of very short duration returned by plasmas created by lightning flashes, there is no reason to assume that other plasmas could not be detected by search radars if the plasmas were sufficiently separated from other targets. The radar echoes would probably appear as point targets and if the duration were sufficient to compute a speed, it would correspond to that of the plasma. The possible range of speeds of plasma blobs cannot be given since so little is known about the phenomenon.

In addition to reflections of the radar pulse there is another source of signals from the lightning discharge, those that are radiated by the lightning discharge itself. These signals, called sferics, appear on the PPI as radial rows of dots, as one or more short radial lines, or as a combination of dots and lines (Ligda, 1956). Atlas (195 8b) states that 10 cm. and 23 cm. radars are good sferics detectors while radars such as the 3 cm. CPS-9 have moderately low range capabilities in detecting sferics.

As with the lightning echo, the sferic duration is very short Atlas (195 8b) found an average 480 μ sec. for 489 sferics measured during a severe squall line on 19 June 1957. As a result such sferic signals from a given lightning discharge would only by displayed on one scan of the PPI.

The aurora is a complex phenomenon caused by ionization of the upper atmospheric gases by high-speed charged particles emitted by the sun. Upon entering the earth's upper atmosphere, these charged particles are guided by the earth's magnetic field and give rise to a luminous display visible only at night. The aurora occurs most often in the vicinity of 67° geomagnetic latitude. In the zone of maximum auroral activity, visual displays can be seen almost every clear night.

Increased auroral activity is found to follow solar magnetic storms. A direct correlation exists between sunspot activity and the intensity and extent of aurora. The increased auroral activity follows a solar disturbance by about one or two days, the time required for the charged particles to travel from the sun to the earth. During these times, auroras may be seen at latitudes far removed from the normal auroral zones.

Auroral displays occur in the ionosphere at altitudes ranging from 54-67 mi. The ionization which is seen as a visual auroral display is formed into long slender columns which are aligned with the earth's magnetic field. This formation results in strong aspect sensitivity which means that radar reflections occur only when the radar beam is approximately at right angles to the earth's magnetic field. Echo strength is proportional to the radar wavelength raised to the third or fifth power; consequently, most radar observations occur at VHF or lower UHF.

As a result only lower frequency UHF search radars within 1000 mi. of the Arctic or Antarctic Circles would be capable of detecting auroral echoes. The echoes would generally appear at true ranges of 60-180 mi. for a few minutes to several hours. The echoes would be mainly stationary and could be either distributed or point targets usually in the magnetic north azimuths in the northern hemisphere or magnetic south azimuths in the southern hemisphere.

Meteors are small solid particles that, when they enter the earth's atmosphere, leave an ionized trail from which radar echoes are returned. The majority are completely ablated at altitudes ranging from 50-75 mi. Visible meteors vary in size from about 1 gm. to about 1 μgm. The ionized trail produced by a 0.1 gm. meteor is miles long and only a few feet in diameter.

The meteor particle itself is far too small to be detected. Meteors are observed both visually and by radar by the trail of ionization they produce. Because of the distance and the small cross-section of the trail, meteor ionization can be detected by radar only when the trail is orientated at right angles to the radar beam.

Although most meteor echoes last no more than a fraction of a second when observed with VHF radar, a few echoes persist for many seconds. The duration of the meteor echo is theoretically proportional to the square of radar wavelengths, and the power returned is proportional to the wavelength cubed. For these reasons, meteor echoes are seldom detected at frequencies above VHF.

Meteor echoes on a low frequency UHF radar usually appear as point targets with a duration of a few seconds or less. Ranges center around 120 mi.

Very, very infrequently meteors occur that are large enough to survive atmospheric entry. They usually produce a spectacular visual display, referred to as fireballs. Such meteorites are detectable by sensitive search radars operating at any frequency and at any angle to its path. Echoes appear as point targets with a duration of a few seconds. The true range would be less than 120 mi. and the range rate generally would be less than 20,000 mph.

BALLOONS

Balloons and instrument packages or reflectors carried by balloons can be detected by search radars. More than 100 balloons are released over the United States at least twice a day from Weather Bureau, Navy, and Air Force Stations for the measurement of upper atmospheric conditions. A number of these balloons carry radar reflectors as well as an instrument package, and some are lighted for theodolite (visual) tracking. Echoes from these point targets move at the speed of the wind at the altitude of the balloon. Balloon altitudes vary widely and may reach 100,000 ft. so that ground speeds vary from near zero to well over 100 knots. When a balloon bursts and the instrument package abruptly starts a descent which is normally slowed by parachute, there could be an abrupt change in the behavior of the echo on the PPI. A balloon that had been rising in a direction away from the station would show the range gradually increasing. Then if it descended rapidly the range could appear to decrease which could be interpreted as a reversal of course.

"CHAFF," "WINDOW," AND "ROPE"

When radar was developed as a means for aiming searchlights and antiaircraft guns during World War II, countermeasures were promptly devised. What was needed was something inexpensive and expendable that would give a radar return comparable with the echo from the aircraft. Small metallic foil strips which act as dipole reflectors were employed. The strips are released from an aircraft, and they are wind-scattered which results in a cloud with a radar cross-section comparable to a large aircraft.

The terms "chaff," "window," and "rope" are used to designate particular types of materials. Chaff consists of various lengths of material. Chaff having the same length is called window. Rope is a long roll of metallic foil or wire designed for broad, low-frequency response.

Metallized nylon monofilaments have replaced metal foil in the construction of chaff and window. The nylon type is lighter, hence has a slower rate of descent, and is more compact. A typical package of X-band chaff is a cylinder 1 in. in diameter and 1.5 cm. (one half the 3 cm. wavelength) long. The cylinder contains approximately 150,000 filaments and weighs 6.5 gm. and forms a cloud with a radar cross-section of about 25 m^2. The filaments descend at about 2 ft/sec in still air at lower altitudes, so that if dispensed at 40,000 ft. they take about four hours to reach the ground. Turbulence causes the chaff cloud to grow and disperse, so that generally the signal becomes so much weaker that sometimes the chaff cloud cannot be tracked all the way to the ground.

Since chaff contains a large number of elements the radar signal is similar to that from precipitation. Also it moves with the wind at its altitude. Therefore, it is difficult to distinguish between precipitation and a cloud of chaff by briefly examining the PPI display. When chaff is distributed along a relatively extended path as opposed to only a point distribution, the echo is elongated and does appear to be dissimilar to precipitation.

Rope is a 60-80 ft. piece of narrow metallized material such as mylar. It is weighted at one end and has a drag mechanism at the other. When deployed it has a rate of descent about twice as fast as chaff so it would take about two hours to fall from 40,000 ft. to the surface. Usually a number of rope elements are deployed together so there will be some increase in the size of the cloud as it descends.

SMOKE

Hiser (1955) reports detecting smoke from fires at a city disposal dump about 15 mi. from the site of a 10 cm. search radar. The radar echo from the smoke plume was evident on the PPI extending in a northeasterly direction to a range of

50 mi. Goldstein (1951) mentions a case where an airplane was directed to an echo observed by a 10 cm. radar. Only several columns of smoke from brush fires were found. Smoke particle size and concentrations are so small that one would be highly skeptical about echoes from the smoke itself. The returns may arise from refractive index discontinuities at the boundaries of the smoke plume. Plank (1956) suggests that echoes from the vicinity of fires may be from either particles (neutral or ionized) carried aloft by convective currents or from atmospheric inhomogeneities created by the fire.

DISTANT GROUND RETURN AND "ANGLES"

Local terrain features and, at sea, the ocean surface are detected by radar. The range to which such clutter is detected is a function of antenna height, elevation angle and beamwidth, and the distribution of temperature and humidity along the propagation path. Since normal ground clutter is present day after day, radar operators become familiar with it and may even use some prominent points to check the azimuthal accuracy of the radar. There are circumstances in which distant, rarely detected terrain features or surface objects return echoes to a radar. The phenomenon referred to as "angels" is also included in this section since at least some of the angels appear to be distant ground return that is detected by reflection or forward scatter of the radar beam by atmospheric inhomogeneities.

To investigate the phenomena of distant ground return it is first necessary to review some of the fundamentals of the propagation of electromagnetic radiation through the atmosphere. The interested reader can find a comprehensive treatment of tropospheric radar propagation in a book on radio meteorology by Bean (1966) which covers in detail the topics in the following brief review.

In a vacuum, electromagnetic energy is propagated in straight lines at the velocity of light, 3×10^8 m/sec. This constant is usually designated by the symbol "c." In a homogeneous medium, the direction of propagation remains constant,

$$V = \frac{c}{\sqrt{\mu\kappa}} \qquad (1)$$

but velocity (V) is reduced and where μ is the magnetic per-

$$\sqrt{\mu\kappa} = n = \frac{c}{V}$$

meability of the medium and κ is its dielectric constant and where n is the index of refraction.

When electromagnetic wave energy encounters a surface of discontinuity in refractive index in a medium, the wave is partly *reflected* and partly refracted.* The angle of the incident ray (Θ) is related to the angle of the refracted ray (Θ') by the equation:

$$\frac{\text{Sin } \theta}{\text{Sin } \theta'} = \frac{n'}{n} \qquad (2)$$

where Θ and Θ' are the angles of incidence and refraction respectively in the first and second medium, and n and n′ are the values of the refractive index for the first and second medium respectively.

The ray is always refracted towards the medium of higher refractive index. A portion of the energy will also be reflected in the same plane and at an angle equal to the angle of incidence if the energy encounters a sudden change in the refractive index; this is a partial reflection. Total reflection occurs when the angle of incidence exceeds a critical value given by (with $n_1 < n_2$):

$$\theta_1 = \frac{\sin^{-1} n_1}{n_2} \qquad (3)$$

In the atmosphere, discontinuities in refractive index sharp enough to cause reflection of the incident wave back to the radar are believed to exist on occasion. Because of the difficulty in making suitable measurements of the physical factors involved, some uncertainty attends the understanding of this mechanism under practical conditions. Detailed discussion of this aspect of propagation is deferred until later where radar 'angels' are described. In the present context, discussion of the effects of refractive index inhomogeneities will be confined to refraction.

Where the refractive index gradient is changing continuously as is normally the case in the natural atmosphere as the height above the earth's surface increases, a ray of electromagnetic energy will follow a curved path. The change of direction that this produces may be evaluated by reference to Snell's law by the expression

$$n_h (a + h) \cos \beta = n_s a \cos \beta o \qquad (4)$$

where n_h is the refractive index at height h, n_s is the refractive

* For a more complete discussion of atmospheric refraction of electromagnetic rays, see Section III, Chapter 5 and Section VI, Chapter 4/ Note, however, the difference in the factors contributing to the refractive index at radar and at optical frequencies.

index at the surface, a is the radius of the spherical earth, β is the ray elevation angle at height h and β_0 is the ray elevation angle at the earth's surface (See Fig. 7).

A most important consequence of this is that *the effects of a vertical gradient of refractive index are most apparent at low (10° or less) angles of elevation.*

Where the refractive index gradient is constant ($n_h = n_s$) or varies regularly, the curvature of the path of rays of radar energy may be readily determined by reference to the foregoing expressions. In more complicated conditions more sophisticated techniques are available for tracing the path of such rays.

In terms of the real atmosphere, at radar frequencies the refractive index varies as a function of pressure, temperature, and water vapor content. An equation relating the various parameters as given by Smith (1953) is:

$$(n-1)\ 10^6 = \frac{77.6P}{T} + \frac{3.73 \times 10^5 e}{T^2} \tag{5}$$

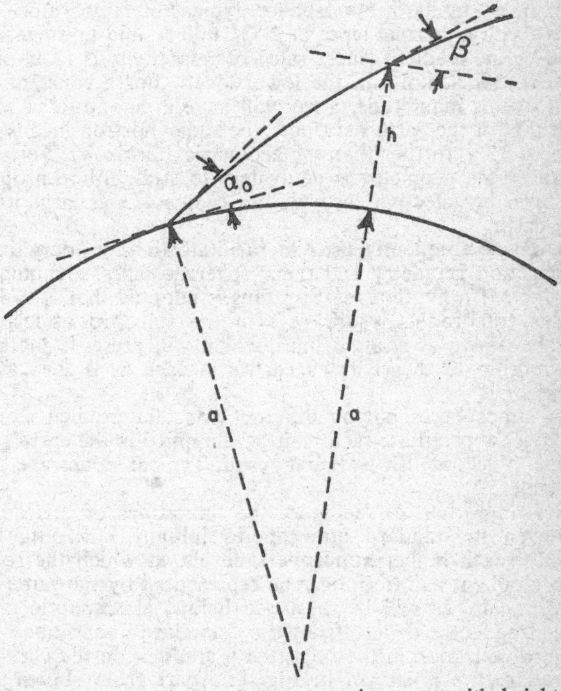

Fig. 7 Curvature of electromagnetic waves with height

where P = total pressure (millibars)
T = absolute temperature (degrees Kelvin)
e = partial pressure of water vapor (millibars)

When the available data are given in terms of relative humidity, e may be replaced by e_s R.H., where e_s is saturation vapor pressure at the pressure and temperature of interest and R.H. is relative humidity expressed as a decimal.

For convenience, the left hand side of the equation is commonly designated N (refractivity) and is expressed in N-units, i.e., $N = (n-1)\ 10^6$.

Values of N are conveniently derived from meteorological parameters by the use of tables or nomograms, such as those given by the U.S. Navy (1960).

At sea level, a typical value of n is 1.00035, i.e., the refractivity is 350 N units. But depending upon pressure, temperature and humidity the sea level refractivity may range from 250 to 450 N units.

Since pressure, temperature, and water vapor normally decrease with height the refractivity normally decreases with altitude. In a 'standard' atmosphere, typical of temperature latitudes (with a thermal lapse of 2°C/1000 ft. and uniform R.H. of 60%, the gradient (lapse rate) of refractivity is 12 N-units/ 1000 ft. 39 N. km^{-1} in the lower levels. For a constant gradient of this magnitude, a ray will have a curvature of about ¼th that of the earth's surface (the radar horizon in this case is about 15% further than the geometrical horizon). For short distances the geometry is equivalent to straight-line propagation over an effective earth with a radius 4/3 as large as the true earth.

A device frequently used to facilitate the consideration of propagation geometry and radar coverage takes advantage of this fact. If a fictitious earth radius is adopted that is 4/3 the earth's true radius, radar rays in the standard atmosphere may be drawn as straight lines, which will preserve the same relationship to the redrawn earth's surface as is the case in reality.

In atmospheres having different constant gradients of refractivity appropriate factors may be applied to the earth's true radius to accomplish a similar result. Typical values are given in Table 5.

It is important to recognize the limitations of this device, for even in standard atmospheres initially horizontal rays rapidly reach higher atmospheric levels, at which the refractivity gradient can no longer be represented by the same constant. Again, as will be discussed below, atmospheric conditions frequently depart from the "standard" conditions. The effect of variation in the refractivity gradient on the curvature of radar rays is shown in Fig. 8. Apart from showing the

Table 5

Effective earth radius for several atmospheres

Atmosphere	Typical $\frac{dN}{dz}$	Effective earth radius for typical $\frac{dN}{dz}$
Standard	-12 N-units/1000 ft.; -39 km^{-1}	1.33 actual radius
Subrefractive	+10(> 0); +33 km^{-1}	0.82
"Normal"*	-15(0 to -24); -50 km^{-1}	1.47
Superrefraction	-30 (24-48); -100 km^{-1}	2.68
Trapping	-48 (or greater); -157 km^{-1}	∞ (or negative; i.e., concave earth)

* For an average temperate zone climate; northern climates (e.g. England) tend to be "standard," tropical climates tend to be near-superrefractive (e.g. -80 km^{-1}).

range of curvatures in atmospheres having constant refractivity gradients, this figure indicates the way in which rays can be deflected in passing through atmospheric layers. More specifically, the deflection of a ray in milliradians ($\Delta\tau$) in passing through a layer with constant N-gradient is given by:

$$\Delta\tau = \frac{N_B - N_T}{500\ (\tan\beta_B + \tan\beta_T)} \qquad (7)$$

where the subscripts B and T refer to the bottom and top of the layer respectively. The values of β are determined at each level in terms of βo, N_s (surface refractivity), N_h (refractivity at height h) and h, using Snell's Law (equation 4).

Procedures based on these relationships may be used to trace the path of rays to determine the detailed effect of refraction on radar propagation under any given condition of atmospheric stratification.

The broad pattern of refractive effects, however, is as follows:

Where the general refractivity gradient lies between O N-units/1,000 ft. and 24 N-units/1,000 ft. (100 km^{-1}) propagation is described as *normal*. Refractivity gradients less than

O N-units/1,000 ft. are *subrefractive* and cause upward bending of radar waves with a reduction of distance to the radar horizon. Such conditions may occur where the temperature lapse rate is well above average, or where the atmosphere is drier at lower levels than aloft.

Where the refractivity gradient exceeds 24-N units/1,000 ft. conditions are said to be *superrefractive* and radar waves curve down more strongly. Such conditions result from thermal

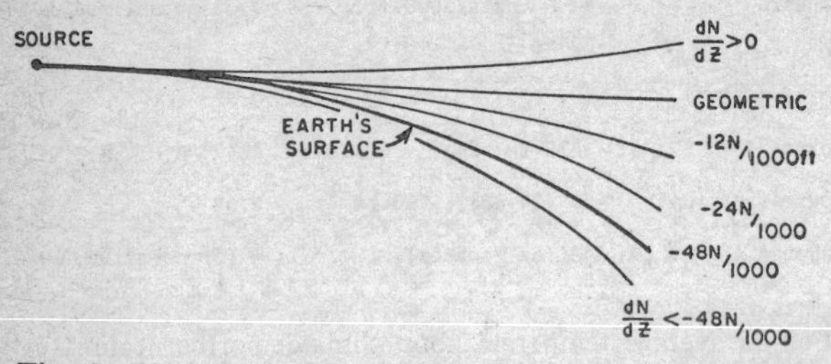

Fig. 8 Variations in curvature with different refractivity gradients

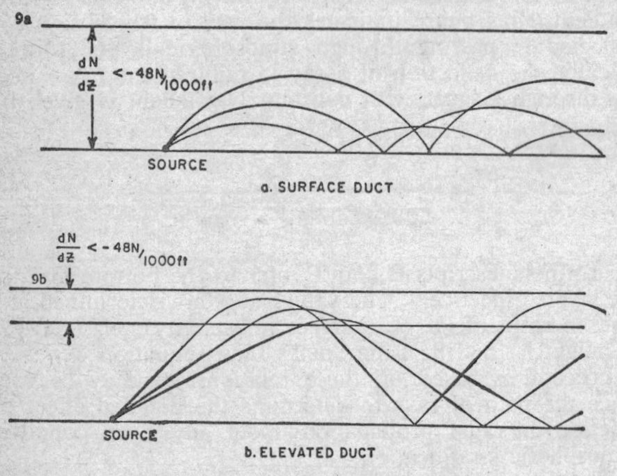

Fig. 9 Ray paths through 'ducts'

inversions, i.e., where temperature increases with height, or where the decrease of water vapor content with height is excessive.

For refractivity gradients greater than 48-N/1,000 ft. (157

km^{-1}), the ray curvature will be greater than that of the earth's surface and trapping is said to occur.

This condition gives rise to marked anomalies in propagation and, provided the layer through which such a gradient occurs is deep enough, the radar energy will be guided within a duct bounded by the earth's surface and the upper level of the layer. In such cases, exceptionally long detection ranges are achieved, well beyond the normal radar horizon (See Fig. 8). Where a marked negative refractive gradient occurs in a layer adjacent to the ground, a surface duct is formed (Fig. 9a). An elevated layer of strong negative gradient can also produce ducting (Fig. 9b).

Surface ducts are commonly caused by radiative cooling of the earth's surface at night, leading to a thermal inversion in the air near the surface. In this case, the extreme refractivity gradient is mainly due to temperature effects and such ducts can occur in quite dry air. Where humidity at the surface is higher than usual and falls off rapidly with height, a strong negative refractivity gradient is also established. Evaporation from water surfaces or wet soil can produce these conditions and a particularly common example occurs in warm dry air from the land when it is advected over the sea. This type of duct is commonly found in tropical areas, where temperature and humidity both decrease with height; the inversion type of duct is more common in temperate and artic areas (Bean, 1966).

Elevated layers of extreme refractivity gradient are caused by similar meteorological mechanisms but often occur on a somewhat broader scale. Certain areas of the world are particularly prone to such layers; the California coastal area is a good example. Plate 66 (Blackmer, 1960) shows an example of the PPI during a trapping situation off the California Coast. In this case echoes were presented on the PPI on second and third sweeps but could be correlated with islands and mountainous terrain. Elevated layers such as this are commonly found in the southeast (northeast at S latitudes) quadrants of trade-wind anticyclonic systems.

The anomalous propagation to which such irregular refractivity conditions give rise is of considerable significance to the problem of target identification and false targets. In the first place, the whole basis of the radar technique depends upon knowing the direction in which the radar energy is propagated. For normal practice, propagation must be close to rectilinear. When the radar energy is being strongly curved, information on a target's location derived from the position of the radar antenna can thus be highly erroneous. Again, echoes may be received from the ground or from other targets that are not normally within the range of the radar or within its 'field of view' at any given antenna elevation. Ground echoes from beyond the normal radar horizon are cases in point.

An especially significant condition arises when the antenna is elevated in a direction which is near a critical angle for trapping or ducting. In this case, while much of the energy may be propagated in a direction approximating that intended, because of the finite dimensions of the radar beam, some energy may be severely refracted. This is illustrated diagrammatically in Figure 10.

With such a mechanism an aircraft could be tracked fairly accurately, but in addition, echoes could be received from the ground (intermittently if the surface reflectivity or propagation conditions are variable as might be the case in areas of thunderstorms). Such echoes would be displayed as though they were due to targets seen at the angle of elevation of the antenna, and thus at heights which would depend upon their range. A great variety of such possibilities can occur depending upon the geometry involved, the refractive conditions, and the nature of the terrain.

The range of possibilities is further extended if the distribution of radar energy in the side lobes is taken into consideration. With a side lobes strength 30 dB below the main beam (a factor of 1000 in power), a side lobes target will yield a return equal in strength to the main beam return of an identical target at a range 5.6 times greater (the 4th root of 1,000). Thus a target detectable at 100 mi. in the main beam might be detected by the (first) side lobes at a range of up to 18 mi.

Anomalous propagation of the type described is also significant in determining the distribution of energy within the envelope of the main beam, particularly in broad vertical beam systems. At low angles some energy within the beam impinges on the earth's surface near the radar and is reflected, still within the envelope of the beam. Because the path followed by such energy is necessarily longer than the direct path and because of the wave nature of the energy, in-phase and out-of-phase interference will occur, leading to a vertical lobe structure in the beam envelope (see Fig. 10). Anomalous propagation conditions can readily produce variations in the normal distribution of energy within the beam due to this mechanism and thus can easily lead to unexpected variations in signal intensity from distant targets.

It is important to recognize the difficulties that are inherent in establishing whether propagation conditions are anomalous in certain cases. Where the gradient of refractivity extends uniformly over large horizontal areas, there is little difficulty in determining the situation either from conventional meteorological data or from the manifestation of the anomalous performance of the radar itself (for example, the detection of ground clutter to abnormally large ranges). In some cases it is possible to infer, with some confidence, from the meteorological conditions (especially if data on the vertical profile of temperature and humidity are available) that anomalous propagation is *not* present. In many cases, however, the causative conditions may be very variable in space and time, and it is then

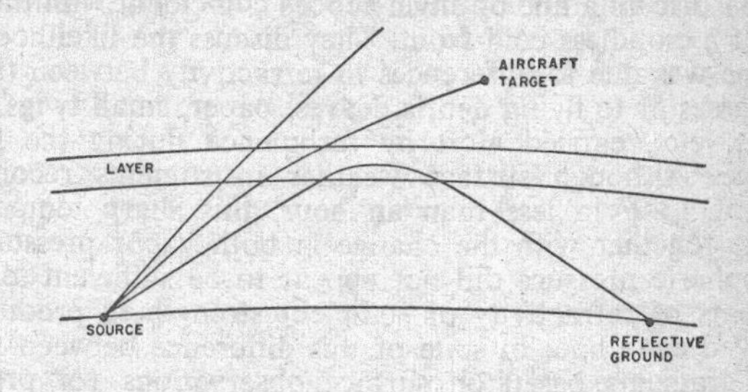

Fig. 10 Ducting of a portion of the radar beam. Both surface and elevated target are detected

difficult to be at all confident about the nature of propagation at any particular time or in any particular place. Even if timely radiosonde data are available from a nearby location, the information they provide on the thermal and humidity gradient is often inadequate for the assessment of the refractive conditions. In particular, special experimental observations have shown that shallow layers of abnormal refractivity commonly occur either close to the surface or at various levels aloft.

It is often possible to infer only the likelihood or improbability of anomalous propagation conditions by reference to the general meteorological conditions that prevail. Thus one would expect normal propagation in the daytime in a well-mixed, unstable airstream with moderate winds over a dry surface, while expecting marked superrefraction over moist ground during a calm clear night following the passage of a front that brought precipitation in the late afternoon.

Localized conditions favorable for superrefraction are also caused by showers and thunderstorms (Ligda, 1956). The cold downdraft beneath thunderstorms can cause colder air near the surface than aloft while evaporation from the rain and rain-soaked surface, causes locally higher humidities.

In addition to the detection of distant ground targets by refraction of the radar beam, there is the possibility of reflection or forward scatter of the beam to ground targets. Whether or not layers that would reflect the beam to the ground would also be detected by the radar has been part of the controversy concerning the nature of invisible targets in clear air. These so-called "angel" echoes have been observed since the early days of radar (Plank, 1956; Atlas, 1959 and 1964; Atlas, 1966a). Detailed case studies of selected angel situations illustrate the difficulty of determining the nature of the targets causing the angel echoes. For example, Ligda and Bigler, (1958) discuss a line of angel echoes coincident with the location of a cloudless cold front. They discuss the likelihood that the line was due to differences in refractivity between the two air masses or to flying debris, leaves, paper, small twigs, birds, insects, etc., carried aloft by turbulence during the frontal passage. Although surface weather instruments recorded a drop of 13°F in less than an hour, this sharp temperature change together with the change in both vapor pressure and atmospheric pressure did not appear to be sufficient to cause gradients of refractivity of sufficient strength to produce the observed echo line. In spite of this difference between refractivity gradients based on surface observations (of pressure, temperature, and moisture) and those required to explain the source of the echo, Ligda and Bigler found serious objections to any hypothesis other than that the echo was due to refractivity gradients. They mention the need for instruments capable of measuring sharp refractivity gradients.

Atlas (1959) studied in detail a situation at Salina, Kans. on 10 September 1956 where cellular and striated echoes covered much of the PPI to ranges of 85 mi. He concluded that the echoes were due to forward scatter from a patterned array of refractive index inhomogeneities to ground targets and back. Recently Hardy and Katz (1968) discussed a very similar radar pattern. They concluded that insects were responsible for the echoes and that cellular pattern of insects was due to atmospheric circulation. Atlas (1968c) agreed that insects may be responsible for some echoes but that the forward scatter explanation is valid in other instances.

Investigations of angel echoes with high-power, high-resolution radars at three different wavelengths have made it possible to learn much about the nature of targets producing various types of angel echoes. Simultaneous observations at 3 cm., 10.7 cm., and 71.5 cm. with the ultrasensitive MIT Lincoln Laboratory Radars at Wallops Island, Va. have been described by Hardy, Atlas, and Glover (1966), Atlas and Hardy (1966a), and Hardy and Katz (1968a). They found two basic types of angel echoes: dot or point echoes and diffuse echoes with horizontal extent. The dot angels are incoherent at long ranges or when viewed with broad beams but are discrete coherent echoes when viewed by a radar with high resolution. They may occur in well defined layers and may have movements different from the wind at their altitude. Their cross-sections and wavelength dependence are consistent with radar returns to be expected from insects. Since no other explanation fits all the observations of these dot angels, it is concluded that the targets are insects.

Extensive diffuse echo layers have been noted at a variety of heights and sometimes exhibit an undulation or wave motion. The height of these layers coincides with levels at which refractive inhomogeneities may be expected, e.g., at the tropopause. It can be shown theoretically (as summarized by Hardy (1968b) that the measured radar reflectivity of such layers accords well with the theory of the scattering of electromagnetic energy by dielectric inhomogeneity due to Tatarski (1966). The reflectivity η is related to wavelength λ and the coefficient C^2, which describes the degree of refractive inhomogeneity due to turbulence, by the expression from which

$$\eta = 0.39 \, C_n^2 \, \lambda^{-1/3} \tag{10}$$

it will be seen that such layers are more likely to be detected by radars operating at shorter wavelengths. Although, because this simple relationship does not apply in the dissipation range of the turbulence spectrum the largest values of η occur at about 5 cm (Atlas 1966b). These phenomena have been much studied recently in connection with the detection of clear air turbulence. (Hardy, 1968b; Ottersten, 1968: and Atlas, 1968b). It is concluded that such turbulence may be detected with ultra high performance radars but only when well marked. (Note that the significant physical feature detected, i.e., the dielectric inhomogeneities, is caused in these cases by the turbulent condition of the atmosphere.)

Radars of the type normally used for tracking and surveillance are unlikely to detect such layers. On the other hand, it has been suggested that on occasion at low levels where marked intermixing of dry and moist air is present, dielectric inhomogeneities will be sufficiently marked and be present in sufficient quantity to produce detectable echoes with radars of relatively modest performance.

Measurements made by Atlas (1953, 1959) and others indicated that atmospheric layers occasionally exist having power reflection coefficients, at normal incidence, of 10^{-14} or greater (i.e., 140 db attenuation). The power reflection coefficient of such layers would be greatly magnified if the radar energy impinged on the layer at a small grazing angle. The increase is roughly proportional to the 6th power of the cosecant of the grazing (i.e., elevation) angle. Thus at a grazing angle of about 10 mrad, the reflected signal would be as high as 10^{-2}

(a 20 db attenuation). Under actual atmospheric conditions the partially reflected signal of ground objects for example, would be expected to be detectable only at grazing angles (and thus, initial elevation angles) low enough to produce return signals above the noise threshold of the radar receiver. This would produce a "forbidden cone" effect, where no such anomalous signals would be detected closer than a certain range (because of elevation angle, range relation of a layer at a constant height); this has been actually observed in several cases (see Section III, Chapter 5).

It is conceivable that there could be rare occasions when only isolated atmospheric inhomogeneities existed or when the inhomogeneities were such that only the most reflective ground targets were detectable. In such situations only one or two unusual ground targets would appear on the PPI. Levine (1960), in a discussion of mapping with radar, points out how certain combinations of ground and man-made structures act as 'corner reflectors' and return a much stronger signal to the radar than is returned by surrounding features. The sides of buildings and adjacent level terrain, or even fences and level terrain, constitute such reflectors. He states that in areas where fences and buildings are predominantly oriented north-south and east-west, the 'glint' echoes from the corner reflector effect appear at the cardinal points of the compass and have therefore been called a "cardinal point effect." In addition, different types of vegetation have different reflectivities and these vary further according to whether they are wet or dry.

From the above discussion it is obvious that the identification of targets as being ground return due to forward scatter or reflection is difficult in any but the most obvious situations. Still it should be realized that situations do occur when only very localized areas of ground return may be detected and due to the detection mechanism the location of the intersection of the radar beam with the ground may vary from sweep to sweep of the radar antenna. The problem of verifying whether the target is ground return is greatly complicated by the fact that measurements of refractivity gradients cannot currently be made in sufficient detail around the radar site to describe with precision the medium through which the radar beam is being propagated.

RADIO FREQUENCY INTERFERENCE

During the past 15 years, electromagnetic compatibility (EMC) has emerged as a new branch of engineering concerned with the increasing problems of radio frequency interference (RFI) and the overcrowding of the radio frequency spectrum. The EMC problem is increasing so rapidly that considerable engineering efforts are included in the design, development, RFI testing and production of all new electronic equipment from the electric razor and TV set to the most sophisticated of electronic equipments, such as computer and radar systems. This is true for entertainment, civil, industrial, commercial, and military equipment. The problems are compounded not only because the frequency spectrum is overcrowded, but much earlier generation equipment, which is more susceptible to and is a more likely source of interference, is not made obsolete or scrapped. New generation equipment is potentially capable of interaction problems among themselves, as well as playing havoc with older equipment. Each year sees new users bring new equipment into the frequency spectrum: such as UHF television, garage door openers, automatic landing control systems, city traffic management and control systems, and a vast array of new electronic devices being introduced into tactical and strategic defense systems.

RFI contributes to the information displayed on radar scopes. It is caused by the radiation of spurious and/or undesired radio frequency signals from other non-associated electronic equipment, such as navigational aids, data processing computers, voice communication systems, other radars, and from more common sources, such as ignition and electric motor control systems. RFI can also be emitted from the radar system's own components, causing self-induced interference.

Much interference may be sporadic, producing only a short lived 'echo.' There may be instances, however, when the interference occurs at regular intervals that could nearly coincide with the antenna rotation rate so that the spurious 'echo' might appear to be in approximately the same position or close enough to it that the operator would assume there was a target moving across the scope.

Radio frequency interference can enter the radar system in many places:

(1) In the transmitter where it can affect the stability and fidelity of the transmitted output pulse waveform;

(2) In the receiver local signal-generating and amplifying circuitry where its effects can be similar to the transmitter perturbations;

(3) In the external transmitter/receiver space link where the interference effectiveness depends upon its intensity, frequency, power level, direction of arrival and signal spectral characteristics.

External interference entering on the link through the antenna input is the most common of these possible interference sources. Plate 67 shows some of the more easily recognizable radio frequency interference patterns from other radar systems. This type of interference considerably reduces the effectiveness of the radar, but this type of interference, taken alone, is usually readily identifiable by operating personnel. This might not be as true when it occurs in conjunction with extraordinary meteorological, propagation, and equipment degradation phenomena.

The photographs in Plate 66 are time exposures of the PPI. The camera shutter is left open for a full rotation of the antenna so the photograph is generated by the intensity of the cathode ray tube electron beam as it rotates with the antenna. This is in contrast to an instantaneous photograph that would be brightest where the trace was located at the instant of exposure and, depending on the persistence of the cathode ray tube, much less bright in other regions. While the interference in these photographs appears as lines it would appear as points at any given instant. The lines are generated by the time exposure as the points move in or outward along the electron beam. The photographs also show precipitation echoes. Examination of the photographs shows that the interference does not mask the larger precipitation echoes to any appreciable extent but might mask small point targets.

A radar receiver has a limited bandwidth over which it will accept and detect electromagnetic signals. In this acceptance band, the receiver reproduces the signals at the receiver output and displays them on the radar presentation display. Thus any interfering signals that fall within this band will be detected and displayed by the very sensitive receiver. In an S-band (2ghz) pulse radar, the typical bandwidth of the receiver will be 20-50 ghz. Any weak signals in this frequency band will be detected. Even out-of-band signals can interfere if they are of sufficient signal intensity to overpower the receiver out-of-band rejection characteristics. For instance, a very strong out-of-band signal of 10 watts might be typically attenuated by the receiver preselection filter by 60 db, reducing it to a signal of −20 db. To the radar receiver, this can still be a powerful signal, as it might have a sensitivity of displaying signals as weak as from −50 to −80 db or less. It is also likely that the out-of-band interference will be derived from the nonlinear interaction of the desired return signal and the out-of-band interfering signal. The resulting interaction (mixing) of these signals in the receiver can generate still weaker intermodulation products that fall within the passband of the system circuits so that they are displayed. Spurious responses can occur at other than the frequency to which the radar is tuned because of inadequacies in the rejection of the unwanted frequencies in the receiver. The inadequacy is caused by insufficient out-of-band filter rejection coupled with a high level of RFI.

Increasingly more powerful transmitters and more sensitive receiver radar systems need even greater relative suppression of unwanted emission, to prevent the absolute level of out-of-band interference from rising to intolerable levels, thus causing interference to and from other electronic systems.

Even if normally operating radars are not affected by this interference most of the time, the degradation of the radar components or of nearby systems can cause the temporary increase in interference at the radar site. Radar personnel are continually concerned with this problem. Such acts as opening an electronic cabinet can cause the local RFI to increase sufficiently to create an RFI nuisance to the radar system.

Each radar system has been designed to fulfill a single class of target tracking function, being optimized to provide proper and reliable target data a high percentage of the time. However all systems, including radar systems, have their limitations. Thus, it must be recognized that there will be times when other systems will interfere, component parts will either gradually degrade or catastrophically fail, propagation and meteorological conditions will deviate far from the normal environment, and maintenance and operating personnel will occasionally fail to function effectively. For all radar and other electronic systems, an increasing amount of effort is expended to reduce the occurrence of these degradations or failures and to minimize their effects.

Lobes and Reflections

Because of radar engineering design limitations, it is not possible to direct all of the transmitter energy into the main antenna beam and small but measurable amounts of energy are transmitted in many other directions. Similarly, energy can be received from such directions, in what are known as the side lobes of the antenna, and can give rise to erroneous directional information. Particularly complicated situations arise when side lobe problems are associated with building or ground reflection mechanisms. For example, if a radar antenna is radiating 100,000 watts peak power in the main beam, 100 watts can be simultaneously radiated from a −30 db side lobe in another direction. Fig. 11 (adapted from Skolnik, 1962) shows a radiation pattern for a particular parabolic reflector. Note that if the main beam is radiating 100 Kw, the first side lobe, the first minor and the spillover lobe radiate about 100 watts. This 100-watt radiation will be reflected from large targets in this side lobe heading but will be shown on the PPI as having the same bearing as the main beam of the antenna. This display of a false target is called a ghost. In this particular instance two targets having identical radar cross-sections would appear as returns of equal intensity if one were in the main beam and the other in the side lobe but 5.6 times closer to the radar.

Highly reflective targets can often be detected in the side lobes. Thus a single large target detected in the numerous side lobes can be displayed in a number of places simultaneously. Since, in radar displays, target echoes are represented as being in the direction in which the antenna is pointing, not in the direction from which the energy is returning at the time of the detection, side lobe echoes from a single target can be

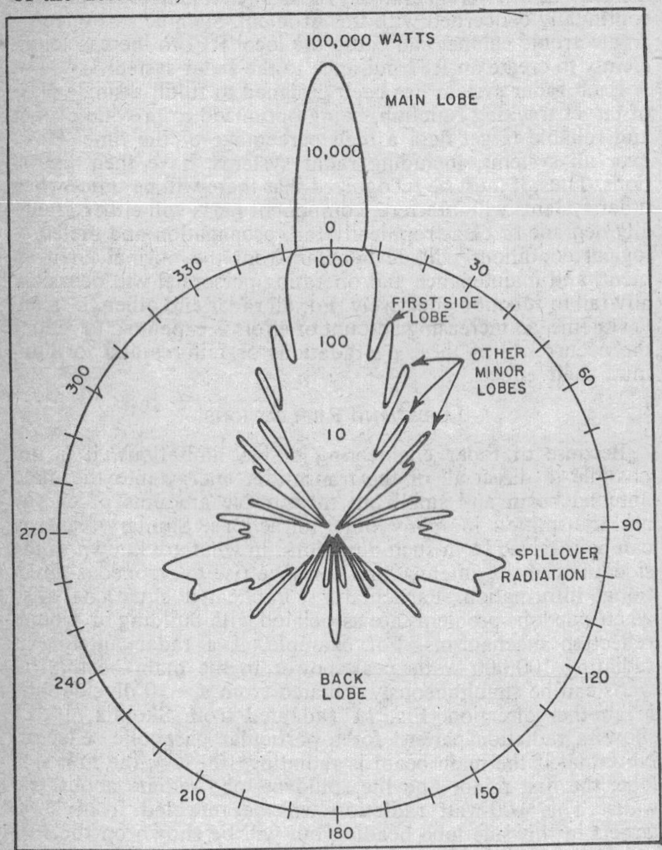

Fig. 11 Lobe pattern of a radar antenna

shown as a collection of false targets. Such target outputs from side lobe returns are generally systematically located in the display relative to the main beam return signal. Therefore, in general, side lobe return signals are readily identifiable by the operator and will tend to cause obliteration of other nearby target returns. Side lobe return signals usually bear a fixed relationship of adjacent blips on an arc about each side of the main target return. This is a common problem in ship radars where another ship is being scanned broadside. The highly reflective ship might have a return signal that will occur at the true range of the ship, but will be contained in an arc exceeding 10° or 15° instead of a single narrow blip.

Detection from vertical side lobes can cause strange effects when "radio dusting" is present. Many radars are constructed so that the antenna cannot be pointed at very low elevation angles, in order to avoid the most severe anomalous propagation effects or, more often, to avoid ground reflections. Assume, for example, a radar with a beam width of (nominally) 1°, having a minimum at say 1.5° and a side lobe at 2°. Assume also that the antenna is constrained to elevation angles of 1.5° or greater. If a surface duct is present, the strongest signals would be attained by pointing the antenna (and the main beam) at an elevation angle of 0°, but this cannot be done. However, ducted targets could be detected with the first (vertical) side lobe, and in this case the maximum AP signals (ducted) would be attained at an apparent elevation angle of 2° (so that the main side lobe was at 0°), and the intensity of these false target signals would decrease or even disappear if the antenna were lowered to its minimum setting of 1.5°. This sort of behavior has apparently led some investigators of specific UFO incidents to discount the possibility of anomalous propagation as the source of unknown radar targets.

Smith (1962) discusses the effects of side lobes on observed echo patterns during thunderstorms and periods of anomalous propagation. In both situations echoes were observed extending from the surface up to 70,000 ft. (the upper limit of the RHI scope). Before these vertical protrusions to high altitudes were observed during anomalous propagation conditions when the echoes were known to be from ground clutter, it was not realized that they were from side lobes. As a result, the side lobe echoes had not been recognized when measuring thunderstorm heights and reported heights were much too great. On the RHI side lobe, echoes took the form of narrow echo protrusions above the location of strong targets. These protrusions were often segmented due to nulls between side lobes, but in some cases were continuous.

One effect of such lobes is that when the antenna of a search radar is elevated (so that at longer ranges no ground return should be evident) ducted side lobe radiation results in echoes on the PPI. Without understanding what is happening, the operator would logically assume a strong target at high altitudes.

Angle of arrival measurements by a radar, like other measurement devices, will be limited in accuracy by noise and interference. Other limiting factors can be the reflection caused by the wave characteristics of electromagnetic radiation. Reflections from the ground in front of the antenna system or from a nearby building or mountain can be minimized by proper antenna location. These effects can seldom be reduced to zero and are detrimental to an extent that depends on the antenna lobe pattern, geographical, and extraordinary meteorological conditions, thus causing residual reflection problems.

Another phenomenon explaining strange and erratic radar returns has been observed with echoes occurring at locations where no targets are to be found. Analysis of these observations shows that the echoes are from ground or airborne objects which are being detected by radiation reflected from mirror-like plane surfaces of vehicles or buildings in the neighborhood of the radar. If the reflector is moving, then the reflected ground target behaves like a moving target. It changes its apparent distance and direction relative to the radar. The double reflecting return echo is shown in the PPI display in the direction at which the first reflecting surface is found. The echo may, however, be displayed at a point at which there is no actual target. Moving objects, such as automobiles or other objects capable of reflecting electromagnetic waves may be observed on the PPI by ground clutter so they are not identified. It is obvious that ghost echoes can show movement which is not possible with real vehicles. Many unusual PPI observations have been explained in this manner.

Mechanisms of multiple reflections which serve to produce ghosts are illustrated in Fig. 12. These involve spectacular reflection from the first target, effectively deflecting a significant amount of radar energy to a second target at a different azimuth, which is oriented so as to reflect most of the radiation incident on it. Either of the reflecting targets can be stationary or moving objects. In Fig. 12 the radar is at the point labeled "1." A reflector is a point "2" and real targets are at the points labeled "3." Due to reflections from the reflector to the targets, ghost echoes will appear at the points labeled "4." The appearance of the ghost on the PPI is one possible explanation for perplexing unidentified target motions. If one of the two reflectors is an aircraft and undertakes any maneuvers, the path followed by the ghost is especially erratic. As viewed on a PPI scope perhaps it first recedes from, then "flies" parallel to, and finally overtakes or appears to collide or pass the real aircraft.

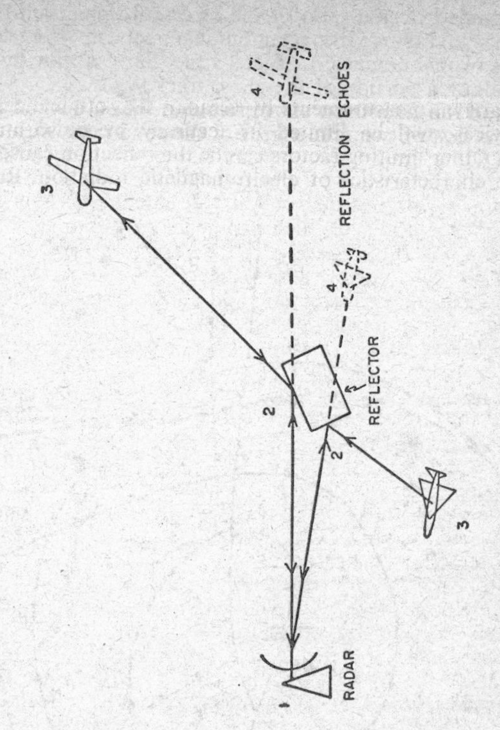

Fig. 12 Geometry of reflection echoes

Fig. 13 (adapted from Levine 1960) shows the outline of a conventional aircraft surveillance radar PPI (included within the circle). The solid line (A) shows the return echo path of an aircraft traveling at 300 knots. The dashed line (B) shows the echo path that will also result when sufficient radar energy is scattered from the aircraft to a prominent ground reflector located at C, and then reflected back to the aircraft and then to the receiver. In this example, the aircraft is the first of the reflectors, so that the phantom echo always occurs at the same azimuthal bearing as the aircraft, while its range always exceeds that of the aircraft. Consequently, on the PPI, the path of this ghost always lies outside the aircraft path. However, if the aircraft overflies the ground object, the phantom echo and the aircraft echo will almost merge. In addition, as the apparent range of the phantom is greater with the same radial speed as the aircraft, the apparent velocity of the ghost will be magnified by the ratio of the aircraft-to-phantom distance from the radar. The phantom can appear to exceed 2,000 knots in this manner. In Fig. 13 the ghost is moving at 900 knots along a portion of the ghost track.

Fig. 13 and the discussion above relate to the case when the aircraft is the first of two reflectors. For the conditions with the

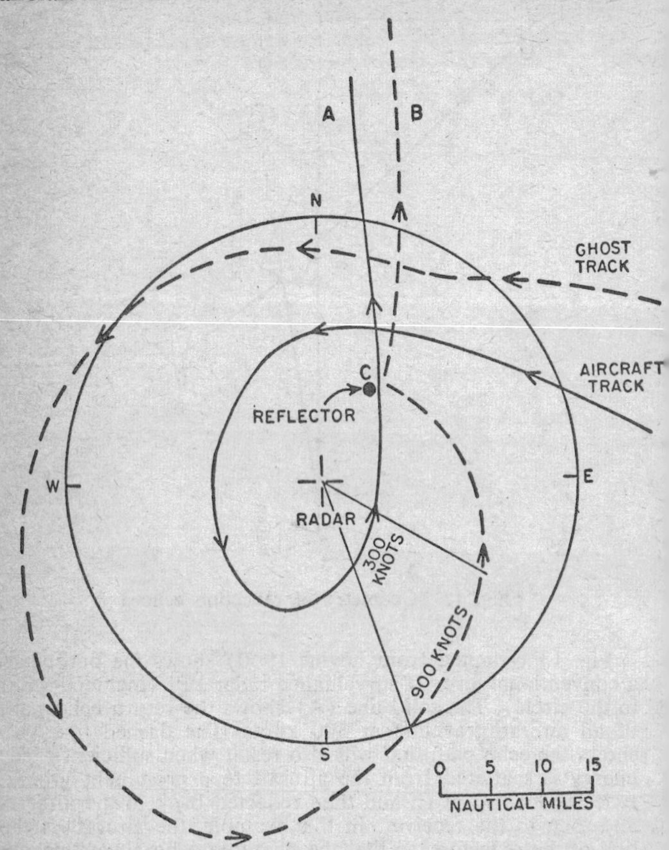

Fig. 13 Track of ghost echo caused by reflection from aircraft to ground reflector

ground object as the first of the two reflectors, the phantom echo always occurs at the same azimuth bearing as the ground object. For example, in Fig. 14 (also adapted from Levine,

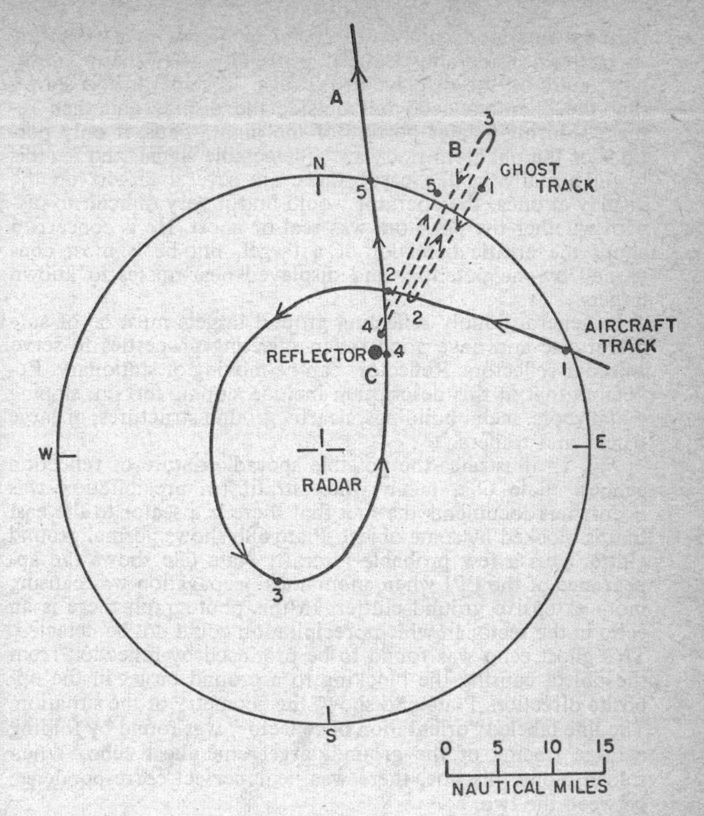

Fig. 14 Track of ghost echo caused by reflection from ground reflector to aircraft

1960) the solid line (A) applies to scattering from the first reflector to the aircraft and back to the receiver. The inward and outward excursions of this path actually occur along a single radial line from the radar site through the first reflector.

In any actual situation, only fractional portions of the ghost echo paths might be of sufficient signal strength to appear on the display. Those particular returns that are closest to the ground object or where the reflector has the most favorable reflecting properties will most likely be displayed. In a radar detecting only moving targets, a stationary ground object might not appear as a target on the scope. Thus, in this manner, the operator's ability to correlate ghosts to a reflecting surface is considerably reduced, especially when many known targets are on the display. From Figs. 13 and 14, it is shown that the phantom echo fell outside the display and then returned during a later portion of the flight. Thus, if only portions of the phantom track are a detectable signal, and if (this would usually be the case) there are several targets on the display at once, the operator would find it very difficult to discern whether the phantom was real or ghost. He is concerned about the erratic behavior of a target, but he is most concerned by the potential and displayed near-misses to known targets.

In general doubly reflecting ground targets must be of sufficient size and have good radar-reflecting properties to serve as radar-reflectors. Reflectors can be moving or stationary. Reflectors that fit this description include sloping terrain, sloping metal roofs, metal buildings, nearby ground structures, or large trucks and trailers.

Fig. 13 illustrates the possible sporadic nature of reflection echoes. Plate 68a, taken when stratiform precipitation was occurring, documents the fact that there is a sector to the east that is blocked by some object. Plate 68b shows normal ground clutter plus a few probable aircraft. Plate 68c shows the appearance of the PPI when anomalous propagation was causing more extensive ground clutter. In this photograph there is an echo in the sector in which precipitation could not be detected. This ghost echo was found to be produced by reflection from the object causing the blocking to a ground target in the opposite direction. Plate 68d shows the geometry of the situation. The line labeled "orientation of reflector" was found by folding a large tracing of the ground target and ghost echo. When folded along this line, there was near perfect correspondence between the two.

More complex reflection occurrences require a rare combination of reflector/target radar geometry and reflectivities. Analysis indicates that they occur occasionally. However, unless accurate data are recorded at the time of the event, ray tracing techniques will be almost impossible to use in order to reconstruct the possible circumstances. In addition to phantoms, caused by reflecting objects, other types of spurious target returns can be occurring at the same time, further increasing the difficulty of analyzing the unusual sighting. Such things as extraordinary meteorological conditions, and multiple-time-around echoes can also be contributing effects, making the analysis that much more difficult. When interference problems, operator interpretation, and equipment reliability factors are included, one begins to realize that the explanation of reported unusual observations requires extensive research for each incident, and such research is not possible unless all pertinent information has been documented in detail.

7. *Evaluation of Radar Echoes to Identify Targets*

When there is an echo on the PPI of a search radar, the operator must determine the nature of the target. The information he has is relative signal intensity, some knowledge of fluctuation in intensity, position, velocity, and behavior relative to other targets. In addition he may be able to infer altitude if he is able to elevate the beam and reduce the gain to find an angle of maximum signal intensity. Previous sections of this chapter have briefly described a number of targets that search radars are capable of detecting. From the discussion it is apparent that there is overlap in the characteristics of different types of targets. Signal intensities, for example, range over several orders of magnitude. Wind-borne and powered targets may have comparable ground speeds depending on the wind speed. Many different types of targets show echo fluctuations. Thus there is no specific set of characteristics that will permit a given echo to be unambiguously identified as a specific target. At best all one can do is say that a given echo *probably* is, or is not, a specific target based on some of the observed characteristics.

TARGET VELOCITY

Determination of the direction and speed of an echo in the PPI of a search radar requires some assumptions. A long range search radar antenna generally rotates at about 4-8 rpm. At 6 rpm, an antenna rotates through 360° in 10 sec. (=36°/-sec). If the horizontal beam-width of the antenna is 3.6° a point target will be within the beam for 0.1 sec. as the beam sweeps past. Then 9.9 sec. elapse until the beam again sweeps the target. If on this next revolution there is an echo in the general vicinity of the target detected on the previous sweep the operator must decide whether this echo is from the same target that was detected previously or is from a new target. If he assumes the two echoes are from the same target, he can then compute a velocity. If his assumption was correct, if his computations are accurate, and if the target is at the indicated locations, the computed ground speed is correct. If, however, the two echoes are not from the same target or are from a target that is not at the indicated location, then the computed speed will have no meaning.

The speed computed from the displacement of the echoes from a target at the indicated location represents the ground speed of the target. To aid in the identification of slow moving targets, it is necessary to determine its airspeed. This requires knowledge of the wind velocity at the location including altitude and time of the detection, and the assumption that the target is in essentially level flight. It is often difficult to determine precisely the wind velocity at a given point due to the wide spacing of stations that measure winds aloft and the six-hour interval between observations. Except in complex situations, it is usually possible, however, to extrapolate measured winds for a given location with sufficient accuracy to determine whether the target velocity and wind velocity have sufficient similarity to justify a conclusion that the target is probably windborne. Conversely if there is a large disparity between wind velocity and target velocity a logical conclusion would be that the target could not be windborne.

When an echo that has been moving in an orderly manner on the PPI suddenly disappears, the information for computing its speed also disappears. Any attempts to guess the speed would require the operator to make specific assumptions of the reason for the disappearance. He might assume that the target moved out of range during the brief time required for one antenna revolution. Such an assumption would probably require a very high speed target. Or the operator might assume that the target decreased altitude to a position below the radar horizon. If the target was located close to the radar horizon, an altitude change of a few tens of feet would be sufficient for it to disappear and the required speed (vertical velocity) would be quite small.

TARGET INTENSITY AND FLUCTUATIONS

The power received from a point target is directly proportional to the radar scattering cross-section of the target and inversely proportional to the fourth power of the distance from the radar to the target. Therefore, for an equal signal to be received from two targets, a target 10 mi. from the radar would have to have a radar cross-section 10,000 times as large as a target at 1 mi. Examples of targets with differences in cross-sections of this order of magnitude are birds with cross-sections of 0.01 m^2 or less and aircraft with cross-sections of up to 100 m^2. Intensity differences such as these can be measured (by gain reduction to threshold of detection), but the nature of display systems such as PPI's is such that differences are considerably reduced. An echo on the PPI is composed of many small dots that result from an electron beam that excites the coating on the face of the tube causing it to emit light. The coating may be designed to emit light only when the electron beam excites it or may continue to emit light for some time after the excitation has ceased (persistence). The later is usually the case for PPI's where the operator depends on persistence to see the 360° coverage provided by the rotating antenna. Haworth (1948) states that from 150-200 spots can be resolved along the radius of magnetically deflected radar tubes. Gunn (1963) points out that since the PPI trace lines converge at the center the light output per unit area of the tube face will decrease with increasing radical distance from the center. As a result echoes near the center are 'painted' with a higher intensity than echoes of comparable strength anywhere else on the display. These characteristics of the display system act to conceal further the relative magnitudes of the signal intensity of targets at different ranges, so that the operator loses much of the available radar information when it is displayed on the PPI. Fluctuations are smoothed out, and the intensities are normalized to some extent. The result is that he can give some information on an unknown target in comparison with a known target *at the same range*. Positive knowledge of the nature of a target at a given range can only result from auxiliary data. For example, if the operator is in contact with an aircraft that is over a given point and he has an echo at that point he will logically assume the echo is from the aircraft if the echo is moving on the course and at the speed reported by the pilot. He could then compare the intensity and fluctuations of other targets at that range with those of the known target and draw some conclusions as to whether they might be larger or smaller than the aircraft.

BEHAVIOR RELATIVE TO OTHER TARGETS

Very little can be said about a target from the examination of a single echo but some information can be obtained by comparing the echo with other echoes on the remainder of the PPI. When the echo is interpreted in terms of the appearance and behavior of other echoes a logical explanation may become evident.

For example, the author has seen isolated targets on the PPI that were moving toward the radar in a direction opposite to that of the wind, so that it was obvious that they could not be windborne. A slight elevation of the antenna caused them to disappear so it was apparent that they were at low levels. No attempt was made to send aircraft to the vicinity to look for targets. All other attempts to interpret the nature of real targets on that half of the PPI that would return the displayed echoes were futile. When the remainder of the PPI was examined it was found that the speed of a line of thunderstorms moving toward the station was the same as that of the echoes to the east. The direction of movement, however, was the same as that of the wind and not opposite, as with the echoes to the east. Further, the distance to the thunderstorms to the west was the same as the distance to the unknown echoes to the east. With this additional information it seemed likely that the echoes to the east were reflections of portions of the thunderstorms to the west. The obstacles causing the reflections were subsequently identified as large nearby chimneys that extended only slightly higher than the height of the radar so that when the antenna was elevated slightly the chimneys were below the main beam and no longer caused reflections.

Since the reflectors (chimneys) were very narrow, the reflection echoes were very narrow but their length was equal to the diameter of the precipitation area. The echoes therefore had a long, narrow (cigar-shaped) appearance. Since the apparent lengths in some cases were 10-15 mi. they were not mistaken for some type of flying vehicle.

Although the solution of the case discussed here is a simple, and, on the surface, obvious one, it does demonstrate the necessity of studying the entire PPI, not just one or two odd echoes. The case also illustrates how echo characteristics become distorted when the return is from a target not at the indicated location. The long, narrow shapes of the reflection echoes, a vertical extent of only 1°-2° at ranges less than 50 mi., and movement against the wind all tended to rule out precipitation as the target.

The problem of identifying reflections is very difficult. The simplest case is where the reflector and reflected target are both fixed. The reflected echo is always in the same position and whether it appears or not depends on propagation conditions and if the reflector is of limited vertical extent on antenna elevation angle.

When the reflector is fixed and the target is moving the reflected echo also moves but in a different direction than the true target. Still the geometry is relatively simple and the reflected echo will move toward or away from the radar along a radial line extending from the radar across the reflector. The reflected echo will appear to move toward the radar when the distance from the radar to the true target is decreasing and away from the radar when the distance from the radar to the true target is increasing. The apparent speed of the reflected echo toward or away from the radar corresponds to the speed of the true target toward or away from the reflector. This is *not its actual ground speed*. A target could move at 500 knots along a constant-distance circle from the reflector, yet the reflected echo would be stationary. Only if the target moved directly toward or away from the reflector would the reflected echo have the same speed as the target; but the speed of the reflected echo can never exceed that of the target.

When the reflector is moving and the target is stationary (see discussion of Fig. 13) the reflected echo track is always further from the radar than the reflector track. The reflection echo will follow roughly the same track as the reflector but its apparent speed may be much greater depending on the distance between the reflector and target. When the reflector is far from the target the apparent speed of the reflected echo will be much greater than the true speed of the reflector. When the reflector is very close to the target the reflected echo will be close to the position of the reflector and its apparent speed will be comparable to that of the reflector.

The situation where both the reflector and the target are moving is very complex. The apparent speed of the reflected echo will depend on the relative speeds of both reflector and target. When the reflector is moving slowly, the condition of a stationary reflector will be approached but not quite realized. That is, the reflected echo will have a maximum apparent speed that does not greatly exceed that of the target, but since the reflector is moving, the reflection echo will not be restricted to motion along a single radial line.

When the reflector is moving rapidly compared to the target, the result is similar to the case of a fixed target, that is the reflected echo track approximates the reflector track but its apparent speed will be greater. When the target moves, the track correspondence is not as good and the reflected echo's apparent speed may greatly exceed that of the reflector.

The most complex cases are those in which a moving reflector is not illuminating a single target but may show a different target on each scan of the radar. In these cases there is no correspondence between reflected echo track and reflector track. Speed computations in these cases are erroneously based on multiple targets. Attempts to compute a speed therefore produce values that can vary from some very low speeds to thousands of knots.

It is obvious from the preceding discussion that it is nearly impossible to identify an unknown target working in real time at the PPI. To establish that an unknown is a reflection echo requires a determination of whether it is at the same azimuth as a reflector. Since any one of many other echoes could be the possible reflector, the geometry would have to be applied to each one in turn. When numerous echoes are on the PPI this is impossible.

Much valuable information can be recorded for later detailed study by photographing the PPI with a radarscope camera during each revolution of the radar antenna. Later the films can be studied, either as time-lapse motion pictures or frame by frame. For many years this type of radarscope photography has been used for studies of radar-detected precipitation patterns and has provided insights into meteorological phenomena that would have been impossible from subjective verbal descriptions of the echo patterns.

Radarscope photographs of the PPI have all the limitations of the PPI presentation itself. They cannot show intensity differences or minor intensity fluctuations. They do have the powerful advantage of making it possible to review a puzzling echo hundreds of times at various rates of viewing and to study the appearance and behavior of *all* echoes before, during, and after the episode. Only by the study of radarscope films and many other supporting data is it possible to arrive at even a tentative conclusion that a given echo cannot be explained.

8. Conclusions

Radar is a valuable instrument for detecting and ranging targets that are not visible to an observer due to darkness, extreme distance, intervening rain, cloud cover, haze, or smog. Radar can also detect, or reflect from, atmospheric discontinuities that are not visible to the eye. The echoes of real targets and apparent targets that result from RFI, reflections, or system noise may on occasion produce scope presentations that are extremely difficult or impossible to interpret. The major difficulty is that while radar is designed to beam radiation in a specific direction and detect targets within a specific distance, it does not always do so. The transmitted radiation, while concentrated in a main beam, goes out as well, in many other directions. Portions of the main beam and the lobes may be reflected in other directions by nearby objects, by solid targets a considerable distance from the radar, or by layers or small volumes of atmospheric inhomogeneities. All of this radiation in various directions is refracted by atmospheric temperature and moisture profiles to deviate further from its original path. Portions of this radiation that impinge upon any of a wide variety of targets are reflected back along a reciprocal path and presented on the PPI as if they were at the position determined by the antenna elevation and azimuth, and the time required for the most recently transmitted pulse to travel out and back. Some of the displayed echoes will represent targets at the indicated locations. Some of the displayed echoes will be from targets not at the indicated position, and some of the echoes will not represent targets at all, but will be due to system noise or RFI. Since radar does not differentiate between the unique characteristics of different types of targets, it is impossible for even the most experienced radar operator to look at the PPI and positively identify all echoes on the scope.

Some auxiliary information on the possible nature of the

targets may be derived from the study of the appearance of the PPI on successive antenna revolutions or from a series of PPI photographs. These successive presentations show the interpreter apparent motion and changes in intensity. This additional information is useful but still does not permit positive identification of the target. Only such generalizations may be made as that the target appears to be moving at 250 knots so it cannot be precipitation, birds, or a balloon. To even make this generalization the operator has to know or make some assumptions about the probable wind speed in the vicinity of the apparent target.

The data presented on the PPI of a single radar, therefore, do not permit the operator to say very much about the possible nature of a target displayed as an echo on the PPI. Many additional data are required such as meteorological conditions between the radar and the apparent location of the target, and auxiliary radar information such as target elevation angle and the bearing of the target from another radar. The detection of a target at the same location by two or more radars with different characteristics would usually rule out multiple trip echoes, reflections, and detection by side lobes. Surveillance by more than one radar would also aid in establishing continuity along an echo track if the rotation rate of the two radars was such that they were 180° apart so that one would "see" the echo when the other was "looking" 180° from it. The problem of determining speed is based on the assumption that a single target has moved a specific distance during the time that the beam is not aimed at it. In many cases this may be an erroneous assumption, and it requires either continuous tracking or surveillance by numerous radars to determine whether only a single target is involved.

It is hoped that this discussion of radar has convinced the reader that radar data are only a tool to be used in conjunction with many other bits of information for the solution of various problems. Radar alone cannot specify the exact nature of all targets especially when it was probably specifically designed to detect specific target types. It can only provide the operator with some generalized information about the target and he can only draw some general conclusions based on a number of assumptions he must make. If he makes the wrong assumption, he will come to an erroneous conclusion.

This does not mean that radar could not be a useful tool in any further studies of the UFO problem; it simply points out the need for, and problems of, gathering photographic and other data from a number of different types of radar on specific incidents before the data could be carefully analyzed and interpreted with any degree of confidence.

Allen, R. J. and M. G. H. Ligda. "Services for Bird Counter Study and Design," *Final Report, Contract DA 42-007 AMC-306 (Y)*, Stanford Research Institute, Menlo Park, (1966).

Atlas, D. "Radar Lightning Echoes and Atmospherics in Vertical Cross Section," *Recent Advances in Atmospheric Electricity*, Pergamon Press, New York, (1958a), 441-459.

———. "Radar as a Lightning Detector," *Proc. Seventh Wx. Radar Conf.*, Miami Beach, Fla. (Available from American Meteorological Society, Boston, Mass.), (1958b), C-1-C-8.

———. "Sub-Horizon Radar Echoes by Scatter Propagation," *J. Geophysical Res.*, Vol. 64, (1959), 1205-1218.

———. "Advances in Radar Meteorology," *Advances in Geophysics*, Vol. 10, Academic Press, New York, (1964), 317-478.

———. "Further Remarks on Atmospheric Probing by Ultrasensitive Radar," Paper presented to the Panel on Remote Atmospheric Probing of the National Academy of Sciences, Chicago, Ill., (1968).

Atlas, D. and K. R. Hardy. "Radar Analysis of the Clear Atmosphere: Angels," Paper presented to the XV General Assembly of the International Scientific Radio Union, Munich, (1966a).

Atlas, D., K. R. Hardy, and K. Naito. "Optimizing the Radar Detection of Clear Air Turbulence," *J. Appl. Meteor.*, Vol. 5, (1966b), 450-460.

Battan, L. J. "Duration of Connective Radar Cloud Units," *Bull. AMS*, Vol. 34, (1953), 224-228.

Bauer, J. R. "The Suggested Role of Stratified Elevated Layers in Transhorizon Short Wave Radio Propagation, "*Tech. Rep., No. 124*, Lincoln Lab. M.I.T., (1956).

Bean, B. R. and E. J. Dutton. "Radio Meteorology," *NBS Monograph 92*, U.S. Government Printing Office, Washington, D.C. (1966).

Blackmer, R. H., Jr. "The Lifetime of Small Precipitation Echoes," *Proc. Fifth Wx. Radar Conf.* Asbury Park, N.J., (1955), 103-108.

———. "Anomalous Echoes Observed By Shipborne Radars," *Proc. Eighth Wx. Radar Conf.*, San Francisco, Calif. (available from AMS, Boston, Mass.), (1960), 33-38.

Blackmer, R. H. Jr. and S. M. Serebreny. "Analysis of Maritime Precipitation Using Radar Data and Satellite Cloud Photographs," *J. Appl. Meteor.*, Vol. 7, (1968), 122-131.

Bonham, L. L. and L. V. Blake. "Radar Echoes from Birds and Insects," *The Scientific Monthly*, (April, 1956), 204-209.

Borden, R. C. and T. K. Vickers. "A Preliminary Study of Unidentified Targets Observed on Air Traffic Control Radars," *Technical Development Report No. 180*, Civil Aeronautics Administration Technical Development and Evaluation Center, Indianapolis, (1953).

Browning, D. A. and D. Atlas. "Velocity Characteristics of Some Clear-Air Dot Angels," *J. Atmos. Sci.*, Vol. 23, (1966), 592-604.

Eastwood, E. *Radar Ornithology*, Methuen and Co., Ltd., 11 New Fetter Lane, London, 1967.

Eastwood, E., G. A. Isted and G. C. Rider. "Radar Ring Angels and the Roosting Behaviour of Starlings," *Proc. Royal Soc.*, London, Vol. 156, (1962), 242-267.

Eastwood, E. and G. C. Rider. "Some Radar Measurements of the Altitude of Bird Flight," *British Birds*, Vol. 58, (1965), 393-420.

Edrington, T. S. "The Amplitude Statistics of Aircraft Radar Echoes," *Trans. IEEE*, Vol. MIL 9, (1965), 10-16.

Ferrari, V. J. "An Epidemiologic Study of USAF Bird Strike Damage and Injury, 1960 to 1965," Life Sciences Division, Norton Air Force Base, California, (1966).

Geotis, S. G. "Some Radar Measurements of Hailstones," *J. Appl. Meteor.*, Vol. 2, (1963), 270-275.

Glick, P. A., "The Distribution of Insects, Spiders and Mites in the Air," Tech. Bull. No. 673, U.S. Dept. of Agriculture, (1939).

Goldstein, H., D. E. Kerr, and A. E. Bent. "Meteorological Echoes," *M.I.T. Rad. Lab. Series,* McGraw Hill, New York, Vol. 13, (1951), 588-640.

Glover, K. M., K. R. Hardy, C. R. Landry, and T. Konrad. "Radar Characteristics of Known Insects in Free Flight," *Proc. Twelfth Wx. Radar Conf.*, Norman, Oklahoma, (1966), 254-258.

Gunn, K. L. S. "Tube Face Filters for Line Space Compensation," *Proc. Tenth Wx. Radar Conf.*, Washington, D.C. (available from AMS, Boston, Mass.), (1963), 361-364.

———. "Tube Space Filters for Line Space Compensations," *Proc. Tenth Wx. Radar Conf.*, Wash., D.C., (1965).

Gunn, K. L. S., and T. W. R. East. "The Microwave Properties of Precipitation Particles," *Q. J. Roy. Meteor. Soc.*, Vol. 80, (1954), 552-545.

Hajovsky, R. G., A. P. Deam, and A. H. La Grone. "Radar Reflections from Insects in the Lower Atmosphere," *IEEE Trans.*, Vol. AP-14, (1966), 224-227.

Hansford, R. F. (Editor) *Radio Aids to Civil Navigation,* Heywood and Co. Ltd., London, 1960.

Hardy, K. R., D. Atlas, and K. M. Glover. "Multiwavelength Backscatter From the Clear Atmosphere," *J. Geophys. Res.*, 71, No. 6, (1966), 1537-1552.

Hardy, K. R. and I. Katz. "Probing the Atmosphere with High Power, High Resolution Radars," Paper presented to the Panel on Remote Atmospheric Probing of the National Academy of Sciences, Chicago, Ill. (1968a).

Haworth, L. J. "Introduction to Cathode Ray Tube Displays," *M.I.T. Rad. Lab. Series,* Vol. 22, Edited by T. Soller, M. A. Starr, and G. E. Valley, Jr., McGraw Hill, New York, (1948).

Hilst, G. R., and G. P. MacDowell. "Radar Measurements of the Initial Growth of Thunderstorms," *Bull. AMS,* 31, (1950), 95-99.

Hiser, H. W. "Some Interesting Radar Observations at the University of Miami," *Proc. Fifth Wx. Radar Conf.*, Asbury Park, N.J., (1955), 287-293.

Houghton, E. "Detection, Recognition and Identification of Birds on Radar," *Proc. Eleventh Wx. Radar Conf.*, (1964), 14-21.

Konrad, T. G., J. J. Hicks, and E. B. Dobson. "Radar Characteristics of Birds in Flight," *Science,* Vol. 159, (1968), 274-280.

Lack, D. and G. C. Varley. "Detection of Birds by Radar," *Nature,* Vol. 156, (1945).

La Grone, A., A. Deam, and G. Walker. *Radio Sci. J. Res.* (1964, 1965), 68D, 895.

Lane, J. A. "Small Scale Irregularities of the Radio Refractive Index of the Troposphere," *Nature,* Vol. 204, (1964), 438-440.

Levine, D. *Radargrammetry,* McGraw Hill, N.Y. 1960.

Ligda, M. G. H. "Radar Storm Observation," *Compendium of Meteorology,* AMS, Boston, Waverly Press, Baltimore, Md., 1951, 1265-1262.

———. "The Radar Observation of Lightning," *J. Atmos. and Terrestrial Physics,* Vol. 9, (1956), 329-346.

———. "Middle-Latitude Precipitation Patterns as Observed by Radar" (a collection of composite radar observations), *Scientific Report No. 1, Contract AF 19(604)-1564,* Texas A&M College, College Station, Tex., (1957).

———. "Radar Observations of Blackbird Flights," *Texas J. of Science*, Vol. 10, (1958), 225-265.

Ligda, M. G. H., and S. G. Bigler. "Radar Echoes From a Cloudless Cold Front," *J. Meteor.*, Vol. 15, (1958), 494-501.

Ligda, M. G. H., R. T. H. Collis, and R. H. Blackmer, Jr. "A Radar Study of Maritime Precipitation Echoes," *Final Report, Contract NOas 59-6170-a, SRI Project 2829*, Stanford Research Institute, Menlo Park, Calif., (1960).

Myres, M. T. "Technical Details of Radar Equipment Detecting Birds, and a Bibliography of Papers Reporting the Observation of Birds with Radar," *Field Note No. 9*, The Associate Committee on Bird Hazards to Aircraft, National Research Council of Canada, Ottawa, (1964).

Nagle, R. E. and R. H. Blackmer, Jr. "The Use of Synoptic-Scale Weather Radar Observations in the Interpretation of Satellite Cloud Observations," *Final Report, Contract AF 19 (628)-284, SRI Project 3947*, Stanford Research Institute, Menlo Park, Calif., (1963).

Page, R. M. "Radar Goes to Sea," (Unpublished report of early tests of the XAF radar by the U.S. Naval Research Laboratory. Described by Bonham and Blake 1956, (1939).

Pererson, A. M., R. L. Leadabrand, W. E. Jaye, R. B. Dyce, L. T. Dolphin, R. I. Presnell, L. H. Rorden, and J. C. Schobom. "Radar Echoes Obtained from Earth Satellites, 1957, Alpha and 1957, Beta," *Avionics Research*, Pergamon Press, N.Y., (1960), 140-145.

Plank, V. G. "A Meteorological Study of Radar Angels," *Geophysical Research Papers No. 52*, Air Force Cambridge Res. Lab., Bedford, Mass., (1956).

Plank, V. G., R. M. Cunningham, and G. F. Campen, Jr. "The Refractive Index Structure of a Cumulus Boundary and Implications Concerning Radio Wave Reflection," *Proc. Sixth Wx. Radar Conf.* Cambridge, Mass., (1957), 273-280.

Rainey, R. C. "Radar Observations of Locust Swarms," *Science*, Vol. 157, No. 3784, (1967), 98-99.

Ritchie, D. J. *Ball Lightning*, Consultants Bureau, New York, 1961, 70.

Rockney, V. D. "The WSR-57 Radar," *Proc. Seventh Wx. Radar Conf.*, Miami Beach, Florida, (1958), F-14 to F-20.

Schelling, J. G., C. R. Burrows, and E. B. Ferrell. "Ultra-short Wave Propagation," *Proc. IRE*, Vol. 21, (1933), 427-463.

Senn, H. V. and H. W. Hiser. "Major Radar Parameters for Airborne Weather Reconnaissance," *Proc. Tenth Wx. Radar Conf.*, Washington, D.C. (available from the AMS, Boston, Mass.), (1963), 341-347.

Skolnik, M. I. *Introduction to Radar Systems*, McGraw Hill, New York, 1962, 648.

Smith, E. K. Jr. and S. Weintraub. "The Constants in the Equation for Atmospheric Refractive Index at Radio Frequencies," *Proc IRE*, Vol. 41, (1953), 1035-1037.

Smith, R. L. "Vertical Echo Protrusions Observed by WSR-57 Radar," *Progress Report No. 10 on WSR-57 Radar Program*, Dept. of Commerce, Weather Bureau, Washington, D.C., (1962), 20-30.

U.S. Air Force. "Ground Radar Equipment Characteristics Digest," ADCM 50-12, Air Defense Command, Colorado Springs, Colo., (1954).

U.S. Navy. "Meteorological Aspects of Radio Radar Propagation," NAVWEPS 50-IP-550, U.S. Navy Weather Research Facility, Norfolk, Virginia, (1960).

Walker, W. "Use of Sun to Check WSR-57 Azimuth and Height Accuracy," *Progress Report No. 10 on WSR-57 Radar Program*, U.S. Dept. of Commerce, Washington, (1962), 15-19.

Williams, E. L. "Progress Report on the AN/CPS-9 Radar Program," *Proc. Third Wx. Radar Conf.* McGill University, Montreal, (1952).

Chapter 6 Sonic Boom / William Blumen

1. *Introduction*

Observers of unidentified flying objects report a variety of sound effects associated with the phenomenon. Some report sharp, explosive sound during rapid acceleration or high-speed flight. Others refer to humming, whining or whirring noise while the UFO is hovering or moving at relatively slow speeds (Hall, 1964). Still others mention whistling or swishing sounds suggestive of rushing air.

More remarkable than any of the foregoing, however, are reports that describe the UFO as moving at velocities far in excess of the maximum speed of sound in the earth's atmosphere without producing any noise or shock wave that would normally be expected under such conditions of atmospheric displacement. No characteristic "boom" is heard in these instances.

The absence of a sonic boom in these cases remains a mystery. Possible explanations are that: a) actual speed was overestimated; b) a natural atmospheric effect that could suppress the sonic boom was present; or c) the object or phenomenon did not displace the atmospheric gases through which it was passing at supersonic speeds.

In this chapter we shall present the basic concepts involved in the production of the sonic boom or shock wave resulting from the passage of an object through the atmosphere at speeds greater than that of sound at the altitude of flight. Natural effects that are theoretically capable of rendering such waves inaudible at ground level will also be discussed, as will current research aimed at suppression of sonic booms by aircraft design modification and other means.

In general, it would be unrewarding to analyze each UFO report in conjunction with meteorological data to determine if a sonic boom from a particular object flying at supersonic speed would be heard at ground level. The difficulties are two-fold: first, the existing state of knowledge concerning meteorological effects on sonic booms is sufficient only to provide information in terms of statistical probabilities (Roberts, 1967); and second, local meteorological features which occur between weather observing stations and/or which occur between the times of scheduled observations would not be observed.

2. *Sonic Boom Generation*

Sound waves are a manifestation of the compressibility of air. A source capable of compressing air produces pressure fluctuations, called sound or compression waves, which travel through the atmosphere. The peaks and troughs of the waves correspond to maxima and minima of the pressure fluctuations.

The leading edge of the wave or wave front is approximately spherical in shape, and the pressure disturbance propagates away from the source in a series of concentric spheres. The speed of propagation of these waves, the sound speed, varies with the temperature and pressure of the air through which the waves travel. The maximum value for speed of sound waves is generally at ground level and reaches about 760 mph. The sound speed may show considerable variation in the atmosphere, alternately decreasing and increasing with altitude. A minimum value of 580 mph is reached at approximately 50 miles above the earth's surface. However, these values are principally a function of altitude, but they also vary with the time of day, season and latitude and longitude. The following are approximate average values:

Height (feet)	*Speed of Sound (miles per hour)*
0	760
10,000	735
20,000	707
30,000	679

Pressure disturbances are generated whenever a body, such as an airplane, moves through the atmosphere and displaces the air around it. In subsonic flight the speed of the aircraft is less than the local sound speed and the wave disturbances propagate away from the plane in all directions. These pressure variations are generally weak and too slowly varying to be detected by the ear (Carlson, 1966).

An aircraft travelling at supersonic speeds moves faster than the pressure disturbances it generates. When this occurs the plane is always ahead of the wave front and the spherical waves emitted at successive points along the flight path become tangent to lines sloping backward from the bow of the plane. These lines form a cone, the surface of which is the shock wave. Shock waves are formed by each protuberance on the plane's exterior. However, with distance, the various shock fronts tend to coalesce into two large shock fronts, usually attributed to the bow and to the tail of the plane. Fig. 1a shows how the fronts intersect level ground from a hypothetical flight path parallel to the ground surface at constant sound speed and with no wind. The indicated abrupt pressure rise and fall is responsible for the sonic booms heard at the earth's surface. Two booms will be heard as the "bow" and "tail" shocks successively pass over an observer but the ear may not always register the separate shocks when they are of different intensities (Carlson, 1966) or when the observer is taken by surprise.

The ratio of aircraft speed to the sound speed at its altitude is called the Mach number. The limiting value at which no sonic boom is heard, because of atmospheric effects, is called the cutoff Mach number (Wilson, 1962). Studies made by Wilson (1962), Kane (1966) and Roberts (1967) have established that the cutoff Mach number ranges roughly between about 1.0 and 1.3 depending on atmospheric conditions and the altitude of the plane. This means that sonic booms produced by objects moving faster than 1.3 times the sound speed should be heard at ground level.

The angle between the shock front and the ground becomes smaller as the aircraft speed increases relative to the sound speed. In this situation the sonic boom may not be heard at ground level until the plane has passed from view. Wilson (1962) has estimated that the plane may be as much as 25 miles away from the point on the ground where the sonic boom is heard.

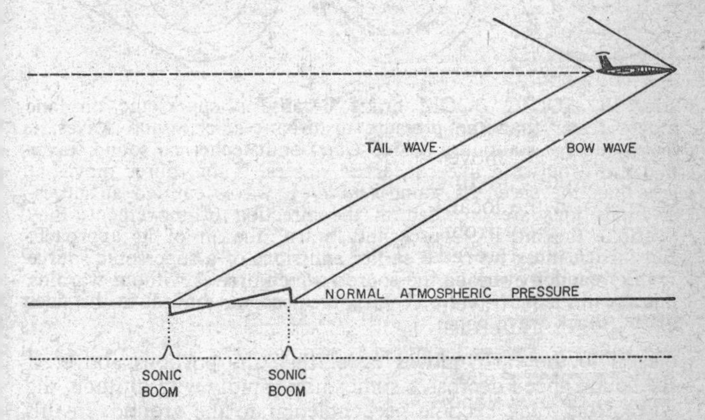

Fig. 1a SHOCK WAVES created by the passage through the air of a supersonic airplane coalesce into two large cone-shaped shock fronts, shown here in cross section, that are carried along with the airplane. Each front is a region of compressed air that creates a distinct "pressure jump" at the ground. The changes in atmospheric pressure are heard by an observer as two sonic booms in succession.

3. *Atmospheric Effects on Sonic Boom Propagation*

When the actual wind and temperature variations that occur in the atmosphere are taken into account, the simple conical pattern of the shock front may become quite distorted. The sound speed generally decreases with altitude between the ground and the plane. Therefore, as a propagating shock wave descends toward the ground, the portion of the wave front

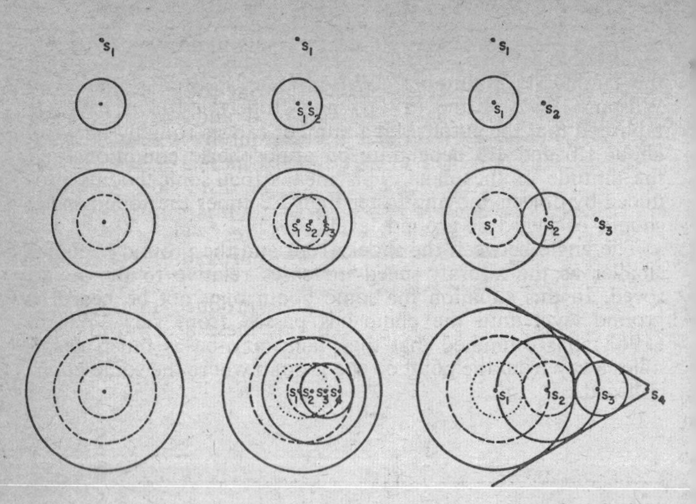

Fig. 1b SONIC BOOM arises because a supersonic airplane moves faster than the pressure disturbances, or sound waves, it propagates. A stationary source (*left*) emits spherical sound waves that move outward like concentric ripples. If the source moves at less than the speed of sound (*middle*), waves emitted at successive positions are crowded in the direction of movement; they overtake the moving source and "warn" the air of its approach. But disturbances from the earlier emissions of a supersonic source (*right*) cannot overtake the source, which arrives without warning and creates a shock wave. The spheres become tangent to the sides of the shock wave cone.

closest to the earth moves faster than the portions above. If the sound speed decreases sufficiently rapidly with altitude, the wave front may become perpendicular to the ground. In this situation the shock never reaches the ground because it begins to travel parallel to the ground before it gets there (Carson, 1966). Physical requirements for such an effect, however, are unlikely, even under extremely abnormal atmospheric conditions. In any event, an object moving through the atmosphere at any altitude parallel to the earth's surface, at a speed greater than the speed of sound at ground level would inevitably produce a sonic boom.

The decrease of sound speed with altitude also affects the portion of the wave front that spreads out to the sides of the plane. An investigation of the effect by Kane (1966), under conditions of no wind, shows that the lateral extent of the sonic boom at ground level ranges from about 10 to 35 miles on either side of the ground track of the plane. Furthermore, the intensity of the shock wave will be diminished as it spreads out.

Consequently the boom will become less intense on either side of the flight track.

When wind is present, the wave front progresses at a rate which is the sum of the sound speed and the wind speed. Therefore the effect on the wave front by the temperature decrease is counteracted if a tail wind increases with altitude. If a tail wind decreases with altitude the distortion of the wave front caused by the temperature variation is reinforced, while a head wind produces the opposite effect. The situation becomes more complicated when the horizontal variations of wind and temperature are considered.

Other atmospheric features could produce unusual sonic boom patterns at the ground. Among these are: turbulent air motions in the lowest few thousand feet of the atmosphere, the type of clouds present and their spatial distribution, and temperature inversions. None of these meteorological phenomena have been studied in sufficient detail to produce conclusive results about their effects on sonic booms. However preliminary investigations have been reported (Roberts, 1967).

4. *Design Modifications and Maneuvers*

Although various government agencies, industrial organizations and university research projects are currently engaged in seeking methods to reduce sonic boom intensities, all known practical supersonic airplane designs will produce sonic booms (National Academy of Sciences, 1967). Furthermore, according to the Academy report. "The possibility that unconventional configurations may be devised which will yield significant reductions cannot be disallowed but, at present, the future must be viewed in terms of small reductions obtained through better understanding of theory, design refinements of conventional aircraft and improvements in propulsive efficiency and operating procedures." Research efforts are continuing in an effort to find an unconventional design, with practical aerodynamic characteristics, which would minimize or eliminate the sonic boom.

The various research efforts to suppress sonic boom intensities which are under investigation are reviewed below.

The pressure distribution at ground level, shown in Fig. 1a and 1b is the so-called "farfield" signature. The shock fronts emanating from protuberances on the aircraft have little effect on the pressure pulse at ground level. The sonic boom can be reduced, but not necessarily eliminated, if the aircraft climbs at subsonic speeds before making the transition to supersonic speeds at high-altitude cruising levels. Optimization of the arrangement of the various components, such as the shape and position of the wings, may lessen sonic boom intensity. Long, slender and blended configurations appear to offer the best compromise between maximum aerodynamic performance and low sonic boom levels. Reduction of the peak pressures at ground level by design modifications is also being attempted. For example, a "stretched" design would alter the point at which the various waves form a bow and tail shock. With this type of design a less rapid rate of pressure rise would be produced at ground level and consequently a less audible boom would result (McLean, 1966; NAS, 1967).

Aircraft accelerations and maneuvers at various altitudes cause sonic booms of varying intensities in localized regions at or above ground level. It is possible, during common flight maneuvers, to produce local pressure buildups which may be more than twice as large as those produced by the same aircraft in level, unaccelerated flight. The subsequent "superbooms" occur at isolated points at ground level in contrast to the ordinary booms that move with the aircraft. Limitations on rapid accelerations and maneuvers would reduce the intensity and frequency of "superbooms" but could not be expected to suppress sonic booms altogether (Maglieri, 1966).

In subsonic flight, pressure disturbances propagate ahead of the aircraft altering the airstream in such a way that abrupt pressure changes do not occur. In supersonic flight however, pressure disturbances cannot propagate ahead. In order to prevent the buildup of a shock wave in supersonic flight, the Northrup Corporation is currently working on a method to modify the airstream through an electromagnetic force field concentrated at the nose of the aircraft. This work is still in preliminary stages and experiments have only been undertaken in wind tunnels (Aviation Week and Space Technology, 1968).

5. *Comments*

Although sonic boom research has progressed rapidly since the early 1950's, the complete suppression of sonic booms at ground level by means of present technology does not appear imminent. This does not mean that sonic booms are always heard in conjunction with supersonic flight. Some meteorological factors occasionally could reduce sonic boom intensities or, even more rarely, prevent sonic booms from reaching the ground at all. However, the reported total absence of sonic booms from UFOs in supersonic flight and undergoing rapid accelerations or intricate maneuvers, particularly near the earth's surface, cannot be explained on the basis of current knowledge. On the contrary, intense sonic booms are expected under such conditions.

ACKNOWLEDGEMENT

Discussions with Professor Adolph Busemann, Aerospace Engineering Sciences Department of the University of Colorado, have been extremely helpful in the preparation of this manuscript.

References

Aviation Week and Space Technology, 88 (1968), p. 21.

Carlson, H. W. and F. E. McLean. "The sonic boom," *Int. Sci. Tech,* No. 55 (1966), p. 70.

Hall, R. H., (ed.). *The UFO Evidence.* National Investigations Committee on Aerial Phenomena, Washington, D.C.: 1964.

Kane, E. J. "Some effects of the nonuniform atmosphere on the propagation of sonic booms," *J. Acoust. Soc. Amer.,* 39 (1966), S26-S30.

Maglieri, D. J. "Some effects of airplane operations and the atmosphere on sonic-boom signatures," *J. Acoust. Soc. Amer.,* 39 (1966), S36-S42.

McLean, F. E. and B. L. Shrout. "Design methods for minimization of sonic-boom pressure-field disturbances," *J. Acoust. Soc. Amer.,* 39 (1966), S19-S25.

National Academy of Sciences. *Report on Generation and Propagation of Sonic Boom.* 1967.

Roberts, C., W. Johnson, G. Herbert, and W. A. Hass. *Meteorological Investigations in Sonic Boom Experiments at Edwards AFB* National Sonic Boom Evaluation Office, Arlington, Virginia, D1-D11, (1967).

Wilson, H. A., Jr. "Sonic boom," *Sci. Amer.* 206 (1962), 36-43.

Chapter 7 Atmospheric Electricity and Plasma Interpretations of UFOs / Martin D. Altschuler

Research into atmospheric electricity is important and difficult. Although many aspects are now becoming clear, much remains controversial or unknown. Even common events, such as the thunderstorm and the lightning flash, continue to provide fascinating challenges to science.

Electric fields are produced by clouds, fog, rain, sleet, snow, tornadoes, dust devils, volcanos, earthquakes, meteors, and contaminants in air. On mountains, electrical activity often becomes intense. Experienced climbers can tell bizarre stories of mountaintop electricity. Researchers themselves have often been astonished at nature's complexity. Ball lightning, for example, although witnessed and reported many times in the past, has only with difficulty been established as a genuine scientific problem. Years of patient effort were required to distinguish ball lightning from retinal after-images and optical illusions. In view of the numerous manifestations of atmospheric electricity, it is reasonable to try to determine whether or not some luminescent UFOs are indicative of yet another electrical phenomenon of nature.

Much research has been done theoretically, in the laboratory, and in the field that bears on the problems of atmospheric electricity and the plasma state of matter. Here we emphasize the more unusual (and often speculative) aspects of these subjects and their possible correlation with descriptions of UFO behavior. People who have witnessed unusual electrical phenomena of the types reviewed in this chapter are invited to send reports to

Dr. Bernard Vonnegut
Earth Science Building, Room 323
State University of New York at Albany
1400 Washington Avenue
Albany, New York 12203
or phone them to 518-457-4607 or 518-457-3898.

The author thanks Drs. Sydney Chapman, John Firor, Sadami Matsushita, and J. Doyne Sartor of the National Center for Atmospheric Research, and Professor Julius London of the Department of Astrogeophysics, University of Colorado, for reviewing portions of this manuscript, for informative and pleasant discussions, and for useful references. He is also indebted to Dr. Edmond M. Dewan of the Air Force Cambridge Research Laboratories for a file of useful reprints.

1. Definition of a Plasma

In its lowest energy state, an atom contains an equal number of electrons and protons, and is electrically neutral. By gaining or losing electrons, an atom or molecule can acquire an electric charge. A charged atom or molecule is called an ion. If some of the atoms of a gas become ions, the gas is said to be partially-ionized. Where there are enough ions or electrons to affect the physical properties of the gas, the gas is called a plasma. The "plasma state of matter" refers to an ionized medium.

An atom may become ionized by (a) absorbing a quantum of high energy electromagnetic radiation, (b) colliding with a fast particle (atom, ion, or electron), (c) capturing an electron. In processes (a) and (b), atoms lose one or more electrons and become positive ions. In process (c), atoms gain an electron and become negative ions. The ionization of the outermost layers of the atmosphere (above 65 km) is caused primarily by the absorption of solar ultraviolet radiation and x-radiation (process [a]). The weak ionization in the lower atmosphere is largely an effect of cosmic ray particles (mostly fast protons) (process [b]). Free electrons in the lower atmosphere are quickly captured by oxygen molecules, which then become negative ions (process [c]).

When large electric fields are present, electrons and ions are accelerated to high velocities in short distances, and may acquire enough kinetic energy to ionize neutral atoms upon collision. The new charges are accelerated in turn by the electric field, collide with still other neutral atoms, and produce more electrons and ions. The ionization of a neutral gas by the acceleration of a few electrons and ions in a large electric field is called an avalanche process. The avalanche process is responsible for coronal point discharge (St. Elmo's fire), lightning flashes, neon and fluorescent lighting, and Geiger counters.

Since electrons can be accelerated by high-frequency electric fields, ionization is sometimes possible in the presence of microwaves. High temperature shock waves surrounding meteors and reentering space vehicles also cause ionization in the atmosphere.

When a free electron and a positive ion collide, the electron may be captured. When a negative and a positive ion collide, an electron may be transferred from the negative to the positive ion. In such collisions, called recombination processes, ions are neutralized and become atoms or molecules. In the lower atmosphere, plasma (such as that created in a lightning flash) is rapidly neutralized through such processes. Radiation may be emitted during recombination.

2. *Occurrence of Plasma*

Probably 99% of all the matter in the universe is in the plasma state. Within the stars, hydrogen, helium, and the other abundant atoms are completely ionized.

The visible surface of the sun, called the photosphere, is host to a mysterious plasma phenomenon, the sunspot. The strong magnetic fields which emanate from sunspots interact with the plasma of the outer solar atmosphere. As a consequence, violent events, known as solar flares, are often generated in regions where the magnetic field gradient is large. During a solar flare, ions and electrons are accelerated out of the sun's atmosphere into interplanetary space. Some of these fast charged particles interact with the earth's magnetic environment, and contribute to short-wave radio blackouts, auroras (Northern and Southern Lights), and geomagnetic storms.

Basic plasma research is vital in many technological areas. In the field of communication, problems arise in connection with radio and radar transmission through plasma regions such as the ionosphere and the ionized sheath surrounding re-entering spacecraft. Laboratory effects are under way to control the reactions of nuclear fusion for power generation. If successful, present experiments may lead to efficient sources of power which do not require fossil fuel or fissionable materials. In the field of space technology, engineers are developing low thrust ion rocket engines to propel the next generation of interplanetary spaceships.

3. *Plasma Properties of the Lower Atmosphere*

The lower atmosphere (below 60 km) is not a plasma under normal conditions. In every cubic meter of air at sea level, the fair weather atmosphere contains roughly 3×10^{25} electrically neutral molecules and only about 5×10^8 ions. About 10^7 ion pairs are created per cubic meter every second by ionizing radiation, and a like number are neutralized by recombination processes. The lifetime of a light ion is several hundred seconds. When dust particles are present, light ions are rapidly absorbed, and long-lived heavy ions are created. Over land at ground level, gamma rays emitted by natural radioactive substances are the primary cause of atmospheric ionization. Above a few hundred meters over land, and everywhere over the oceans, cosmic ray particles and secondaries are the major source of ionization. In the lower atmosphere (below 60 km) unattached electrons are immediately captured by oxygen molecules.

The presence of even a few ions in the lower atmosphere means that air is not a perfect insulator. An electric charge placed on a metal sphere which is insulated from the ground and suspended in air, will leak into the atmosphere; the higher the altitude of the sphere, the faster will be the leakage of electric charge.

Where air pollution is prevalent, the light ions are collected on heavy dust particles, creating heavy less-mobile ions. The electric medium bounded by electrically conducting layers (or than that of clean air.

The earth's atmosphere may be represented as a leaky dielectic medium bounded by electrically conducting layers (or equipotentials) at sea level and at about 60 km height. Sea level is taken as the zero reference or ground potential. The layer at 60 km, now called the electrosphere, is the lowest level in the atmosphere of uniform electrical potential. This article deals with the electrical effects that are possible in the lower atmosphere, where UFO's are reported.

4. The Fair Weather Electric Field

At sea level in fair weather, there exists an average electric field of about 130 volt/m directed downward. The potential of the electrosphere is about 300,000 volts positive with respect to the earth's surface. The earth's surface contains over its entire area a net negative charge of 5×10^5 coulombs (or 10^{-9} coulomb/m^2). An equal positive charge resides in the atmosphere above the ground. Because air is not a perfect insulator, an electric current of 1800 amp (or 3.6×10^{-12} amp/m^2) flows downward (i.e. positive ions migrate downward, negative ions migrate upward). At higher altitudes, the current remains constant but the electric field decreases as the electrical conductivity increases. At the height of commercial jet aircraft (12 km), the electrical potential of air has reached 90% of the potential of the electrosphere (i.e. about 270,000 volts). This indicates that most of the positive charge resides in the troposphere in the form of positive ions.

With the values known for the electrical conductivity of air, the negative charge on the earth's surface should leak away in about five minutes. To maintain the negative charge on the earth's surface, and consequently the electric field of the lower atmosphere, a charging mechanism is needed which acts continuously.

5. *Thunderstorms and the Electric Circuit of the Atmosphere*

Thunderstorms maintain the fair weather electrostatic field. Every hour, several hundred thousand lightning flashes and coronal point discharges transfer negative charge from the bases of thunderclouds to the ground. The average charge transmitted by a lightning flash is estimated to be about 20 coulombs. Positive ions also rise from the tops of thunderclouds.

Many theories have been proposed to explain how negative and positive charges are separated in a thundercloud. The mechanism must (1) give a positive charge to the upper part of the cloud and a negative charge to the lower part of the cloud, (2) provide a charge separation rate of several amperes.

It is generally believed that as precipitation particles fall they acquire negative electric charge. Consequently, negative charge is carried to the bottom of the cloud. A detailed understanding of the mechanisms involved in transferring charge between precipitation particles (and air pollutants) is of major scientific importance.

Strong evidence that thunderclouds act as batteries for the atmosphere is provided by the daily fluctuations in the fair weather electric field. Over the oceans the fair weather electric field fluctuates 15 to 20% about its mean value, and reaches a maximum at 1900 Greenwich Mean Time everywhere over the earth regardless of the local time. Smaller secondary maxima occur at 1500 GMT and at 0700 GMT. Much of the earth's thunderstorm activity occurs in tropical regions during midafternoon when surface heating is most apt to produce strong convection. At 1900 GMT, it is midafternoon in the Amazon basin; at 1500 GMT, it is midafternoon in Africa; at 0700 GMT, it is midafternoon in Indonesia. The minimum fair weather field occurs at 0300 GMT when it is midafternoon in the middle of the Pacific Ocean.

If each thunderstorm supplies a charging current of 1 amp, there must be at least 1800 thunderstorms raging simultaneously over the earth at any one time to maintain the fair weather electric field. This is not an unreasonable estimate. It seems probable, therefore, that thunderstorms are the prime cause of the earth's electrical activity.

6. *Properties of Lightning*

Current surges in the atmosphere are known as lightning. Lightning limits the magnitude of the electrical dipole of a thundercloud. Only about 20% of all lightning fiashes are between cloud and ground. The majority of flashes occur within clouds. Here we briefly describe only the cloud-to-ground event, for which better information is available.

What appears to the eye as a single lightning flash is actually a number of individual charge surges, called strokes, recurring in rapid succession. A flash consists of between one and forty main strokes, each of which is preceded by a leader stroke. The median number of strokes in a lightning flash is about three.

When electric field strengths build up to values of about 3×10^6 volt/m near the edge of a cloud, avalanche processes become important. The visible lightning event begins with the initiation of a stepped leader from the cloud region where the electric field is most intense. The stepped leaser is a conducting channel, perhaps a few centimeters in diameter, which is at essentially the same potential as the base of the cloud. Consequently, as the leader progresses downward away from the cloud, the electric field (i.e. the potential gradient) between the tip of the leader and the surrounding air continually increases, so that further ionization becomes easier.

After advancing about 20 meters (the exact distance depending on the field strength), the leader pauses for about 50 microseconds, forges ahead another 20 meters, stops again, and so on. (It is believed that the ionization of the air immediately ahead of the stepped leader is initiated by an avalanche region called a pilot streamer.) The stepped leader advances downward toward the ground along a zigzag path roughly parallel to the electric field. After about 100 steps and 50 milliseconds, the stepped leader has almost traversed the 2 km or so between the cloud base and the ground. When the stepped leader descends to about 20 meters altitude, it is met by a positive streamer from the earth. (The potential difference between the cloud and the ground may reach 10^8 or 10^9 volts before a lightning flash).

As soon as the conducting channel between the cloud and the ground is completed, the main (or return) stroke begins. In less than 10 microseconds, a current of about 20,000 amp is forcing its way through a conducting channel only a few millimeters in diameter. (The maximum current ever recorded in a lightning flash was 345,000 amp.) On the average, about 10^9 joules (an energy equivalent to ¼ ton of TNT) are released in the flash event.

The temperature in the lightning channel, measured spectroscopially, reaches 30,000°K only 12 microseconds after the passage of the tip of the return stroke, but decays so rapidly that it falls to 5,000°K in about 50 microseconds. If thermalization is achieved, these temperatures are hot enough to cause considerable dissociation and ionization of air molecules. Some scientists argue, however, that thermal temperatures never exceed a few thousand degrees Kelvin. The precise time variation of the thermal temperature is important in estimating lightning damage by acoustic shocks.

Magnetic field strengths associated with lightning are in the neighborhood of 1 tesla ($=10^4$ gauss), so that the plasma pinch effect is probably of importance. Possible magnetic effects of a lightning stroke have been considered in connection with ball and bead lightning.

After the first leader and return stroke, the lightning flash may continue with another current surge along the same conducting channel. This second stroke is initiated by a dart leader, which advances continuously (not in steps) and more rapidly than the stepped leader. The dart leader follows the main channel to the ground and ignores the ungrounded branch channels of the first stroke. When the dart leader reaches the ground, a return stroke follows.

Recombination processes work rapidly in the atmosphere. Only 100 milliseconds after the cessation of a return stroke, the lightning channel is no longer sufficiently conducting to guide a dart leader. The lightning flash is then completed. Another stroke from the same part of a cloud must follow a completely new path, one created by a new stepped leader. For this reason, reports of ball lightning lasting as long as a few seconds were discounted or considered to be afterimages of the eye. There is still no satisfactory explanation for long-lived isolated electrical luminescence in the atmosphere.

7. *Ball Lightning*

Among the most mysterious manifestations of atmospheric electricity is the phenomenon of ball lightning or Kugelblitz. A glowing ball either (1) appears after a cloud-to-ground lightning flash and remains near the ground, or (2) is first seen in midair, descending from a cloud or arising from no obvious cause, thereafter remaining aloft until it vanishes. Collisions with aircraft have caused verified damage, indicating that ball lightning is not restricted to ground level.

Most witnesses report that ball lightning is clearly visible in daylight although not as bright as an ordinary lightning flash. Some 85% of the observers agree that the size and brightness of the ball remains roughly constant throughout the period of observation and that no changes occur even immediately prior to its disappearance. A minority report brightening and color changes just before the ball vanishes. The colors red, orange, and yellow are most common, but most other colors are seen occasionally. Some researchers believe that blue or blue-white Kugelblitz is associated with higher energy, although there is no statistical basis for such an assertion. The reported diameters of Kugelblitz range between 5 and 80 cm with a median of about 30 cm. One survey lists three complexions of ball lightning: (1) a solid appearance with a dull or reflecting surface, or a solid core within a translucent envelope, (2) a rotating structure, suggestive of internal motions, (3) a structure with a burning appearance. The last type seems most common. About ⅓ of the witnesses detect internal motions or rotation of the ball itself, although this may depend on the distance of the observer.

A majority of onlookers report the motion of the ball to be slow (about 2 meters/sec.) and horizontal, with no apparent guidance by the wind or by the ground. One in six observers report speeds in excess of 25 m/sec. Several reports do indicate some guidance from telephone or power lines and by grounded objects. An odor of brimstone (burning sulfur) is often reported by nearby observers, especially at the time of decay.

The median lifetime of ball lightning is roughly four seconds, with 10% reporting over 30 seconds. Determination of lifetime is difficult because (1) subjective time during an exciting event is often in error, and (2) few observers see a ball from the time it is created until the time it disappears. In any case, since an ordinary lightning channel can remain electrically conducting for only 0.1 second, a 10 second lifetime is two orders of magnitude beyond expectation.

Not long ago, considerable scientific discussion ensued on the question of whether ball lightning is a real phenomenon. Scientists believed that ball lightning could be (1) a retinal afterimage of a lightning flash, (2) an intense coronal point discharge near a lightning target below a thundercloud, (3) some burning or incandescent material thrown from the impact point of a lightning bolt. Today most researchers believe that Kugelblitz is a genuine electrical effect. A recent survey indicates that ball lightning may be extremely commonplace, but that the observer must be relatively close to the ball to be able to see it. Kugelblitz is probably invisible or indistinguishable in daylight at distances greater than 40 meters, which would explain why it is incorrectly believed to be a rare phenomenon.

The median distance between an observer outdoors and ball lightning is 30 meters. Sometimes ball lightning floats through buildings. The median distance between indoor observers and ball lightning is only 3 meters. The reported distance of the observer seems to be closely correlated with the reported size of the ball. A more distant observer is (1) less likely to notice luminous balls of small diameter, and (2) more likely to misjudge the diameter. The second difficulty is somewhat mitigated since in most cases of ball lightning terrestrial landmarks can be used for reference in estimating distances and sizes. On the other hand, estimates of the distance and size of a luminous sphere seen against the sky can be quite inaccurate.

In one report, a red lightning ball the size of a large orange fell into a rain barrel which contained about 18 liters of water. The water boiled for a few minutes and was too hot to touch even after 20 minutes. Assuming (1) that the water temperature was initially 20°C, (2) that 1 liter of water evaporated, and (3) that 17 liters were raised to 90°C, one needs roughly 8×10^6 joules of energy (equivalent to 2 kg of TNT). For a ball 10 cm in diameter (the size of a large orange), the energy density is then 5×10^9 joule/m^3. But if all the air in a volume were singly-ionized, the energy density would be only 1.6×10^8 joule/m^3. Both the energy content and the energy density of ball lightning as derived from the singular rain barrel observation seem incompatible with the non-explosive character of most Kugelblitz. Although many lightning balls emit a loud explosive (or implosive) noise upon decay, effects characteristic of the release of energies of the order of 2 kg of TNT have rarely been reported (understandably if the observer was within 3 meters). Moreover, explosive or implosive decays have been noted indoors with no apparent heat or damage to nearby ceramic objects. Nevertheless, there are enough well-documented cases of extremely high energy Kugelblitz to make the water barrel report very believable. Probably there is a wide range of possible energies for a lightning ball, with the vast majority of Kugelblitz possessing energy densities less than that of singly-ionized air. The minimum possible energy of a lightning ball is that required to illumine a sphere about 25 cm in diameter with the brightness of a fluorescent lamp. With 10% efficiency, this means a source of 250 watts for 4 sec., or about 1000 joules of energy. We can only conclude with certainty that the energy of a lightning ball lies somewhere between 10^3 and 10^7 joules.

Theoretical efforts have focused on the energy estimate of the rain barrel observation. To maintain a fully-ionized, perhaps doubly-ionized mass of air requires either (1) a large amount of energy concentrated in a small volume and shielded from the surrounding air by a remarkably stable envelope, or (2) a continuous energy flow into a small volume, presumably by focusing power from the environment.

Theories which attempt to bottle fully-ionized plasma by magnetic fields or magnetovortex rings are faced with severe stability problems. There is no known way to contain plasma in the atmosphere for as long as a few seconds. Moreover, a fully-ionized plasma ball would be hotter and probably less dense than the surrounding air, so that it would tend to rise rather than descend or move horizontally. Chemical combustion theories cannot explain the high energy content or the remarkable antics of the ball. Nuclear reactions would require an electric potential of at least 10^6 volts between the center and surface of the ball, and a mean free path for the ions as long as the potential gap. This situation seems unlikely, and faces similar problems of stability.

Theories which depend on an outside source of energy such as microwaves or concentrated d-c fields cannot explain how ball lightning can survive indoors.

If energies as high as several megajoules are not required, we can try other hypotheses. One suggestion is that the lightning ball is a miniature thundercloud of dust particles, with a very efficient charge separation process. Continuous low energy lightning flashes are illuminating the cloud. Another idea is that a small amount of hydrocarbon, less than that required for combustion, is suddenly subjected to strong electric fields. The hydrocarbons become ionized and form more complex hydrocarbon molecules which clump together. Eventually there is enough combustible material in the center to allow a burning core. If the concentration of hydrocarbon decreases, the ball disappears; if the concentration increases, the ball ignites explosively. (This represents the swamp gas theory for ball lightning.)

Much depends on a reliable energy estimate for the Kugelblitz. If the energy is as high as indicated by the water barrel report, we have a real dilemma. At present no mechanism has been proposed for Kugelblitz which can successfully explain all the different types of reports. Probably several completely different processes can produce luminescent spheres in the atmosphere.

We conclude this section with summaries of several eyewitness reports of Kugelblitz.

The first few cases concern aircraft.

1. A commercial airliner (LI-2) was struck by ball lightning on 12 August 1956 while flying in the lower Tambosk region of the USSR. Before being struck, the aircraft had been flying at 3.3 km altitude through a slowly moving cold front which contained dense thunderclouds. During a penetration of one thundercloud, where the air temperature was about $-3°C$, the crew saw a rapidly approaching dark red almost orange fireball 25 to 30 cm in diameter to the front and left of the aircraft. At a distance of not more than 30 to 40 cm in front of the nose, the ball swerved and collided with a blade of the left propeller, exploded in a blinding white flash, and left a

flaming tail along the left side of the fuselage. The sound of the explosion was loud enough to be heard over the noise of the engine. No substantial damage could be found. One of the left propeller blades had a small fused area 4 cm along the blade and less than 1 cm in depth. Around the damaged region was a small area of soot, which was easily wiped off.

2. In 1952, a T-33 jet trainer was flying near Moody AFB in Georgia. Because of a thunderstorm, the pilot was told to proceed to Mobile, Ala. As the T-33 rolled out onto a westerly heading at 4 km altitude, it collided with a "big orange ball of fire" that hit the nose head-on. The jolt was such that the student pilot believed there had been a midair collision with another aircraft. The low frequency radio compass no longer functioned, and they had to receive radio guidance to another base. On examination of the aircraft, they did not find a single mark or hole. The only damage was to the radio compass unit in the nose of the T-33 which was practically melted inside and was rendered useless. After the radio compass was replaced, everything functioned normally.

3. Another pilot distinguishes ball lightning from balls of St. Elmo's fire, and states that he has only seen "true" ball lightning near severe thunderstorms associated with squall lines, mountainous terrain, and significant cloud-to-cloud lightning. He defines "true" ball lightning as having the following characteristics: (1) diameters between 15 and 30 meters, (2) never originates outside the main thunderstorm cloud, (3) generates from a single point and expands in exactly the same manner as the fireball of an atomic explosion, but with a longer lifetime, (4) earphones detect soft sibilant hiss, easily distinguishable from crash static, which gradually increases in loudness concurrent with the growth of the ball, then rapidly decreases in loudness after peak brightness, (5) no apparent thunder. He considers smaller luminous balls seen near his aircraft to be St. Elmo's fire. If Kugelblitz within clouds can be as large as is estimated by this pilot, then ground-based observations reflect only weak manifestations of the phenomenon.

4. In Klass's book there is a remarkable photograph taken by an RCAF pilot in 1956, which seems to confirm the above observations. The pilot was flying westward at 11 km altitude over the foothills of the Canadian Rockies near Macleod, Alberta, through what he describes as the most intense thunderstorm he ever saw in North America. Cloud pillars extended above 12 km. The sun was setting behind the mountains and was obscured from view. The ground was dark. Through a break in the clouds he observed a bright stationary light with sharply defined edges "like a shiny silver dollar." The light was nestled deep within the thunderstorm, suspended above some

cumulus reported at 4 km altitude. The object remained in view for 45 seconds as he flew across the cloud break. The diameter of the light is estimated to be at least 15 to 30 meters.

The following case is indicative of high-energy ball lightning.

5. At 3:30 p.m. on 26 April 1939, following a moderate rainstorm at Roche-fort-sur-Mer (France), an extremely brilliant flash of lightning branched into three directions. At the first impact point, a witness described a ball 15 to 20 cm in diameter and 2.5 meters above the ground which passed only 4 meters in front of him. He felt a breeze of air at the same time. The globe climbed an iron cable which it melted and pulverized, producing smoke in the process. The electrical conduits of an adjoining house were burned and the meter was damaged. The observer, who was installing a gas pipe, received a shock. At the second impact point several workers saw a globe also 15 to 20 cm in diameter touch the top of a crane. There ensued a great explosive noise accompanied by a blue spark as large as an arm which flew 40 meters and struck the forehead of a dock worker, knocking him to the ground. A dozen shovelers working 10 to 50 meters from the crane received shocks and were knocked over, one being thrown 60 cm into the air. The shovels were torn from their hands and thrown 3 or 4 meters away. No smoke or odor was perceived. At the crane, current flowed along the electric cable, boiled the circuit breaker board and the windings of the crane's electric motor. The chief electrician received a violent shock and was unable to free his hands from the controls. At the third impact point, a ball of fire as large as two fists hit a lightning rod and descended along the conductor to the ground, disappearing behind a building. Two workers saw a ball of fire roll very rapidly along the ground.

6. In Hanover, Germany during a July thunderstorm in 1914, a fire-ball the size of an egg came through the window, left a burnt spot near the ceiling, travelled down the curtain, and disappeared in the floor. No burnt marks were found in the floor or curtains, but the ceiling had a slightly charred mark the size of a penny.

Cases like these are not unusual. Ball lightning has been known to cut wires and cables, to kill or burn animals and people, to set fire to beds and barns, to chase people, to explode in chimneys, and to ooze through keyholes and cracks in the floor. It has even been reported in the passenger compartment of a DC-3 aircraft. Moreover, lightning conductors are not always able to dissipate the energy of Kugelblitz. In St. Petersburg, Fla., during the summer of 1951 an elderly woman was found burned to death in an armchair near an open window. Above one meter, there were indications of intense heat—melted candles, cracked mirror, etc. A temperature of 1400°C would have been needed to produce such effects. But below one meter there was only one small burned spot on the rug and the melted plastic cover of an electric outlet. A fuse had blown, stopping a clock in the early morning hours. Since lightning is common near St. Petersburg, this case has all the marks of Kugelblitz.

7. "On 3 March 1557, Diane of France, illegitimate daughter of Henri II, then the Dauphin, married Francois de Montmorency. On the night of their wedding, an oscillating flame came into their bedroom through the window, went from corner to corner, and finally to the nuptial bed, where it burnt Diane's hair and night attire. It did them no other harm, but their terror can be imagined."

8. *Coronal Effects*

A sharp point which extends from a charged conducting surface is a region of maximum electric field. During a thunderstorm, therefore, we can expect large electric fields near trees, towers, tall buildings, the masts of sailing ships, and all other points rising from the earth's conducting surface.

If the electric field becomes large enough, avalanche processes can cause electrical breakdown of the surrounding air and a sustained coronal discharge. Coronal effects may transfer more charge between cloud and ground than does lightning.

St. Elmo's fire appears as a glowing luminescence hovering above a pointed object or near a wire conductor. It is usually oval or ball-shaped, between 10 and 40 cm in diameter, and has a glowing blue-white appearance. Its lifetime exceeds that of ball lightning, sometimes lasting several minutes. The decay is silent but may be sudden or slow. Sometimes hissing or buzzing noises can be detected.

The primary difference between ball lightning and St. Elmo's fire is that St. Elmo's fire remains near a conductor. It has been observed to move along wires and aircraft surfaces, sometimes pulsating. Foo-fighters are probably a manifestation of St. Elmo's fire. Eyewitness reports of coronal discharge are presented in Section 14. Here is an account of St. Elmo's fire from the same pilot who gave observation 3 of the previous section.

"The smaller 'ball lightning' I have always associated as being the phenomenon known as St. Elmo's fire; however, St. Elmo's fire generally consists of an infrequent blanket covering the leading edges and trailing edges of an aircraft. It does not blind or brighten but is merely irritating as it prevents clear radio reception. The 'small ball' formation varies in size from two inches (5 cm) to a foot and half (46 cm) in diameter and generally 'rolls around' the aircraft apparently unaffected by the movement of the aircraft. On one occasion a small ball (about six inches (15 cm) in diameter) of yellowish-white lightning formed on my left tiptank in an F-94B then rolled casually across the wing, up over the canopy, across the right wing to the tiptank and thence commenced a return, which I didn't note, but I was advised by my observer that it disappeared as spontaneously as it had arisen. I have seen this form several times but rarely for as long as a period which I would estimate to be about two minutes in duration. Sometimes the balls are blue, blue-green, or white though it appears to favor the blue-green and yellow-white. It might be of interest to you to know that subsequent to the 'small ball' rolling over my aircraft, the aircraft was struck three times by conventional lightning bolts which melted four inches (10 cm) off the trailing edge of each tiptank and fused about a four inch section covering my tail lights."

9. Ignis Fatuus

In swamps and marshes, methane, CH_4 (and also phosphine PH_3), is released by decaying organic matter. When the methane ignites, either by spontaneous combustion or by electrical discharges produced during times of thunderstorm activity, luminous globes which float above the swamp can be seen. These are not plasma effects, but resemble them in appearance. They are called Ignis Fatuus (foolish fire), jack-o-lanterns, will-o-the-wisp, or simply swamp (or marsh) gas. The colors are reported to be yellow, sometimes red or blue. Thunderstorms and other electrical activity around swamps seem to stimulate this effect.

Occasionally observers have placed their hands into these luminescent gases without feeling any heat. Dry reeds did not catch fire. Copper rods did not heat up. Occasionally however paper was ignited.

There is little doubt that Ignis Fatuus is the source of some ghost stories and UFO reports.

10. Tornado Lightning

In certain situations, cold dry air (from the Rocky Mountains) flows over warm moist air (from the Gulf of Mexico) which is moving in a different horizontal direction. As a result, wind shear and strong convection produce active thunderstorm cells along a line of instability some tens of kilometers ahead of the cold front. These thunderstorm cells and the opaque clouds connecting them are known as a squall line. Squall lines are the source of most tornadoes.

The characteristic feature of the tornado is the funnel-shaped cloud that hangs from the sky and moves around like the trunk of an elephant. The destructive capability cf the tornado is the result of an extremely sudden pressure drop of roughly 0.1 atmosphere between the inside and outside of the funnel. Winds can range in speed from 100 to 330 m/sec.

Without question, the most concentrated and powerful manifestations of atmospheric electricity occur in conjunction with tornadoes. Tornadoes are associated with continuous lightning, point discharges, and ball lightning. Early theories of the 19th century maintained that the tornado is a conducting channel for lightning between cloud and ground. Present thought attributes the origin of tornadoes to violent convective air motions near squall lines.

Although many convective events, such as isolated thunderstorms, dust devils, hurricanes, etc., occur in the atmosphere, these have energy concentrations much smaller than that of a tornado. Consequently, several researchers believe that a tornado can be maintained only by an intense and continuous lightning discharge along its axis. Such a discharge heats the air within the funnel, thereby causing violent updrafts and vortex motions. Whether or not this theory is correct, there is little doubt that the electrical power generated during a single tornado event is at least 2×10^{10} watts, or about 1/10 of the combined power output of all the electrical generators in the United States.

From radio emissions (spherics), it is estimated that about 20 lightning flashes occur each second in a tornado cloud. Assuming 20 coulombs per lightning discharge, the average current flowing through a tornado is about 400 amperes. Magnetic field measurements near a tornado indicate that such a current is not unreasonable. Using 10^9 joules per lightning flash, we find 2×10^{10} watts for the electrical power generated by a tornado.

Such estimates may be too conservative. Tornado lightning is reported to be brighter, bluer, and more intense than its thunderstorm counterpart. Long before a tornado is observed, lightning interlaces the clouds. About 15 minutes prior to the appearance of the funnel, the lightning becomes intense and continuous. After the funnel descends, the sky is reported to be in a blaze of light with never ceasing sheet lightning.

Large hailstones are commonly produced both by tornadoes and by severe isolated thunderstorms. Hail is closely correlated with intense electrical activity. Observations of burned, wilted, and dehydrated vegetation, and odors of brimstone (burning sulfur) provide further evidence of electrical action. The tornado funnel is usually preceded by a peculiar-whining sound, a noise indicative of coronal discharge.

Eyewitness accounts are interesting in the present context because it has been suggested that many UFOs are luminous tornado clouds whose funnels have not reached the ground.

1. "After a tornado passed over Norman, Oklahoma and headed north, personnel at Tinker Field heard a sharp hissing sound overhead combined with a lowpitched continuous roar. We were conscious of an unusual and oppressive sensation. The noise source was definitely above us. When it was nearest us, I saw the sky above gradually grow lighter, then fade to black. The light was greenish in color. Associated with the light was a strong sensation of heat radiating downward. The noise increased in volume and then faded out as though it came from the south and passed us going north. The rain had stopped while this phenomenon was overhead."

2. "As the storm was directly east of me, I could see fire up near the top of the funnel that looked like a child's Fourth of July pinwheel. There were rapidly rotating clouds passing in front of the top of the funnel. These clouds were illuminated only by the luminous band of light. The light would grow dim when these clouds were in front, and then it would grow bright again as I could see between the clouds. As near as I can explain, I would say that the light was the same color as an electric arc-welder but very much brighter. The light was so intense that I had to look away when there were no clouds in front of it."

3. "The funnel from the cloud to the ground was lit up. It was a steady deep blue light—very bright. It had an orange-color fire in the center from the cloud to the ground. As it came along my field, it took a swath about 100 yards wide. As it swung from left to right, it looked like a giant neon tube in the air, or a flagman at a railroad crossing. As it swung along the ground level, the orange fire or electricity would gush out from the bottom of the funnel and the updraft would take it up in the air causing a terrific light—and it was gone! As it swung to the other side, the orange fire would flare up and do the same."

4. "There was a screaming, hissing sound coming directly from the end of the funnel. I looked up, and to my astonishment I saw right into the heart of the tornado. There was a circular opening in the center of the funnel, about fifty to one hundred ft. (15 to 30 m) in diameter and extending straight upward for a distance of at least half a mile (800 m), as best I could judge under the circumstances. The walls of this opening were rotating clouds and the whole was brilliantly lighted with constant flashes of lightning, which zig-zagged from side to side."

5. "We looked up into what appeared to be an enormous hollow cylinder bright inside with lightning flashes, but black as blackest night all round. The noise was like ten million bees plus a roar that beggars all descriptions."

6. "A few minutes after the storm passed, there was a taste and smell in the air like that of burnt sulfur. The air was clammy, and it was hard for me to breathe. The sensation was like being smothered."

7. ". . . burned up the trees that lay within its circumference, and uprooted those which were upon its line of passage. The former, in fact, were found with the side which was exposed to

the storm completely scorched and burned, whereas the opposite side remained green and fresh."

8. ". . . suddenly it turned white outside. This whiteness definitely was not fog. I would say it appeared to be giving off a light of its own."

9. "The beautiful electric blue light that was around the tornado was something to see, and balls of orange and lightning came from the cone point of the tornado."

10. "The most interesting thing I remember is a surface glow—some three or four feet deep—rolling noise, etc."

If a researcher had never heard of a tornado, and were asked to compare the eyewitness accounts of tornadoes (such as these) with those concerning UFOs, he would probably find the tornado reports to be more fantastic and incredible. Luminous tornado clouds with no funnels to the ground are possible causes of several UFO reports.

11. Dust Devil Electricity

During the heat of the day, the air temperature is high at the desert floor but decreases rapidly with height. At some critical temperature gradient (called the autoconvective lapse rate) violent upward convection of heated air occurs. Under certain desert conditions, the upward convection may be rather intense in small areas. Rapidly rising air is replaced by cooler air which flows inward horizontally and asymmetrically, thereby creating a vertical vortex funnel. Such a desert vortex made visible by dust and sand particles, is known as a dust devil. Unlike the tornado, however, the dust devil begins from the ground and rises upward. Although it can sometimes blow a man over, it is much less powerful than a tornado.

Recent measurements indicate that strong electric fields are generated by dust devils. The precise nature of the charge separation process is not understood, but in this case at least, the electrical effects are almost certainly the result of convective motions and particle interactions.

Luminescent effects of dust devils have never been reported and would be extremely difficult to detect in the daytime. Since dust devils do not occur at night when the desert floor is cooler than the air above, this phenomenon can not explain UFOs reported at night.

12. Volcano Lightning

Undersea volcanic eruptions began on the morning of 14 November 1963, only 23 km from the southern coast of Iceland, where the water depth was 130 m. Within 10 days an island was created which was nearly 1 km long and 100 m above sea level. Motion pictures showed clouds rising vertically at 12 m/sec to an altitude of 9 km. The cloud of 1 December contained intense, almost continuous light, presumably the result of large dust particles and perhaps electric effects of sulfur.

Aircraft flights through the volcanic cloud were made during periods of no lightning. Large electric fields were measured, sometimes exceeding 11,000 volt/m.

The production of lightning by volcanoes is of considerable interest for atmospheric electricity. Nevertheless, there is no evident relation between volcano lightning and UFO reports.

13. Earthquake-Associated Sky Luminescence

Intense electrical activity has often been reported prior to, during, and after earthquakes. Unusual luminescent phenomena seen in the sky have been classified into categories: (1) indefinite instantaneous illumination: (a) lightning (and brightenings), (b) sparks or sprinkles of light, (c) thin luminous stripes or streamers; (2) well-defined and mobile luminous masses: (a) fireballs (ball lightning), (b) columns of fire (vertical), (c) beams of fire (presumably horizontal or oblique), (d) luminous funnels; (3) bright flames and emanations: (a) flames, (b) little flames, (c) many sparks, (d) luminous vapor; (4) phosphorescence of sky and clouds: (a) diffused light in the sky, (b) luminous clouds. The classification is somewhat ambiguous, but is rather descriptive of luminous events associated with earthquakes.

The earliest description of such phenomena was given by Tacitus, who describes the earthquake of the Achaian cities in 373 B.C.E. Japanese records describe luminous effects during many severe earthquakes. In the Kamakura Earthquake of 1257, bluish flames were seen to emerge from fissures opened in the ground.

Flying luminous objects are mentioned in connection with the earthquake at Yedo (Tokyo) during the winter of 1672. A fireball resembling a paper-lantern was seen flying through the sky toward the east. During the Tosa earthquake of 1698, a number of fireballs shaped like wheels were seen flying in different directions. In the case of the Great Genroku Earthquake of 31 December 1730 in Tokaido, luminous "bodies" and luminous "air" were reported during the nights preceding the day of severest shock. Afterwards a kind of luminosity resembling sheet lightning was observed for about 20 days, even when there were no clouds in the sky. One record of the Shinano Earthquake of 1847 states: "Under the dark sky, a fiery cloud appeared in the direction of Mt. Izuna. It was seen to make a whirling motion and then disappeared. Immediately afterward, a roaring sound was heard, followed by severe earthquakes." In Kyoto in August, 1830, it is reported that during the night preceding the earthquake luminous phenomena were seen in the whole sky; at times, illumination emitted from the ground was comparable in brightness to daylight. In the Kwanto Earthquake of 1 September 1923, a staff member of the Central Meteorological Observatory saw a kind of stationary fireball in the sky of Tokyo.

The earthquake at Izu, 26 November 1930, was studied in detail for associated atmospheric luminescence. Many reports of sightings were obtained. The day prior to the quake, at 4 p.m., a number of fishermen observed a spherical luminous body to the west of Mt. Amagi, which moved northwest at considerable speed. Fireballs (ball lightning) and luminous clouds were repeatedly observed. A funnel-shaped light resembling a searchlight was also seen. Most witnesses reported pale blue or white illumination, but others reported reddish or orange colors.

That large electrical potentials can be created by the slippage or shearing of rocks is not surprising. Nevertheless, associated ball lightning and luminous clouds are of significance to this study. Of possible importance is the use of electrical measurements to provide some advance warning of an impending earthquake.

14. Mountaintop Electricity

Mountains are sharp projections which rise from the conducting surface of the earth. The electrical potential of a mountain is essentially equal to that of the surrounding lowlands. Consequently, when an electric field is set up between cloud and ground, the potential gradient (or electric field strength) reaches a maximum between the mountaintop and the overlying clouds.

The large potential gradient which often exists on a mountaintop may give rise to a number of events related to coronal discharge. Physiological effects of large electric fields are frequently reported by mountaineers. Many of these effects are also occasionally reported in connection with UFOs. In this section we summarize eyewitness reports from mountaintops.

1. A graduate student of the University of Colorado was climbing Chimborazo, a high and isolated mountain in Ecuador. The summit is a large flat plateau 400 meters in diameter and 6266 meters above sea level. He and a companion left their camp at 5700 meters on the morning of 1 March 1968. At 10 a.m. clouds started forming at the peak. and a small amount of graupel began to fall. When they reached the summit, between 2 and 2:30 p.m., there was considerable cloudiness. Just as they were about to take the traditional photograph of conquest, the graupel began to fall more heavily. Suddenly they felt an odd sensation about their heads, described as mild electric shocks and crackling and buzzing sounds. Their aluminum glacier goggles began to vibrate, and their hair stood on end.

The climbers dived into the snow and waited. Thunder was heard in the distance. They found that whenever they raised their heads off the ground, the electrical effects recurred. It seemed as if there were an oppressive layer 50 cm above the surface. After waiting half an hour, the climbers crawled off the peak on their bellies. They proceeded in this manner for an hour and a half, 400 meters across the plateau and down the slope. After descending 60 meters, they found they could stand up. By this time the fall of graupel and the sounds of thunder had ceased.

During the 1870's and 1880's, the Harvard College Observatory maintained a meteorological station at the top of Pike's Peak. The journal of this expedition makes fascinating reading:

2. "16 July 1874. A very severe thunderstorm passed over the summit between 1 and 3 p.m., accompanied by mixed rain and hail. Sharp flashes and reports came through the lightning arrester, to the terror of several lady visitors; outside the building the electric effects were still more startling. The strange crackling of the hail, mentioned before, was again heard, and at the same time the observer's whiskers became strongly electrified and repellent, and gave quite audible hissing sounds. In spite of the cap worn, the observer's scalp appeared to be pricked with hundreds of red hot needles, and a burning sensation was felt on face and hands. Silent lightning was seen in all directions in the evening, and ground-currents passed incessantly through the arrester."
3. "21 July 1874. Not only did the constant crackling of the fallen hail indicate the highly electrified state of the summit, but from the very rocks proceeded a peculiar chattering noise, as if they were shaken by subterranean convulsions."
4. "25 May 1876. At 6 p.m. continued thunder was heard overhead and southeast of the peak. The arrester was continually making the usual crackling noise. About this time, while outdoors, the observer heard a peculiar "singing" at two or three places on the wire very similar to that of crickets. When the observer approached near one of these places the sound would cease, but would recommence as soon as he withdrew two or three feet distant."
5. "18 August 1876. During the evening the most curiously beautiful phenomenon ever seen by the observer was witnessed, in company with the assistant and four visitors. Mention has been made in journal of 25 May and 13 July of a peculiar "singing" or rather "sizzling" noise on the wire, but on those occasions it occurred in the daytime. Tonight it was heard again, but the line for an eighth of a mile (200 m) was distinctly outlined in brilliant light, which was thrown out from the wire in beautiful scintillations. Near us we could observe these little jets of flame very plainly. They were invariably in the shape of a quadrant, and the rays concentrated at the surface of the line in a small mass about the size of a currant, which had a bluish tinge. These little quadrants of light were constantly jumping from one point to another of the line, now pointing in one

direction, and again in another. There was no heat to the light, and when the wire was touched, only the slightest tingling sensation was felt. Not only was the wire outlined in this manner, but every exposed metallic point and surface was similarly tipped or covered. The anemometer cups appeared as four balls of fire revolving slowly round a common center; the wind vane was outlined with the same phosphorescent light, and one of the visitors was very much alarmed by sparks which were plainly visible in his hair, though none appeared in the others'. At the time of the phenomenon snow was falling, and it has been previously noticed that the "singing" noise is never heard except when the atmosphere is very damp, and rain, hail, or snow is falling."

6. "16 June 1879. (During afternoon). One of those electric storms peculiar and common to Pike's Peak prevailed. A queer hissing sound issued from the telegraph line, the wind-vane post, and another post standing in a deep snow drift near by. Observer stepped out to view the phenomenon, but was not standing in the snow drift long, when the same buzz started from the top of his head; his hair became restless, and feeling a strange creeping sensation all over his body, he made quick steps for the station."

7. "10 July 1879. At 5 p.m. the hail turned to snow, and ceased at 5:30 p.m., the wind being gentle throughout. On stepping to the door at 6 p.m., observer states that he felt a peculiar sensation about the whole body, similar to that of an awakening limb after being benumbed; that his hair stood straight out from his head, and seemed to produce a peculiar "singing" noise like that of burning evergreens; the telegraph line and all metallic instruments producing a noise like that of swarming bees. When he put on his hat, the prickly sensation became so intense that he was compelled to remove it, his forehead smarting as though it had been burned for fully three hours later. At 7 p.m. the electric storm had ceased."

With the exception of tornado situations described earlier (where heat is also present), it is not likely that electrical sensations are anywhere more intense than on mountaintops. UFO reports sometimes indicate creepy, crawling sensations, much less pronounced, however, than those experienced by mountaineers.

15. Meteor Ionization and Meteor Sounds

A meteor is a streak of light produced by the interaction with the atmosphere of a solid particle (or meteoroid) from interplanetary space. Most meteoroids, particularly those that appear on schedule during certain times of the year, are probably dust balls which follow the orbit of a comet. When they enter the atmosphere they produce short-lived streaks of light commonly known as shooting stars.

A fireball or bolide (Greek for javelin) is a meteor with a luminosity that equals or exceeds that of the brightest planets (apparent magnitude −5). A solid object called a meteorite may be deposited on the earth's surface after a bolide, but never after scheduled meteor showers. The appearance of a bolide is random, and not correlated either in space or in time with comet orbits and the usual meteor showers. Bolides are believed to be caused by solid fragments from the asteroid belt, whereas the scheduled meteors are caused by dust balls from cometary orbits.

When a meteoroid passes through the upper atmosphere, a shock wave is generated, accompanied by intense heating of the surrounding air and the meteoroid surfaces. Atoms which boil off the meteoroid surface possess thermal speeds of about 1 km/sec and directed velocities of up to 72 km/sec. They collide with surrounding air molecules, and create an envelope of ionization and excitation. A meteorite only a few tens of centimeters wide may be surrounded by an ionized sheath of gas some tens of meters or more in diameter. De-excitation and recombination processes give rise to the long visible trail behind the meteoroid. Meteor trails are visible at altitudes between 110 and 70 km.

The brightest bolides can cast shadows over a radius of 650 km. To be as bright as the full moon, meteoroids of at least 100 kg are required. About 1500 meteoroids enter the earth's atmosphere each year, each with a mass greater than 100 kg.

The visual appearance of a bolide differs considerably from that of a shooting star. Vivid colors and color changes are common. Bolides have been seen to break apart, with fragments circling slowly on the way down or flying in a line or in an apparent formation. The trajectory of a bolide can appear almost horizontal to the observer. Because of the extreme brightness and the large diameter of the ionization envelope, distances to bolides are always underestimated, particularly if it should flare up toward the end of the descent. Odors of brimstone near the impact point have also been reported.

Meteor trains associated with bolides sometimes remain luminescent for an hour or so. Such a train may appear as a glowing column about one kilometer in diameter. The mechanism which allows certain meteor trains to glow for so long a time is not known. Radar trails of ordinary meteors last only 0.5 sec. Spectral analysis of glowing meteor trails reveals many bright emission lines from excited air atoms. Radiation from the hot surface of a meteoroid has also been detected on rare occasions. These emission lines reveal only common elements (such as iron, sodium, magnesium, and other minerals), implying a chemical composition similar to the earth and to the asteroids. During the day, a bolide train is seen as a pillar of dust at lower altitudes rather than as a glowing column in the upper atmosphere.

Some minutes after exceptionally bright bolides, some witnesses have heard sounds described as thunder, the boom of a cannon, rifle or pistol fire, etc. These sounds are produced by the fall and deceleration of a massive meteorite or of several fragments.

There are also a significant number of reports concerning sounds heard while the bolide was still descending from the sky, perhaps a hundred kilometers above the ground. These sounds are described as hissing, swishing, whizzing, whirring, buzzing, and crackling, and are attributed to bolides with an average apparent magnitude of −13 (about the brightness of the full moon). Such noises could not have propagated all the way from the meteorite, since sound travels too slowly.

At one time it was believed that people who observed bolides imagined the sounds, as a psychological association with noise from sparklers and other fireworks. Meteor sounds are now regarded as physical effects. On several occasions the observer first heard the noise and then looked upward to seek the cause. (Similar noise has also been reported during times of auroral activity.)

One hypothesis is that low frequency electromagnetic radiation is emitted by bright bolides and detected by human sense organs. Human subjects exposed to radar beams of low intensity have perceived sensations of sound described as buzzing, clicking, hissing or knocking, depending on the transmitter characteristics. A pulse-modulated signal with a peak electromagnetic radiation flux of 4 watt/m^2 at the observer was perceived as sound by subjects whose audible hearing was good above 5 kHz. If the background noise exceeded 90 decibels, the radio frequency sound was masked, but earplugs improved the reception.

During the fall of one of the largest bolides, near Sikhote-Alin, near Vladiovostok (USSR), an electrician on a telephone pole received a strong electric shock from disconnected wires at the instant the bolide became visible. The shock may have been due to other causes, but the possibility of strong electromagnetic effects is not ruled out.

At present, measurements made during smaller meteor events (of the dust ball variety) give no indication of significant radio emission. Magnetic effects are insignificant.

Another conjecture is that atomic collisions in the vicinity of a meteorite bring about a separation of charge along the ionization trail of the bolide. For coronal discharge effects to occur at ground level, however, the bolide would have to separate many thousands (or even tens of thousands) of coulombs about 30 km. along its ionization trail. Such a process seems unlikely.

The noises which appear simultaneously with the bolide are

not understood. If strong electrical fields accompany a bolide, other effects such as lightning or ball lightning may occur. Both lightning and ball lightning have occasionally been reported in clear non-stormy weather. There are also several reports of large chunks of ice falling out of cloudless skies. They are not believed to have fallen from aircraft. The ice chunks may arise from electrical effects of bolides, or (more probably) may be the meteorites themselves.

16. Micrometeorites of Antimatter

The existence of anti-protons, anti-electrons, anti-neutrons, etc. is no longer a subject for speculation. A particle and its anti-particle annihilate one another on contact, creating radiant energy. Consequently, we do not find antimatter on the earth. It is not known how much antimatter exists elsewhere in the universe.

In June of 1908, a bolide of enormous magnitude fell near the Tunguska River about 800 km. north of Lake Baikal in Siberia. The light was possibly as bright as the sun and was seen over a radius of 700 to 1000 km. Acoustic noises from the shock were heard as far away as 1000 km. No trace of a crater has ever been found, but within a radius of 40 km., exposed trees were flattened with their tops pointing radially away from the epicenter. Witnesses felt intense heat on their skin. Metal objects near the impact point were melted. Trees were scorched for 18 km around. An earthquake was detected on seismographs at the Irkutsk Magnetic and Meteorological Observatory which corresponds in time to the impact of the bolide. Barometric waves circled the globe. Magnetic disturbances were reported on many continents. The energy released by the Tunguska bolide is estimated between 10^{16} and 10^{17} joules (the energy range of hydrogen bombs).

Several million tons of dust may have been injected into the atmosphere. For several weeks after the event, luminous clouds in Europe and Western Siberia made it possible in certain areas to read at midnight under the open sky. The observatory at Irkutsk could not see the stars. A traveller noted in his diary that night never came. The nature of these luminous clouds is still a matter of debate.

The composition of the bolide and the cause of the explosion are not known. A very massive meteorite should impact with the ground and leave a large crater (even though the meteorite and part of the ground would be immediately vaporized). The Tunguska bolide, however, apparently exploded some 3 km or so above ground level.

Several hypotheses have been advanced concerning the nature of the bolide and the explosion: (1) a meteorite of large initial mass with an almost horizontal trajectory; (2)

a collision with a comet containing an ice or dust nucleus; (3) a high energy chemical reaction initiated by radicals in a head of a comet; (4) a nuclear explosion initiated by the shock wave of a large meteorite; (5) an antimatter meteoroid of a few hundred grams.

The first two hypotheses are conventional. Even so, it is extremely difficult to evaluate quantitatively the optical, acoustical, and thermal effects that might occur under all possible circumstances. The remaining hypotheses were proposed to explain the thermal effects.

The fourth hypothesis seems unlikely. A fission reaction of such magnitude would require that large almost-critical masses of fissionable material be suddenly brought together. A fusion reaction would require an initial temperature of several million degrees Kelvin. Neither of these possibilities seems reasonable.

The fifth hypothesis has measurable consequences. When matter and antimatter come into contact, they annihilate each other, and produce gamma ray, kaons, and pions. If an antimatter meteoroid were to collide with the atmosphere, negative pions would be produced. The nuclei of the surrounding air atoms would absorb the negative pions and release the neutrons. Nitrogen nuclei would capture the neutrons and be turned into radioactive carbon 14. As carbon dioxide, the radiocarbon would be dispersed throughout the atmosphere and be absorbed by living organisms.

The energy of the Tunguska bolide was estimated from a study of the destruction that occurred. The initial quantity of antimatter and the amount of radioactive carbon dioxide produced was then estimated. Sections of trees which grew in 1908 were analysed for radiocarbon. The conclusion of several scientists is that the Tunguska meteor was probably not composed of antimatter. The best guess is that a comet collided with the earth in June, 1908.

Nevertheless, the hypothesis of antimatter meteorites is intriguing. If a significant amount of antimatter does exist in the universe, it is possible that antimatter supernovae might eject tiny grains of anti-mass at relativistic speeds. Such a grain might penetrate our galaxy and collide with the earth's atmosphere. Entering at relativistic speeds, the grain might survive until it reached the troposphere. A fraction of a microgram of antimatter would destroy an equal mass of matter and release many megajoules of energy, perhaps creating luminous spheres. However, the annihilation of a fast antimatter meteorite has never been calculated in detail, and possible visual effects are unknown. Moreover, since small grains of antimatter would leave virtually no trace, this hypothesis remains as pure speculation.

Two articles and one popular book have been written on plasma interpretations of UFOs by P. J. Klass. Klass was impressed by reports of UFOs in close association with high tension power lines near Exeter, New Hampshire. Many popular books assert that UFOs are extraterrestrial spaceships which hover over power lines to refuel. Klass believes that some UFOs are an unusual form of coronal discharge analogous to St. Elmo's fire.

In his first article, ball lightning is assumed to be a manifestation of extreme coronal discharge. Klass points out that ball lightning and the Exeter UFOs compare favorably with regard to color, shape, sound, dynamics, lifetime, and size. According to those reports, the diameters of the UFOs ranged from the size of a basketball to 60 meters. This size range may be due to the difficulty of making distance estimates at night without visible reference points. Exeter is close enough to the sea for salt to form on high tension wires and had very little rainfall that summer to wash away the salt, thus providing points from which coronal discharge could occur.

Criticisms are (1) that other seacoast towns with high tension wires did not report UFO activity during the drought period, and (2) the luminosity, although near the wires, was occasionally some angular distance away.

Klass also examined other UFO reports including those seen at aircraft altitudes. In his second article, which is concerned with the general UFO problem he asserts that ball lightning may occur under many situations, and consequently may be the cause of many unusual UFO sightings. Various aspects of ball lightning and the laboratory creation of luminous plasma by microwaves and gas discharges are briefly discussed. Klass argues that plasma blobs would have the same characteristics and would cause the same effects as those occasionally attributed to UFOs, including the abrupt (sometimes explosive) disappearances, maneuvers near aircraft, rapid accelerations, stalled automobiles, heat, prickling sensations, irritated eyes, etc. He discusses one observation of an UFO seen through Polaroid sunglasses and one report of an agitated magnetic compass.

The book, *UFOs Identified,* is an expanded version of the two articles, and contains background of the author's investigation. He discusses ball lightning, the behavior and appearance of UFOs, radar and photographic evidence, the various reactions to his articles, and an account of a couple who claim they were held prisoner in an UFO. The book does not attempt to summarize any of the fundamental principles of atmospheric electricity, plasma physics, or atmospheric dynamics.

About reports of automobiles stalled near UFOs, Klass

writes: "Because a plasma contains a cloud of electrified particles, there is no doubt that if an auto battery were enveloped by such a plasma the battery could be short-circuited. But it is difficult to explain how an UFO-plasma could gain entry to the car battery in the engine compartment without first dissipating its energy to the metal body of the car. Another possible explanation is based on the fact that an electric charge in the vicinity of a conducting surface, such as a car's hood, creates a mirror image of itself on the opposite side of the conducting surface." The implication here is mistaken: the image charge discussed in electrical theory is not an actual charge on the other side of a metal shield, but a mathematical fiction that is used to describe the alteration of the electric field by redistribution of electric charges on the metal shield.

Alleged automobile malfunctions are discussed in Section III, Chapter 5 of this report, and was purposely omitted here. However, a few remarks may be in order. As Klass points out, some motorists have reported that both headlights and engine failed. Others have reported that only the engine or only the headlights failed. Often police cars have chased UFOs for tens of kilometers so engine failure does not always occur. Moreover, no unusual magnetic patterns have so far been detected in auto bodies.

When radar was secretly being developed by the RAF prior to the London Blitz (World War II), some of the local people of Burnham-on-Crouch were convinced that the mysterious masts recently erected had stopped passing automobiles. Presumably when the purpose of radar became known, cars were no longer stalled.

In addition to ball lightning and coronal discharge, he also suggests tornado clouds with no funnel to ground, luminescence generated during snowstorms, rotating dust vortices, and small charged ice crystals. Another one of his ideas is that occasionally a highly charged aircraft may release ions into a large wingtip vortex. The vortex remains luminous for awhile, to be encountered shortly thereafter by another aircraft. Although coronal effects occur on aircraft surfaces, it is unlikely that a lightning ball could detach from an aircraft and remain luminous for more than a few seconds.

18. Plasma UFO Conference

On 27 and 28 October 1967, several physicists expert in either plasma physics or atmospheric electricity met in Bouler, Colo. to discuss the UFO problem with staff members of this project.

Participants in the plasma UFO conference were:

Marx Brook: New Mexico Inst. of Mining and Technology

Keith A. Brueckner: University of California (San Diego)
Nicolas C. Christofilos: University of California (Livermore)
Ronald T. H. Collis: Stanford Research Institute
Edmond M. Dewan: Air Force Cambridge Research Lab.
Herman W. Hoerlin: Los Alamos Scientific Lab.
Bernd T. Matthias: University of California (San Diego)
Arnold T. Nordsieck: Santa Barbara, California
Marshall N. Rosenbluth: James Forrestal Research Center
John H. Taylor: University of California (San Diego)
UFO Study Members

Various aspects of atmospheric electricity were reviewed, such as ball lightning, and tornado and earthquake luminescence. Unusual UFO reports were presented for discussion. These included a taped report by a B-47 pilot whose plane was paced for a considerable time by a glowing object. Ground radar reported a pacing blip which appeared to be 16 km from the aircraft. After review the unanimous conclusion was that the object was not a plasma or an electrical luminosity by the atmosphere.

Participants with a background in theoretical or experimental plasma physics felt that containment of plasma by magnetic fields is not likely under atmospheric conditions for more than a second or so. One participant listed the characteristics that would be expected to accompany a large plasma. These are (1) thermal emission, (2) production of ozone and odor of N_2O, (3) convective air motions, (4) electrical and acoustic noise, (5) unusual meteorological conditions.

Another plasma physicist noted that a plasma explanation of certain UFO reports would require an energy density large enough to cause an explosive decay. Atmospheric physicists, however, remarked that several reports of ball lightning do indicate unusually high energy densities.

All participants agreed that the UFO cases presented contained insufficient data for a definitive scientific conclusion.

References and Notes

Sections 0, 1, 2:

A review of atmospheric electricity, which contains about 1000 references to previous work in the field, is:

1. *Atmospheric Electricity,* (2nd edition), J. Alan Chalmers: Permagon Press, 1967.

A readable introduction to plasma physics is:

2. *Elementary Plasma Physics,* Lev. A. Arzimovich: Blaisdell Publ., 1965 (Russian edition, 1963).

An extremely engrossing scientific detective story is:

3. *Cosmic Rays,* Bruno Rossi: McGraw-Hill Books, 1964.

For the sun and the earth, the following articles are useful for background:

4. *Our Sun,* (revised edition), Donald H. Menzel: Harvard Univ. Press, 1959.
5. *Sunspots,* R. J. Bray and R. E. Loughhead: John Wiley & Sons, 1965.

6. *Solar Flares,* Henry J. Smith and Elske V. P. Smith: Macmillan Co., 1963.
7. Magnetic Fields on the Quiet Sun, William C. Livingston: Scientific American, November, 1966.
8. "Magnetosphere," Laurence J. Cahill, Jr.: *Scientific American,* March, 1965.
9. Aurora, Syun-Ichi Akasofu: Scientific American, December, 1965.
10. Keoeeit. The Story of the Aurora Borealis, William Petrie: Pergamon Press, 1963.
11. Auroral Phenomena, Martin Walt (editor): Stanford Univ. Press, 1965.
12. The Earth's Magnetism (2nd edition), Sydney Chapman: Methuen, London, 1951.

Radio propagation through the ionosphere and plasma technology are discussed in:

13. Radio Amateur's Handbook: American Radio Relay League, Newington, Connecticut, 1968.
14. Progress Toward Fusion Power, T. K. Fowler and R. F. Post: Scientific American, December, 1966.
15. Shock Waves and High Temperature, Malcolm McChesney: Scientific American, February, 1963.
16. Electrical Propulsion in Space, Gabriel Giannini: Scientific American, March, 1961.
17. Electric Propulsion, Robert G. Jahn: American Scientist, vol. 52, p. 207, 1964.

Section 3:

1. Exploring the Atmosphere, G. M. B. Dobson: Clarendon Press Oxford, 1963.
2. The Science of Weather, John A. Day: Addison Wesley Books, 1966.
3. Introduction to the Atmosphere, Herbert Riehl: McGraw-Hill, 1965.
4. Meteorology, William L. Donn: McGraw-Hill, 1965.
5. Weather, Philip D. Thompson and Robert O'Brien: Time-Life Books, 1965.

An advanced treatise is:

7. Physics of the Atmosphere, P. N. Tverskoi: Israel Program for Scientific Translations, Jerusalem, 1965 (Russian edition, 1962) (NASA TT F-288, U.S. Dept. of Commerce).

Sections 4, 5, 6:

In addition to Chalmer's book cited earlier, detailed treatises are:

1. Electricity of the Free Atmosphere, I. M. Imyanitov and E. V. Chubarina: Israel Program for Scientific Translations, Jerusalem, 1967. (Russian edition, 1965) (NASA TT F-425, U.S. Dept. of Commerce).
2. Physics of Lightning, D. J. Malan: English Univ. Press, 1963.

Temperature in a lightning stroke is discussed in:

3. Pressure Pulse from a Lightning Stroke, E. L. Hill, and J. D. Robb: Journal of Geophysical Research, vol. 73, p. 1883, 1968.

An elementary account of lightning is:

4. The Lightning Book, Peter E. Viemeister: Doubleday, 1961.

A recent theory of charge separation in thunderstorms is:

5. The Role of Particle Interactions in the Distribution of Electricity in Thunderstorms, J. D. Sartor: Journal of Atmospheric Sciences, vol. 24, p. 601, 1967.

Section 7:

Surveys of ball lightning are:

1. Preliminary Report on Ball Lightning, J. Rand McNally, Jr.: Second Annual Meeting, Div. of Plasma Phys., Amer. Phys. Soc., Gatlinburg, Tenn. Nov. 2-5, 1960.
2. Ball Lightning Characteristics, Warren D. Rayle: NASA TN D-3188, January, 1966.
3. Ball Lightning, James Dale Barry: Master's Thesis, California State College, 1966.
4. Ball Lightning, J. Dale Barry: Journal of Atmospheric and Terrestrial Physics, vol. 29, p. 1095, 1967.

Bibliographies of earlier ball lightning work are contained in reference #3 above and in:

5. Ball Lightning Bibliography 1950-1960: Science and Technology Division, Library of Congress, 1961.
6. Ball Lightning (A Collection of Soviet Research in English Translation), Donald J. Ritchie (editor): Consultants Bureau, New York, 1961.

A theory based on standing microwave patterns is given in:

7. The Nature of Ball Lightning, P. L. Kapitsa: in Ball Lightning, Consultants Bureau, N.Y., 1961 (Doklady Akademii Nauk SSSR, vol. 101, p. 245, 1955).

A theory based on external d-c electric fields is given in:

8. Ball Lightning, David Finkelstein and Julio Rubinstein: Physical Review, vol. 135, p. A390, 1964.
9. A Theory of Ball Lightning, Martin A. Uman and Carl W. Helstrom: Journal of Geophysical Research, vol. 71, p. 1975, 1966.

Theories based on magnetic containment are given by:

10. Ball Lightning and Self-Containing Electromagnetic Fields, Philip O. Johnson: American Journal of Physics, vol. 33, p. 119, 1965.
11. Ball Lightning, E. R. Wooding: Nature, vol. 199, p. 272, 1963.
12. On Magnetohydrodynamical Equilibrium Configurations, V. D. Shafranov: in Ball Lightning, Consultants Bureau, N.Y., 1961 (Zhurnal Eksperimentalnoi i Teoreticheskoi Fiziki, vol. 37, p. 224, 1959).
13. Magneto-Vortex Rings, Yu. P. Ladikov: in Ball Lightning, Consultants Bureau, N.Y., 1961 (Izvestiya Akademii Nauk SSSR, Mekhanika i Mashinostroyenie, No. 4, p. 7, July-Aug., 1960).

A theory of ball lightning as a miniature thundercloud is given in:

14. Ball Lightning as a Physical Phenomenon, E. L. Hill: Journal of Geophysical Research, vol. 65, p. 1947, 1960.

The creation of ball lightning by man-made devices is discussed in:

15. Ball Lightning and Plasmoids, Paul A. Silberg: Journal of Geophysical Research, vol. 67, p. 4941, 1962.

Ball Lightning as burning hydrocarbon is discussed in:

16. Laboratory Ball Lightning, J. Dale Barry: Journal of Terrestrial Physics, vol. 30, p. 313, 1968.

The above list of ideas on the nature of ball lightning is far from exhaustive. A skeptical view of ball lightning theories is given in:

17. Attempted Explanations of Ball Lightning, Edmond M. Dewan: Physical Sciences Research Paper #67, AFCRL-64-927, November, 1964.

An elementary review of ball lightning is:

18. Ball Lightning, H. W. Lewis: Scientific American, March, 1963.

The first eyewitness account presented in this review is found in:

19. The Nature of Ball Lightning, G. I. Kogan-Beletskii: in Ball Lightning, Consultants Bureau, N.Y., 1961 (Prioroda, No. 4, p. 71, 1957).

Eyewitness accounts 2, 3, 5, 6, 7, and many others even more incredible are found in:

20. Eyewitness Accounts of Kugelblitz, Edmond M. Dewan: CRD-25, (Air Force Cambridge Research Laboratories) March, 1964.

Account 4 concerns a photograph taken by Robert J. Childerhose of the RCAF. The description is found in the book by Klass, which is cited below.

The strange case in St. Petersburg, Florida is discussed in:

21. Theory of the Lightning Balls and Its Application to the Atmospheric Phenomenon Called "Flying Saucers," Carl Benedicks: Arkiv for Geofysik (Sweden), vol. 2, p. 1, 1954.

Section 8:

An advanced treatise, primarily concerned with laboratory experiments, is:

1. Electrical Coronas (Their Basic Physical Mechanisms), Leonard B. Loeb: Univ. of California Press, 1965.

See also:

2. "High Voltage Transmissions," L. O. Barthold and H. G. Pfeiffer: Scientific American, May, 1964.
3. Corona Chemistry, John A. Coffman and William R. Browne: Scientific American, June, 1965.

Section 9:
See reference #3 in ball lightning, and
1. The Nature of Light and Colour in the Open Air, M. Minnaert: Dover Publ., 1954.

Section 10:
1. Tornadoes of the United States, Snowden D. Flora: Univ. of Oklahoma Press, 1954.
2. Tornadoes, Morris Tepper: Scientific American, May, 1958.
3. On the Mechanics of a Tornado, J. R. Fulks: National Severe Storms Project Report No. 4, U.S. Dept. of Commerce, February, 1962.
4. Electrical Theory of Tornadoes, Bernard Vonnegut: Journal of Geophysical Research, vol. 65, p. 203, 1960.
5. Tornadoes: Mechanism and Control, Stirling A. Colgate: Science, vol. 157, p. 1431, 1967.

Magnetic measurements near a tornado are reported in:

6. Electric Currents Accompanying Tornado Activity, Marx Brook: Science, vol. 157, p. 1434, 1967.

The eyewitness reports used in this review came from a number of sources, and were collected in:

7. Electromagnetic Phenomena in Tornadoes, Paul A. Silberg: Electronic Progress, Raytheon Company, Sept.-Oct., 1961.
8. Dehydration and Burning Produced by the Tornado, P. A. Silberg: Journal of the Atmospheric Sciences, vol. 23, p. 202, 1966.
9. Luminous Phenomena in Nocturnal Tornadoes, B. Vonnegut and James R. Weyer: Science, vol. 153, p. 1213, 1966.

Section 11:
1. The Electric Field of a Large Dust Devil, G. D. Freier: Journal of Geophysical Research, vol. 65, p. 3504, 1960.
2. The Electric Field of a New Mexico Dust Devil, W. D. Crozier: Journal of Geophysical Research, vol. 69, p. 5427, 1964.

Section 12:
1. Whirlwinds Produced by the Eruption of Surtsey Volcano, Sigurdur Thorarinsson and Bernard Vonnegut: Bulletin American Meteorological Society, vol. 45, p. 440, 1964.
2. Electricity in Volcanic Clouds, Robert Anderson et al.: Science, vol. 148, p. 1179, 1965.

Section 13:
1. On Luminous Phenomena Accompanying Earthquakes, Torahiko Terada: Bulletin of the Earthquake Research Institute, Tokyo Imperial University, vol. 9, p. 225, 1931.
2. Raccolta e Classificazione di Fenomeni Luminosi Osservati nei Terremoti, Ignazio Galli: Bolletino della Societa Italiana, vol. 14, p. 221, 1910.

For background:

3. Long Earthquake Waves, Jack Oliver: Scientific American, March, 1959.
4. The Plastic Layers of the Earth's Mantle, Don L. Anderson: Scientific American, July, 1962.

Section 14:
1. Personal communication from Thomas Bowen, Dept. of Anthropology, University of Colorado, 1968.
2. Extract from Daily Journal, Summit of Pike's Peak, Colorado: Annals of the Observatory of Harvard College, vol. 22, p. 459, 1889.

Section 15:
1. Meteors, Comets, and Meteorites, Gerald S. Hawkins: McGraw-Hill, 1964.
2. Meteorites, Fritz Heide: Univ. of Chicago Press, 1964 (German edition, 1957).
3. Out of the Sky (An Introduction to Meteoritics), H. H. Nininger: Dover Publ., 1952.
4. Strange Sounds from the Sky, Mary F. Romig and Donald L. Lamar: Sky and Telescope, October, 1964.
5. Principles of Meteoritics, E. L. Krinov: Pergamon Press, 1960 (translated from Russian).

6. Giant Meteorites, E. L. Krinov: Pergamon Press, 1966 (translated from Russian).
7. Meteor Science and Engineering, D. W. R. McKinley: McGraw-Hill, 1961.
8. Fossil Meteorite Craters, C. S. Beals: Scientific American, July, 1958.
9. High Speed Impact, A. C. Charters: Scientific American, October, 1960.
10. Note on Persistent Meteor Trails, Sydney Chapman: in The Airglow and the Aurorae, (Belfast Symposium, 1955), E. M. Armstrong and A. Dalgarno (editors), Pergamon Press, 1956.

Section 16:

The description of the 1908 bolide is found in reference #6 above by Krinov. Evidence that anti-matter is not involved, is discussed in:

1. Possible Anti-Matter Content of the Tunguska Meteor of 1908, Clyde Cowan, C. R. Alturi, and W. F. Libby: Nature, vol. 206, p. 861, 1965.
2. Non-anti-matter Nature of the Tunguska Meteor, L. Marshall: Nature, vol. 212, p. 1226, 1966.

Anti-matter in the universe is discussed in:

3. Anti-Matter, Geoffrey Burbidge and Fred Hoyle: Scientific American, April, 1958.
4. Worlds-Antiworlds, Hannes Alfvén: W. H. Freeman and Co., 1966.
5. Anti-Matter and Cosmology, Hannes Alfvén: Scientific American, April, 1967.

Chemical radicals are discussed in:

6. Frozen Free Radicals, Charles M. Herzfeld and Arnold M. Bass: Scientific American, March, 1957.
7. Production and Reactions of Free Radicals in Outer Space, F. O. Rice: American Scientist, vol. 54, p. 158, 1966.

Also for background:

8. Chemistry at High Velocities, Richard Wolfgang: Scientific American, January, 1966.

An alien spaceship theory is advocated in:

9. Unidentified Flying Objects, Felix Zigel: Soviet Life, February, 1968.

Section 17:

1. Plasma Theory May Explain Many UFO's, Philip J. Klass: Aviation Week and Space Technology, p. 48, August 22, 1966.
2. Many UFOs are Identified as Plasmas, Philip J. Klass: Aviation Week and Space Technology, p. 54, October 3, 1966.
3. UFOs Identified, Philip J. Klass: Random House, 1968.

Stalled automobiles in connection with radar are mentioned in:

4. Full Circle (The Tactics of Air Fighting 1914-1964), Group Captain John E. Johnson: Ballantine Books, 1964.

Vortices created by aircraft are discussed in:

5. Boundary Layer, Joseph J. Cornish III: Scientific American, August, 1954.
6. Shape and Flow, Ascher H. Shapiro: Doubleday Anchor Books, 1961.
7. Airman's Information Manual, Part I: Federal Aviation Administration, November, 1967.

Criticisms of Klass' ideas are found in:

8. UFOs: An International Scientific Problem, James E. McDonald: Astronautics Symposium, Canadian Aeronautics and Space Institute, Montreal, Canada, 12 March 1968.

Section 18:

The difficulties involved in the magnetic confinement of a plasma are discussed in:

1. Leakage Problems in Fusion Reactors, Francis F. Chen: Scientific American, July, 1967.

Section 19:

In addition to the aspects of atmospheric electricity mentioned in this review, many other physical phenomena and psychological effects may be involved in many (if not all) sightings. For background reading in addition to Minnaert's book cited in Section 9:

1. Flying Saucers, Donald H. Menzel: Harvard Univ. Press, 1953.

2. The World of Flying Saucers, Donald H. Menzel and Lyle G. Boyd: Doubleday & Co., 1963.
3. Afterimages, G. S. Brindley: Scientific American, October, 1963.
4. Illusion of Movement, Paul A. Kolers: Scientific American, October, 1964.
5. Texture and Visual Perception, Bela Julesz: Scientific American, February, 1965.
6. Psychological Time, John Cohen: Scientific American, November, 1964.
7. Aerial Migration of Insects, C. G. Johnson: Scientific American, December, 1963.
8. Biological Luminescence, W. D. McElroy and H. H. Seliger: Scientific American, December, 1962.
9. Various Colorado newspapers, April 11, 1966.
10. The Elements Rage, Frank W. Lane: Chilton Books, 1965.

Chapter 8 Balloons—Types, Flight Profiles and Visibility / Vincent E. Lally

1. *Types of balloons*

Three kinds of balloons can give rise to UFO sightings: neoprene or rubber balloons which expand during ascent from six feet to 30 ft. in diameter; polyethylene balloons which are partially inflated on the ground and fill out at float altitude to a diameter of 100 ft. to 400 ft.; and small super-pressure balloons called "ghost" balloons.

NEOPRENE BALLOONS

When neoprene or rubber balloons which are used to carry radiosondes begin their ascent, they have a diameter of six feet. They continue to expand as they rise, and the balloons that reach an altitude of 140,000 ft. are 55 ft. in diameter. All of these balloons shatter when they reach a volume at which a weakness develops. One of these balloons has flown as high as 156,000 ft., higher than the largest polyethylene balloons. These balloons are used to make measurements of air temperature, humidity, and winds. Approximately 90% of the neoprene balloons reach 80,000 ft.; probably 50% of them reach 100,000 ft. The neoprene balloon at any altitude has a brighter reflectance than either the polyethylene or the "ghost" balloon. It is opaque on the ground. As it rises and expands, its skin becomes thinner and reflects and scatters light. They are used in quite large numbers in many places for routine observation because of their low cost. About 100,000 of these a year are flown in the United States, with most launches at scheduled times from airports and military installations. During their ascent up to 20,000 ft., the neoprene balloons are visible to the naked eye during the daytime, but once they attain an altitude of 20,000 ft. or higher they cannot be seen from the ground.

SUPER-PRESSURE BALLOONS

The other small balloons are the super-pressure "ghost" balloons. In general these have payloads of a few grams. The balloons are usually spherical and size is a function of altitude; five feet in diameter at 20,000 ft., seven feet at 40,000 ft., ten feet at 60,000 ft. A few larger balloons have been flown at higher altitudes. Over 300 super-pressure balloons have been flown in the Southern Hemisphere. Several balloons have flown for over 300 days in the Southern Hemisphere with two balloons still flying which have been in the air for more than 11 mo. Not more than 20 long duration flights have been made in the Northern Hemisphere.

POLYETHYLENE BALLOONS

At launch polyethylene balloons are filled with a gas bubble varying from 20-70 ft. in diameter. Twenty feet of gas will lift a small balloon to 100,000 ft. A 70-ft. bubble is required to carry the Stratoscope II with a 7,000-lb. telescope. Scientists flying this type of balloon usually want to attain altitudes between 80,000 and 120,000 ft. to gather data on atmospheric radiation or composition. The "cosmic ray community" is the largest user of "ghost" balloons. The diameter of these balloons at altitude is anywhere from 60-250 ft. The 250-ft. size is for the Stratoscope II system. The largest balloons, those approximating 300 ft., are designed for very high altitudes. The largest balloon that has been flown to date holds 2.6×10^7 cu. ft. of gas and is just under 400 ft. in diameter. There are a large number of 10,000,000 cu. ft. balloons being flown, approximately half from Palestine, Tex. A few years ago the most common balloon was the 3,000,000 cu. ft. size.

2. *Visibility*

The relative visibility of a balloon depends on its type, size, material, time-of-day, and altitude. The human eye can usually detect a balloon against a bright sky background when the intercepted arc is 0.5 mil or greater. The radiosonde balloon is visible in daylight to a distance of two to four miles. During ascent, the "ghost" balloon is visible against the bright sky background at a distance of about two miles. At altitude the intercepted arc of "ghost" balloon varies from between 0.2-0.6 mil. The polyethylene balloon provides a target of one to two mils at altitude.

The large polyethylene balloons absorb about 5% of sunlight; however, they scatter and reradiate as much as 20-30% of the incident light. This scattering is very much a function of angle. Polyethylene balloons are always visible at altitude during daylight hours when the sky is clear. It is often difficult to focus the eyes on the balloon, but once seen it is easy to relocate the balloon. The "ghost" balloon is not visible above 20,000 ft. during daylight hours.

Polyethylene balloons are shaped more like a pear than a sphere, although they always appear spherical from the ground to the naked eye. Glass fiber tapes affixed to the gore seams are used to strengthen polyethylene balloons carrying heavy payloads. Observed from the ground through a telescope, a shell effect gives a taped balloon a saucer-like appearance. The tape itself, which is the basic reflecting element, is quite shiny and reflects well. On very lightly loaded systems the balloons are tapeless; heavier loads require the glass fiber tapes. As seen through the telescope, then, the taped balloons appear much shinier and are distinguished by their scalloped appearance.

3. *Derelicts and cutdown*

Another phenomenon that might be witnessed by an observer during the day is what is known as the "cutting down" of a balloon. When the decision has been made to terminate a balloon's flight, the tracking aircraft will send a destruct signal to the balloon's control and command mechanism and a squib will fire. This will detach the payload and shatter the balloon. The payload is then tracked by the plane as it parachutes to the ground. Occasionally, however, the balloon will not shatter.

The shattering of a balloon during payload detachment is easily visible (especially in the late afternoon or early morning). However, the entire operation is not. The payload chute is only 60 ft. in diameter so that it is barely visible. The tracking plane which sends the destruct signal may be 30-40 mi. away from the balloon. The "cutting down" of a balloon is usually accomplished one or two hours before sunset or just after dawn so that the pilot can visually track the parachute down. When the balloon does shatter, a large part of the balloon comes down in one piece as a flapping mass. There is little side motion or apparent hovering. Its speed of descent depends on how the balloon breaks up.

With improved balloon materials, there were a number of cases in 1966 where the balloon did not shatter but continued its ascent. Normally, if the balloon does not shatter, it should rise so fast after the shock that the gas does not escape rapidly enough to prevent bursting. Occasionally the balloon will begin to stretch, and if there is no weakness in it, the balloon could remain aloft at that higher altitude for four or five days. It might fly at 130,000 or 140,000 ft. until sunset at which time the gas will cool, reducing the volume by 5%. This causes the balloon to descend a few thousand feet. In daytime, at high altitudes the balloon's skin tends to run colder than the atmospheric temperature. As the balloon cools in the evening, it starts to descend because it has lost its volume. When it gets to approximately 60,000-70,000 ft., where the atmospheric temperatures are colder, the balloon is warmer than ambient temperature. It then picks up the 5% lost solar heat and continues to float along at this altitude until the next morning when it warms up and returns to maximum altitude.

For example, a 1,000,000 cu. ft. balloon, launched in France came down in Montana in August 1966, after having remained aloft for 27 days. This balloon had been traveling at 60,000 to 100,000 ft.

4. Balloon motion

Actual balloon movement during the day is no more discernible than the movement of hands on a clock. At many times a balloon will appear to move if there are clouds in the sky just as a flagpole might seem to fall over when one is looking at it while lying on his back. The moon demonstrates this same phenomenon when it seems to move across fields and jump fences while looked at from a moving automobile. Anytime there are clouds, a balloon may appear to move at extreme speed.

A small balloon observed in the first thousand feet of ascent, of course, will be quite obviously moving. Our very large balloons climb at a rate of 700-1,000 ft./min.; radiosonde balloons ascend at 1,000-1,200 ft./min. As these balloons reach higher altitudes, they could encounter strong wind shears (changes in velocity associated with changes in altitude) of the order of 30 knots/1,000 ft. Hence, velocity could change by as much as 30 knots in a minute, but even this would not make a large change in position. The angular movement would always be small over any one-minute period.

With respect to daylight sightings, pilots invariably estimate that balloons they see are considerably lower than their true height. For example, a pilot flying at 30,000 or 40,000 ft. will always report that the balloon is between 10,000 and 40,000 ft. above him. He will never say it is 100,000 ft. above him. The difficulty arises because no one conceives of a balloon 300 ft. in diameter. There is no depth to the balloon and no background which permits an estimate of either size or distance.

A frequent occurrence in Boulder, Colo., when searching for a balloon which has been recently launched, is to focus on the fluffy balls from a cottonwood tree floating 50-100 ft. above the observer. The cottonwood ball has been tracked on several occasions for two to three minutes before its motion convinced the observer that it was a one-inch cottonwood ball at 100 ft. and not a 10-ft. balloon at 10,000 ft.

5. Twilight effects

Just after sunset, a balloon may still be in sunlight. At this time the contrast becomes sharp and the balloon is clearly visible. A good bright balloon appears at least as bright as the brightest we ever see Venus when the planet is high in the sky. This "twilight effect" may continue from 20 min. to two hours.

At high altitudes we have another striking effect for the last few minutes before the sun sets at balloon altitude. This is caused by the sun reflecting off the balloon producing a rosy pink and later bright red color as the sun's rays pass through a hazy atmosphere and only the red end of the spectrum reaches the balloon. This has generated reports of fiery objects in the sky.

The neoprene balloons are also visible at twilight. An Australian scientist made experiments at NCAR for about a year using a new technique for measuring ozone. He flew a neoprene balloon with a little stopper attached which permitted the gas to escape and enabled the balloon to remain aloft for one or two hours at altitude instead of ascending and bursting. To make measurements of the reflectance of the sun on the balloon and determine the ozone concentration, he launched the balloons so that they would reach 100,000 ft. above the observing site just after sunset. These balloons were plainly visible about sunset, continued to become brighter and brighter, and then receded to a faint glow before disappearing.

6. Lighted balloons

Small rubber pilot balloons are still being used in many countries. For night soundings these two-foot diameter rubber balloons are tracked by small candles placed under the balloon. A single candle in a little holder has been used. The holder creates an even glow and keeps the candle from going out. The candle has been replaced in most countries by small battery-powered bulbs of approximately two candle power. Although the pilot balloon tracked by theodolite is no longer in common use in the U.S., a light is still used on radiosonde balloons at night to assist the observer to acquire the balloon, particularly if the night is dark and the trackers have had difficulty locking the radar set on the target. The blinking, bobbing light swaying under a pilot balloon or radiosonde balloon produces an exciting and attractive UFO. The FAA requires that large polyethylene scientific balloons carry lights when below 60,000 ft. at night. They can provide an awesome sight as they slowly ascend.

7. Frequency of flights

About 100 polyethylene balloons are flown each year from Palestine, Tex. San Angelo, Tex. has been an active launch area with as many as 100-200 per year. Chico, Calif., during the winter months has about ten flights, and Holloman AFB, N. M. (White Sands), has approximately 50-100 per year. Minneapolis remains still a center of balloon activities with 20-50 flights per year—usually of small polyethylene balloons.

In addition, there are other field programs during the year that are undertaken by universities and manufacturers. Ten to 20 flights are made from Cardington, England each summer. A continuing flight program is conducted from Aire sur L'Adior, France. Australia, Russia, India, and Brazil have active flight programs using large polyethylene balloons.

About 100,000 of the small neoprene balloons are flown each year in the United States for routine observation. Radiosonde balloon flights constitute a vast undocumented area. They are generally sent up four times a day. Flight schedules are all based on Greenwich time. At some times of the year at some places in the country, the balloons will be going into altitude at twilight. There are approximately 100 sites in the United States that send up radiosondes four times a day. Records of launch time and location for these balloons are kept in Asheville, N. C.

A radiosonde balloon ascending to 100,000 ft. at twilight and then shattering can be the source of reports of a fiery object in the skies which disappears in a burst of flame.

8. *Balloon UFOs*

Two situations are illustrated that have produced UFO reports. In January 1964, a large balloon was flown from the Glen Canyon Dam area near Pago, Ariz. It was a 6,000,000 cu. ft. balloon with a light payload. The balloon, which was flying at 135,000 ft., had encountered extremely strong winds. About three hours after it reached altitude it was decided to cut the balloon down. By this time the balloon was over Okla. It did not burst during payload detachment, but maintained its integrity and continued to ascend to 140,000 ft. When, just after sunset, it came over the East Coast at 140,000 ft., a number of pilot reports were received of a balloon sighted at 60,000-70,000 ft. Because it was at twilight on a very clear day, a number of people saw the balloon. This triggered a rash of flying saucer stories. For example, in Va. the people of a small town gathered a posse together to go out into a field to pick up the little green men. The sheriff attempted to halt them, but after a gun-waving encounter was forced to give up. The towns people then went out into the field and fortunately failed to find their little men.

At altitudes of 5,000-10,000 ft. we fly a different kind of "ghost" balloon. This cylinder-shaped balloon is approximately 20 ft. long and about two feet in diameter. We flew one of these from Boulder on 23 June 1965 at an altitude of 6,500 ft. We lost the balloon after a few hours. It went through some rather heavy showers, and seventeen days later over the Azores a silvery object like a long spear was sighted in the sky. At the same time as the silvery object was seen—all of the clocks on the Azores stopped. Later investigation determined that an electrician short-circuited the island's clock power supply while he was working on a fuse box.

9. *Conclusions*

The public at large and even many scientists are unaware of the great number of balloon launchings that occur every year in all parts of the world. The majority of such launchings are for meteorological studies, but some relate to other atmospheric or astronomical research.

By far most of the balloons launched for whatever purpose go unobserved except by those directly interested in their performance. They perform their missions and are cutdown or burst unnoticed by the public. This is due to the fact that most launchings take place at times and under conditions which make observation—and misidentification—of them unlikely or impossible. As a result, when a balloon is observed under unusual conditions by individuals not familiar with the kinds of devices described in this chapter it may be erroneously reported as an UFO.

Chapter 9 Instrumentation for UFO Searches / Frederick Ayer II

1. *Introduction*

Most of the thousands of existing reports of UFO phenomena are poor sources of information. They contain little or no data, are reports of hoaxes, or are the result of misidentification of familiar objects. Only a very small percentage of these reports provide concrete information from which any inferences can be drawn.

The need for instrumented observation of UFO phenomena arises from the fact that an observer's unaided senses are not reliable recorders of scientific data. Further, the ability of an observer to supply useful information is affected by his training, his state of mind at the time of the observation, and his suggestibility, both during and after the event. Accuracy requires instruments to measure precisely data such as angles, apparent or real velocities, distance, color, and luminance.

Even an observer with optimal training, objective state of mind, and minimal suggestibility is hard pressed when unassisted by instruments, to provide useful scientific information. This is especially true in the case of UFO phenomena, which are typically of short duration, occur in an unfamiliar environment, and lack points of reference from which reasonable inferences as to distance, size, and velocity can be drawn.

Even when instruments are available to him, the observer and the analyst of his report must be aware of a process inherent in any scientific inquiry; namely, the tendency of the investigator to look for evidence to support or discount a given hypothesis. In this state of mind, the investigator tends to disregard all data from his instruments that are irrelevant to his predetermined goal. An air traffic controller, for example, concentrates on radar echoes that he feels quite certain are those that come from those aircraft for which he is responsible. A meteorologist focusses his attention on quite different data on the radar scope: thunderstorm, tornado, and frontal activity. The military observer pays less heed to natural phenomena and concentrates on data on the scope that might signify the approach of ballistic or orbiting bodies.

In other words, almost all investigative processes begin with a built-in "filter" designed to minimize whatever, for the investigator concerned, constitutes "noise." But one man's noise is frequently another man's data. The physicist interested in the elastic scattering cross-section of pi-mesons interacting with protons begins his analysis by setting up criteria that tend to eliminate all inelastic events.

This filtering process turned out to be at work when researchers in atmospheric physics examined the read-out of a scanning photometer, an instrument normally used in studies of airglow. The device scans a sector of the sky and records the result as a trace on paper tape. The zodiacal light and the Milky Way appear as broad humps; stars and planets as sharp spikes. An UFO would also appear as such a spike, but its motion would cause the spike to appear in different parts of the sky in successive scans.

Would the operator of the scanner notice such a trace? Or would he ignore it, along with the star and planet "noise"? Since his attention is focused on the traces that indicate airglow, it seemed likely that he would fail to notice any trace attributable to an UFO.

This proved to be the case. Examination by project investigators of a zodiacal light photometer read-out made at the time of a visual sighting revealed four spikes in successive scans that could not be attributed to stars or planets. The personnel analyzing the data had ignored them. Geometric reconstruction of the object's path established that the photometer had recorded a ballistic missile in trajectory over the Pacific Ocean. Details are found in Section 8 of this chapter, "Haleakala II."

But even if the operator of an instrument fails to notice

what, to him, is noise, another operator employing the same device for a different purpose has access to all the recorded data and can therefore search for the specific information of interest to him. As demonstrated in the case of the scanning photometer, the instrument *can* be employed to provide a record of an UFO that can later be subjected to scientific analysis. Not all existing instruments, however, have adequate resolving power or other design features for effective searches for UFO phenomena.

Future studies of UFO phenomena should, in my judgment, be based upon information recorded by suitable instruments. This chapter will discuss existing instruments and instrument systems with special reference to their suitability for an UFO search. It will also suggest what instruments and instrument systems might be devised that would more readily yield suitable data for the study of UFO phenomena.

2. *The All-Sky Camera*

The all-sky camera was developed in order that permanent photographic records of the time of occurrence, intensity and location of auroral and airglow displays could be made automatically. During the International Geophysical Year, (1957-1958) 114 all-sky cameras were in operation at sites from near the North Pole to the South Pole.

The cameras are designed to photograph about 160° of the sky and to record angular distances from the zenith by means of lights. Photosensitive detectors switch the cameras on at dark and off at daylight. Exposures are short and can be set to any desired value. Local or Universal Time and length of exposure are recorded on each frame. Table 1 lists the salient points of the cameras of several participating countries. For further details see: Annals (1962) Gartlein (1947).

The film is examined by trained personnel and the data on auroral position and brightness in each of three areas, as a function of time, are entered on a five-line format called an "ascaplot." The three areas are the northern, zenith and southern. The northern and southern zones cover the regions lying between 60° and 80° from the zenith, and the zenith area takes in the whole of the sky between 60° and the zenith.

At a height of 100 km., the lowest altitude at which auroras generally exist, the camera covers a region of about 3° of latitude.

Most of the cameras record on 16 mm. film, and the diameter of the circular sky image is about 10 mm. Since the individual silver grains in the emulsion are of the order of 1μ (= 0.001 mm.) in diameter, an image less than 20μ is very poorly resolved. To produce a 20μ image, an object 100 km. distant would have to be no less than 600 meters in diameter.

Table 1

Features of Some I. G. Y.

All-Sky Cameras

Country	Film width mm.	Number of exposures per hour	Exposure in seconds	Film Type	Time Accuracy
U.S.A.	16	60-80 alternating	10-20, 15,48	Eastman Kodak Tri-x, Ilford HP-3	± 10 sec. to ± 2 minutes
Canada	35	60	4-40 alternating	Eastman Kodak Tri-x Pan.	± 3 sec. to ± 1 minute
Canada	16	60	30	Eastman Kodak Tri-x Neg.	± 1 minute
U.S.S.R.	35	12,60,120, 180 alternating	5,10,20 alternating	High sensitivity Negative Pan.	± 2.5 sec.
Japan	16	240	13	High sensitivity Pan.	± 0.3 minutes
Argentina	16	60,48	20	Eastman Kodak Tri-x	± 1 minute

It is apparent that the resolution of such an instrument is not adequate for objects of more terrestrially common dimensions.

The sensitivity of the all-sky camera is also disappointingly low for purposes of UFO search. For instance, referring to point sources, Dr. Gerald M. Rothberg, in his report on one month's observation with one of these cameras, states that five miles is "roughly the maximum distance at which we can detect the landing lights on commercial airliners, as determined from photographs of planes . . ."

The sky-coverage of these instruments is very good, however, amounting to about 83% of a hemisphere of the same radius. However, each camera can sample only about 0.2% of the volume of sky 100 km. high over the continental United States, which amounts to about 9×10^8 km³.

A thorough test of a 16 mm, U.S. all-sky camera was made by Dr. Rothberg during August 1967 (Case 27). The camera was operated for about 150 hours on seventeen nights. Exposures started at dusk and ended at dawn. The camera made one 40-sec. exposure per minute. The total number of frames taken was about 9,000 during a period when 106 local UFO sightings were reported. Rothberg states that

> . . . continued at high frequency during the feasibility study, less than 12 of 9,000 all-sky camera exposures contained images not immediately identifiable. Only two of these coincided in time and azimuth with a sighting report. Study of one negative suggests that the image is either that of a meteor whose path was at or nearly at a right angle to the focal plane or that an emulsion defect or impurity is responsible for the image. The other negative's image was identified as a probable aircraft (Case 27).

One UFO sighting was definitely recorded by the camera; the objects were three garment-bag balloons which were photographed repeatedly over a period of 15 min.

In appraising the value of the all-sky camera as the instrument to use in any follow-up investigations, Dr. Rothberg is "less than enthusiastic about (their) use" for an UFO search.

Put very simply, a camera designed for the observation of airglow and auroral phenomena, both of which are large, amorphous luminous regions, does not have the resolution necessary for investigating phenomena such as fireballs, ball lightning, tornadoes, or UFOs.

3. *The Prairie Network*

Instrumented meteor astronomy is a comparatively young field dating back not much before 1936 when the Harvard Meteor Project began. Determination of mass distribution, size and composition has been difficult because results have to be arrived at by inference only instead of from studies of samples collected in the field.

Current theory holds that meteors originate from two sources: comets and asteroids. It is thought that meteors which survive long enough in our atmosphere to reach the surface are asteroidal in origin. From spectroscopic evidence it appears as if comets were composed of solid particles—"dust"—weakly bound by material which can exist in solid form only at very low temperatures. Only the dust can exist for an appreciable time in the solar system, and it is these solids which appear as cometary meteoroids. As a matter of interest, this does not preclude the deep penetration of our atmosphere by large cometary fragments. The Tunguska Meteor of 1908 is thought to have been such a fragment, and the devastating effect of this encounter is still visible today (Krinov, 1963).

Almost all meteorites in museum collections were found accidentally and the time of landing for about half of them is unknown. Seeking to increase the recovery rate and to pinpoint the time of arrival, the Smithsonian Institution began to design the Prairie Network in the early 1960s (McCrosky, 1965) in such a way as to increase the area coverage over that of the Harvard Project and to improve the probability of observing large, bright objects. Between 1936 and 1963 four technical advances proved particularly important in the basic design of the system: the Super-Schmidt camera, much faster photographic emulsions, radar, and the image orthicon. The Super-Schmidt and high-speed film were originally used in an effort to determine the trajectories of faint meteors having initial masses of $\sim 10^{-2}$ gm. The radar and image orthicon have been combined into a system for the study of meteors which are fainter than the Super-Schmidts were capable of detecting, and which are presumed to be of cometary origin. A grant from NASA established the network and the first prototype photographic station went into operation at Havana, Ill. in March 1963. About a year later, the network first functioned when ten stations began working reliably.

The complete network now consists of 16 stations of four cameras each, located at the apices of a set of nesting equilateral triangles having a separation of 225 km. Each of the four cameras is aligned with a cardinal point of the compass with the diagonal of its 9.5 sq. in. film oriented vertically. The optical axis of the camera is elevated at an angle of 35° to the horizon, but as the effective field of the present lenses is $\sim 100°$ one corner of the film will photograph $\sim 10°$ below the horizon and the extreme of the opposite corner falls short of covering the zenith by $\sim 10°$ (See Fig. 1). As a result, there are five blind spots, one vertical and the other four at true compass bearings of 45°, 135°, 225° and 315°, amounting to about 20% of the total hemisphere. All 16 interlocking stations cover a total impact area of 1,500,000 km^2.

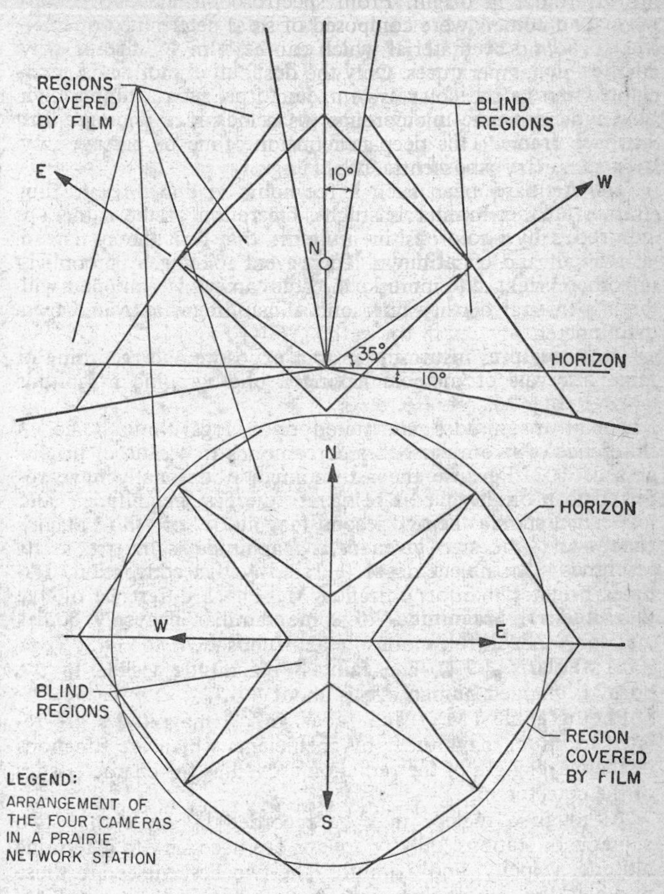

Fig. 1 Arrangement of the four cameras in a prairie network station

The Super-Schmidts are capable of recording stars with a photographic magnitude of as low as $M_{pg} = +3$, but the network cameras have considerably lower sensitivity, computed at $M_{pg} = -3$.

The angular velocity of the meteorite is determined by interrupting the streak of its path on the film by means of a shutter that runs continuously. The shutter motion is interrupted at regular intervals in order to produce a timing code that indicates time in reference to a clock face photographed on each frame. This permits fixing the time of passage with respect to the exposure interval.

The standard exposure is three hours so that three to four frames are produced each night. Operation of the camera is controlled by photosensitive switches that turn the system on at twilight and off at dawn. To prevent fogging by moonlight or other bright sky conditions, each camera is equipped with both a neutral density filter and a diaphragm activated by a photometer.

Other features insure the proper exposure and recording of time intervals of meteors having a photographic magnitude greater than $M_{pg} = -6$.

Stellar magnitudes are stated on a logarithmic scale. A difference of five magnitudes corresponds to a ratio of brightness of 100. Because the astronomers traditionally have referred to a bright star as being of "the first magnitude," and less bright stars as being "second magnitude" or "third magnitude" stars, the sign given to a magnitude is inverse to its brightness. An object of M_v -1 is, by this convention, 100 times brighter than an object of M_v $+4$ (a difference of five magnitudes). Magnitudes of some familiar heavenly bodies are: sun -26.72; full moon ≈ -12; Venus -3.2 to -4.3; Vega $+0.1$; Polaris $+2.1$. The faintest magnitude visible to the normal, unaided human eye is about $+6$.

Photographic (M_{pg}) and radar (M_{rad}) magnitudes are related to visual magnitudes by coefficients which are functions of the wavelength of the radiation as well as the characteristics of the detector.

Although a meteor may be recorded by more than two cameras or stations, only two views are necessary to determine altitude, velocity, and azimuth. The two best views are those in which the line joining them is the most nearly perpendicular to the trajectory. Such stereopairs will detect meteors at altitudes of 40-120 km. If the measurements indicate that the meteor may land in a region relatively accessible to network personnel, a third view of the trajectory, downstream from the first pair, and where the meteor has fallen to an altitude of between 10 and 40 km., is then measured to determine the rate of momentum loss from which the impact ellipse is computed.

Exposed film from one-half of the stations is collected every two weeks and scanned at field headquarters in Lincoln, Neb. The rate of acquisition of film is ~500 multi-station and ~500 single-station meteors per year. Frames with meteors from one station are cut out of the film strip and a search is made for views of the same event taken at other stations. The assembled events are then sent to Cambridge, Mass. for measurement. It is necessary to measure the length of every interval on the meteor track produced by the shutter, the positions of about forty stars, and to make densitometric measurements of the trace.

One of the most important functions of the network is to facilitate recovery of meteoritic material. The network's design is adequate to provide an "impact error" of 100 meters for the "best determined objects." But such accuracy fails to guarantee recovery because the object of search is nearly indistinguishable from the more common field stones. One recent search occupying 150 man-days resulted in no recovery. Since the start of the project some 500 man-days of search have yielded no recoveries.

In contrast, the Canadian "network," which was not yet in operation by June 1968, has already recovered at least one meteor by careful and extensive interrogations of persons who had witnessed meteor falls. Similarly, in Czechoslovakia, four pieces, out of the many which make up the Pribram meteor, were recovered before the impact point had been determind from data obtaind by a simple two-station system not designed for this purpose.

4. *Evaluation of the Prairie Network*

Colorado project scientists attempted to evaluate the usefulness of the Prairie Network as an instrumented system for UFO searches. A list of UFO sightings dating back to 1965 that occurred within the network limits was presented to the supervisor of the field headquarters in Lincoln, Neb. He was requested to produce those plates which might conceivably have been able to photograph the objects which gave rise to the sightings. Information supplied to the supervisor was deliberately limited to case number, year, month, day, time, city, duration, direction, and location. Duration of the sighting was given in minutes. Direction in the sighting reports referred either to the direction in which the observer was looking, or the direction of motion of the object. Location was specified by the coordinates of an atlas. Presenting the information in this form avoided biases based on preconceptions and placed more emphasis on the immediate environs of the sighting point. The assumption that an UFO was in the immediate neighborhood of the sighting was made so as to combat any tendency to attribute sightings to distant objects, that is, to astronomical bodies.

A map was prepared for each case (see Fig. 2) and each film scanned for exceptionally bright objects and planes or satellites. Tracks of bright meteors were never seen because the films on which they appeared had been sent to Cambridge, but the azimuth, elevation, and trajectory of these meteors were available and correlated with the sighting report. Angular positions of bright objects were roughly determined by means of a template.

The following criteria were applied to the reports and to the films:

Not operating (NO): cameras do not operate before dusk or after dawn and they sometimes malfunction or run out of film.

Meteor (M): a fireball with a known trajectory computed by its film tracks at several stations.

Overcast (O): this applied to cases where two nearby stations were so overcast that no star images showed, and where there was little information on films from more distant stations.

No information (NI): this classification was used when the report failed to state the direction in which the observer was looking or the direction in which the object was moving, or both.

No conclusion (NC): the report information was so fragmentary that no correlation between the objects on the photograph and those reported, was possible, or the films gave no information which could confirm that an object was seen.

Inconclusive identification (II): if the photographic evidence showed the presence of a body which could have been responsible for the sighting with a fair degree of probability, the case was called inconclusively identified.

Conclusive identification (CI): when description in the visual report was confirmed with a high degree of probability in all characteristics, the case was considered to be conclusively identified.

The following rules were adopted:

a) All NI cases became NC
b) No NO cases were labelled NC
c) Some O cases were classified NC

Of 114 cases, two were identified as meteors, one conclusively and one inconclusively, four cases received conclusive

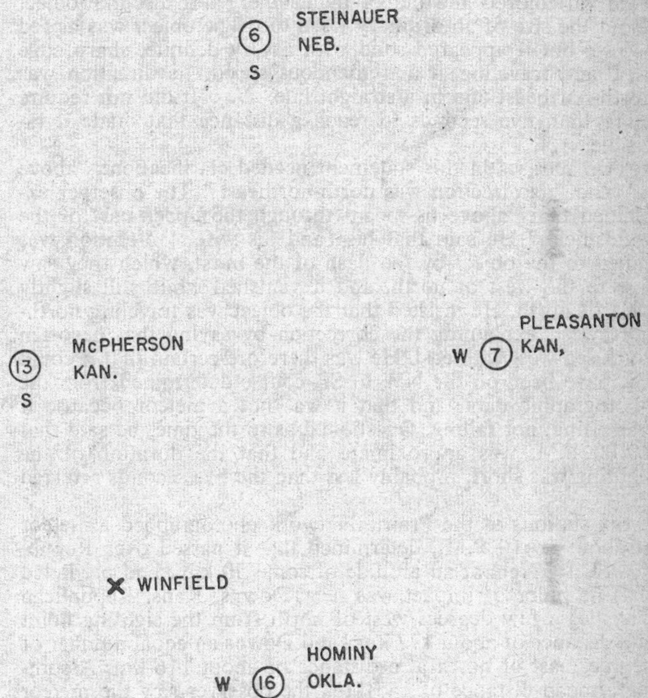

STEINAUER
(6) NEB.
S

McPHERSON
(13) KAN.
S

PLEASANTON
W (7) KAN,

✕ WINFIELD

HOMINY
W (16) OKLA.

Fig. 2

and 14 inconclusive identifications. Of the remaining cases 80 were classified NC; and 14, NI or NI combined with NO and O.

The sighting identified conclusively as a meteor was made by a couple who were driving north on Highway 281, six miles north of Great Bend, Kans., at 2200 CST. They reported that they saw ". . . a flash or burst of fireworks above car, not unlike the usual Fourth of July fireworks, except that this was much larger and much higher. The fireworks or sparkles were varicolored and out of them emerged a disc-like object about the size of an ordinary wash tub. The object was as red as fire, but it appeared solid with a very definite, sharp edge . . . and traveling at a tremendous speed. Its direction was north-northeast and in a straight line. . . . It did not require more than five seconds to reach a distance that made it invisible . . ."

Two phrases in this statement needed clarification: "above us" and "its direction was north-northeast." The observer explained that "above us meant through the upper part of the windshield." He said that his (and his wife's) attention was called to the object by the flash of the burst, which they saw just to the west of north, and it vanished while still slightly west of north. He insisted that the object was traveling north-northwest, explaining the correction by saying that he often confused west with east. He was therefore certain that it could not have been on the NW to SE course determined from the photographic data, and that it was not a meteor because it was rising, not falling. Questioned as to the time, he said that 10:00 P.M. was approximate and that the duration of the sighting was short, probably less than the five seconds referred to.

Six stations of the Prairie Network photographed a meteor at about 10:10 P.M., determined that it passed over Republican City, Neb. at an altitude of some 50 km., and predicted that its point of impact was near Downs, Kans. Republican City lies a few degrees west of north from the sighting point at a distance of about 177 km., and Downs an equal number of degrees east of north at a distance of about 116 km. Assuming a mean distance of 145 km., the observer saw the meteor at an elevation of approximately 19°. The elevation of the top of a windshield of an American two-door sedan from the eye level of a man of average height is about 25° or less.

The observer's impression was that the object was rising. This would be expected if it were approaching him at a constant altitude. His strong feeling that it was on a northerly course, and therefore receding, is explained by recalling the very short time during which he saw it.

Considering the general agreement as to time, elevation and

region of viewing, the probability is high that the object seen was the meteor photographed.

The second case was labeled inconclusive because, in spite of the paucity of information available about it, there was a relatively close agreement between the time of the sighting (0001 CST, 26 January 1967) and the time of a meteor recorded on three network stations (2341:51 CST, 25 January 1967). The discrepancy of only 18 minutes leads to a probable identification of the sighting as the meteor, but the identification cannot be made conclusive.

A striking example of the lack of correlation that can occur between a familiar object and the interpretation of a sighting is related in the case where a large, helmet-shaped, luminous body appeared overhead from behind a cliff. The observer was driving west. He reported that the object stayed nearly overhead for 45 min. until it disappeared behind a hill to the southwest at an altitude of about 40°.

Network photographs show the moon moving from 245° to 270° at a starting elevation of 85° dropping to 45°. Stars and a plane also appeared on the film, but their positions did not tally with the report.

Neither the observer nor the Air Force interviewer mentioned that the moon was visible, but the conclusion appears to be inescapable that the object seen was the moon. A summary of the results of this study is presented in Table 2.

Bearing in mind that Prairie Network optics and geometry were designed to detect bright astronomical objects at high angular velocities, it is not surprising that 100% of the conclusive and 67% of the inconclusive identifications relate to astronomical objects. In fact, any future investigation utilizing the network should guard against a possible bias arising from its design features.

The network's identification of 18% of all sightings with a fair degree of probability, does not constitute as poor a performance as might be thought since 34% could not be recorded because of overcast and 43% were so deficient in information that, even if an object had been recorded by the film it would have been impossible to correlate it with the sighting.

5. *The Tombaugh Survey*

In 1923, Dr. W. H. Pickering called attention to the possibility that undiscovered small natural earth satellites might exist. In 1952, after a long period of searching for trans-neptunic planets and "lost" asteroids, during which the planet Pluto was found, Dr. Clyde W. Tombaugh began a search for small satellites which might be in circular geocentric orbits having radii between 5,000 and 26,000 mi.

Table 2

Prairie Network Study

Summary of Sighting Identifications

State	O	NI	NO	total	NC	M	CI	II	conclusively astronomical	inconclusively astronomical
S. Dak	0	0	0	5	2		0	3		2
Neb.	4	6	0	10	8		1		1	
Kans.	3	9	1	14	9	1	0	3		1
Mo.	10	7	2	27	17	1	3	3	3	2
Iowa	3	2	1	11	8		0	2		
Ill.	11	16	5	33	27		0	1		1
Okla	3	3	3	14	9		0	2		2
Total	34	43	12	114	80	2	4	14	4	8
% Total	30	38	11		70	2	4	12	100	67

In searching for small, high-velocity bodies having a luminance close to the photographic threshold, it is essential to avoid "trailing"; that is, the image must be kept stationary with respect to the film. For example, if a star image 0.04 mm. in diameter trails over the emulsion for a distance of 10 mm., its brightness at any point will be diminished in the ratio 0.04/10.0 = 1/250 times. The resulting trail image may be below the film's threshold. Therefore, Dr. Tombaugh's experimental method was based on searching the surfaces of a large number of spherical shells, each concentric with the earth. The angular velocity of the search in each shell was made equal to the angular velocity a body moving in the gravitational field of the earth would have at a geocentric distance equal to the radius of that shell. (Tombaugh, 1959.)

The minimizing of trailing permitted the recording of images down to the M_{pg} = +15 in a 2 min. exposure. A dark rock, four feet in diameter, having a reflectivity equal to that of the moon, at a geocentric distance of 26,200 miles, would produce an image of this photographic magnitude.

The project was terminated at the end of June 1956. The number of concentric shells searched was over 100, resulting in a collection of 13,450 photographs. A few dozen possible natural satellite images having photographic magnitudes lying between +16 and +14 were found and attempts were made to recapture them by repeatedly photographing the shells in which they occurred, but with no success. The conclusion is that these images were either film defects, very small asteroids in elliptical orbits around the sun, or natural satellites in elliptical, rather than circular, orbits around the earth.

As a by-product of this project, a search for moon satellites was made during the lunar eclipse of November 1956. Three telescopes, monitored by a sky photometer, produced a total of 25 plates, recording point images down to about M_{pg} = +17. Some 500 candidates were found in the region between the moon's surface and a lunicentric distance of 37,000 miles, but none survived a detailed analysis.

A program of visual observation for nearby objects at very low latitudes began at the end of 1955 and continued through 1958. The equatorial plane, at distances between 600 and 2,500 miles from the surface of the earth, was searched with a twelve inch Newtonian reflecting telescope and 10x80 binoculars. The telescope had a limiting visual magnitude of +11 at 100 miles and +13 at 2,400 miles, while the binoculars could detect objects of M_v = +8 at 100 miles and of M_v = +9 at 2,800 miles. No satellites were seen. In the words of the report:

It is most unlikely that any objects larger than [two feet in diameter at an altitude of 100 miles or twenty feet at 2,500 miles as seen by binoculars, and several inches at 100 miles or three feet at 2,500 miles as seen by the telescope] existed . . . during 1956, or that any natural objects have since entered these regions.

The method used by Dr. Tombaugh, while admirably suited to orbiting bodies, is not appropriate for the observation of aerial phenomena that are not constrained in circular orbits. If their distances from the cameras were large they would not be detected due to the effect of trailing. For this reason a search on satellite survey films for reported UFOs was not attempted.

6. *Scanning Photometers*

Photometry of the night sky is carried out by means of photomultipliers which sweep out circles parallel to the horizon (almucantars) at various zenith angles Z(Z = 90°-altitude). Photometers used in airglow studies have a 5° field and sweep at the rate of 10°/sec horizontally and 5°/ sec vertically. A "sky survey" consists in making 360° sweeps at each of six zenith angles as follows: scanning clockwise at Z = 80° at the rate of 10°/sec, counter-clockwise at Z = 75° at 5°/sec and repeating the process at the same rate at Z = 70°, 60°, 40°, and 0°. A survey requires 4.1 min. Often a series of surveys is made using different filters depending on the nature of the investigation.

The output of the instrument consists of pulses, the amplitude of which is proportional to the intensity of the light sensed by the photometer. In older models the output is recorded analogically by a pen on paper tape. Since the distance along the length ("x" axis) of the tape is proportional to the time of the scan, it is therefore an indicator of the azimuth and zenith angle of the light source represented by the pulse. Data are analysed by measuring the height of pulses of interest ("y" axis) and determining their azimuth at each zenith angle. This measurement is done manually or in the new model, by recording the coordinates directly on machine-readable magnetic tape.

The angular size of the field, sweep rate, and other quantities differ depending on the use to which the instrument will be put. A zodiacal light photometer, for example, has a narrower field, 3°, scans at about 2°/sec and sweeps out almucantars at much smaller zenith distances, that is at altitudes much closer to the zenith.

Bodies brighter than $M_v = +3$ can readily be identified by their angular coordinates coupled with pulse height which is a measure of their magnitude. In practice, however, identification is rarely carried out because investigators of airglow and zodiacal light are interested in diffuse light phenomena rather than in single bright objects.

The sky coverage of the photometers is large since they can be made to scan an entire hemisphere as in the case of the all-sky cameras. The fact that they do not do so in the same short period of time as the cameras is not very important since at large distances the linear sweep speed approaches the velocity of light. Because their observations are made over a longer period of time and their angular data is recorded over a very much larger area, they have a greater resolution; azimuth and altitude are presented more accurately and the direction of motion is non-ambiguous.

Colorado project scientists thoroughly searched two such photometer sky surveys. The first search was made on an airglow survey chosen at random and the results are summarized in section 7 of this chapter. The second search was prompted by a visual sighting by three trained persons of a bright object in retrograde (E to W) motion during the operation of a zodiacal light photometer.

Scanning photometers can also sense different colors on separate surveys. The instrument's ability to measure the degree and direction of polarization can also aid in determining whether the object is self-luminous or its light is reflected. For these reasons, and because of their relatively extensive sky coverage, scanning photometers can be considered useful instruments in the conduct of UFO searches.

7. Haleakala I

A search was made of the taped output of an airglow photometer survey recorded around midnight, Hawaiian Standard Time (HST), 11-12 February 1966 in order to see if all bright objects could be identified as stars or planets. This survey was chosen at random from a sample of surveys made under particularly good conditions, that is, on nights during the dark of the moon with the minimum interference from clouds. The taped data, consisting of brightness as a function of azimuth, was plotted by machine in two ways, the first showing the raw data which included light from all sources, and the second, the raw data from which the background of zodiacal light, Milky Way and integrated starlight had been subtracted. On both plots, individual stars and planets stand out as narrow pulses, their height being proportional to their apparent magnitudes. The brightness is measured in terms of the number of 10th visual magnitude stars per square degree of sky, that is, in "S_{10}(vis)" units.

The observations of that night were made through three filters successively: 6300 ±5 Å, 5577 ± 5 Å and 5300 ±

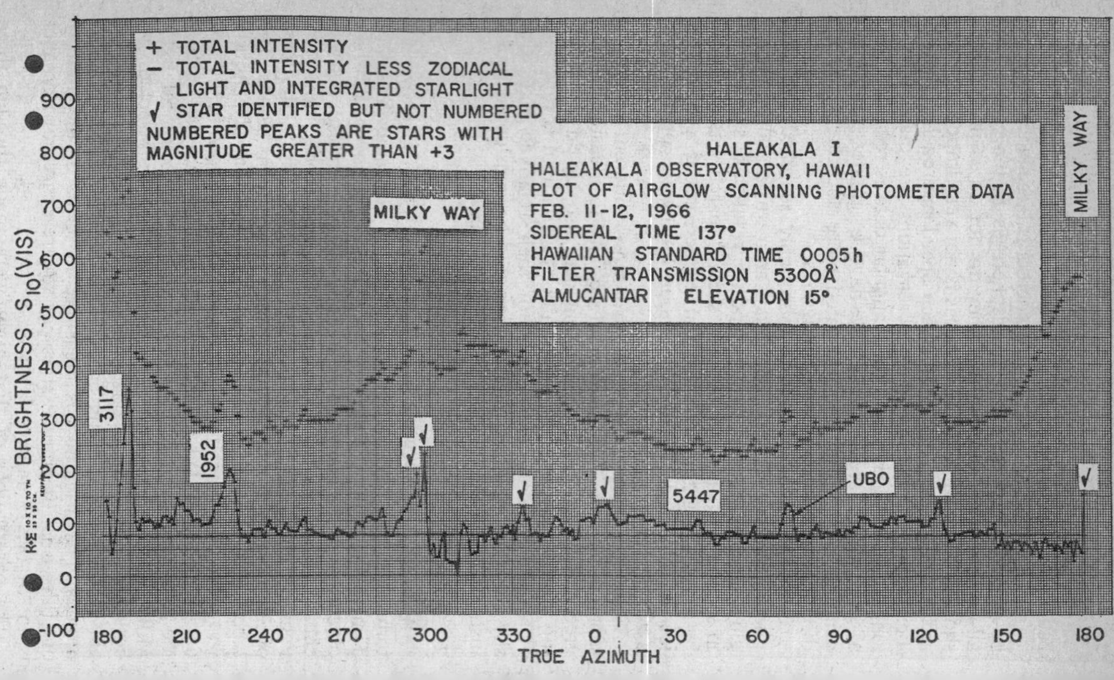
+ TOTAL INTENSITY
− TOTAL INTENSITY LESS ZODIACAL LIGHT AND INTEGRATED STARLIGHT
√ STAR IDENTIFIED BUT NOT NUMBERED
NUMBERED PEAKS ARE STARS WITH MAGNITUDE GREATER THAN +3
HALEAKALA I
HALEAKALA OBSERVATORY, HAWAII
PLOT OF AIRGLOW SCANNING PHOTOMETER DATA
FEB. 11-12, 1966
SIDEREAL TIME 137°
HAWAIIAN STANDARD TIME 0005h
FILTER TRANSMISSION 5300Å
ALMUCANTAR ELEVATION 15°
MILKY WAY
MILKY WAY
3117
1952
5447
UBO
BRIGHTNESS S10(VIS)
900
800
700
600
500
400
300
200
100
0
-100
180
210
240
270
300
330
0
30
60
90
120
150
180
TRUE AZIMUTH

Fig. 3

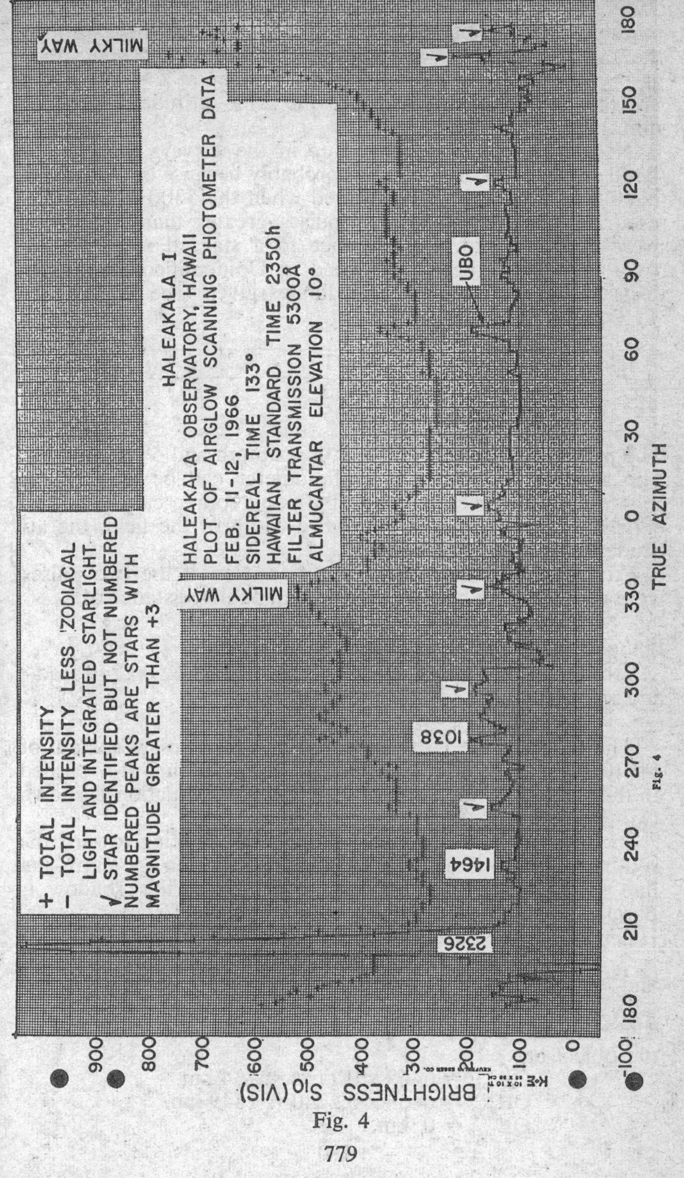

+ TOTAL INTENSITY
— TOTAL INTENSITY LESS ZODIACAL LIGHT AND INTEGRATED STARLIGHT
✓ STAR IDENTIFIED BUT NOT NUMBERED
NUMBERED PEAKS ARE STARS WITH MAGNITUDE GREATER THAN +3
HALEAKALA I
HALEAKALA OBSERVATORY, HAWAII
PLOT OF AIRGLOW SCANNING PHOTOMETER DATA
FEB. 11-12, 1966
SIDEREAL TIME 133°
HAWAIIAN STANDARD TIME 2350h
FILTER TRANSMISSION 5300Å
ALMUCANTAR ELEVATION 10°
MILKY WAY
MILKY WAY
UBO
1038
1464
2326
BRIGHTNESS S10(VIS)
TRUE AZIMUTH
180 210 240 270 300 330 0 30 60 90 120 150 180
-100 0 100 200 300 400 500 600 700 800 900

Fig. 4

25 Å. As each survey through each filter requires about four minutes, successive sweeps at the same zenith distance through the same filter occur at ~15 min. intervals, and one sweep at, say Z = 80°, will be followed by a sweep at Z = 75° about 36 seconds later and repeated at the same altitude about 15.5 min. later.

No stars or planets showed up in the surveys through the 6300 Å and 5577 Å filters, but probably because of its broader band-pass, many more apppeared when the 5300 Å filter was used. In this survey, all star pulses greater than $M_v = +3$ were accounted for by reference to a star atlas, except for two. These have been designated as Unidentified Bright Objects (UBO), having the coordinates given (see Figs. 3 and 4) (see also Figs. 5 and 6).

Angle Z	HST	Azimuth
80°	2350	68°T
75°	0005	72°T

The pulses were separated by 4° in azimuth and 5° in altitude. The azimuthal error in this photometer can be as great as ± 4°. Since the field is 5° and the point source can be sensed equally well over almost the entire width of the field, the altitude uncertainty may be ± 5°.

From the recorded values of the angles, if the two pulses were made by one body, it moved an angular distance of

$$\Phi = \sqrt{4^2 + 5^2} = 6.5° \equiv 0.1134 \text{ rad}$$

If the errors are in phase, then, maximally:

$$\Phi\text{max} = \sqrt{(4+4)^2 + (5+5)^2} = 12.8° \equiv 0.2240 \text{ rad}$$

and minimally

$$\Phi\text{min} = \sqrt{(4-4)^2 + (5-5)^2} = 0°$$

The fact that the UBO appeared on only two sweeps out of many surveys may be interpreted to mean that it vanished in the shadow of the earth at Z ≈ 75°. This situation is shown two-dimensionally in Figs. 3 and 4.

In Fig. 5, which is a view of the earth, looking toward the southern hemisphere, Haleakala (21°N) lies on the earth-sun line at 2400 HST, and the edge of the earth's shadow is parallel to it. In the first approximation, the distance d from Haleakala to the shadow line in an easterly direction is

$$d \sim R = 6371 \text{ km.}$$

and

$$OH = d/\cos 10° = 6469 \text{ km.}$$

The nominal, maximum and minimum distances travelled by the object are:

$$OB_{nom} = 6469 \times 0.1134 = 734 \text{ km.}$$
$$OB_{max} = 6469 \times 0.2240 = 1449 \text{ km.}$$
$$OB_{min} = 0 \text{ km.}$$

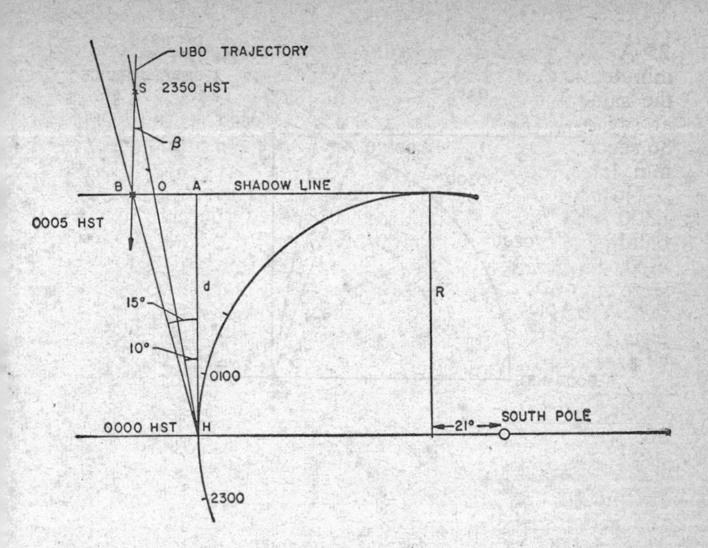

in 15 min., for a velocity of:

$$V_{nom} = 48.9 \text{ km/min}$$
$$V_{max} = 96.6 \text{ km/min}$$
$$V_{min} = 0 \text{ km/min}$$

These velocities should be compared with those of the UBO in Haleakala II, that is, ~ 142 mi/min ≡ 228 km/min. If the UBO was in orbit, the distance OB is the projection of its path SB making an angle β with the line of sight. Assuming that the velocity in Haleakala II is typical, then

$$\sin\beta_{nom} \sim \frac{48.9}{228} \sim 0.214$$
$$\beta_{nom} \sim 12^\circ$$

and the object was in a highly elliptical orbit. Alternatively, the distance OB might have been the projection of the apogee of the ballistic trajectory of a body launched in a retrograde direction.

Investigation showed that no sub-orbital missiles were launched from Vandenberg AFB or Pt. Mugu until one or more hours after this sighting. The Aerial Phenomena Office at Wright-Patterson AFB suggests that it might have been an artificial satellite on which information is not readily available. The object is thus in the unidentified category.

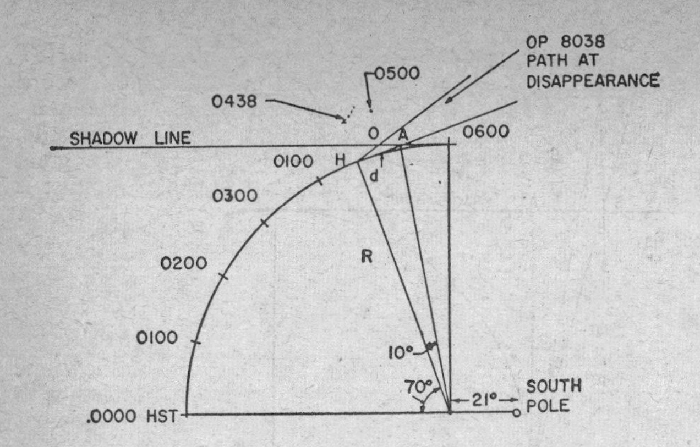

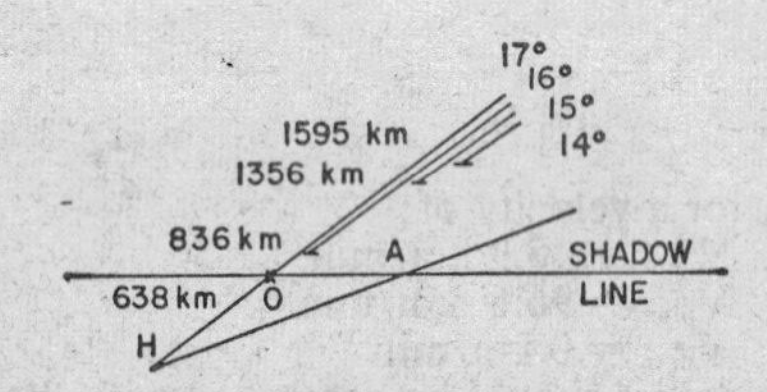

8. *Haleakala II*

On 10-11 September 1967 three observers at the Haleakala Observatory who were operating two scanning photometers saw a bright object move from NE to W at a low elevation. The paper tape outputs of each instrument were examined; the airglow photometer was operating with red filters and did not record anything which stood out against the background, but the zodiacal light photometer detected the object four times through a 5080 ± 30 Å filter. Other prominent astronomical features, such as η Canis Majoris, labelled ηCMa were readily identified.

The characteristics and operation of this photometer are somewhat different from the one used in airglow measurements. Its field is 3°; its sweep rate is 2°/sec; and almucantar increments are 1°. Because the focus of attention is the brightness of the zodiacal light a few degrees on each side of the plane of the ecliptic, the sweep was restricted to 160° starting from 0°T, each sweep being completed in 80 sec.

The survey in which the UBO appeared began at 0419 HST and ended at 0451 HST, on 11 September. The tape record is reproduced in Fig. 1 and the data summarized in Table 3.

The object was identified as OP 8038, a sub-orbital missile, which lifted off Vandenberg AFB at 0425 HST. The great circle distance, d, between launch and observation points, is calculated from the rough coordinates:

	Lat.	Long.
Vandenberg	34.5°N.	120.7°W.
Haleakala	21.0°N.	156.0°W.

and it is found that

$$d = 3762 \text{ km}.$$

The position of Haleakala with respect to the shadow-line of the earth is shown in Fig. 5, which is a view of the earth with the southern hemisphere toward the reader. On 11 September the sun rose at 0618.

Table 3

Photometer Data of UBO Sighting

Sighting	HST h	HST m	HST s	Elevation	Azimuth = ψ	τ min	Δψ
1st	04	34	25	14°	47°	----	--
2nd	04	35	28	15°	41°	1.05	6°
3rd	04	37	45	16°	36°	2.28	5°
4th	04	38	37	17°	37°	0.87	-1°

At 0439 HST the point of observation, H, was 70° east of its position at midnight. The distance to the point where the body was last seen is HO which, from known quantities is

$$HO = 638 \text{ km},$$

so that by the time the object vanished, it had travelled a great circle distance

$$d' \sim 3100 \text{ km}$$

in 13 m 37 s for an average velocity over the earth's surface of

$$V \sim 228 \text{ km/min}.$$

The distance, d, of the body from the observer at each sighting until its disappearance, which is assumed to be coincident with the time of last observation, is shown in Fig. 6. From the angular velocity, the angle of approach, β, can be approximately computed; the relevant quantities are listed in Table 4, where ω°, ω_r is the angular displacement in degrees and radians, respectively, Φ is the projected displacement in kilometers and

$\overline{V}$ the average velocity between each observing interval, in km/min. The measure of ellipticity is, as before, Sin $\beta = V/228$, where β is the angle between the trajectory and the line of sight.

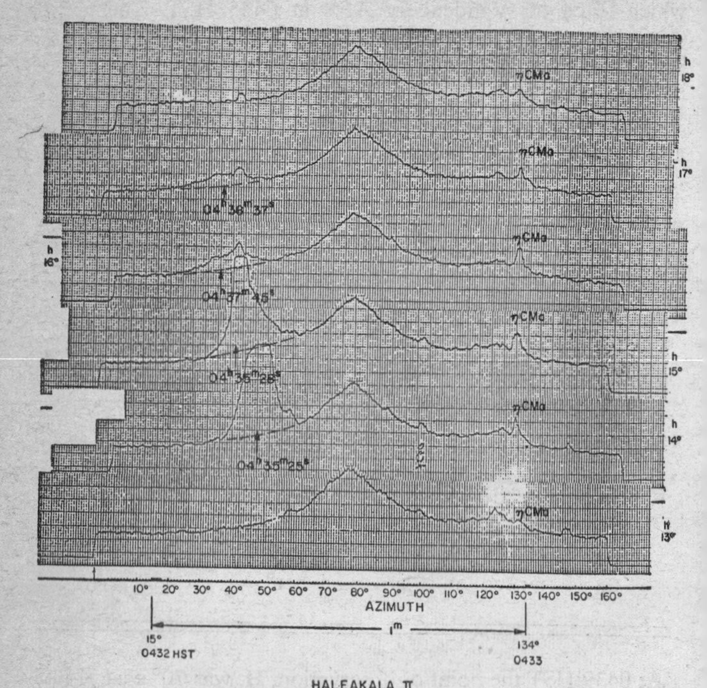

HALEAKALA II

COMPOSITE CHART OF SIX SCANS OF A ZODICAL SCANNING PHOTOMETER, SEPT. 10-11, 1967, SHOWING FOUR BRIGHT PEAKS INDICATED BY THEIR TIMES.

FILTER TRANSMISSIONS: 5080 Å
ALMUCANTAR ELEVATION, h, IN DEGREES
HORIZONTAL SCALE: AZIMUTH INCREASING TO THE RIGHT
VERTICAL SCALE: BRIGHTNESS IN ARBITRARY UNITS

The data were obtained directly from the output tape, eliminating almost completely errors due to manual data reduction. Backlash errors in azimuth are negligible. As a field is only 3°, the uncertainty in altitude is smaller than with a larger field, and remains ± 1.5°, the error in Φ for the first interval ~ 5%, for the second ~ 10% and very high for the third. However, it must be emphasized that the geometrical reconstruction was quite crude and errors introduced by it are probably greater than instrumental errors. Absence of information about the trajectory introduces the most serious uncertainty and the values for d, Φ, $\overline{V}$ and β should be regarded skeptically. The errors shown in Table 4 are derived entirely from the uncertainty in the field.

Table 4

Sighting Interval	ω^o	ω_r	d	ϕ	$\overline{V}$	Sin β	β
1-2	$6.2^{+.3}_{-.2}$	$0.108^{+.05}_{-.03}$	1595	172	164	0.72	46°
2-3	$5.1^{+.5}_{-.1}$	$.089^{+.009}_{-.002}$	1356	121	53	0.23	13°
3-4	$1.4^{+1.3}_{-.4}$	$.023^{+.024}_{-.005}$	836	19	22	0.10	6°

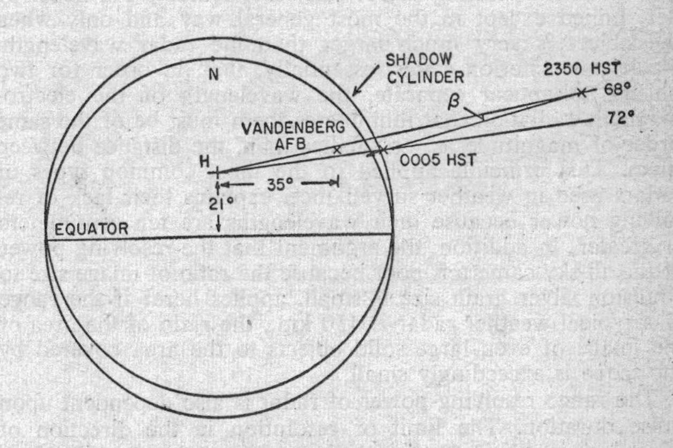

Even though the reconstruction is very approximate, the magnitude of β indicates a sub-orbital trajectory, because when last seen the body was

$$h \sim 638 \sin 17° + \frac{638^2}{8 \times 6371} \sim 194\text{km}$$

above the surface of the earth, and at this distance it would be expected that $\beta \approx 17°$ for an object in orbit.

9. *Radar*

The use of radar has spread into many diversified fields since its introduction as an aircraft-tracking instrument at the beginning of World War II. One of the first non-military uses it was put to was tracking weather balloons. Not long after, it was discovered that, given the proper wavelength, radar could detect clouds and the position of rain and hail in storms. Since then its use has extended to tracking satellites, investigating the atmospheres of several planets in the solar system, including our own, determining the trajectory of meteors and predicting their points of impact and studying lightning and violent storms (Battan, 1962).

In general, radar provides information for determining the velocity, range, elevation and azimuth of the reflecting objects in its field of view. Indirectly, it will furnish some data on the state of the matter which is backscattering (reflecting) radio energy; other variables such as temperature and index of refraction can sometimes be inferred.

The resolving power of radar, defined as the minimum distance between two objects (or two parts of one object) necessary to make them appear separate, is poor. Details of the shape of the reflecting object and other features can never be determined except in the most general way and only when the object is very much larger than the radar wavelength. Rayleigh's criterion states, essentially, that, in order for two objects to appear separate, the wavelength of the electromagnetic radiation that illuminates them must be of the same order of magnitude as, or smaller than, the distance between them. This principle applied to the most common types of radars used in weather surveillance, explains their lack of resolving power because their wavelengths are ten centimeters or greater. In addition, the argument that the resolving power of the all-sky camera is poor because the ratio of image size to emulsion silver grain size is small, applies here: if the range of a typical weather radar is 450 km., the ratio of the area of the image of even large solid objects to the area covered by the scope is exceedingly small.

The range resolving power of radar is also dependent upon pulse duration. The limit of resolution in the direction of propagation is half the linear dimension of the pulse because at intervals less than that the echo formed by the leading edge of the pulse reaching the more distant object overlaps the echo formed by the trailing edge of the pulse returning from the nearer object. Thus, if the radar is "looking" at two objects in its "line of sight," and if its pulse duration is 1 μsec., it will not display as separate from other, in-line targets whose ranges differ by less than 500 ft.

Radar reports information in three coordinates: range, elevation, and azimuth. The resolving power in the range coordinate is determined by pulse duration. Resolving power in elevation and azimuth depend upon the same conditions that apply to optical resolution. Rayleigh's criterion for the optical resolution of a telescope can be used for this purpose, if the radar antenna is circular and its diameter is regarded as its aperture. Resolving power is proportional to the ratio of the wavelength to aperture (diameter). This is another way of saying that the ratio determines the angular beam width of a radar transmitting-receiving antenna. Resolving power is determined for this case by the equation

$$r = 70° \left(\frac{\lambda}{D}\right)$$

where λ is wavelength, D is antenna diameter, and 70°(=1.22 rad.) is the angular size of diffraction disc image of a point source for unit $\frac{\lambda}{D}$ ratio as derived by Rayleigh. (For other than antennas with a circular aperture, resolving power must be separately computed for the vertical and horizontal planes). Applying the equation to a radar with a wavelength of 3 cm., and whose parabolic antenna has a diameter of 3 m., the beam width, and therefore the resolving power, is found to be 0.7° of arc in elevation and azimuth.

Radar is frequently able to see targets virtually undetectable by the unaided eye or on photographic film. This greater sensitivity is due to marked differences in the signal-to-noise ratio of wavelengths employed by radar compared to the optical wavelengths upon which the eye and the camera must rely. The atmosphere is almost completely transparent to radar wavelengths between 3 cm. and 10 cm. It scatters such waves hardly at all. At optical wavelengths, it is still relatively transparent, but air scatters energy appreciably, especially at the short (blue) wavelengths (Rayleigh scattering): hence, the blue sky. In addition, unlike the radar case, there is a powerful source of optical noise present in the daytime sky—the sun. Thus, a pale blue object seen against the sky is nearly invisible to the retina or to photographic film, yet, if constructed of metal, the object will reflect radar waves strongly.

Design of a radar to track targets very much smaller than the wavelength takes into account that for a given wavelength, backscattering power varies as the sixth power of the target size (Rayleigh's Law of Scattering) and, conversely, for a given target size the power varies inversely as the fourth power of the wavelength. Furthermore, atmospheric attenuation of the beam increases as frequency increases. The balancing of these factors results in the choice of a 10-20 cm. wavelength for radar which are to survey extensive storms such as hurricanes; 3-10 cm. for tracking metallic objects; and 1-3 cm. for studies of rain and hail distributions (Battan, 1959).

The first exact theory of scattering of electromagnetic waves by a sphere was developed by Gustav Mie in 1908. In this theory, the dielectric constant and therefore the index of refraction of the sphere determines in large part the amount of backscatter at any wavelength (Born, 1964). For example, the backscatter from a hailstone is enormously greater than that from a raindrop of equal size, and, as a result, radar can provide data for estimating the amount of ice or hail in a storm cloud. In effect, therefore, it can give information on the state of matter in the scattering object, for example; it can distinguish between wet and dry hailstones.

Anomalous reflections called "angels" can sometimes be ascribed to certain atmospheric conditions. Temperature inversions cause rapid changes in the index of atmospheric refraction at the interfaces of the layers and such changes can give rise to radar echoes exactly as similar conditions account for mirages in the case of visible wavelengths. (See Section III, Chapter 5 and Section VI, Chapter 5.)

As would be expected from Maxwell's equations, radar echoes will be produced by regions of high ionization where there is an appreciable density of free charges. This is the reason why lightning paths are visible to radar. The density of charges in the trail of a meteor is different from that in the immediately surrounding space, and the radar echo arises from this difference in space charge, not by reflection from the nucleus of the meteor itself (Lovell, 1954). Depending upon the magnitude of the radar "cross-section" some "angels" can be ascribed to echoes from birds or even insects. "Cross-section" is better defined as the ratio of the reflected power per unit solid angle, to the incident power density; in other words, it is a measure of the effectiveness of the target in reflecting radiation and will have a different value for each wavelength. Inasmuch as birds and insects are usually smaller than radar wavelengths, their actual dimensions cannot be measured, although their radar cross-section can be (Glover, 1966). This quantity, for several species of birds and insects is tabulated below as a function of radar wavelength:

The extreme sensitivity of radar is well illustrated here: The insect targets were at least 10 km. distant and the birds at ranges between 10 and 20 km. when the measurements were made. Because of the poor resolution of the radars, the cross-section is simply a measurement of relative backscattered power and now the actual spatial extent of the object on the radar scope. In other words, the moth can be distinguished

Table 5

Target	Wavelength	Mean cross-section cm^2
Hawkmoth	10.7	1.0
Honeybee	10.7	3.0×10^{-3}
Sparrow	10.2	15.0
	71.5	2.5×10^{-2} (a)
	3.5	1.9
Pigeon	10.2	80.0
	71.5 (a)	11.0
Pigeon	3.5	15.0
	3.5	1.1 head
		100.0 broadside
		1.0 tail

(a) Transmitted beam vertically polarized; received echo also vertically polarized.

(Table taken from Glover (1966) and Conrad (1968).

from the sparrow only by determinations of the power received rather than by shape and size; the head of a pigeon cannot be differentiated from the tail.

> The radar return does, however, contain information which provides a basis for identifying an unknown point target as a bird. . . .
>
> Thus, the radar return from single birds in flight differs . . . from other possible point or dot targets, such as aircraft, swarms of insects, several birds together, or small clouds or other meteorological structures (Conrad, 1968).

Weather Radar:

Of the 14 types of radars used by the U.S. Weather Bureau, only the WSR-57 which is equipped with a 35 mm.

WSR-57

Wave Length cm.	Pulse Length Rep. rate	Peak Power Output K.W.	Beam Width	Sweep Characteristics	Scopes	Range	Altitude
10.3 (5 and 2.5 cm. planed but not yet on order)	0.5 micro/sec at 658 pulses per sec. or 4.0 micro/sec at 164 pulses per sec.	500	2°	Automatic, manual in altitude or azimuth at 0-24°/sec	PPI RHI R A	464km.	-10° to +40°

(Source: U.S. Dept of Commerce)

camera appears to be adaptable to UFO searches. The salient features of this instrument are enumerated on page 789.

These radars are placed around the perimeter of the Weather Network and are interspersed with the eastern stations of the Prairie Network in Minnesota, Iowa, Kansas, Oklahoma, Missouri and Illinois. They are, therefore, well located to furnish corroboration of sightings in any future investigations.

The sky coverage of these radars is obviously less than that of the airglow photometers since they are limited in their choice of elevation and they have only a 2° sweep width.

The photographic program which has been carried over the last few years consists in taking one scope picture of one sweep every 15 min. in times of clear weather and more frequently when storms were developing. These films are available for inspection, but the Colorado project made no attempt to search for confirmatory evidence of reported sightings because each photograph covers only 1.7% of each hour of elapsed time.

METEOR RADAR

The facilities of the Radar Meteor Project of the Smithsonian Institution are located at Long Branch, some seven miles south of Havana, Ill. They consist of a network of eight receivers and one 4 Mw, 40 MHz transmitter, with antennas bearing 113°T. This direction was chosen as the most favorable one for the detection of faint meteor trails.

The main lobe of the radiation pattern from the two transmitting antennas is inclined upward at 45° and has a half-power horizontal width of ~ 20° and a half-power vertical width of ~ 11°.

Pulses of 6 μsec. duration are emitted at the rate of about 1300 per second, so that the echo from an object 200 km. distant will return within one pulse cycle. An object in the beam at 200 km. will be about 140 km. above Decatur. Ill. The Havana radar is thus designed to scan approximately the same volume of sky monitored by an image orthicon located at Sidell, (near Urbana) Ill. (see Section 12).

The radar will detect meteors as faint as $m_{rad} = +13$ for counting purposes, and $m_{rad} = +11$ and will acquire echoes from 3,000-4,000 meteors/hr.

The system is capable of receiving echoes from objects at almost any distance from the transmitter. In order to limit the information to "suitable" meteors, meteor-recognition logic has recently been installed which filters out extraneous signals such as those from aircraft. These echoes are, however, visible on the monitoring oscilloscopes and are characterized by a persistence greater than that of meteors. Data pertaining to "suitable" echoes is recorded on magnetic tape. Similar, but unfiltered data is simultaneously recorded on film (Smithsonian, 1966).

During 1967, many non-meteoritic echoes were seen on the oscilloscopes and recorded in the Havana log book. Using the film record, the Colorado project sought to determine how many of the UFOs sighted during 1967 in a radius of ~ 140 km. from Havana, had resulted in an echo which had been both filmed and logged. Of nine cases (the same used to test the orthicon), seven had occurred when the station was not operating. The eighth case covered a series of sightings over a period of 10 days during which the station was operating. Unfortunately, only very sketchy observing data were available. The object was seen from Kilbourne, about five miles south of the transmitter, "over the west south-west horizon." Station attendants had been alerted that unusual objects had been seen in the area. The absence of entries in the log book implies that nothing unusual appeared on the scopes. This is not surprising because echoes of objects very close to the station are lost in the display formed by the transmitted pulse, particularly at low altitudes. If the objects had been farther away but bearing ~ 140°T (WSW) they would not have been located within the main lobe of radiation bearing ~ 113°T. Objects outside this zone of maximum transmitted power would return echoes too faint to be observed against background "noise."

The ninth object is the one that the image orthicon recorded in a test run on November 7th, 1967 at 2330 ± 3 m. It was subsequently identified as a fireball. No simultaneous radar sighting was made because the radar was not in operation.

10. The Image Orthicon

One of the important problems in meteor physics is the cross-correlation by simultaneous radar and optical meteor observations of ionization and luminous efficiencies as functions of velocity.

The development of the image orthicon has made such cross-correlation studies feasible. The instrument is a conventional vidicon television camera modified so as to increase its sensitivity. This is achieved by adding an image intensifier ahead of the scanning mechanism in the camera. The result yields a sensitivity equivalent to an ASA rating of 100,000. Such extreme sensitivity permits detection of meteors having a limiting magnitude of about +7. This is well within the equivalent M_{rad} range detectable by radar, and considerably superior to the capability of any photographic system except the 48 in. Schmidt telescope at Mt. Palomar. Tests show that the image orthicon will detect 20-30 meteoroids per hour.

The image orthicon site in Sidell, Ill., about 35 mi. SE of

Urbana, was chosen by the Smithsonian Institution with two objectives in mind. Using a lens having a 16° field (the optimum lens for meteor surveys), the image orthicon is sited to survey approximately the same area of sky over Decatur as that covered by the 20° beam of the Long Branch radar (see previous section). But whereas the radar is sited so as to track the meteor trails at about right angles, the image orthicon is located so that its optical axis is more nearly parallel to the meteors' paths.

Linked by microwave and radio, the radar and the image orthicon are able to determine times within 10^{-2}sec., thereby minimizing ambiguities as to the identity of the objects observed.

As in conventional television, an 875-line scan samples the tube target in two sets of sweeps of alternate lines, each requiring 1/60 sec. When the alternate sweeps are interlaced, flicker and resolution are greatly improved. The electronic image is recorded on magnetic tape and can be immediately played back for viewing on a monitor. Used in this way, the high sensitivity of the image orthicon permits the acquisition of moving aerial objects that would be undetectable photographically because of the effect of trailing. Photographic records of the monitor images can be recorded by a 35 mm. camera operating at any desired frame speed.

The sensitivity of some image orthicons can be further increased by operating them in the integrating mode. In this procedure, the electronic image is swept away less frequently, thereby allowing the photoelectron population due to ultra-faint images to build up. The Smithsonian image orthicon has no provision for this technique, nor does its camera permit the making of time-lapse photographs which are preferable when the device is operating in the integrating mode (Williams, 1968).

During 1967 there were nine sightings of UFOs within a distance of ~ 200 km. from Urbana. (These were the same sightings which were correlated with the radar records.) Eight of the sightings occurred before testing of the image orthicon began in August. The ninth was a sighting on 7 November at 2230 ± 3 min., of a bright object between Urbana, Ill. and Lafayette, Ind. This event was recorded on the image orthicon tape during a test. A film of the tape clearly shows a bright mass moving rapidly across a corner of the field. The object is badly resolved due to its great brightness, but the shape of the image suggests that the meteoroid had already broken into two pieces. Preceding the meteoroid image is a large ghost image which is the result of reflections between the lens elements. Just prior to the appearance of the meteor, a small object can be seen moving at 90° to the fireball trajectory.

This object has been identified by Wright-Patterson AFB as a satellite.

11. Proton Magnetometers

The variation in the magnitude and direction of both the horizontal and vertical components of the earth's magnetic field is of such importance in geophysics that a network of some 240 geomagnetic observatories have been deployed by several countries at stations all over the globe (NAS 1968). Thirteen of these stations exist in the continental United States and of these, three are situated on the western edge of the Prairie and Weather Radar networks.

Most of the instruments at the geomagnetic stations are proton magnetometers. These instruments have a sensitivity of about 1 γ (= 10^{-5} gauss) in magnetic field strength. This means that the instrument is capable of detecting at a distance of 185 m. the field strength along the axis of a single-turn circular conductor 20 m. in diameter in which a 100 amp. direct current is flowing. In addition to this extreme sensitivity to field-strength fluctuations, the proton magnetometer is capable of detecting 0.1′ of arc in declination, defined as the deviation of the horizontal component of the earth's magnetic field from 0°T. Since the mean strength of the earth's magnetic field at midlatitudes is about 50,000 γ, the instruments are sensitive to about one part in 50,000 of the earth's field.

Assuming a model consisting of a line current in the vortex extending from the ground to a height of 10 km. and an image current of equal length in the earth, Brook (1967) calculates that the current in a tornado, which caused a 15γ deflection in a magnetometer 9.6 km. distant, was about 1,000 amp. Revising the model to make it more realistic, he assumes that a 20 km. horizontal line current 6 km. above the earth joins a 6 km. vertical line current to the earth together with an equal earth image. The current necessary to produce the observed 15γ field is then only 225 amp.

Consideration of the electromagnetic effects produced by tornadoes suggests that some UFO sightings may have been stimulated by these storms, and that continued photographic, geomagnetic and radar observations would be useful in studying them.

The claim that UFOs produce powerful magnetic fields could also be investigated by proton magnetometer measurements. The problem, however, is a familiar one: thus far it has not been possible to bring instrumentation to the scene of a sighting while UFO phenomena were still observable.

Papers by Vonnegut and Weyer (1966) and Colgate (1967) contain extensive lists of references on tornado energy phenomena. Much of the information for this section was supplied by Dr. Joseph H. Rush, High Altitude Observatory, National Center for Atmospheric Research, Boulder, Colo.

12. *Lasers*

The use of lasers in tracking objects is analogous to the use of radar, the principal difference lying simply in the wavelength of the radiation in the emitted pulse. As in radar tracking, the information obtained is range, azimuth, and altitude, but the accuracy of laser ranging is expected to be better than in 3 cm. radar by a factor of two, because of the smaller effect of atmospheric water vapor on the refractive index at the laser wavelength.

The extremely good collimation of a laser beam, where the angular spread is less than 2×10^{-5} radians (a few seconds of arc), is a two-edged sword insofar as the development of laser ranging is concerned. The narrow beam increases the accuracy of azimuthal data and diminishes the transmitted power required to yield a detectable return signal; but this very narrowness increases the difficulty of scoring a hit on a rapidly moving object in low orbit.

Laser ranging has been in the developmental stage for only a few years and, at the present state of the art would be of only limited value in UFO investigations. However, laser technology is advancing rapidly and it seems quite probable that future laser ranging devices could be useful in UFO searches.

13. *Observations and Comments*

The description of a phenomenon requires the collection of many of its qualitative and quantitative aspects. If the data relating to these aspects is sufficient to permit the construction of a model then this model can be identified as belonging to one or another known category of phenomena if their mutual similarities are not numerous enough. Conversely, if the similarities are not numerous enough, it may be necessary to identify the model as a member of a completely new category.

In the majority of UFO sightings, the amount, type and quality of the data have been insufficient even to describe the event, to say nothing of identifying it with a known classification. Data from many other sightings have been adequate for identification with familiar phenomena, to a reasonable level of confidence, but in no case have the data been either detailed or accurate enough to class the event as a new phenomenon.

The lack of instrumented observations has curtailed investigation of a number of events which sounded fascinating and on the threshold of revealing something novel. No matter how detailed or how intelligent the reports of observers, qualitative statements could not serve to define an unfamiliar phenomenon. To do so requires a quantitative description of a number of basic characteristics, some of which are listed below:

1. Dimensions.
2. Position, that is, coordinates in some frame of reference, usually with respect to the observer.
3. Shape.
4. Mass.
5. Motion—velocity and acceleration, particularly with reference to the method of propulsion.
6. Interactions with other systems—effects of electric and magnetic fields on surrounding objects, emission of energy in the form of exhaust, light and sound, aerodynamic lift, ionization.
7. Matter primarily involved—the composition and state of matter and its temperature, rigidity and structure.
8. Origin—the genesis of the phenomenon, the conditions which gave rise to it, its presence in and mode of transport to the region in which it was observed.

Instrumentation to acquire knowledge of these characteristics must be designed with appropriate regard for the behavior shown both by UFOs and some other phenomena which can be loosely classed together as objects difficult to identify. Any instrumentation for the detection and identification of these objects must be elastic enough to cover the wide range of expected behavior. A comparison of various salient characteristics of some objects observed in the atmosphere is set out in Table 6.

An explanation of some of the statements in the table is of interest.

Duration:

1) The large majority of meteors have been observed to have a duration shorter than 15 sec. Thus if a meteor moving at 30 km/sec at an altitude of 80 km. is visible over 160° of sky, its path length will be

$$d = 2 \times \frac{80 \text{ km.}}{\tan 10^\circ} = 900 \text{ km.}$$

so that it will have a maximum distance from the observer of 450 km. Therefore, it will be visible for not more than

$$t = \frac{900}{30} = 30 \text{ sec.}$$

However, most meteors do not usually have the luminance to be seen at a distance of 450 km.

2) In the case of satellites, one which has a 90 min. period at an altitude of 200 km., and can be seen over 160°

Table 6

Characteristics of Some Objects Observed in the Atmosphere

	Meteors	Satellites and Satellite re-entries	Aircraft	Tornadoes	UFOs
Point source (P.S.) or extended object (E.O.)	P.S. unless fireball	P.S. unless re-entry	P.S. by night E.O. by day	E.O.	P.S. by night E.O. by day
Self-luminous	yes	reflected light yes (re-entries)	yes, navigation lights	yes?*	yes, at night
Luminance	high	low	low	low	low to high
Direction of motion-unpredictable, linear, ballistic or orbital	linear or ballistic	linear or orbital	straight or slowly curving	slowly varying	unpredictable
Electromagnetic effects, other than visual	some evidence exists**	none	none	possible but not established**	sometimes
Close approach to or contact with ground	infrequently	re-entry only	yes	yes	so reported
Distance to observer	many miles	many miles	from close to far	usually several miles	from close to many miles

*(Vonnegut and Weyer 1966)
**(Romig, 1963)
***(Vonnegut, 1968)

Table 6 (cont'd)

Characteristics of Some Objects Observed in the Atmosphere

	Meteors	Satellites and Satellite re-entries	Aircraft	Tornadoes	UFOs
Duration of appearance	1-15 sec.	<5 min.	<5 min.	a few sec. to many min.	a few sec. to many min.
Velocity range	<17 km/sec	<8 km/sec	<0.6 km/sec	<0.03 km/sec	unpredictable
Altitude	10-100 km.	100-2,200 km.	<26 km.	>13 km. and <19 km.	zero to very high
Direction	isotropic	Constant; W to E, polar or E to W	isotropic	isotropic	isotropic
Other			characteristic illumination	most common in central states	no apparent geographical distribution

of sky, will be visible for about 4.5 min.

3) Tornadoes occasionally persist for a long time and travel many miles.

Velocity range:

1) The lowest meteor velocity (prior to the last few seconds before impact) is ~ 17 km/sec. The greatest velocity imparted artificially to a small object is ~ 14 km/sec by means of a four-stage rocket in a ballistic trajectory and a final boost with a shaped charge. (McCrosky, 1968)

2) Satellites with a near-escape velocity of 17,000 mph have a velocity of only 7.6 km/sec.

3) For aircraft, 2,000 km/sec. or ~ 0.6 km/sec.

4) A tornado usually moves at 5-70 mph., (0.002-0.03 km/sec).

Altitude:

1) The Prairie Network attempts to get stereo-pairs of meteor photographs for trajectories at 40-80 km. in altitude and downstream single photos at 10-40 km. altitude to predict the point of impact.

2) Perigee and apogee of most satellies lie in the range of 100-2,000 km.

3) Aircraft: 26 km. $\equiv$ 16 mi. $\approx$ 80,000 ft.

4) Vonnegut (1968) states that although thunderstorms spawn tornadoes, the higher the storm the greater the probability of formation. "Ordinary" thunderstorms at an altitude of about 8 mi. rarely produce tornadoes while those at 12 mi. often do.

Azimuth:

1) Meteors appear in a region bounded by a few degrees on each side of the plane of the ecliptic and their trajectories will be oriented isotropically with respect to their points of origin.

2) Satellites launched from Cape Kennedy will travel from west to east, with a small southward component; those launched from Vandenberg AFB are most often in a polar orbit, though some are in retrograde orbit.

3) Aircraft, of course, will be seen moving in any direction.

4) Tornadoes seem to have no observable directional pattern.

Review and Discussion of Several Instrumental Methods

1) The Prairie Network covers about 80% of the volume of space above each camera station. This is as good a coverage as can be found with any instrument except certain types of radar, all-sky cameras, and airglow photometers.

2) The coverage is continuous, during periods of good

visibility from dusk to dawn, or, roughly, about 30% out of every day. Radar has the advantage of daytime coverage over optical systems, but resolution and identification is not as good. The presence of "angels" and other anomalies, complicates the interpretations.

3) Certain other means of detection, such as photometric scans, have much longer ranges and therefore probe very much larger volumes of sky. But these systems suffer from the same disadvantages as radar.

4) No other optical network exists which is as extensive as the Prairie Network, the coverage of which is ~0.13 of the sky over the U. S.

5) The network has been designed to produce data which allows the direct computation of altitude, azimuth, velocity, and brightness from which loss of momentum and impact coordinates can be found. Radar will acquire the same data but will record neither the visual identifying signals emitted by a plane nor the brightness of a meteor.

6) Objects recorded by a photographic time exposure show a continuous projection of their position in time. In many radars the object is located only once every sweep and since each sweep may have a period of six to 15 sec., rapid course changes may result in an inability to identify successive images as belonging to the same object.

7) Although the network is at present purely pictorial, it may shortly be improved by the addition of a spectrometric camera at each station.

8) Devices such as airglow photometers cover the sky well but also have shortcomings similar to radar because each scan at a given zenith angle requires a relatively long time and a complete sky survey requires several scans taking several minutes.

9) Most photometric scanners plot intensities as a function of time on paper tape. Reduction of this data to coordinates is not as accurate as interpretation of the network film, although it is good enough for airglow and aurora studies.

10) Differentiation between near-orbital or ballistic objects and the star background is much simpler in network photographs than on photometric scan tapes because star trajectories on film are obvious, whereas on tapes a pulse produced by a reflecting or self-luminous object can be distinguished from a pulse produced by a star only by comparing its coordinates with those given for stars.

11) Scanning radar sky coverage is very good, but identification of objects photographed on the radar scopes is much more difficult that objects seen photographically, both because of poor resolution and because of the lack of char-

acteristic patterns such as flashing lights on planes, and so forth. Weather radar, however, would be a useful adjunct to a photographic patrol, particularly since a portion of the weather radar system is interlaced with the network. In general, it can be said that the most effective use of radar lies in confirmation of velocity, range and direction.

12) Image Orthicons and Vidicons: The use of these photoelectric devices is growing, largely because their sensitivity is greater than film by a factor up to 10^4. Such systems can also store and reproduce the image immediately. These attributes make them valuable instruments in investigations of aerial phenomena of any kind, including UFOs.

13) A number of UFO reports have indicated electromagnetic interactions with terrestrial systems: radio and TV interference, stalled internal combustion engines, and the like. It would be desirable to investigate the frequency with which UFOs exhibit such interactions as well as the field strengths and direction. No network of stations making routine recordings of atmospheric electric potential exists at present in the U.S. Electric potential measuring devices might be incorporated into joint geomagnetic weather radar and Prairie Network system at a later time.

14) There have been persistent reports that sometimes sounds accompany the passage of large meteors (fireballs) and the re-entry of satellite debris. There is evidence that these sounds have been heard at great distances, sometimes simultaneously with the time of passage. This suggests that fireballs give rise to electromagnetic fields which either interact with the surroundings of the observer, or directly with the observer himself, to produce audible waves (Romig, 1963, 1964). Stations containing geomagnetic or electric tape recorders and appropriate acoustical sensing devices.

15) Other instruments such as ultra-violet and infra-red sensors, and radiation-counters would also be desirable.
tape recorders and appropriate acoustical sensing devices.

Existing Instrument Systems of Limited Value

1) The Super-Schmidt cameras developed for meteor studies are sensitive and have a 55° field but they are few in number and individually cover only a hundredth of the area of sky covered by one Prairie Network station. The Baker-Nunn cameras which were designed for satellite tracking have a much smaller field, and although there are perhaps 16 of them in all, they are scattered all over the world.

2) Sky surveys made through large astronomical telescopes cover too little sky at each exposure. Because of their slow photographic speed, only very bright objects moving with respect to the star background will be recorded.

3) The Tombaugh Survey for small natural earth satel-

lites was an extremely systematic search (Tombaugh, 1959). This technique would hardly be suitable for photographing UFOs.

The capabilities of existing instrumental systems to record the characteristics necessary for quantitative descriptions of UFOs vary widely. The Prairie Network can supply data on position and motion at all times under ideal conditions it might be capable of determining dimensions and shape but it cannot directly describe mass, interactions, the matter associated with the event, its origin or manner of locomotion.

Radar is more limited in its information return. It can report position and motion, even when the phenomenon is invisible to the network, but it cannot furnish information on any other characteristic, with the possible exception of the state of matter. Photometric scanners are even more limited.

Determining mass and kind of matter, and extensive analysis of structure and organization of an UFO require that such an object, if one exists, be made continuously available for instrumented study.

If all the eight characteristics listed at the beginning of this section describe adequately an UFO, then no network, simple or complex as presently constituted, can help us far along the road toward the identification of that type of event which today defies explanation.

What is required is a modified and extended network, so designed that its component systems complement each other, and so integrated that it can provide storable data in a form suitable for interdisciplinary study.

More specifically, the network should be organized along the following lines:

1. In the interests of economy and speed, arrangements should be made to have access to the output of the Prairie Network, and the cooperation of its investigators.
2. Similar arrangements should be made with the Weather Radar Network and a program of photography developed along lines suitable for the acquisition of data on tornadoes and other transient phenomena not detected by time-exposure photographs.
3. Simultaneous observations with the several geomagnetic observatories which lie in or near the combined Prairie Network Weather Radar nets should be provided for.
4. Link these three networks, and other devices, such as tape recorders and radiation monitors, together to a single time base. This step is important, for example, in testing reports that fireballs have been heard at the same time as their appearance, although their distance from the observer would normally require a many-second interval between sight and sound.

5. The tedium of a patrol can be relieved by the installation of various automatic sensors, but the degree of discrimination offered by these devices is often not as great as that of the human eye. It is true that the eye is, in general, incapable of making quantitative and reliable observations suitable for network studies, but it is a very sensitive detector with a wide angle of view and search, and these qualities should be used. It will be recalled that Tombaugh supplemented instrumental with visual search for small natural satellites. Visual search could probably benefit from a tie to an "early warning" communications network of amateur radio operators.

6. Photoelectric and electromagnetic sensors can not only give early warning of the approach of an event of interest, but also are capable of actuating detecting and recording instruments much more rapidly than the human on patrol.

7. The operation of the network can be made flexible. Costs can be reduced by maintaining a minimum staff in maximum collaboration with other search organizations.

8. Combined network operations should start as soon as the photographic, radar and geomagnetic nets are linked in time. Installation of additional instrumentation should be deferred until a backlog of observations has been studied.

The cost of a program organized in this way should be two to three orders of magnitude less than most current proposals. The capital and operating expenses of the Smithsonian Meteorite Recovery Project can be taken as a measure of these costs. It is estimated that to duplicate the Prairie Network would cost about $150,000, not including the cost of the cameras and lenses which were lent by the U.S. Air Force.

It is difficult to arrive at that part of the total operating expense for meteorite research applicable to an UFO network because the cost figures include operation and data reduction of Super-Schmidt cameras at Wallops Island, and the new image orthicon installation at Urbana in conjunction with the radar at Havana, Ill. The total annual expense, however, can serve as a guide for the proposed combined network:

Running and maintenance, Lincoln, Neb.	$25,000
Supplies: film, chemicals for 64 cameras ($500/camera/year)	32,000
Scanning of film	10,000
Data reduction, all projects	65,000
Astronomers' salaries etc.	28,000
	$160,000

Assuming that the combined network will not have to bear any of these costs, it would seem that, initially, at least, its expenses could be limited to the salaries of a principal investigator, a junior investigator and one technician, the cost of film exposed by the Weather Radar scope cameras, travelling expenses and miscellaneous items. It would be surprising if expenses would exceed $50,000 annually.

Because of the rarity of the UFO phenomena, the investigation should continue for a minimum of five years. It is anticipated that the total cost would exceed $250,000, however, because preliminary results would suggest equipment modifications and additions.

14. Recommendations

The problems involved in sightings of UFOs warrant the mounting of an instrumented effort to arrive at reasonable identifications of the several phenomena involved, and to add to the limited knowledge which exists about those phenomena. Present knowledge amounts to little more than suppositions.

Popular preoccupation with the notion that UFOs may be intelligently guided extraterrestrial space ships has had one undesirable effect: it has imbedded in the term "UFO" the unfortunate connotation that if a phenomenon is unidentified it must somehow be extraterrestrial.

It has become apparent that the clarification of the "unidentifiable 1%" referred to by Hynek (1966) may more likely result from investigating several rare phenomena, rather than one. If evidence of extraterrestrial intelligence is uncovered by the study, then the goal of the research can be changed and a full-scale investigation launched.

Until that time comes—if it does—the pursuit of knowledge about the less dramatic phenomena can go on in a modest way, using already established facilities, extended when, as and if the need arises, with additional equipment.

With the de-emphasizing of the ETI hypothesis must also come a complete elimination of the term "UFO." Its connection with an otherwise soundly-based research program can serve only to impair that program's effectiveness. After all, it is beginning to look like a misnomer in certain cases: the sighting may not involve an "object," meaning a solid mass; it may not "fly" in the sense of having aerodynamic lift, and often it remains "unidentified" only briefly.

Several suggestions have been made on investigating what will now be called "strange phenomena." Dr. James E. McDonald, of the University of Arizona has recommended a program of several steps, the cost of which would range from "a few tens of millions of dollars" to "global expenditures at the level of billions of U.S. dollars per year." McDonald, 1967, 1968).

W. T. Powers of the Dearborn Observatory has discussed the design of a new photographic network covering 1% of the area of the United States; the cost for this coverage would amount to about $\$2 \times 10^6$ and $\$2 \times 10^7$ for a 10% coverage of the U.S. (Powers, 1968). Dr. G. H. Rothberg in his report to this project of an attempt at first-hand observations and UFO photography recommends new camera design and a "small" effort costing perhaps $\$1 \times 10^7$ (see Case 27). Larry W. Bryant, after suggesting an Earth-surveillance satellite especially designed for the purpose of monitoring UFO activities, finds that it might cost $\$5 \times 10^7$ and require five years' effort from funding and design until launch (Bryant, 1967).

The UFO phenomenon is extremely rare. Whereas some 500 meteors per year have trajectories which can be reconstructed from photographs, and none has been recovered in the three or four years of the Prairie Network's existence, Hynek states that only 600 UFO sightings since 1947 have remained unidentified by the Air Force (Hynek, 1966). If this number is adopted as the equivalent of the "1% unidentifiable" events, sightings due to strange phenomena occur at the rate of only 30 per year. Other arguments further lower this figure to 18 or less per year (Page, 1968).

The number of sightings of rare phenomena is so low that it is impossible to make a meaningful geographical distribution. Whether the site of the Prairie—Weather Radar—Geomagnetic Network will eventually turn out to be the best location cannot now be predicted; its present advantage lies in the fact that the three detecting systems are interlaced over a small area, thus facilitating an investigation involving several disciplines.

It is because these sightings are so infrequent that the recommendation is made to use existing facilities, wherever they happen to be, and to proceed with such studies in a measured and thoughtful manner.

Chapter 10 Statistical Analysis / Paul Julian

> For the most part, statistics is a method of investigation that is used when other methods are of no avail; it is often a last resort and forlorn hope. M. J. Moroney, *Facts from Figures.*

Statistical analysis may be described as the quantitative treatment of uncertainty. In the broad sense, it is certainly more than that. To many people the term 'statistics' is synonymous with 'data' and a large portion of those who do statistical analysis concern themselves with collecting and summarizing data. But when data so treated are used to formulate and test hypotheses, probability is immediately involved and the quantitative treatment of uncertainty begins.

The malaise engendered when one deals with uncertainty and an insufficient knowledge of statistics probably account for the viewpoint expressed by Moroney. Many people, scientists among them, are uncomfortable dealing with uncertainty (even though, without being aware of the fact, they are constantly doing so) and their opinion of statistics is consequently somewhat colored.

We are interested here in whether or not statistical analysis of UFO sighting reports is likely to be informative as to what the phenomena are but not as to how they are reported. We make a distinction, initially, between studying the phenomena of UFOs and studying how people report UFOs. It is likely that the two cannot be completely untangled and, further, that the former is impossible without some idea of the latter. However, attempts have been made and probably will in the future be made to use aggregated sighting report data to study the UFO phenomena because that data source is certainly the largest and most comprehensive of any we have available with which to attack the problem. Throughout this chapter we will be concerned, then, with the role of statistical methodology in studying the UFO phenomena.

Since statistics deal with uncertainty it might seem an attractive candidate for a central methodology in UFO research. The purpose of this chapter is to discuss the place of statistical analysis in the study of the UFO problem. We will be specifically interested in the testing of hypotheses and with decision procedures and not simply in the aggregation of data.

The nature of the UFO problem coupled with the nature of statistical methodology, first of all, results in questions posed in the hypotheses which may not be particularly satisfying. For example, we might want to ask "Is there a 95% (or 90% or 99%) chance that UFO sighting reports include observations of objects not of terrestrial origin?" But by the nature of the data we are forced to ask questions such as "Is there a 95% (etc.) chance that the characteristics of reports classified as 'knowns' differ from those for which no explanation has been suggested?"

One reason for the inability to ask questions or state hypotheses which are directed specifically at solving the problem of UFO phenomena is that they occur in nature and out of our direct control. Except perhaps for some psychological studies, we cannot place 'the UFO problem' in a laboratory and measure and study it—we must accept it as it happens. In statistical terms, we cannot design statistical experiments to test particular questions.

The second, and more profound, difficulty is presented by the rather obvious fact that it is impossible to formulate meaningful statements, questions, or hypotheses about the manifestations of unknown phenomena. We can, of course, examine the data and see what manifestations there are in the sample data, but we are severely limited in the nature of the conclusions we can draw, again, because of the unknown nature of the phenomena. The difference here is subtle, perhaps, but important.

An instructive, but certainly not unique, way of looking at this difference is to invoke the traditional dichotomy between inductive and deductive reasoning in science. The deductive approach would operate by, say, assuming that UFOs are a manifestation of Extra Terrestrial Intelligence; or, perhaps, simply represent a class of unknown atmospheric optical or electromagnetic phenomena. Given one or the other assumption it would next follow that some hypotheses about the characteristics of UFO reports be constructed. But because in both assumptions we are dealing with something unknown, how would we go about setting up such hypotheses? Such an approach from a statistical point of view at any rate seems so difficult to pursue as to be essentially valueless.

An inductive approach would, in this case, be something as follows. Let us aggregate a sample of UFO reports and examine their characteristics with the objective of establishing beyond some reasonable doubt that the characteristics are thus and so. From there we must try to build a theory which explains those characteristics.

Nearly all science operates in practice by a combination and alternation of inductive and deductive methods and in both statistics as a research tool is generally used. However there are some important differences in statistical method depending upon whether we look at that data or evidence in order to formulate a hypothesis or whether we wish to establish a degree of reliability for the validity of what we hypothesize. Perhaps the commonest misuse of statistics is represented by efforts to do both of these at once.

In statistical language, the expression of hypothesis formation after the fact, after examining the data, is called *a posteriori* hypothesis formation. The erection of a hypothesis before the data are examined is called *a priori* formation. The former follows rather easily as a result of the inductive approach and the latter from the deductive method. *A posteriori* hypothesis formation unless properly tested represents the previously mentioned attempt simultaneously to formulate a hypothesis and establish its significance.

In addition to the difficulties in hypothesis formation presented by the UFO problem, there is another problem which should be discussed. This problem, nearly always a crucial one and not as unique to the UFO problem as the one just mentioned, is the sampling problem. Granted that some hypothesis be formulated either *a priori* or *a posteriori,* we then must test the hypothesis on a randomly selected sample of data. We cannot enter into a complete discussion of random sample selection here, but must simply point out that if we hope to establish the true statistical significance of a hypothesis the selection of sighting reports cannot be biased either in favor of or against that hypothesis to be tested.

For example, let us suppose that we want to test the hypothesis that UFO sighting reports contain a significant (in some statistical sense) number in which the estimated apparent speed exceeds sonic or aircraft speed. Such an experiment could be set up and a sample of report data gathered on which to test the hypothesis. However, unless great care is used in selecting cases for inclusion in the sample, a non-random component is likely to be encountered. This is because it is very likely that it is precisely *because* the UFO exhibited what to someone was supersonic speed that it is reported and included in UFO files of one sort or another. Such a bias in the sample negates the possibility of a statistically reliable answer to the question embodied in the hypothesis.

The preceding example brings up a very perplexing problem. Just what should constitute the population of UFO reports? Should we include all UFO reports regardless of probable explanation, or just those reports for which no rational explanation can be given? It seems intuitively obvious that an observation which is almost certainly of, for example, Venus should not be included in the population *of UFOs.* But the possible dangers of biasing the sample of reports examined by such intuitive reasoning seem to be serious, to say nothing of the problem of determining the division between known and unknown cases. Again, it seems that the unknown nature of the phenomena poses some serious questions as to the definition of the population and therefore to the kinds of questions we might ask of report data.

Some UFO literature has used aggregates of report data to search for "trends" or "patterns," either implicitly or explicitly stated. The basic assumption seems to have been that trends and patterns in UFO reports might provide information on the nature of the phenomenon. This approach appears to be mostly inductive—perhaps not surprisingly so in view of the difficulties in the deductive approach in the UFO problem.

There are two important comments on this assumption. The first is that any examination of report data is bound to turn up *some* pattern—we would be quite surprised if the reports were completely featureless. The second is that, as already mentioned, since the patterns were detected from the sample in hand some procedure for testing the significance of the patterns on independent data samples is necessary.

The Vallees (1966) recommend a search for spatial and temporal patterns in the report data. They report 1) a claimed tendency for report positions in a given calendar day to be located in patterns that can be joined by nets of straight lines (the controversial 'orthoteny' hypothesis), 2) a difference in the diurnal variation of different types of UFO reports, and 3) a 26-month periodicity (adjusted for annual variation) in report data. Only in the first instance do the Vallees report any test as to the statistical significance of the claimed pattern. They establish some basic criteria giving the distribution of the number of points determining straight lines used to join nets of points when the points are randomly distributed in space. They do not report, however, testing the straight line hypothesis on a data sample other than the one used to formulate the orthoteny hypothesis.

For the moment, let us assume that all three features may be tested according to the methodology of statistical hypothesis testing and any one proves significant—that is, the null hypothesis of 1) a spatially random distribution of daily report locations, or 2) no difference in the diurnal variation of types of sightings, or 3) a temporally random distribution of monthly total number of reports is rejected at, say, the 95% level. Therefore, we conclude with a risk of 95% that *some* non-random spatial or temporal variation occurs in sighting report data. This 'risk level' is a measure of how confident we can be of rejecting the null hypothesis when it is in reality true. Most statistical tests are of this basic type.

However there is another type of statistical error which is inherent in this type of hypothesis testing which generally speaking should be taken into account. We should (if possible) try to determine what is the risk of accepting the null hypothesis when it is in fact false. Normally this type of error is guarded against by formulating the problem so that the *status quo* is represented by the null hypothesis. The *rationale* for this choice is that it is better to err on the conservative side, since generally the risk of accepting the status quo (null hypothesis) when it is in fact false is higher than the risk of rejecting it when actually true. The complete formulation of the problem in these terms would be an exercise in decision theory. Because of the interest aroused by the UFO problem, both scientific and social interest, it appears that a most interesting and appealing exercise would be an attempt to formulate some problems in terms of decision theory.

Even assuming that the decision problem can be attacked and solved and we accept the rejection of one of the null hypotheses, what have we learned? Obviously we are faced with strong evidence that there is something very peculiar about the distribution in space or time of sighting reports. But the use we could make of this peculiarity in drawing conclusions about the nature of UFOs would be limited because of numerous alternative explanations of a peculiar distribution of reports. Statistical reasoning in this hypothetical situation could tell us that the reports are significantly non-random in their spatial or temporal distribution and that the probability is large that there is something there to investigate, but statistical reasoning could tell us nothing about how to *interpret* this non-randomness. In addition the word 'significance' is used in the statistical sense and has no connotation at all of 'importance.'

A useful analogy here might be the cigarette smoking-lung cancer relationship which has also been a storm center of controversy. The statistical significance of a relationship between the two has been established to be very high and almost everyone accepts the level of statistical significance as indicative of a relationship. However, this significance in no way proves a *causal* relationship between smoking and lung cancer—that is merely one of a number of alternative explanations of the statistical result. Most people, in addition, would accept the significance level as evidence that there is certainly something to investigate. The use of statistical evidence to choose what to do next rather than to choose between terminal acts involves decision theory, rather than classical statistical hypothesis testing. This type of analysis has already been mentioned above.

To summarize, the UFO phenomena presents some difficult and challenging problems to statistical methodology. We are dealing with unknown phenomena, at least in part, which is manifested by subjective, qualitative reports from observers with a wide spectrum of ability to report what they see. We cannot place the phenomena in the laboratory to study them and design experiments on them. There are very fundamental problems such as defining the population to be used in statistical studies, and formulating hypotheses about characteristics or report data *a posteriori* and attempting to interpret these as manifestations of unknown phenomena.

The physical scientist conversant with statistics and statistical studies, and formulating hypotheses about characteristics about the possibility of productive use of statistics in the UFO problem. Considering the difficulties described above he may conclude that the methodology of statistical analysis does not offer satisfying answers to the important, central questions of the UFO phenomena, and that efforts should be directed at increasing understanding of atmospheric optics, etc. or in attempting to make some measurement of some physical quantity associated with an UFO. Or he might take the position that difficulties of statistical analysis in this instance should not prevent efforts to make analyses, because the risk of throwing away valuable information by ignoring sighting report data should not be overlooked. This position must be taken with some care, however, for he would be taking it as "a last resort and forlorn hope" as Moroney puts it.

The social scientist, on the other hand, might take a different position. Instead of concerning himself with report sightings as a measure of a physical phenomena he might be attracted by the data as a source of information on psychological and social-psychological problems of perception, reporting, etc. We do not regard ourselves as qualified to pursue this point further. Mention of it was made at the beginning of this chapter and additional discussion may be found in Section VI in Chapters 1 and 2.

As a result of considering the problem of the role of statistical analysis of report data in investigating UFO phenomena we conclude that very grave difficulties are present involving rather fundamental aspects of statistical methodology. It is our feeling that little value to the physical sciences will result from "searching" the report data for "significant" features.

We qualify this view in two ways: First, we are not able, of course, to perceive the future and it may be that an innovative worker paying careful attention to the demands of methodology might well produce a study which represents a real increase in knowledge about UFOs. We should in this regard give the decision-theory approach some thought: we should attempt to evaluate the consequences of statistical error of both kinds and to consider the problems posed by questions of the "where do we go from here?" type. Second, efforts to investigate UFO *reports* rather than the UFO phenomena seem to offer fertile ground for future study.

Section VII

APPENDICES

APPENDIX A: Special Report of the USAF Scientific Advisory Board Ad Hoc Committee to Review Project "Blue Book"

MARCH 1966

TABLE OF CONTENTS

SPECIAL REPORT OF THE USAF SCIENTIFIC ADVISORY BOARD AD HOC COMMITTEE TO REVIEW PROJECT "BLUE BOOK"

MARCH 1966

MEMBERS PARTICIPATING

Dr. Brian O'Brien (Chairman)
Dr. Launor F. Carter
Mr. Jesse Orlansky
Dr. Richard Porter
Dr. Carl Sagan
Dr. Willis H. Ware

SAB SECRETARIAT

Lt. Col. Harold A. Steiner

SPECIAL REPORT OF THE USAF SCIENTIFIC ADVISORY BOARD AD HOC COMMITTEE TO REVIEW PROJECT "BLUE BOOK"

MARCH 1966

I. *INTRODUCTION*

As requested in a memorandum from Major General E. B. LeBailly, Secretary of the Air Force Office of Information, dated 28 September 1965 (Tab A), an SAB Ad Hoc Committee met on 3 February 1966 to review Project "Blue Book." The objectives of the Committee are to review the resources and methods of investigation prescribed by Project "Blue Book" and to advise the Air Force of any improvements that can be made in the program to enhance the Air Force's capability in carrying out its responsibility.

In order to bring themselves up to date, the members of the Committee initially reviewed the findings of previous scientific panels charged with looking into the UFO problem. Particular attention was given to the report of the Robertson panel which was rendered in January 1953. The Committee next heard briefings from the AFSC Foreign Technology Division, which is the cognizant Air Force agency that collates information on UFO sightings and monitors investigations of individual cases. Finally, the Committee reviewed selected case histories of UFO sightings with particular emphasis on those that have not been identified.

II. *DISCUSSION*

Although about 6% (646) of all sightings (10,147) in the years 1947 through 1965 are listed by the Air Force as "Unidentified," it appears to the Committee that most of the cases so listed are simply those in which the information available does not provide an adequate basis for analysis. In this connection it is important also to note that no unidentified objects other than those of an astronomical nature have ever been observed during routine astronomical studies, in spite of the large number of observing hours which have been devoted to the sky. As examples of this the Palomar Observatory Sky Atlas contains some 5000 plates made with large instruments with wide field of view; the Harvard Meteor Project of 1954-1958 provided some 3300 hours of observation; the Smithsonian Visual Prairie Network provided 2500 observing hours. Not a single unidentified object has been reported as appearing on any of these plates or been sighted visually in all these observations.

The Committee concluded that in the 19 years since the first UFO was sighted there has been no evidence that unidentified flying objects are a threat to our national security. Having arrived at this conclusion the Committee then turned its attention to considering how the Air Force should handle the scientific aspects of the UFO problem. Unavoidably these are also related to Air Force public relations, a subject on which the Committee is not expert. Thus the recommendations which follow are made simply from the scientific point of view.

III. *CONCLUSIONS AND RECOMMENDATIONS*

It is the opinion of the Committee that the present Air Force program dealing with UFO sightings has been well organized, although the resources assigned to it (only one officer, a sergeant, and secretary) have been quite limited. In 19 years and more than 10,000 sightings recorded and classified, there appears to be no verified and fully satisfactory evidence of any case that is clearly outside the framework of presently known science and technology. Nevertheless, there is always the possibility that analysis of new sightings may provide some additions to scientific knowledge of value to the Air Force. Moreover, some of the case records which the Committee looked that were listed as "identified" were sightings where the evidence collected was too meager or too indefinite to permit positive listing in the identified category. Because of this the Committee recommends that the present program be strengthened to provide opportunity for scientific investigation of selected sightings in more detail and depth than has been possible to date.

To accomplish this it is recommended that:

A. Contracts be negotiated with a few selected universities to provide scientific teams to investigate promptly and in depth certain selected sightings of UFO's. Each team should include at least one psychologist, preferably one interested in clinical psychology, and at least one physical scientist, preferably an astronomer or geophysicist familiar with atmospheric physics. The universities should be chosen to provide good geographical distribution, and should be within convenient distance of a base of the Air Force Systems Command (AFSC).

B. At each AFSC base an officer skilled in investigation (but not necessarily with scientific training) should be designated to work with the corresponding university team for that geographical section. The local representative of the Air Force Office of Special Investigations (OSI) might be a logical choice for this.

C. One university or one not-for-profit organization should be selected to coordinate the work of the teams mentioned under A above, and also to make certain of very close communication and coordination with the office of Project Blue Book.

It is thought that perhaps 100 sightings a year might be subjected to this close study, and that possibly an average of 10 man days might be required per sighting so studied. The information provided by such a program might bring to light new facts of scientific value, and would almost certainly provide a far better basis than we have today for decision on a long term UFO program.

The scientific reports on these selected sightings, supplementing the present program of the Project Blue Book office, should strengthen the public position of the Air Force on UFO's. It is, therefore, recommended that:

A. These reports be printed in full and be available on request.

B. Suitable abstracts or condensed versions be printed and included in, or as supplements to, the published reports of Project Blue Book.

C. The form of report (as typified by "Project Blue Book" dated 1 February 1966) be expanded, and anything which might suggest that information is being withheld (such as the wording on page 5 of the above cited reference) be deleted. The form of this report can be of great importance in securing public understanding and should be given detailed study by an appropriate Air Force office.

D. The reports "Project Blue Book" should be given wide unsolicited circulation among prominent members of the Congress and other public persons as a further aid to public understanding of the scientific approach being taken by the Air Force in attacking the UFO problem.

DEPARTMENT OF THE AIR FORCE

Washington

OFFICE OF THE SECRETARY

MEMORANDUM FOR MILITARY DIRECTOR, SCIENTIFIC ADVISORY BOARD

SUBJECT: Unidentified Flying Objects (UFOs)

In keeping with its air defense role, the Air Force has the responsibility for the investigation of unidentified flying objects reported over the United States. The name of this project is Blue Book (Attachment 1). Procedures for conducting this program are established by Air Force Regulation 200-2 (Attachment 2).

The Air Force has conducted Project Blue Book since 1948. As of 30 June 1965, a total of 9267 reports had been investigated by the Air Force. Of these 9267 reports, 663 cannot be explained.

It has been determined by the Assistant Deputy Chief of Staff/Plans and Operations that Project Blue Book is a worthwhile program which deserves the support of all staff agencies and major commands and that the Air Force should continue to investigate and analyze all UFO reports in order to assure that such objects do not present a threat to our national security. The Assistant Deputy Chief of Staff/Plans and Operations has determined also that the Foreign Technology Division (FTD) at Wright-Patterson Air Force Base should continue to exercise its presently assigned responsibilities concerning UFOs.

To date, the Air Force has found no evidence that any of the UFO reports reflect a threat to our national security. However, many of the reports that cannot be explained have come from intelligent and technically well qualified individuals whose integrity cannot be doubted. In addition, the reports received officially by the Air Force include only a fraction of the spectacular reports which are publicized by many private UFO organizations.

Accordingly, it is requested that a working scientific panel composed of both physical and social scientists be organized to review Project Blue Book—its resources, methods, and findings—and to advise the Air Force as to any improvements that should be made in the program in order to carry out the Air Force's assigned responsibility.

Doctor J. Allen Hynek who is the Chairman of the Dearborn Observatory at Northwestern University is the scientific consultant to Project Blue Book. He has indicated a willingness to work with such a panel in order to place this problem in its proper perspective.

Doctor Hynek has discussed this problem with Doctor Winston R. Markey, the former Air Force Chief Scientist.

/s/
E. B. LeBAILLY
Major General, USAF
Director of Information

2 Attachments
1. Blue Book Report
2. AFR 200-2

AD HOC COMMITTEE ON
UNIDENTIFIED FLYING OBJECTS (UFOs)

AGENDA

Thursday, 3 February 1966

0800	Welcoming Remarks	Commander or Vice Commander, FTD
0805	Introduction	Dr. O'Brien, SAB
0810	The Air Force Problem	Lt. Col. Spaulding, SAFOI
0830	Briefing on Project Blue Book	Major Quintanilla, FTD
1000	Break	
1015	Review of Selected Case Histories	FTD Staff
1145	Lunch	
1315	Executive and Writing Session	

22 December 1965

SPECIAL REPORT OF THE USAF SCIENTIFIC ADVISORY BOARD AD HOC COMMITTEE TO REVIEW PROJECT "BLUE BOOK"

DISTRIBUTION

	SYMBOL	*COPIES*
Secretary of the Air Force Office of Information	SAFOI	25
Military Director, DCS/R&D	AFRDC	1
Committee Members (1 each)		6
Dr. Brian O'Brien (Chairman)		
Dr. Launor F. Carter		
Mr. Jesse Orlansky		
Dr. Richard Porter		
Dr. Carl Sagan		
Dr. Willis H. Ware		
Commander, Foreign Technology Division		5
DCS/Foreign Technology (AFSC)	SCF	2
Chairman, SAB	AFBSA	1
SAB Secretariat	AFBSA	1

Meeting statistics bearing on this report including all times, dates, places, a listing of persons in attendance and purposes therefor, together with their affiliations and material reviewed and discussed, are available in the SAB Secretariat offices for review by authorized persons or agencies.

APPROVED BY:

(s)

HAROLD A. STEINER, Lt Colonel, USAF
Assistant Secretary
USAF Scientific Advisory Board

APPENDIX B: AFR NO. 80-17. UNIDENTIFIED FLYING OBJECTS

AIR FORCE REGULATION NO. 80-17

DEPARTMENT OF THE AIR FORCE
Washington, D. C. 19 September 1966

Research And Development

UNIDENTIFIED FLYING OBJECTS (UFO)

This regulation establishes the Air Force program for investigating and analyzing UFOs over the United States. It provides for uniform investigative procedures and release of information. The investigations and analyses prescribed are related directly to the Air Force's responsibility for the air defense of the United States. The UFO Program requires prompt reporting and rapid evaluation of data for successful identification. Strict compliance with this regulation is mandatory.

SECTION A—GENERAL PROVISIONS

Paragraph

SECTION B—PUBLIC RELATIONS, INFORMATION, CONTACTS, AND RELEASES

SECTION C—PREPARING AND SUBMITTING REPORTS

SECTION A—GENERAL PROVISIONS

1. Explanation of Terms. To insure proper and uniform usage of terms in UFO investigations, reports, and analyses, an explanation of common terms follows:

a. *Unidentified Flying Objects.* Any aerial phenomenon or object which is unknown or appears out of the ordinary to the observer.

b. *Familiar or Known Objects/Phenomena.* Aircraft, aircraft lights, astronomical bodies (meteors, planets, stars, comets, sun, moon), balloons, birds, fireworks, missiles, rockets, satellites, searchlights, weather phenomena

This regulation supesedes AFR 200-2, 20 July 1962
OPR: AFRSTA
DISTRIBUTION: S

(clouds, contrails, dust devils), and other natural phenomena.

2. Program Objectives. Air Force interest in UFOs is twofold: to determine if the UFO is a possible threat to the United States and to use the scientific or technical data gained from study of UFO reports. To attain these objectives, it is necessary to explain or identify the stimulus which caused the observer to report his observation as an unidentified flying object.

a. *Air Defense.* The majority of UFOs reported to the Air Force have been conventional or familiar objects which present no threat to our security.

(1) It is possible that foreign countries may develop flying vehicles of revolutionary configuration or propulsion.

(2) Frequently, some alleged UFOs are determined to be aircraft. Air Defense Command (ADC) is responsible for identification of aircraft. Except as aircraft are determined to be the stimulus for a UFO report, aircraft are not to be reported under the provisions of this regulation.

b. *Technical and Scientific.* The Air Force will analyze reports of UFOs submitted to it to attain the program objectives. In this connection these facts are of importance:

(1) The need for further scientific knowledge in geophysics, astronomy, and physics of the upper atmosphere which may be provided by study and analysis of UFOs and similar aerial phenomena.

(2) The need to report all pertinent factors that have a direct bearing on scientific analysis and conclusions of UFO sightings.

(3) The need and the importance of complete case information. Analysis has explained all but a small percentage of the sightings which have been reported to the Air Force. The ones that have not been explained are carried statistically as "unidentified." Because of the human factors involved and because analysis of a UFO sighting depends primarily on a personal impression and interpretation by the observer rather than on scientific data or facts obtained under controlled conditions, the elimination of all unidentifieds is improbable. However, if more immediate, detailed, and objective data on the unidentifieds had been available and promptly reported, perhaps these, too, could have been identified.

3. Program Responsibilities:

a. *Program Monitor.* The Deputy Chief of Staff, Research and Development, is responsible for the overall program, evaluation of investigative procedures, and the conduct of separate scientific investigations.

b. *Resources.* The Air Force Systems Command will support the program with current resources within the Foreign Technology Division (FTD) at Wright-Patterson Air Force Base, Ohio, to continue the Project Blue Book effort. Other AFSC resources normally used by FTD for this effort will continue to be made available.

c. *Investigation.* Each commander of an Air Force base will provide a UFO investigative capability. When notice of a UFO sighting is received, an investigation will be implemented to determine the stimulus for the sighting. An Air Force base receiving the notice of a UFO sighting may not be the base nearest the locale of the sighting. In that event, the reported UFO sighting will be referred to the Air Force base nearest the sighting for action.

EXCEPTIONS: FTD at Wright-Patterson Air Force Base, Ohio, independently or with the help of pertinent Air Force activities, may conduct any other investigation to conclude its analysis or findings. HQ USAF may arrange for separate investigations.

d. *Analysis.* FTD will:

(1) Analyze and evaluate all information and evidence reported to bases on those UFOs which are not identified at the base level.

(2) Use other Government agencies, private industrial companies, and contractor personnel to assist in analyzing and evaluating UFO reports, as necessary.

e. *Findings.* FTD, Wright-Patterson AFB, Ohio, will prepare a final case report on each sighting reported to it after the data have been properly evaluated. If the final report is deemed significant, FTD will send the report of its findings to AFSC (SCFA), Andrews AFB, Wash DC 20331, which will send a report to HQ USAF (AFRDC), Wash DC 20330.

f. *Cooperation.* All Air Force activities will cooperate with UFO investigators to insure that pertinent information relative to investigations of UFO sightings are promptly obtained. When feasible, this will include furnishing air or ground transportation and other assistance.

SECTION B—PUBLIC RELATIONS, INFORMATION, CONTACTS, AND RELEASES

4. Response to Public Interest. The Secretary of the Air Force, Office of Information (SAF-OI), maintains contact with the public and the news media on all aspects of the UFO program and related activities. Private individuals or organizations desiring Air Force interviews, briefings, lectures, or private discussions on UFOs will be instructed to direct their requests to SAF-OI. Air Force members not officially connected with UFO investigations covered by this regulation will refrain from any action or comment on UFO reports which may mislead or cause the public to construe these opinions as official Air Force findings.

5. Releasing Information. SAF-OI is the agency responsible for releasing information to the public and to the news media.

a. *Congressional and Presidential Inquiries.* The Office of Legislative Liaison will:

(1) With the assistance of SAF-OI, answer all Congressional and Presidential queries regarding UFOs forwarded to the Air Force.

(2) Process requests from Congressional sources in accordance with AFR 11-7.

b. *SAF-OI will:*

(1) Respond to correspondence from individuals requesting information on the UFO Program and evaluations of sightings.

(2) Release information on UFO sightings and results of investigations to the general public.

(3) Send correspondence queries which are purely technical and scientific to FTD for information on which to base a reply.

c. *Exceptions.* In response to local inquiries regarding UFOs reported in the vicinity of an Air Force base, the base commander may release information to the news media or the public after the sighting has been positively identified. If the stimulus for the sighting is difficult to identify at the base level, the commander may state that the sighting is under investigation and conclusions will be released by SAF-OI after the investigation is completed. The commander may also state that the Air Force will review and analyze the results of the investigation. Any further inquiries will be directed to SAF-OI.

SECTION C—PREPARING AND SUBMITTING REPORTS

6. General Information:

a. The Deputy Chief of Staff, Research and Development, USAF and the ADC have a direct and immediate interest in UFOs reported within the US. All Air Force activities will conduct UFO investigations to the extent necessary for reporting action (see paragraphs 9, 10, 11, and 12). Investigation may be carried beyond this point when the preparing officer believes the scientific or public relations aspect of the case warrants further investigation. In this case, the investigator will coordinate his continued investigation with FTD.

b. Paragraph 7 will be used as a guide for screenings, investigations, and reportings. Paragraph 11 is an outline of the reporting format.

c. Inquiries should be referred to SAF-OI (see paragraph 5).

d. If possible, an individual selected as a UFO investigator should have a scientific or technical background and experience as an investigator.

e. Reports required by this regulation are excluded from assignment of a reports control symbol in accordance with paragraph 3k, AFR 300-5.

7. Guidance in Preparing Reports. The usefulness of a UFO report depends largely on accuracy, timeliness, skill and resourcefulness of the person who receives the initial information and makes the report. Following are aids for screening, evaluating and reporting sightings:

a. Activities receiving initial reports of aerial objects and phenomena will screen the information to determine if the report concerns a valid UFO as defined in paragraph 1a. Reports not falling within that definition do not require further action. Aircraft flares, jet exhausts, condensation trails, blinking or steady lights observed at night, lights circling near airport and airways, and other aircraft phenomena should not be reported as they do not fall within the definition of a UFO.

EXCEPTION: Reports of known objects will be made to FTD when this information originally had been reported by local news media as a UFO and the witness has contacted the Air Force. (Do NOT solicit reports.) News releases should be included as an attachment with the report (see paragraph 8c).

b. Detailed study will be made of the logic, consistency, and authenticity of the observer's report. An interview with the observer, by persons preparing the report, is especially valuable in determining the reliability of the source and the validity of the information. Factors for particular attention are the observer's age, occupation, and education, and whether he has a technical or scientific background. A report that a witness is completely familiar with certain aspects of a sighting should indicate specific qualifications to substantiate such familiarity.

c. The following procedures will assist the investigating officer in completing the report and arriving at a conclusion as required in paragraph 11.

(1) When feasible, contact local aircraft control and warning (ACW) units, and pilots and crews of aircraft aloft at the time and place of sighting. Contact any persons or organizations that may have additional data on the UFO or can verify evidence—visual, electronic, or other.

(2) Consult military or civilian weather forecasters for data on tracks of weather balloons or any unusual meteorological activity that may have a bearing on the stimulus for the UFO.

(3) Consult navigators and astronomers in the area to determine if any astronomical body or phenomenon might account for the sighting.

(4) Consult military and civilian tower operators, air operations units, and airlines to determine if the sighting could have been an aircraft. Local units of the Federal Aviation Agency (FAA) can be of assistance in this regard.

(5) Consult persons who may know of experimental aircraft of unusual configuration, rocket and guided missile firings, or aerial tests in the area.

(6) Consult local and State police, county sheriffs, forest rangers, and other civil officials who may have been in the area at the time of the sighting or have knowledge of other witnesses.

8. Transmittal of Reports:

a. *Timeliness.* Report all information on UFOs promptly. Electrical transmission with a "Priority" precedence is authorized.

b. *Submission of Reports.* Submit multiple-addressed electrical reports to:

(1) ADC.

(2) Nearest Air Division (Defense).

(3) FTD WPAFB. (First line of text: FOR TDETR.)

(4) CSAF. (First line of text: FOR AFRDC.)

(5) OSAF. (First line of text: FOR SAF-OI.)

c. *Written Reports.* In the event follow-up action requires a letter report, send it to FTD (TDETR), Wright-Patterson AFB, Ohio 45433. FTD will send the reports to interested organizations in the US and to SAF-OI if required.

d. *Reports from Civilians.* Advise civilians to report UFOs to the nearest Air Force base.

e. *Negative or Inapplicable Data.* If specific information is lacking, refrain from using the words "negative" or "unidentified" unless all logical leads to obtain the information outlined in paragraph 11 have been exhausted. For example, the information on weather conditions in the area, as requested in paragraph 11g, is obtainable from the local military or civilian weather facility. Use the phrase "not applicable (NA)" only when the question really does not apply to the sighting under investigation.

10. Comments of Investigating Officer. This officer will make an initial analysis and comment on the possible cause or identity of the stimulus in a supporting statement. He will make every effort to obtain pertinent items of information and to test all possible leads, clues, and hypotheses. The investigating officer who receives the initial report is in a better position to conduct an on-the-spot survey and follow-up than subsequent investigative personnel and analysts who may be far removed from the area and who may arrive too late to obtain vital data or information necessary for firm conclusions. The investigating officer's comments and conclusions will be in the last paragraph of the report submitted through channels. The reporting official will contact FTD (Area Code 513, 257-0916 or 257-6678) for verbal authority to continue investigations.

11. Basic Reporting Data and Format. Show the abbreviation "UFO" at the beginning of the text of all electrical reports and in the subject of any follow-up written reports. Include required data in all electrical reports, in the order shown below:

a. Description of the Object(s):

(1) Shape.

(2) Size compared to a known object.

(3) Color.

(4) Number.

(5) Formation, if more than one.

(6) Any discernible features or details.

(7) Tail, trail, or exhaust, including its size.

(8) Sound.

(9) Other pertinent or unusual features.

b. Description of Course of Object(s):

(1) What first called the attention of observer(s) to the object(s)?

(2) Angle of elevation and azimuth of object(s) when first observed. (Use theodolite or compass measurement if possible.)

(3) Angle of elevation of object(s) upon disappearance. (Use theodolite or compass measurement if possible.)

(4) Description of flight path and maneuvers of object(s). (Use elevations and azimuth, not altitude.)

(5) How did the object(s) disappear? (Instantaneously to the North, for example.)

(6) How long were the object(s) visible? (Be specific—5 minutes, 1 hour, etc.)

c. Manner of Observation:

(1) Use one or any combination of the following items: Ground-visual, air-visual, ground-electronic, air-electronic. (If electronic, specify type of radar.)

(2) Statement as to optical aids (telescopes, binoculars, etc.) used and description thereof.

(3) If the sighting occurred while airborne, give type of aircraft, identification number, altitude, heading, speed, and home station.

d. Time and Date of Sighting:

(1) Greenwich date-time group of sighting and local time.

(2) Light conditions (use one of the following terms: Night, day, dawn, dusk).

e. Location of Observer(s). Give exact latitude and longitude coordinates of each observer, and/or geographical position. In electrical reports, give a position with reference to a known landmark in addition to the coordinates. For example, use "2 mi N of Deeville"; "3 mi SW of Blue Lake," to preclude errors due to teletype garbling of figures.

f. Identifying Information on Observer(s):

(1) Civilian—Name, age, mailing address, occupation, education and estimate of reliability.

(2) Military—Name, grade, organization, duty, and estimate of reliability.

g. Weather and Winds-Aloft Conditions at Time and Place of Sightings:

(1) Observer(s) account of weather conditions.

(2) Report from nearest AWS or US Weather Bureau Office of wind direction and velocity in degrees and knots at surface, 6,000',

10,000′, 16,000′, 20,000′, 30,000′, 50,000′, and 80,000′, if available.

(3) Ceiling.

(4) Visibility.

(5) Amount of cloud cover.

(6) Thunderstorms in area and quadrant in which located.

(7) Vertical temperature gradient.

h. Any other unusual activity or condition, meteorological, astronomical, or otherwise, that might account for the sighting.

i. Interception or identification action taken (such action is authorized whenever feasible and in compliance with existing air defense directives).

j. Location, approximate altitude, and general direction of flight of any air traffic or balloon releases in the area that might possibly account for the sighting.

k. Position title and comments of the preparing officer, including his preliminary analysis of the possible cause of the sighting(s). (See paragraph 10.)

12. Reporting Physical Evidence:

a. *Photographic:*

(1) Still Photographs. Forward the original negative to FTD (TDETR), Wright-Patterson AFB, Ohio 45433, and indicate the place, time, and date the photograph was taken.

(2) Motion Pictures. Obtain the *original* film. Examine the film strip for apparent cuts, alterations, obliterations, or defects. In the report comment on any irregularities, particularly in films received from other than official sources.

(3) Supplemental Photographic Information. Negatives and prints often are insufficient to provide certain valid data or permit firm conclusions. Information that aids in plotting or in estimating distances, apparent size and nature of object, probable velocity, and movements includes:

(a) Type and make of camera.

(b) Type, focal length, and make of lens.

(c) Brand and type of film.

(d) Shutter speed used.

(e) Lens opening used; that is, "f" stop.

(f) Filters used.

(g) Was tripod or solid stand used.

(h) Was "panning" used.

(i) Exact direction camera was pointing with relation to true North, and its angle with respect to the ground.

(4) Other Camera Data. If supplemental information is unobtainable, the minimum camera data required are the type of camera, and the smallest and largest "f" stop and shutter speed readings of the camera.

(5) Radar. Forward two copies of each still camera photographic print. Title radarscope photographic prints per AFR 95-7. Classify radarscope photographs per AFR 205-1.

NOTE: If possible, develop film before forwarding. Mark undeveloped film clearly to indicate this fact, to avoid destruction by exposure through mail channels to final addressees.

b. *Material.* Air Force echelons receiving suspected or actual UFO material will safeguard it to prevent any defacing or alterations which might reduce its value for intelligence examination and analysis.

c. *Photographs, Motion Pictures, and Negatives Submitted by Individuals.* Individuals often submit photographic and motion picture material as part of their UFO reports. All original material submitted will be returned to the individual after completion of necessary studies, analysis, and duplication by the Air Force.

BY ORDER OF THE SECRETARY OF THE AIR FORCE

J. P. McCONNELL
General, U.S. Air Force
Chief of Staff

OFFICIAL

R. J. PUGH
Colonel, USAF
Director of Administrative Services

AIR FORCE REGULATION DEPARTMENT OF THE AIR FORCE
NO. 80-17 (C2) Washington, *30 September 1968*

Research and Development

UNIDENTIFIED FLYING OBJECTS (UFO)

AFR 80-17, 19 September 1966, and change 1, 26 October 1967, are changed as follows:

8b(3). FTD WPAFB. (First line of text: FOR TDPT (UFO).)

8b(6). Delete.

BY ORDER OF THE SECRETARY OF THE AIR FORCE

OFFICIAL

J. P. McCONNELL, *General, USAF*
Chief of Staff

JOHN F. RASH, *Colonel, USAF*
Director of Administrative Services

DISTRIBUTION: S

AIR FORCE REGULATION NO. 80-17 (C1)

DEPARTMENT OF THE AIR FORCE
Washington, *26 October 1967*

Research and Development

UNIDENTIFIED FLYING OBJECTS (UFO)

AFR 80-17, 19 September 1966, is changed as follows:

★**3c.** *Investigation.* Each commander of an Air Force base within the United States will provide a UFO . . . sighting for action.

3c. *EXCEPTIONS:* FTD at Wright-Patterson . . . for separate investigations. The University of Colorado, under a research agreement with the Air Force, will conduct a study of UFOs. This program (to run approximately 15 months) will be conducted independently and without restrictions. The university will enlist the assistance of other conveniently located institutions that can field investigative teams. *All* UFO reports will be submitted to the University of Colorado, which will be given the fullest cooperation of all UFO Investigating Officers. Every effort will be made to keep all UFO reports unclassified. However, if it is necessary to classify a report because of method of detection or other factors not related to the UFO, a separate report including all possible information will be sent to the University of Colorado.

★**6a.** The Deputy Chief of Staff, . . . reported within the United States. All Air Force activities within the United States will conduct UFO . . . investigations with FTD.

8b(6). University of Colorado, Boulder CO 80302, Dr. Condon. (Mail copy of message form.)

★**8c.** *Reports.* If followup action is required on electrically transmitted reports, prepare an investigative report on AF Form 117, "Sighting of Unidentified Phenomena Questionnaire," which will be reproduced locally on 8″ x 10½″ paper in accordance with attachment 1 (9 pages). Send the completed investigative report to FTD (TDETR), Wright-Patterson AFB OH 45433. FTD will send the reports to interested organizations in the United States and to Secretary of the Air Force (SAFOI), Wash DC 20330, if required.

8e. Negative or Inapplicable Data. Renumber as paragraph 9.

11k. Position title, name, rank, official address, telephone area code, office and home telephone, and comments of the preparing officer, including his preliminary analysis of the possible cause of the sighting. (See paragraph 10.)

BY ORDER OF THE SECRETARY OF THE AIR FORCE

OFFICIAL

J. P. McCONNELL, *General,*
USAF Chief of Staff

R. J. PUGH, *Colonel, USAF*
Director of Administrative Services

1 Attachment
AF Form 117, "Sighting of Unidentified Phenomena Questionnaire"

This regulation supersedes AFR 80-17A, 8 November 1966.
OPR: AFRDDG
DISTRIBUTION: S

SIGHTING OF UNIDENTIFIED PHENOMENA QUESTIONNAIRE	*BUDGET BUREAU APPROVAL NUMBER 21-R258*

THIS QUESTIONNAIRE HAS BEEN PREPARED SO THAT YOU CAN GIVE THE U.S. AIR FORCE AS MUCH INFORMATION AS POSSIBLE CONCERNING THE UNIDENTIFIED PHENOMENON THAT YOU HAVE OBSERVED. PLEASE TRY TO ANSWER ALL OF THE QUESTIONS. THE INFORMATION YOU GIVE WILL BE USED FOR RESEARCH PURPOSES. YOUR NAME WILL NOT BE USED IN CONNECTION WITH ANY OF YOUR STATEMENTS OR CONCLUSIONS WITHOUT YOUR PERMISSION. RETURN TO AIR FORCE BASE INVESTIGATOR FOR FORWARDING TO FTD (TDETR), WRIGHT-PATTERSON AFB, OHIO 45433, IAW AFR 80-17. *(IF ADDITIONAL SHEETS ARE NEEDED FOR NARRATIVE OR SKETCHES ATTACH SECURELY TO THIS FORM OR ANNOTATE WITH YOUR NAME FOR IDENTIFICATION.)*

1. WHEN DID YOU SEE THE PHENOMENON?

DAY________ MONTH________ YEAR________

2. WHAT TIME DID YOU FIRST SIGHT THE PHENOMENON?

HOUR________ MINUTES________ ☐ A.M. ☐ P.M.

3. WHAT TIME DID YOU LAST SIGHT THE PHENOMENON?

HOUR________ MINUTES________ ☐ A.M. ☐ P.M.

4. TIME ZONE ☐ DAYLIGHT SAVINGS ☐ STANDARD

☐ EASTERN ☐ CENTRAL ☐ MOUNTAIN ☐ PACIFIC ☐ OTHER

5. WHERE WERE YOU WHEN YOU SAW THE PHENOMENON? IF IN CITY, GIVE THE NEAREST STREET ADDRESS AND INDICATE ON A HAND DRAWN MAP WHERE YOU WERE STANDING WITH REFERENCE TO THE ADDRESS. IF IN THE COUNTRY, IDENTIFY THE HIGHWAY YOU WERE ON OR NEAR AND TRY TO FIX A DISTANCE AND DIRECTION FROM SOME RECOGNIZABLE LANDMARK.

6. IMAGINE YOU ARE AT THE POINT SHOWN IN THE SKETCH. PLACE AN "A" ON THE CURVED LINE TO SHOW HOW HIGH THE PHENOMENON WAS ABOVE THE HORIZON, OR SKYLINE, WHEN FIRST SEEN. PLACE A "B" ON THE SAME CURVED LINE TO SHOW HOW HIGH ABOVE THE HORIZON THE PHENOMENON WAS WHEN LAST SEEN.

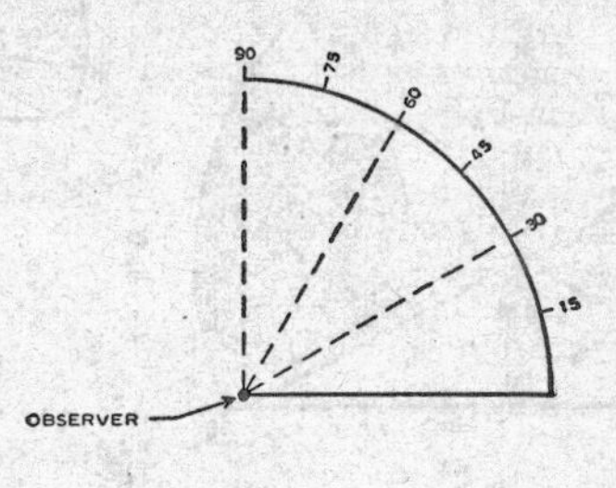

AF FORM AUG 67 117

Attachment 1
(Becomes Attachment 1 to AFR 80-17)

6A. NOW IMAGINE YOU ARE AT THE CENTER OF THE COMPASS ROSE. PLACE AN "A" ON THE COMPASS TO INDICATE THE DIRECTION TO THE PHENOMENON WHEN FIRST SEEN. PLACE A "B" ON THE COMPASS TO INDICATE THE DIRECTION TO THE PHENOMENON WHEN LAST SEEN.

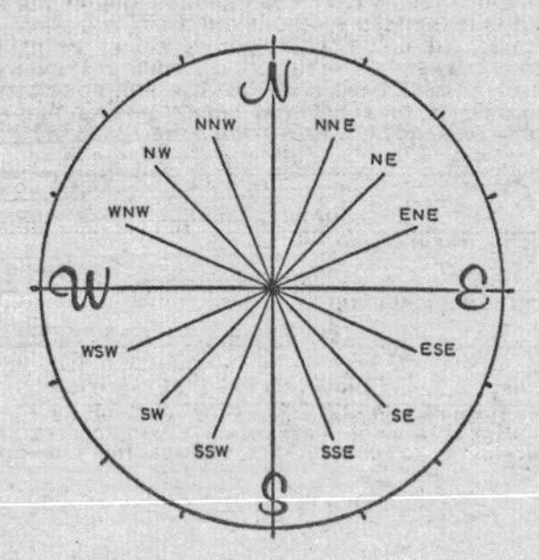

7. IN THE SKETCH BELOW, PLACE AN "A" AT THE POSITION OF THE PHENOMENON WHEN FIRST SEEN, AND A "B" AT THE POSITION OF THE PHENOMENON WHEN LAST SEEN. CONNECT THE "A" AND "B" WITH A LINE TO APPROXIMATE THE MOVEMENT OF THE PHENOMENON BETWEEN "A" AND "B". THAT IS, SCHEMATICALLY SHOW WHETHER THE MOVEMENT APPEARED TO BE STRAIGHT, CURVED OR ZIG-ZAG. REFER TO SMALLER SKETCH AS AN EXAMPLE OF HOW TO COMPLETE THE LARGER SKETCH.

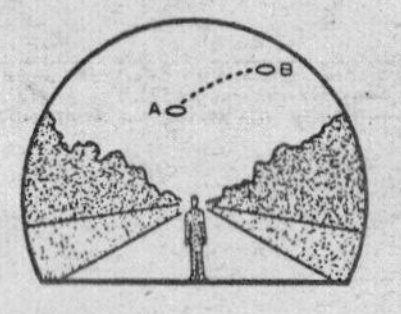

Attachment 1
(Becomes Attachment 1 to AFR 80-17)

8.	WHERE WERE YOU WHEN YOU SAW THE PHENOMENON? *(Check appropriate blocks.)*		
	OUTDOORS		IN BUSINESS SECTION OF CITY
	IN BUILDING		IN RESIDENTIAL SECTION OF CITY
	IN CAR ☐ AS DRIVER ☐ AS PASSENGER		IN OPEN COUNTRYSIDE
	IN BOAT		NEAR AIRFIELD
	IN AIRPLANE ☐ AS PILOT ☐ AS PASSENGER		FLYING OVER CITY
	OTHER		FLYING OVER OPEN COUNTRY
			OTHER

A. IF YOU WERE IN A VEHICLE, COMPLETE THE FOLLOWING:

WHAT DIRECTION WERE YOU MOVING?				HOW FAST WERE YOU MOVING?
	NORTH		EAST	
	SOUTH		WEST	DID YOU STOP ANYTIME WHILE OBSERVING THE PHENOMENON?
	NORTHEAST		SOUTHEAST	
	NORTHWEST		SOUTHWEST	☐ YES ☐ NO

EXPLAIN WHETHER SUCH MOVEMENT AFFECTS YOUR SKETCHES IN ITEMS 5 AND 6

DESCRIBE TYPE OF VEHICLE YOU WERE IN AND TYPE OF ROAD, TERRAIN OR BODY OF WATER YOU TRAVERSED DURING THE SIGHTING. STATE WHETHER WINDOWS OR CONVERTIBLE TOP WERE UP OR DOWN.

HOW MUCH OTHER TRAFFIC WAS THERE?

DID YOU NOTICE ANY AIRPLANES? ☐ YES ☐ NO. IF "YES," DESCRIBE WHEN THEY WERE IN SIGHT RELATIVE TO THE TIME OF SIGHTING THE PHENOMENON AND WHERE THEY WERE IN THE SKY RELATIVE TO THE POSITION OF THE PHENOMENON.

9.	HOW LONG WAS THE PHENOMENON IN SIGHT?			
LENGTH OF TIME		CERTAIN OF TIME		NOT VERY SURE
		FAIRLY CERTAIN		JUST A GUESS

HOW WAS TIME DETERMINED?

WAS THE PHENOMENON IN SIGHT CONTINUOUSLY? ☐ YES ☐ NO. IF "NO," INDICATE WHETHER THIS IS DUE TO YOUR MOVEMENT OR THE BEHAVIOR OF THE PHENOMENON, AND DESCRIBE SUCH MOVEMENT OR BEHAVIOR. INDICATE DISAPPEARANCES ON PREVIOUS SKETCHES.

10 IF THERE WERE MORE THAN ONE PHENOMENON, HOW MANY WERE THERE? DRAW A PICTURE TO SHOW HOW THEY WERE ARRANGED. DID THIS ARRANGEMENT CHANGE DURING THE SIGHTING?

11 CONDITIONS (*Check appropriate blocks.*)

A. SKY		B. WEATHER			
	DAY		CUMULUS CLOUDS (*Low fluffy*)		FOG OR MIST
	TWILIGHT		CIRRUS CLOUDS (*High fleecy or Herring-bone*)		HEAVY RAIN
	NIGHT				LIGHT RAIN OR DRIZZLE
	CLEAR		NIMBUS CLOUDS (*Rain*)		HAIL
	PARTLY CLOUDY		CUMULONIMBUS CLOUDS (*Thunderstorms*)		SNOW OR SLEET
	COMPLETELY OVERCAST				UNKNOWN
			HAZE OR SMOG		NONE OF THE ABOVE

C. IF THE SIGHTING WAS AT TWILIGHT OR NIGHT, WHAT DID YOU NOTICE ABOUT THE STARS AND MOON?

(1) STARS		(2) MOON			
	NONE		BRIGHT MOONLIGHT		NO MOONLIGHT
	A FEW		MOON WITH HALO		UNKNOWN
	MANY		MOON HIDDEN BY CLOUDS		
	UNKNOWN		PARTIAL (*New or quarter*)		

D. IF SIGHTING WAS IN DAYLIGHT, WAS THE SUN VISIBLE? ☐ YES ☐ NO. IF "YES," WHERE WAS THE SUN AS YOU FACED THE PHENOMENON?

	IN FRONT OF YOU		TO YOUR RIGHT		OVERHEAD (*Near noon*)
	IN BACK OF YOU		TO YOUR LEFT		UNKNOWN

E. SPECIFY THE MAJOR SOURCE OF ILLUMINATION PRESENT DURING THE SIGHTING, SUCH AS THE SUN, HEADLIGHTS OR STREET LAMP, ETC. FOR TERRESTRIAL ILLUMINATION, SPECIFY DISTANCE TO LIGHT SOURCE.

12 GIVE A BRIEF DESCRIPTION OF THE PHENOMENON, INDICATING WHETHER IT APPEARED DARK OR LIGHT, WHETHER IT REFLECTED LIGHT OR WAS SELF-LUMINOUS AND WHAT COLORS YOU NOTICED. DESCRIBE YOUR IMPRESSION OF WHETHER IT WAS SOLID OR TRANSPARENT, WHETHER EDGES WERE SHARP OR FUZZY. DESCRIBE THE SHAPE OR INDICATE IF IT APPEARED AS A POINT OF LIGHT. INDICATE COMPARISONS WITH OTHER OBSERVED OBJECTS, LIKE STARS, A LIGHT OR OTHER OBJECT IN YOUR FIELD OF VIEW.

Attachment 1
(Becomes Attachment 1 to AFR 80-17)

13. DID THE PHENOMENON	YES	NO	UNKNOWN
MOVE IN A STRAIGHT LINE?			
STAND STILL AT ANYTIME?			
SUDDENLY SPEED UP AND RUN AWAY?			
BREAK UP IN PARTS AND EXPLODE?			
CHANGE COLOR?			
GIVE OFF SMOKE?			
CHANGE BRIGHTNESS?			
CHANGE SHAPE?			
FLASH OR FLICKER?			
DISAPPEAR AND REAPPEAR?			
SPIN LIKE A TOP?			
MAKE A NOISE?			
FLUTTER OR WOBBLE?			

14. WHAT DREW YOUR ATTENTION TO THE PHENOMENON?

A. HOW DID IT FINALLY DISAPPEAR?

B. DID THE PHENOMENON MOVE BEHIND OR IN FRONT OF SOMETHING, LIKE A CLOUD, TREE, OR BUILDING AT ANY TIME?
☐ YES ☐ NO. IF "YES," DESCRIBE.

Attachment 1
(Becomes Attachment 1 to AFR 80-17)

15. DRAW A PICTURE THAT WILL SHOW THE SHAPE OF THE PHENOMENON. INCLUDE AND LABEL ANY DETAILS THAT MIGHT HAVE APPEARED AS WINGS OR PROTRUSIONS, AND INDICATE EXHAUST OR VAPOR TRAILS. INDICATE BY AN ARROW THE DIRECTION THE PHENOMENON WAS MOVING.

16. WHAT WAS THE ANGULAR SIZE? HOLD A MATCH AT ARM'S LENGTH IN FRONT OF A KNOWN OBJECT, SUCH AS A STREET LAMP OR THE MOON. NOTE HOW MUCH OF THE OBJECT IS COVERED BY THE HEAD OF THE MATCH. NOW IF YOU HAD BEEN ABLE TO PERFORM THIS EXPERIMENT AT THE TIME OF THE SIGHTING, ESTIMATE WHAT FRACTION OF THE PHENOMENON WOULD HAVE BEEN COVERED BY THE MATCH HEAD.

Attachment 1
(Becomes Attachment 1 to AFR 80-17)

17. DID YOU OBSERVE THE PHENOMENON THROUGH ANY OF THE FOLLOWING? INCLUDE INFORMATION ON MODEL, TYPE, FILTER, LENS PRESCRIPTION OR OTHER APPLICABLE DATA.

	EYEGLASSES		CAMERA VIEWER
	SUNGLASSES		BINOCULARS
	WINDSHIELD		TELESCOPE
	SIDE WINDOW OF VEHICLE		THEODOLITE
	WINDOWPANE		OTHER

A. DO YOU ORDINARILY WEAR GLASSES? ☐ YES ☐ NO

B. DO YOU USE READING GLASSES? ☐ YES ☐ NO

18. WHAT WAS YOUR IMPRESSION OF THE SPEED OF THE PHENOMENON? GIVE ESTIMATE OF SPEED ____________

19. WHAT WAS YOUR IMPRESSION OF THE DISTANCE OF THE PHENOMENON? GIVE ESTIMATE OF DISTANCE ____________.

20. IN ORDER THAT WE MAY OBTAIN AS CLEAR A PICTURE AS POSSIBLE OF WHAT YOU SAW, DESCRIBE IN YOUR OWN WORDS A COMMON OBJECT OR OBJECTS WHICH, WHEN PLACED IN THE SKY, SIMILAR TO WHERE YOU NOTED THE PHENOMENON, WOULD BEAR SOME RESEMBLANCE TO WHAT YOU SAW. DESCRIBE SIMILARITIES AND DIFFERENCES BETWEEN THE COMMON OBJECT AND WHAT YOU SAW.

21. DID YOU NOTICE ANY ODOR, NOISE, OR HEAT EMANATING FROM THE PHENOMENON OR ANY EFFECT ON YOURSELF, ANIMALS OR MACHINERY IN THE VICINITY? ☐ YES ☐ NO. IF "YES," DESCRIBE.

A. DID THE PHENOMENON DISTURB THE GROUND OR LEAVE ANY PHYSICAL EVIDENCE. ☐ YES ☐ NO. IF "YES," DESCRIBE.

22. HAVE YOU EVER SEEN THIS OR A SIMILAR PHENOMENON BEFORE? ☐ YES ☐ NO. IF "YES," GIVE DATE AND LOCATION.

23. WAS ANYONE WITH YOU AT THE TIME YOU SAW THE PHENOMENON? ☐ YES ☐ NO. IF "YES," DID THEY SEE IT TOO? ☐ YES ☐ NO.

a. LIST THEIR NAMES AND ADDRESSES

24. GIVE THE FOLLOWING INFORMATION ABOUT YOURSELF

LAST NAME, FIRST NAME, MIDDLE NAME

ADDRESS *(Street, City, State and Zip Code)*

TELEPHONE *(Area code and number)*	AGE		MALE		FEMALE

INDICATE ADDITIONAL INFORMATION INCLUDING OCCUPATION AND ANY EXPERIENCE WHICH MAY BE PERTINENT.

25 WHEN AND TO WHOM DID YOU REPORT THAT YOU HAD SIGHTED THIS PHENOMENON?

NAME ______________ DAY ______ MONTH ______ YEAR ______

26. DATE YOU COMPLETED THIS QUESTIONNAIRE.

DAY ______ MONTH ______ YEAR ______

Attachment 1
(Becomes Attachment 1 to AFR 80-17)

27. INFORMATION WHICH YOU FEEL IS PERTINENT BUT WHICH IS NOT ADEQUATELY COVERED IN THIS QUESTIONNAIRE. ALTERNATIVELY PROVIDE A NARRATIVE EXPLANATION OF THE SIGHTING

PAGE 9 OF 9 PAGES

Attachment 1
(Becomes Attachment 1 to AFR 80-17)

CHANGE | AFR 80-17A

AIR FORCE REGULATION NO. 80-17A

DEPARTMENT OF THE AIR FORCE
Washington, 8 November 1966

Research and Development

UNIDENTIFIED FLYING OBJECTS (UFO)

AFR 80-17, 19 September 1966, is changed as follows:

3c. *EXCEPTIONS:* FTD at Wright-Patterson . . . for separate investigations. The University of Colorado will, under a research agreement with the Air Force, conduct a study of UFOs. This program (to run approximately 15 months) will be conducted independently and without restrictions. The university will enlist the assistance of other conveniently located institutions that can field investigative teams. *All* UFO reports will be submitted to the University of Colorado, which will be given the fullest cooperation of all UFO Investigating Officers. Every effort will be made to keep all UFO reports unclassified. However, if it is necessary to classify a report because of method of detection or other factors not related to the UFO, a separate report including all possible information will be sent to the University of Colorado.

8b(6). University of Colorado, Boulder, Colorado 80302, ATTN: Dr. Condon. (Mail copy of message form.)

8e. Negative or Inapplicable Data. Renumber as paragraph 9.

11k. Position title, name, rank, official address, telephone area code, office and home phone, and comments of the preparing officer, including his preliminary analysis of the possible cause of the sighting(s). (See paragraph 10.)

BY ORDER OF THE SECRETARY OF THE AIR FORCE

OFFICIAL

J. P. McCONNELL
General, U. S. Air Force
Chief of Staff

R. J. PUGH
Colonel, USAF
Director of Administrative Services

DISTRIBUTION: S

APPENDIX C: Presentation at Arizona Academy of Science Meeting, 29 April 1967, by Gerard Kuiper, Lunar and Planetary Laboratory, University of Arizona

It is difficult to summarize adequately the very complex set of problems posed by the UFO reports. I think that Dr. McDonald is performing a service to science and the country in attempting to raise the standards of reporting and analysis; but I would differ with him on several points of emphasis.

My own involvement with UFO reports dates back to 1947 when they first became popular. I was then Director of the University of Chicago's Yerkes Observatory in Southern Wisconsin, and the Chicago Daily News and other newspapers contacted me frequently for my evaluation as reports were received from the wire services. I was also intermittently teaching at Chicago on Campus and approached by students who had made puzzling observations of their own. These latter reports were usually disposed of rather easily. Several of them were related to observations of the planet Jupiter seen around 4 AM between passing clouds. I also made a UFO "observation" of my own! It occurred at the McDonald Observatory, in daytime, while I was observing the planet Venus with the 82-inch telescope. I was amazed to see in the daytime sky a number of objects, almost stellar in appearance, with the approximate brightness of Venus. Quick focal measurements with the telescope's finders established that these objects were a few hundred feet above the observatory and moved approximately with the direction and velocity of the wind. They turned out to be spiders floating over the Rocky Mountains on their webs, causing bright star-like diffraction images when seen almost in the direction of the sun.

I also learned first hand of reports circulating in Southern California during visits to Mt. Palomar. In that area there was a cult which organized sunset or sunrise meetings for the observation of UFO's, the details of which were truly astounding. The Palomar astronomers were accused by members of the cult of keeping their secrets on the UFO's seen and captured (one of which was the 18-foot diameter bowl-shaped Hartmann diaphragm used in testing the 200-inch Hale telescope!). I became acquainted with the role of Mr. Adamski who lived at the foot of Palomar Mt. and who teamed up with an Englishman who was a writer. Together they produced a book, "Flying Saucers Have Landed," that became a best seller. The lore concerning authors of this book who frequently visited Mt. Palomar, was the subject of much conversation among the Palomar and Mt. Wilson service staffs, and revealed much on the reliability or lack thereof in the material presented.

I should correct a statement that has been made that scientists have shied away from UFO reports for fear of ridicule. As a practicing scientist, I want to state categorically that this is nonsense. A scientist's research is self-directed. He knows how limited and cut-up is the time he can devote to research, between his numerous other duties. He selects his area of investigation not because of pressures but because he sees the possibility of making some significant scientific advance. We are living in a period of explosive growth of science, and the scientist has dozens of choices. He selects in much the same manner in which a hiker selects a path over a dangerous mountain slope or through a jungle. At all times he fights against time and he knows that his scientific reputation is at stake. If his judgment was right, he will get results and be praised by his peers. A scientist would consider the discovery of evidence of life on another planet as perhaps the greatest contribution he could make and one that might earn him the Nobel Prize. But this is no reason for him to chase every will-o'-the-wisp. A scientist chooses his field of inquiry because he believes it holds real promise. If later his choice proves wrong, he will feel very badly and try to sharpen his criteria before he sets out again. Thus, if society finds that most scientists have not been attracted to the UFO problem, the explanation must be that they have not been impressed with the UFO reports. In my own case, after having examined several dozen of them during the past twenty years, I have found nothing that was worthy of further attention. Each scientist must, of course, make this kind of decision for himself. Anyone who is curious or impressed has the privilege to follow them up and is free to solicit the interest of others.

The subject of the UFO reports may be put in perspective by looking at two somewhat analogous cases: (1) the announcement of the discovery of extraterrestrial living organisms in meteorites; and (2) the case of Martian "canals." Most people, even scientists, have little appreciation for the extreme hostility to life of outer space; and most of us, through education or cultural tradition, would like to believe that life on earth is not alone. Every straw in the wind that might point toward the existence of life elsewhere is seized upon and made an object of veneration, if not of a new cult.

In both the detection of organisms in meteorite falls and in establishing that some UFO's may come from outer space, we have the difficulty that *our test areas, the earth and its atmosphere, are literally crowded with organisms and gadgets; and that the atmosphere itself exhibits ever-changing meteorological and electrical phenomena.* The problem is more difficult than finding a needle in a haystack; it is finding a piece of extra-terrestrial hay in a terrestrial haystack, often on the basis of reports of believers in extra-terrestrial hay. The initially enthusiastic reports of finds of extra-terrestrial organisms in meteorites are now attributed to terrestrial contaminations. The "unpopular" scientist who at the outset discounted this "evidence" as preposterous has been vindicated; but society has suffered "the loss of a dream," and some of its members may bear a grudge to those who destroyed the dream.

The canals of Mars were reported by Schiaparelli, a well-known Italian scientist of the last century, who made them the basis of major speculation on the presence of intelligent life on Mars. These ideas were taken over by enthusiastic persons with literary interest in the U. S. and further developed. The careful observers with better telescopes who continued to denounce the "canals" as optical elusions were castigated. This controversy brought disrepute to planetary science and weakened its status in universities. To this day the effects have not been overcome and affect even the NASA programs adversely through inadequate academic scientific support. Mariner IV seems to have done what these careful observers of the past half century were unable to do, namely, to destroy in the public mind the myth of the canals of Mars and all that it implied. This indicates, if such were necessary, that even reports by scientists may at times be found to be premature or foolish and that no subject is so well established that continued and more careful scientific investigation is superfluous.

Before leaving the subject of the Martian canals it is instructive to see how the cult was perpetuated in the semi-professional literature for decades. For many years W. H. Pickering, the brother of the famous Harvard astronomer E. C. Pickering, collected amateur observations of Martian canals and published the results in 44 reports in *Popular Astronomy*. The amateur observers were "rated" by the number of "canals" they had noted. Thus, there was a premium on reporting many canals. Pickering himself compared them in one of these *Popular Astronomy* reports with the hedges he had seen while flying over the Azores, speculating that the Martian canals were hedges designed to prevent dust and vegetation from blowing from one area to another (the "hedges" were often hundreds of miles long and 25-100 miles wide).

What then, may be regarded as scientific "truth" and a proper standard of finding this truth? How does this affect the scientist's position to the UFO's? I believe that most scientists hold one or two of their senior colleagues in such high regard that they limit their standard of reference largely to them. In physics, in the 1920's and 30's, Niels Bohr had this distinction in Europe, and later Fermi in the U. S.

To a person seriously proposing that 100 or more of the 10,000 UFO's recorded arrived on earth from outer space, a few questions should be put. One is that of the planets in our solar system (other than earth) only Mars appears to have a remote possibility of harboring life. The very tenuous atmosphere (ground pressure about 1% of the terrestrial atmosphere) and the absence of free oxygen, coupled with the extremely low water-vapor content and the penetration of near-ultraviolet radiation to the Martian surface, combine almost certainty to exclude Mars as a suitable breeding ground for *energetic* "beings" such as would build and man "space vehicles." If it is assumed instead that the UFO's come from *outside* the solar system, one finds that the nearest possible location would be planets accompanying stars more than 4-10 light years away. Since it is impossible to exceed the velocity of light and or even approach it with finite energies, one must assume that the space voyages would last decades or centuries. Then it is hard to see how there could have been a sudden increase in a few years; also, how any civilization could afford so many missions per year, all to *one* distant planet! This is certainly entirely inconceivable here. Further, why intelligent beings would wish to investigate remote deserts (such as in New Mexico) instead of obvious evidence of intelligence on earth, such as large cities. Also, why this remote development would occur just as our own development of aircraft and space vehicles took place in a total life span of the universe of over 10 billion years. Further, why have no UFO's been observed by groups of competent observers working over many years in such countries as England (Members of the British Astronomical Association).

Finally, it has been stated at this meeting that the Robertson Report was unfortunate and was used to suppress evidence. Since it is admitted even by UFO advocates that some 99% are terrestrial and based on faulty interpretation, it must have seemed proper for a responsible group advising the Government to caution against hysteria at the time when our military forces were experimenting with new equipment, scientists were using new types of balloons and other atmospheric devices, and international tensions were high. Since it is the Department of Defense that has the duty to guard against unwanted aerial invasion, it is logical and proper that they have the responsibility for watching for unexpected aircraft and other aerial devices; and it would seem proper for the Robertson Report to contain a statement that no hostile craft had so far been sighted.

It is reiterated that no greater progress in science can be made than through discovery of a totally new phenomenon. However, only when UFO observations are made that convince a number of competent scientists that something really significant may have occurred, will they drop their active programs and redirect their efforts. The near absence of present scientific participation can only reflect that the reports have been found wanting.

Again, if one proposes that UFO reports merit scientific inquiry, one must also admit that in no other field of inquiry the scientist is so handicapped by an odd and discouraging assemblage of "data." More than 90% of these reports are found to be hoaxes or poor accounts of well-known or trivial events. Under those circumstances an unexplained residue of perhaps 10% is no basis to believe in miracles. It is more reasonable to assume that this residue is so distorted or incomplete as to defy all analysis.

If this were a period in science of exceptional dullness, it might be still possible to arouse interest; but with the incredible progress currently being made in all fields of the natural and biological sciences, few professional scientists will feel called upon to enter the jungle.

Since the Department of Defense has both the obligation and the means to observe foreign spacecraft and similar devices, and since this Department also has access to information on experimental "aircraft," this channel appears to be the only logical one to bring a measure of reliability and sanity into this subject. Until not 100 but *one* case is established to be of scientific interest, the entire subject will remain fanciful to most practicing scientists. They may quote Einstein, whose opinion was asked on UFO reports: "I am sure they saw something."

In assessing the UFO reports one must make allowances for the lack of experience of most observers in reporting precisely and objectively on natural phenomena. Thus in the reports, the observations themselves may be buried beneath interpretations that reflect the mental reference frame of the reporters. Much of the present generation has been weaned on science fiction, and the *UFO reports reflect not only the images thus acquired but its cavalier disregard of natural law*. Earlier generations had different backgrounds and believed in and reported seeing mermaids on rocks, miracles, and more recently, sea serpents.

It is surprisingly difficult to devise adequate scientific surveys of very rare natural phenomena. The experience of the Smithsonian Prairie Meteorite Network, organized through numerous stations equipped with the most modern cameras and supporting electronic equipment, illustrates this point: No meteorites have so far been recovered from the mass of excellent photographic trajectories obtained over a period of about 3 years. Similarly, no adequate data yet exist of ball lightning (a phenomenon known for at least a century) and other atmospheric plasma phenomena. Nevertheless, a special effort could be made in the Department of Defense or the Federal Aviation Agency, largely with existing facilities, to obtain reliable records of any unexpected objects or phenomena that may occur in our atmosphere. This would clear away the present jungle of uncertainty, hopes, disillusionment, and frustration; and would probably lead to new discoveries about our environment.

APPENDIX D: Letter—J. E. Lipp to Brigadier General Putt
Project "Sign" No. F-TR-2274-IA Appendix "D"

13 December 1948 AL-1009

Brigadier General Putt
United States Air Force
Director of Research and Development
Office, Deputy Chief of Staff, Materiel
Washington 25, D.C.

Dear General Putt:

Please refer to your letter of 18 November 1948 relative to the "flying object" problem and to Mr. Collbohm's reply dated 24 November 1948. In paragraph (b) of the reply, Mr. Collbohm promised (among other things) to send a discussion of the "special design and performance characteristics that are believed to distinguish space ships."

This present letter gives, in very general terms a description of the likelihood of a visit from other worlds as an engineering problem and some points regarding the use of space vehicles as compared with descriptions of the flying objects. Mr. Collbohm will deliver copies to Colonel McCoy at Wright-Patterson Air Base during the RAND briefing there within the next few days.

A good beginning is to discuss some possible places of origin of visiting space ships. Astronomers are largely in agreement that only one member of the Solar system (besides Earth) can support higher forms of life. It is the planet Mars. Even Mars appears quite desolate and inhospitable so that a race would be more occupied with survival than we are on Earth. Reference 1 gives adequate descriptions of conditions on the various planets and satellites. A quotation from Ref. 1 (p. 229) can well be included here.

> "Whether intelligent beings exist to appreciate these splendors of the Martian landscape is pure speculation. If we have correctly reconstructed the history of Mars, there is little reason to believe that the life processes may not have followed a course similar to terrestrial evolution. With this assumption, three general possibilities emerge. Intelligent beings may have protected themselves against the excessively slow loss of atmosphere, oxygen and water, by constructing homes and cities* with the physical conditions scientifically controlled. As a second possibility, evolution may have developed a being who can withstand the rigors of the Martian climate. Or the race may have perished.
>
> "These possibilities have been sufficiently expanded in the pseudo-scientific literature to make further amplification

superfluous. However, there may exist some interesting restrictions to the anatomy and physiology of a Martian. Rarity of the atmosphere, for example, may require a completely altered respiratory system for warm-blooded creatures. If the atmospheric pressure is much below the vapor pressure of water at the body temperature of the individual, the process of breathing with our type of lungs becomes impossible. On Mars the critical pressure for a body temperature of 98.6°F. occurs when a column of the atmosphere contains one sixth the mass of a similar column on the Earth. For a body temperature of 77°F. the critical mass ratio is reduced to about one twelfth, and at 60°F. to about one twenty-fourth. These critical values are of the same order as the values estimated for the Martian atmosphere. Accordingly the anatomy and physiology of a Martian may be radically different from ours—but this is all conjecture.

"We do not know the origin of life, even on Earth. We are unable to observe any signs of intelligent life on Mars. The reader may form his own opinion. If he believes that the life force is universal and that intelligent beings may have once developed on Mars, he has only to imagine that they persisted for countless generations in a rare atmosphere which is nearly devoid of oxygen and water, and on a planet where the nights are much colder than our arctic winters. The existence of intelligent life on Mars is not impossible but it is completely unproven."

It is not too unreasonable to go a step further and consider Venus as a possible home for intelligent life. The atmosphere, to be sure, apparently consists mostly of carbon dioxide with deep clouds of formaldehyde droplets, and there seems to be little or no water. Yet living organisms might develop in chemical environments that are strange to us: the vegetable kingdom, for example, operates on a fundamentally different energy cycle from Man. Bodies might be constructed and operated with different chemicals and other physical principles than any of the creatures we know. One thing is evident: fishes, insects, and mammals all manufacture within their own bodies complex chemical compounds that do not exist as minerals. To this extent, life is self-sufficient and might well adapt itself to any environment within certain limits of temperature (and size of creature).

Venus has two handicaps relative to Mars. Her mass, and gravity, are nearly as large as for the Earth (Mars is smaller) and her cloudy atmosphere would discourage astronomy, hence space travel. The remaining Solar planets are such poor prospects that they can be ignored.

In the next few paragraphs, we shall speak of Mars. It should be understood that most of the remarks apply equally well to Venus.

Various people have suggested that an advanced race may have been visiting Earth from Mars or Venus at intervals from decades to eons. Reports of objects in the sky seem to have been handed down through the generations. If this were true, a race of such knowledge and power would have established some form of direct contact. They could see that Earth's inhabitants would be helpless to do interplanetary harm. If afraid of carrying diseases home, they would at least try to communicate. It is hard to believe that any technically accomplished race would come here, flaunt its ability in mysterious ways and then simply go away. To this writer, long-time practice of space travel implies advanced engineering and science, weapons and ways of thinking. It is not plausible (as many fiction writers do) to mix space ships with broadswords. Furthermore, a race which had enough initiative to explore among the planets would hardly be too timid to follow through when the job was accomplished.

One other hypothesis needs to be discussed. It is that the Martians have kept a long-term routine watch on Earth and have been alarmed by the sight of our A-bomb shots as evidence that we are warlike and on the threshold of space travel. (Venus is eliminated here because her cloudy atmosphere would make such a survey impractical). The first flying objects were sighted in the Spring of 1947, after a total 5 atomic bomb explosions, i.e., Alamogordo, Hiroshima, Nagasaki, Crossroads A and Crossroads B. Of these, the first two were in positions to be seen from Mars, the third was very doubtful (at the edge of Earth's disc in daylight) and the last two were on the wrong side of Earth. It is likely that Martian astronomers with their thin atmosphere, could build telescopes big enough to see A-bomb explosions on Earth, even though we were 165 and 153 million miles away, respectively, on the Alamogordo and Hiroshima dates. The weakest point in the hypothesis is that a continual, defensive watch of Earth for long periods of time (perhaps thousands of years) would be dull sport, and no race that resembled Man would undertake it. We haven't even considered the idea for Venus or Mars, for example.

The chance that Martians, under such widely divergent conditions, would have a civilization resembling our own is extremely remote. It is particularly unlikely that their civilization would be within a half century of our own state of advancement. Yet in the last 50 years we have just started to use aircraft and in the next 50 years we will almost certainly start exploring space.

Thus it appears that space travel from another point within the Solar system is possible but very unlikely. Odds are at least a thousand-to-one against it.

This leaves the totality of planets of other stars in the Galaxy as possible sources. Many modern astronomers believe that planets are fairly normal and logical affairs in the life history of a star (rather than cataclysmic oddities) so that many planets can be expected to exist in space.

To narrow the field a little, some loose specifications can be written for the star about which the home base planet would revolve. Let us say that the star should bear a family resemblance to the Sun, which is a member of the so-called "main-sequence" of stars, i.e., we eliminate white dwarfs, red giants and supergiants. For a description of these types, see reference 2, chapter 5. There is no specific reason for making this assumption except to simplify discussion: we are still considering the majority of stars.

Next, true variable stars can be eliminated, since conditions on a planet attached to a variable star would fluctuate too wildly to permit life. The number of stars deleted here is negligibly small. Reference 3, pages 76 and 85 indicate that the most common types are too bright to be in nearby space unnoticed. Lastly, we shall omit binary or multiple stars, since the conditions for stable planet orbits are obscure in such cases. About a third of the stars are eliminated by this restriction.

As our best known sample of space we can take a volume with the Sun at the center and a radius of 16 light years. A compilation of the 47 known stars, including the Sun, within this volume is given in reference 4, pages 52 to 57. Eliminating according to the above discussion: Three are white dwarfs, eight binaries account for 16 stars and two trinaries account for 6 more. The remainder, 22 stars, can be considered as eligible for habitable planets.

Assuming the above volume to be typical, the contents of any other reasonable volume can be found by varying the number of stars proportionately with the volume, or with the radius cubed, $S_e = 22 \times \left(\frac{r}{16}\right)^3$, where S_e is number of eligible stars and r is the radius of the volume in light years. (This formula should only be used for radii greater than 16 light years. For smaller samples we call for a recount. For example, only one known eligible star other than the Sun lies within eight light years).

Having an estimate of the number of useable stars, it is now necessary to make a guess as to the number of habitable planets. We have only one observed sample, the Solar system, and the guess must be made with low confidence, since intelligent life may not be randomly distributed at all.

The Sun has nine planets, arranged in a fairly regular progression of orbits (see reference 1, Appendix I) that lends credence to theories that many stars have planets. Of the nine planets, (one, the Earth) is completely suitable for life. Two more (in adjacent orbits) are near misses: Mars has extremely rigorous living conditions and Venus has an unsuitable atmosphere. Viewed very broadly indeed, this could mean that each star would have a series of planets so spaced that one, or possibly two, would have correct temperatures, correct moisture content and atmosphere to support civilized life. Let us assume that there is, on the average, one habitable planet per eligible star.

There is no line of reasoning or evidence which can indicate whether life will actually develop on a planet where the conditions are suitable. Here again, the Earth may be unique rather than a random sample. This writer can only inject some personal intuition into the discussion with the view that life is not unique on Earth, or even the random result of a low probability, but is practically inevitable in the right conditions. This is to say, the number of inhabited planets is equal to those that are suitable!

One more item needs to be considered. Knowing nothing at all about other races, we must assume that Man is average as to technical advancement, environmental difficulties, etc. That is, one half of the other planets are behind us and have no space travel and the other half are ahead and have various levels of space travel. We can thus imagine that in our sample volume there are 11 races of beings who have begun space explorations. The formula on page 3 above now becomes

$$R = 11 \times \left(\frac{r}{16}\right)^3$$

where R is the number of races exploring space in a spherical volume of radius $r > 16$ light years.

Arguments like those applied to Martians on page 2 need not apply to races from other star systems. Instead of being a first port-of-call, Earth would possibly be reached only after many centuries of development and exploration with space ships, so that a visiting race would be expected to be far in advance of Man.

To summarize the discussion thus far: the chance of space travelers existing at planets attached to neighboring stars is very much greater than the chance of space-traveling Martians. The one can be viewed almost as a certainty (if the assumptions are accepted), whereas the other is very slight indeed.

In order to estimate the relative chances that visitors from Mars or star X could come to the Earth and act like "flying objects," some discussion of characteristics of space ships is necessary.

To handle the simple case first, a trip from Mars to Earth should be feasible using a rocket-powered vehicle. Once here, the rocket would probably use more fuel in slowing down for a landing than it did in initial takeoff, due to Earth's higher gravitational force.

A rough estimate of one way performance can be found by adding so-called "escape velocity" of Mars to that of the Earth plus the total energy change (kinetic and potential) used in changing from one planetary orbit to the other. These are 3.1, 7.0, and 10.7 miles per second, respectively, giving a total required performance of 20.8 miles per second for a one-way flight. Barring a suicide mission, the vehicle would have to land and replenish or else carry a 100% reserve for the trip home.

Let us assume the Martians have developed a nuclear, hydrogen-propelled vehicle (the most efficient basic arrangement that has been conceived here on Earth) which uses half its stages to get here and the remaining stages to return to Mars, thus completing a round trip without refueling, but slowing down enough in our atmosphere to be easily visible (i.e., practically making a landing). Since it is nuclear-powered, gas temperatures will be limited to the maximum operating temperatures that materials can withstand (heat must transfer from the pile to the gas, so cooling can't be used in the pile). The highest melting point compound of uranium which we can find is uranium carbide. It has a melting point of 4560°R. Assume the Martians are capable of realizing a gas temperature of 4500°R (= 2500°K), and that they also have alloys which make high motor pressures (3000 psi) economical. Then the specific impulse will be I = 1035 seconds and the exhaust velocity will be c = 33,400 ft/sec (reference 5). Calculation shows that using a single stage for each leg of the journey would require a fuel/gross weight ratio of 0.96 (for each stage) too high to be practical. Using two stages each way (four altogether) brings the required fuel ratio down to 0.81, a value that can be realized.

If, by the development of strong alloys, the basic weight could be kept to 10% of the total weight for each stage, a residue of 9% could be used for payload. A four-stage vehicle would then have a gross weight $\left(\frac{100^4}{9}\right) = 15{,}000$ times as great as the payload; thus, if the payload were 2,000 pounds, the gross weight would be 30 million pounds at initial takeoff (Earth pounds).

Of course, if we allow the Martians to refuel, the vehicle could have only two stages* and the gross weight would be only $\left(\frac{100^2}{9}\right) = 123$ times the payload, i.e., 250,000 pounds. This would require bringing electrolytic and refrigerating equipment and sitting at the South Pole long enough to extract fuel

*Actually three stages. On the trip to Earth, the first stage would be filled with fuel, the second stage would contain partial fuel, the third would be empty. The first stage would be thrown away during flight. On the trip back to Mars, the second and third stages would be filled with fuel. The gross weight of the initial vehicle would be of the order of magnitude of a two-stage rocket.

for the journey home, since they have not asked us for supplies. Our oceans (electrolysis to make H_2) would be obvious to Martian telescopes and they might conceivably follow such a plan, particularly if they came here without foreknowledge that Earth has a civilization.

Requirements for a trip from a planet attached to some star other than the Sun can be calculated in a similar manner. Here the energy (or velocity) required has more parts: (a) escape from the planet, (b) escape from the star, (c) enough velocity to traverse a few light years of space in reasonable time, (d) deceleration toward the Sun, (e) deceleration toward the Earth. The nearest "eligible" star is an object called Wolf 359 (see reference 4, p. 52), at a distance of 8.0 light years. It is small, having an absolute magnitude of 16.6 and is typical of "red dwarfs" which make up more than half of the eligible populations. By comparison with similar stars of known mass, this star is estimated to have a mass roughly 0.03 as great as the sun. Since the star has a low luminosity (being much cooler and smaller than the Sun) a habitable planet would need to be in a small orbit for warmth.

Of the changes of energy required as listed in the preceding paragraph, item (c), velocity to traverse intervening space, is so large as to make the others completely negligible. If the visitors were long-lived and could "hibernate" for 80 years both coming and going, then 1/10 the speed of light would be required, i.e., the enormous velocity of 18,000 miles per second. This is completely beyond the reach of any predicted level of rocket propulsion.

If a race were far enough advanced to make really efficient use of nuclear energy, then a large part of the mass of the nuclear material might be converted into jet energy. We have no idea how to do this, in fact reference 6 indicates that the materials required to withstand the temperatures, etc., may be fundamentally unattainable. Let us start from a jet-propellant-to-gross-weight ratio of 0.75. If the total amount of expended material (nuclear plus propellant) can be 0.85 of the gross weight, then the nuclear material expended can be 0.10 of the gross. Using an efficiency of 0.5 for converting nuclear energy to jet energy and neglecting relativistic mass corrections, then a rocket velocity of half the velocity of light could be attained. This would mean a transit time of 16 years each way from the star Wolf 359, or longer times from other eligible stars. To try to go much faster would mean spending much energy on relativistic change in mass and therefore operating at lowered efficiency.

To summarize this section of the discussion, it can be said that a trip from Mars is a logical engineering advance over our own present technical status, but that a trip from another star system requires improvements of propulsion that we have not yet conceived.

Combining the efforts of all the science-fiction writers, we could conjure up a large number of hypothetical methods of transportation like gravity shields, space overdrives, teleports, simulators, energy beams and so on. Conceivably, among the myriads of stellar systems in the Galaxy, one or more races have discovered methods of travel that would be fantastic by our standards. Yet the larger the volume of space that must be included in order to strengthen this possibility, the lower will be the chance that the race involved would ever find the earth. The Galaxy has a diameter of roughly 100,000 light years and a total mass about two hundred billion times that of the Sun (reference 4). Other galaxies have been photographed and estimated in numbers of several hundred million (reference 2, p. 4) at distances up to billions of light years (reference 7, p. 158). The number of stars in the known universe is enormous, yet so are the distances involved. A super-race (unless they occur frequently) would not be likely to stumble upon Planet III of Sol, a fifth-magnitude star in the rarefied outskirts of the Galaxy.

A description of the probable operating characteristics of space ships must be based on the assumption that they will be rockets, since this is the only form of propulsion that we know will function in outer space. Below are listed a few of the significant factors of rocketry in relation to the "flying objects."

(a) Maneuverability. A special-purpose rocket can be made as maneuverable as we like, with very high accelerations either along or normal to the flight path. However, a high-performance space ship will certainly be large and unwieldy and could hardly be designed to maneuver frivolously around in the Earth's atmosphere. The only economical maneuver would be to come down and go up more or less vertically.

(b) Fuel reserves. It is hard to see how a single rocket ship could carry enough extra fuel to make repeated descents into the Earth's atmosphere. The large number of flying objects reported in quick succession could only mean a large number of visiting craft.

Two possibilities thus are presented. First, a number of space ships could have come as a group. This would only be done if full-dress contact were to be established. Second, numerous small craft might descend from a mother ship which coasts around the Earth in a satellite orbit. But this could mean that the smaller craft would have to be rockets of satellite performance, and to contain them the mother ship would have to be truly enormous.

(c) Appearance. A vertically descending rocket might well appear as a luminous disk to a person directly below. Observers at a distance, however, would surely identify the rocket for what it really is. There would probably be more reports of oblique views than of end-on views. Of course, the shape need not be typical of our rockets; yet the exhaust should be easy to see.

One or two additional general remarks may be relevant to space ships as "flying objects." The distribution of flying objects is peculiar, to say the least. As far as this writer knows, all incidents have occurred within the United States, whereas visiting spacemen could be expected to scatter their visits more or less uniformly over the globe. The small area covered indicates strongly that the flying objects are of Earthly origin, whether physical or psychological.

The lack of purpose apparent in the various episodes is also puzzling. Only one motive can be assigned; that the space men are "feeling out" our defenses without wanting to be belligerent. If so, they must have been satisfied long ago that we can't catch them. It seems fruitless for them to keep repeating the same experiment.

Conclusions:

Although visits from outer space are believed to be possible, they are believed to be very improbable. In particular, the actions attributed to the "flying objects" reported during 1947 and 1948 seem inconsistent with the requirements for space travel.

Very truly yours,
J. E. Lipp
Missiles Division

JEL:sp

References (Included in original letter)

1. "Earth, Moon and Planets," by F. L. Whipple, Harvard Books on Astronomy, Blakiston, 1941.
2. "Atoms, Stars and Nebulae," by Goldberg and Aller; Harvard Books on Astronomy, Blakiston, 1943.
3. "The Story of Variable Stars," by Campbell and Jacchia, Harvard Books on Astronomy, Blakiston, 1945.
4. "The Milky Way," by Bok and Bok, Harvard Books on Astronomy, Blakiston, 1941.
5. Calculated Properties of Hydrogen Propellant at High Temperatures. Data provided to RAND by Dr. Altman, then at JPL. Unpublished.
6. "The Use of Atomic Power for Rockets," by R. Serber, Appendix IV Second Quarterly Report, RA-15004, Douglas Aircraft Co., Inc., Project RAND.
7. "Galaxies," by Shapley, Harlow; Harvard Books on Astronomy, Blakiston, 1943.

S-11750

APPENDIX E: Report on Numerical Experiment on the Possible Existence of an "Anti-Earth," by Dr. R. L. Duncombe, U.S. Naval Observatory

To experimentally determine the dynamical effects of a planet located on the other side of the Sun from the Earth, an extra body was introduced at this position in the initial conditions for a simultaneous numerical integration of the equations of motions for the major planets of the solar system.

The numerical integration used was the Stumpf-Schubart program, described in Publications of the Astronomischen Rechen-Institut, Heidelberg, No. 18 (1966). The calculations were performed on an IBM 360/40 computer at the U. S. Naval Observatory.

The initial coordinates and velocities were derived from those given in the above reference by integrating the system to the desired epoch. All the planets from Venus to Pluto were included; the mass of Mercury was included with that of the Sun. On runs in which the anti-Earth planet, Clarion, was included, its initial coordinate and velocity vectors were taken to be the negative of those for the Earth-Moon barycenter at epoch.

The initial epoch was J.D. 244 0000.5 and the integration, using a 2 day step length, was done backward to J.D. 240 0000.5, a period of approximately 112 years. From the integrated coordinates an ephemeris was generated at a 40 day interval.

Four integrations were made. The first was the solar system alone, for use as a comparison standard. The other three included Clarion with three different mass values: Earth + Moon, Moon, and zero. These three integrations were then compared to the solar system standard integration and the differences for all the planets were expresesd in ecliptic longitude, latitude, and radius vector. In addition, the separation of Clarion from a straight line through the perturbed Earth-Moon barycenter and Sun was computed in longitude, latitude, and radius vector.

Since the principal perturbations occur in longitude, the following discussion of the three cases is confined to a description of the amplitude of the differences in this coordinate.

Case 1. Mass of Clarion equals Earth + Moon mass.

Separation of Clarion from the center of the Sun exceeded the mean solar radius of 960″ after about 10,000 days and reached an amplitude of 10,000″ in 112 years. Perturbations of Venus exceeded 1″ after 80 days, while perturbations of the Earth and Mars exceeded 1″ after 100 days. At the end of 112 years the perturbations induced by Clarion in the motions of Venus, Earth, and Mars reached 1200″, 3800″, and 1660″ respectively.

Case 2. Mass of Clarion equals mass of Moon.

Separation of Clarion from the center of the Sun exceeded the mean solar radius after 17,600 days and in 112 years had reached 3470″. Perturbations of the Earth exceeded 1″ after 5120 days and reached 26″ in 112 years. Perturbations of Venus and Mars exceeded 1″ after 2160 days and 2800 days respectively, and reached 15″ and 20″ respectively in 112 years.

Case 3. Clarion assumed to have zero mass.

As expected there was no effect on the motions of the other planets, but the separation of Clarion from the Sun was very nearly the same amplitude as for Case 2.

Conclusions:

The separation of Clarion from the line joining the Earth and the Sun shows a variation with increasing amplitude in time, the effect being most pronounced for the largest assumed mass. During the 112 years covered by the integration the separation becomes large enough in all cases that Clarion should have been directly observed, particularly at times of morning or evening twilight and during total solar eclipses. The most obvious effect of the presence of Clarion, however, is its influence on the positions of the other planets. During the past 150 years precise observations by means of meridian circles have been made of the motions of the principal planets of the solar system. Differences introduced, by the presence of an anti-Earth (Clarion) of non-negligible mass, in the motions of Venus, Earth, and Mars could not have remained undetected in this period.

APPENDIX F: FAA Notice N7230.29

NOTICE

FEDERAL AVIATION AGENCY
Washington, D.C.

N 7230. 29
4/4/67

Cancellation
Date: 12/31/67

SUBJ: REPORTING OF UNIDENTIFIED FLYING OBJECTS (RIS: AT 7230-96)

1. *PURPOSE.* This notice establishes procedures for reporting of unidentified flying objects (UFO's) by air traffic control specialists.

2. *EFFECTIVE DATE.* April 20, 1967.

3. *REFERENCES.* Aeronautical Communications and Pilot Services Handbook 7300.7.

4. *BACKGROUND.* The University of Colorado is conducting a study project on UFO's. One of their problems is to develop detailed and credible data. Since air traffic control specialists are skilled observers and in many facilities have access to radar, their cooperation is invaluable to the project success.

5. *PROCEDURES.* All reports submitted for this project are on a voluntary basis, but it should be noted that reports will be held in strict confidence and no details of sightings or names of persons will be released to news media. Telephone reports of radar UFO sightings shall not include names of radar sites from which the data was derived. This is to preclude release of classified information on joint-use radar.

   a. Initial reports on UFO sightings should be transmitted immediately on the FTS system to the University of Colorado by dialing 8-303-447-1000 and requesting phone number 443-6762. When the switchboard operator at the University of Colorado answers, advise that the Federal Aviation Agency is calling with a UFO report and the party designated to accept the call will be connected.

   b. Report should be brief and include such information as:

      (1) Time, place and duration of sighting.

      (2) Method of observation (radar, visual or both). Do not include name of radar site.

(3) Number of objects seen.

(4) Size, distance and motion of object.

(5) Name of person calling and facility of employment.

c. After initial reports of sightings, a later follow up by University of Colorado and collaborating scientists at other universities will take place in the form of interviews. Interviews will be conducted only on those sightings that hold special interest for UFO research and will be held at the convenience of the personnel. If the interview concerns a UFO sighting derived from joint-use radar, security clearances at the secret level must be confirmed for the interview group. A listing of those persons cleared will be provided to the air route traffic control centers through Compliance and Security channels.

d. Sighting information received from outside sources shall be handled as specified in Handbook 7300.7, paragraph 463.

APPROVED APRIL 4, 1967

APPENDIX G: U.S. Weather Bureau Operations Manual Letter 67-16

WEATHER BUREAU

SILVER SPRING, MARYLAND 20910

Operations Manual Letter 67-16

Date of Issue: November 1, 1967 **Effective Date:** November 1, 1967
In Reply Refer To: W1421 **File With:** B-99

Subject: Reporting of Unidentified Flying Objects

The University of Colorado, under sponsorship of the U.S. Air Force, is conducting a study of UFO's. Since "ESSA scientists and personnel are among the most skilled and careful observers to be found," the University has asked our cooperation.

All reports submitted for this project are on a voluntary basis and will be held in strict confidence by the University of Colorado.

Weather Bureau observers at stations in the 48 contiguous United States are requested to report any UFO sightings to the University of Colorado by FTS system, telephone 303-447-1000 and request number 443-6762. When the switchboard operator at the University of Colorado answers, advise that the Weather Bureau is calling with a UFO report and the party designated to accept the call will be connected.

Include in the report such information as:

(1) Time, place and duration of sighting
(2) Number of objects seen
(3) Size, distance and motion if known
(4) Your name and station

The University may arrange an interview with, and at the convenience of, the person making the report if the sighting holds special interest for UFO research.

Your cooperation in this important project is appreciated.

This OML is intended for information only at stations in Alaska and in the Pacific since they are not included in this program.

(s)
Karl R. Johannessen
Associate Director
Meteorological Operations

APPENDIX H: U.S. Dept. of Agriculture Forest Service, Rocky Mtn. Region, Memorandum to Forest Supervisors

TO: Forest Supervisors File No. 1740
5100

FROM: D. S. Nordwall, Regional Forester, By John B. Smith Date: November 24, 1967

SUBJECT: Memorandums of Understanding Fire Control

Dr. Edward Condon, Department of Physics, University of Colorado, Boulder has requested Region 2 of the Forest Service to cooperate with the University on its UFO (Unidentified Flying Objects) Study. Although the study terminates June 30, 1968, they are anxious to provide a procedure for getting reports from Forest Service observers.

From their standpoint, this is not for the purpose of getting more data, but to get better data. Forest Service people, because of experience, background, and training, should be able to provide more accurate reports—if they observe a UFO. Such reports would become part of a scientific study, and involvements with reporters or news sources should be avoided. The University has also requested reports from FAA and the Weather Bureau.

Standard procedure for Ranger Districts and National Forests to use to report a UFO follows:

A. Report information should include:
   1. Time, place, and duration of sighting.
   2. Number of objects seen and description of each.
   3. Positive identification of a substantive object.
   4. Size, distance, and motion if known.
   5. Observer's name and station.

B. Report procedure:
   1. Ranger District and Forest personnel should report through the Forest Dispatcher (or Forest Supervisor).
   2. Forest Dispatcher should notify the Regional Dispatcher or, if no answer, call persons in order listed in the Emergency Forest Fire Plan.
   3. Regional Dispatcher (or alternate) will report to Mr. Robert J. Low, University Project Coordinator, UFO Study. On the FTS system, call 303-447-1000 and ask for 443-2211 to reach Mr. Low.

So far as we know, Forest Service people in Region 2 have not sighted a UFO, but the above establishes procedure, and a report should be made if a UFO is sighted.

(s)
JOHN B. SMITH

APPENDIX I: Individuals Who Participated in the Early Warning Network

Alexander, Frank
Anderson, Dr. Kenneth V.
Ansevin, Dr. Krystyna
Armstrong, W. P.
Biller, Dr. Harold
Boltjes, Dr. Ben H.
Brake, Robert V.
Bryan, Kenneth E.
Buckalew, Dr. Mary
Cahn, Dr. Harold A.
Callina, Joseph A.
Cecin, Jose A.
Cerny, Paul C.
Ciarleglio, Frank J.
Clapp, Mrs. Carol
Cleaver, Marshall
Cobb, Mrs. Robert
Conron, Frederick E.
Craig, Clark
Darling, Spenser
Davis, Luckett V.
Dibblee, Grant
Donavan, William D.
Dorris, Ralph M.
Duncan, Robert A.
Earley, George W.
Eldridge, Raymond
Emerson, Col. Robert B.
Epperson, Mrs. Idabel
Faulkner, Richard Louis
Fowler, Raymond E.
Friezo, James V.
Frye, Ronald K.
Funk, Carl F.
Ginnings, Dr. G. K.
Grant, Mrs. Verne
Gregory, Jeanne L.
Haber, Dan
Harder, Dr. James
Heiglig, Robert B.
Henry, Dr. Richard C.
Inderwiesen, F. H.
Johnson, Mrs. Jeanne Booth
Kammer, David
Klingaman, David C.
Lansden, David V.
Larson, Mrs. June
Laufer, Dr. L. Gerald
Lewis, Robert M.
Lillian, Irving
Loftin, Capt. Robert E.
Lohr, Lloyd A.
MacDonald, Cynthia M.
McCown, Lowell E.
McLeod, John F.
Meloney, John
Mood, Douglas A.
Morse, Robert F.
Moss, Richard D.
Murdock, Roy E.
Murphy, Terry
Murphy, William
Murray, Dr. Robert
Olson, Donald L.
Park, Dr. Nelson A.
Peterson, Dr. W. C.
Reichman, Louis
Rice, Dr. Herman
Robie, Carl
Roth, Herbert
Rowe, Dr. William E.
Russell, Betty
Rygwalski, Eugene
Salisgury, Dr. Frank B.
Sanders, Rayford R.
Sayer, Dr. Gordon C.
Scegner, Dr. James
Schneider, Dr. Richard V.
Scott, Thomas J.
Seamands, Robert E.
Seff, Dr. Philip
Sipprell, James
Smith, Eugene P.
Sorenson, Arthur
Stokesberry, John L.
Strand, Lt. Col. Howard C.
Stringfield, Leonard H.
Stroud, Walter J.
Sutton, Charles M.
Swann, Dr. A. Henry
Tull, Clancy D.
Utke, Dr. Allen R.
Wambaugh, Helen A.
Webb, Walter N.
Williams, Roy P.
Worstell, Paula
Zechman, Richard W.

APPENDIX J: Early Warning Report Form

Date____________ Time________ Zone______

Place________________ Classification______

Duration____________ Direction disappeared______

Visual observers________ Radar?________

Objects__________ Size__________

Shape____________ Color__________

Distance__________ Motion__________

Other features____________________

Weather________________________

Known traffic_____________________

Observer—Name________________ Age______

Address_______________________

Phone__________ Occupation________

Reporter—Name_____________________

Address_______________________

Phone__________ Occupation________

Receiver—__________ Date________ Time______

Please fill in all possible blanks with relevant information. Use the back of this sheet for a running description of the event.

DRS—6/6/67 (Rev)

APPENDIX K: Field Kit Inventory List

1. *INSTRUMENTS AND MISCELLANEOUS*
    a. Camera (diffraction grating, filters, operating instructions if necessary, and *film*)
    b. Movie Camera
    c. Binoculars
    d. Geiger Counter
    e. Flashlight
    f. Compass
    g. Magnifying Glass
    h. Sample Containers
    i. Tape Recorder (Tapes)
    j. Tape Measure
    k. Plaster Casting Material
    l. Pocket Spectroscope
    m. Geologist's Kit
    n. String
    o. Star Finder
    p. Nautical Almanac
    q. Elevation Indicator
    r. Arc Indicator (Size?)
    s. Police Radiomonitor
2. *PAPER*
    a. Notebook and Address Book (Contacts)
    b. Identification Card
    c. Copy of Contract
    d. Orders
    e. Letter of Authorization
    f. Maps (of specific areas)
    g. Road Atlas
    h. Auto Sun-visor Identification Card
    i. Sighting Report Forms/Interview Forms
    j. Copies of 80-17A, 80-17
    k. Tax Exempt Certificates
3. *PERSONAL*
    a. Boots
    b. Warm Clothing if necessary
    c. Air Tickets (or others)
    d. Money or Traveler's Checks
    e. Credit Cards
    f. Briefcase

NOTE: *Carry essentials on person*—airline luggage can be delayed.

APPENDIX L: Weather Conditions and Radar Echoes Near Washington, D.C., and Norfolk, Va., on 19-20 and 26-27 July 1952

Loren W. Crow

CERTIFIED
CONSULTING METEOROLOGIST

Phone (303) 722-8665 or 756-3971
2422 South Downing Street
Denver, Colorado 80210

April 1, 1968

The following is a summary of weather conditions surrounding UFO visual sightings and co-incident radar echoes near Washington, D.C. and Norfolk, Virginia on the nights of July 19-20, 1952, and July 26-27, 1952.

SOURCES OF DATA

Radiosonde and wind data from—

Washington, D.C., Norfolk, Virginia, and Richmond, Virginia

Surface weather observations surrounding the times of sightings from—

Washington National Airport
Bolling AFB
Andrews AFB
Norfolk, Virginia
Newport News, Virginia
Langley AFB

GENERAL WEATHER SITUATION

The general weather situation during both nights was "hot and muggy." Maxima temperatures of the previous day, the minima and maxima on the following day were:

	19th max.	20th min.	20th max.	26th max.	27th min.	27th max.
Washington	93°	76°	90°	90°	75°	94°
Norfolk	98°	78°	95°	89°	72°	98°

On the night of the 19-20 a large, flat high-pressure area of 1020 millibars was located over the Middle Mississippi Valley and a very minor trough existed off the east coast. There were no fronts in the immediate area of either Washington or Norfolk. The general flow of air was from west to east.

On the night of the 26-27, both Washington and Norfolk were near the center of a flat high-pressure wedge extending from Texas to several hundred miles east of New York City. A light drift from south to north characterized the air flow outward from the central portion of the wedge. Again, there were no fronts in the immediate area of either station.

THE INCIDENCE OF SCATTERED CLOUDS

It would have been possible for observers on the ground to have seen small clouds at both low and middle heights at various times during each of the two nights. Some cloud cover—mostly scattered clouds—was recorded by nearly all the observing stations where trained observers were on duty. A summary of cloud cover conditions is as follows:

a. *At Washington* on the night of July 19-20.

At 9:30 P.M. the observer mentioned a few altocumulus at 8,000 feet. These altocumulus were not mentioned in subsequent reports until 0454 A.M. on the morning of the 20th when again in the remarks column a few altocumulus were mentioned. The hourly summary indicates a height of these clouds observed near sunrise at 18,000 feet and movement of the cloud from the northwest. The observer at Bolling AFB, just across the river from Washington National Airport, recorded various quantities of middle cloud estimated at 12,000 and 15,000 feet during the early part of the night before 10:30 P.M. No such clouds were reported between 10:30 P.M. and 3:30 A.M. At 4:30 A.M. the observer on duty at Bolling AFB reported scattered clouds at 14,000 feet and a few cumulus clouds at 5,000 feet. Observers at both Washington National Airport and Bolling AFB reported various amounts of cirrus clouds at 25,000 feet.

No low or middle clouds were being reported during the darker portion of the night. It is not uncommon that observations made by trained observers during brief trips outdoors from a lighted room to view a darkened sky fail to report scattered cloud conditions. Another observer who has remained outside long enough for his eyes to adjust to darkened conditions can often see some scattered clouds. Conditions of cloudiness on this night would let some scattered clouds form and dissipate in a reasonably short period of time in any one portion of the sky.

There may have been a few clouds visible to ground observers in the Washington area although they were not being reported by the official observing stations. Both the 19-20 and 26-27 nights occurred during the darker portion of the month since a full moon in July, 1952, occurred on July 7.

At Norfolk on the night of July 19-20.

The scattered conditions at 4,000 feet and varying quantities of cloud at approximately 12,000 feet would have made it possible for a few scattered clouds to have been seen on an intermittent basis at various times during the night.

b. *At Washington* the night of July 26-27.

Clear conditions prevailed throughout most of the night but when daylight began to arrive between 4:00 and 5:00 A.M., cloudiness was reported as a few stratocumulus at 2,000 feet and some thin scattered cirrus at 25,000 feet. It would have been possible for some clouds to have been visible in the area during the darker portion of the night if an observer permitted his eyes to adjust to the darkness.

At Norfolk the night of July 26-27.
The cloud conditions in the Norfolk area varied considerably between the Norfolk Municipal Airport and the observations made at Langley AFB several miles north of there. Langley reported clear conditions while broken or overcast cloudiness was being reported near 5,000 feet at the Norfolk Municipal Airport.

There would have been a marginal area of dissipating cloud cover somewhere between Norfolk Municipal Airport and Langley AFB. Thus, multiple observers could have had a wide variety of possible cloud sightings.

TEMPERATURE, MOISTURE AND WIND PROFILES

The conditions of the atmosphere were capable of generating anomalous propagation on weather radar displays on both nights. In Battan's book on RADAR METEOROLOGY, published in 1959, page 21, is found the following:

> "Nocturnal radiation, which occurs on clear nights, especially in the summer when the ground is moist, leads to a temperature inversion at the ground and a sharp decrease in moisture with height. It is found that these conditions frequently produce abnormal propagation, which becomes more pronounced as the temperature and humidity lapse rates become larger. . . . These conditions which favor ducts at the ground occur most frequently over large land areas in the summer and can be thought of as situations of 'radiative superrefraction.' "

More recent studies of anomalous propagation on radar have been made at Texas A & M. They have further confirmed the appearance of radar echoes during night and early morning hours under clear sky conditions when low level inversions and fluctuating quantities of moisture characterize the surrounding atmosphere.

In Figures 1-4, profiles of temperature and dew point, plus wind direction and velocity, are presented. In most instances the vertical profiles *near the ground* would have had several degrees variation in and around each of the two stations where the radars were located. Using surface temperatures at the several airports and the actual radar sights, there would have been variations of from 3-5°F. in the first few hundred feet. Relatively small change in the vertical profiles would have occurred during the night at elevations greater than 2,500 feet. Respective percentages of relative humidity are recorded next to the moisture profile. The dashed lines report observations made at 10:00 P.M. The solid lines report values at 10:00 A.M. the following morning. The profiles would have changed gradually during the night-time hours but would have remained somewhere between these two soundings. The greatest variability in the local area would have been in the lowest few hundred feet. Near the surface, indications for 4:00 A.M. were made from surface observations.

Of some importance is the fact that rain showers were reported in the Washington area during late afternoon on the 19th of July. Amounts reported at the three stations in the Washington area ranged from .10 through .13. This would have wet the ground and furnished a variable moisture source in different portions of the surrounding country side.

SUMMARY

It is the author's opinion that hot, humid air prevailed on both nights in both Washington and Norfolk. The general weather would have been considered fair weather by the trained observers at the various airports and they may not have reported all the scattered clouds which actually existed. It would have been considered an "easy shift." Visibilities remained above six miles at all times. The horizontal movement of scattered clouds, plus formation and dissipation of some few low clouds, both could have been seen at various times by ground observers whose eyes were well adjusted to the darkened sky. Anomalous propagation could have been observed on weather radar units during both nights at both locations. The echoes due to anomalous propagation would have had horizontal motion similar to the clouds.

(s)
LOREN W. CROW
Certified Consulting
Meteorologist

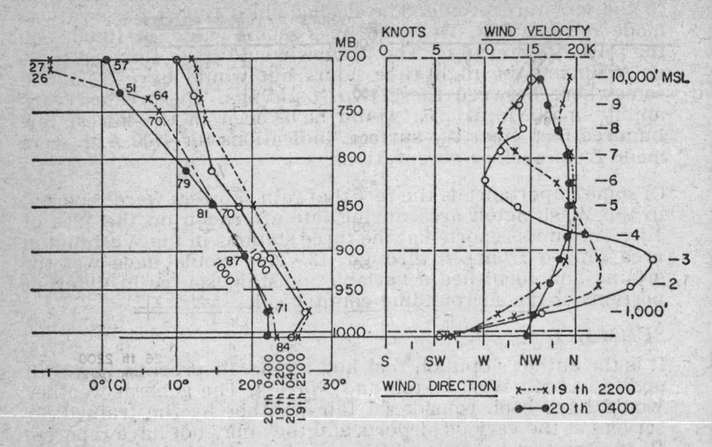

Fig. 1. Profiles of Temperature, Dew Point, Relative Humidity, Wind Direction and Velocity related to UFO sightings during the night of July 19-20, 1952 near Washington, D. C.

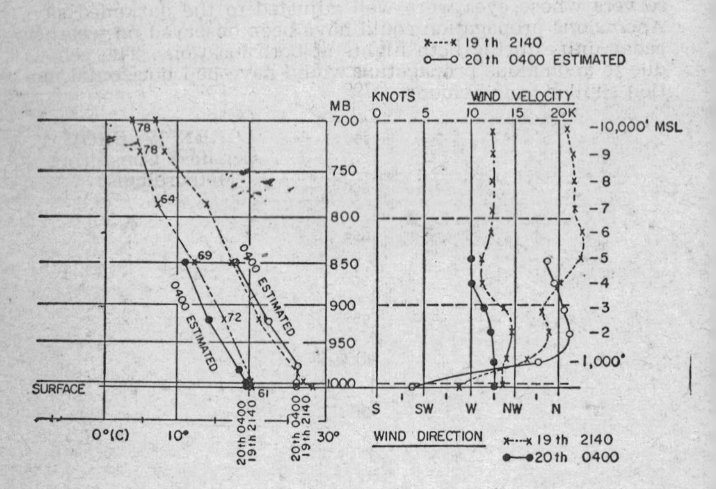

Fig. 2. Profiles of Temperature, Dew Point, Relative Humidity, Wind Direction and Velocity related to UFO sightings during the night of July 19-20, 1952, near Norfolk, Virginia.

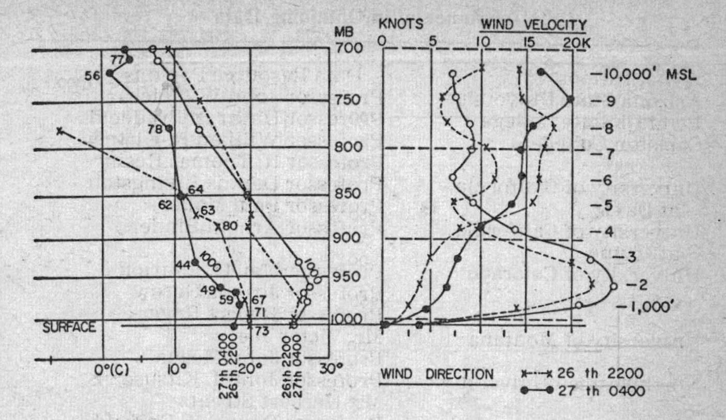

Fig. 3. Profiles of Temperature, Dew Point, Relative Humidity, Wind Direction and Velocity related to UFO sightings during the night of July 26-27, 1952, near Washington, D. C.

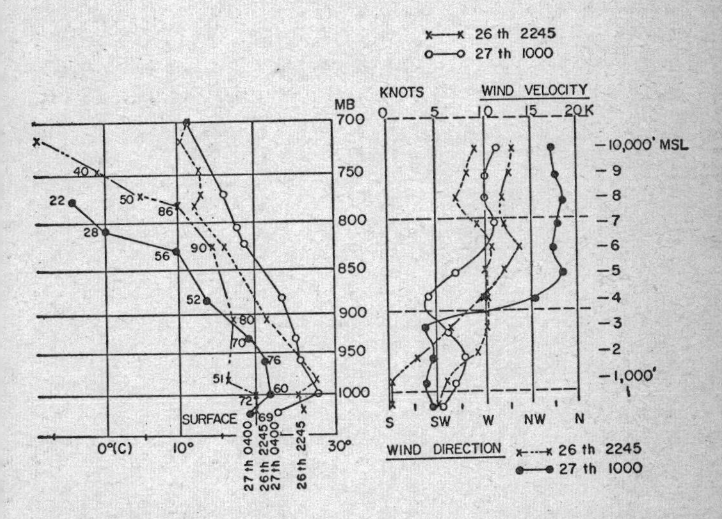

Fig. 4. Profiles of Temperature, Dew Point, Relative Humidity, Wind Direction and Velocity related to UFO sightings during the night of July 26-27, 1952, near Norfolk, Virginia.

APPENDIX M: Sources of College Survey Data and Persons Instrumental in Obtaining Data

Institutions	Data Resource Persons
Arizona State University	Professor John W. Reich
Bemidji State College	Professor Kathryn Bradfield
Carleton College	Professor William R. Kirtner Professor R. Thomas Rosin
University of California at Davis	Professor Dennis Livingston Professor Paul Moller
University of California at Irvine	Professor Arnold Binder
University of Colorado	Professor Neil G. Fahrion Professor Joshua Gerow Professor Robert Rogers
University of Montana	Mr. Victor Joe Professor John Means
Northwestern University	Professor John I. Kitsuse Mr. Herbert Strentz
University of Utah	Professor Donna M. Gelfand Professor Donald P. Hartman
Wesleyan University	Professor Thornton Page

APPENDIX N: UFO Opinion Questionnaire

The following statements all have to do with Unidentified Flying Objects—often called "U-F-O's." One type of U-F-O is a "flying saucer." The statements are ideas, or opinions, not necessarily facts—so people differ in the degree to which they believe them to be true or false.

For each of the statements shown below, please indicate the degree to which you feel the statement to be either true or false:

1. *Definitely false* means that you are fully convinced the statement is false, and you would act without hesitation on this belief. You would question the wisdom of anyone who disagreed with you.
2. *Probably false* means that you are not sure whether the statement is true or false, but that if you had to act on it, you would regard the statement as more likely false than true. Your opinion might be changed by discussion with another person.
3. *Probably true* means that you are not sure whether the statement is true or false, but that if you had to act on it, you would regard the statement as more likely true than false. Your opinion might be changed by discussion with another person.
4. *Definitely true* means that you are fully convinced that the statement is true, and you would act without hesitation on this belief. You would question the wisdom of anyone who disagreed with you.

To indicate your belief, place an X in the appropriate box next to the item. Do not skip any item.

	Definitely False	Probably False	Probably True	Definitely True
1. Some flying saucers have tried to communicate with us.				
2. All UFO reports can be explained either as well understood happenings or as hoaxes.				
3. The Air Force is doing an adequate job of investigation of UFO reports and UFOs generally.				
4. No actual, physical evidence has ever been obtained from a UFO.				
5. A government agency maintains a Top Secret file of UFO reports that are deliberately withheld from the public.				

	Definitely False	Probably False	Probably True	Definitely True
6. No airline pilots have seen UFOs.				
7. Most people would not report seeing a UFO for fear of losing a job.				
8. No authentic photographs have ever been taken of UFOs.				
9. Persons who believe they have communicated with visitors from outer space are mentally ill.				
10. The Air Force has been told to explain all UFO sightings reported to them as natural or man-made happenings or events.				
11. Earth has been visited at least once in its history by beings from another world.				
12. The government should spend more money than it does now to study what UFOs are and where they come from.				
13. Intelligent forms of life cannot exist elsewhere in the universe.				
14. Flying saucers can be explained scientifically without any important new discoveries.				
15. Some UFOs have landed and left marks in the ground.				
16. Most UFOs are due to secret defense projects, either ours or another country's.				
17. UFOs are reported throughout the world.				
18. The government has done a good job of examining UFO reports.				
19. There have never been any UFO sightings in Soviet Russia.				
20. People want to believe that life exists elsewhere than on Earth.				
21. There have been good radar reports of UFOs.				

	Definitely False	Probably False	Probably True	Definitely True
22. There is no government secrecy about UFOs.				
23. People have seen space ships that did not come from this planet.				
24. Some UFO reports have come from astronomers.				
25. Even the most unusual UFO report could be explained by the laws of science if we knew enough science.				
26. People who do not believe in flying saucers must be stupid.				
27. UFO reports have not been taken seriously by any government agency.				
28. Government secrecy about UFOs is an idea made up by the newspapers.				
29. Science has established that there are such things as "Unidentified Flying Objects."				

APPENDIX O: A-B Scale

This scale is an abridgment of Rotter's I-E Scale (Rotter, 1966), which measures the tendency of the individual to perceive events as contingent on his own behavior or independent of it (i.e., contingent upon forces external to him).

Here are six sets of statements. For each set please tell me which comes closer to being true, in your opinion. There are no right or wrong answers—just pick one statement in each set that comes closest to how you feel.

A. First—

Without the right breaks one cannot be an effective leader. 1

—or that—

Capable people who fail to become leaders have not taken advantage of their opportunities. 2

B. Next, which comes closest to your opinion—

Becoming a success is a matter of hard work, luck has little or nothing to do with it. 1

—or that—

Getting a good job depends mainly on being in the right place at the right time. 2

C. Which comes closest to your opinion—

Who gets to be the boss often depends on who was lucky enough to be in the right place first. 1

—or that—

Getting people to do the right thing depends upon ability, luck has little or nothing to do with it. 2

D. Which comes closest to your opinion—

As far as world affairs are concerned, most of us are victims of forces we can neither understand nor control. 1

—or that—

By taking an active part in political and social affairs the people can control world events. 2

E. Next,

Most people don't realize the extent to which their lives are controlled by accidental happenings. 1

—or that—

There really is no such thing as "luck." 2

F. Finally,

Many times I feel that I have little influence over things that happen to me. 1

—or that—

It is impossible for me to believe that change or luck plays an important role in my life. 2

INSTRUCTIONS FOR THE A-B SCALE

Each item consists of a pair of statements lettered a or b. *For each set, circle the letter which stands for the one which comes closer to being true, in your opinion.* There are no right or wrong answers—just pick one statement in each set that comes closest to how you feel.

a b 1. a) Children get into trouble because their parents punish them too much.

b) The trouble with most children nowadays is that their parents are too easy with them.

a b 2. a) In the long run people get the respect they deserve in this world.

b) Unfortunately, an individual's worth often passes unrecognized no matter how hard he tries.

a b 3. a) Without the right breaks one cannot be an effective leader.

b) Capable people who fail to become leaders have not taken advantage of their opportunities.

a b 4. a) Becoming a success is a matter of hard work, luck has little or nothing to do with it.

b) Getting a good job depends mainly on being in the right place at the right time.

a b 5. a) When I make plans, I am almost certain that I can make them work.

b) It is not always wise to plan too far ahead because many things turn out to be a matter of good or bad fortune anyhow.

a b 6. a) In my case getting what I want has little or nothing to do with luck.

b) Many times we might just as well decide what to do by flipping a coin.

a b 7. a) Who gets to be the boss often depends on who was lucky enough to be in the right place first.

b) Getting people to do the right thing depends upon ability, luck has little or nothing to do with it.

a b 8. a) As far as world affairs are concerned, most of us are the victims of forces we can neither understand, nor control.

b) By taking an active part in political and social affairs the people can control world events.

a b 9. a) Most people don't realize the extent to which their lives are controlled by accidental happenings.

b) There really is no such thing as "luck."

a b 10. a) It is hard to know whether or not a person really likes you.

b) How many friends you have depends upon how nice a person you are.

a b 11. a) A good leader expects people to decide for themselves what they should do.

b) A good leader makes it clear to everybody what their jobs are.

a b 12. a) Many times I feel that I have little influence over the things that happen to me.

b) It is impossible for me to believe that chance or luck plays an important role in my life.

APPENDIX P: Current Events Questionnaire
OPINIONS ON CURRENT ISSUES

For each of the statements shown below, please indicate whether you feel the statement is: Definitely True, Probably True, Probably False, or Definitely False.

	Definitely False	Probably False	Probably True	Definitely True
VIET NAM				
1. The U. S. should intensify bombing in Viet Nam.				
2. The U. S. Government should work harder toward peace negotiations in Viet Nam.				
3. More troops should be sent to Viet Nam.				
4. The United States should get out of Viet Nam.				
WAR ON POVERTY				
1. The War on Poverty is necessary to help the poor become self-sufficient.				
2. Too much money is going into government programs to fight poverty.				
3. Poor people should help themselves, instead of relying on the Government for help.				
4. The problems of the poor and uneducated is properly a major concern of the Federal Government.				
KENNEDY ASSASSINATION				
1. Kennedy was shot by a man who was not a part of any conspiracy to kill the President.				
2. Lee Harvey Cswald was a member of, or was used by, a secret group who wanted Kennedy dead.				

	Definitely False	Probably False	Probably True	Definitely True
3. The Warren Report's conclusion that Oswald, alone and without help, assassinated Kennedy is correct.				
4. Either a foreign government or a secret branch of the U. S. Government was responsible for the Kennedy assassination.				
RACE PROBLEMS 1. The Communists have stirred up Negroes and poor whites.				
2. Society, as a whole, is responsible for the current racial tensions.				
3. Racial discrimination is primarily to blame for the summer riots.				
4. The minority groups want to move too fast.				

APPENDIX Q: Weather Conditions in the Area Between Dallas and Mineral Wells, Texas, 19 September 1957

Loren W. Crow

CERTIFIED
CONSULTING METEOROLOGIST

Phone (303) 722-8665 or 756-3971
2422 South Downing Street
Denver, Colorado 80210

June 10, 1968

The following is a summary of weather conditions to determine whether or not the atmosphere was favorable to producing optical mirages and anomalous radar propagation for an area from 50 miles east of Dallas to Mineral Wells, Texas, during the time period from 2:00 A.M. to 3:00 A.M., Central Standard Time, September 19, 1957, for an aircraft flying in that region at elevations between 10,000 to 30,000 feet.

SOURCES OF DATA

Radiosonde and wind data from—
Carswell AFB at Fort Worth

Surface weather observations surrounding the time of UFO sightings from—

Love Field—Dallas, Naval Air Station—Dallas, Carter Field—Fort Worth, Mineral Wells, Tyler, College Station, Perrin AFB, Connolly AFB, Gray AFB.

A special study—
"On the Effects of Atmospheric Refraction on Radar Ground Patterns" by the Department of Oceanography and Meteorology, Texas A & M University, 1963.

National Bureau of Standards Monograph 92—

"Radio Meteorology," U.S. Department of Commerce, 1966.

GENERAL WEATHER SITUATION

The weather which prevailed in the entire northeast part of Texas during the early morning hours of September 19, 1957, consisted of a stable air mass with clear conditions. Air movement near the surface was from the southeast at all stations. Table I on the following page presents the actual condition for ceiling, visibility, temperature, dew point, wind direction and velocity at the surface for several surrounding stations. Figure 1 presents the conditions at 2:00 A.M. for these same stations and is representative of conditions that continued beyond 3:00 A.M.

VERTICAL PROFILE OF TEMPERATURE, HUMIDITY AND WIND

The vertical soundings of the atmosphere made about three hours before the UFO sightings and an equal time following gives the vertical profile of atmospheric conditions in the immediate vicinity of the sightings. The radiosondes were released at 11:30 P.M. and 5:30 A.M. respectively from Carswell AFB which is near Fort Worth, Texas.

Probably the most significant portion of the profile is the very rapid decrease in moisture content at a level between 6000 feet and 7000 feet. Temperatures increased with height in this same layer. Beneath this inversion layer the wind direction changed from southerly in the lower part of the atmosphere to a westerly and northerly direction at approximately 6000 feet. Wind velocities increased during the night in the layer between 2000 feet and 5000 feet. Figure 2 presents this pattern for the two different soundings.

EFFECTS OF TEMPERATURE AND HUMIDITY ON REFRACTIVE INDEX

If a radio ray (including radar) is propagated in free space, where there is no atmosphere, the path followed by the ray is a straight line. However, a ray that is propagated through the earth's atmosphere encounters variations in the atmospheric refractive index along its trajectory that caused the ray path to become curved. The total angular refraction of the ray path between two points is commonly called the "bending" of the ray. This "bending" is strongly influenced by rapid changes in refractive index within the atmosphere and such rapid changing in refractive index is caused by rapid changes in the moisture in the air. The *typical temperature inversion* permits the temperature to increase over a fairly short increase in height, while at the same time the amount of moisture decreases rapidly. Experimental work has developed relationships between the moisture content and the refractive index so that data obtained in the vertical sounding of temperature and humidity from a radiosonde can be converted to corresponding values of refractive index. Figure 3 presents the profile of refractive index that directly corresponds with the vertical temperature and humidity profile in Figure 2.

In Figure 3 a *critical gradient* line is drawn for change in refractive index with height. Later discussion will indicate the importance of this critical gradient.

STANDARD ATMOSPHERE VERSUS ACTUAL ATMOSPHERE

When only a standard atmosphere is considered the change in temperature and humidity with height is quite gradual and there are no sharp changes due to rapid decreases in humidity. Figure 4 gives the typical profiles for a standard atmospheric profile in the top part of the figure. The middle portion and the lower portion of Figure 4 indicate the corresponding effect on the change in refractive index with height as inversions are observed near the surface and at some elevated layer. In both of the non-standard patterns the gradient of N is somewhat greater than the critical value capable of producing ducting of microwave energy.

EXTRAORDINARY RADAR ECHOES

Of special importance in this investigation was some research work done at Texas A & M using their 3.2-Cm. AN/CPS-9 weather radar. The report, prepared by L. B. Cobb and V. E. Moyer, covers research carried out in 1962 and 1963, supported by National Science Foundation Grant NSF G-13834. This study was particularly interested in abnormal PPI presentations of radar echoes that occurred during clear weather.

The effect of atmospheric refraction on microwave propagation in the lower troposphere is a problem with which radio engineers and radio meteorologists have been vitally concerned since World War II. Prior to that time, the speed of propaga-

Table I. Hourly Weather Conditions Observed Early Morning Hours, September 19, 1957

2:00 A.M.

	Ceiling	Visibility	Temperature	Dew Point	Wind Direction & Velocity
Perrin AFB	clear	15 miles	72°F	66°F	SE 9
Mineral Wells	clear	25	72	66	SE 9
Ft. Worth	clear	15+	72	66	SE 10
Naval Air Station	clear	15	75	69	SE 16
Love Field-Dallas	clear	15	74	68	SE 10
Tyler	clear	12	70	67	SE 5
Connally AFB	clear	15	73	67	SSE 3
Gray AFB	clear	15	73	67	SE 4

3:00 A.M.

	Ceiling	Visibility	Temperature	Dew Point	Wind Direction & Velocity
Perrin AFB	clear	15	71	66	SE 9
Mineral Wells	clear	25	71	66	SE 10
Ft. Worth	clear	15+	72	67	SE 9
Naval Air Station	clear	15	75	69	SE 14
Love Field-Dallas	clear	15	73	67	SE 10
Tyler	clear	12	70	66	SE 5
Connally AFB	clear	15	72	67	SSE 3
Gray AFB	clear	15	72	64	SSE 6

tion of electromagnetic energy had been considered to be a constant, that of the speed of light in a vacuum. As radar, missiles, and other radio-controlled equipment were developed and became more complex, evidence of small changes in the speed of propagation due to atmospheric conditions began to mount. These small changes in speed are very important as they cause refraction, or a change in the direction of propagation, of the electromagnetic energy. Radar trapping, errors in the positioning of targets, the radio hole, fading of radio signals, and "anomalous" echoes on weather radar scopes are

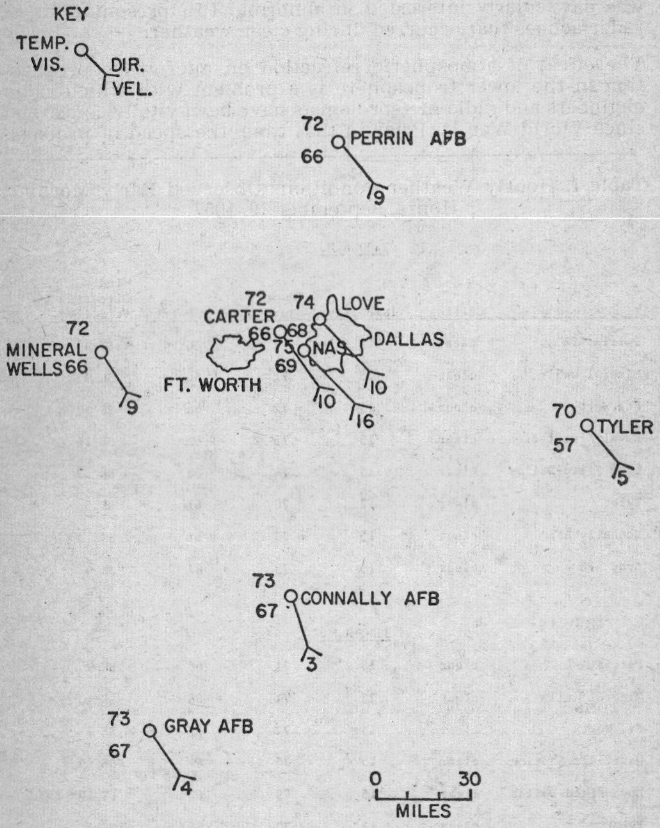

Fig. 1 Multiple Reports of Surface Wind, Temperature and Dew Point as Observed by Trained Weather Observers at 2:00 a.m., September 19, 1957.

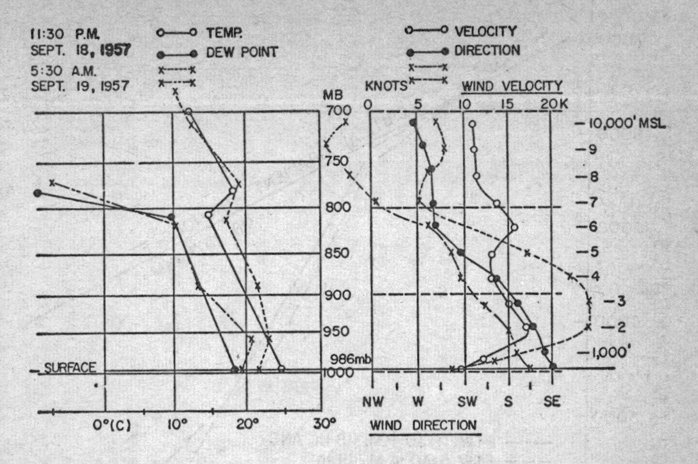

Fig. 2 Profiles of Temperature, Dew Point, Relative Humidity, Wind Direction and Velocity at Ft. Worth, Texas, during night and early morning hours, September 18-19, 1957.

some of the problems encountered. Any observer who makes critical deductions based on radar observations may be tricked into bad decisions unless he is familiar with the limitations of the equipment under *nonstandard atmospheric conditions.* Radar echoes of unknown origin near a vertical beam above the earth's surface are commonly called "angels." Unusual echoes from the surface are generally referred to as "anomalous propagation" or "AP." Both of these phenomena have been ascribed to abnormal refraction of the radio ray.

A study of abnormal radar echoes made at Texas A & M dealt primarily with anomalous propagation brought about by ducting or bending of radar beams due to inversions near the surface. They studied the expansion of ground clutter echoes due to increased gradient of refractive index near the surface. They examined large areas of anomalous echoes separated from the normal ground clutter pattern brought about by both strong surface inversions and strong upper level inversions.

The index of refraction, n, of electromagnetic energy in a non-dispersive medium such as the troposphere is defined as the ratio of the speed of propagation in a vacuum to the speed of propagation in the medium:

$$n = \frac{c_{vacuum}}{v_{air}} \qquad (1)$$

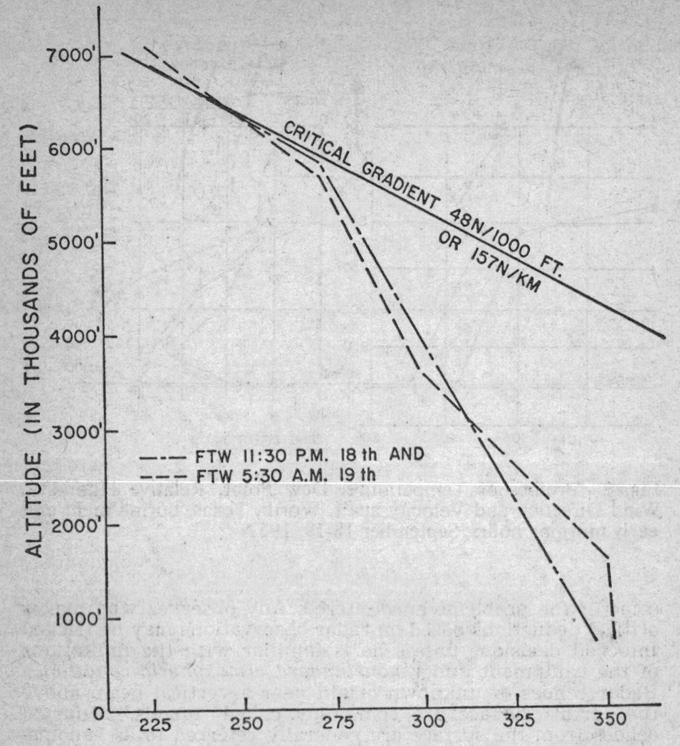

Fig. 3 Refractivity profiles at Ft. Worth, Texas, Carswell AFB, 11:30 p.m. September 18 and 5:30 a.m., September 19, 1957. Note critical gradient of N for microwave ducting in the vicinity of 6000 feet to 7000 feet altitude.

The speed of radar energy in the atmosphere is slightly less than the speed in a vacuum, so that the index of refraction always is very close to, but in excess of, unity. A typical example is 1.000287. For convenience in handling, the index of refraction is converted to a "refractive modulus," N, which is referred to most frequently as "refractivity":

$$N = (n - 1)10^6. \qquad (2)$$

The refractivity for the above example would be 287.

The index of refraction is a function of temperature, pressure, and humidity, their relationship being given by the equation

$$N = (n - 1)10^6 = \frac{Ap}{T} + \frac{ABe}{T^2} \qquad (3)$$

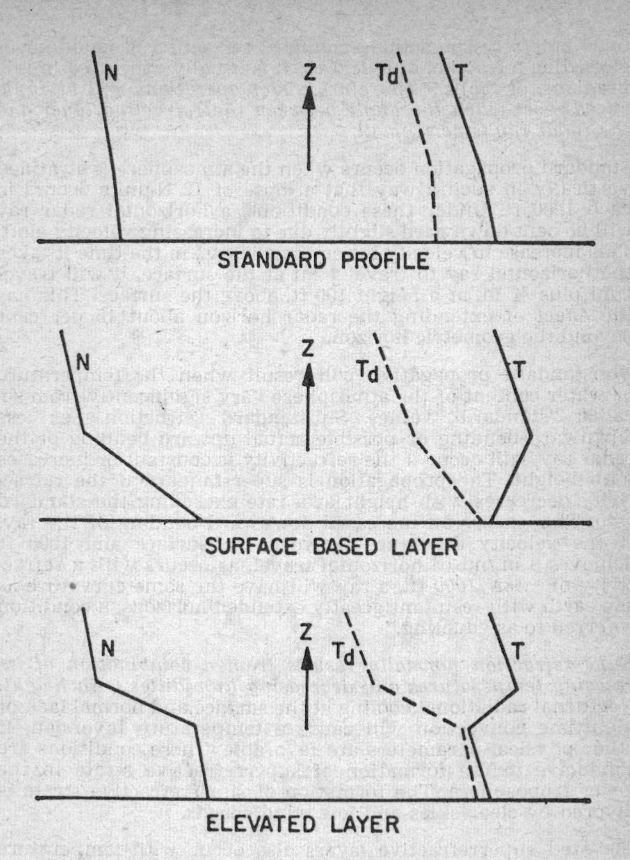

Fig. 4 Typical refractive index (N) profiles and sounding curves for three refractive index models. Solid curves on the right are for temperature—dashed curves for dew point temperature.

where p is the total atmospheric pressure in millibars, e is the partial pressure of atmospheric water vapor in millibars, T is the temperature in degrees Kelvin, and the constants A (= 76.6 deg/mb)* and B (= 4810 deg)* are average values recommended by Smith and Weintraub. A is the dielectric constant for dry air and B is the water vapor dipole moment. The formula is correct to within 0.5 per cent for the temperature range of −50C to 40C and the frequency range of 30 mc/sec

* slightly different than values presented by Bean and Dutton.

to 30 kmc/sec. The actual amount of refraction is small, never exceeding a fraction of a degree; it is usually expressed in milliradians, or "mils." *Therefore, radar operations will be influenced most when the angle between the refracting layer and the radar ray is very small.*

Standard propagation occurs when the atmosphere is stratified vertically in such a way that a lapse of 12 N-units occurs in each 1000 ft. Under these conditions, a horizontal radar ray will be bent downward slightly due to increasing velocity aloft. This increase in velocity is very small; e.g., in the time it takes the horizontal ray to travel 1 mi at the surface, it will travel 1 mi plus ¾ in. at a height 100 ft. above the surface. This has the effect of extending the radar horizon about 15 per cent beyond the geometric horizon.

Nonstandard propagation will result when the temperature or water content of the atmosphere vary significantly from so-called "standard" values. Substandard refraction, i.e., less downward bending or possible actual upward bending of the radar ray, will occur if the refractivity is constant or increases with height. The propagation is superstandard if the refractivity decreases with height at a rate exceeding the standard rate. This causes an increased downward bending of the ray. If the velocity difference between the surface and 1000 ft achieves 3 in./mi of horizontal travel, as occurs with a refractivity of *−48N/1000* ft., a ray will have the same curvature as the earth with resultant greatly extended horizons, a condition referred to as "ducting."

Superrefraction normally results from a combination of increasing temperatures and decreasing humidities with height. Nocturnal radiational cooling at the surface and normal lack of nighttime convection will cause a temperature inversion, if other physical parameters are favorable. These conditions are conducive to the formation of superrefractive strata in the lower troposphere. The formation of superrefractive strata is favored by clear skies and low wind speeds.

Elevated superrefractive layers also occur with temperature inversions or in stable layers in which there is a decrease in moisture with height. Subsidence inversions are the most common cause of this situation.

LOCAL TERRAIN SURROUNDING COLLEGE STATION, TEXAS

When the beam of a radar unit is used to cover a large horizontal area—from 200 to 300 miles—the elevation angle of the beam must be at or near zero. Near the radar site, even when the antenna is several feet above the ground, part of the energy is "echoed" back from nearby objects and/or the ground itself. As the energy goes farther and farther from the radar site the curvature of the earth permits the beam to extend into the air mass higher and higher above the earth's surface. The local terrain surrounding any particular radar location helps define the typical ground pattern. Figure 5 shows the topographic map of area within 150 miles of College Station, Texas.

NORMAL GROUND PATTERN

A standard pattern must be determined if one wishes to ascertain the degree of abnormality of nonstandard patterns. Figure 6 presents the PPI (Plan Position Indicator) pattern for College Station with the elevation angle set at 0° and a full gain setting of the receiver. It is the ground return pattern associated with standard refraction in the atmosphere. The black circle shown in Figure 6 encloses an area inside 25 miles from the radar site at College Station (CCL). The terrain features in Figure 5 are reflected in this normal ground pattern. For example, the line of echoes oriented southwest-northeast (approximately 25 miles south of CCL) represents the ridge which rises south of Yegua Creek west of Navasota. The low ground along the three streams—Brazos River, Yegua Creek, Navasota River—is indicated by the converging blue lines which join to form the expanded Brazos River near Navasota before it heads southeastward to empty into the Gulf at Freeport.

Figure 6 can be reproduced with a 0° beam angle and a near standard atmosphere day after day at College Station, Texas, and can be considered the normal ground pattern. A standard pattern must be determined if one wishes to ascertain the degree of abnormality of nonstandard patterns.

EXPANSION OF NORMAL GROUND PATTERN

Eleven cases were studied in which anomalous propagation caused an expansion of the normal ground pattern. The amount of additional echo observed varies from scattered, small additions to large areas of anomalous echoes which extend beyond the 50 mi range. The eleven cases were divided roughly according to whether they had small or large amounts of AP. Examples from each division are shown in Figures 7 and 8 (photo section). The black circles enclose the same 25 mile radius area in these figures as in Figure 6.

The common feature of all cases was a surface refracting layer less than 2000 ft thick, overlain by air of standard or near-standard refraction. The difference in refractivity between the two divisions is reflected in the extent to which the ground pattern is expanded. The smaller expansions of AP echoes are associated with smaller refractivity values, and larger amounts with larger values. All cases with greater amounts of AP were from periods of higher temperatures than those with lesser amounts. Warmer air masses, with their larger values of temperature and humidity, have greater values of refractivity. However, the *gradient of N*, rather than the discrete values of N, is most important in determining the refracting properties of an air mass.

The difference in amount of anomalous echoes appear to depend upon the gradient and thickness of the surface refracting

Fig. 5 Topographic Map of Area within 150-mi Radius of CLL.

layer. All of the smaller amounts occurred with gradients between 18N/1000 ft and 30N/1000 ft; the larger amounts occurred with gradients between 26N/1000 ft and 40N/1000 ft. In general, the refracting layer was thicker when the larger amounts of anomalous echoes were observed. However, the thickness of the surface refracting layer was less than 1600 ft in all cases.

The anomalous echoes are related to the topographic features. Comparison of Figure 7 (photo section) with a map of the terrain shows that the excess echoes (indicated by white arrows) are reflections from hills at those locations. These hills are not detected under standard refractive conditions, but are detected when the radar ray is bent one and one-half to two times the standard rate of bending. Greater bending of the ray will cause additional topographic features to be presented on the PPI (Figure 8 [photo section]).

LARGE AREAS OF ECHO SEPARATED FROM THE NORMAL GROUND PATTERN

The examples that are included in this group are those which have anomalous echoes at a considerable distance from the normal ground pattern. In some cases, these echoes encircle the local area; in others, they are confined to one or two quadrants. In most cases, they appear to be caused by an elevated ducting layer.

Two examples of anomalous echoes which encircle the local area are considered first. Figures 9 and 10 (photo section) are examples of "radial patterns" which occurred on 7 May 1962 and 12 February 1962. The black circles again show an area of 25 miles radius nearest CLL. A polaroid photograph is presented for 7 May because the regular photographs were not usable. In the case of 12 February, there had been a complete ring of echoes earlier, but those in the eastern quadrants had begun to disappear by 0820CST, when the photograph was taken. The refractivity profiles for both dates were very similar.

A large anticyclone was located over the Gulf of Mexico at the surface, with a smaller high-pressure area aloft centered over Texas, on both 7 May 1962 and 12 February 1962. Thus, there was a layer of moist Gulf air near the surface, overlain by a very dry layer caused by subsidence. Noctural radiational cooling at the surface, together with the subsidence warming aloft, created a very sharp inversion. *These are the ideal conditions for the formation of an elevated superrefractive layer*, with near-standard refractive conditions above and below the layer. The effect of the elevated layer on the radar ray is dependent on the location of the antenna relative to the layer, and on the antenna elevation angle. If the antenna is located well below the layer, total bending of the ray may be considerable at low elevation angles, but the ray will emerge on the top side of the layer. When the antenna is located just below the layer (within several thousand feet) and elevated less than 2 deg, the ray may be trapped or totally refracted.

There are several characteristics which distinguish these echoes from those discussed previously. First, a radial pattern is caused by total or near-total refraction from an elevated layer, so that its location is dependent on the vertical distance between the radar and the layer, as well as on the antenna elevation angle. Terrain features are of secondary importance in giving the pattern its shape and location. Second, these echoes usually persist longer because it takes much more convective mixing to destroy an elevated layer than is needed to destroy a layer next to the surface. Third, elements of a second ring of echoes are often observed; they probably result from a second "bounce" of the ray between the surface and the refracting layer.

A good example of anomalous echoes associated with the formation of an elevated refracting layer occurred during the night of 27 April 1962. An elongated low-pressure trough aloft, extending from Illinois to central Texas, triggered severe thunderstorms as it moved eastward during the day. Clearing occurred over the southern half of the state during the afternoon, but thunderstorms continued in the Dallas-Shreveport area. Moist Gulf air was flowing northward aloft, ahead of the trough, at the time of the 0000UT radiosonde soundings; it was replaced by very dry air from the west after passage of the trough. Figure 11 shows the refractivity profiles for San Antonio (SAT) and Lake Charles (LCH) at 0000 Universal Time (UT) and 1200UT, 28 April (1800CST, 27 April and 0600CST; 28 April); the profile for Ft. Worth (ACF) is not shown as it did not change appreciably from one sounding to the next. The formation of an elevated superrefractive layer is clearly indicated at both stations between the times of the two soundings.

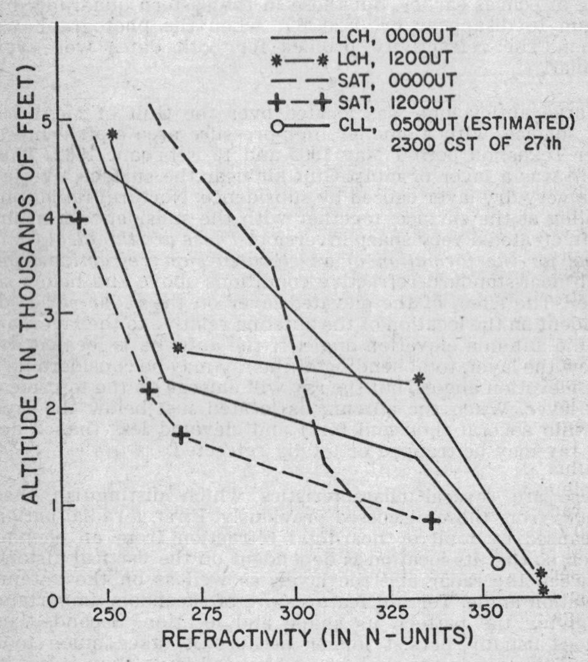

Fig. 11 Refractivity Profiles for 0000UT and 1200T, 28 April 1962.

Figure 12 (photo section) shows the AP echoes which had formed in the southern quadrants by 2250CST (skies were then clear); the echoes to the north were caused by thunderstorms.

The last example to be considered in this group occurred on 9 February 1962 (Figure 13a-e [photo section]). Skies were generally clear over the state, except for some early morning fog along the coast and low stratus clouds which dissipated as the temperature increased. A large high-pressure area was situated over the southeastern United States, so that warm, moist air was flowing northward from the Gulf at the lower levels. Cold, dry air aloft had entered Texas from the northwest; the 1200UT refractivity profiles (Figure 14) indicate that this air had not reached LCH. Very strong superrefractive layers existed at ACF and SAT; it appears to be a reasonable assumption that such a layer existed at CLL also, if one considers the amount of anomalous echoes that were occurring (Figure 13a-e [photo section]). Both the profiles and the photographs demonstrate that the pattern was not a true radial pattern at 0850CST, although echoes occurred in all directions. During the next 15 min, heating and convective mixing began to destroy the superrefractive layer next to the surface; an elevated layer was created and the echoes moved outward from the center (Figure 13b [photo section]). Continued heating and convection during the next 26 min destroyed much of the radial pattern (Figure 13c, 0931CST); in the following 13 min, all the echoes in the northwest quadrant disappeared and new echoes appeared in the southwest quadrant (Fig 13d, 0944CST). Nearly all the echoes had disappeared by 1021CST, except several in the eastern quadrants beyond 100 mi, indicating that the low-level refracting layer was virtually destroyed. This example tends to confirm all previous conclusions concerning the relationship between anomalous echoes and the location and strength of superrefractive layers.

OPTICAL AND RADIO PROPAGATION

In Chapter 13 of the Handbook of Geophysics for Air Force Designers, published by the U.S. Air Force in 1957, various equations, tables, and nomograms are presented covering electromagnetic wave propagation in the lower atmosphere. Figures 15 and 16, as copied from that book, show how refractive modulus values vary with altitude for both optical and radio wavelengths. As shown in Figure 16 the two curves for optical and radio wavelengths converge at altitudes greater than 20,000 feet. This would indicate that any abnormal ducting of optical and/or radar type images might be similarly distorted to observers in aircraft flying above 20,000 feet when atmospheric abnormalities are uniquely favorable for anomalous propagation.

AIRCRAFT PENETRATION OF CLEAR AIR "ANGELS"

At the Ninth Weather Radar Conference in Kansas City in 1961, R. Q. Tillman, R. E. Ruskin, and M. N. Robinson of the U.S. Naval Research Laboratory, reported on the tracking of

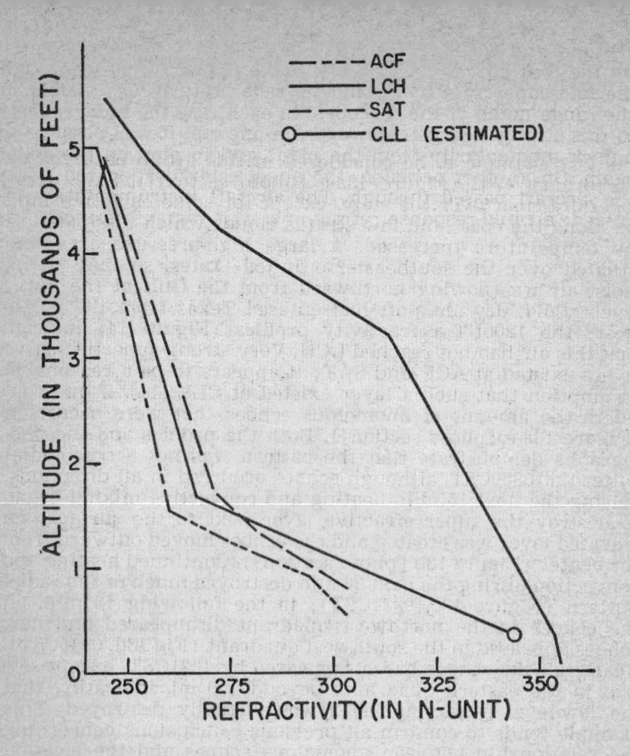

Fig. 14 Refractivity Profiles for 1200UT, 9 February 1962.

approximately 500 clear air "angel" echoes. Most of the "angels" plotted had radar cross sections between approximately 0.2 and 2 cm².

The maximum detectable range usually fell between 2,000 and 4,000 yards. On occasion, distinct angels with the appearance and characteristics of large airplanes or vessels were tracked, presenting targets roughly 100 times the minimum detectable target at that range. The physical extent of most of the angels, as deduced from manually varying the range setting across the target, was approximately 35 yards.

A series of attempts was made to vector an instrumented WV-2 Super-Constellation aircraft through the apparent location of the angel echoes. Of 28 attempts, 4 were successful. The plane was directed by radio by the radar operators, using the altitude and heading information from the plotting boards. On the four successful runs the plane passed directly through the telescope cross hairs, and its radar return was visible in the range notch of the A-scopes. In each case the radar shifted to this stronger target. However, in one run it was possible to unlock momentarily from the plane and to pick up the angel again. On another occasion, the angel echo disappeared when the aircraft passed through. The aircraft instrumentation included: a rapid-response refractometer, a vortex thermometer, electric field and conductivity instruments, and space charge detector. In none of the four instances was there any correlation between the records of these instruments and the angel location. Slight turbulence was encountered in close proximity of several of the angels, but no definite correlation could be ascertained.

SUMMARY

Cloudless skies and good visibility prevailed at the time of the UFO sightings in an area from 50 miles east of Dallas to Mineral Wells, Texas in the early morning hours of September, 19, 1957. Therefore, the UFO sightings were not related to cloudiness, lightning, or radar echoes from shower activity near the flight path.

The vertical profile of the atmosphere as measured at Ft. Worth did contain a sharp temperature inversion near the 6000-7000 foot level (Figure 2). The temperature increased and moisture content decreased rapidly with height in this layer. The change with height was great enough to permit a corresponding gradient of refractive index near the critical level which allows extensive anomalous propagation of either optical or radar energy (see Figures 3 and 16). The aircraft crew, although flying above the ducting layer, could have been receiving echoes and/or images of objects or lights many miles from the path of the aircraft. The ground operators of radar, located below the ducting layer, probably were observing echoes which were part of an anomalous propagation pattern transmitted to them due to the elevated refracting layer.

The air mass itself would have been changing slowly with respect to time during the night time hours. From a fixed position the ground radar operators would have been able to detect anomalous propagation near one particular position for fairly long periods. By contrast the airborne equipment would have been constantly changing its position relative to both the surrounding atmosphere and terrain. The probable ducting of images from considerable distances through the layered atmosphere would have tended to keep the images in the same general direction from the aircraft and at some distance away from the aircraft itself. This is in some ways similar to the observation of a rainbow from a moving automobile.

It is worthy to note that a large fraction of the reports on detailed research which have been used as references for the conclusions in this study have publication dates after September 1957. Even in 1968 it is not likely that the results of such research are common knowledge to a high fraction of aircraft crews who might on rare occasions fly near a "ducting layer" which is invisible in a cloudless atmosphere.

The detailed observations are being retained in my files. Should they be of further use to you please let me know.

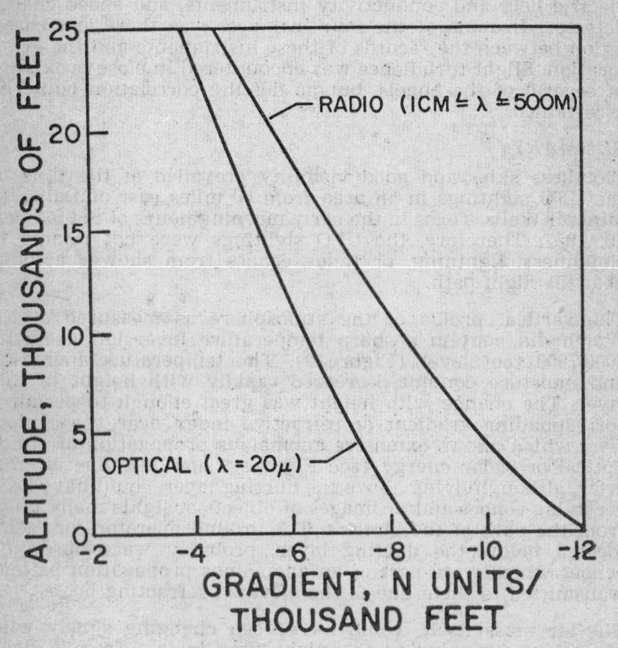

Fig. 15 Variation of Standard Gradient of Refractive Modulus with Altitude.

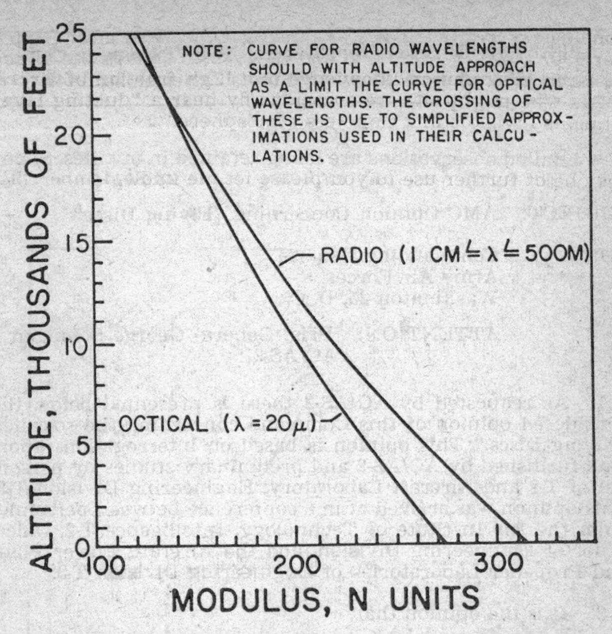

Fig. 16 Variation of Standard Refractive Modulus with Altitude.

APPENDIX R: Letter from General N. F. Twining to Commanding General, Army Air Forces 23 September 1947

(COPY)

23 September 1947

SUBJECT: AMC Opinion Concerning "Flying Discs"

TO: Commanding General
Army Air Forces
Washington 25, D. C.

ATTENTION: Brig. General George Schulgen
AC/AS-2

1. As requested by AC/AS-2 there is presented below the considered opinion of this Command concerning the so-called "Flying Discs." This opinion is based on interrogation report data furnished by AC/AS-2 and preliminary studies by personnel of T-2 and Aircraft Laboratory, Engineering Division T-3. This opinion was arrived at in a conference between personnel from the Air Institute of Technology, Intelligence T-2, Office, Chief of Engineering Division, and the Aircraft, Power Plant and Propeller Laboratories of Engineering Division T-3.

2. It is the opinion that:

a. The phenomenon reported is something real and not visionary or fictitious.

b. There are objects probably approximating the shape of a disc, of such appreciable size as to appear to be as large as man-made aircraft.

c. There is a possibility that some of the incidents may be caused by natural phenomena, such as meteors.

d. The reported operating characteristics such as extreme rates of climb, maneuverability (particularly in roll), and action which must be considered evasive when sighted or contacted by friendly aircraft and radar, lend belief to the possibility that some of the objects are controlled either manually, automatically or remotely.

e. The apparent common description of the objects is as follows:

(1) Metallic or light reflecting surface.

(2) Absence of trail, except in a few instances when the object apparently was operating under high performance conditions.

(3) Circular or elliptical in shape, flat on bottom and domed on top.

(4) Several reports of well kept formation flights varying from three to nine objects.

(5) Normally no associated sound, except in three instances a substantial rumbling roar was noted.

(6) Level flight speeds normally above 300 knots are estimated.

f. It is possible within the present U.S. knowledge—provided extensive detailed development is undertaken—to construct a piloted aircraft which has the general description of the object in subparagraph (e) above which would be capable of an approximate range of 7000 miles at subsonic speeds.

g. Any developments in this country along the lines indicated would be extremely expensive, time consuming and at the considerable expense of current projects and therefore, if directed, should be set up independently of existing projects.

h. Due consideration must be given the following:

(1) The possibility that these objects are of domestic origin—the product of some high security project not known to AC/AS-2 or this Command.

(2) The lack of physical evidence in the shape of crash recovered exhibits which would undeniably prove the existence of these objects.

(3) The possibility that some foreign nation has a form of propulsion possibly nuclear, which is outside of our domestic knowledge.

3. It is recommended that:

a. Headquarters, Army Air Forces issue a directive assigning a priority, security classification and Code Name for a detailed study of this matter to include the preparation of complete sets of all available and pertinent data which will then be made available to the Army, Navy, Atomic Energy Commission, JRDB, the Air Force Scientific Advisory Group, NACA, and the RAND and NEPA projects for comments and recommendations, with a preliminary report to be forwarded within 15 days of receipt of the data and a detailed report thereafter every 30 days as the investigation develops. A complete interchange of data should be effected.

4. Awaiting a specific directive AMC will continue the investigation within its current resources in order to more closely define the nature of the phenomenon. Detailed Essential Elements of Information will be formulated immediately for transmittal thru channels.

N. F. TWINING
Lieutenant General, U.S.A.
Commanding

APPENDIX S: Directive—Major General L. C. Craigie to Commanding General Wright Field (Wright-Patterson AFB) —Disposition and Security for Project "SIGN," Dated 30 December 1947

(COPY)

30 December 1947

SUBJECT: Flying Discs

TO: Command General
Air Material Command
Wright Field, Dayton, Ohio
Attn: TSDIH

1. Reference is made to three inclosures, memoranda from your office to this headquarters, subject as above.

2. It is Air Force policy not to ignore reports of sightings and phenomena in the atmosphere but to recognize that part of its mission is to collect, collate, evaluate and act on information of this nature.

3. In implementing this policy, it is desired that the Air Material Command set up a project whose purpose is to collect, collate, evaluate and distribute to interested government agencies and contractors all information concerning sightings and phenomena in the atmosphere which can be construed to be of concern to the national security. It is desired that appropriate recommendations be forwarded to this Headquarters, wherever action is indicated which falls outside the field of the Air Material Command.

4. It is suggested that the activities of this project include the preparation and distribution of an initial report, as recommended in Inclosure 1, and that subsequent reports be issued on a quarterly basis. Supplementary reports should be issued at more frequent intervals should the need for same be indicated. This project is assigned priority 2A, with a security classification of "restricted" and Code Name of "SIGN." Where data of a classification higher than restricted is handled by the project such data should be classified accordingly. A complete interchange of data should be effected as recommended in Inclosure 1.

BY COMMAND OF THE CHIEF OF STAFF:
L. C. CRAIGIE
Major General, U.S. Air Force
Director of Research and Development
Office, Deputy Chief of Staff, Material

4 Incls

1. Memo dtd 23 Sept '47
   from AMC to AC/AS-2
   (Gen Schulgen)

2. Memo dtd 24 Sept '47
   from AMC to AC/AS-2
   (Gen McDonald)

3. Memo dtd 19 Dec '47
   to Gen Craigie

4. R&R from Dir of Intell. w/2 Dools

APPENDIX T: G. E. Valley, Interpretation of Reports of Unidentified Flying Objects, Project "SIGN," No. F-TR-2274-IA, Appendix "C"

Appendix "C"

Some Considerations Affecting the Interpretation of Reports of Unidentified Flying Objects

By

G. E. Valley, Member Scientific Advisory Board,
Office of the Chief of Staff, United States Air Force

The writer has studied summary abstracts and comments pertaining to unidentified flying objects, which were forwarded by Air Force Intelligence. These remarks are divided into three main parts: the first part is a short *summary* of the reports; the second part consists of a general survey of various *possibilities* of accounting for the reports; the third part contains certain *recommendations* for future action.

PART I—*SHORT SUMMARY OF OBSERVATIONS*

The reports can be grouped as follows:

Group 1—The most numerous reports indicate the daytime observation of metallic disk-like objects, roughly in diameter ten times their thickness. There is some suggestion that the cross section is asymmetrical and rather like a turtle shell. Reports agree that these objects are capable of high acceleration and velocity; they often are sighted in groups, sometimes in formation. Sometimes they flutter.

Group 2—The second group consists of reports of lights observed at night. These are also capable of high speed and acceleration. They are less commonly seen in groups. They usually appear to be sharply defined luminous objects.

Group 3—The third group consists of reports of various kinds of rockets, in general appearing somewhat like V-2 rockets.

Group 4—The fourth group contains reports of various devices which, in the writer's opinion, are sounding balloons of unusual shape such as are made by the General Mills Company to Navy contract.

Group 5—The fifth group includes reports of objects in which little credence can be placed.

General Remarks

In general, it is noted that few, if any, reports indicate that the observed objects make any noise or radio interference. Nor are there many indications of any material affects or physical damage attributable to the observed objects.

Summary—PART I

This report will consider mainly the reports of Groups 1 and 2.

PART II—ON POSSIBLE EXPLANATIONS OF THE REPORTS

Section A—What can be deduced concerning the nature of an unknown aerial object from a single sighting?

Here, there are two problems: first, how much can be deduced concerning the nature of the objects from geometrical calculations alone; second, how much more can be deduced if, in addition, it is assumed that the objects obey the laws of nature as we know them.

Concerning the first problem, it can be stated that only ratios of lengths, and rates of change of such ratios, can be accurately determined. Thus, the range and size of such objects cannot be determined; and it is noticeable that reports of size of the observed objects are widely at variance. However, angles, such as the angle subtended by the object, can be observed. Likewise there is fair agreement among several observers that the diameter of the objects of Group 1 is about ten times their thickness. Although velocity cannot be determined, angular velocity can be, and in particular the flutter frequency could, in principle, be determined.

All that can be concluded about the range and size of the objects, from geometrical considerations alone, is: 1) from the fact that estimated sizes vary so widely, the objects were actually either of different sizes, or more likely, that they were far enough from the observers so that binocular vision produced no stereoscopic effect; this only means that they were farther off than about thirty feet; 2) since objects were seen to disappear behind trees, buildings, clouds, etc., they are large enough to be visible at the ranges of those recognizable objects.

Now, it is obviously of prime importance to estimate the size and mass of the observed objects. This may be possible to some extent if it is permissible to assume that they obey the laws of physics. Since the objects have not been observed to produce any physical effects, other than the one case in which a cloud was evaporated along the trajectory, it is not certain that the laws of mechanics, for instance, would be sufficient.

But suppose that mechanical laws alone are sufficient, then the following example is sufficient proof that at least a length could, in principle, be determined: suppose a simple pendulum were observed suspended in the sky; then after observing its frequency of oscillation, we could deduce from the laws of mechanics its precise length.

This suggests that something could be deduced from the observed fluttering motion of some of the objects of Group 1. Assume that we know the angular frequency and angular amplitude of this fluttering motion (they can be measured in principle from a motion picture). Then for purposes of calculation assume the object to be thirty feet in diameter, to be as rigid as a normal aircraft wing of 30-foot span, to be constructed of material of the optimum weight-strength ratio and to be a structure of most efficient design. It is now possible to calculate how heavy the object must be merely to remain rigid under the observed angular motion. Let the calculation be made for a plurality of assumed sizes 1, 2, 4, 8, 16, 32, 64—up to say 200 feet, and let calculated mass be plotted versus assumed size. The non-linear character of the curve should indicate an approximate upper limit to the size of the object.

If, in addition, it is assumed that the flutter is due to aerodynamic forces, it is possible that more precise information could be obtained.

The required angular data can probably be extracted from the witnesses most reliably by the use of a demonstration model which can be made to oscillate or flutter in a known way.

Summary—PART II, Section A

Geometrical calculations alone cannot yield the size of objects observed from a single station; such observation together with the assumption that the objects are essentially aircraft, can be used to set reasonable limits of size.

Section B—The possibility of supporting and propelling a solid object by unusual means.

Since some observers have obviously colored their reports with talk of rays, jets, beams, space-ships, and the like, it is well to examine what possibilities exist along these lines. This is also important in view of the conclusions of PART II, Section A, of this report.

Method I—Propulsion and support by means of "rays" or "beams."

By "rays" or "beams" are meant either purely electromagnetic radiation or else radiation which is largely corpuscular like cathode-rays or cosmic-rays or cyclotron-beams.

Now, it is obvious that any device propelled or supported by such means is fundamentally a reaction device. It is fundamental in the theory of such devices that a given amount of energy is most efficiently spent if the momentum thrown back or down is large. This means that a large mass should be given a small acceleration—a theorem well understood by helicopter designers.

The beams or rays mentioned do the contrary, a small mass is given a very high velocity, consequently enormous powers, greater than the total world's power capacity, would be needed to support even the smallest object by such means.

Method II—Direct use of Earth's Magnetic Field

One observer (incident 68) noticed a violent motion of a hand-held compass. If we assume from this that the objects produced a magnetic field, comparable with the Earth's field, namely, 0.1 gauss, and that the observer found that the object subtended an angle Θ at his position, then the ampere-turns of the required electromagnetic is given by:

$$ni = \frac{30R}{\Theta^2} \text{ where R is the range of the object.}$$

For instance, if R is one kilometer and the object is 10 meters in diameter, then ni $\neq$ 1 billion ampere-turns.

Now if the object were actually only 10 meters away and were correspondingly smaller; namely, 10 cm in diameter, it would still require 10 million ampere-turns.

These figures are a little in excess of what can be conveniently done on the ground. They make it seem unlikely that the effect was actually observed.

Now, the Earth's magnetic field would react on such a magnet to produce not only a torque but also a force. This force depends not directly on the Earth's field but on its irregularity or gradient. This force is obviously minute since the change in field over a distance of 10 meters (assumed diameter of the object) is scarcely measurable, moreover the gradient is not predictable but changes due to local ore deposits. Thus, even if the effect were large enough to use, it would still be unreliable and unpredictable.

Method III—Support of an electrically-charged object by causing it to move transverse to the Earth's magnetic field.

A positively-charged body moving from west to east, or a negatively-charged body moving from east to west will experience an upward force due to the Earth's magnetic field.

A sphere 10 meters diameter moving at a speed of one kilometer/second would experience an upward force of one pound at the equator if charged to a potential of 5×10^{12} volts. This is obviously ridiculous.

Section D—The anti-gravity shield

It has been proposed, by various writers, perhaps first by H. G. Wells, that it might be possible to construct a means of shielding a massive body from the influence of gravity. Such an object would then float. Recently, there appeared in the press a notice that a prominent economist has offered to support research on such an enterprise.

Obviously, conservation of energy demands that considerable energy be given the supported object in order to place it on the shield. However, this amount of energy is in no way prohibitive, and furthermore it can be gotten back when the object lands.

Aside from the fact that we have no suggestions as to how such a device is to be made, the various theories of general relativity all agree in assuming that gravitational force and force due to acceleration are indistinguishable, and from this assumption the theories predict certain effects which are in fact observed. The assumption, therefore, is probably correct, and a corollary of it is essentially that only by means of an acceleration can gravity be counteracted. This, we can successfully do for instance by making an artificial satellite, but this presumably is not what has been observed.

Summary—Part II, Section B

Several unorthodox means of supporting or propelling a solid object have been considered, all are impracticable. This finding lends credence to the tentative proposed assumption of Part II, that the objects are supported and propelled by some normal means, or else that they are not solids. No discussion of the type of Part II, Section B, can, in principle, of course, be complete.

Section C—Possible causes for the reports

Classification I—Natural terrestrial phenomena

1. The observations may be due to some effect such as ball of lightning. The writer has no suggestions on this essentially meteorological subject.

2. The objects may be some kind of animal.

Even in the celebrated case of incident 172 where the light was chased by a P51 for half an hour and which was reported by the pilot to be intelligently directed, we can make this remark. For considering that an intelligence capable of making so remarkable a device would not be likely to play around in so idle a manner as described by the pilot.

In this connection, it would be well to examine if some of the lights observed at night were not fire-flies.

3. The observed objects may be hallucinatory or psychological in origin. It is of prime importance to study this possibility because we can learn from it something of the character of the population; its response under attack; and also something about the reliability of visual observation.

One would like to assume that the positions held by many of the reported observers guarantee their observations. Unfortunately, there were many reports of curious phenomena by pilots during the war—the incident of the fire-ball fighters comes to mind. Further, mariners have been reporting sea-serpents for hundreds of years yet no one has yet produced a photograph.

It would be interesting to tabulate the responses to see how reliable were the reports on the Japanese balloons during the war. There we had a phenomenon proven to be real.

It is interesting that the reports swiftly reach a maximum frequency during the end of June 1947 and then slowly taper off. We can assume that this is actually an indication of how many objects were actually about, or, quite differently, we can take this frequency curve as indicating something about mass psychology.

This point can be tested. Suppose the population is momentarily excited; how does the frequency of reports vary with time? A study of crank letters received after the recent publicity given to the satellite program should give the required frequency distribution.

It is probably necessary but certainly not sufficient that the unidentified-object curve and the crank-letter curve should be similar in order for the flying disks to be classed as hallucinations.

A large-scale experiment was made at the time of Orson Welles' "Martian" broadcast. Some records of this must persist in newspaper files.

Classification II—Man-made terrestrial phenomena

1. The objects may be Russian aircraft. If this were so, then the considerations of Sections A and B indicate that we would have plenty to worry about. It is the author's opinion that only an accidental discovery of a degree of novelty never before achieved could suffice to explain such devices. It is doubtful whether a potential enemy would arouse our curiosity in so idle a fashion.

Classification III—Extra-terrestrial objects

1. Meteors: It is noteworthy that the British physicist Lovell writing in "Physics Today" mentions the radar discovery of a new daytime meteorite stream which reached its maximum during June 1947. The reported objects lose little of their interest, however, if they are of meteoritic origin.

2. Animals: Although the objects described act more like animals than anything else, there are few reliable reports on extra-terrestrial animals.

3. Space Ships: The following considerations pertain:

a. If there is an extra-terrestrial civilization which can make such objects as are reported then it is most probable that its development is far in advance of ours. This argument can be supported on probability arguments alone without recourse to astronomical hypotheses.

b. Such a civilization might observe that on Earth we now have atomic bombs and are fast developing rockets. In view of the past history of mankind, they should be alarmed. We should, therefore, expect at this time above all to behold such visitations.

Since the acts of mankind most easily observed from a distance are A-bomb explosions we should expect some relation to obtain between the time of A-bomb explosions, the time at which space ships are seen, and the time required for such ships to arrive from and return to home-base.

PART III—RECOMMENDATIONS

1. The file should be continued.

2. A meteorologist should compute the approximate energy required to evaporate as much cloud as shown in the incident 26 photographs. Together with an aerodynamicist he should examine whether a meteorite of unusual shape could move as observed.

3. The calculations suggested in Part II, Section A, should be estimated by an aerodynamicist with such changes as his more detailed knowledge may suggest.

4. The mass-psychology studies outlined in Part II, Section C, Classification I 3 should be carried out by a competent staff of statisticians and mass-psychologists.

5. Interviewing agents should carry objects or moving pictures for comparison with reporter's memories. These devices should be properly designed by a psychologist experienced in problems pertaining to aircraft and design of aircraft-control equipment so that he shall have some grasp of what it is that is to be found out. If the Air Force has reason to be seriously interested in these reports, it should take immediate steps to interrogate the reporters more precisely.

6. A person skilled in the optics of the eye and of the atmosphere should investigate the particular point that several reports agree in describing the objects as being about ten times as wide as they are thick; the point being to see if there is a plurality of actual shapes which appear so, under conditions approaching limiting resolution or detectable contrast.

APPENDIX U: Report of Meetings of Scientific Advisory Panel on Unidentified Flying Objects (Robertson Panel) 14-18 January 1953

INDEX

(SECRET) UNCLASSIFIED

16 February 1953

MEMORANDUM FOR:

FROM :

SUBJECT : Report of Meetings of the Scientific Advisory Panel on Unidentified Flying Objects, January 14-18, 1953

PURPOSE

The purpose of this memorandum is to present:

a. A brief history of the meetings of the Advisory Panel On Unidentified Flying Objects (Part I),

b. An unofficial supplement to the official Panel Report: setting forth comments and suggestions of the Panel Members which they believed were inappropriate for inclusion in the formal report (Part II).

PART I: HISTORY OF MEETINGS

GENERAL

After consideration of the subject of "unidentified flying objects" at the 4 December meeting of the the following action was agreed:

"The will:

a. Enlist the services of selected scientists to review and appraise the available evidence in the light of pertinent scientific theories. . . ."

Following the delegation of this action to the and preliminary investigation, an Advisory Panel of selected scientists was assembled. In cooperation with the Air Technical Intelligence Center, case histories of reported sightings and related material were made available for their study and consideration.

Present at the initial meeting (0930 Wednesday, 14 January) were: Dr. H. P. Robertson, Dr. , Dr. Thornton Page, Dr. Samuel A. Goudsmit,

and the writer. Panel Member, Dr. Lloyd V. Berkner, was absent until Friday afternoon. Messrs. were present throughout the sessions to familiarize themselves with the subject, represent the substantive interest of their Divisions, and assist in administrative support of the meetings. (A list of personnel concerned with the meetings is given in Tab A.

WEDNESDAY MORNING

The opened the meeting, reviewing CIA interest in the subject and action taken. This review included the mention of the Study Group of August 1952 culminating in the briefing of the the ATIC November 21 briefing, 4 December consideration, visit to ATIC Robertson and , and concern over potential dangers to national security indirectly related to these sightings. Mr. enumerated these potential dangers. Following this introduction, Dr. turned the meeting over to Dr. Robertson as Chairman of the Panel. Dr. Robertson enumerated the evidence available and requested consideration of specific reports and letters be taken by certain individuals present (Tab B). For example, case histories involving radar or radar and visual sightings were selected for Dr. while reports of Green Fireball phenomena, nocturnal lights, and suggested programs of investigation were routed to Dr. Page. Following these remarks, the motion pictures of the sightings at Tremonton, Utah (2 July 1962) and Great Falls, Montana (15 August 1950) were shown. The meeting adjourned at 1200.

WEDNESDAY AFTERNOON

The second meeting of the Panel opened at 1400. Lt. USN, and Mr. of the USN Photo Interpretation Laboratory, Anacostia, presented the results of their analyses of the films mentioned above. This analysis evoked considerable discussion as elaborated upon below. Besides Panel members and CIA personnel, Capt. E. J. Ruppelt, Dr. (2-a-2), and Dr. were present.

Following the Photo Interpretation Lab presentation, Mr. E. J. Ruppelt spoke for about 40 minutes on ATIC methods of handling and evaluating reports of sightings and their efforts to improve the quality of reports. The meeting was adjourned at 1715.

THURSDAY MORNING

The third and fourth meetings of the Panel were held Thursday, 15 January, commencing at 0900 with a two-hour break for luncheon. Besides Panel members and CIA personnel, Mr. Ruppelt and Dr. were present for both sessions. In the morning, Mr. Ruppelt continued his briefing on ATIC collection and analysis procedures. The Project STORK support at was described by Dr. . A number of case histories were discussed in detail and a motion picture film of seagulls was shown. A two hour break for lunch was taken at 1200.

THURSDAY AFTERNOON

At 1400 hours gave a 40-minute briefing of Project TWINKLE, the investigatory project conducted by the Air Force Meteorological Research Center at Cambridge, Mass. In this briefing he pointed out the many problems of setting up and manning 24-hour instrumentation watches of patrol cameras searching for sighting of U.F.O.'s.

At 1615 joined the meeting with expressed his support of the Panel's efforts and stated three personal opinions:

a. That greater use of Air Force intelligence officers in the field (for follow-up investigation) appeared desirable, but that they required thorough briefing.

b. That vigorous effort should be made to declassify as many of the reports as possible.

c. That some increase in the ATIC section devoted to U.F.O. analysis was indicated.

This meeting was adjourned at 1700.

FRIDAY MORNING

The fifth session of the Panel convened at 0900 with the same personnel present as enumerated for Thursday (with the exception of .

From 0900-1000 there was general discussion and study of reference material. Also, read a prepared paper making certain observations and conclusions. At 1000 gave a briefing on his fifteen months experience in Washington as Project Officer for U.F.O.'s and his personal conclusions. There was considerable discussion of individual case histories of sightings to which he referred. Following presentation, a number of additional case histories were examined and discussed with Messrs. Ruppelt, and . The meeting adjourned at 1200 for luncheon.

FRIDAY AFTERNOON

This session opened at 1400. Besides Panel members and CIA personnel, Dr. was present. Dr. Lloyd V. Berkner, as Panel Member, was present at this meeting for the first time. Progress of the meetings was reviewed by the Panel Chairman and tentative conclusions reached. A general discussion followed and tentative recommendations considered. It was agreed that the Chairman should draft a report of the Panel to that evening for review by the Panel the next morning. The meeting adjourned at 1715.

SATURDAY MORNING

At 0945 the Chairman opened the seventh session and submitted a rough draft of the Panel Report to the members. This draft had been reviewed and approved earlier by Dr. Berkner. The next two and one-half hours were consumed in discussion and revision of the draft. At 1100 the joined the meeting and reported that he had shown and discussed a copy of the initial rough draft to the Director of Intelligence, USAF, whose reaction was favorable. At 1200 the meeting was adjourned.

SATURDAY AFTERNOON

At 1400 the eighth and final meeting of the Panel was opened. Discussion and rewording of certain sentences of the Report occupied the first hours. (A copy of the final report is appended as Tab C.) This was followed by a review of work accomplished by the Panel and restatement of individual Panel Member's opinions and suggestions on details that were felt inappropriate for inclusion in the formal report. It was agreed that the writer would incorporate these comments in an internal report to the . The material below represents this information.

PART II: COMMENTS AND SUGGESTIONS OF PANEL GENERAL

The Panel Members were impressed (as have been others, including personnel) in the lack of sound data in the great majority of case histories; also, in the lack of speedy follow-up due primarily to the modest size and limited facilities of the ATIC section concerned. Among the case histories of significant sightings discussed in detail were the following:

Bellefontaine, Ohio (1 August 1952); Tremonton, Utah (2 July 1952); Great Falls, Montana (15 August 1950); Yaak, Montana (1 September 1952); Washington, D. C. area (19 July 1952); and Haneda A.F.B., Japan (5 August 1952); Port Huron, Michigan (29 July 1952); and Presque Isle, Maine (10 October 1952).

After review and discussion of these cases (and about 15 others, in less detail), the Panel concluded that reasonable explanations could be suggested for most sightings and "by deduction and scientific method it could be induced (given additional data) that other cases might be explained in a similar manner." The Panel pointed out that because of the brevity of some sightings (e.g. 2-3 seconds) and the inability of the witnesses to express themselves clearly (semantics) that conclusive explanations could not be expected for every case reported. Furthermore, it was considered that, normally, it would be a great waste of effort to try to solve most of the sightings, unless such action would benefit a training and educational program (see below). The writings of Charles Fort were referenced to show that "strange things in the sky" had been recorded for hundreds of years. It appeared obvious that there was no single explanation for a majority of the things seen. The presence of radar and astronomical specialists on the Panel proved of value at once in their confident recognition of phenomena related to their fields. It was apparent that specialists in such additional fields as psychology, meteorology, aerodynamics, ornithology and military air operations would extend the ability of the Panel to recognize many more categories of little-known phenomena.

ON LACK OF DANGER

The Panel concluded unanimously that there was no evidence of a direct threat to national security in the objects sighted. Instances of "Foo Fighters" were cited. These were unexplained phenomena sighted by aircraft pilots during World War II in both European and Far East theaters of operation wherein "balls of light" would fly near or with the aircraft and maneuver rapidly. They were believed to be electrostatic (similar to St. Elmo's fire) or electro-magnetic phenomena or possibly light reflections from ice crystals in the air, but their exact cause or nature was never defined. Both Robertson and had been concerned in the investigation of these phenomena, but David T. Griggs (Professor of Geophysics at the University of California at Los Angeles) is believed to have been the most knowledgeable person on this subject. If the term "flying saucers" had been popular in 1943-1945, these objects would have been so labeled. It was interesting that in at least two cases reviewed that the object sighted was categorized by Robertson and as probably "Foo Fighters," to date unexplained but not dangerous; they were not happy thus to dismiss the sightings by calling them names. It was their feeling that these phenomena are not beyond the domain of present knowledge of physical sciences, however.

AIR FORCE REPORTING SYSTEM

It was the Panel's opinion that some of the Air Force concern over U.F.O.'s (notwithstanding Air Defense Command anxiety over fast radar tracks) was probably caused by public pressure. The result today is that the Air Force has instituted a fine channel for receiving reports of nearly anything anyone sees in the sky and fails to understand. This has been particularly encouraged in popular articles on this and other subjects, such as space travel and science fiction. The result is the mass receipt of low-grade reports which tend to overload channels of communication with material quite irrelevant to hostile objects that might some day appear. The Panel agreed generally that this mass of poor-quality reports containing little, if any, scientific data was of no value. Quite the opposite, it was possibly dangerous in having a military service foster public concern in "nocturnal meandering lights." The implication being, since the interested agency was military, that these objects were or might be potential direct threats to national security. Accordingly, the need for deemphasization made itself apparent. Comments on a possible educational program are enumerated below.

It was the opinion of Dr. Robertson that the "saucer" problem had been found to be different in nature from the detection and investigation of German V-1 and V-2 guided missiles prior to their operational use in World War II. In this 1943-1944 intelligence operation (CROSSBOW), there was excellent intelligence and by June 1944 there was material evidence of the existence of "hardware" obtained from crashed vehicles in Sweden. This evidence gave the investigating team a basis upon which to operate. The absence of any "hardware" resulting from unexplained U.F.O. sightings lends a "will-of-the-wisp" nature to the ATIC problem. The results of their investigation, to date, strongly indicate that no evidence of hostile act or danger exists. Furthermore, the current reporting system would have little value in the case of detection of enemy attack by conventional aircraft or guided missiles; under such conditions "hardware" would be available almost at once.

ARTIFACTS OF EXTRATERRESTRIAL ORIGIN

It was interesting to note that none of the members of the Panel were loath to accept that this earth might be visited by extraterrestrial intelligent beings of some sort, some day. What they did not find was any evidence that related the objects sighted to space travelers. Mr. in his presentation, showed how he had eliminated each of the known and probable causes of sightings leaving him "extra-terrestrial" as the only one remaining in many cases.   's background as an aeronautical engineer and technical intelligence officer (Project Officer, BLUEBOOK for 15 months) could not be slighted. However, the Panel could not accept any of the cases cited by him because they were raw, unevaluated reports. Terrestrial explanations of the sightings were suggested in some cases and in others the time of sighting was so short as to cause suspicion of visual impressions. It was noted by Dr. Goudsmit and others that extraterrestrial artifacts, if they did exist, are no cause for alarm; rather, they are in the realm of natural phenomena subject to scientific study, just as cosmic rays were at the time of their discovery 20 to 30 years ago. This was an attitude in which Dr. Robertson did not concur, as he felt that such artifacts would be of immediate and great concern not only to the U.S. but to all countries. (Nothing like a common threat to unite peoples!) Dr. Page noted that present astronomical knowledge of the solar system makes the existence of intelligent beings (as we know the term) elsewhere than on the earth extremely unlikely, and the concentration of their attention by any controllable means confined to any one continent of the earth quite proposterous.

TREMONTON, UTAH, SIGHTING

This case was considered significant because of the excellent documentary evidence in the form of Kodachrome motion picture films (about 1600 frames). The Panel studied these films, the case history, ATIC's interpretation, and received a briefing by representatives of the USN Photo Interpretation Laboratory on their analysis of the film. This team had expended (at Air Force request) approximately 1000 man-hours of professional and sub-professional time in the preparation of graph plots of individual frames of the film, showing apparent and relative motion of objects and variation in their light intensity. It was the opinion of the P.I.L. representatives that the objects sighted were not birds, balloons or aircraft, were "not reflections because there was no blinking while passing through 60° of arc" and were, therefore, "self-luminous." Plots of motion and variation in light intensity of the objects were displayed. While the Panel Members were impressed by the evident enthusiasm, industry and extent of effort of the P.I.L. team, they could not accept the conclusions reached. Some of the reasons for this were as follows:

a. A semi-spherical object can readily produce a reflection of sunlight without "blinking" through 60° of arc travel.

b. Although no data was available on the "albedo" of birds or polyethylene balloons in bright sunlight, the apparent motions, sizes and brightnesses of the objects were considered strongly to suggest birds, particularly after the Panel viewed a short film showing high reflectivity of seagulls in bright sunlight.

c. P.I.L. description of the objects sighted as "circular, bluish-white" in color would be expected in cases of specular reflections of sunlight from convex surfaces where the brilliance of the reflection would obscure other portions of the object.

d. Objects in the Great Falls case were believed to have probably been aircraft, and the bright lights such reflections.

e. There was no valid reason for the attempt to relate the objects in the Tremonton sighting to those in the Great Falls sighting. This may have been due to misunderstanding in their directive. The objects in the Great Falls sighting are strongly suspected of being reflections of aircraft known to have been in the area.

f. The intensity change in the Tremonton lights was too great for acceptance of the P.I.L. hypothesis that the apparent motion and changing intensity of the lights indicated extremely high speed in small orbital paths.

g. Apparent lack of guidance of investigators by those familiar with U.F.O. reports and explanations.

h. Analysis of light intensity of objects made from duplicate rather than original film. The original film was noted to have a much lighter background (affecting relative brightness of object) and the objects appeared much less bright.

i. Method of obtaining data of light intensity appeared faulty because of unsuitability of equipment and questionable assumptions in making averages of readings.

j. No data had been obtained on the sensitivity of Kodachrome film to light of various intensities using the same camera type at the same lens openings.

k. Hand "jitter" frequencies (obtainable from early part of Tremonton film) were not removed from the plots of the "single pass plots" at the end of the film.

The Panel believed strongly that the data available on this sighting was sufficient for positive identification if further data is obtained by photographing polyethylene "pillow" balloons released near the site under similar weather conditions, checking bird flight and reflection characteristics with competent ornithologists and calculating apparent "G" forces acting upon objects from their apparent tracks. It was concluded that the results of such tests would probably lead to creditable explanations of value in an educational or training program. However, the Panel noted that the cost in technical manpower effort required to follow up and explain every one of the thousand or more reports received through channels each year (1,900 in 1952) could not be justified. It was felt that there will always be sightings, for which complete data is lacking, that can only be explained with disproportionate effort and with a long time delay, if at all. The long delay in explaining a sighting tends to eliminate any intelligence value. The educational or training program should have as a major purpose the elimination of popular feeling that every sighting, no matter how poor the data, must be explained in detail. Attention should be directed to the requirement among scientists that a new phenomena, to be accepted, must be completely and convincingly documented. In other words, the burden of proof is on the sighter, not the explainer.

POTENTIAL RELATED DANGERS

The Panel Members were in agreement with opinion that, although evidence of any direct threat from these sightings was wholly lacking, related dangers might well exist resulting from:

a. Misidentification of actual enemy artifacts by defense personnel.
b. Overloading of emergency reporting channels with "false" information ("noise to signal ratio" analogy—Berkner).
c. Subjectivity of public to mass hysteria and greater vulnerability to possible enemy psychological warfare.

Although not the concern of CIA, the first two of these problems may seriously affect the Air Defense intelligence system, and should be studied by experts, possibly under ADC. If U.F.O.'s become discredited in a reaction to the "flying saucer" scare, or if reporting channels are saturated with false and poorly documented reports, our capability of detecting hostile activity will be reduced. Dr. Page noted that more competent screening or filtering of reported sightings at or near the source is required, and that this can best be accomplished by an educational program.

GEOGRAPHIC LOCATIONS OF UNEXPLAINED SIGHTINGS

The map prepared by ATIC showing geographic locations of officially reported unexplained sightings (1952 only) was examined by the Panel. This map showed clusters in certain strategic areas such as Los Alamos. This might be explained on the basis of 24-hour watchful guard and awareness of security measures near such locations. On the other hand, there had been no sightings in the vicinity of sensitive related AE establishments while there were occasionally multiple cases of unexplained sightings in non-strategic areas. Furthermore, there appeared to be no logical relationship to population centers. The Panel could find no ready explanation for these clusters. It was noted, however, that if terrestrial artifacts were to be observed it would be likely that they would be seen first near foreign areas rather than central U. S.

INSTRUMENTATION TO OBTAIN DATA

The Panel was of the opinion that the present ATIC program to place 100 inexpensive 35 mm. stereo cameras in the hands of various airport control tower operators would probably produce little valuable data related to U.F.O.'s. However, it was recognized that such action would tend to allay public concern in the subject until an educational program had taken effect. It was believed that procurement of these cameras was partly the result of public pressure in July 1952. With the poor results of the year-long Project TWINKLE program of 24-hours instrumentation watch (two frames of film showing nothing distinguishable), a widespread program of sky-watching would not be expected to yield much direct data of value.

There was considerable discussion of a possible "sky patrol" by amateur astronomers and by wide-angle cameras (Page). Dr. Page and Dr. Robertson pointed out that at present a considerable fraction of the sky is now—and has been for many years—under surveillance every clear night in several meteor and aurora observing programs as well as sky mapping programs at the various locations listed below. Although the attention of these astronomers is largely directed toward identified rather than unidentified objects, no case of any striking unidentified object is known to Dr. Page or Dr. ———. Such an object would most certainly be reported if found on patrol plates.

A case was cited where an astronomer refused to interrupt his exposure in order to photograph an alleged sighting in a different part of the sky. This led Dr. ——— to say that, if a program of watching could be an adjunct of planned astronomical programs, little cost would be involved and that the trained astronomical personnel might photograph a sighting of an unidentified object.

The location of some of these programs and their directors are believed to be:

a. Harvard University, Cambridge and New Mexico (meteor patrol)—Whipple.
b. Yerkes Observatory, University of Chicago and Fort Davis, Texas (several programs)—Meinel (auroras), Kuiper (asteroids), Morgan (wide angle camera).
c. University of Alaska, Fairbanks (aurorae)—Elvey
d. Dominion Observatory, Ottawa (meteors)—Millman
e. Palomar Observatory, California (sky map)—Minkowski
f. Lick Observatory, California (sky map)—Shane

It was agreed by the Panel that no government-sponsored program of optical nation-wide sky patrol is worthwhile at the present time, and that the encouragement of amateur astronomers to undertake such a program might have the adverse effect of over-emphasizing "flying saucer" stories in the public mind. However, the issue of radar scope cameras for recording peculiar radar echoes would serve several purposes, including the better understanding of radar interference as well as identification of U.F.O.'s.

RADAR PROBLEM OF MUTUAL INTERFERENCE

This characteristic problem of radar operation wherein the pulse signal (of approximately the same frequency) from station A may be picked up on the screen of station B and show as a high-speed track or series of dots was recognized to have probably caused a number of U.F.O. reports. This problem was underlined by information received indicating ADC concern in solving this problem of signal identification before service use of very high-speed aircraft or guided missiles (1955-1956).

Dr. Berkner believed that one answer to this problem was the use of a "doppler filter" in the receiving circuit. Dr. ——— suggested that the problem might be better solved by the use of a "controlled jitter" wherein the operator receiving "very fast tracks" (on the order of 1000- 10,000 m.p.h.) would operate a circuit which would alter slightly his station's pulse frequency rate. If the signal received on the screen had been caused by mutual interference with another station, the track would now show itself at a different distance from the center of the screen, if it still appeared at all. Dr. ——— felt such a technical solution was simpler and would cost much less than a "doppler filter."

UNEXPLAINED COSMIC RAY PHENOMENA

Two reported cases were examined: one at Palomar Mountain, California, in October 1949, when cosmic ray counters went "off scale for a few seconds," apparently while a "V" of flying saucers was observed visually; and two, a series of observations by the "Los Alamos Bird Watchers Association" from August 1950 to January 1951, when cosmic ray coincidence counters behaved queerly. Circuit diagrams and records were available for the latter, and Dr. ——— was able quickly to point out that the recorded data were undoubtedly due to instrumental effects that would have been recognized as such by more experienced observers.

The implication that radioactive effects were correlated with unidentified flying objects in these two cases was, therefore, rejected by the Panel.

EDUCATIONAL PROGRAM

The Panel's concept of a broad educational program integrating efforts of all concerned agencies was that it should have two major aims: training and "debunking."

The training aim would result in proper recognition of unusually illuminated objects (e.g., balloons, aircraft reflections) as well as natural phenomena (meteors, fireballs, mirages, noctilucent clouds). Both visual and radar recognition are concerned. There would be many levels in such education from enlisted personnel to command and research personnel. Relative emphasis and degree of explanation of different programs would correspond to the categories of duty (e.g., radar operators; pilots; control tower operators; Ground Observer Corps personnel; and officers and enlisted men in other categories). This training should result in a marked reduction in reports caused by misidentification and resultant confusion.

The "debunking" aim would result in reduction in public interest in "flying saucers" which today evokes a strong psychological reaction. This education could be accomplished by mass media such as television, motion pictures, and popular articles. Basis of such education would be actual case histories which had been puzzling at first but later explained. As in the case of conjuring tricks, there is much less stimulation if the "secret" is known. Such a program should tend to reduce the current gullibility of the public and consequently their susceptibility to clever hostile propaganda. The Panel noted that the general absence of Russian propaganda based on a subject with so many obvious possibilities for exploitation might indicate a possible Russian official policy.

Members of the Panel had various suggestions related to the planning of such an educational program. It was felt strongly that psychologists familiar with mass psychology should advise on the nature and extent of the program. In this connection, Dr. Hadley Cantril (Princeton University) was suggested. Cantril authored "Invasion from Mars," (a study in the psychology of panic, written about the famous Orson Welles radio broadcast in 1938) and has since performed advanced laboratory studies in the field of perception. The names of Don Marquis (University of Michigan) and Leo Roston were mentioned as possibly suitable as consultant psychologists. Also, someone familiar with mass communications techniques, perhaps an advertising expert, would be helpful. Arthur Godfrey was mentioned as possibly a valuable channel of communication reaching a mass audience of certain levels. Dr. Berkner suggested the U. S. Navy (ONR) Special Devices Center, Sands Point, L. I., as a potentially valuable organization to assist in such an educational program. The teaching techniques used by this agency for aircraft identification during the past war was cited as an example of a similar educational task. The Jam Handy Co. which made World War II training films (motion picture and slide strips) was also suggested, as well as Walt Disney, Inc. animated cartoons. Dr. ——— suggested that the amateur astronomers in the U. S. might be a potential source of enthusiastic talent "to spread the gospel." It was believed that business clubs, high schools, colleges, and television stations would all be pleased to cooperate in the showing of documentary type motion pictures if prepared in an interesting manner. The use of true cases showing first the "mystery" and then the "explanation" would be forceful.

To plan and execute such a program, the Panel believed was no mean task. The current investigatory group at ATIC would, of necessity, have to be closely integrated for support with respect to not only the historical cases but the current ones. Recent cases are probably much more susceptible to explanation than older ones; first, because of ATIC's experience and, secondly, their knowledge of most plausible explanations. The Panel believed that some expansion of the ATIC effort would certainly be required to support such a program. It was believed inappropriate to state exactly how large a Table of Organization would be required. Captain Ruppelt of ATIC unofficially proposed, for purposes of analyzing and evaluating reports:

a. An analysts' panel of four officers
b. Four officer investigators
c. A briefing officer
d. An ADC liaison officer
e. A weather and balloon data officer

f. An astronomical consultant

g. A group Leader, with administrative assistant, file clerks and stenographers.

This proposal met with generally favorable comment. The Panel believed that, with ATIC's support, the educational program of "training and debunking" outlined above might be required for a minimum of one and one-half to two years. At the end of this time, the dangers related to "flying saucers" should have been greatly reduced if not eliminated. Cooperation from other military services and agencies concerned (e.g., Federal Civil Defense Administration) would be a necessity. In investigating significant cases (such as the Trementon, Utah, sighting), controlled experiments might be required. An example would be the photographing of "pillow balloons" at different distances under similar weather conditions at the site.

The help of one or two psychologists and writers and a subcontractor to produce training films would be necessary in addition. The Panel considered that ATIC's efforts, temporarily expanded as necessary, could be most useful in implementing any action taken as a result of its recommendations. Experience and records in ATIC would be of value in both the public educational and service training program envisaged. Dr. Robertson at least was of the opinion that after public gullibility lessened and the service organizations, such as ADC, had been trained to sift out the more readily explained spurious sightings, there would still be a role for a very modest-sized ATIC section to cope with the residuum of items of possible scientific intelligence value. This section should concentrate on energetically following up (perhaps on the advice of qualified Air Force Scientific Advisory Board members) those cases which seemed to indicate the evidence of unconventional enemy artifacts. Reports of such artifacts would be expected to arise mainly from Western outposts in far closer proximity to the Iron Curtain than Lubbock, Texas!

UNOFFICIAL INVESTIGATING GROUPS

The Panel took cognizance of the existence of such groups as the "Civilian Flying Saucer Investigators" (Los Angeles) and the "Aerial Phenomena Research Organization (Wisconsin)." It was believed that such organizations should be watched because of their potentially great influence on mass thinking if widespread sightings should occur. The apparent irresponsibility and the possible use of such groups for subversive purposes should be kept in mind.

INCREASE IN NUMBER OF SIGHTINGS

The consensus of the Panel was, based upon the history of the subject, that the number of sightings could be reasonably expected to increase again this summer.

(SECRET) **UNCLASSIFIED**

REPORT OF THE SCIENTIFIC PANEL ON UNIDENTIFIED FLYING OBJECTS

1. Pursuant to the request

, the undersigned Panel of Scientific Consultants has met to evaluate any possible threat to national security posed by Unidentified Flying Objects ("Flying Saucers"), and to make recommendations thereon. The Panel has received the evidence as presented by cognizant intelligence agencies, primarily the Air Technical Intelligence Center, and has reviewed a selection of the best documented incidents.

2. As a result of its considerations, the Panel *concludes*:

a. That the evidence presented on Unidentified Flying Objects shows no indication that these phenomena constitute a direct physical threat to national security.

We firmly believe that there is no residuum of cases which indicates phenomena which are attributable to foreign artifacts capable of hostile acts, and that there is no evidence that the phenomena indicates a need for the revision of current scientific concepts.

3. The Panel further *concludes*:

a. That the continued emphasis on the reporting of these phenomena does, in these parlous times, result in a threat to the orderly functioning of the protective organs of the body politic.

We cite as examples the clogging of channels of communication by irrelevant reports, the danger of being led by continued false alarms to ignore real indications of hostile action, and the cultivation of a morbid national psychology in which skillful hostile propaganda could induce hysterical behavior and harmful distrust of duty constituted authority.

4. In order most effectively to strengthen the national facilities for the timely recognition and the appropriate handling of true indications of hostile action, and to minimize the concomitant dangers alluded to above, the Panel *recommends*:

a. That the national security agencies take immediate steps to strip the Unidentified Flying Objects of the special status they have been given and the aura of mystery they have unfortunately acquired;

b. That the national security agencies institute policies on intelligence, training, and public education designed to prepare the material defenses and the morale of the country to recognize most promptly and to react most effectively to true indications of hostile intent or action.

We suggest that these aims may be achieved by an integrated program designed to reassure the public of the total lack of evidence of inimical forces behind the phenomena, to train personnel to recognize and reject false indications quickly and effectively, and to strengthen regular channels for the evaluation of and prompt reaction to true indications of hostile measures.

/s/ *H. P. Robertson, Chairman*
California Institute of Technology

/s/ *Luis W. Alvarez*
University of California

/s/ *Lloyd V. Berkner*
Associated Universities, Inc.

/s/ *S. A. Goudsmit*
Brookhaven National Laboratories

/s/ *Thornton Page*
Johns Hopkins University

(SECRET) **UNCLASSIFIED**

TAB B

SCIENTIFIC ADVISORY PANEL ON UNIDENTIFIED FLYING OBJECTS

14-17 January 1953

EVIDENCE PRESENTED

1. Seventy-five case histories of sightings 1951-1952 (selected by ATIC as those best documented).
2. ATIC Status and Progress Reports of Project GRUDGE and Project BLUE BOOK (code names for ATIC study of subject).
3. Progress Reports of Project STORK contract work supporting ATIC).
4. Summary Report of Sightings at Holloman Air Force Base, New Mexico.
5. Report of USAF Research Center, Cambridge, Mass., Investigation of "Green Fireball" Phenomena (Project TWINKLE).
6. Outline of Investigation of U.F.O.'s Proposed by Kirtland Air Force Base (Project POUNCE).
7. Motion Picture Films of sightings at Tremonton, Utah, 2 July 1952 and Great Falls, Montana, August 1950.
8. Summary Report of 89 selected cases of sightings of various categories (Formations, Blinking Lights, Hovering, etc.).
9. Draft of manual: "How to Make a FLYOBRPT," prepared at ATIC.
10. Chart Showing Plot of Geographic Location of Unexplained Sightings in the United States during 1952.
11. Chart Showing Balloon Launching Sites in the United States.
12. Charts Showing Selected Actual Balloon Flight Paths and Relation to Reported Sightings.
13. Charts Showing Frequency of Reports of Sightings, 1948-1952.
14. Charts Showing Categories of Explanations of Sightings.

15. Kodachrome Transparencies of Polyethylene Film Balloons in Bright Sunlight Showing High Reflectivity.

16. Motion picture of seagulls in bright sunlight showing high reflectivity.

17. Intelligence Reports Relating to U.S.S.R. Interest in U.S. Sightings.

18. Samples of Official USAF Reporting Forms and Copies of Pertinent Air Force, Army and Navy Orders Relating to Subject.

19. Sample Polyethylene "Pillow" Balloon (54 inches square).

20. "Variations in Radar Coverage," JANP 101 (Manual illustrating unusual operating characteristics of Service radar).

21. Miscellaneous official letters and foreign intelligence reports dealing with subject.

22. Copies of popular published works dealing with subject (articles in periodicals, newspaper clippings and books).

APPENDIX V: The Natural Philosophy of Flying Saucers,

R. V. Jones

"I could more easily believe that two Yankee professors would lie than that stones would fall from heaven." If President Thomas Jefferson could say this so unluckily in 1807, what should we say today to the contention that our earth is visited not merely by stones but by craft manned by intelligent beings? Jefferson's disbelief had in effect already been dealt with by Chladni, famous for his vibrating plates, in a battle with the French Academy that had reached its height about 1790. By that time, as Paneth has said, men of science were far too sophisticated to accept such yarns as that stones should fall out of the sky; but Chladni, who was a lawyer as well as a scientist, believed from his legal experience that eyewitnesses to meteorite falls were genuinely describing a natural phenomenon. After a 10 year battle, he ultimately convinced the French Academy that it was wrong, and that meteorites were real.

Perhaps my one claim to be writing this article is that to some extent I share Chladni's experience, for as an Intelligence Officer I had often to investigate the evidence of witnesses when it conflicted with established 'science', and sometimes it was the 'science' that was wrong. Let me therefore look as dispassionately as possible at the character of the evidence regarding 'flying saucers'. The phrase itself dates from 24 June 1947, but it seems that the apparitions to which it refers had occurred many times before then. Whether or not it was in the heavens that Ezekiel saw his wheels, the sky was a sufficient source of signs for the Roman augurs to scan it in their prognostic routine and it seems to have encouraged the Emperor Constantine handsomely with a χ–ρ celestial monogram before the battle of the Milvian Bridge. In the same tradition, some of us can remember the Angels of Mons.

It may indeed turn out that apparitions have been seen in the sky as long as human records have been kept. In his *History of the English Church and People,* Bede (735) described what would today almost certainly be claimed as flying saucers; and I remember reading an 11th or 12th century account where an object in the sky had caused "multum terrorem" to the brothers in a monastery. And perhaps for almost as long, the tendency of humanity to scare itself has been exploited by the hoaxer. I have read that Newton as a boy of 12 caused much alarm in his Lincolnshire village by flying a kite with a lantern at night.

There was much concern in England in 1882 when as objective an observer as E. W. Maunder of the Royal Observatory saw what he considered to be a celestial visitor. The object was also seen on the Continent by a future Nobel Laureate, the famous spectroscopist Zeeman. It was described in various ways—'spindle shaped', 'like a torpedo, or weaver's shuttle', 'like a discus seen on edge' and so forth. It was said to glow with a whitish colour. From measurements made on it, it must have been very large—perhaps 70 miles long and situated more than 100 miles above the earth's surface. Although Maunder said that it was different from any auroral phenomenon that he had seen, it is noteworthy that there was an intense magnetic storm at the time, coinciding with one of the largest sunspots ever recorded. It is therefore likely that Maunder's object was an unusual feature of an auroral display. There was another scare in 1897, when something like a winged cigar projecting a brilliant light from its head was seen over Oakland, California (Fort 1941). Similar objects

Based on a lecture given to the North Eastern Branch of the Institute and Society and the Newcastle Astronomical Society.

were soon seen throughout the United States, but while some were undoubtedly the work of hoaxers, the cause of the original incident remains obscure.

My own contact with the subject goes back to about 1925, when I was told at Oxted in Surrey of a bright light that slowly made its way across the sky every night. In fact, I knew of one married couple who sat up all night watching it. It was Venus, which had attracted them by its brilliance; they had never before noticed that all the planets and stars seem to move across the sky. Venus, indeed, has caused much trouble through the years. In 1940 or 1941 there was an alarm that the Germans had a new high flying aircraft, because this was what was reported by the predictor crew of an antiaircraft battery somewhere, I think, in the Borders. The aircraft, they said, was showing a light and they had determined its height with their rangefinder. The answer was, as far as I can remember, 26,000 ft and we wondered how they had managed to get such a precise measurement. Investigations showed that this was the last graduation on their range scale and that what they had tried to range upon was, once again, Venus. The same explanation has been true of several flying saucers that have been drawn to my attention in the north of Scotland; it has sometimes been possible to predict the nights on which reports would come in, depending on whether or not Venus was bright and visible.

It is necessary, in any discussion of flying saucers, to consider the nature of the evidence concerning them; it may therefore be relevant if I recount some of my experiences in similar matters, for the tensions associated with war provided fertile ground for the conception of apparitions. I can remember the Russians with the snow on their boots who came to Britain in 1914. One of my uncles was among the hundreds of people who saw them although, in his case, he could not see the snow because they were in a train going over a railway bridge. In fact no detachment of Russian troops ever came to this country. Years later I was told the explanation by the Chief of our Secret Service. In prewar days there used to be large consignments of eggs imported from Russia, and one of the ports at which they were landed was Aberdeen. An agent in Aberdeen on this particular occasion sent a telegram to his London headquarters to warn them that the eggs had been landed and were on the train. With telegraphic economy he sent a signal such as "100,000 Russians now on way from Aberdeen to London" and inadvertently started the legend.

The years before 1939 were full of stories of an engine stopping ray. As I heard the story in 1937 or 1938 it was that an English family on holiday in Germany would be travelling in a car when its engine would suddenly fail, invariably on a country road, and usually at the edge of a wood. A German sentry would then step out of the trees and tell them that there were special tests in progress and that they would be unable to proceed. Some time later he would come back and tell them that it was all right for them to start the engine again and the engine would immediately fire and they were able to drive off.

By this time I was becoming concerned with Intelligence, and one of my tasks was to ascertain the truth about the mysterious rays. At about the same time someone thought that it was a pity that the Germans should have a monopoly in the story and a parallel story was deliberately spread, hinting that we, too, had a ray. Within a short time we in Intelligence were flooded out with stories of similar events in England. We were astonished at the circumstantial detail that the public had added. In one instance, said to have occurred on Salisbury Plain, it was no ordinary family that were in their car, but a family of Quakers—and Quakers, it was added, were well known for telling the truth.

Eventually, I got to the bottom of the story. The places most mentioned in Germany were the regions around the Brocken in the Harz, and the Feldberg near Frankfurt. These were the sites of the first two television towers in Germany. A Jewish radio announcer at Frankfurt who escaped to this country was at first puzzled when I told him the story and then, with a chuckle, he told me that he could see how it had happened. In the days before the television transmitters had been erected, the engineers made field strength surveys, but these surveys were rendered difficult by interference from the engines of motor vehicles. Under an authoritarian regime such as that of the Nazis it was simple to eliminate this trouble by stopping all cars in the area around the survey receiver for the period of the test. Sentries, who were probably provided by the German Air Force, were posted on the roads, and at the appointed hour would emerge and stop all vehicles. At the end of the test they would then give the drivers permission to proceed. It only required a simple transposition in the story as subsequently told by a driver for the vehicle to have stopped before the sentry appeared, giving rise to a two year chase after the truth.

The beginning of the second World War took me for a few weeks to Harrogate, where part of the Air Ministry was evacuated. I soon saw a flying saucer. It was high in the blue of a clear midday sky, gleaming white, and appearing hardly to move. Everyone stopped to watch it, but it was merely an escaped balloon. Such objects appeared throughout the war and were even reported by fighter pilots who tried to intercept them, only to find that the objects were too high. There were indeed enough such incidents for part of the Intelligence Organization to suppose that the Germans had developed a special high flying version of the Junkers 86 aircraft known as the Ju 86P, P indicating that the cabin was pressurized (an unusual step in those days) for the crew. It was further supposed that these Ju 86Ps were flying photographic reconnaissances of this country and that we were powerless to intercept them. I doubt in fact whether any such reconnaissances were made—certainly, and very surprisingly, there was no photographic reconnaissance of London by the Germans from 10 January 1941 until 10 September 1944 when the Me 262 jet became available.

1940 was a grand time for scares. Many people saw flares fired up by Fifth Columnists to guide the German bombers to their targets; I even had an eyewitness account from an RAF friend who had worked with me in finding the German navigational beams. I was involved in a hunt for Fifth Columnists in Norfolk in which the details were far more convincing than those of any Flying Saucer story that I have encountered but the explanation turned out to be quite innocent. Happily, observations of curious lights were not confined to one side. I was delighted to watch the pilots of Kampfgruppe 100 (the 'crack' beam bombing unit of the German Air Force) conduct a three week test of a theory that our Observer Corps was indicating the presence of German bombers to our fighters by switching on red lights whenever a German bomber was overhead. At the end of the check the Kgr 100 crews reported that they had confirmed the observation, despite the fact that we were doing no such thing.

Air crew, because of the intense strain involved, appeared to be especially susceptible to apparitions. Air Commodore Helmore, one of our ablest pilots in World War I, recalled to me in 1939 that he and his contemporaries had been scared of a particular kind of German antiaircraft shell which burst with a purple flash. The legend was that these shells somehow radiated venereal disease—one can only guess at the chain of events that led up to these speculations.

In World War II our bomber crews repeatedly reported that they were shadowed by German single engine night fighters carrying yellow lights in their noses. The oddness of this observation was that, apart from the difficulty of putting a light in the nose of a single engine aircraft, there were at that time no German single engine fighters flying at night. No one ever completely explained the story. When I did get a chance to ask a German nightfighter crew whether they knew what the explanation was they said that they also knew that no single engine fighters were flying but that they had seen much the same thing as I described to them. American aircraft, later in the war, also saw what may have been the same phenomenon, both over Europe and over Japan. One theory, advanced by Professor Menzel (1953), who has studied such incidents in detail, is that it may have been some effect of light reflected from condensation in wing tip eddies.

Another of the aircrew theories, which ultimately did us very great harm, was that the control of German searchlights was mysteriously put out of action if our bomber switched on its radar identification device. Some of our most experienced and cool headed pilots believed this story, although one could see that it was ridiculous. Even if, by some accident, the German radar control had been upset originally by the radiation from our identification set, the Germans would very clearly have remedied the defect and used the radiation from our set as a means of identifying and locating our bombers—for we had thereby presented them with the answer to one of the most difficult problems in combat, that of getting your enemy positively to identify himself. They indeed exploited this technique towards the end of the war when their main radar equipment was jammed, and it cost us many bombers before we persuaded the Command that it must get the IFF sets switched off. There was another story that a beer bottle thrown out of a bomber would defeat the German radar, and I can remember Lord Cherwell's humorous question "Must it be a freshly opened bottle?" being solemnly recorded in the minutes of a War Cabinet discussion.

I had often to assess the evidence of eyewitnesses but even when these were observers who were anxious to help us, it was sometimes surprising how much in error their descriptions could be. I received, for example, three reports within a few weeks of one another in 1941 regarding German constructional activity on Mont Pinçon in Normandy. One report said that it was an underground aerodrome, the second that it was a long range gun and the third that it was a radio mast about 1100 ft high. Faced with such diversity, I guessed that none of these descriptions was correct but that, from the site, the construction was probably a radio navigational beam station, with an aerial (which was, incidentally, about 40 ft high) which could be rotated on a turntable of about 100 ft diameter. Photographic reconnaissance showed that my guess was correct; it also illustrated a more general point that witnesses were usually right when they said that something had happened at a particular place, although they could be wildly wrong about what had happened.

Another example that occurred, not to me but to Professor Charles Kittel, the American solid state physicist, may also be salutary. He and a British theoretical physicist were given the problem of establishing the pattern on which the Germans laid their mines at sea, the principal evidence being derived from the reports of minesweeper crews regarding the range and bearing of the mines as they were exploded by the passage of minesweepers. Kittel proposed to go on a minesweeping sortie, to get the feel of the evidence. His British counterpart refused to go, on the grounds that since they would only be making one trip the evidence that they were likely to obtain would be highly special to that particular trip and might colour their general judgement. Kittel at once found out the surprising fact that the reports of the crews were completely unreliable as regards range and bearing estimation, and that the only part of the evidence on which he could rely was whether the explosion had occurred to port or starboard. I believe that he managed to solve the problem of the pattern on this evidence alone, but that his colleague remained perplexed until the end of the war through accepting the ranges and bearings as accurate.

I have made this discursion into some of my war experience because it is relevant to the flying saucer story in that it illustrates the difficulty of establishing the truth from eyewitness reports, particularly when events have been witnessed under stress. I do not, of course, conclude that eyewitness reports must be discarded; on the contrary, excluding hoaxers and liars, most witnesses have genuinely seen something, although it may be difficult to decide from their descriptions what they really had seen.

The end of the war brought me an experience that was directly connected with the flying saucer problem. In fact, although the term was invented in America as the result of something seen by Kenneth Arnold, piloting a private plane near Mt Ranier on 24 June 1947, the modern scare about strange celestial objects started in Sweden early in 1946. I was Director of Intelligence on the Air Staff at the time and I had to decide whether or not there was anything in the story. I am not sure of the incident that started it off, but the general atmosphere was one of apprehension regarding the intentions of the Russians, now that their post-war attitude was becoming clear. It was, for example, the time of Winston Churchill's 'iron curtain' speech. At any rate, a number of stories began about people seeing things in the sky over Sweden, and this gained such volume that the Swedish General Staff asked the population in general to keep its eyes open. The result, of course, was an immediate spate of reports. Many of these could be quickly dismissed by explanations such as wild geese seen at a distance, but one or two were so widely reported that they must have been something more unusual.

Some of the technical officers on my staff were quite convinced and subscribed to the Swedish explanation that the objects were long range flying bombs being sent over Sweden by the Russians. Even such a cool headed judge as Field Marshal Smuts was convinced enough to refer to them in a broadcast talk as evidence of the Russian threat. The belief was strongly aided by what I think must have been two unusually bright meteors, which were clearly visible in daylight. One of these led to many reports almost simultaneously, from a wide area of Sweden; an enthusiastic Intelligence officer joined all the reports up into one track according to the times of the individual reports and this track seemed to show that the object sometimes hovered and sometimes flew for hundreds of miles within half a minute. What he had failed to notice was that almost every report said that the object had been seen to the east of the observer, and this would have been impossible if his track was genuine. The explanation, of course, was that the individual times of sighting that were reported represented the scatter of errors in the individual watches of the observers, and that they had all been witnessing one event; this was a large, bright meteor that had appeared over the Gulf of Finland.

However, such a simple explanation did not satisfy some of my officers, who clearly disapproved of my scepticism. I pointed out to them that since we had two years before studied the behaviour of German flying bombs, we knew the order of reliability of such missiles, which was such that 10% or so would come down accidentally through engine failure. The Russians were supposedly cruising their flying bombs at more than twice the range that the Germans had achieved, and it was unlikely that they were so advanced technologically as to achieve a substantially greater reliability at 200 miles than the Germans had reached at 100 miles. Even, therefore, if they were only trying to frighten the Swedes, they could hardly help it if some of their missiles crashed on Swedish territory. The alleged sightings over Sweden were now so many that, even giving the Russian the greatest possible credit for reliability, there ought to be at least 10 missiles already crashed in Sweden. I would therefore only believe the story if someone brought me in a piece of a missile.

I did not have to wait long. The other Director of Intelligence on the Air Staff, an Air Commodore who tended to side with those who believed in the story, telephoned me to say that while the Swedes had not actually picked up a crashed missile, someone had seen objects fall from one of the missiles and had collected them. The Swedish General Staff handed them to us for examination; they were a miscellaneous collection of irregular lumps of material. The piece that I remember best was perhaps three inches across, grey, porous and shiny, and with a density not much more than that of water. Charles Frank (now Prof. F. C. Frank of Bristol) and I looked at it and at one another, and laughed; but since we had been set a silly problem we thought that we would deal with it in a suitable manner, and so we sent the collection of specimens to the chemical department at Farnborough for a formal analysis. We did not foresee the scare that was then to arise; Farnborough, instead of sending the report of their analysis directly back to us, sent it to the technical officers who were among the believers.

My Air Commodore friend telephoned me to say that he now had the Farnborough report and that it substantiated the idea that the specimens had come from something quite mysterious, because one of them contained over 98% of an unknown chemical element. It was the grey porous specimen that was the cause of the trouble; Farnborough had analysed it for such elements as iron, manganese and so forth and had found traces of all of them adding up to less than 2%. The remaining 98% they had been unable to identify. Charles Frank and I were delighted. I telephoned the head of the chemical department at Farnborough (now a Fellow of the Royal Society) and asked him whether he really believed in the analysis that his Section had done. When he said that he did, I asked him how he could be satisfied with an analysis that left 98% of the substance unidentified, and he agreed that it was rather a puzzle. I then asked him whether they had tested for carbon. There was something of an explosion at the other end of the telephone. Carbon would not have shown up in any of the standard tests, but one had only to look at the material, as Charles Frank and I had done, to see that it was a lump of coke.

These were the only specimens that were ever claimed to have come from a Russian flying bomb, and the story might then had died. But by this time it had gone round the world and we received a signal from the British mission in Tokyo because General MacArthur had asked them to enquire into the story that a missile had fallen in England during the previous few weeks. The same Air Commodore telephoned me, asking how he should reply to the signal. I told him that, so far as I knew, nothing like a missile had fallen in England since the end of the war, and to this he replied: "Well, it might tie up with the Westerham incident." When I asked him what Westerham incident, he said: "Good God, I was supposed not to tell you about that." And then, of course, he had to tell me.

It transpired that on the previous Saturday one of my technical officers had received a telephone call from a man who said that his name was Gunyon, and that one of these newfangled contraptions had fallen out of the sky into one of his fields, and that he thought it was the Air Ministry's business to come and remove it. The technical officer concerned happened to be one of the believers and he saw a chance of convincing his Director that the Russian flying bomb really existed. He therefore asked farmer Gunyon how to find his farm, and was told that if one drove from Croydon to Westerham one should look out for a public house called 'The White Dog' and drive up the lane beside it, and that the farm was at the end of the lane. The technical intelligence resources of the Air Ministry were immediately mobilized and the two staff cars full of officers set off to find farmer Gunyon. When they got into the right area, they were disappointed to find no public house of the right name. But, being good Intelligence officers, they realized that the name may have been misheard over the telephone. They therefore enquired whether there were any public houses with similar names, and they were soon directed to one called 'The White Hart.' They were beginning, in any event, to need a drink, and they asked the publican whether he knew where farmer Gunyon lived. The pubkeeper did not know anyone by the name of Gunyon but, again, they asked whether he knew of anyone with a name that they could have mistaken for Gunyon over the telephone. Happily, he did. There was a farmer called Bunyan about three miles over the hill, and this astonished man duly received the full force of Air Technical Intelligence. Ultimately, he satisfied them that he had not telephoned the Air Ministry and that all his fields were in good order. They returned sadly to London. On the way, in seeking an explanation, they concluded that their Director had decided to have some fun with them and had made them waste their Saturday on a wild goose chase, just to teach them a lesson for their credulity. The only satisfaction left to them, they thought, was not to let their Director know how well he had succeeded, and they had therefore decided that they would not tell me what had happened. Although I appreciated their respect in giving me credit for such a happy hoax, I had in fact nothing to do with it, and I still do not know who thought of it. Even after that, some still believed in a Russian flying bomb, but the scare in Sweden and Britain gradually died down.

Even so, the Swedish scare had sensitized the western world so much that Kenneth Arnold's 1947 story set up a secondary scare in America that quickly overshadowed the primary source. Arnold was flying his own aircraft near Mt Ranier in Washington State on 24 June, when he saw "a chain of small saucer-like things at least five miles long swerving in and out of the high mountain peaks." There is no reason to doubt that Arnold genuinely saw something but, as D. H. Menzel has suggested, it may have been no more than snow swirling off the peaks or small clouds forming over them. Arnold's story triggered off a wave of sightings, with saucers appearing almost daily over one part or the other of the United States and since the Russians were at that time considered incapable of making apparitions cruise at such a long range, some other origin had to be found. The United States Air Force went even further than the Royal Air Force had done and set up an official investigation 'Project Saucer' on 22 January 1948 (this was succeeded in February 1949 by 'Project Grudge' and in March 1952 by 'Project Bluebook', which survives today). Eventually, in January 1953, a special Panel under CIA and USAF auspices was called to assess the evidence. The Chairman of the Panel was H. P. Robertson, the distinguished relativist, and with him were L. W. Alvarez, L. V. Berkner, S. A. Goudsmit and T. L. Page. They concluded, briefly, that there was no evidence for any "artefacts of a hostile foreign power", and that there should be a "debunking of the flying saucers".

The verdict of the Robertson Panel did much to restore a critical view of flying saucer stories and to offset the efforts of publicity seeking charlatans; but the Panel could not, of course, quell the enthusiasts who claimed to discern in its conclusions a range of motives that included the 'whitewashing' of the United States Air Force and its inability to cope with the invaders, celestial or otherwise (others even postulated that the unfortunate USAF had itself started the flying saucer stories by trying out a new secret weapon). If I may interject a personal comment here, it happens that I knew H. P. Robertson well; he was the representative appointed in 1943 by the American Chiefs of Staff to decide whether or not we in Britain were being hoaxed by the Germans regarding the existence of the V-1 flying bomb. He was immediately convinced by our evidence, and we owe him much, both for his personal help and for the promptness of the American technical support that followed his conclusion. He was always as anxious as anyone I know to establish the truth, and he would never have made an attempt to suppress it if it proved unpalatable; the same is true of the other members of his Panel who are known to me. Nevertheless, their findings have recently been criticized again, especially by a distinguished meteorologist, Dr James E. McDonald (1967) of the University of Arizona and by Dr J. Allen Hynek (1966), Director of the Dearborn Observatory of Northwestern University. Dr Hynek's criticism is the more interesting for the fact that he has been for 20 years a consultant to the United States Air Force, and he was an associate member of the Robertson Panel. For most of this time he held that saucers were fictions, and he contributed an article to the *Encyclopaedia Britannica* (1964) that threw much doubt on their existence. Recently, however, he appears to have changed his mind, and he now believes that there are sufficient unexplained pieces of sound evidence to justify a new examination. As a result, the United States Air Force has set up a fresh investigation at the University of Colorado, Boulder, headed by Dr Edward Condon, the former Director of the National Bureau of Standards. The study was initiated in October 1966 and is expected to take 18 months at a cost of $300,000.

It appears that the Russians, too, have been facing similar doubts, for Air Force General Anatoli Stolyarov has recently been appointed head of a committee of investigation (*The Times,* 13 November 1967). Again, this comes some years after *Pravda* had published official denials of flying saucers in 1961.

Let us consider the difficulties that face these new investigations. Apart from the liars and hoaxers who have done much to confuse the issue, and those witnesses who have simply had hallucinations, there are many witnesses who have genuinely observed something. Some of these witnesses have seen manmade vehicles such as balloons, aircraft, rockets and satellites, but have misidentified them in unfamiliar circumstances. Others have seen natural phenomena including mirages, ice haloes, mock suns, Brocken ghosts, lenticular clouds, phosphorescence at sea, ball lightning, Venus and so forth. Some have seen and have even photographed convincing artefacts such as the detached image of the plane of a Herald aircraft through complex refraction at the edge of one of the cabin windows. Others have observed unusual echoes on radar screens such as the 'ring angels' due to the morning flight of starlings.

The foregoing explanations account for the majority of flying saucer reports. The size of the unexplained residue may be gauged from the statement of the Under Secretary of State for Defence in the House of Commons on 9 November 1967. Over the period 1 January 1959 to 30 September 1967, 625 reports were received by the Ministry of Defence; 70 remain unexplained after investigation. For comparison, the American figures, given by the Staff of Project Bluebook in a report of February 1966, are 6817 alleged sightings in the years 1953-65 inclusive; of these, 1248 were reported too vaguely to allow an attempt at explanation. Of the remaining 5569, there were 237 for which explanations could not be found.

Summarizing the British and American experience, it appears that perhaps 10% of the alleged sightings cannot be explained. In this residue, it is probable that the majority of witnesses have made substantial errors in their descriptions. A point of dispute is whether, after such errors have been allowed for, there is enough left that is unexplained to make us think that there is a gap in our knowledge either of natural phenomena or of an extraterrestrial invasion of our atmosphere, perhaps by intelligently controlled spacecraft.

Those who have pressed the last explanation, and especially those who have believed in little men from Venus or Mars, must have been discouraged by the latest evidence regarding surface conditions on those planets. But I doubt whether they will be any more finally discouraged than were those who believed in the Russian flying bombs over Sweden. Hope is not the only thing that springs eternal in the human breast. If Earth proves to be the one planet in the solar system that supports intelligent life, it is still possible that intelligent beings from a more distant system have found the way to cross intervening space in small craft without ageing on the long journey; and, although it is unlikely, it is just possible that the craft are small enough not to have shown up on astronomical or radar surveys. Jesse Greenstein of Mt Wilson and Palomar Observatories has calculated that a vehicle 100 ft in diameter would easily show up at a height of 50 miles on any of the 5000 plates of the Palomar Sky Survey.

Perhaps I may be permitted to make some remarks on resolving the confusion of evidence, for I have had to do this before. In particular, I had to sort out the true from the false in the scare of 1943 about the threat of the German rocket. In the early stages this was not difficult, since there were few reports, and they were substantially secret and independent. But as the stories grew, it was almost impossible to tell whether or not a particular report came from someone who genuinely knew something or whether he was repeating a rumour. By that time there was no question about whether or not there was a rocket—the question was what it weighed. Finally I found a touchstone—I would accept a weight only from a report that had also mentioned that liquid oxygen was one of the fuels, which I by then knew to be true. The result was spectacular; out of hundreds of conflicting reports this touchstone selected only five, and these pointed consistently to a total weight of about 12 tons with a warhead from one to two tons, in contradistinction to the 80 tons with a 10 ton warhead that had been mooted. These five surviving reports thus led me to the correct answer.

Unfortunately, I have not found a similar touchstone for flying saucer reports. We are then left with assessing probabilities from what we know about the physical world, but we cannot reject the flying saucer hypothesis simply because it is unlikely. This would merely lead to the danger of repeating the error of the French Academy regarding meteorites. But are flying saucers simply of the first order of unlikeliness? I think not, for I would apply the same argument as I used regarding the apparitions in Sweden. There have been so many flying saucers seen by now, if we were to believe the accounts, that surely one of them must have broken down or left some trace of its visit. It is true that one can explain the absence of relics by supposing that the saucers have a fantastic reliability, but this adds another order of unlikeliness. At least the French Academy had some actual meteorites to examine.

I think that this is where the natural philosopher must take his stand, for there is a well tried course in such a situation. This is to apply 'Occam's razor'—hypotheses are not to be multiplied without necessity. Of all the possible explanations for a set of observations, the one with the minimum of supposition should be accepted, until it is proved wrong. Otherwise one lives in a fearsomely imaginative world in which rational conduct becomes impossible. There is a story of one of my more eccentric colleagues that will illustrate what I mean. He was at the time a Fellow of one of the men's colleges in Oxford, but he happened also to tutor some of the women students in philosophy. One of the girls went into his room for a tutorial one day, only to find that he seemed not to be there. However, she was accustomed to some of the curiosities in his behaviour and she was not unduly surprised when, a minute or two after she had sat down, his voice boomed from under the table: "Read your essay!" This she proceeded to do, and then waited for his comments. Something that she had said reminded him of Occam's razor and he proceeded to give her an example. Poking his head out from under the tablecloth he said: "Supposing that I was to say to you that there is a tiger outside the door, but that the tiger is frightened of me so that every time I go to the door to see it, it runs away and hides round the corner. If I were to tell you that this was the explanation of why I see no tiger outside my door, you would say that I was mad—or, at least, a little peculiar!" Are flying saucers as imaginary as my colleague's tiger?

Of course, the difficulty in applying Occam's razor is in deciding which explanation of flying saucers involves the minimum hypothesis. Jefferson was committing scientific suicide with the razor when he preferred to believe that professors would lie. And it is also true that the explanation with the minimum of hypothesis is not always the right one. I can recall just one occasion when Occam led me astray in this way. This was towards the end of 1943 when the method of propulsion of the German flying bombs was unknown. I thought that I was able to deduce it from a set of facts as follows. On the plans of one of the flying bomb sites that had been sent to us by one of our spies, backed up by what we could see on aerial photographs, there seemed to be one fuel store on each site. Indeed, it was so labelled on the plan. The store was divided into two parts, and I concluded from the disposition of the entrances and blast walls that two kinds of fuel were to be used and that the designer was taking unusual precautions to prevent them from coming into contact. I already knew of two such fuels, hydrogen peroxide and sodium permanganate. These were already being used in rocket propelled glider bombs, and I even managed to establish that some of the servicing crews for these particular fuels were being allocated to the flying bomb sites. Moreover, when I checked the volume of peroxide that could be held in the store, it was enough to propel 20 peroxide rockets to London, and this was consistent with the storage in the rest of the site for 20 flying bomb bodies. There was therefore no need to postulate any other engine, on this evidence, for the flying bomb beyond a development of the peroxide rocket engine. Everything was consistent and had been well supported by evidence. And yet the conclusion was wrong. A more complicated hypothesis turned out to be right. The peroxide was used merely for firing the bombs from their catapults, and their main means of propulsion was a new type of engine, the Argus tube, which burned ordinary fuel. The reason that this ordinary fuel did not show up on the site was that the bombs arrived already filled with fuel from a central store.

At the same time, I must emphasize that in compensation for this one instance where Occam's razor led me astray, there were many instances where it led me to the truth when many other people were confused. The essential thing in applying the Razor is that one must be completely honest in realizing that, while it dictates the best operational course, it can lead to the wrong result and one must not cling to the simple explanation to which it leads if subsequent observations show that this is incorrect.

Here it is advisable to remember the advice of Pasteur (1854):

> Preconceived ideas are like searchlights which illumine the path of the experimenter and serve him as a guide to interrogate nature. They become a danger only if he transforms them into fixed ideas—this is why I should like to see these profound words inscribed on the threshold of all the temples of science: 'The greatest derangement of the mind is to believe in something because one wishes it to be so.'

Keeping all these facts in mind, the balance of the evidence regarding flying saucers as I see it—viewed against the critical situations in which I used to have to decide on courses of action based on evidence from eyewitnesses and other sources—is heavily against their being intelligently controlled vehicles. But I also know that, even if the current American and Russian investigations come to this same conclusion or even a stronger one, it will not discourage the flying saucer believers. For these investigations are faced with the impossible job, if flying saucers do not exist, of proving a completely negative case. This is one of the most difficult of all Intelligence tasks, and even if the investigation is as thorough as humanly possible, the flying saucer exponents will always be able to conjure new hypotheses that had not been considered.

If known natural phenomena are insufficient to explain everything that has been genuinely seen, the alternative to the intelligently controlled vehicles is an as yet unrecognized natural phenomenon. This is distinctly possible—the case may be similar to that of ball lightning, the occurrence of which has long been both asserted and disputed. But ball lightning has been seen by many observers with a scientific training, including a Deputy Director of the Meteorological Office. In this it appears (apart from a few recent reports from Russia) to differ from the flying saucer and since there is no reason to expect that scientists are more likely to be favoured relatively to laymen by ball lightning than by flying saucers, we may conclude that either the saucers are much rarer even than the comparatively rare ball lightning, or that the latter has often been mistaken by lay observers for saucers.

In coming to a conclusion about the existence of flying saucers, there is a strong temptation to be overcautious, because if you turn out to be wrong in denying their existence the error will be blazoned in the history of science; but if you merely turn out to be right, there will be little credit in proving a negative case. My own position has been that if at any time in the last 20 years I had had to take a vital decision one way or the other according to whether I thought that flying saucers were fact or fantasy, Russian or extraterrestrial (why has China never been credited, by the way?), I would have taken that decision on the assumption that they were either a fantasy or an incorrect identification of a rare and unrecognized phenomenon; and while I commend any genuine search for new phenomena, little short of a tangible relic would dispel my scepticism of flying saucers.

ACKNOWLEDGEMENTS

I am grateful for help from Messrs Brownlee Haydon, Amrom Katz and Merton Davies of the Rand Corporation in providing copies of US literature, and from the staff of the Ministry of Defence.

FURTHER READING

FORT, C., 1941, *The Books of Charles Fort* (New York: Holt and Co.). A source book for pre-saucer apparitions.

HYNEK, J. A., 1964, *Encyclopaedia Britannica* 22, 696 (Chicago: Benton).

——, 1966, *Science*, 154, 329.

LANE, F. W., 1966, *The Elements Rage* (Newton Abbot: David and Charles). A general account of meteors and other phenomena.

McDONALD, J. E., 1967, *Paper to the American Society of Newspaper Editors*, 22 April.

——, 1967, *Statement to the Outer Space Affairs Group, United Nations Organisation*, 7 June.

MENZEL, D. H., 1953, *Flying Saucers* (London: Putnam).

——, and BOYD, L. G., 1963, *The World of Fying Saucers* (New York: Doubleday).

MINNAERT, M., 1940, *Light and Colour in the Open Air*, reprinted 1959 (London: Bell).

PASTEUR, L., 1954, Reported in DUBOS, R. J., 1964, *Louis Pasteur* (London: Gollanez).

APPENDIX W: Acknowledgments

We express here our grateful appreciation to the many organizations and individuals who have rendered valuable assistance to our study. It is impracticable to list all of the hundreds of members of the general public who have made suggestions or written about their experiences. We apologize if we have overlooked any who should be specially recognized. Those to whom we owe particular thanks are:

National Research Council of Canada, particularly Dr. Peter M. Millman, for detailed information about UFO matters in Canada.

National Aeronautics and Space Administration, which appointed Dr. Urner Liddel as liaison officer to this study, and also for cooperation of the astronauts with Dr. Roach in the preparation of Section III, Chapter 6.

Environmental Science Services Administration, particularly to Dr. George S. Benton and Dr. C. Gordon Little who arranged for us to have the services of Mr. Gordon Thayer in the preparation of Section III, Chapter 5, and for critical review of early drafts of Section VI, Chapter 5; and for general cooperation of the Weather Bureau.

U.S. Naval Observatory, particularly Dr. R. L. Duncombe, director, Nautical Almanac Office, who carried out the perturbation calculations on *Clarion* mentioned in Section II (p. 42).

Alcohol and Tobacco Tax Division, Internal Revenue Service, particularly Mr. Maynard J. Pro who arranged for the neutron activation analysis of a magnesium sample mentioned in Case 4 (p. 391).

U.S. Forest Service, particularly Mr. C. A. Shields, director of division of administrative management, for information about local areas of forest damage.

Federal Aviation Agency, particularly Mr. Clyde Dubbs, and Mr. Newton Lieurance, for general cooperation of air traffic controllers in relation to UFO reports. (Section III, Chapter 1.)

Library of Congress, particularly Miss Lynn Catoe, for information on published material on UFOs.

U.S. Department of State, for assistance in securing information about the UFO interests of foreign governments (Section V, Chapter 3) particularly Dr. Walter Ramberg, science attaché in Rome, Italy for information for Section V, Chapter 2.

U.S. Air Force, particularly Lt. Col. Robert Hippler and Lt. Col. Hector Quintanilla, and Dr. William Price and Dr. J. Thomas Ratchford of the Air Force Office of Scientific Research, for prompt and efficient responses to our requests for information, and great tact in not influencing the course of the study. Also the UFO officers at all of the various Air Force bases for reports and general cooperation.

The University of Arizona, particularly the Lunar and Planetary Laboratory, for arranging for the study to have the services of Dr. William K. Hartmann who prepared Section III, Chapter 2, and Section IV, Chapter 3. Also the Institute of Atmospheric Physics whose Dr. James E. McDonald gratuitously supplied information and criticism, especially in regard to UFO matters in Australia, New Zealand and Tasmania, which he studied during a trip there which was sponsored by the U.F. Office of Naval Research.

University of Wyoming, for the assistance of Prof. R. Leo Sprinkle in connection with Case 42 (p. 598).

University of Colorado, (in addition to those on the project staff), to Prof. Ned Bowler, Department of Audiology and Speech Pathology for sonograms of bird calls and other sounds used in study of Case 20 (p. 468); to the School of Medicine, for the services of Dr. Mark Rhine in the preparation of Section VI, Chapter 3; to Dr. William A. Scott, Dr. Thomas O. Mitchell, Mr. Ronnal L. Lee, Dr. David R. Saunders, Miss Dorothy R. Davis and Miss Marilyn R. Bradshaw for contributions to Section III, Chapter 7.

Stanford Research Institute, particularly Dr. R. T. H. Collis, who arranged for the study to have the services of Dr. William Viezee and Dr. Roy H. Blackmer, Jr., in preparation of Section VI, Chapters 4 and 5. Thanks are also due Mr. Roy M. Endlich and Dr. Edward E. Uthe and also Dr. J. V. Dave of the International Business Machines Corporation of Palo Alto for assistance in this connection.

Smithsonian Astrophysical Observatory, particularly Dr. Fred H. Whipple for the cooperation extended in connection with their Prairie Network, discussed in Section VI, Chapter 9. Also to Dr. Donald H. Menzel for much information and advice based on his long and critical study of UFO matters.

Northwestern University, Dearborn Observatory, for information and consultation voluntarily supplied by Dr. J. Allen Hynek and others on his staff, particularly Dr. Jacques Vallee and Dr. William Powers.

Illinois Institute of Technology Research Institute, for the loan of the all-sky camera used in Case 27 (p. 508).

National Center for Atmospheric Research, and its director, Dr. Walter Orr Roberts, for the services of: Dr. Joseph H. Rush, who consulted on instrumentation problems and critically edited many of the case reports in Section IV; Dr. Vincent Lally in preparing Section VI, Chapter 8; Dr. Paul Julian in preparing Section VI, Chapter 10; Dr. Martin Altschuler in preparing Section VI, Chapter 7; Dr. Julian Shedlovsky, who provided information on radio-activity induced in various materials on exposure to radiation in outer space; and for many consultations on special problems.

Ford Motor Company, particularly to Dr. Michael J. Ference, vice-president for research, Mr. Frederick J. Hooven, now of Dartmouth College, and Mr. David F. Moyer, for assistance on alleged effects of UFOs on automobiles. (Section III, Chapter 4, p. 151; Case 12, p. 432; and Case 39, p. 582.)

Dow Chemical Company, particularly Dr. R. S. Busk and Dr. D. R. Beaman, for information and analyses of a magnesium sample (Case 4, p. 391).

Raytheon Company, Autometrics Division, for the services of Mr. Everitt Merritt in connection with photogrammetric studies. (Section II, p. 50.)

Volunteer Flight Officer Network, and particularly Mr. H. E. Roth, United Airlines, for reports of sightings by commercial air transport pilots (p. 84).

Aerial Phenomena Research Organization, particularly James and Coral Lorenzen, for information and samples particularly referring to South American cases, and for the cooperation of many of its members in supplying prompt notice of UFO sightings to our Early Warning System (Section III, Chapter 1, p. 84).

National Investigations Committee for Aerial Phenomena, particularly Donald Keyhoe and Richard H. Hall, for supplying copies of case reports from NICAP files, and for the cooperation of many of its members in supplying prompt notice of UFO sightings to our Early Warning Network (Section III, Chapter 1, p. 84); and to Raymond E. Fowler of Wenham, Mass., in connection with the study of UFO reports in the New England region.

Ottawa New Sciences Club, particularly Mrs. Carol Halford-Watkins, for information about a metallic mass claimed to have UFO significance.

Mr. Gerard Piel, publisher of the *Scientific American* for valuable advice on editorial matters and particularly for having helped secure the services of Mr. Daniel S. Gillmor as editor of this report.

Mr. Philip J. Klass, senior editor of *Aviation Week and Space Technology*, for assistance in connection with atmospheric plasmas in relation to UFO reports, and for helpful information on UFO developments in Washington.

Mr. Philip Wittenberg, member of the New York bar and author of *The Protection of Literary Property;* Mr. Charles Williams, Mr. Edwin Kahn, Mr. J. Michael Farley, Mr. John Holloway, and the late Mr. Phillip Danielson, members of the Colorado bar, for valuable advice on legal problems related to the study.

Mrs. LaVern Knoll, reference librarian at the Great Falls, Montana, public library, for searching files of *Great Falls Leader* in connection with Case 47 (p. 626).

Mr. Gary Rosenberger of Boulder, Colo., for use of his automobile and assistance in magnetic measurements involved in Case 38 (p. 582).

American Institute of Public Opinion, for providing the original records of their 1966 poll on flying saucers, and for permission to use the results in Section III, Chapter 7.

Opinion Research Organization, particularly Leonard F. Newton, Isabelle N. Rhodes and James C. Manuel, who conducted the 1968 study reported in Section III, Chapter 7, under contract with this project.

To the following individuals who assisted in the study of Case 22 (p. 484): Wing Commander D. F. Robertson, Canadian Forces Headquarters; Royal Canadian Air Force Squadron Leader Paul Bissky; Royal Canadian Mounted Police CIB Superintendents G. H. Miller and I. C. Shank, Cpl. G. J. Davis and Constable Zaccherias; Dr. Edward C. Shaw; Director B.

C. Cannon and members J. B. Thompson and E. J. Epp of the Canadian Aerian Phenomena Research Organization.

Hauser Research and Engineering Company, Boulder, Colo., for chemical analysis of material identified as chaff in Case 3, p. 388.

Several scientists who gave us useful information on condition that their names would not be mentioned.

And, finally, I would like to add my special thanks to the typists and editorial assistants who handled the monumental task of typing, proofing, correcting, and assembling this report, remaining with the study until its completion: Miss Beth Allman, Miss Ashley Baker, Mrs. Carol Love, Miss Brenda Montalvo and Mrs. Sue Wood. And, above all, to Mrs. Kathryn Shapley, who served loyally and efficiently as my secretary throughout the entire study.

APPENDIX X: Authors and Editors—Staff of the Colorado Project

JOHN B. AHRENS (Research Psychologist) received his B.S. at the University of Wyoming where he assisted Dr. D. Foulkes in research.

ROBERT J. ALLEN (Section VI, Chapter 5) senior research engineer, Radar Aerophysics Group, Stanford Research Institute, specialized in the development of acoustic miss-distance scoring systems for small arms and special radar-data processing unit. He holds the degrees of B.S. EE., B.S., and M.S.

BETH ALLMAN (Assistant Editor) holds a B.A. (University of Colorado) in comparative literature. Prior to her work on this report, she was engaged in personnel work at Thompson-Ramo-Woolridge and as a production assistant for Henry Z. Walck, Publishers.

MARTIN D. ALTSCHULER (Section VI, Chapter 7) is associated with NCAR as research assistant. He holds a Ph.D. (Yale) in astronomy and physics, and since 1965 has been a member of the Department of Astrophysics at the University of Colorado.

FREDERICK AYER II (Section VI, Chapter 9) received his M.S. (New York University) in physics. He has been consultant and research associate at the Brookhaven National Laboratory, and has recently done research on high-energy physics at the University of Colorado.

VICTORIA SIEGFRIED BARKER (Indexer) received her B.S. (Stanford) in library science. She has served as librarian for the University of Colorado, and as chief librarian of the Boulder Laboratories, U.S. Department of Commerce, National Bureau of Standards (1951-1964).

ROY H. BLACKMER, JR. (Section VI, Chapter 4) currently directs a series of projects for improved observation and prediction of weather phenomena for Stanford Research Institute. His M.S. (M.I.T.) is in meteorology.

WILLIAM BLUMEN (Section VI, Chapter 6) is assistant professor of Astrophysics at the University of Colorado. His Ph.D. (M.I.T.) is in physics. He has done research in dynamic meteorology at NCAR.

WILLIAM B. CARSON (Programmer) was mathematics technician with the Institute for Environmental Research, ESSA, and the National Bureau of Standards.

RONALD T. H. COLLIS (Section VI, Chapter 5) manages the Aerophysics Laboratory at Stanford Research Institute. A graduate of the Royal Naval School of Meteorology, he received his M.S. from Oxford University.

EDWARD U. CONDON (Scientific Director) is professor of Physics and Astrophysics, and is a Fellow of the Joint Institute for Laboratory Astrophysics at the University of Colorado. He is former director of the National Bureau of Standards and a member of the National Academy of Sciences. He received his Ph.D. in physics from the University of California and has served faculties of Princeton University, the University of Minnesota, Oberlin College, and Washington University, St. Louis. He has been associate director of research for the Westinghouse Electric Corporation, and director of research for Corning Glass Works. In 1941 he was named to the committee which established the U.S. atomic bomb program. He has also served as scientific advisor to a special Senate atomic energy committee, and to the President's Evaluation Commission for Naval Atomic Bomb Tests (1946). He is a member of the American Academy of Arts and Sciences, the American Philosophical Society, the American Association for the Advancement of Science (president, 1953), the American Physical Society (president, 1946), the American Association of Physics Teachers (president, 1964), the Society for Social Responsibility in Science (president, 1968-69), and of scientific organizations in Sweden, France, and Great Britain.

STUART W. COOK (Principal Investigator) is co-director of the University of Colorado Institute of Behavioral Science research program, having recently completed five years as chairman of the Department of Psychology. He is also chairman of the American Psychological Association's committee on research ethical standards. His research has involved the development, modification, and measurement of attitudes, social behavior, and intergroup relationships. He holds a Ph.D. (Minn.) and is a diplomate in clinical psychology from the American Board of Examiners in Professional Psychology.

ROY CRAIG (Section III, Chapters 1, 3, and 4) was an associate professor and coordinator of Physical Science in the Division of Integrated Studies at the University of Colorado for two years and has also taught at Clarkson College. He has been research assistant at Iowa State University Institute for Atomic Research and at the California Institute of Technology. His Ph.D. (Iowa State) is in physical chemistry.

LOREN W. CROW (Consulting Meteorologist) has served as Special Assistant for Industrial Meteorology, ESSA.

DANIEL S. GILLMOR (Editor) has been a journalist since 1939 as newspaper reporter, magazine editor, and free-lance writer, specializing in the sciences. The author of one book, he has served in various capacities on the scientific and general publications in the United States, Canada, Great Britain, and France.

CARL D. HEROLD (Section VI, Chapter 5) is Senior Research Engineer in the Systems Evaluation Department of Stanford Research Institute. His B.S. (Case) is in electrical engineering.

WILLIAM K. HARTMANN (Section III, Chapter 2; Section VI, Chapter 2) is assistant professor at the University of Arizona's Lunar and Planetary Laboratory. He was named co-winner of the 1964-65 Ninninger Meteorite Award. The previous year he had acted as consultant to North American Aviation for LESA studies (NASA). He was also a member of Geosciences Panel to recommend post-Apollo lunar research. He has made lunar and planetary photoanalyses in Mexico, Hawaii and Arizona volcanic fields. His Ph.D. (Ariz.) is in astronomy.

HARRIET HUNTER (Section V, Chapter 3) was Associate Editor of this report. She was an administrative aide to the director of NCAR and the center's conference manager. She has studied at Michigan State University and the University of Colorado, and is presently an administrative assistant to the Dean of the Graduate School at the latter.

PAUL R. JULIAN (Section VI, Chapter 10) is on the research staff at NCAR and is an affiliate professor for the University of Chicago. His Ph.D. (Pennsylvania State) is in meteorology. For five years he served on the staff of the High Altitude Observatory in Boulder, Colorado.

VINCENT E. LALLY (Section VI, Chapter 8) is currently employed at NCAR in balloon and instrument experimentation. His M.S. (M.I.T.) is in business and engineering administration.

ALDORA LEE (Section III, Chapter 7) received her Ph.D. (Colorado) in social psychology. She has taught at the University of Colorado and has done research at mental health centers and hospitals in California and Colorado.

NORMAN E. LEVINE (Research Associate) received his Ph.D. from the University of Arizona, where he is currently an assistant engineer in research.

ROBERT J. LOW (Project Coordinator) is special assistant to the Vice-President and Dean of Faculties at the University of Colorado. He received his B.S. EE (Harvard) and his M.B.A. (Columbia), and has done graduate work at Oxford and the University of Colorado. He conducted curriculum studies for the state of Florida and the American Institute of Biological Sciences. Prior to assuming his duties on the project, he was assistant dean of the University of Colorado's Graduate School.

RONALD I. PRESNELL (Research Associate) is on the staff of Stanford Research Institute as Senior Research Engineer in the Radio Physics Laboratory. His M.S. (Stanford) is in engineering.

MARK W. RHINE (Section VI, Chapter 3) is an assistant professor of psychiatry at the University of Colorado Medical Center. His M.D. is from Harvard.

FRANKLIN E. ROACH (Section III, Chapter 6), a Principal Investigator of the project, is Professor Adjoint in the Astrogeophysics Department of the University of Colorado; he is also consultant to NASA. He has taught at the University of Arizona and has done research at various governmental agencies including the National Bureau of Standards. His B.S. is from the University of Michigan, and his M.S. and Ph.D. (Chicago) is in astrophysics.

SAMUEL ROSENBERG (Section V, Chapter 1) is a documentary film producer and director. As a photojournalist he has had articles published in *Life* and has directed and produced 12 documentary films for television. He has served as a consultant in matters involving the United Nations. He has given two one-man shows of drawings in Washington and New York. A personal memoir is scheduled for publication in 1969 by Prentice-Hall.

GERALD M. ROTHBERG (Research Associate) is associate professor of Physics, Stevens Institute of Technology. His Ph.D. (Columbia) is in physics.

JOSEPH H. RUSH (Consultant) received his Ph.D. (Duke) in physics. He has taught at various institutions in Texas and was a physicist for the A-bomb project at Oak Ridge, Tennessee, and the High Altitude Observatory in Colorado. He is presently employed at NCAR.

DAVID R. SAUNDERS (Principal Investigator) is professor of psychology at the University of Colorado and assistant director of its Department of Testing and Counseling. He holds a Ph.D. (Ill.) in psychology.

WILLIAM A. SCOTT (Co-principal Investigator) is professor of psychology at the University of Colorado. For eight years he was director of the University's graduate program in personality and social psychology. His Ph.D. is from the University of Michigan.

MARGARET C. SHIPLEY (Indexer) has a B.S. from Scripps College. She is currently writer and editor in the University of Colorado's School of Engineering.

HERBERT J. STRENTZ (Research Associate) is visiting professor of journalism at the University of Kentucky. His M.A. (Syracuse) is in journalism.

GORDON D. THAYER (Section III, Chapter 5) received his B.S. in physics from the University of Colorado and attended the U.S. Army Signal Corps radar school, and was assigned to White Sands Proving Grounds for research analysis. He is currently with ESSA. (In the preparation of his chapter Mr. Thayer was assisted by Burgette A. Hart.)

WILLIAM VIEZEE (Section VI, Chapter 4) research meteorologist at the Stanford Research Institute, received his M.S. (California) in meteorology. He has been engaged in studies related to numerical weather predictions, clear-air turbulence, satellite meteorology, and applications of laser radar to atmospheric research.

JAMES E. WADSWORTH (Research Associate) received his B.A. at the University of North Carolina and was research assistant with the Institute of Behavioral Sciences at the University of Colorado.

MICHAEL M. WERTHEIMER (Section VI, Chapter 2) is a professor of experimental psychology at the University of Colorado. His Ph.D. is from Harvard. He has done research in perception, physiological, abnormal and social psychology, and in psychological theory.

INDEX